Basic Forms

1. $\displaystyle\int u\,dv = uv - \int v\,du$

2. $\displaystyle\int u^n du = \frac{1}{n+1}u^{n+1} + C, \qquad n \neq -1$

3. $\displaystyle\int \frac{du}{u} = \ln|u| + C$

4. $\displaystyle\int e^u du = e^u + C$

5. $\displaystyle\int a^u du = \frac{1}{\ln a}a^u + C$

6. $\displaystyle\int \sin u\,du = -\cos u + C$

7. $\displaystyle\int \cos u\,du = \sin u + C$

8. $\displaystyle\int \sec^2 u\,du = \tan u + C$

9. $\displaystyle\int \csc^2 u\,du = -\cot u + C$

10. $\displaystyle\int \sec u \tan u\,du = \sec u + C$

11. $\displaystyle\int \csc u \cot u\,du = -\csc u + C$

12. $\displaystyle\int \tan u\,du = \ln|\sec u| + C$

13. $\displaystyle\int \cot u\,du = \ln|\sin u| + C$

14. $\displaystyle\int \sec u\,du = \ln|\sec u + \tan u| + C$

15. $\displaystyle\int \csc u\,du = \ln|\csc u - \cot u| + C$

16. $\displaystyle\int \frac{du}{\sqrt{a^2-u^2}} = \arcsin\frac{u}{a} + C$

17. $\displaystyle\int \frac{du}{a^2+u^2} = \frac{1}{a}\arctan\frac{u}{a} + C$

18. $\displaystyle\int \frac{du}{u\sqrt{u^2-a^2}} = \frac{1}{a}\operatorname{arcsec}\frac{u}{a} + C$

19. $\displaystyle\int \frac{du}{a^2-u^2} = \frac{1}{2a}\ln\left|\frac{u+a}{u-a}\right| + C$

20. $\displaystyle\int \frac{du}{u^2-a^2} = \frac{1}{2a}\ln\left|\frac{u-a}{u+a}\right| + C$

Forms Involving $\sqrt{a^2+u^2}$

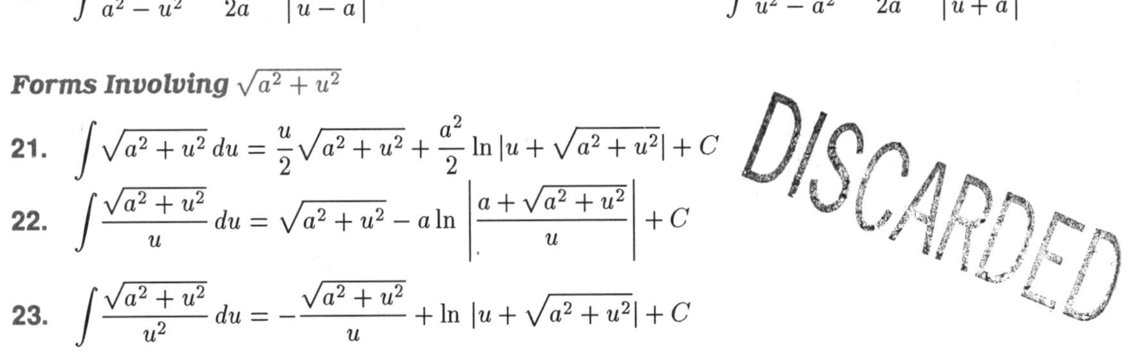

21. $\displaystyle\int \sqrt{a^2+u^2}\,du = \frac{u}{2}\sqrt{a^2+u^2} + \frac{a^2}{2}\ln|u+\sqrt{a^2+u^2}| + C$

22. $\displaystyle\int \frac{\sqrt{a^2+u^2}}{u}\,du = \sqrt{a^2+u^2} - a\ln\left|\frac{a+\sqrt{a^2+u^2}}{u}\right| + C$

23. $\displaystyle\int \frac{\sqrt{a^2+u^2}}{u^2}\,du = -\frac{\sqrt{a^2+u^2}}{u} + \ln|u+\sqrt{a^2+u^2}| + C$

24. $\displaystyle\int \frac{u^2du}{\sqrt{a^2+u^2}} = \frac{u}{2}\sqrt{a^2+u^2} - \frac{a^2}{2}\ln|u+\sqrt{a^2+u^2}| + C$

25. $\displaystyle\int \frac{du}{\sqrt{a^2+u^2}} = \ln|u+\sqrt{a^2+u^2}| + C$

26. $\displaystyle\int \frac{du}{u\sqrt{a^2+u^2}} = -\frac{1}{a}\ln\left|\frac{\sqrt{a^2+u^2}+a}{u}\right| + C$

27. $\displaystyle\int \frac{du}{u^2\sqrt{a^2+u^2}} = -\frac{\sqrt{a^2+u^2}}{a^2u} + C$

28. $\displaystyle\int \frac{du}{(a^2+u^2)^{3/2}} = \frac{u}{a^2\sqrt{a^2+u^2}} + C$

29. $\displaystyle\int u^2\sqrt{a^2+u^2}\,du = \frac{u}{8}(a^2+2u^2)\sqrt{a^2+u^2} - \frac{a^4}{8}\ln|u+\sqrt{a^2+u^2}| + C$

(continued on next page)

Forms Involving $\sqrt{a^2 - u^2}$

30. $\displaystyle\int \sqrt{a^2-u^2}\,du = \frac{u}{2}\sqrt{a^2-u^2} + \frac{a^2}{2}\arcsin\frac{u}{a} + C$

31. $\displaystyle\int \frac{\sqrt{a^2-u^2}}{u^2}\,du = -\frac{1}{u}\sqrt{a^2-u^2} - \arcsin\frac{u}{a} + C$

32. $\displaystyle\int u^2\sqrt{a^2-u^2}\,du = \frac{u}{8}(2u^2-a^2)\sqrt{a^2-u^2} + \frac{a^4}{8}\arcsin\frac{u}{a} + C$

33. $\displaystyle\int \frac{\sqrt{a^2-u^2}}{u}\,du = \sqrt{a^2-u^2} - a\ln\left|\frac{a+\sqrt{a^2-u^2}}{u}\right| + C$

34. $\displaystyle\int \frac{u^2\,du}{\sqrt{a^2-u^2}} = -\frac{u}{2}\sqrt{a^2-u^2} + \frac{a^2}{2}\arcsin\frac{u}{a} + C$

35. $\displaystyle\int \frac{du}{u\sqrt{a^2-u^2}} = -\frac{1}{a}\ln\left|\frac{a+\sqrt{a^2-u^2}}{u}\right| + C$

36. $\displaystyle\int \frac{du}{u^2\sqrt{a^2-u^2}} = -\frac{1}{a^2u}\sqrt{a^2-u^2} + C$

37. $\displaystyle\int \frac{du}{(a^2-u^2)^{3/2}} = \frac{u}{a^2\sqrt{a^2-u^2}} + C$

38. $\displaystyle\int (a^2-u^2)^{3/2}du = -\frac{u}{8}(2u^2-5a^2)\sqrt{a^2-u^2} + \frac{3a^4}{8}\arcsin\frac{u}{a} + C$

Forms Involving $\sqrt{u^2 - a^2}$

39. $\displaystyle\int \sqrt{u^2-a^2}\,du = \frac{u}{2}\sqrt{u^2-a^2} - \frac{a^2}{2}\ln|u+\sqrt{u^2 = a^2}| + C$

40. $\displaystyle\int u^2\sqrt{u^2-a^2}\,du = \frac{u}{8}(2u^2-a^2)\sqrt{u^2-a^2} - \frac{a^4}{8}\ln|u+\sqrt{u^2-a^2}| + C$

41. $\displaystyle\int \frac{\sqrt{u^2-a^2}}{u^2}\,du = -\frac{\sqrt{u^2-a^2}}{u} + \ln|u+\sqrt{u^2-a^2}| + C$

42. $\displaystyle\int \frac{u^2\,du}{\sqrt{u^2-a^2}} = \frac{u}{2}\sqrt{u^2-a^2} + \frac{a^2}{2}\ln|u+\sqrt{u^2-a^2}| + C$

43. $\displaystyle\int \frac{\sqrt{u^2-a^2}}{u}\,du = \sqrt{u^2-a^2} - a\arccos\frac{a}{u} + C$

44. $\displaystyle\int \frac{du}{\sqrt{u^2-a^2}} = \ln|u+\sqrt{u^2-a^2}| + C$

45. $\displaystyle\int \frac{du}{u^2\sqrt{u^2-a^2}} = \frac{\sqrt{u^2-a^2}}{a^2u} + C$

46. $\displaystyle\int \frac{du}{(u^2-a^2)^{3/2}} = -\frac{u}{a^2\sqrt{u^2-a^2}} + C$

Forms Involving $a + bu$

47. $\displaystyle\int \frac{u\,du}{a+bu} = \frac{1}{b^2}(a+bu-a\ln|a+bu|) + C$

48. $\displaystyle\int u\sqrt{a+bu}\,du = \frac{2}{15b^2}(3bu-2a)(a+bu)^{3/2} + C$

49. $\displaystyle\int \frac{u^2du}{a+bu} = \frac{1}{2b^3}[(a+bu)^2 - 4a(a+bu) + 2a^2\ln|a+bu|] + C$

50. $\displaystyle\int \frac{du}{u(a+bu)} = \frac{1}{a}\ln\left|\frac{u}{a+bu}\right| + C$

51. $\displaystyle\int \frac{du}{u^2(a+bu)} = -\frac{1}{au} + \frac{b}{a^2}\ln\left|\frac{a+bu}{u}\right| + C$

52. $\displaystyle\int \frac{u\,du}{(a+bu)^2} = \frac{a}{b^2(a+bu)} + \frac{1}{b^2}\ln|a+bu| + C$

53. $\displaystyle\int \frac{du}{u(a+bu)^2} = \frac{1}{a(a+bu)} - \frac{1}{a^2}\ln\left|\frac{a+bu}{u}\right| + C$

54. $\displaystyle\int \frac{u^2du}{(a+bu)^2} = \frac{1}{b^3}\left(a+bu-\frac{a^2}{a+bu} - 2a\ln|a+bu|\right) + C$

55. $\displaystyle\int \frac{u\,du}{\sqrt{a+bu}} = \frac{2}{3b^2}(bu-2a)\sqrt{a+bu} + C$

56. $\displaystyle\int \frac{u^2du}{\sqrt{a+bu}} = \frac{2}{15b^3}(8a^2+3b^2u^2-4abu)\sqrt{a+bu} + C$

(continued on back page)

THE OREGON STATE UNIVERSITY
CALCULUS CONNECTIONS PROJECT

Calculus of a Single Variable

Thomas P. Dick

Charles M. Patton

PWS PUBLISHING COMPANY
BOSTON

PWS Publishing Company is a division of Wadsworth, Inc.

I(T)P

International Thomson Publishing
The trademark ITP is used under license

Library of Congress Cataloging-in-Publication Data

Dick, Thomas P.
Calculus of a single variable / Thomas P. Dick, Charles M. Patton
p. cm.
Includes index.
ISBN 0-534-93936-8
1. Calculus. I. Patton, Charles M. II. Title.
QA303.D59 1994
515--dc20 94-2244
CIP

Sponsoring Editor Steve Quigley
Developmental Editors Barbara Lovenvirth, David Dietz
Editorial Assistant John Ward
Marketing Manager Marianne Rutter
Production Editor Helen Walden
Manufacturing Coordinator Ellen Glisker
Cover Designer Elise Kaiser
Text Printer/Binder Courier
Cover Printer Henry N. Sawyer Company
Cover Image Stephen Hunt

Contents

0 *Preliminaries* 1

1 *Fundamentals of Functions* 47

2 *Limits -- Local and Global Behavior of Functions* 103

3 *The Derivative* 159

Preface to the Instructor

Curriculum revision is generally a process of gradual evolution of scope and sequence, occasionally punctuated by calls for more fundamental changes in content or delivery. The launching of Sputnik precipitated such a call for reform in mathematics education in the 1950s. We now find ourselves in the midst of a new period of widespread revitalization efforts in mathematics curriculum and instruction. A forward-looking vision of the entire K-12 mathematics curriculum is outlined in the *Curriculum and Evaluation Standards* of the National Council of Teachers of Mathematics. The Mathematical Sciences Education Board has made an eloquent and urgent case for revitalizing mathematics instruction at all levels in preparation for our country's future workforce needs in *Everybody Counts*. Both of these influential documents recognize the emergence of sophisticated computer and calculator technology as redefining the tools of mathematics education.

Calculus occupies a particularly critical position in mathematics education as the gateway to advanced training in most scientific and technical fields. It is fitting that calculus should receive particular attention as we prepare for the needs of the twenty-first century. The Sloan Conference (Tulane, 1986) and the Calculus for a New Century Conference (Washington, 1987) sounded the call for reform in the calculus curriculum. Now the entire introductory course in calculus is being reexamined under the closest scrutiny that it has received in several years. Through a special funding initiative, the National Science Foundation has made resources available for a variety of calculus curriculum revision efforts to be tried and implemented. The Calculus Connections Project is one of these NSF-funded efforts, and this book is a major result of the project.

MAJOR THEMES

The text does not differ radically from a traditional calculus text in terms of major topics. This is as it should be - calculus reform will not change the importance and vitality of the major ideas of calculus, and any wholesale departure from those ideas should be viewed with great skepticism. What *is* possible is a fresh approach to these important ideas in light of the availability of modern technology. In particular, the technology can invite us to change or adopt new emphases in instruction.

Making intelligent use of technology

Computer algebra systems, spreadsheets, and graphing calculators are just a few of the readily available technological tools providing students with new windows of understanding and new opportunities for applying calculus. However, technology should not be viewed as a panacea for calculus instruction. This book seeks to take advantage of these new tools, while at the same time alerting the student to their inherent limitations and the care that must be taken to use technology wisely.

While being technology-aware, the text itself does not assume the availability of any particular machine or software. To do so would invite immediate obsolescence and ignore how quickly technology advances. Rather, the text adopts a language appropriate for the kinds of numerical, graphical, and symbolic capabilities that are found (and will continue to be found) on a wide variety of computer software packages and sophisticated calculators. For example, the language of "zooming in" on the graph of a function is powerfully suggestive without the need for listing specific keystrokes or syntax.

Technology can provide students new opportunities for understanding calculus, but it must be used with care. Numerical computations performed by a machine are subject to magnitude and precision limitations. For example, the calculation of difference quotients is naturally prone to cancellation errors. Machine-generated graphs can also provide misleading information, since graphs consist of discrete collections of pixels whose locations are computed numerically. Symbolic algebra results need to be interpreted in context. Helping students understand the limitations of technology is a major goal of this text. Students are reminded of the care that must be taken to make intelligent use of technology without becoming a victim of its pitfalls.

Since no specific hardware or software is assumed, an instructor will need to judge the appropriateness of any particular activity in light of the technology available. However, the exercises are designed to be compatible with a very wide variety of available software and hardware. A graphing calculator will be adequate for most of the activities.

Multiple representation approach to functions

The most important concept in all of mathematics is that of *function*, and the function concept is central in calculus. The idea of a function as a process accepting inputs and returning outputs can be captured in a variety of representations - numerically as a table of input-output pairs, graphically as a plot of outputs vs. inputs, and symbolically as a formula describing or modeling the input-output process. The interpretations of the core calculus topics of limits and continuity, differentiation, and integration all have different flavors when approached through different representations. The connections we forge among them enrich our personal concept of function.

All too often, students leave the calculus course with an impoverished mental image of function formed in a context dominated by symbolic forms. This book seeks to take a more balanced three-fold approach to functions. With each new topic or result, an explicit effort is made to interpret the meaning and consequences in a numerical, graphical, and symbolic context. Such an approach does not require technology, but the availability of an appropriate device allows us greater access to numerical and graphical representations, while at the same time reducing the need for heavy emphasis of rote "by hand" symbol manipulation skills.

Visualization and approximation

Two themes that become increasingly important with the availability of technology are visualization and approximation. The ability to obtain a machine-generated graph as a first step instead of a last one can completely turn around our approach to a variety of calculus topics. Graphical interpretation skills become primary. In particular, graphing can be used as a powerful problem-solving aid, both in estimating and in monitoring the reasonableness of results obtained numerically or symbolically. Whenever possible, explicit mention is made of the visual interpretation of definitions, theorems, and example solutions, often with direct reference to machine-generated graphs.

Much of calculus grew out of problems of approximation, and many of the key concepts of calculus are best understood as limits of approximations. Numerical tools make once exorbitantly tedious calculations into viable computational estimation strategies.

Accordingly, approximation and estimation techniques are given a high priority throughout the text.

Overview of the materials

Chapter 0 is a brief introduction to the major ideas of calculus, including a discussion of how the notions of infinite processes and approximation arise naturally in the study of real number measurement. Review material on absolute value and interval notation is included. Important issues in the use of technology in calculus are addressed, particularly the limitations of computers and calculators, such as numerical precision and the discrete nature of machine graphics. Functions are introduced as input-output processes, with an emphasis on multiple representations that recurs throughout the text. For students who do not have previous experience with the use of graphing calculators or software, the section on using graphing as a tool will provide a good introduction. Depending on the backgrounds of your students, the amount of time spent on Chapter 0 will vary widely from instructor to instructor.

Chapter 1 presents a library of functions. From the outset, transcendental functions are treated, including trigonometric, exponential, logarithmic, and inverse trigonometric functions. With respect to terminology and notation, the distinctions between variables, constants, and parameters are highlighted.

Chapter 2 discusses limits and continuity. Numerical and graphical approaches receive equal if not greater emphasis than symbolic techniques. The rigorous epsilon-delta definitions are included, but these are explained with reference to their numerical and graphical consequences, rather than a heavy emphasis on proofs. For example, the definition of continuity of a function has a dynamic interpretation in terms of the scaling of a graphing window. The "delta-hunt" for a particular epsilon becomes a search for a certain horizontal scaling, given a vertical scaling. Numerically, epsilons and deltas can be interpreted as output and input tolerances.

Chapter 3 starts with a review of linear functions, and then uses piece-wise linear functions to discuss the notions of *local slope* and *local linearity*. Differentiable functions can then be considered as *approximately* locally linear functions, an idea visually reinforced by zooming in on the graphs of functions. The physical interpretation of derivative as a rate of change is motivated by the problem of estimating a car's speedometer reading using its odometer and a stopwatch.

Difference quotients are used repeatedly to approximate derivative values, and are not considered just an artifact of the formal definition of derivative. Derivative properties and rules are developed and a dictionary of derivative formulas for all the basic algebraic and transcendental functions is included at the end of the chapter. Extra exercises on the mechanics of computing derivatives can be found in the appendices.

Chapter 4 emphasizes the use of the derivative as a measurement tool. The chapter begins by discussing the physical interpretation of derivative as a rate of change. A tangent line is considered as the graph of the best linear approximation of a differentiable function at a point (first-order Taylor forms). The use of the derivative to analyze function behavior, critical points, and extrema, and the consequences of the Mean Value Theorem are interpreted from both physical and graphical perspectives.

Chapter 5 treats applications and extensions of the derivative. The use of calculus to solve optimization problems is illustrated with examples and exercises drawn from the context of the day-to-day operations of a manufacturing facility. Higher-order derivatives are introduced using the physical example of a car's acceleration, and then used in a discussion of concavity and inflection points. This chapter also treats implicit differentiation and its application to related rates, and parametric equations and their application to particle motion.

Chapter 6 motivates the idea of definite integral through both the geometrical interpretation of area and the physical interpretation of accumulated change. By using piece-wise linear functions as examples, many of the properties of definite integrals are explored without the necessity of special summation formulas. A Riemann sum is then motivated as a reasonable approximation technique for more general functions. Antiderivatives are introduced by reversing the problem of determining a car's speedometer reading from its odometer and clock readings to one of determining distance covered from speed and time readings. *Slope fields* (direction fields) are used as a graphical means of approximating the graph of an antiderivative. Noting that $d = rt$ represents the area under the graph of a car's *constant* speed r over time t leads to the more general conjecture that definite integrals can be used to generate antiderivatives. The two fundamental theorems of calculus tie together differentiation and integration. Chapter 6 closes with a discussion of numerical and symbolic techniques of integration. The method of substitution is discussed as the integral counterpart to the chain rule. Additional material on techniques of integration can be found in the appendices.

Chapter 7 emphasizes applications of the definite integral as a measurement tool. The role of Riemann sums in modeling measurements involving continuously varying quantities is highlighted over and over again. Geometric examples include the measurement of area, volume, and arc length. Many of the definite integrals encountered in this chapter require the use of machine numerical integration. There is a discussion of applications of integration to measuring various averages, including moving averages. In turn, the notion of average value of a function suggests a Monte Carlo technique of numerical integration. The chapter then turns to physical applications such as velocity, force, and work, and ends with an introduction to improper integrals.

Chapter 8 discusses differential equations from a variety of viewpoints. Integration by parts is discussed as the counterpart to the product rule in searching for antiderivatives. Slope fields are used to visualize solutions to differential equations. The first fundamental theorem of calculus is reviewed for its use in creating antiderivatives. Exponential and logarithmic functions are both re-examined as the solutions of special differential equations. Applications of exponential functions to problems of growth and decay are included. Chapter 8 ends by treating Euler's method as a graphical application of the fundamental theorem of calculus.

Chapter 9 deals with function approximations. Error bounds for numerical integration are discussed from the point of view of interpolating polynomials. After Taylor polynomials are further developed as function approximations, techniques for using graphics to compare functions are discussed. This leads naturally to a revisiting of limits and indeterminate forms (L'Hopital's Rule). Chapter 9 concludes by examining cubic splines, which combine some of the attributes of both interpolating polynomials and Taylor polynomials (this section can be readily omitted without loss of continuity in the material).

Chapter 10 opens with a discussion of long division as a familiar example of an infinite process that can produce an infinite sequence of approximations. Several examples of sequences, including recursive and iterative sequences, are examined. Root-finding methods, including the bisection method and Newton's method, are also included as examples of iterative techniques yielding sequences of approximations. The Archimedean property of real numbers and Zeno's paradox are used to motivate the idea of a series. A series is then defined as the limit of a sequence of partial sums. Tests of convergence include the Nth term test, comparison and limit comparison tests, the integral test, the alternating series test, and the root and ratio tests. Absolute and conditional convergence are contrasted. After a discussion of power series, including interval and radius of convergence, this chapter concludes with a closer look at iterative methods in general.

The appendices provide review material on trigonometry as well as additional material on techniques of integration (including the method of partial fractions), polar coordinates, complex numbers, and Taylor's formula. The appendices conclude with additional practice exercises for differentiation and integration. Besides short answers to almost all the odd-numbered exercises, several useful formulas and tables can be found in the end pages of the book.

Corrections, comments, and criticisms of the materials are welcomed, and can be directed to the authors.

ANCILLARIES

The ***Instructor's Resource Manual*** provides answers to all the exercises, a pool of test items for each chapter (with answers), and additional commentary on goals and philosophy of the book, suggestions for pacing, and section-by-section notes to aid instructors using the materials.

The ***Student's Resource Manual*** is a supplement that provides detailed answers to selected exercises, as well as programs for graphing calculators that should prove useful in the sections on numerical integration, slope fields, Newton's method, and Euler's method.

If your school makes use of a computer algebra system in teaching calculus, or if students have access to such software - Mathematica, Maple, Derive, or Theorist - other resources are available from PWS Publishing Company. ***Notebooks*** have been prepared to accompany this book for each of these computer algebra systems. Each includes examples of step-by-step worked exercises from the text. Contact your bookstore for more information.

Preface to the Student

Books are written to be read. Yes, that is true even of mathematics books! We strongly encourage you to read the chapter introductions and the explanations in each section carefully, and to follow closely the discussion of examples. Perhaps you are accustomed to skipping to the exercises of a mathematics textbook first, and then searching back for an example that is a "clone" of the problem at hand that you can mimic. Certainly, this book has many examples and exercises to illustrate and help you practice your calculus skills. But there are also many problems in this text that ask you to reflect on and explain in your own words some of the important ideas of calculus. Other problems are designed to force you to think about these ideas in new ways. You may feel frustrated at times, but keep in mind that the effort you make to really understand the ideas in calculus will give you an ownership of them that will last long after you forget some of the specific technical details.

USING TECHNOLOGY TO STUDY CALCULUS

Some of the technology made possible by calculus includes devices such as graphing calculators and computers. We live in an exciting age where these powerful computational tools enable us to perform complex numerical and symbolic computations and provide tremendous graphics capabilities at our fingertips. In turn, we now have both new ways to understand the ideas of calculus and new opportunities to apply calculus.

However, even the most powerful technology is of little use if we do not know how it can and cannot be applied. We recognize that new technological tools are available and this book was written with the *intelligent* use of those tools in mind. The use of technology to study functions is not without its pitfalls. To use calculators and computers intelligently requires a knowledge of their limitations. Solving important mathematical problems will always require the inspiration, recognition, and application of the right idea at the right time.

If you have access to one of the computer algebra systems now being used to teach calculus at many schools - Mathematica, Maple,

Derive, or Theorist - you may be interested in another problem-solving aid provided by the publisher. The *Notebooks* prepared to accompany this book are data disks comprised of worked examples and exercises from the text. The examples on each disk show, step-by-step, how to use a particular computer algebra system to solve selected problems from the text. (Contact your bookstore for more information.)

In calculus and other branches of mathematics, you will often encounter problems for which there is no specific recipe to solve them. Even in these instances, there are a variety of strategies you can use to make progress toward a solution. The next section gives you some hints from a master problem solver. We hope you find them useful.

GENERAL HINTS FOR SOLVING PROBLEMS: POLYA'S FOUR STEPS

George Polya (1887-1985) was considered by many as the greatest teacher of mathematical problem solving. In his work *How To Solve It*, Polya discusses in detail many aspects of the problem-solving process. He provides several useful general strategies (or heuristics) for mathematical problem solving. Here are the four basic steps Polya outlined in the problem-solving process.

POLYA'S FOUR STEPS IN PROBLEM SOLVING

1. UNDERSTAND THE PROBLEM
2. DEVISE A PLAN
3. CARRY OUT THE PLAN
4. LOOK BACK

Let's elaborate on these problem-solving steps.

1. UNDERSTAND THE PROBLEM

This means *understand what the problem is asking for.* While that may seem obvious, there are many times when we dive into a problem and waste a lot of time and effort that could have been saved by a few extra moments of reflection at the beginning. Ask yourself these questions: Do I understand all the terminology? What is given? What is the goal? Am I required to find something or to prove something? Is there enough information? Is there extraneous information? Have I seen a similar problem before? Rewriting the problem in your own words, drawing a figure, trying some examples are all ways to clarify a problem statement.

The full power of algebra and calculus can be unleashed if we can model a problem situation as a function or as an equation or inequality. We may be able to introduce a coordinate system for the purposes of graphing. The act of identifying and labeling variable quantities in and of itself may clarify aspects of the problem to us.

2. DEVISE A PLAN

Devise a plan of action for the problem. If you don't know where to begin, then try a general problem-solving heuristic or strategy. Three very useful heuristics include:

Trial and Error. At worst, you may get a better feel for the constraints of the problem situation. At best, you may stumble on the answer directly. Trial and error doesn't necessarily mean blind guesswork; our early guesses can help guide us in making better guesses. Making a list of the results of our trials may reveal a pattern or relationship. Mathematics is sometimes called the science or art of finding patterns.

Try a Simpler Problem. If the original problem seems too complex or confusing, try simplifying it first and solving that version. The solution to the simpler problem may give insights on how to solve the original problem. Exactly how do you make a problem simpler? Some of the ways include: substituting a smaller number in place of a larger one given in the problem; substituting a specific numerical value for an unknown constant or parameter (0 or 1 are often good substitution choices); making up a related problem that involves fewer dimensions or unknowns; and adding or dropping some of the problem constraints.

Try Extreme or Special Cases. We may get a special understanding from examining the problem situation in extreme or special cases. For example, if a problem involved the *elliptical* orbits of planets, we might benefit by considering the special case of a *circular* orbit. Substituting extreme values for an unknown variable can also give us useful information. For example, a question involving lines in the plane can be examined for the special cases of horizontal (zero slope) and vertical (undefined slope) lines. Making a list of special cases may also reveal a pattern or relationship.

3. CARRY OUT THE PLAN

Carry out your plan of action. Implement the strategy you've chosen until the problem is solved or until a new course of action is suggested. Give yourself a reasonable period of time to solve the problem. Monitor yourself. If you feel that you've embarked on a dead-end road then consider a change of strategy. Don't be afraid of starting all over. Many times a fresh start and a new strategy lead to success. You can have a flash of insight when you least expect it!

4. LOOK BACK

Check your answer to see if it really satisfies the requirements of your problem. Looking back means more than just checking your answer, though. Also look at your method of solution. Can you see another way of coming up with the answer? Can you see how your method could be used on other problems? Look forward to how you might generalize or extend your solution.

Calculus arose in response to the need to solve certain problems, and to understand the what and why of calculus requires understanding how, when, and where calculus can be used to solve problems. Calculus provides some very powerful tools for calculating quantities related to change. The derivative provides a means of measuring rates of change, and the integral provides a means of measuring accumulated change. This book is devoted to helping you understand these fundamental ideas so that you can successfully apply calculus to solving problems.

Your study of calculus can be an exciting intellectual adventure. Good luck on your journey!

Acknowledgments

The Calculus Connections Project has been made possible with the support of the National Science Foundation, Oregon State University and the Lasells Stewart Foundation, the Hewlett-Packard Corporation, and PWS Publishing Company.

This book was prepared using Donald Knuth's TeX with Textures (Blue Sky Research) and the AMS-TeX - Version 2.0 macro package (American Mathematical Society). Thanks to Marilyn Wallace, Donna Kent, D'Anne Hammond, and Colleen Dick for their contributions to the technical typesetting of the text. The illustrations were produced using MacPaint and MacDraw II (Claris), Adobe Illustrator, PSMathgraphs II (Maryann software), and Grapher 881 (thanks to Steve Scarborough). Thanks to George Dick for his painstaking preparation and revisions of the illustrations.

A project such as this owes thanks to many people. First and foremost, we wish to thank Dr. Dianne Hart for her exemplary work throughout the life of this project, including the preparation of supporting materials for instructors, coordination of so many of the project's instructional activities, and most importantly, for her research on students' use of multiple representations and technology. Special thanks are also due to Howard L. Wilson of Oregon State University, for his exceptional instructional and in-service work with the Calculus Connections project. We would also like to acknowledge our appreciation for the efforts and support of many others:

To the mathematics department at Oregon State University, for its encouragement of the laboratory approach to calculus, and to all the faculty and graduate teaching assistants involved in the experimental calculus program at Oregon State University.

To Kathy Dukes, Alison Warr, Michelle Jones Zandieh, and Dianne Hart, for preparation of answers to exercises and other instructional resources.

To past and present advisors and consultants to the project: Bert Waits (Ohio State University), Franklin Demana (Ohio State University), Gregory D. Foley (Sam Houston State University), Thomas Tucker (Colgate University), Robert Moore (University of Washington), William Wickes (Hewlett-Packard), John Kenelly (Clemson University), Don

LaTorre (Clemson University), and Jeanette Palmiter (Portland State University).

Many people reviewed and/or pilot tested the preliminary edition drafts and revisions. We wish to acknowledge them for their many useful suggestions and constructive criticisms.

Nacer Abrouk	Rose-Hulman Institute of Technology
Nancy Baggs	University of Colorado - Colorado Springs
Maureen A. Bardwell	Westfield State College
Barry Bergman	Clackamas County Community College
Marcelle Bessman	Frostburg State University
E. E. Burniston	North Carolina State University
Herb Brown	SUNY at Albany
Dan Chiddix	Ricks College
Mary Louise Collette	Mount St. Mary's College
Debra Crawford	Riverside High School
Carol Crawford	United States Naval Academy
Deborah Crocker	Miami University (Ohio)
Catherine Curtis	Mt. Hood Community College
Gerald Daniels	Mitchell High School
Wade Ellis	West Valley College
Kevin Fitzpatrick	Greenwich High School
William Francis	Michigan Technological University
Dewey Furness	Ricks College
Charles Geldaker	Lakeridge High School
Anthony J. Giovannitti	University of Southern Mississippi
Ron Goolsby	Winthrop University
Mary Ann Gore	Warner Robins High School
Samuel Gough	East Meklenburg High School
Karen Graham	University of New Hampshire
Murli Gupta	George Washington University
James Hall	Westminster College
Donnie Hallstone	Green River Community College
Betty Hawkins	Shoreline Community College
Warren Hickman	Westminster College
Mark Howell	Gonzaga College High School
Howard Iseri	Mansfield University
Gary S. Itzkowitz	Glassboro State College
William Kiele	United States Air Force Academy
Elaine Klett	Brookdale Community College
Paul Latiolais	Portland State University
Tom R. Lucas	University of North Carolina - Charlotte
Lewis Lum	University of Portland
Mary Martin	Winthrop College
Marian McCain	Centennial High School
Joan McCarter	Arizona State University
Richard Metzler	University of New Mexico
Dennis Mick	Carroll College
Teresa Michnowicz	Jersey City State College
Laura Moore-Mueller	Green River Community College
Lawrence Morgan	Montgomery County Community College
Stephen Murdock	Tulsa Junior College

Mel Noble	Olympic High School
Michele Olsen	College of the Redwoods
John Oman	University of Wisconsin - Oshkosh
Robert Piziak	Baylor University
Priscilla Putman-Haindl	Jersey City State College
William Raddatz	Linfield College
Carla Randall	Lake Oswego High School
Laurel Rogers	University of Colorado - Colorado Springs
Audrey Rose	Tulsa Junior College
Donald Rossi	DeAnza College
David Royster	University of North Carolina - Charlotte
G.T. Springer	Alamo Heights High School
Larry Sternberger	Tulsa Junior College
Ted Sundstrom	Grand Valley State University
W. Todd Timmons	Westark Community College
Sandra Vrem	College of the Redwoods
John Whitesitt	Southern Oregon State College
Kei Yasuda	Lane Community College

To the hundreds of other instructors and the thousands of students who used the published preliminary edition, for their valuable feedback. Special thanks to Lewis Lum, William Kiele, and James Hall, for their very detailed reviews of the book, and for the improvements in exposition and problems they suggested to us.

To the editorial and production staff at PWS Publishing Company, for their support and expertise in helping disseminate the work of the project: David Dietz, Steve Quigley, Christian Gal, Barbara Lovenvirth, Helen Walden, and John Ward.

Finally, to Leslie and Colleen, Daniel, Jean, Connor, Eamon, and Eleanor, for enduring the authors throughout this project with love and support, we dedicate this book.

Thomas P. Dick
Charles M. Patton

Corvallis, Oregon

About the Authors

Calculus of a Single Variable is the product of five years of intensive experimentation, writing, and revision by Drs. Thomas Dick and Charles Patton. The textbook is the outgrowth of the authors' interest in the teaching and learning of calculus, and how emerging technologies can be intelligently used to enhance students' understanding of calculus.

Thomas Dick is the director of the Calculus Connections Project, a program funded by the National Science Foundation as part of a major effort to revise the calculus curriculum in preparation for the needs of a new century. He earned his Ph.D. at the University of New Hampshire, where he served as the coordinator of the UNH Calculus Testing Center for two years before joining the mathematics faculty of Oregon State University. In 1988 he received the Carter Award for outstanding and inspirational undergraduate teaching in Oregon State University's College of Science. He has been widely involved in high school and college teacher education, particularly in calculus and the use of technology in the mathematics classroom. He has served both as a reader and as a consultant for the Advanced Placement Program in Mathematics, and has directed several workshops and institutes for teachers and instructors. Dr. Dick is on the editorial board of the Journal of Computers in Mathematics and Science Teaching, and has been appointed a member of the Committee on Research in Undergraduate Mathematics Education by the American Mathematical Society. He has written extensively on the use of technology in the mathematics classroom, including papers for *The Computing Teacher*, the Mathematical Association of America's *Calculus as a Laboratory Course*, and the National Council of Teachers of Mathematics 1992 Yearbook on *Calculators in Mathematics Education.*

Charles Patton earned his Ph.D. at the State University of New York at Stonybrook, studying also at the Mathematical Institute, Oxford, and Institute des Hautes Etudes Scientifique, France. His doctoral work was in the mathematical foundations of relativity and quantum mechanics. He was awarded an American Mathematical Society Postdoctoral Research Fellowship and has been a member of the Institute for Advanced Study, Princeton. After teaching mathematics at the University of Utah, Dr. Patton joined the Calculator Research and

Development team for Hewlett-Packard, where he has been instrumental in the first implementation of a computer algebra system on hand-held computers. He has been awarded several patents for his work related to computational systems for computer algebra. Dr. Patton has numerous publications on representation theory and twistor theory in such journals as the *Transactions* and the *Bulletin of the American Mathematical Society*.

0

Preliminaries

What is *calculus*? The word itself suggests calculations, but to think of calculus merely as a collection of computational techniques does a grave injustice to the subject. Rather, calculus is a network of fundamentally important mathematical *ideas*. These ideas originated in attempts to solve particular measurement problems in geometry and physics. Specifically, the problems of measurement of length, area, and volume in geometry and the problems of measuring force, velocity, and acceleration in physics gave birth to the calculus. Today the applications of calculus reach far and wide to quantitative analysis in fields ranging from archaeology to zoology.

There are two major branches of calculus. The *differential calculus* involves measuring the instantaneous rate of change of one quantity relative to the change in another quantity. This physical measurement problem in differential calculus corresponds to a geometric measurement problem—finding the slope of a graph at a specific point. *Integral calculus* has its origins in the geometric problems of measuring length, area, and volume, but it has found wide applications to problems of measuring accumulated change. The realization of the inverse nature of these two branches marked the dawn of the modern age of calculus.

Why is calculus useful? Understanding the dynamics of *change* is a primary goal in the study of any system, whether it be physical, biological, economic, or social. When we analyze processes involving continuous change, calculus allows us to describe and measure the rate of that change and its total effects. By harnessing the notion of *infinite processes*, especially as they relate to approximation, calculus provides both powerful tools and an effective language for describing and measuring change.

Calculus—past and future

Whether calculus was *invented* or *discovered* is a matter for philosophical debate. Many of the ideas and insights of calculus stem from geometrical and physical observations. In that regard, calculus was discovered. But ideas and insights arise within our minds, and the language and notation with which we communicate them are very much a creative endeavor, so calculus was also invented. In any case, the development of calculus is one of the crowning intellectual achievements of the human race.

The impact of calculus on technological progress alone makes its development of great historical significance. But calculus is a living, growing body of knowledge whose importance to the quantitative understanding of the world around us remains vital. As we move into the next century and address increasingly complex problems, knowledge of calculus will be indispensable to analyzing and describing the dynamics of change.

0.1 REAL NUMBERS

Measurement is a fundamental theme in all of mathematics. Two of our earliest mathematical experiences have to do with measurement: counting and using a ruler. Counting necessarily uses only whole numbers 0, 1, 2, 3, ..., and counting problems occupy much of what is called *discrete mathematics.*

We associate ruler measurement, on the other hand, with the system of **real numbers**. Indeed, the *real number line* can be thought of as an infinitely long continuous ruler, with each real number associated with exactly one point on the line and, conversely, every point on the line corresponding to a unique real number (Figure 0.1). The problems of measurement with real numbers are said to belong to *continuous mathematics.*

While the whole numbers can be thought of as particular real numbers, there is a major distinction between counting problems and real-number measurement problems. For example, suppose you were asked to count the number of letters on the page you are now reading. By directly counting, you have every reason to expect your answer to be exactly correct.

On the other hand, suppose you were asked to measure the height of the page. If you chose a ruler to make the measurement, your answer could hardly be more accurate than the thickness of the marks on the ruler. Even if you have a sophisticated optical scanner providing a digital readout of the height, the precision of the measurement you obtain is limited.

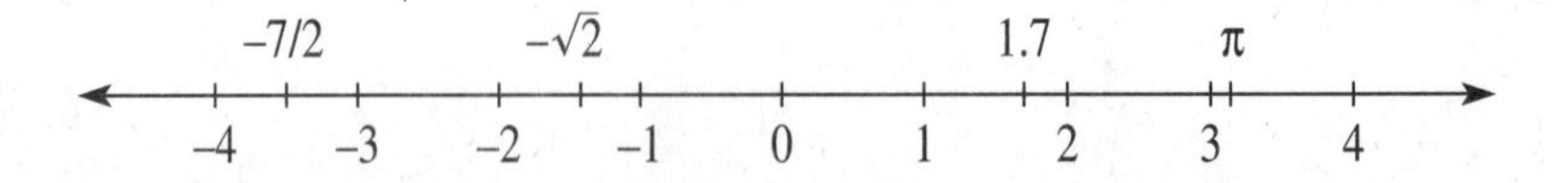

Figure 0.1 The real number line.

This imprecision is a fact of life when we deal with any measuring instrument. Mathematics, however, can provide us with *precise* relationships between quantities. For example, the familiar Pythagorean theorem tells us that

$$a^2 + b^2 = c^2$$

when a, b, and c represent the leg lengths and hypotenuse length, respectively, of a right triangle. Provided that we know the exact values of a and b, we can compute the exact value of c. Or can we?

Rational and irrational numbers

One problem of measurement that the ancient Greeks wrestled with had to do with the diagonal of a square with sides of unit length.

If we consider the diagonal of the square shown in Figure 0.2 as being the hypotenuse of a right triangle with legs each of one unit length, then the Pythagorean theorem tells us that the diagonal has length $\sqrt{1^2 + 1^2} = \sqrt{2}$. The difficulty the ancient Greeks had was not with the Pythagorean theorem, but with the number $\sqrt{2}$ itself. They expected $\sqrt{2}$ to be a **rational number** (that is, a *ratio* p/q of two integers p and q). However, $\sqrt{2}$ is an example of an **irrational number**, because it is a real number that *cannot* be expressed as the ratio of two integers.

Real numbers can be represented in other ways. Perhaps the most common representation of real numbers is by decimal notation. Any real number has a (possibly infinitely long) decimal representation. The decimal representations of rational numbers either terminate or have a finite block of digits that repeats indefinitely.

For example, the rational number $22/7$ (a common approximation of the *irrational* number π) can be written as

$$\frac{22}{7} = 3.\overline{142857} = 3.142857142857142857142857\ldots$$

where the overline indicates that this block of six digits repeats indefinitely.

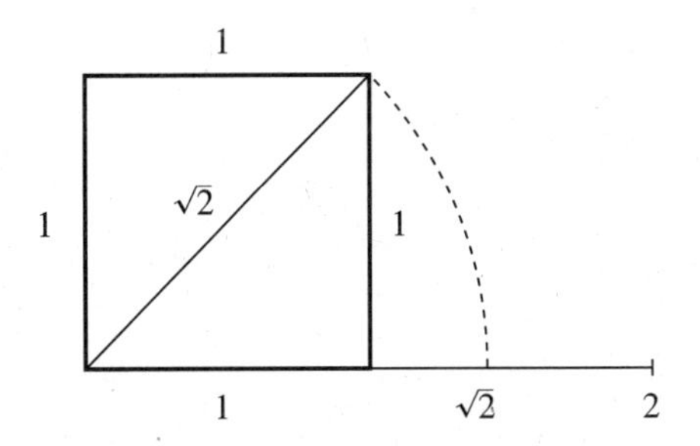

Figure 0.2 Measuring the length of the diagonal of a unit square.

This notation allows us to communicate the entire decimal expansion, even though it is infinitely long.

The decimal representation of $\sqrt{2}$ will not reveal any such block of repeating digits:

$$\sqrt{2} = 1.41421356\ldots$$

Here, the use of "..." means only that the decimal representation continues; it is not meant to convey that some repeating pattern exists. How can we say that we *know* $\sqrt{2}$ is a perfectly good real number representing a point on the number line, if we have no way of knowing all of the digits in its decimal representation?

Infinite processes and approximations

The fundamental problem of representing real numbers like $\sqrt{2}$ is at the heart of calculus. While it's physically impossible to write down the entire decimal representation of $\sqrt{2}$, we *can* describe an *infinite process* that would yield a sequence of decimal approximations, each closer to the exact value of $\sqrt{2}$. Let's see how. Here's a fact we'll use:

> NOTE: If x and y are *positive real numbers* and $x^2 < y^2$, then $x < y$.

So, if we can find two positive real numbers x and y such that $x^2 < 2 < y^2$, we can conclude that $x < \sqrt{2} < y$. Our strategy is to approximate $\sqrt{2}$ by keeping it "trapped" between two numbers with a finite number of decimal places.

First, we can see that

$$1 < \sqrt{2} < 2$$

because $1^2 = 1 < 2 < 4 = 2^2$. This just tells us that $\sqrt{2} = 1.\textit{something}$.

If we compute $(1.1)^2$, $(1.2)^2$, $(1.3)^2$, and so on, we will be able to determine the first decimal place of $\sqrt{2}$. Try it, and you'll see that

$$(1.4)^2 = 1.96 < 2 < 2.25 = (1.5)^2,$$

so we must have $1.4 < \sqrt{2} < 1.5$.

Now we can determine the second decimal place by checking the values $(1.41)^2$, $(1.42)^2$, and so on. We have

$$(1.41)^2 = 1.9881 < 2 < 2.0164 = (1.42)^2,$$

so $1.41 < \sqrt{2} < 1.42$.

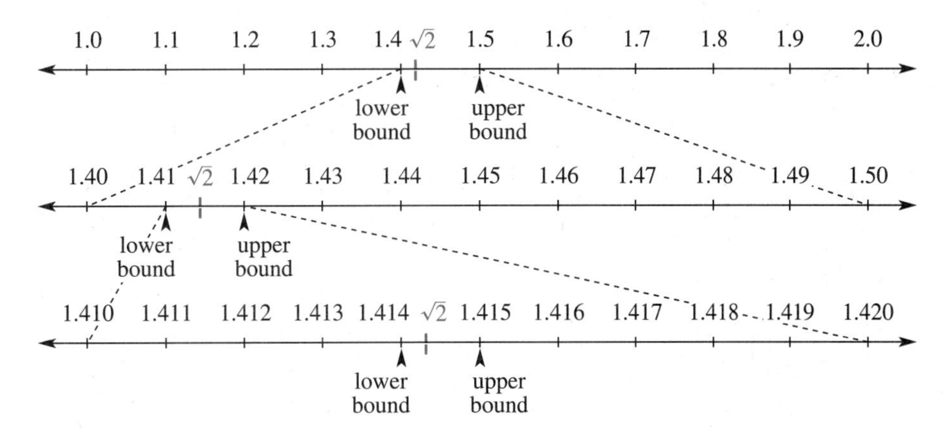

Figure 0.3 Three steps in approximating $\sqrt{2}$.

We can continue in this way. Since $(1.414)^2 = 1.999396 < 2 < 2.002225 = (1.415)^2$, we have $1.414 < \sqrt{2} < 1.415$.

For these first three steps, Figure 0.3 illustrates on a number line the lower and upper bounds trapping $\sqrt{2}$. If we use the lower of the two approximations at each step of this process, we obtain a sequence of numbers: $1, 1.4, 1.41, 1.414, 1.4142, \ldots,$ where each number in the sequence determines another decimal place of $\sqrt{2}$. The upper approximation at each step differs from the lower approximation by one digit in the last decimal place, and these upper approximations also give us a sequence of numbers *converging* on $\sqrt{2}$.

While this process never ends after a finite number of steps, it really can be thought of as *determining* the square root of two. The difference between the upper and lower estimates can be made as small as we like by just continuing the process. Only *one* number can fit between every pair of approximations, and, by design, we have guaranteed that $\sqrt{2}$ is between every pair of approximations. Hence, $\sqrt{2}$ is the *unique* number determined by this sequence of inequalities.

Of numbers and symbols

Of course, using a decimal approximation of $\sqrt{2}$ to several thousand digits would be silly in performing computational work with physical measurements, which are precise to only a few decimal places. Is there ever any advantage to using the symbol $\sqrt{2}$ as opposed to simply using a sufficiently accurate decimal approximation? Some might maintain that $\sqrt{2}$ is *exact* or somehow more aesthetically pleasing. But the real advantage to the symbol $\sqrt{2}$ is that it reminds us of the defining characteristic of the number: $\sqrt{2}$ is that *unique* positive real number whose square is 2, and whose decimal representation is trapped by the infinite approximation process we just described. Once we use a decimal approximation for $\sqrt{2}$, it becomes

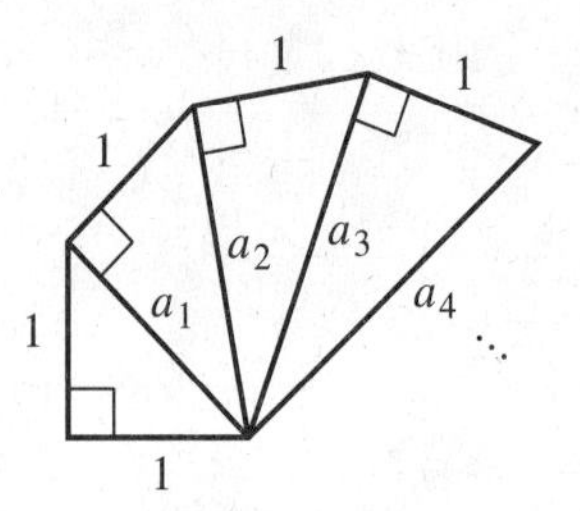

Figure 0.4 A "spiral" of right triangles.

anonymous and its defining characteristic is lost amid other calculations. Carrying the true identity of a number through our calculations can prove to be extremely helpful in discovering an important pattern or relationship.

Look at the right triangles shown in Figure 0.4. The first triangle has legs of unit length and hypotenuse a_1. The second triangle has one leg of unit length and the hypotenuse of the first triangle as its other leg. Similarly, the third triangle has one leg of unit length and the hypotenuse of the second triangle as its other leg. We could imagine building these triangles *ad infinitum.* (Of course, they will eventually "spiral" around and overlap the earlier triangles.) Is there a pattern to the lengths of the hypotenuses, which we have labeled $a_1, a_2, a_3, a_4, \ldots$ (where a_n represents the hypotenuse of the nth triangle)?

Using a calculator and the Pythagorean theorem, we obtain:

$$\begin{aligned} a_1 &\approx 1.414213562, \\ a_2 &\approx 1.732050807, \\ a_3 &\approx 1.999999999, \\ a_4 &\approx 2.236067977, \\ &\vdots \end{aligned}$$

but by maintaining the "radical" notation, we obtain

$$a_1 = \sqrt{2},\ a_2 = \sqrt{3},\ a_3 = \sqrt{4},\ a_4 = \sqrt{5},\ \ldots.$$

From which sequence could you most easily predict the value of a_{99}?

EXERCISES for Section 0.1

For exercises 1–4: Consider all proper fractions p/q (that is, p and q are positive integers with $p < q$) with denominators $q \leq 10$.

1. How many *different* real numbers are represented?

2. Exactly which of these fractions have terminating decimal representations?

3. Which of these fractions is closest to $\sqrt{2}/2$?

4. Which of these fractions is closest to $\pi/4$?

---

5. If a rational number p/q is in reduced form (in other words, p and q have no common integer factors greater than 1), how can one tell whether the number has a terminating decimal representation without actually doing the long division?

6. Give an example of a rational number having two different decimal representations. (Hint: $3 \times \frac{1}{3} = 1$.)

7. In the decimal representation of $22/7$, there is a block of 6 digits that repeats indefinitely. Can the number of digits in the repeating block of the decimal representation of p/q ever be equal to or greater than q, the denominator? If so, give an example. If not, explain why.

8. Is $0.101001000100001000001\ldots$ a rational number? Why or why not?

For exercises 9–16: Refer to Figure 0.4 in the text.

9. What is the value of a_{99} if we continue the sequence of right triangles?

10. What is the area of the 100th triangle?

11. What is the value of a_n if we continue the sequence of right triangles?

12. What is the area of the nth triangle?

13. Suppose that we use each hypotenuse a_n as the diameter of a circle. What would be the area of the nth circle?

14. What is the measure of the smallest angle in the 100th triangle?

15. What is the measure of the smallest angle in the nth triangle?

16. For what value of n does the nth triangle overlap the first triangle?

---

17. Railroad tracks have small gaps between sections to allow for expansion and contraction of the metal due to temperature changes. Suppose that someone lays a 1-mile stretch of metal track with no gaps between two walls, and on a hot summer day the track expands 1 inch in length for every 100 feet. If one end of the track stays fixed to the ground, and the track does not curve, how high will the other end of the track have to rise to compensate for the new length?

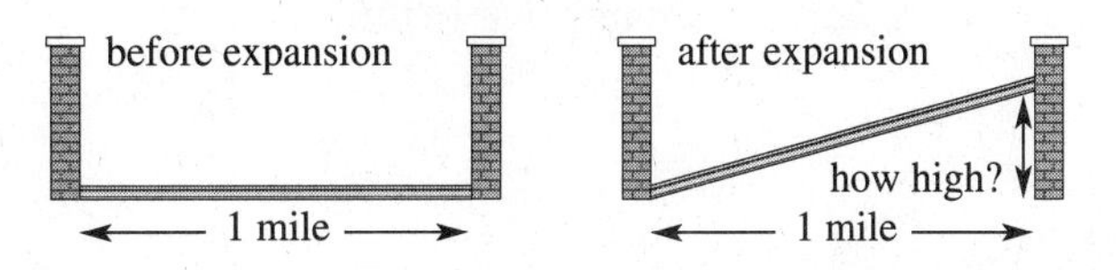

For Exercise 17

18. Assume that the circumference of the earth at the equator is exactly 25000 miles. If a rope is wrapped around the earth at the equator so that it is 3 feet off the ground at all points, how much more than 25000 miles of rope is needed?

0.2 MACHINE COMPUTATIONS

Calculators and computers are machines that can greatly enhance our computational powers. Originally, these technological devices were considered primarily as "number crunchers." Now, they are also valued highly for their graphic and even symbolic calculation facilities. The emergence of such machines as readily available additions to our mathematical toolkits is changing the landscape of mathematics. To use calculators and/or computers effectively and intelligently in calculus, you should be aware of some of the limitations of machine computations.

Magnitude—underflow and overflow errors

Machine numerical computations are generally limited in **magnitude**. By *magnitude* we mean the *size* of the numbers: what are the largest and smallest numbers (in absolute value) that can be handled or represented by the calculator or computer? Errors related to magnitude are called **overflow** (too large) or **underflow** (too small) errors.

EXAMPLE 1 Suppose that we have a machine capable of displaying eight digits, so that the largest-magnitude numbers it can handle are

$$99999999 \qquad \text{and} \qquad -99999999$$

and the smallest-magnitude *nonzero* numbers it can handle are

$$.00000001 \qquad \text{and} \qquad -.00000001.$$

What happens when we attempt to compute

$$.0000006 \div 300 \times 50000000$$

on this machine?

▶▶▶ **Reminder: The hierarchy or order of arithmetic operation evaluations is understood to be:**
1. parenthetical expressions,
2. exponentiations,
3. multiplications and divisions from left to right,
4. additions and subtractions from left to right.

Solution Since division and multiplication are on the same level of the hierarchy of arithmetic operations, this is understood to be $(.0000006 \div 300) \times 50000000$ and *not* $.0000006 \div (300 \times 50000000)$. Now, $.0000006 \div 300 = .000000002$, so we will either get an *underflow* error message or the machine will simply round the result to 0, in which case we'll end up with a final result of 0 instead of the correct result, .1. ■

EXAMPLE 2 Explain what happens when we try to compute $400 \times 30000000 \times .0000006$ on the same eight-digit machine.

Solution We could receive either an *overflow* error message or an intermediate result of 99999999 for the product 400×30000000. ■

Of course, a calculator or computer displaying more than just eight digits would have no trouble with these specific calculations, but it would be a simple matter to come up with similar examples that also result in underflow or overflow for these machines. The next example shows how we can extend the usefulness of a computational machine by using a little forethought.

EXAMPLE 3 How can we compute $400 \times 30000000 \times .0000006$ on the eight-digit machine without an overflow problem?

Solution If we first compute $30000000 \times .0000006$ (using the fact that real-number multiplication is *associative*), we obtain

$$400 \times 18 = 7200.$$

(Can you see a way to evaluate the expression in Example 1 on the same machine that avoids the intermediate underflow result?) ■

Exponential notation can allow a much wider range of values to be represented. For example, the numbers involved in the computation of Example 1 might be displayed as

$$6.0E{-7} \div 3.0E2 \times 5.0E7.$$

Here rEn stands for $r \times 10^n$. While the use of exponential notation makes overflow and underflow errors less likely, nevertheless there is some ceiling on how large the exponents can be. Ultimately, there are limitations on the magnitude of numbers represented by any machine.

Precision—round-off and cancellation errors

By **precision**, we mean the *relative accuracy* of the numbers represented by a machine. The precision of a calculator or computer can be measured by the number of *digits* that can be used to represent a decimal number.

EXAMPLE 4 If a machine uses exponential notation, how many digits of precision are required to *exactly* display 0.00327 and 40.0056007?

Solution $0.00327 = 3.27E{-3}$ requires only 3 digits of precision to be displayed exactly, while $40.0056007 = 4.00056007E1$ requires 9 digits of precision. ■

In practical terms of measurement in the physical world, we should use only the number of digits warranted by the accuracy of our measuring devices. Any calculator or computer that can display or store only a limited number of digits must either truncate (drop off the digits beyond a certain place) or round off the real numbers it represents as decimals. The cumulative effects of these **round-off errors** through a sequence of computations can be very severe.

EXAMPLE 5 Suppose that we have a machine that rounds to 8 digits of accuracy. Describe what happens when we calculate the following:

$$\frac{(1000 + 0.12345) - (1000.123 + 0.00044)}{0.0000001}.$$

Solution If we compute the value of the expressions within parentheses first, then the calculator must round each of them to the fourth decimal place, giving us

$$\frac{1000.1235 - 1000.1234}{0.0000001} = \frac{0.0001}{0.0000001} = 1000$$

when the *actual* result is only 100. ■

Here the round-off errors have led to a special phenomenon, which we refer to as **cancellation error**. Cancellation errors can occur when we compute the (relatively) small difference between two (relatively) large quantities. Can you see another way to perform the computation (with the same machine) that would avoid this difficulty? Again, another machine having more digits of precision certainly could have handled this particular calculation without any trouble, but no matter how many digits of precision our machine can muster, we can devise other examples that result in significant cancellation errors.

Note that a machine's precision is described in terms of the maximum number of digits it can handle, and not in terms of the smallest number that it can represent. Machine precision also affects our ability to distinguish between two numbers. Suppose our machine can handle only 8 digits of precision. The numbers 12345.6789 and 12345.6794 are indistinguishable on this machine, because both are rounded to 12345.679.

In summary, machine limitations on magnitude limit how far we can look up and down the real number line, while machine limitations on precision blur our vision when looking close-up at points on the line. The computational speed offered by calculators and computers is great, but you must keep these limitations in mind if you are to take full advantage of their numerical capabilities.

Machine symbolic computations

A **computer algebra system** is a machine or software package capable not only of numerical and graphical computations but also of symbolic computations. Perhaps the most important thing to keep in mind when using a computer algebra system for symbolic computation has to do with the importance of context. By *context*, we mean that the same symbols can carry different meanings and interpretations, depending on when and where we use them. For example,

$$y = 3$$

can represent simply a specific replacement value for the variable y in one context, or it might refer to a defining formula for a *constant function* in another context. The symbol dy/dx has a very important meaning in calculus that is quite different from another interpretation as a quotient of two algebraic quantities.

In order to manipulate symbolic expressions, a computer algebra system must "know" the context in which it is working. If we do not communicate this context effectively to the system, it may be forced to make some assumptions that do not match our intentions. For example, cancelling the *d*'s in dy/dx would be grossly inappropriate in the context of the expression's usual meaning in calculus.

In short, symbols carry meanings that often depend on context. Computer algebra systems (and people, for that matter) manipulate symbols according to certain procedures and patterns. For those manipulations to make sense, we need to monitor closely the match between the context the system assumes and the meanings we intend for the symbols.

Technology can give us tremendous power and offer opportunities for new insights in the study of calculus. To take full advantage of that power and those opportunities requires knowing the technology's limitations and both how to recognize and when to expect their effects. One goal of this book is to show some of the ways you can exploit calculators and computers to aid your understanding and appreciation for calculus. The goal is to use technology *intelligently*, so that you can reap its benefits while avoiding its pitfalls.

EXERCISES for Section 0.2

For exercises 1–8: Assuming that a machine uses exponential notation, how many digits of precision are required to display each of the following numbers *exactly*?

1. 0.000000125

2. 2000.0002

3. 2001

4. 2.125×10^{468}

5. 2000000

6. -34.780×10^{-3}

7. 0

8. π

For exercises 9–12: Suppose that a machine rounds to 8 digits of precision (but doesn't use exponential notation).

9. How could you compute the result in Example 1 and avoid the underflow problem?

10. How many *different* numbers between 100000 and 100002 can this machine display?

11. How many *different* numbers between -1 and 1 can this machine display?

12. How could you compute the value of the expression in Example 5 and avoid the cancellation problem?

For exercises 13–16: Suppose that a machine rounds to 12 digits of accuracy and uses exponential notation for exponents $-99 \leq n \leq 99$.

13. What is the smallest possible positive number this machine can display?

14. What is the largest possible positive number this machine can display?

15. How many different numbers between 10 and 11 can this machine display?

16. How many different numbers between 100 and 101 can this machine display?

---

17. Explain the statement, "A machine can distinguish between two numbers best when both are close to zero. "

18. Three students with different machines attempt to take the square root of -1. One obtains a display of the letter "E," one obtains a display of the letter "i," and the third obtains $(0, 1)$. Explain the three results.

0.3 ABSOLUTE VALUE AND INTERVAL NOTATION

Mathematical notation has a purpose, and it is rarely chosen arbitrarily. Its goal is to communicate important information effectively and concisely. Absolute value notation is used to communicate the *distance* between two numbers.

Definition 1

The **absolute value** of a real number x is defined as follows:

$$|x| = \begin{cases} x \text{ if } x \geq 0 \\ -x \text{ if } x < 0. \end{cases}$$

This is an example of a *split formula*, meaning that the rule for evaluating the expression depends on the value of the variable x.

Geometrically, $|x|$ can be thought of as the distance between the point with coordinate x and the origin 0. The absolute value of the difference of two real numbers, $|a - b|$ represents the (nonnegative) distance between the points with coordinates a and b, respectively. This is true regardless of the relative order of a and b on the number line (see Figure 0.5).

Suppose that we measure the length of a building as 23 meters, with an error tolerance of $\pm.025$ m. In other words, if x is the true length of the building (in meters), then we know that

$$22.975 \leq x \leq 23.025.$$

This way of writing the inequality has the advantage of giving us the lower and upper bounds on the possible values of x directly.

Using absolute value notation, we could write this inequality as

$$|x - 23| \leq .025.$$

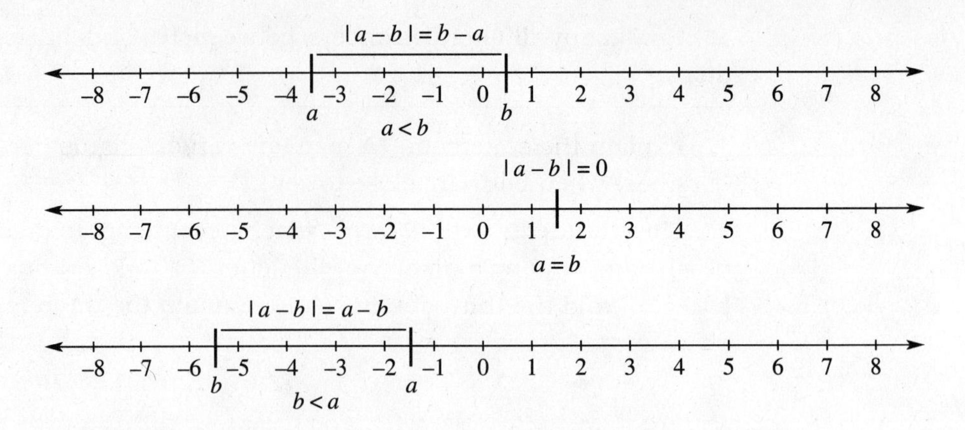

Figure 0.5 Absolute value measures distance between points.

The absolute value notation provides a different advantage: we can read off both the measured value 23 and the error tolerance .025 for x directly.

In general, suppose that we have made a measurement of some quantity x (in some given units), arriving at a measurement of a units with an error tolerance *less than* $\pm\delta$ units. To emphasize that the lower bound for x is $a - \delta$ and the upper bound for x is $a + \delta$, the range of possible values for x can be written

$$a - \delta < x < a + \delta.$$

Alternatively, to emphasize the measured value a and the error tolerance δ, we can write $|x - a| < \delta$. (Note that δ is the Greek letter delta, which corresponds to the letter d, for *distance*.)

We need to take special care with algebraic manipulations that depend on the *sign* of the value of an expression. In particular, the absolute value marks cannot be dropped from an expression involving unknowns without a careful analysis of the possible values that expression could have.

EXAMPLE 6 Express $|-2x - 3|$ without the use of the absolute value symbols.

Solution It would be *incorrect* to simply drop the "−" symbols without any knowledge of the possible replacement values for x. Using Definition 1, we can say

$$|-2x - 3| = \begin{cases} -2x - 3 \text{ if } -2x - 3 \geq 0 \\ 2x + 3 \text{ if } -2x - 3 < 0. \end{cases}$$

We simplify each part of this split formula by solving the "if" inequalities:

$$|-2x - 3| = \begin{cases} -2x - 3 \text{ if } x \leq -\dfrac{3}{2} \\ 2x + 3 \text{ if } x > -\dfrac{3}{2}. \end{cases}$$

In this example, we use $(-2x-3)$ to evaluate $|-2x-3|$ when $x \leq -3/2$, and we use $(2x+3)$ when $x > -3/2$.

For instance, if $x = -7$, then $|-2x-3| = -2(-7) - 3 = 14 - 3 = 11$.

If $x = -1/2$, then $|-2x-3| = 2(-\frac{1}{2}) + 3 = -1 + 3 = 2$. ■

Sets

Definition 2

A **set** is simply a collection of objects. The objects in a set are called **elements** or **members** of the set. We use the notations

$$x \in A \qquad x \notin B$$

to denote, respectively, that the object x is a member of the set A, but x is not a member of the set B.

Sets of real numbers can be described in a variety of ways. If a set contains only a few numbers, we can simply enclose the list of these numbers in braces to denote that set. For example, the set containing the real numbers -1, $\frac{2}{3}$, $-\frac{17}{8}$, $\sqrt{2}$, 6, and π can be denoted as

$$\{-1,\ \frac{2}{3},\ -\frac{17}{8},\ \sqrt{2},\ 6,\ \pi\}.$$

This is called the **roster** notation for sets, since we are simply listing the elements as on a roster. This method of denoting a set is fine as long as the number of elements in the set is small. We could even use the roster notation for a set with infinitely many elements as long as we could effectively communicate exactly which elements belong to the set.

EXAMPLE 7 Express the set E of all positive even integers using roster notation.

Solution $E = \{2, 4, 6, 8, \ldots\}$. ■

This use of the roster notation depends heavily on the reader discerning the intended pattern. For example, writing $\{2, 4, \ldots\}$ out of any context would make it difficult for the reader to know whether the set intended was the set of positive even integers, the set of positive integer powers of 2, or perhaps some other infinite set.

The **rule** notation for sets gives us much more flexibility and precision for denoting a set of real numbers. The general form for such a set is

$$\{x : \text{a property involving } x\}.$$

We read this notation as "the set of all real numbers x such that x satisfies the given property." (Some mathematicians use the vertical bar "|" to denote the "such that" part of this notation.)

EXAMPLE 8 Express the set E of all positive even integers using rule notation.

Solution $E = \{x : x = 2n \text{ for some positive integer } n\}$. ■

Definition 3

The **set of all real numbers** is denoted by $\mathbb{R}$. If we are using rule notation for a set and we want to emphasize that the elements are real numbers, we write

$$\{x \in \mathbb{R} : \text{a property involving } x\}.$$

The set containing no elements whatsoever is called the **empty set** and is denoted by the symbol $\emptyset$ or by a pair of empty braces $\{\ \}$.

▶▶▶ **Do not overdo the use of braces. The symbol $\mathbb{R}$ denotes the set of all real numbers and the symbol $\emptyset$ denotes the empty set. However, $\{\mathbb{R}\}$ and $\{\emptyset\}$ are entirely different. Each is a set containing exactly one element that also happens to be a set.**

Definition 4

If A and B are two sets of real numbers, then

$$A \cup B = \{x : x \in A \textit{ or } x \in B\}$$

and is called the **union** of A and B.

$$A \cap B = \{x : x \in A \textit{ and } x \in B\}$$

and is called the **intersection** of A and B. If every element of A is also an element of B, then we write $A \subseteq B$ and say that A is a **subset** of B.

Note that if $A = B$, we could still say $A \subseteq B$. In fact, if we have both $A \subseteq B$ and $B \subseteq A$, then we can conclude that $A = B$. If A is not a subset of B, we write $A \not\subseteq B$.

Suppose that $A = \{2, 4, 6, 8\}$, $B = \{3, 4, 5, 6\}$, and $C = \{2, 4, 6\}$. Then we have $A \cup B = \{2, 3, 4, 5, 6, 8\}$, $B \cup C = \{2, 3, 4, 5, 6\}$, and $A \cup C = A$, while $A \cap B = B \cap C = \{4, 6\}$ and $A \cap C = C$. We can also see that $C \subseteq A$, but $C \not\subseteq B$.

Interval notation

Some special sets of real numbers arise so frequently in our study of calculus that special shorthand notation has been devised for them. **Intervals** are sets of real numbers containing *no gaps*. Given any two distinct real numbers in an interval, all of the numbers between them also belong to the interval. We can think of intervals geometrically as representing unbroken pieces of the real number line. Definition 5 is a glossary of the special notation used for intervals of various types.

Definition 5

Glossary of interval notation. If $a < b$ are real numbers, then

$[a, b] = \{x : a \le x \le b\}$ $(a, b) = \{x : a < x < b\}$
$[a, b) = \{x : a \le x < b\}$ $(a, b] = \{x : a < x \le b\}$
$[a, \infty) = \{x : a \le x\}$ $(a, \infty) = \{x : a < x\}$
$(-\infty, b] = \{x : x \le b\}$ $(-\infty, b) = \{x : x < b\}$

The set of all real numbers can be written as the interval: $\mathbb{R} = (-\infty, \infty)$.

When they appear as shown here, the real numbers a and b are called **endpoints** of the interval. If an interval has two endpoints, we call it a **bounded** interval. Otherwise, we say that the interval is **unbounded**. The intervals

$$[a, b], \quad (a, b), \quad [a, b), \quad (a, b]$$

are bounded intervals, while

$$[a, \infty), \quad (a, \infty), \quad (-\infty, b], \quad (-\infty, b), \quad (-\infty, \infty)$$

are unbounded intervals.

Note that the endpoints of an interval do not necessarily have to belong to the set of real numbers in that interval. An interval is called **closed** if all of its endpoints are included in the interval. A closed interval can be unbounded. The intervals

$$[a, b], \quad [a, \infty), \quad (-\infty, b]$$

are closed. An interval is called **open** if it does *not* include any of its endpoints. The intervals

$$(a, b), \quad (a, \infty), \quad (-\infty, b)$$

are open. The intervals $[a, b)$ and $(a, b]$ are called **half-open** (equivalently, **half-closed**) for obvious reasons. Technically, we would call the interval $(-\infty, \infty)$ both open and closed, because it has no endpoints at all!

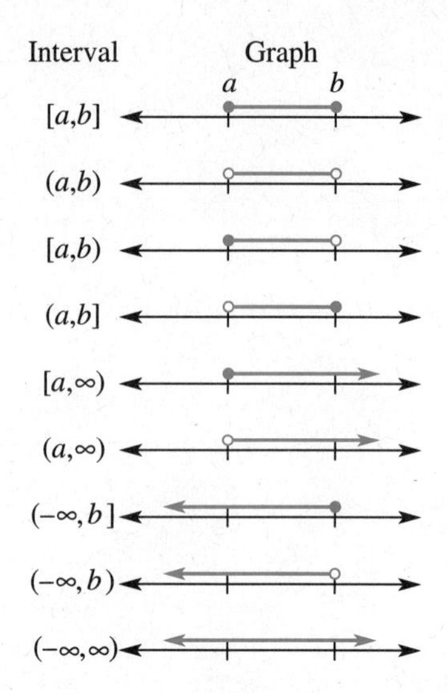

Figure 0.6 Graphs of intervals on the real number line.

The symbols ∞ and $-\infty$, which we read as "positive infinity" and "negative infinity," do not represent real numbers.

They are simply convenient shorthand symbols used here to indicate that an interval extends without end in one or both directions. If an interval of real numbers is intended, it is *never* appropriate to use a left square brace "[" adjacent to the symbol $-\infty$ or a right square brace "]" adjacent to the symbol ∞.

We can graph intervals on a number line by marking endpoints with either a small filled-in or empty circle (for included and nonincluded endpoints, respectively) and shading the portion of the number line included in the interval. If an interval extends indefinitely in a direction, we use an arrowhead to communicate this information. Figure 0.6 shows a graph for each of the intervals in our glossary.

Using absolute value notation for intervals

Absolute value notation is sometimes used to express an interval of real numbers. For example, the interval $[-2, 4]$ can be described as the set of all real numbers x at a distance of 3 units or less from 1. We could thus write

$$[-2, 4] = \{x : |x - 1| \leq 3\}.$$

This way of expressing an interval emphasizes the *center* and the *radius* of the interval, as shown in Figure 0.7.

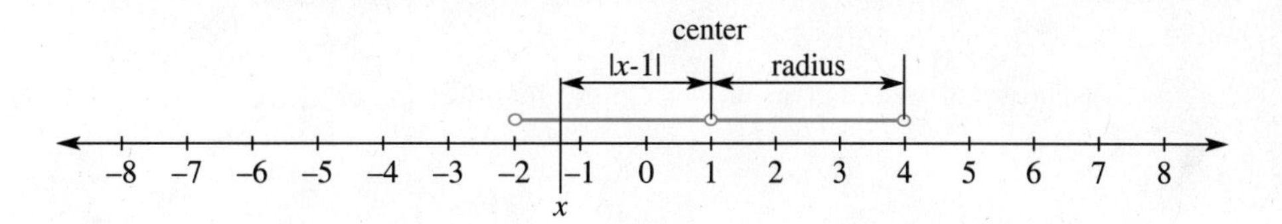

Figure 0.7 Graph of $[-2, -4] = \{x : |x - 1| \leq 3\}$.

EXAMPLE 9 Express the open interval $(-7, -2)$ using absolute value notation.

Solution Representing the interval graphically can be very helpful. The graph of the interval $(-7, -2)$ is shown in Figure 0.8. The center of the interval $(-7, -2)$ is the average of the endpoints:

$$\frac{(-7) + (-2)}{2} = -\frac{9}{2}.$$

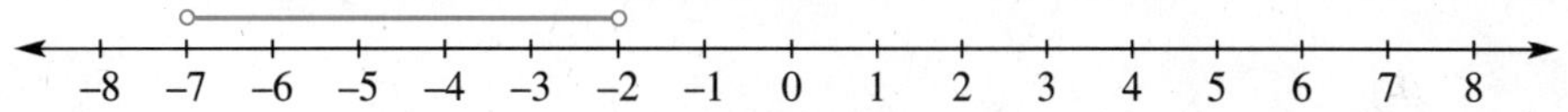

Figure 0.8 Graph of $(-7, -2)$.

The radius of the interval is half the distance between endpoints:

$$\frac{|(-7) - (-2)|}{2} = \frac{|-5|}{2} = \frac{5}{2}.$$

So, the interval can be expressed as the set of all real numbers x at a distance of less than $5/2$ units from $-9/2$, or

$$(-7, -2) = \{x : |x - (-9/2)| < 5/2\} = \{x : |x + 9/2| < 5/2\}.$$ ■

EXAMPLE 10 Express $\{x : |x + 2| \leq 5\}$ using interval notation.

Solution $|x + 2| = |x - (-2)|$, so our set of real numbers all lie 5 units or less from -2.

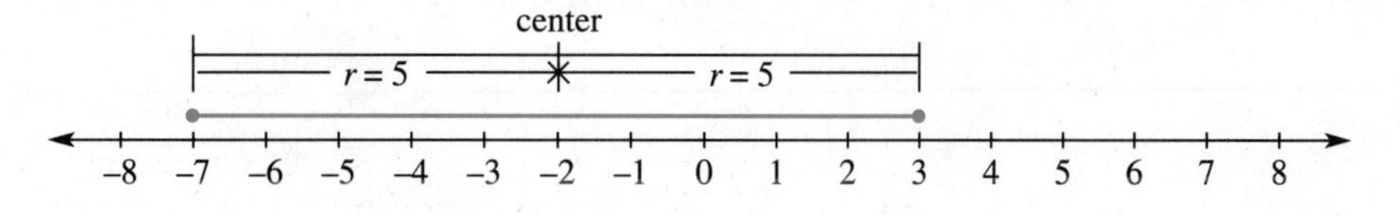

Figure 0.9 Graph of $|x + 2| \leq 5$.

Figure 0.9 illustrates that -2 is at the center of the interval and that the radius of the interval is 5. The endpoints of the interval are $((-2) + 5) = 3$ and $((-2) - 5) = -7$. Since these endpoints are included, we have a closed interval

$$\{x : |x + 2| \leq 5\} = [-7, 3].$$ ■

EXAMPLE 11 Express $\{x : x^2 > 4\}$ using interval notation.

Solution If $x^2 > 4$, then $x^2 - 4 > 0$. Factoring, we have

$$x^2 - 4 = (x + 2)(x - 2),$$

and this expression is positive precisely when both factors $(x+2)$ and $(x-2)$ have the same sign. This is the case when either $x > 2$ or $x < -2$, so we can write

$$(-\infty, -2) \cup (2, \infty)$$

to express the set in interval notation. ■

EXAMPLE 12 Express $\{x : |x| > 4\}$ using interval notation.

Solution If $|x| > 4$, then either $x > 4$ or $-x > 4$ (that is, $x < -4$), so we can write

$$(-\infty, -4) \cup (4, \infty)$$

to express the set in interval notation. ■

EXERCISES for Section 0.3

For exercises 1–6: Express the given inequality using absolute value notation.

1. $-8 \leq x \leq -2$

2. $-1 < x < 4$

3. $x > 3$ or $x < -3$

4. $x \geq 10$ or $x \leq 4$

5. $x \neq -3$

6. $-5 \leq x \leq 1$

For exercises 7–12: Express each interval or union of intervals using absolute value notation. Graph each set on the real number line.

7. $[-5, 0]$

8. $(4, 11)$

9. $[-2, 19]$

10. $(-13, -5]$

11. $(-\infty, -3) \cup (3, \infty)$

12. $[2, \infty) \cup (-\infty, -1]$

For exercises 13–20: Find all real values of x satisfying these inequalities. Express each of these sets of real numbers using interval notation. Graph each interval on the real number line.

13. $x^2 - 4 \leq 5$

14. $2|x - 9| \geq 1$

15. $\dfrac{x}{1 + 2x} < 3 - x$

16. $|x^2 - 9| \geq 2$

17. $\dfrac{1}{|2x - 3|} < 4$

18. $x^3 - x < 0$

19. $x^2 + 4x + 6 \leq 1$

20. $x^2 - 2x + 3 > 1$

For exercises 21–26: Express each set using interval notation.

21. $\{x : |x - 3| < 7\}$

22. $\{x : |x + 4| \leq 3\}$

23. $\{x : |x| < 1\}$

24. $\{x : |x - a| < \delta\}$ where $\delta > 0$

25. $\{x : |2x - 6| > 7\}$

26. $\{x : |4x + 5| \geq 3,\ x \neq -1/2\}$

For exercises 27–34: Graph the following sets of real numbers. If the set is an interval, indicate whether it is open, closed, both, or neither, and indicate whether the interval is bounded or unbounded.

27. $[2, \infty) \cup (-\infty, 2]$

28. $[2, \infty) \cap (-\infty, 2]$

29. $(2, \infty) \cup (-\infty, 2)$

30. $(2, \infty) \cap (-\infty, 2)$

31. $[-2, \infty) \cup (-\infty, 2]$

32. $[-2, \infty) \cap (-\infty, 2]$

33. $(-2, \infty) \cup (-\infty, 2)$

34. $(-2, \infty) \cap (-\infty, 2)$

35. Suppose that I want to cut out a cube of wood with a volume of $1000\ \text{cm}^3$. How accurate must my measurements of each side of the cube be (in cm) if I want the volume to be within $1\ \text{cm}^3$ of the desired volume?

36. Suppose that I want to cut out a cube of wood with a volume of $1\ \text{m}^3$. Within what accuracy (in cm) must my measurements of each side of the cube be if I want the volume to be within $1\ \text{cm}^3$ of the desired volume?

37. To achieve acceptable fitting accuracy in a manufactured product, a machine tool must be set at 3.72 cm, with an allowable error tolerance in either direction of at most 0.003 cm. Express the set of permissible settings x in both interval notation and absolute value notation.

38. A person charges $\$1.50$ per square foot to refinish wood floors. Suppose that she measures a square ballroom floor to be 80 feet on a side, with an accuracy of ± 3 inches. What is the most she might inadvertently overcharge due to her measurement error?

39. Instead of a split formula for the definition of absolute value, someone comes up with the following algebraic formula:

$$|x| = \sqrt{(x^2)},$$

where the square root symbol refers, as usual, to the *nonnegative* square root. Is this definition equivalent to the usual one?

40. The **triangle inequality** states that for any two real numbers a and b (not necessarily distinct), the following inequality is always satisfied:

$$|a| + |b| \geq |a + b|.$$

Under what conditions (in other words, what must be true about a and b) is $|a| + |b| > |a + b|$ true?

0.4 FUNCTIONS AND THEIR REPRESENTATIONS

One of the most important concepts in all of mathematics is that of *function*. The idea of function is central not only to mathematics but to the other disciplines served by mathematics as a tool and a language. Whether the systems we study are physical, biological, social, or economic, we are always on the lookout for significant patterns and connections. The discovery of a functional relationship is particularly important, for it means that we have found a pattern indicating a *very strong* connection. Mathematics provides both the means and the terminology to analyze and describe functional relationships.

Like so many other mathematical terms, the word *function* is also used in everyday language. For example, someone might say that "wisdom is a function of experience" to communicate the idea that one's wisdom is *dependent* on one's experience. Dependence is, in fact, a key feature of the mathematical notion of function. Mathematically, we can think of a function as a special kind of process that accepts certain *inputs* and produces or assigns corresponding *outputs*. That notion is made more precise by Definition 6:

Definition 6

A **function** is any correspondence or process that assigns a single output to each member of a given set of inputs. The set of all possible inputs is called the **domain** of the function.

A function could have virtually any kind of inputs as members of its domain. Likewise, the outputs a function assigns to these inputs could be almost anything—numbers, colors, people, places, sets, or even other functions. In calculus we are most interested in those functions whose inputs and outputs are real numbers (**real-valued** functions.) Calculus gives us extremely powerful ways to study these kinds of functions. The differential calculus allows us to measure the rate of change of the output of a function relative to change in its inputs. The integral calculus allows us to measure such things as the *average* output value of a function over a set of inputs. While those may seem to be simple ideas, they have profound consequences for solving many real-world problems.

The important idea—function as process

We can use a machine diagram to illustrate a function f (see Figure 0.10). A typical input for the function is represented by x, and the corresponding output produced by f is denoted by $f(x)$. The **domain** of the function is

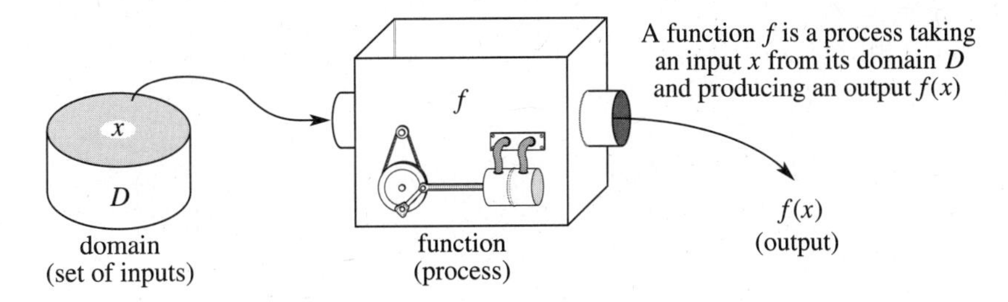

Figure 0.10 Function as process.

pictured as the container of allowable inputs to our function machine f. To *know* a function f requires knowing both the domain of the function and the output $f(x)$ assigned to each input x. We'll emphasize this in our functional notation.

Definition 7

The notation for a real-valued function f with domain D is

$$f : D \longrightarrow \mathbb{R}.$$

The notation for the function assignment process is

$$x \longmapsto f(x).$$

This is read "x is assigned to f of x" or "x maps to f of x."

Note that we use two different arrows in this notation. One ($\longrightarrow$) is used to show that the function f takes its inputs from the domain D and assigns real numbers as outputs. The other ($\longmapsto$) is used to denote the actual assignment process, which takes an *individual* input x and assigns it the output $f(x)$. For example, if $f : [-8, 8] \longrightarrow \mathbb{R}$, where

$$x \longmapsto f(x) = x^3,$$

then the function f assigns the *cube* of each input as output and has the interval $[-8, 8]$ as its domain.

EXAMPLE 13 What is the notation for the function f having the interval $(0, 1)$ as its domain and producing the square of each input as its output?

Solution Using the arrow notation, we write

$$f : (0, 1) \longrightarrow \mathbb{R},$$

and $x \longmapsto f(x)$, where

$$f(x) = x^2.$$

(Figure 0.11 illustrates this squaring function f with a machine diagram.) ■

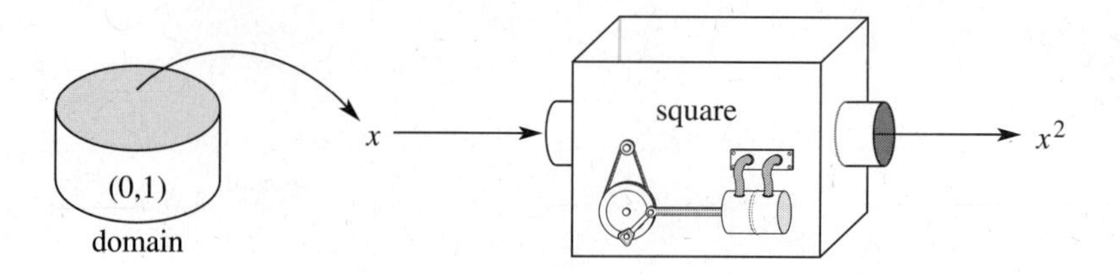

Figure 0.11 Diagram for the squaring function f.

EXAMPLE 14 Find and express with suitable notation the function A that expresses the area of any circle (including the "degenerate" circle consisting of a single point) as a function of its radius.

Solution The formula for the area of a circle is $A = \pi r^2$. The radius r could be any nonnegative real number. So our notation for the area function is

$$A : [0, \infty) \longrightarrow \mathbb{R}.$$

For any particular nonnegative real number r, we have $r \longmapsto A(r)$, where

$$A(r) = \pi r^2.$$

■

We have defined a function as a process assigning an output to each input in the function's domain. We now turn to the multiple ways in which we can represent this process for a given function. Each representation has its own advantages and disadvantages, so it is useful to consider all of them as you analyze a function process.

Numerical representations of functions

An **ordered pair** of real numbers (a, b) is distinguished from a set of two real numbers $\{a, b\}$ by specifying the order of a and b. We call a the **first coordinate** and b the **second coordinate** of the ordered pair (a, b), but there is no specific order intended when we talk of the set $\{a, b\}$. For example, the ordered pairs $(0, 1)$ and $(1, 0)$ are considered different, whereas the sets $\{0, 1\}$ and $\{1, 0\}$ are not.

We could describe a function in terms of *ordered pairs* of its inputs and outputs:

$$f = \{(x, f(x)) : x \in D\}.$$

In other words, f can be represented by the set of all ordered pairs of the form

$$(x, f(x)),$$

where the first coordinate x can be any possible input value in the domain D, and the second coordinate $f(x)$ is the corresponding output value.

If we know the domain of a function and the rule or procedure by which we can assign the output to each input, then we can generate this set of ordered pairs. On the other hand, knowing all these ordered pairs tells us both the domain of the function (just read off the set of first coordinates) and the assignment process linking the inputs to the outputs (just look up the appropriate ordered pair).

EXAMPLE 15 Suppose that the function f has domain $D = \{1, 2, 3, 4\}$ and that $f(x) = 2x - 1$ for each x in the domain. What set of ordered pairs numerically represents the function?

Solution We have

$$f(1) = 1, \quad f(2) = 3, \quad f(3) = 5, \quad \text{and} \quad f(4) = 7.$$

The function f is numerically represented by the set of ordered pairs

$$\{(1,1),\ (2,3),\ (3,5),\ (4,7)\}.$$

It is common to display ordered pairs in the form of a table of inputs and outputs. Table 0.1 shows the table for the function f in this example. ■

input x	output $f(x) = 2x - 1$
1	1
2	3
3	5
4	7

Table 0.1 A table of values for the function $f(x) = 2x - 1$.

Of course, if the domain of a function contains infinitely many possible inputs, it is impossible to list all the ordered pairs in a table. Nevertheless, even a partial table of values can give us some insight or useful information about the nature of the process.

If the inputs and outputs of a particular function are always real numbers, then we refer to the set of ordered pairs of inputs and outputs as the **numerical representation** of the function. Whenever you make a table of inputs and outputs for a function, you are using the numerical representation.

Graphical representations of functions

Ordered pairs of real numbers can be represented as points in a plane by making use of a **rectangular coordinate system**. Two perpendicular real number lines provide the **coordinate axes** for the system, and their point of intersection is called the **origin**. Generally, these two axes are placed so that the first coordinate will correspond to the horizontal axis (with numbers increasing from left to right) and the second coordinate will correspond to the vertical axis (with numbers increasing from lower to higher). This arrangement divides the plane into four distinct regions called **quadrants**, and the quadrants are traditionally numbered I to IV, starting with the upper right and proceeding counterclockwise.

The first and second coordinates of any point are found by locating the real numbers located perpendicularly from it on the horizontal and vertical axes, respectively. Conversely, we can locate any point, given its ordered pair of coordinates (x_0, y_0). Figure 0.12 illustrates a rectangular coordinate system with the quadrants and axes labelled.

A rectangular coordinate system is sometimes called a **Cartesian coordinate system** in honor of the French mathematician and philosopher René Descartes (1596-1650), the founder of analytic geometry.

The **graph** of a function f is obtained by *plotting* the set of ordered pairs (x, y), where x takes on each value in the domain D and $y = f(x)$ is the corresponding output value of the function f. Whenever we examine the graph or a portion of the graph of a function, we are using its **graphical representation**.

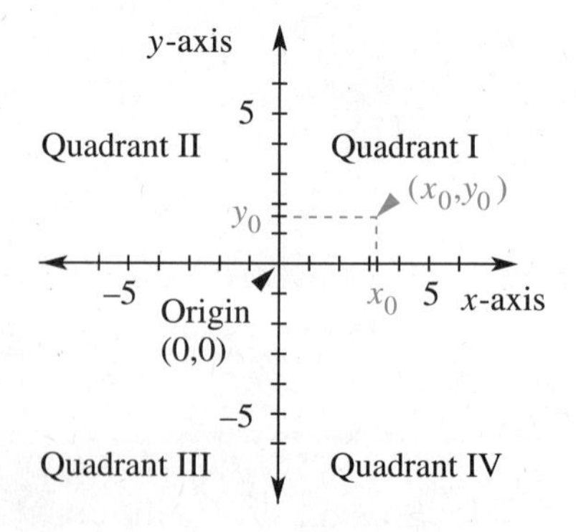

Figure 0.12 A rectangular coordinate system.

Symbolic representations of functions

When it is possible to describe a function process by a symbolic formula

$$y = f(x) = \textit{some expression in terms of } x,$$

we say that we have a **symbolic representation** of the function. It is common to think of symbolic representations first when someone mentions the word "function." For example,

$$y = x^2$$

might be referred to as a function. This notation is certainly concise, but it has some drawbacks. For one thing, it might lead you to think that a function is simply an equation of this form, or that a function can *only* be described by such an equation. In real life, however, functions do not always present themselves in such a nice form. For another thing, the notation $y = x^2$ does not by itself give us the needed information about the domain of the function: what exactly are the allowable input values for x? Of course, it's acceptable to square any real number x, but if x represents the numerical value of a physical quantity such as length, then we might not want to include negative numbers in the domain. (It would also be essential to know what *units* of measurement are being used. Our formula may look quite different, depending on whether x is measured in centimeters, feet, or light-years.)

Interpreting functions in multiple representations

Numeric, graphical, and symbolic representations all have their advantages and disadvantages, and each can give us special insights. Real-valued functions play a prominent role in calculus, and throughout this book we'll draw important connections among the numeric, graphical, and symbolic properties of a function. Let's illustrate by taking another look at the definition of function and how it can be interpreted in the context of each of the three representations.

1. *Numerically*, what distinguishes a function's table of input and output values from just any table of paired values?

▶▶▶ **Since the output of a function is completely determined by the input, we should never see two lines of a function table having the same input but different outputs.**

input	output	input	output	input	output
1	1	1	1	1	1
0	−1	0	0	0	0
−1	−3	1	−1	−1	1
π	$2\pi - 1$	0.81	0.9	0.9	0.81
2.3	3.9	4	−2	−2	4
3/2	2	9/4	3/2	3/2	9/4

Figure 0.13 Three selected tables of paired numbers.

EXAMPLE 16 In Figure 0.13 we see three selected tables of paired numbers from three different sources. Which tables could have been generated by a functional relationship?

Solution The first and third tables could have been generated by a functional relationship, but the second one could not since we can see that the input 1 produces two different outputs.

Note that we said that the first and third tables *could* have come from a functional relationship. Unless these tables are complete—meaning that *all possible inputs* are listed—we cannot be sure that for some unlisted input value we might obtain more than one possible output. Since many processes have infinitely many different possible inputs, we can see that it will be impossible to confirm a functional relationship solely on the basis of a finite table of values. If, however, we note even a single input that produces more than one possible output, we can rule out a functional relationship. ■

Take special note of the third table. These ordered pairs could have been generated by the assignment $x \longmapsto f(x)$, where $f(x) = x^2$. Both of the inputs 1 and -1 are paired with the same output 1.

▶▶▶ **It is perfectly acceptable for a function to produce the same output for different inputs.**

2. *Graphically*, what distinguishes a function graph from just any plot of ordered pairs? Provided we use the horizontal axis to represent inputs and the vertical axis to represent outputs, then the function definition translates to a requirement that no two points of the graph should lie over (or under) the same input value.

▶▶▶ **A function's graph must pass the vertical line test: any vertical line must intersect the graph in at most one point.**

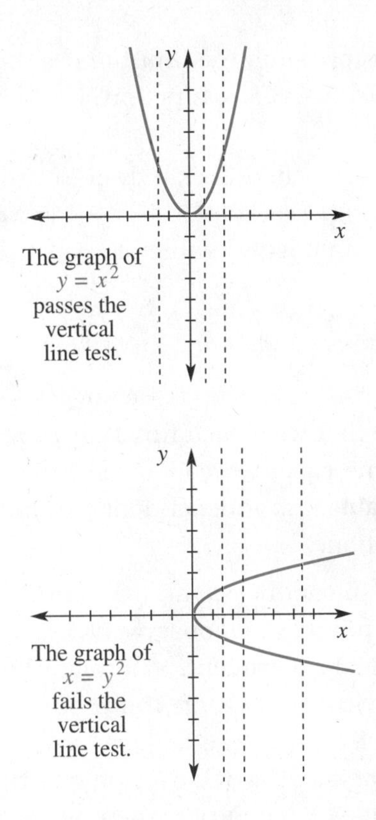

Figure 0.14 The vertical line test for function graphs.

EXAMPLE 17 Apply the vertical line test to the graphs of the two algebraic relationships $y = x^2$ and $x = y^2$.

Solution As shown in Figure 0.14, we see that $y = x^2$ describes y as a function of x, but $x = y^2$ does not. ■

Note that the vertical line test is valid only under the assumption that the horizontal axis represents inputs and the vertical axis represents outputs. The relationship $x = y^2$ *does* describe x as a function of y.

3. *Symbolically*, what distinguishes a formula for a function from just any formula?

▶▶▶ **The requirement for a symbolic expression to describe a function is that we must be able to solve for a unique output value, given any particular input value from the domain.**

EXAMPLE 18 If x represents the input and y the output, does the algebraic relationship $y = x^2$ describe a function?

Solution Yes, since there is exactly one output value determined by each input value. As a non-example, $x = y^2$ yields two possible outputs, $y = \sqrt{x}$ and $y = -\sqrt{x}$, for each positive value of x. ■

Variables, constants, and parameters

A **variable**, as the name suggests, can vary over some set of values. Suppose that we have a function $f : D \longrightarrow \mathbb{R}$ and we let $y = f(x)$ for each $x \in D$. In this case, we call x the **independent variable** and y the **dependent variable**. An independent variable will also be called an **argument** of the function.

In conducting an experiment, a scientist may manipulate the value of one quantity and observe its effects on another quantity. For example, in a medical experiment, she might be interested in understanding the effects of a drug dosage on the production of a certain antibody. The scientist is free to vary the dosage, and for this reason the dosage is termed the *independent* variable in the experiment. The amount of antibody produced will likely depend on the dosage, and for that reason it is called the *dependent* variable in the experiment. The scientist searches for a functional relationship between the manipulated and observed variables. The terminology of *independent* and *dependent* variables for functions follows from this practice of the scientific method of experimentation.

> In graphing a function having real numbers as inputs and outputs, it is traditional to use the horizontal axis for the independent variable and the vertical axis for the dependent variable.

It's true that we generally use letters (such as x, y, h, t) to represent variables. But do NOT think of the word *variable* as synonymous with any letter used symbolically in mathematics. When used in the context of functions, it refers to either the independent (input) or dependent (output) variable.

We also use letters as symbols in a wide variety of other mathematical contexts. Two other ways letters are used are as *constants* or *parameters*. A **constant** represents a quantity that does not change value. For example, 7, $-\sqrt{2}$, and π are constants, as is the irrational number e (≈ 2.7182, used in the study of exponential and logarithmic functions). The value of a constant may be unknown; what is important is that its value stays fixed.

What is a **parameter**? Perhaps the best explanation is that a parameter is a "constant that varies." That sounds contradictory, but the distinctions between variables, constants, and parameters all depend on context. The following example may make this distinction more clear.

EXAMPLE 19 Consider the function $f : \mathbb{R} \longrightarrow \mathbb{R}$, where $f(x) = 2x+b$ and b is an unspecified constant (a parameter). What effect does varying the value of b have on the graph of f?

Solution If we plot the graph of $y = f(x)$ for a fixed value b, we obtain a straight line with slope 2 and y-intercept $(0, b)$.

Now, for each value of the constant b, we get an *entirely new line.* In other words, each value of b corresponds to a *different function.* If we plot each of the functions corresponding to several different values of b, we obtain a family of parallel lines, each with slope 2 (Figure 0.15). ■

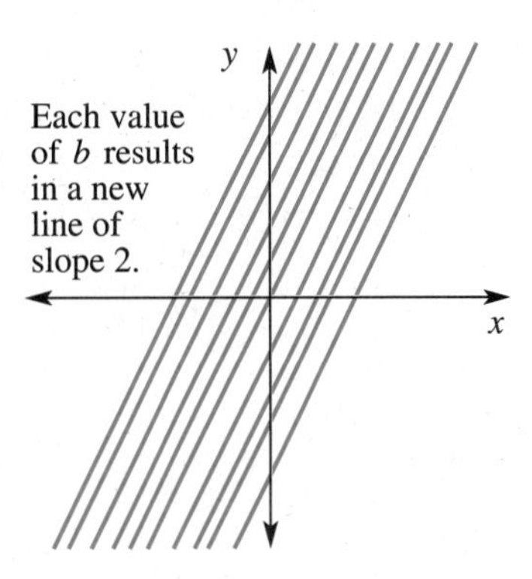

Figure 0.15 The parameter b generates a family of lines $y = 2x + b$.

We say that this family of lines is **parametrized** by b. This process, by which each value of b produces a new line of the form $y = 2x + b$, is itself a function. It takes a real number b as input and produces a *function* as output!

The meaning of mathematical symbolism often depends on the context. For example, $(0, 1)$ could represent either a point or an open interval, depending on the discussion. Whether a particular letter represents a variable, constant, or parameter will also depend on the specific context.

You can think of parameters as "adjustment knobs" on the function process. For example, the slope m and y-intercept b are two parameters in the definition of a linear function

$$f(x) = mx + b.$$

We can adjust the slope of the line by changing the value m, and we can adjust the y-intercept by changing the value b.

Parameters often occur in two special places in a function definition. First, parameters may be involved in some transformation of the *input* before any other operations occur. Second, parameters may be involved in some transformation of the *output* after all other operations are completed. These two kinds of parameters have different effects on the graph of a function.

EXAMPLE 20 Find values for the parameters a and b so that the lowest point on the graph of

$$y = (x + a)^2 + b$$

is the point $(2, 1)$.

Solution Figure 0.16 shows that the graph for $a = 0$ and $b = 0$ has its lowest point at the origin. Changing the value of a moves the graph left or right. Changing the value of b moves the graph up or down. Setting $a = -2$ and $b = 1$ results in the lowest point on the graph being $(2, 1)$. ■

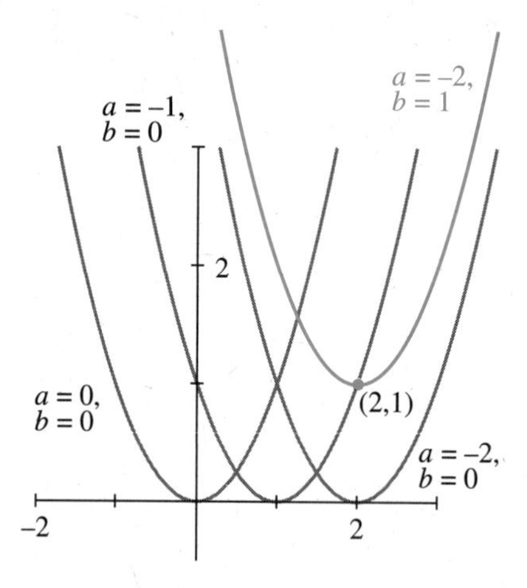

Figure 0.16 Graphing $y = (x + a)^2 + b$ for various values of a and b.

In general, the graph of $y = f(x + a) + b$ can be found directly from the graph of $y = f(x)$ by simply translating each point on the graph $-a$ units horizontally (that is, in the x-direction) and b units vertically (that is, in the y-direction.)

EXERCISES for Section 0.4

For exercises 1–3: Write a suitable notation, specifying the domain, for each function described.

1. The function that expresses the perimeter p of an isosceles right triangle as a function of its leg length ℓ, when it is known that the hypotenuse must be at least 5 units long.

2. The function that expresses the volume V of a sphere as a function of its radius r, when it is known that the sphere must have volume of at least one cubic unit.

3. The function that expresses the surface area S of a sphere as a function of its diameter d, when it is known that the radius must be between 2 and 7 units in length (inclusive).

For exercises 4–6: Which of the following sets of ordered pairs could have been generated by a function?

4. $\{(2,3),\ (4,-1),\ (5,\sqrt{2}),\ (\pi,\pi^2)\}$

5. $\{(1,4),\ (2,4),\ (3,4),\ (4,4)\}$

6. $\{(1.5,7),\ (-4,\sqrt{3}),\ (\frac{3}{2},1),\ (0,0)\}$

For exercises 7–12: Graph the given equation and indicate whether or not the graph could be that of a function $y = f(x)$.

7. $9x^2 + 4y^2 = 36$

8. $9x^2 - 4y^2 = 36$

9. $8y^2 = 2x$

10. $8x^2 = 2y$

11. $xy = 4$

12. $(x+y)^2 = 1$

For exercises 13–18: A family of lines $y = mx - 1$ is parametrized by m, the slope.

13. Graph several members of this family on the same set of coordinate axes. What point do all the graphs have in common?

14. What value of m guarantees that $(-3,6)$ lies on the graph of $y = mx - 1$?

15. What value of m guarantees an x-intercept -5?

16. For what value of m is the graph of the line parallel to the line $y = 3x - 7$?

17. For what value of m is the graph of the line perpendicular to the line passing through $(-1,2)$ and the origin?

18. What value of m guarantees that the point (x_0, y_0) is on the graph? Are there any points (x_0, y_0) for which there is more than one such value for m? Are there any points for which there is no suitable m?

For exercises 19–24: Suppose that a family of functions has graphs given by

$$y = ax^2 + bx + c,$$

with parameters a, b, and c.

19. When is the graph of f a parabola, and when is the graph a straight line? When the graph of f is a straight line, which parameter gives us the slope and which parameter gives us the y-intercept?

20. What effect on the graph does changing the value of c have if we keep a and b fixed? In particular, what predictions can we make when c is positive, negative, and zero?

21. What effect on the graph does changing the value of b have if we keep a and c fixed? In particular, what predictions can we make when b is positive, negative, and zero?

22. What effect on the graph does changing the value of a have if we keep b and c fixed? In particular, what predictions can we make when a is positive, negative, and zero?

23. The **discriminant** d of the function f is given by $d = b^2 - 4ac$. What does the sign (positive, negative, or zero) of d tell us about the graph of the function? (Examine how many times the graph crosses the x-axis.)

24. What happens when $a = b = 0$? Does this change your answer to the previous exercise?

For exercises 25–29: Each of these functions uses parameters a and b in its definition. For each function, find values for these parameters so that the conditions stated in the exercise are met. One strategy is first to graph the function with $a = b = 0$ and determine how the graph needs to change to meet the requirements. Then change a and b separately to see what effect these changes have on the graph. Use this information, together with repeated graphing, to home in on the appropriate values for the parameters.

25. $f(x) = -((x + a)^2) + b$; highest point at $(-1, -5)$

26. $f(x) = |(x + a) - 1| + b$; lowest point at $(2.5, 5)$

27.
$$f(x) = \begin{cases} 1+b & \text{for } x+a<1 \\ 2+b, & \text{otherwise} \end{cases}$$
choose b so that the graph jumps from $(-3,-3)$ to $(-3,-2)$.

28. $f(x) = (x+a)^3 - (x+a) - 1 + b$; the "valley" point at $(0,0)$.

29. $f(x) = 2.5(x+a) + b$; the graph passes through the points $(0,3)$ and $(4,13)$. In this case, find *two* distinct settings of the parameters that work.

---

30. Shown below is a table of selected input and output values for a function $f(x) = (x+a)^3 - (x+a) + b$ corresponding to particular values for the two parameters a and b. Using this table of values, determine the values of the parameters a and b.

Table for f

input	output
-3	-34.375
-2.5	-19
-1.5	-1
-1	3.125
-0.5	5
0	5.375
0.5	5
1	4.625
1.5	5
2	6.875
2.5	11
3	18.125

For Exercise 30

0.5 GRAPHING AS A TOOL

Using numeric, graphical, and symbolic representations gives us multiple avenues for investigating and analyzing functions. Paper and pencil are powerful tools in the hands of a knowledgeable person: the skillful manipulation and interpretation of numbers, pictures, and symbols can provide great insights toward solving problems. But generating a long table of numerical input-output pairs or obtaining a reasonably accurate graph of a complicated function can be very time-consuming if done by hand. Technology in the form of computers and calculators provides us additional tools with which to study functions. We can now use machines to help us compute, graph, and even manipulate symbolic expressions algebraically. Now we have new and expanded opportunities to use multiple representations of functions, particularly numerical and graphical representations.

Graphs are extremely powerful visual aids in the study of functions. A graph provides a useful interpretational tool by giving us a picture of the input-output pairs a function process produces, but it requires much time and effort to prepare graphs by hand. With the availability of computer and calculator graphics technology, we have a much greater opportunity to exploit graphical representations of functions.

▶▶▶ **Be forewarned: the graphical evidence provided by a machine can be open to perceptual illusions and therefore to misinterpretations. To make intelligent use of graphical tools, it is important to understand their limitations.**

In other words, getting the most out of graphics technology requires not only knowing how it can be used but also how it *cannot* be used. Let's take a look at some of the issues you must be concerned with when using graphing technology.

Pixels and resolution

First of all, we need to understand how a graph is produced and displayed by a machine. The screen of a calculator or computer is divided into a grid of small rectangular *picture elements* called **pixels**. The more pixels per square inch of screen area, the higher the *resolution* of the screen. Each pixel has coordinates corresponding to a single point in the plane, but a pixel does not really represent a point. Rather, a pixel represents a small rectangular region including infinitely many points. The specific point corresponding to the coordinates of the pixel may be the center or a corner of the pixel, depending on the particular machine or software. If we want the machine to indicate a certain point in the plane, then we have it light up (or make black) the particular pixel containing that point.

The viewing window

Every graphics package on a computer or calculator has a necessarily limited screen. You might think of this screen as a porthole or window from which you can view a part of the Cartesian plane. By moving this window around the plane, we have the chance to focus our attention on various parts of the graph of a function. This window is also a *lens* through which we can obtain both close-up and distant views of the graph by changing scale. Finding the best window locations and scales are navigational skills for finding our way about a function's graph.

The dimensions of a viewing window can be indicated in a couple of ways. One way to express the dimensions of the viewing window is by specifying the horizontal and vertical ranges with intervals. In this case, we might refer to the **viewing window** $[a, b] \times [c, d]$ to mean a window including all the points (x, y) satisfying $a \leq x \leq b$ (the ***x*-range**) and $c \leq y \leq d$ (the ***y*-range**).

Another way of indicating the dimensions of this same viewing window would be to specify the coordinates of the lower left-hand corner (a, c) and the upper right-hand corner (b, d). See Figure 0.17 for an illustration of a viewing window.

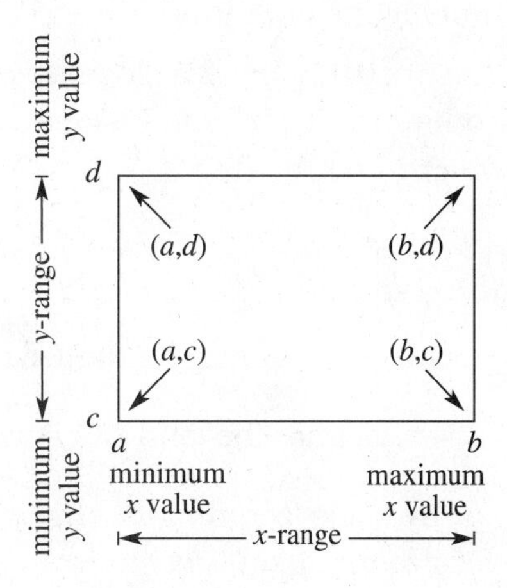

Figure 0.17 Specifying a viewing window.

Connected versus dot modes

When graphing a function, a graphics program or calculator usually starts with the first (left-most) column of pixels, computes the ordered pair $(x, f(x))$ using the first coordinate of that column as the value of x, and lights up the pixel in that column whose y-coordinate is closest to $f(x)$ (provided $f(x)$ is within the vertical range of the window). This process is then repeated for each column of pixels from left to right.

A function grapher may display graphs in either *dot* mode or *connected* mode. (The user may be able to specify either mode.) In dot mode, the function grapher will light up at most one pixel in each column (so the function graph on screen will pass the vertical line test). In connected mode, the function grapher will light up additional pixels to give the visual

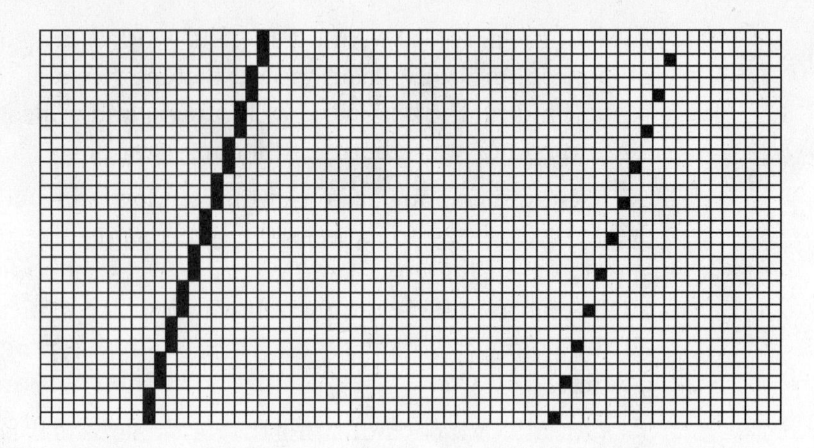

Figure 0.18 Connected and dot modes of machine function plots.

perception of an unbroken graph. In either case, note that the picture is simply a finite collection of pixels, while the true graph generally consists of infinitely many points.

Figure 0.18 shows a close-up of a viewing screen displaying the graphs of two lines with the same slope. One line is plotted in connected mode, the other in dot mode.

Hidden graphical behavior

Graphical behavior can be hidden:

1. by location beyond the bounds of the finite viewing window,

2. by scale (zooming in obscures global information about the graph, whereas zooming out obscures local information about it), and

3. by numerical limitations (the choice of which pixels to light is determined by numerical computations, which in turn are subject to the usual round-off, cancellation, underflow, and overflow errors that may occur).

For example, the graph of the function defined by the formula

$$f(x) = \frac{x^2 - 1}{x - 1}$$

has a *hole* at $x = 1$ (since the output is undefined for $x = 1$). However, a machine plot of this function's graph will have a missing pixel only if the x-coordinate of a pixel is exactly 1. The graph may appear to be continuous if $x = 1$ falls between the x-coordinates of two adjacent pixels.

Keep in mind that you are more likely to observe the visual effects of numerical imprecision at small scalings. The machine-plotted graph of a "well-behaved" function may exhibit jagged jumps or spikes under repeated zooms due to the limited precision of the computed function values. (Try zooming in horizontally on the graph of $y = (1+x)^{1/x}$ to see the graphical effects that limited precision can cause.)

Solving equations graphically

Often the solution to a mathematical problem can be modeled with an equation of the form

$$f(x) = g(x),$$

where f and g are real-valued functions of a real variable x. In this situation, machine graphics can provide us with visual clues to the solution of the equation as the x-coordinate(s) of the intersection(s) of the graphs of $y = f(x)$ and $y = g(x)$. However, since the viewing window of a machine grapher is finite and its resolution limited, the visual search for intersection points may be difficult.

For example, let's investigate the solution to the equation

$$1000x = \frac{(20-x)^3}{8}.$$

We'll label the left-hand side of the equation as $y = f(x) = 1000x$ and the right-hand side of the equation as $y = g(x) = \frac{(20-x)^3}{8}$. Graphing these two functions in a "standard" or "default" viewing window such as $[-10, 10] \times [-10, 10]$ might not show us anything at all (see Figure 0.19). In this case, the slope of the line $y = 1000x$ is so steep that at this scaling, it is indistinguishable from the y-axis. The graph of the cubic $y = \frac{(20-x)^3}{8}$ has no points that are within the viewing window at all.

Autoscaling refers to a feature found on some graphing calculators and software. Given a particular x-range for a viewing window, an autoscaler will *sample* a selection of inputs, calculate the corresponding outputs, and then use this data to determine a y-range that will include the extreme

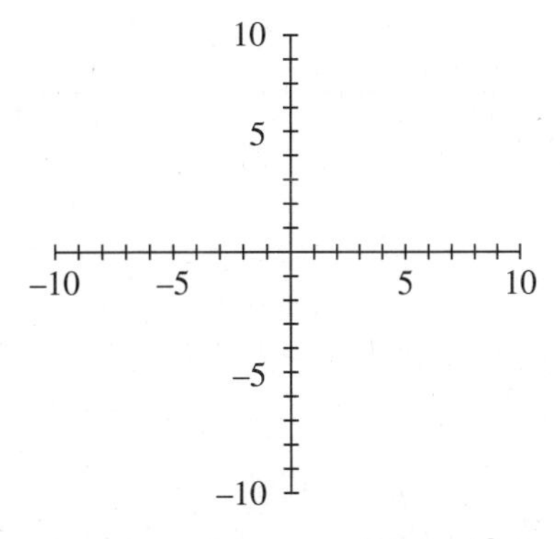

Figure 0.19 Graphs of $y = 1000x$ and $y = \frac{(20-x)^3}{8}$ in $[-10, 10] \times [-10, 10]$.

outputs (lowest and highest). Figure 0.20 shows the graphs of $y = 1000x$ and $y = \dfrac{(20-x)^3}{8}$ over the x-range $[-10, 10]$ with autoscaling. Notice that the autoscaler chose a y-range that just includes the extreme values of $y = 1000x$ over the input interval $[-10, 10]$.

Now we can see an intersection point for the two graphs. Autoscaling definitely helped us in this case, but it is not a cure-all. Notice that autoscaling only chooses the y-range for us. Our chosen x-range must include a solution in order for an intersection point to appear in the viewing window. Even then, the y-range chosen automatically may result in such a distorted picture that we may still have difficulty locating an intersection point. Once we have an intersection point in view, we can zoom in on it to get a more precise idea of its exact location. From our last picture, the intersection appears to be between $x = 0$ and $x = 1$, so we autoscale over this x-range to obtain Figure 0.21.

After repeated zooms, we can continue to refine our estimate of the solution. Figure 0.22 shows the two graphs in a viewing window of width .001. Assuming that the pixels lit up on the screen are accurate, the solution to the original equation must satisfy $0.874 < x < 0.875$. In general, the width of our last window gives us a measure of the precision of our estimate of the solution.

▶▶▶ **Using the width of a viewing window to measure precision assumes that the pixels we see are computed with enough accuracy that the true solution really is within the viewing window. If you zoom in too far, this assumption may become suspect, due to the precision limitations of your machine.**

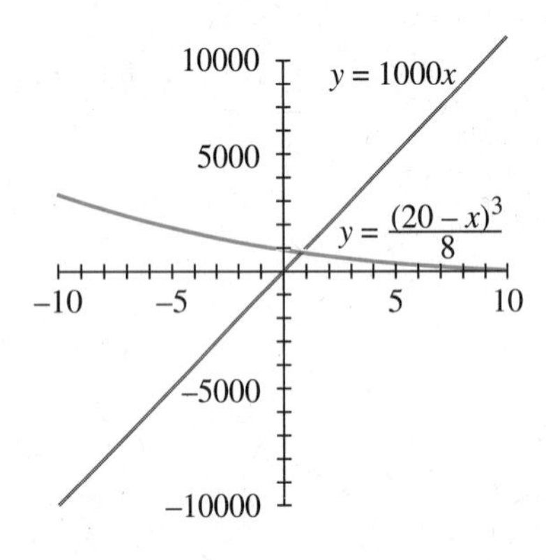

Figure 0.20 Autoscaled graphs of $y = 1000x$ and $y = \dfrac{(20-x)^3}{8}$ over $[-10, 10]$.

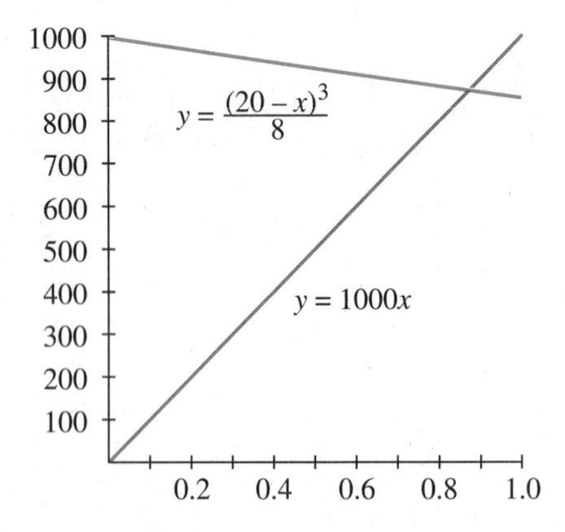

Figure 0.21 Autoscaled graphs of $y = 1000x$ and $y = \dfrac{(20-x)^3}{8}$ over $[0, 1]$.

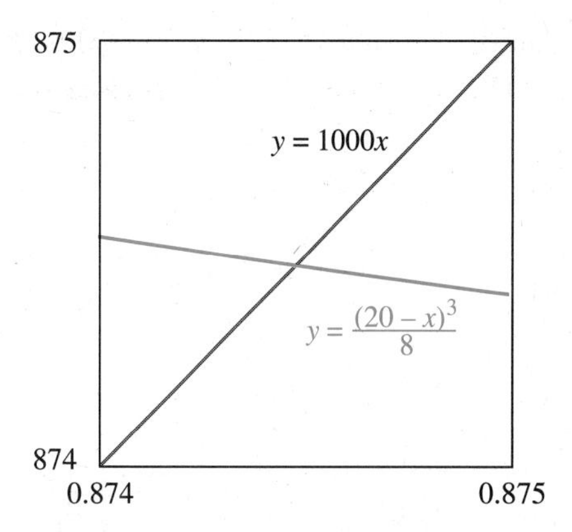

Figure 0.22 Graphs of $y = 1000x$ and $y = \dfrac{(20-x)^3}{8}$ after repeated zooms.

Standardizing the equation

Any equation of the form

$$f(x) = g(x)$$

will have the exact same solutions as the equation

$$f(x) - g(x) = 0.$$

If we graph $y = f(x) - g(x)$, then our task becomes equivalent to finding the zeroes or **roots** of this new function. Visually, we must find where the graph crosses the x-axis.

For example, if we plot $y = 1000x - \dfrac{(20-x)^3}{8}$ over the x-range used in the previous figure, the graph should cross the x-axis as shown in Figure 0.23. You already know that "standardizing" an equation so that one side is 0 can be useful in solving quadratic equations by factoring or by use of the quadratic formula. The same practice can be useful for *any* equation in graphing, for it focuses our attention on a single graph instead of two, and our search is always restricted to the x-intercepts. If the functions involved are *continuous* (a concept we discuss in more detail in Chapter 2), we have an additional way to check the accuracy of our answer. If $f(x) - g(x)$ is calculated to be negative at an input on one side of the apparent root and positive at an input on the other side, then we know that a continuous function's graph must cross the x-axis at least once between those two inputs. (If the functions f and g are not continuous, then we cannot necessarily conclude this.)

We've approximated one solution to the equation $1000x = \dfrac{(20-x)^3}{8}$. How do we know that there aren't others? In short, we *don't* know without

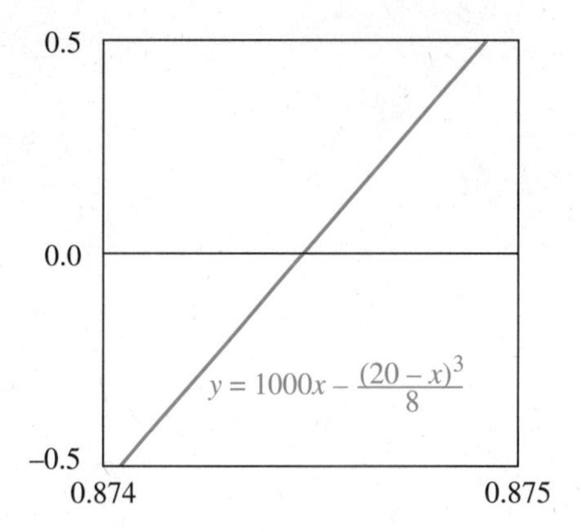

Figure 0.23 Graph of $y = 1000x - \dfrac{(20-x)^3}{8}$.

further analysis. Certainly we could try other viewing windows and search at random for other solutions, but this approach is ultimately futile since we cannot physically check all the infinitely many viewing windows. Instead, we need analysis for a convincing determination of the number of solutions and to locate any additional solutions. In fact, two more solutions do exist to our original equation. Can you find them?

Solving inequalities graphically

While the solutions to an equation can be interpreted as intersection points or as x-intercepts, the solution set to an inequality may include one or more *intervals* of values. Let's illustrate some graphical techniques for solving inequalities through some examples.

EXAMPLE 21 Find the solution set of the inequality

$$x^2 - 7 \leq 5x$$

and express it in interval notation.

Solution We can experiment to determine an appropriate horizontal x-range. Using an x-range of $[-3, 7]$ we obtain the graphs of both $y = x^2 - 7$ and $y = 5x$ as shown below in Figure 0.24. These graphs indicate that the solution set to the inequality is a single interval whose left endpoint is slightly to the left of $x = -1$ and whose right endpoint is slightly to the right of $x = 6$. We can zoom in on the intersection points to refine our estimates of these endpoints. That is, the endpoints occur when the two sides of the inequality are equal.

If we replace the inequality sign "$\leq$" with "$=$," the resulting equation $x^2 - 7 = 5x$ can be solved analytically by the quadratic formula:

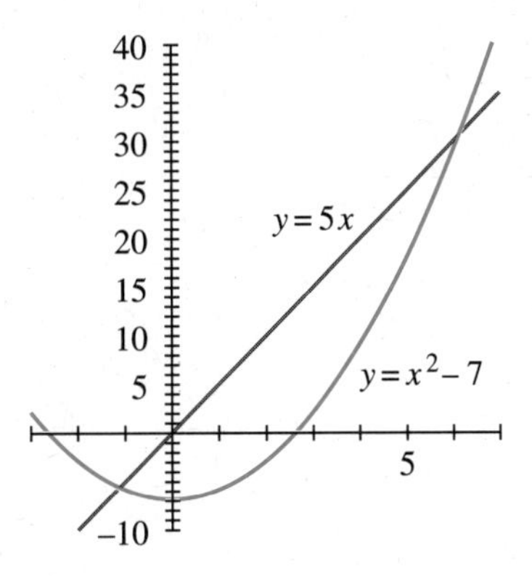

Figure 0.24 Graphs of $y = x^2 - 7$ and $y = 5x$ over $[-3, 7]$.

$$x = \frac{5 + \sqrt{(-5)^2 - 4 \cdot (-7)}}{2} \approx 6.14$$

$$x = \frac{5 - \sqrt{(-5)^2 - 4 \cdot (-7)}}{2} \approx -1.14.$$

The solution set in interval notation is, with these approximate values, $[-1.14, 6.14]$. ■

Note that we can also standardize an inequality in the same way that we standardize an equation.

For example, the solution set to the inequality $x^2 - 7 \leq 5x$ is the same as the solution set to the inequality

$$x^2 - 7 - 5x \leq 0.$$

If we graph the single function $y = f(x) = x^2 - 7 - 5x$, then our task is to find the set of values for which the graph dips below the x-axis, as illustrated in Figure 0.25.

Truth functions

In many systems, an inequality such as $7 > x^2$ or $0.3 \leq \sin x$ can be *evaluated* for any particular real input x to return one real number output value representing "TRUE" if the inequality is true and another real number value representing "FALSE" if the inequality is false. Usually, "TRUE" is represented by 1 and "FALSE" is represented by 0, allowing you to graph a **truth function** representing the inequality. As long as the y-range of the viewing window includes 0 and 1, you will be able to see the output for every input in the viewing rectangle. Figure 0.26 shows the truth plot of the inequality $x^2 - 7 \leq 5x$.

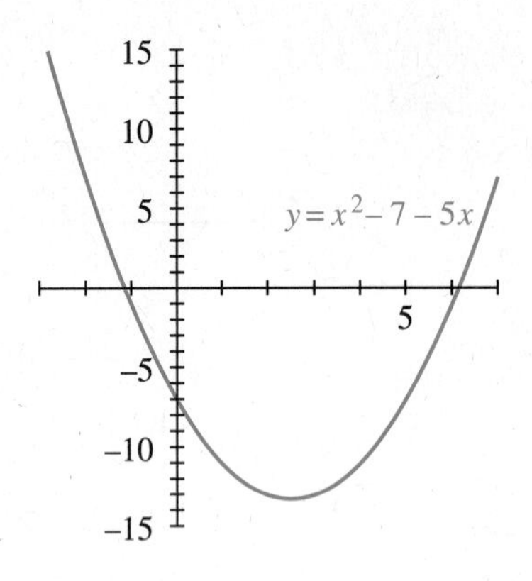

Figure 0.25 Graph of $y = x^2 - 7 - 5x$ over $[-3, 7]$.

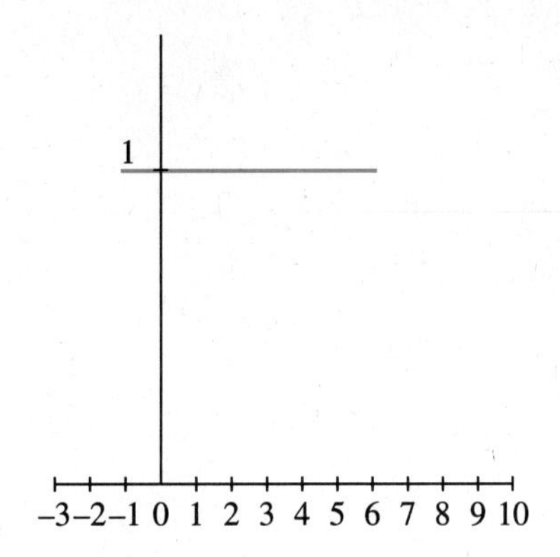

Figure 0.26 Truth plot of the inequality $x^2 - 7 \leq 5x$.

For truth plots, the use of inequality notation such as

$$3 < x < 4$$

does not work very well, because it actually represents two separate inequalities, $3 < x$ and $x < 4$, *both* of which must be satisfied. If the logical connective AND is understood by your system, then you can simply replace $3 < x < 4$ by the mathematically equivalent

$$(3 < x) \text{ AND } (x < 4).$$

Another strategy is to *multiply* the truth functions $(3 < x) \times (x < 4)$. (Why does this work?)

EXERCISES for Section 0.5

For exercises 1–4: Suppose your graphing screen is 101 pixels wide and 101 pixels tall. Explain how the graph of the line $y = x$ would look if you used the given viewing window.

1. $[-10, 10] \times [-10, 10]$
2. $[-.001, .001] \times [-.001, .001]$
3. $[-10, 10] \times [-.001, .001]$
4. $[-.001, .001] \times [-10, 10]$

For exercises 5–14: Graphically find a real number root (accurate to within .001) of the given equation between the values given.

5. $x^2 - 3.2 = 0$; $x = 1$, $x = 2$

6. $x^3 - 23 = 0$; $x = 2$, $x = 3$

7. $\sin(x) = 0.7$; $x = 0.7$, $x = 0.8$

8. $x^5 + 3.6x^4 - 2.51x^3 - 22.986x^2 - 28.24x - 10.4 = 0$; $x = 2$, $x = 3$

9. $x + \sqrt{x} = 7 - \sqrt{x^3}$; $x = 1.8$, $x = 2.6$

10. $x\exp(x^2) - \sqrt{x^2+1} = 0$ (where $\exp(x^2) = e^{x^2}$); $x = 0.4$, $x = 1$.

11. $\ln(x^2 + \ln(x)) = 0$; $x = 0.625$, $x = 1.35$

12. $x^3 - \sqrt{x^2+1} + x - 3 = 0$; $x = 1.1$, $x = 1.6$

13. $3\cos(\cos(x)) = 2x$; $x = 1.1$, $x = 2.2$

14. $\sqrt[4]{x} + x^3 - x - 0.5 = 0$; $x = 0.2$, $x = 1.2$

---

15. Find the other two solutions to the equation $1000x = \dfrac{(20-x)^3}{8}$.

(Hint: context is important! Must the solutions be real numbers?)

For exercises 16–39: Graphically estimate the solution sets to the following inequalities and express each set using interval notation.

16. $x^2 - 4 \le 5$

17. $2|x-9| \ge 1$

18. $x^2 - 2x + 3 > 1$

19. $\dfrac{x}{1+2x} < 3 - x$

20. $|x^2 - 9| \ge 2$

21. $\dfrac{1}{|2x-3|} < 4$

22. $x^3 - x < 0$

23. $x^2 + 4x + 6 \le 1$

24. $|||x| - 1| - 2| - 3 \le 2.7$

25. $\left|\dfrac{1}{x}\right| \ge 2$

26. $x^4 < x < x^2 + 3$

27. $|x+1| < x < |x|$

28. $x^2 - 4 \le \dfrac{x^2}{3}$

29. $2|x-9| \le x + 5$

30. $x^2 + 3 > 1 + 2x$

31. $\dfrac{x}{3-x} < 1 + 2x$

32. $|x^2 - 9| \le 2x$

33. $\dfrac{1}{|2x-3|} < |2x-3|$

34. $|x^3| < x$

35. $|x^2| \le 4x + 6$

36. $|||x| - 1| - 2| \le |x|$

37. $\left|\dfrac{1}{x}\right| \ge 2x + 2$

38. $x^3 < x < x^3 + 3$

39. $|x+1| < x + 1 < |x| + 1$

---

40. A student graphs $y = \cos(x)$ in the viewing window $[-6.28, 6.28] \times [-2, 2]$ and gets the horizontal "line" $y = 1$. Can you explain why?

41. Explain why multiplication is an appropriate operation for truth functions to represent the logical connective AND. (Hint: if a truth function

returns an output of 1 for TRUE and 0 for FALSE, when will the product of two truth functions return an output of 1?)

42. For the union of two or more intervals such as

$$(-\infty, 3] \cup (5, \infty),$$

the logical connective OR is appropriate. In other words, we can represent this set of values as

$$(x \leq 3) \quad \text{OR} \quad (x > 5)$$

for truth plotting. Devise a strategy for representing the truth function if OR is not supported by your system. Consider two cases. First assume that the inequalities are never both true (that is, the corresponding intervals are disjoint.) Then consider the more complicated case when the inequalities might both be true (that is, the intervals may overlap.)

43. Try graphing the function $f(x) = (1+x)^{1/x}$ and zoom in horizontally by a factor of 10 repeatedly. When you approach the precision limitation of the machine, you should see some rather remarkable behavior. Can you explain why this happens?

1

Fundamentals of Functions

The application of mathematics to solving "real-world" problems may be thought of in terms of the diagram in Figure 1.1. In many cases, the mathematical modeling of a problem requires finding a function that describes some real-world process. Mathematical analysis of the function model can lead to a solution of the real-world problem.

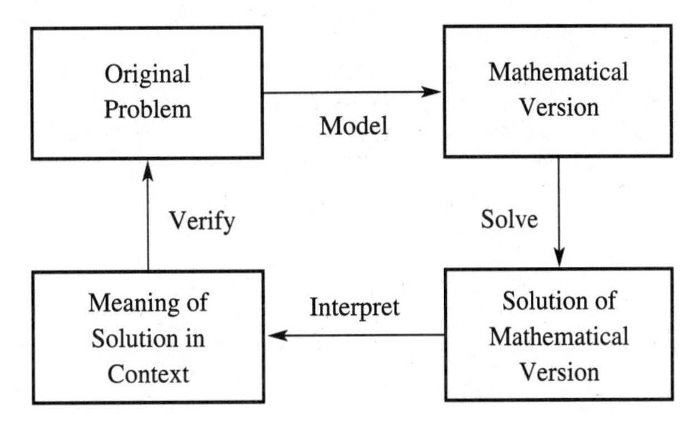

Figure 1.1 Applying mathematics to real-world problems.

Functions having real numbers as inputs and outputs are the central objects of study in calculus. In this chapter, we examine several of the most important types of functions that arise in modeling real-world processes. To analyze the fundamental properties of the functions in our "dictionary," we make use of their numeric, graphical, and symbolic representations. The connections among these function representations can give us valuable insights into the behavior of the process that the function models.

1.1 POLYNOMIAL, RATIONAL, AND POWER FUNCTIONS

Several types of functions occur often enough to deserve special names. In this section we provide part of our dictionary of important functions we study in calculus. Many of them will be familiar to you from your previous study of mathematics.

Polynomial functions

A **polynomial function** has the symbolic form $p : \mathbb{R} \longrightarrow \mathbb{R}$, where

$$p(x) = a_n x^n + a_{n-1}x^{n-1} + \cdots + a_1 x + a_0.$$

Each of the real numbers a_i ($0 \le i \le n$) is called a **coefficient** of the polynomial $p(x)$. Any or all of these coefficients could be 0. Each $a_i x^i$ is called a **term** of the polynomial. The highest power of a *nonzero* term determines the **degree** of a polynomial function.

Two examples of polynomial functions are given by

$$p(x) = 3x^4 - 5x^2 + \sqrt{17} \qquad \text{and} \qquad q(x) = \pi x^2 - x^3.$$

The degree of p is 4, and the degree of q is 3.

> Unless otherwise specified, the domain of any polynomial function is assumed to be $\mathbb{R}$, the set of all real numbers.

Any value x that results in an output value of 0 for a function is called a *root* or *zero* of that function. Recall that $x = r$ is a root of a polynomial function if and only if $(x - r)$ is a factor of the polynomial. For example, the polynomial

$$f(x) = x^3 + 3x^2 - 4x = x(x+4)(x-1) = (x-0)(x-(-4))(x-1),$$

so $x = 0$, $x = -4$, and $x = 1$ are roots of $f(x)$.

This means that a polynomial function of degree n could have, at most, n different real roots. (If it had more than n different roots, then multiplying all the corresponding factors together would result in a polynomial with a degree larger than n.) Let's take a look now at some special cases of polynomial functions.

1. *Constant functions*

A **constant function** is the simplest type of polynomial function, for it assigns exactly the same output value to every input in its domain. A constant function $f : \mathbb{R} \longrightarrow \mathbb{R}$ has the formula

$$f(x) = c,$$

where c is a specific real number.

Note: A *nonzero* constant function is a polynomial function of degree 0.

Keep in mind that a function is an *assignment process* taking inputs and producing outputs. A constant function has the entire set of real numbers as its domain. Hence, any value x can be input, but the same output value is always produced. The graph of a constant function is a horizontal line. On the other hand, the term *constant* (used as a noun) refers to a single fixed real number.

2. *The identity function*

The **identity function** simply returns an output value identical to the input value. The identity function $i : \mathbb{R} \longrightarrow \mathbb{R}$ has the symbolic form

$$i(x) = x.$$

If the scales on the coordinate axes are the same, then the graph of the identity function is a diagonal line rising at a $45°$ angle to the x-axis.

Figure 1.2 illustrates the graph of a constant function f (where $f(x) = 3$ for all values x) and the graph of the identity function i. When we feed a value x to the identity function, the same value is produced as output. Again, it is this *process* of producing an output identical to the input that we call the identity function, and not the variable x by itself.

3. *Linear functions*

A **linear function** $f : \mathbb{R} \longrightarrow \mathbb{R}$ has the formula

$$f(x) = mx + b,$$

where m and b are specific real numbers. The graph of a linear function is a straight line. The parameter m corresponds to the **slope** ("rise/run") of the graph, and b corresponds to the y-intercept.

Constant functions and the identity function are themselves special cases of linear functions. The graph of $y = 3$ has slope $m = 0$ and y-intercept $b = 3$. The graph of $y = x$ has slope $m = 1$ and y-intercept $b = 0$.

A simple example of a linear function is described by the formula relating the Fahrenheit and Celsius temperature scales. If x is the temperature in degrees Celsius, then

$$y = \frac{9}{5}x + 32$$

is the same temperature in degrees Fahrenheit.

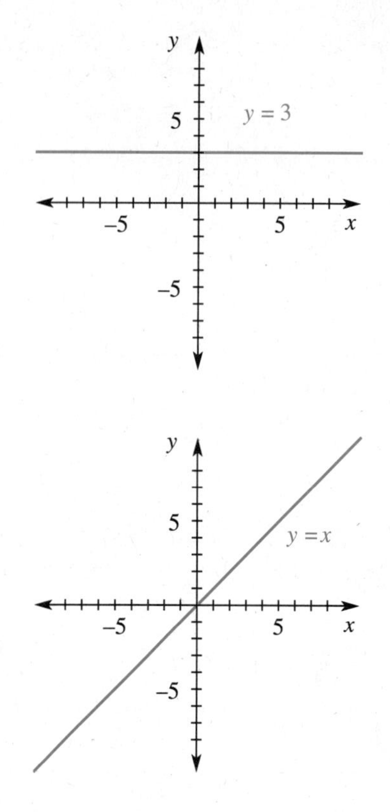

Figure 1.2 Graphs of $y = 3$ and $y = x$.

Linear functions have a special importance in the study of calculus, and we examine them in much greater detail in Chapter 3.

> Note: If the slope $m \neq 0$, then $mx + b$ is a polynomial of degree 1.

4. *Quadratic and cubic functions*

A quadratic function is a polynomial function of degree 2. Any function $p : \mathbb{R} \longrightarrow \mathbb{R}$, where

$$p(x) = ax^2 + bx + c, \quad (a \neq 0)$$

is a quadratic function.

For example, a projectile launched straight up from ground level with velocity 1000 ft/sec will attain, after t seconds, an approximate height h given (in feet) by the quadratic function

$$h(t) = 1000t - 16t^2$$

(provided, of course, that it hasn't returned to earth by time t).

A cubic function is a polynomial function of degree 3. Any function $q : \mathbb{R} \longrightarrow \mathbb{R}$, where

$$q(x) = ax^3 + bx^2 + cx + d, \quad (a \neq 0)$$

is a cubic function.

Graphs of cubic functions are often "glued" together to form smooth curves and outlines in computer-generated illustrations. These curves are called *cubic splines*, and you can find further discussion of them in Chapter 9.

Rational functions

A **rational function** has the symbolic form $f : D \longrightarrow \mathbb{R}$, where

$$f(x) = \frac{p(x)}{q(x)}$$

and $p(x)$ and $q(x)$ are polynomials. Just as a *rational* number is the quotient of two integers, a *rational* function is the quotient of two polynomial functions. Note that any polynomial function can also be considered a rational function with denominator 1, just as any integer can be considered a rational number.

Two examples of rational functions f and g are described by the formulas

$$f(x) = \frac{2x+1}{x^2 - 4x + 3} \qquad \text{and} \qquad g(x) = \frac{\sqrt{2} - 17x^3}{5x^4 - \pi}.$$

Since the formula for a rational function involves a quotient, we must take care to avoid division by zero. Accordingly, the domain D of a rational function f with formula

$$f(x) = \frac{p(x)}{q(x)}$$

is the set of all real numbers x except for those that are roots of $q(x)$. In other words,

$$D = \{x : q(x) \neq 0\}.$$

EXAMPLE 1 Find the domain of the rational functions f and g above.

Solution The domain of f is $D = \{x : x^2 - 4x + 3 \neq 0\} = \{x : x \neq 1, 3\}$.
The domain of g is $D = \{x : 5x^4 - \pi \neq 0\} = \{x : x \neq \pm\sqrt[4]{\frac{\pi}{5}}\}$. ■

We examine the behavior of rational functions in more detail in Chapter 2.

Power functions

A **power function** has the symbolic form $f : D \longrightarrow \mathbb{R}$, with

$$f(x) = ax^b.$$

The behavior and domain of a power function depends on the parameters a and b. Let's look at some special cases.

1. *Monomial functions*

If $a \neq 0$, and n is a nonnegative integer, then ax^n can be called a **monomial** (a polynomial having only one term), and n is the degree. If $a = 0$, then we have a *zero* constant function, and its degree is not defined.

EXAMPLE 2 Find the degrees of the following monomials:

$$-2x^7, \quad -\pi, \quad x, \quad \frac{22}{17}x^{100}, \quad \text{and} \quad 0.$$

Solution In order, the degrees of these five monomials are: 7, 0, 1, 100, and *undefined.* ■

EXAMPLE 3 Explain why the following are not monomials:

$$5x^{2/3}, \quad 3x^{-2}, \quad 2x - 1.$$

Solution Note that $5x^{2/3}$ and $3x^{-2}$ are *not* monomials because the exponent in each case is not a nonnegative integer. Also, $2x - 1$ is not a monomial, because it has more than one term. (We could call it a *binomial*, since it has two terms.) ■

2. *Negative integer power functions*

Monomial functions can be thought of as particularly simple polynomial functions. Negative integer power functions can be thought of as particularly simple rational functions.

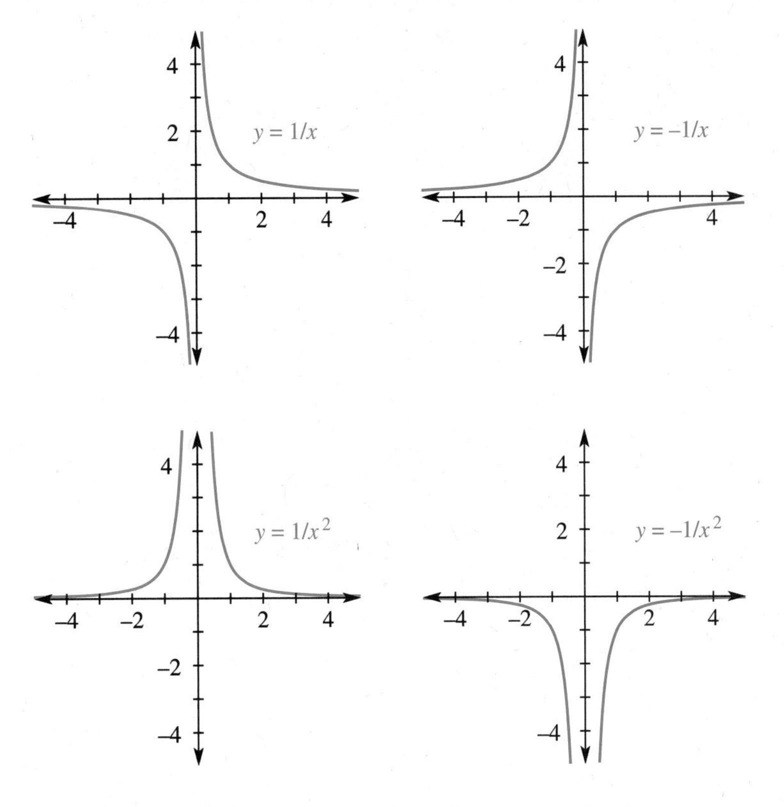

Figure 1.3 Graphs of negative integer power functions.

If $f(x) = ax^{-n}$, where $-n$ is a negative integer, note that we can write

$$f(x) = \frac{a}{x^n}.$$

This expression is undefined only when $x = 0$, so unless otherwise specified, the domain D of f is assumed to be

$$D = \{x : \ x \neq 0\}.$$

Figure 1.3 illustrates the graphs of $y = 1/x$, $y = 1/x^2$, $y = -1/x$, and $y = -1/x^2$. The magnitude of a/x^n is large for values x close to 0 and small when x is far from 0. Put another way:

> $\left|\frac{a}{x^n}\right|$ is large when $|x|$ is small, and $\left|\frac{a}{x^n}\right|$ is small when $|x|$ is large.

A negative power function describes a functional relationship known as *inverse variation.* For example, if x is the distance between two bodies of fixed masses, then the gravitational force $f(x)$ between the two bodies is inversely related to x^2. (The farther apart the two bodies are from each other, the weaker the gravitational attraction between them.) That is,

$$f(x) = \frac{a}{x^2},$$

where a is a constant determined by the masses of the two bodies.

3. *Rational power functions*

The root of a real number can be written using a fractional exponent. If q is a positive integer, then

$$x^{1/q} = \sqrt[q]{x}.$$

For example,

$$9^{1/2} = \sqrt{9} = 3, \qquad \text{and} \qquad (-8)^{1/3} = \sqrt[3]{-8} = -2.$$

If p/q is a rational number in *lowest terms*, such that q is a positive integer and p has *no common factor* with q greater than 1, then we write

$$x^{p/q} = \sqrt[q]{x^p}.$$

For example,

$$4^{3/2} = \sqrt{4^3} = \sqrt{64} = 8.$$

To evaluate the rational power of a real number, it is sometimes easier to perform the equivalent calculation

$$x^{p/q} = (\sqrt[q]{x})^p.$$

For example, $(-125)^{2/3} = (\sqrt[3]{-125})^2 = (-5)^2 = 25$. Unless otherwise specified, the domain D of a rational power function f, with

$$f(x) = x^{p/q},$$

depends on p and q. If the denominator q is even, indicating an even root, then a negative input x will not produce a real-number output. If the numerator p is negative, then $x = 0$ results in division by zero. Taking both of these observations into account, we can categorize the different possible domains as follows:

If $f(x) = x^{p/q}$, with	then the domain D of f is:
p positive, q odd	$D = \mathbb{R}$
p positive, q even	$D = \{x : x \geq 0\}$
p negative, q odd	$D = \{x : x \neq 0\}$
p negative, q even	$D = \{x : x > 0\}$.

Rational power functions form a rich family of functions for study in calculus. In the exercises, you are asked to examine a wide variety of rational power functions.

▶▶▶ **You often need to take special care when using a machine to evaluate a rational power of a real number. The machine may use a different computational procedure, depending on the way you enter the function.**

For example, a machine may give an error message or a complex number result when evaluating $(-8)^{2/3}$. The very same machine may calculate

$$((-8)^2)^{1/3} = 64^{1/3} = 4$$

with no difficulty. You may need to experiment with different forms of expressing a rational power function to make sure your machine computes the values and graphs the points you intend.

Even and odd functions

A power function f, such that $f(x) = ax^n$, where n is an integer, enjoys special properties, depending on whether n is even or odd. These functions provide the motivation for defining *even* and *odd* functions.

Definition 1

A function f is called **even** if the outputs satisfy the property

$$f(x) = f(-x)$$

for *every* real number input x in the domain of f. A function f is called **odd** if the outputs satisfy the property

$$-f(x) = f(-x)$$

for *every* real number input x in the domain of f.

Let's examine the meaning of these definitions in numeric, graphical, and symbolic representations, using $f(x) = x^2$ as an example of an even function f and $g(x) = x^3$ as an example of an odd function g.

Numerically, an even function produces equal outputs for opposite inputs. An odd function produces opposite outputs for opposite inputs.

If $f(x) = x^2$, then

$$f(-2) = (-2)^2 = 4 = 2^2 = f(2),$$

and
$$f(5) = 5^2 = 25 = (-5)^2 = f(-5).$$

On the other hand, if $g(x) = x^3$, then

$$g(-2) = (-2)^3 = -8 \text{ is the opposite of } g(2) = 2^3 = 8,$$

and
$$g(5) = 5^3 = 125 \text{ is the opposite of } g(-5) = (-5)^3 = -125.$$

Graphically, an even function will have a graph that is symmetric about the y-axis. The graph of an odd function has symmetry with respect to the origin.

The graph of an even function over its positive inputs will appear to be a mirror image of the graph over its negative inputs.

We say that the y-axis is a **line of reflection** for the graph of an even function.

If we rotate the graph of an odd function $180°$ about the origin, the graph will lie exactly on top of itself. Another way to think of a graph symmetric with respect to the origin is that, for any input value x, a line segment connecting the points $(x, g(x))$ and $(-x, g(-x))$ will always have its midpoint at the origin.

Figure 1.4 illustrates these symmetry properties of even and odd function graphs.

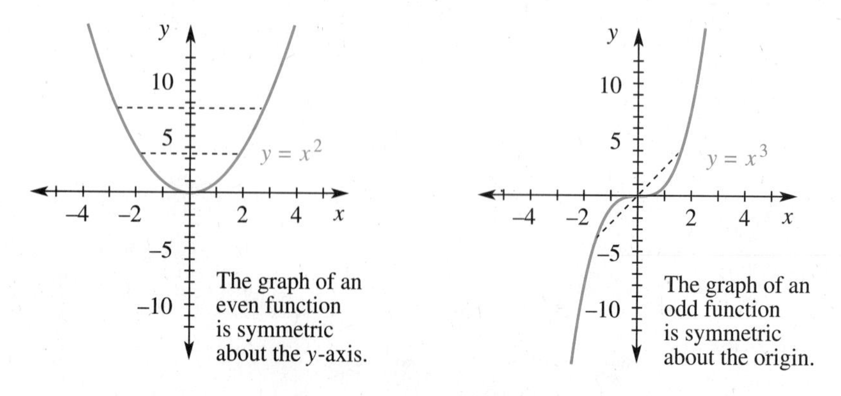

Figure 1.4 Symmetries of even and odd function graphs.

Symbolically, replacing x by $-x$ in the formula of an even function produces the same formula. Replacing x by $-x$ in the formula of an odd function produces the opposite of the original formula.

Note that $$f(-x) = (-x)^2 = x^2 = f(x)$$

for all real values x. On the other hand,

$$g(-x) = (-x)^3 = -x^3 = -g(x)$$

for all real values x.

EXERCISES for Section 1.1

1. When we multiply two nonzero polynomials together, how does the degree of the result compare with the degrees of the original two polynomials?

2. Considering exercise 1, why do you think that the constant polynomial 0 has an undefined degree?

3. When we add two nonzero polynomials together, is it possible for the degree of the result to be less than either of the original polynomial degrees?

4. Some books define a linear function to be a function f with the property

$$f(a + b) = f(a) + f(b)$$

for all possible real values of a and b. Which functions mentioned in this section satisfy this property?

5. The graphs of *all* power functions f with formula $f(x) = x^b$ share one specific point in common. What point is it?

6. Is the constant function f, where $f(x) = 3$ for all x, an even function, an odd function, or neither?

7. Is the identity function i, where $i(x) = x$ for all x, an even function, an odd function, or neither?

8. Can a function be both even and odd? If so, give an example. If not, explain why not.

For exercises 9–20: (a graphing-intensive investigative activity): Suppose the rational power p/q is chosen from the set

$$\{-2/1, -4/3, -3/2, -1/1, -3/4, -2/3, -1/2, 2/1, 4/3, 3/2, 1/1, 3/4, 2/3, 1/2\}.$$

Graph $y = x^{p/q}$ for each of these powers p/q (if you use a machine grapher, make a sketch on paper for comparison and reference). Then identify which of these rational powers result in the given characteristics of the function f with formula

$$f(x) = x^{p/q}.$$

9. Domain is $D = \mathbb{R}$.

10. Domain is $D = \{x : x \neq 0\}$.

11. Domain is $D = \{x : x \geq 0\}$.

12. Domain is $D = \{x : x > 0\}$.

13. All outputs are nonnegative.

14. All outputs are nonzero.

15. Graph has a *cusp* ($\curlyvee$).

16. Graph has a horizontal asymptote.

17. Graph is a straight line.

18. Graph has a vertical asymptote.

19. Function f is even.

20. Function f is odd.

---

21. When is the rational power function f, where $f(x) = x^{p/q}$, an even function, and when is it an odd function? (Does the answer depend on p, q, or both?)

22. Show that if f is an odd function and $f(0)$ is defined, then we must have $f(0) = 0$.

23. A counterexample is an example showing that a statement is false. Find a counterexample to each of the following statements:

(a) If the degree of a polynomial function is even, then it is an even function.

(b) If the degree of a polynomial function is odd, then it is an odd function.

24. Suppose that every term of a polynomial $p(x)$ is even. Is p necessarily an even function? Suppose that every term of a polynomial $q(x)$ is odd. Is q necessarily an odd function?

For exercises 25–30: (a graphing-intensive investigative activity): Suppose $f : \mathbb{R} \longrightarrow \mathbb{R}$, where

$$f(x) = x^3 - x + 1.$$

Graph $y = f(x)$, making note of its zeroes (the x-intercepts) as well as the y-intercept.

25. Graph $y = f(x + a)$ for $a = -3, -2/3, -1, 1/2, 2,$ and 3. Compare the location of the x-intercepts of each graph with those of the graph of $y = f(x)$. Describe in your own words the effect of the parameter a to predict how the graph of $y = f(x + a)$ compares with the graph of $y = f(x)$.

26. Graph $y = f(bx)$ for $b = -3, -2/3, -1, 1/2, 2,$ and 3. Compare the locations of the x-intercepts of each graph with those of the graph of $y =$

$f(x)$. Describe in your own words the effect of the parameter b to predict how the graph of $y = f(bx)$ compares with the graph of $y = f(x)$.

27. Graph $y = cf(x)$ for $c = -3,\ -2/3,\ -1,\ 1/2,\ 2,$ and 3. Compare the locations of the y-intercept of each graph with that of the graph of $y = f(x)$. Describe in your own words the effect of the parameter c to predict how the graph of $y = cf(x)$ compares with the graph of $y = f(x)$.

28. Graph $y = f(x) + d$ for $d = -3,\ -2/3,\ -1,\ 1/2,\ 2,$ and 3. Compare the location of the y-intercept of each graph with that of the graph of $y = f(x)$. Describe in your own words the effect of the parameter d to predict how the graph of $y = f(x) + d$ compares with the graph of $y = f(x)$.

29. Is it possible to find values for the parameters a, b, c, and d so that the graph of $y = cf(bx + a) + d$ has x-intercepts only at -1, 1 and 2, and y-intercept 3? If so, find an example. If not, explain why not.

30. Graph each of the following functions, noting their relationship to the original function f:

$$y = f(|x|) \qquad y = |f(x)| \qquad y = f(1/x) \qquad y = 1/f(x).$$

For exercises 31–35: A projectile launched straight up from ground level at velocity 1000 ft/sec will attain, after t seconds, an approximate height h given (in feet) by the quadratic function

$$h(t) = 1000t - 16t^2$$

(provided, of course, that it hasn't returned to earth by time t).

31. Exactly how long does it take for the projectile to return to earth?

32. Graph $y = h(t)$ over the t-range from $t = 0$ until the projectile returns to earth.

33. During what time interval is the projectile rising?

34. During what time interval is the projectile falling?

35. What is the maximum height achieved by the projectile?

---

36. Find a formula of the form $y = mx + b$ describing the conversion of $x°$ Fahrenheit to $y°$ Celsius temperature.

37. Are the graphs of $y = \sqrt[4]{x^2}$ and $y = (\sqrt[4]{x})^2$ the same over the interval $[-5, 5]$?

38. Why is the expression $x^{p/q}$ ambiguous when p/q is not in lowest terms and $x < 0$? (Hint: consider exercise 37 and $p/q = 2/4$.)

1.2 EXPONENTIAL AND LOGARITHMIC FUNCTIONS

We continue to develop our dictionary of functions in this section by examining exponential and logarithmic functions.

Exponential functions

In general, an **exponential function** has the symbolic form $f : \mathbb{R} \longrightarrow \mathbb{R}$, where

$$f(x) = a^x, \qquad (a > 0, a \neq 1).$$

The domain of an exponential function is $\mathbb{R}$, the set of all real numbers.

Two examples of exponential functions f and g are given by the formulas

$$f(x) = 2^x \qquad \text{and} \qquad g(x) = (2/3)^x.$$

The parameter a is called the **base** of the exponential function. The base of f is 2, and the base of g is $2/3$.

Since the base a must be positive, we can make an important observation:

If $a > 0$, then a^x is positive for all values x.

Note that the formula $h(x) = x^3$ does *not* describe an exponential function. Despite a superficial symbolic similarity between exponential functions and power functions, there is a very important difference: in a power function, the input x is raised to some fixed power, but in an exponential function, x *is* the power.

The graph of $y = a^x$ generally has one of two shapes, depending on whether $a < 1$ or $a > 1$, as illustrated in Figure 1.5. Exponential functions arise quite naturally in descriptions of certain growth (like population) or decay (like radioactivity). Consider a type of bacteria such that each living cell splits into two new cells every hour. Suppose we start out with a single one of these cells, and let t represent the time elapsed in hours. The number of cells $p(t)$ is a function of time t, and we have

$$p(0) = 1, \quad p(1) = 2, \quad p(2) = 4, \quad p(3) = 8, \quad p(4) = 16, \quad \ldots,$$

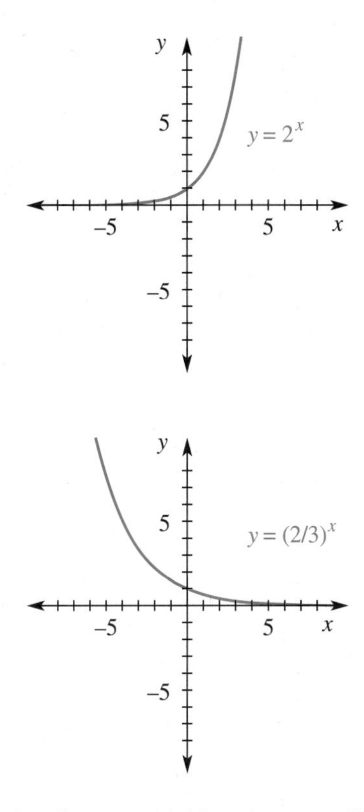

Figure 1.5 Graphs of exponential functions $y = 2^x$ and $y = (2/3)^x$

provided adequate nourishment is available in the cell environment. If we plot the points $(t, p(t))$ for $t = 0, 1, 2, 3, 4, \ldots$, we find that they all lie on the graph of $y = 2^t$, as shown in Figure 1.6.

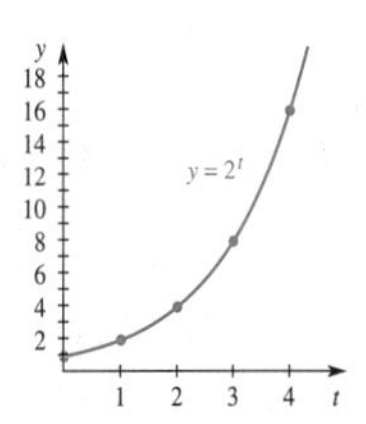

Figure 1.6 Population growth described by an exponential function.

The term **half-life** is used to describe how quickly radioactive material decays. For example, if we start with 100 kg of radioactive material whose half-life is 75 years, and we let $q(t)$ represent the amount of material left after t years, then

$$q(0) = 100 \text{ kg}, \quad q(75) = 50 \text{ kg}, \quad q(150) = 25 \text{ kg}, \quad q(225) = 12.5 \text{ kg}, \quad \ldots$$

We can write a formula $q(t)$ in exponential form for the amount in kilograms of the substance after t years:

$$q(t) = 100 \cdot 2^{-t/75} = 100(2^{-1/75})^t.$$

We can see that the base of this exponential function is

$$2^{-1/75} = \frac{1}{\sqrt[75]{2}} \approx .9908.$$

In general, if we start with an initial amount A_0 of radioactive material having half-life k years, the amount left after t years is

$$q(t) = A_0 \cdot 2^{-t/k} = A_0(2^{-1/k})^t.$$

The natural exponential function

There is one base for exponential functions so important that it deserves a special name and symbol.

Definition 2

The **natural exponential function** exp is defined by

$$\exp(x) = e^x,$$

with the irrational number base $e = 2.71828\ldots$.

Much like the irrational number π, the number e arises over and over again in mathematics, and the natural exponential function exp could lay claim to being the most important function in calculus, as will become apparent later. Chapter 8 discusses some of the applications of the exponential function.

Logarithmic functions

A **logarithmic function** has the symbolic form $f : \{x : x > 0\} \longrightarrow \mathbb{R}$, with

$$f(x) = \log_a x \qquad (a > 0,\ a \neq 1).$$

The parameter a is called the **base** of the logarithm.

The domain D of a logarithmic function is the set of all *positive* real numbers, $D = \{x : x > 0\}$.

A logarithmic equation is equivalent to an exponential equation:

$$y = \log_a x \qquad \text{if and only if} \qquad x = a^y.$$

The value of a logarithm can be determined by solving its associated exponential equation.

EXAMPLE 4 Calculate $\log_3 9$, $\log_5(.04)$, and $\log_8 2$.

Solution In each case, we translate the equation $b = \log_a c$ to $a^b = c$.

If $b = \log_3 9$, then $3^b = 9$, and we see that $b = 2$.

If $b = \log_5(.04)$, then $5^b = .04 = 1/25 = 5^{-2}$, and we see that $b = -2$.

If $b = \log_8 2$, then $8^b = 2$. Since $\sqrt[3]{8} = 2$, we see that $b = 1/3$.

Summarizing, we have $\log_3 9 = 2$, $\log_5(.04) = -2$, and $\log_8 2 = 1/3$. ■

The graph of an exponential function $y = a^x$ and the corresponding logarithmic function $y = \log_a x$ look like mirror images of each other through the line $y = x$. In other words, $y = x$ is a line of reflection for the two graphs. Figure 1.7 illustrates this symmetry property between the graphs of logarithmic functions and exponential functions.

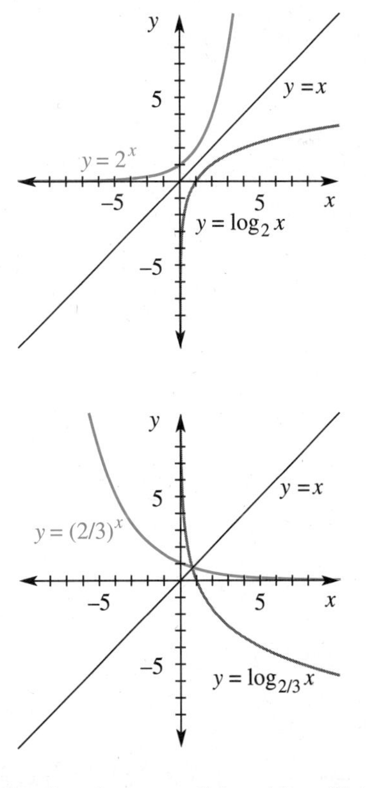

Figure 1.7 Graphs of exponential and logarithmic functions.

Properties of logarithms

Many properties of logarithmic functions follow directly from properties of exponents. We list some of the most important of these properties below:

$$\log_a(bc) = \log_a b + \log_a c \qquad \log_a(b/c) = \log_a b - \log_a c$$

$$\log_a(b^c) = c \log_a b \qquad \log_b c = \frac{\log_a c}{\log_a b}$$

▶▶▶ **It must be emphasized that these properties are valid only for *positive real numbers* a, b, c. If we extend the domain of the logarithm beyond the positive real numbers (as is done in the study of complex numbers), these properties need to be modified, and they lose some of their simplicity.**

The natural and common logarithmic functions

The logarithmic function with base e is called the **natural logarithmic function** and is denoted by the special name $\ln$. In other words,

$$\ln x = \log_e x.$$

The natural exponential and logarithmic functions "undo" each other. More precisely,

$$\exp(\ln x) = x \text{ for all } x > 0, \text{ and } \ln(\exp(x)) = x \text{ for all } x \in \mathbb{R}.$$

Since our decimal system has place values corresponding to powers of 10, many people call $\log_{10}$ the **common logarithmic function**. Most calculators and mathematical software packages have both of these logarithmic functions built in but may not have any others. However, we can use either of these to calculate logarithms to other bases, as shown in the following example.

EXAMPLE 5 Use common logarithms to calculate $\log_3 19$.

Solution Using one of the properties of logarithms, we can write

$$\log_3 19 = \frac{\log_{10} 19}{\log_{10} 3} \approx \frac{1.27875}{0.47712} \approx 2.68014.$$

A calculator having the common logarithmic function was used to calculate $\log_{10} 19$ and $\log_{10} 3$. ■

EXERCISES for Section 1.2

For exercises 1–10: Suppose that you are given the following values:

$$\log_a 2 = .6055, \qquad \log_a 3 = .9597, \qquad \log_a 10 = 2.0115.$$

Use the properties of logarithms to find these values:

1. $\log_a 1$
2. $\log_a 4$
3. $\log_a 5$
4. $\log_a 6$
5. $\log_a 7$
6. $\log_a 8$
7. $\log_a 9$
8. $\log_a 0.5$
9. $\log_a a$
10. $\log_a 15$

For exercises 11–13: The Platypus Company has a manufacturing process that produces a radioactive waste byproduct with a half-life of twenty years.

11. How long must the waste be stored safely to allow it to decay to one-quarter of its original mass?

12. How long will it take to decay to 10% of its original mass?

13. How long will it take to decay to 1% of its original mass?

For exercises 14–16: A rodent pest population triples every 30 days.

14. How long does it take the population to double?

15. If the population starts out with only 10 rodents, how many are there after 1 year?

16. Another population starts out with 100 rodents, and doubles every 20 days. How many are there after 1 year?

For exercises 17–20: If an initial amount P is deposited into a bank account earning r% interest annually, then the amount A in the account after n years is given by

$$A = P(1 + \frac{r}{100})^n.$$

17. How much is in an account where \$1000 is deposited at 6% interest for 5 years?

18. If an initial amount of \$1000 is deposited at 8% annual interest, how long will it take the account balance to double?

19. If an initial amount of \$1000 is deposited for 3 years, what must the annual interest rate be for the account to grow to exactly \$1500?

20. If the annual interest rate is 7.5%, how much should the initial deposit amount be if we want the account balance to be \$1000 after 10 years?

For exercises 21–23: A bacteria colony doubles in size every hour from 6 PM until 6 AM the next morning, when it completely covers the nutrient tray it lives on.

21. At what time was the tray only half-covered with bacteria?

22. At what time was the tray only 10% covered with bacteria?

23. A slow poison is sprayed on the bacteria at 6 AM, causing the bacteria colony to shrink in size by 25% every hour. When will the bacteria colony return to its original size?

For exercises 24–32: Graph $y = 2^x$. If this graph is reflected through the given line or lines, find a formula $y = f(x)$ describing the new graph (i.e., the reflection).

24. reflection through the x-axis

25. reflection through the y-axis

26. reflection through the line $y = x$

27. reflection through the x-axis, then through the y-axis

28. reflection through the y-axis, then through the x-axis

29. reflection through the x-axis, then through the line $y = x$

30. reflection through the y-axis, then through the line $y = x$

31. reflection through the line $y = x$, then through the x-axis

32. reflection through the line $y = x$, then through the y-axis

---

33. Suppose that $\operatorname{expm}(x) = \exp(x) - a$

and
$$\operatorname{lnp1}(x) = \ln(x + b)$$

for certain constants a and b. Find values for a and b such that the graphs of both $y = \operatorname{expm}(x)$ and $\operatorname{lnp1}(x)$ pass through the origin $(0, 0)$.

Note: These functions are defined in ways to take better advantage of machine precision capabilities possible when a graph passes through the origin. The functions expm and lnp1 are actually computed by machines in a distinctly different way than are exp and ln.

For exercises 34–40: (a graphing-intensive investigative activity): Suppose $a > 1$ and that the functions f, g, and h are described by the formulas

$$f(x) = a^x, \qquad g(x) = \log_a x, \qquad h(x) = x^a.$$

For $x > 0$, the function values $f(x)$, $g(x)$, and $h(x)$ all grow larger as x grows larger. Graph each of the three functions for $a = 2$, $a = e$, $a = 3$, and $a = 10$ (twelve graphs in all), and use these graphs to help answer the following questions.

34. For every value $a > 1$, what point do the graphs of $y = a^x$ all have in common?

35. For every value $a > 1$, what point do the graphs of $y = \log_a x$ all have in common?

36. For every value $a > 1$, what point do the graphs of $y = x^a$ all have in common?

37. For a fixed value a, which of the three graphs shows the steepest rise for $0 < x < 1$?

38. For a fixed value a, which of the three graphs shows the steepest rise for $1 < x < a$?

39. For a fixed value a, which of the three graphs shows the steepest rise for $x > a$?

40. The equation $a^x = x^a$ has one obvious solution for x, namely $x = a$. What other positive values x (if any) satisfy the equation for $a = 2$? $a = e$? $a = 3$? $a = 10$?

1.3 TRIGONOMETRIC FUNCTIONS

Trigonometry originated as the study of the relationships between the angle and side measures of triangles. (*Trigonos* and *metrics* are the Greek words for "triangle" and "measurement," respectively.) Historically, trigonometry had a great impact on solving problems in navigation and surveying. The greatest importance of trigonometry today is in its use to describe periodic phenomena and cyclic processes. Planetary orbits, seasonal temperatures, and sound vibrations are just a few of the wide variety of physical processes that can be described using trigonometric functions. The trigonometric functions can also be extremely useful in mathematically describing biological, economic, and even social phenomena that are cyclic or periodic in nature.

At first glance, the study of triangles would appear to have little to do with describing cyclic processes. The key connection is made by relating triangular relationships to a *circle*, as we shall see. (The basics of right-triangle trigonometry are reviewed in the appendices.)

Trigonometric functions as circular functions

The uses of trigonometric functions in modeling cyclic phenomena are made possible by defining them as *circular functions*. To make these definitions, we start out with the **unit circle**, that is, the set of points in the Cartesian plane located exactly one unit from the origin:

$$\{(x, y) : x^2 + y^2 = 1\}.$$

For the time being, let's use θ (theta) to represent the independent variable for trigonometric functions. (The choice of letters or symbols to represent the independent and dependent variables in a function process is really arbitrary. Later we will use x and y to indicate the inputs and outputs of trigonometric functions, as we do for most functions.) The input θ represents the angle in radians measured from the *initial point* $(1, 0)$ on the positive x-axis. As before, positive angle measure is understood to be in the counterclockwise direction and negative angle measure in the clockwise direction. Measured in radians, the angle θ could be any real number, since an angle greater than 2π or less than -2π is obtained by wrapping around the circle more than one full revolution.

Given a specific input angle θ_0, we find its *terminal point* (x_0, y_0) on the unit circle. The output values of the six trigonometric functions sine, cosine, tangent, cosecant, secant, and cotangent are then determined by using one or both of the terminal-point coordinates x_0 and y_0 as follows:

$$\cos(\theta_0) = x_0 \qquad \sin(\theta_0) = y_0 \qquad \tan(\theta_0) = \frac{y_0}{x_0}$$

$$\sec(\theta_0) = \frac{1}{x_0} \qquad \csc(\theta_0) = \frac{1}{y_0} \qquad \cot(\theta_0) = \frac{x_0}{y_0}$$

Figure 1.8 illustrates this process.

When (x_0, y_0) represents a point in the first quadrant (so that x_0 and y_0 are nonnegative), we can consider x_0 and y_0 as the lengths of adjacent and opposite legs of a right triangle (with hypotenuse 1). In this case, these formulas match the right-triangle trigonometric formulas. One advantage of this more uniform method of defining the trigonometric functions is that we are no longer limited to angles between 0 and $\pi/2$.

Output values for the trigonometric functions for some common input values (in both degrees and radians) are shown in Table 1.1 and the graphs of the trigonometric functions are shown in Figure 1.9.

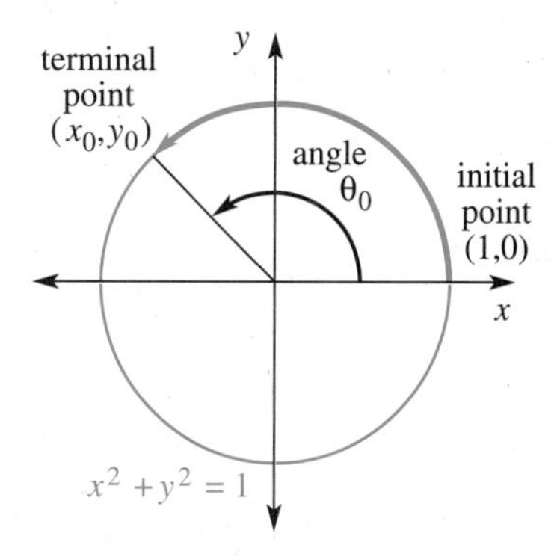

The trigonometric function evaluation process:

1. Measure angle θ_0 from initial point (1,0).
2. Find terminal point (x_0,y_0).
3. Evaluate trigonometric function by its definition.

Figure 1.8 The trigonometric function evaluation process.

▶▶▶ **From here on, unless otherwise stated, all arguments to trigonometric functions will be assumed given in radians.**

Domains of the trigonometric functions

We can evaluate the sine and cosine functions for any real input value θ. Because division is involved in the definitions of the other trigonometric functions, we cannot include any value θ in their domains that would result in division by zero.

Domain of sin and cos: $D=\mathbb{R}$, the set of all real numbers.

Domain of tan and sec: $D=\{\theta:\theta\neq\frac{\pi}{2}+n\pi,\ n \text{ any integer}\}$.

Domain of cot and csc: $D=\{\theta:\theta\neq n\pi,\ n \text{ any integer}\}$.

Periodic functions

The six trigonometric functions have one property in common: the outputs cycle through the same values over and over again. This shouldn't be too surprising, since the trigonometric outputs are all determined

x in radians (in degrees)	trigonometric function values					
	$\sin(x)$	$\cos(x)$	$\tan(x)$	$\csc(x)$	$\sec(x)$	$\cot(x)$
0 (0°)	0	1	0	undefined	1	0
$\pi/6$ (30°)	$\frac{1}{2}$	$\frac{\sqrt{3}}{2}$	$\frac{\sqrt{3}}{3}$	2	$\frac{2\sqrt{3}}{2}$	$\sqrt{3}$
$\pi/4$ (45°)	$\frac{\sqrt{2}}{2}$	$\frac{\sqrt{2}}{2}$	1	$\sqrt{2}$	$\sqrt{2}$	1
$\pi/3$ (60°)	$\frac{\sqrt{3}}{2}$	$\frac{1}{2}$	$\sqrt{3}$	$\frac{2\sqrt{3}}{2}$	2	$\frac{\sqrt{3}}{3}$
$\pi/2$ (90°)	1	0	undefined	1	undefined	0
π (180°)	0	–1	0	undefined	–1	undefined
$3\pi/2$ (270°)	–1	0	undefined	0	undefined	0
2π (360°)	0	1	0	undefined	1	undefined

Table 1.1 Common trigonometric values.

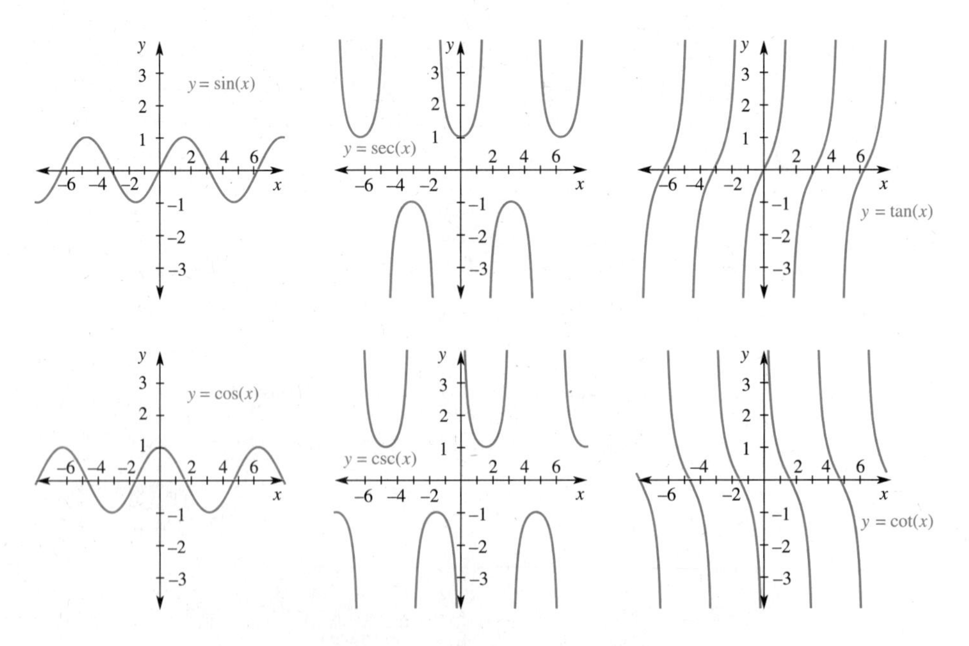

Figure 1.9 Graphs of the six trigonometric functions.

from the coordinates on the unit circle as we wrap around it repeatedly. Functions having this cycling property for their outputs are called **periodic**. In general, a function f is periodic if there is a positive real number p such that

$$f(x+p) = f(x)$$

for all x in the domain of f. The smallest *positive* value of p satisfying this property is called the **fundamental period** of the function. Graphically, if we have a plot of points over an interval of one period, then the rest of the graph is determined since we know how to extend it indefinitely by simply pasting copies of one graph cycle end to end.

The fundamental period of sin, cos, csc, and sec is $p = 2\pi$.

The fundamental period of tan and cot is $p = \pi$.

Because trigonometric functions are used so often in describing cyclic phenomena, their notation is sometimes abbreviated. Take special care to realize that an expression such as

$$\sin^2\theta \qquad \text{means} \qquad (\sin(\theta))^2.$$

The letters sin by themselves designate a function *name*, not a quantity that can be squared or multipled. On the other hand, $\sin(\theta)$ is the *real number output value* of the sine function for the input θ, and this value can certainly be used in an arithmetic or algebraic expression like any other real number.

Trigonometric identities

A **trigonometric identity** is a relationship between the trigonometric function outputs that holds for all acceptable inputs θ. Some trigonometric identities follow directly from the definitions of the functions. For example, from their definitions, we can see that

$$\tan(\theta) = \frac{\sin(\theta)}{\cos(\theta)}$$

for all values $\theta \neq (\pi/2 + n\pi)$, n any integer. Other identities follow from the geometry of the unit circle used in defining the trigonometric functions. For example,

$$\sin^2(\theta) + \cos^2(\theta) = 1$$

for all real values θ, since $x^2 + y^2 = 1$ for any point (x, y) lying on the unit circle. The most commonly used trigonometric identities are summarized here.

Pythagorean identities:

$$\sin^2(\theta) + \cos^2(\theta) = 1 \qquad \tan^2(\theta) + 1 = \sec^2(\theta) \qquad 1 + \cot^2(\theta) = \csc^2(\theta)$$

Fundamental identities:

$$\tan(\theta) = \frac{\sin(\theta)}{\cos(\theta)} \qquad \cot(\theta) = \frac{\cos(\theta)}{\sin(\theta)} \qquad \sec(\theta) = \frac{1}{\cos(\theta)} \qquad \csc(\theta) = \frac{1}{\sin(\theta)}$$

Even/odd identities:

$$\sin(-\theta) = -\sin(\theta) \qquad \cos(-\theta) = \cos(\theta)$$

Double-angle identities:

$$\sin(2\theta) = 2\sin(\theta)\cos(\theta) \qquad \cos(2\theta) = \cos^2(\theta) - \sin^2(\theta)$$

Half-angle identities:

$$\sin^2(\theta/2) = \frac{1 - \cos(\theta)}{2} \qquad \cos^2(\theta/2) = \frac{1 + \cos(\theta)}{2}$$

Sum and difference formulas:

$$\sin(\alpha+\beta) = \sin(\alpha)\cos(\beta)+\cos(\alpha)\sin(\beta) \qquad \sin(\alpha-\beta) = \sin(\alpha)\cos(\beta)-\cos(\alpha)\sin(\beta)$$

$$\cos(\alpha+\beta) = \cos(\alpha)\cos(\beta)-\sin(\alpha)\sin(\beta) \qquad \cos(\alpha-\beta) = \cos(\alpha)\cos(\beta)+\sin(\alpha)\sin(\beta)$$

EXERCISES for Section 1.3

1. Which of the trigonometric functions are even? (Hint: look at the graphs.)

2. Which of the trigonometric functions are odd?

3. A **bounded** function has all of its outputs contained in a bounded interval (of y-values). Which of the trigonometric functions are bounded?

4. Which of the trigonometric functions are unbounded?

For exercises 5–8: (a graphing-intensive investigative activity): Graph $y = \sin(x)$ over the interval $[-2\pi,\ 2\pi]$.

5. Graph $y = A\sin(x)$ for $A = -3,\ -2/3,\ -1,\ 1/2,\ 2,$ and 3. Describe in your own words the effect of the parameter A in comparing the graph of $y = A\sin(x)$ with the graph of $y = \sin(x)$.

6. Graph $y = \sin(Bx)$ for $B = -3, -2/3, -1, 1/2, 2,$ and 3. Describe in your own words the effect of the parameter B in comparing the graph of $y = \sin(Bx)$ with the graph of $y = \sin(x)$.

7. Graph $y = \sin(x - C)$ for $C = -3\pi, -2\pi/3, -\pi, \pi/2, 2\pi,$ and 3π. Describe in your own words the effect of the parameter C in comparing the graph of $y = \sin(x - C)$ with the graph of $y = \sin(x)$.

8. Graph $y = \sin(x) + D$ for $D = -3, -2/3, -1, 1/2, 2,$ and 3. Describe in your own words the effect of the parameter D in comparing the graph of $y = \sin(x) + D$ with the graph of $y = \sin(x)$.

For exercises 9–14: Consider the function $s : \mathbb{R} \longrightarrow \mathbb{R}$, such that

$$s(x) = -3 \sin 2(x - \pi/3) - 1.$$

9. Graph $y = -3 \sin 2(x - \pi/3) - 1$.

10. What is its fundamental period p of the function s?

11. The **frequency** f is defined to be $f = 1/p$, where p is the fundamental period. What is the frequency of the function s?

12. Find the maximum and minimum values of $s(x)$.

13. The **amplitude** of s is defined as half the difference between the maximum and minimum values of $s(x)$. What is the amplitude of s?

14. Find the smallest value $x \geq 0$ such that $s(x)$ is the average of the function's maximum and minimum values. (This is sometimes called the **phase shift** of s relative to $x \longmapsto \sin(x)$.)

For exercises 15–22: A generalized sine function has the formula

$$s(x) = A \sin B(x - C) + D,$$

where A, B, C, and D are parameters. As an example, for $A = -3$, $B = 2$, $C = \pi/3$, and $D = -1$, we have the particular function s described in the exercises above. Describe a formula in terms of the parameters A, B, C, and D for each of the following characteristics of the generalized sine function.

15. the fundamental period p

16. the frequency f

17. the maximum output value

18. the minimum output value

19. the average output value

20. the amplitude

21. the phase shift

22. the y-intercept of the graph

For exercises 23–30: In his 1928 paper "On Certain Topics in Telegraph Transmission Theory," Harry Nyquist described a relationship between frequency and sampling rate that, while initially applied to telegraph operation, is very relevant to digital signal processing (for compact disc, digital audio tape, and digital telephone technology, for example.)

Sampling is the process of converting a continuous signal (also called an *analog signal*), such as sound, into a sequence of numeric values representing the signal strength at successive discrete moments in time. The problem considered here is that of reconstructing the signal from these *digitized* samples—exactly the process involved in playing a CD. In these exercises we will consider a signal, a 4 hz sine wave, described by the function

$$S(t) = \sin(4(2\pi)t).$$

For each sample rate given in exercises 23-30, sample $S(t)$ for one second. (Start at $t = 0$ and space the other values t accordingly.)

(a) Construct a table of samples taken for $0 \le t < 1$.

(b) Find another sine wave of lower frequency ($U(t) = A\sin(B(2\pi)t)$ with $0 \le B \le 4$), which produces exactly the same sample values, if such exist. (A constant signal is considered to have frequency 0.)

23. three samples per second

24. four samples per second

25. five samples per second

26. six samples per second

27. seven samples per second

28. eight samples per second

29. nine samples per second

30. sixteen samples per second

31. Based on the results of the previous exercises, make a conjecture regarding the sampling rate required to unambiguously reconstruct a signal of frequency f. (No fair reading Nyquist's paper!)

32. A CD player advertises "44Khz Sampling Rate!" In what way is this relevant to your musical listening pleasure?

1.4 NEW FUNCTIONS FROM OLD

Functions can be combined algebraically in much the same way that real numbers can be combined arithmetically. Given two functions f and g, we can add, subtract, multiply, and divide them to obtain new functions

$f+g$, $f-g$, fg, and f/g, respectively. To evaluate any of these functions numerically at an input x, we simply evaluate $f(x)$ and $g(x)$ and perform the indicated arithmetic on the results.

For an input x to be acceptable for $f+g$, $f-g$, or fg, it must be acceptable for both of the individual functions f and g. In the language of sets, the domain will be the *intersection* of the domains of f and g. For an input x to be acceptable for f/g, we must also be on guard for division by zero. That is, the domain must not include any input value x such that $g(x)=0$.

EXAMPLE 6 Suppose that $f:\{x : x \neq -1\} \longrightarrow \mathbb{R}$ with

$$f(x) = \frac{2}{x+1},$$

and suppose that $g:\{x : -2 \leq x \leq 2\} \longrightarrow \mathbb{R}$ with

$$g(x) = \sqrt{4-x^2}.$$

Find the evaluation formula and the domain of acceptable inputs for each of the functions $f+g$, $f-g$, fg, and f/g.

Solution The evaluation formulas for $f+g$, $f-g$, and fg are:

$$(f+g)(x) = f(x)+g(x) = \frac{2}{x+1} + \sqrt{4-x^2}$$

$$(f-g)(x) = f(x)-g(x) = \frac{2}{x+1} - \sqrt{4-x^2}$$

$$(fg)(x) = f(x)g(x) = \frac{2\sqrt{4-x^2}}{x+1}$$

The domains of $f+g$, $f-g$, and fg are all the same:

$$D = \{x : -2 \leq x \leq 2 \text{ and } x \neq -1\},$$

the intersection of the domains of f and g. The evaluation formula for f/g is:

$$(f/g)(x) = \frac{f(x)}{g(x)} = \frac{2}{(x+1)\sqrt{4-x^2}},$$

and the domain of f/g is

$$D = \{x : -2 < x < 2 \text{ and } x \neq -1\}.$$

Note that the domain of f/g does not include $x = \pm 2$, since these values result in division by zero. ■

We have already seen the algebra of functions at work. Using just the simple building blocks of the constant functions and the identity function, we can build the polynomials using addition, subtraction, and multiplication (for example, $-5x^3 + 2x = (-5) \cdot x \cdot x \cdot x + 2 \cdot x$). We can build the rational functions from the polynomials using quotients of functions. Similarly, the trigonometric functions tan, cot, sec, and csc can all be expressed in terms of the functions sin and cos.

Composition of functions

Another way of combining functions is through composition. When we compose two functions, we use the output of one function as the input for the other.

Definition 3

If f and g are two functions, then the **composition** of the function g with f is written

$$g \circ f.$$

(We read this as "g composed with f," or simply "g of f.") The outputs of $g \circ f$ are determined by the formula

$$(g \circ f)(x) = g(f(x)).$$

Figure 1.10 illustrates the composition of two functions. The domain D of $g \circ f$ is the subset of inputs in the domain of f that produce outputs in the domain of g. In set notation,

$$D = \{x : x \in (\textit{domain of f}) \text{ and } f(x) \in (\textit{domain of g})\}.$$

EXAMPLE 7 Suppose that $f : \{x : x \neq -1\} \longrightarrow \mathbb{R}$ with

$$f(x) = \frac{2}{x+1},$$

and suppose that $g : \{x : -2 \leq x \leq 2\} \longrightarrow \mathbb{R}$ with

$$g(x) = \sqrt{4 - x^2}.$$

Find the evaluation formula and the domain of acceptable inputs for of the function $g \circ f$.

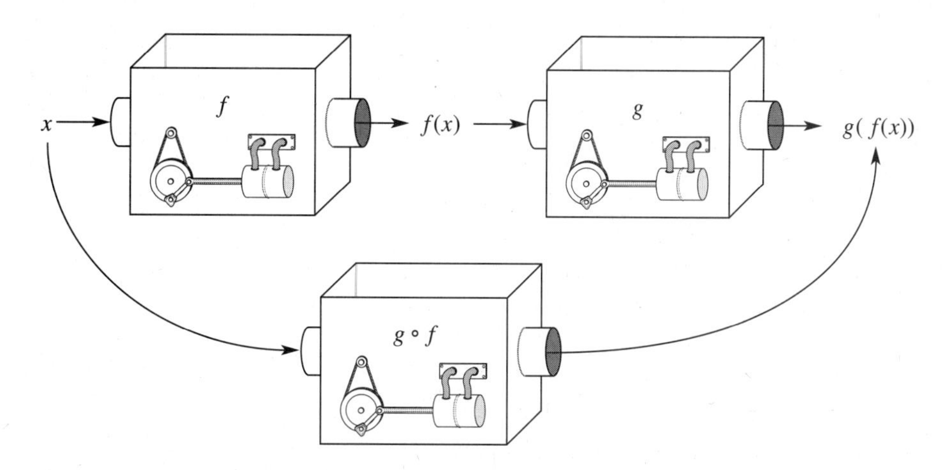

Figure 1.10 Composition of functions.

Solution To find the formula for $g \circ f$, we simply substitute $2/(x+1)$ for each instance of x in the expression $\sqrt{4-x^2}$ to obtain

$$g(f(x)) = \sqrt{4 - \left(\frac{2}{x+1}\right)^2} = \sqrt{4 - \frac{4}{(x+1)^2}} = 2\sqrt{1 - \frac{1}{(x+1)^2}}.$$

The domain D of $g \circ f$ is the set of all real values x in the domain of f ($x \neq -1$) whose output $f(x)$ is in the domain of g. Because of the square root involved, we must have

$$1 - \frac{1}{(x+1)^2} \geq 0$$

in order that this final expression produces real output values. Multiplying both sides of the inequality by always positive value $(x+1)^2$ (remember, we have $x \neq -1$), we obtain

$$(x+1)^2 - 1 \geq 0.$$

Now, $(x+1)^2 - 1 = (x^2 + 2x + 1) - 1 = x^2 + 2x = x(x+2)$, and $x(x+2) \geq 0$ precisely when $x \leq -2$ or $x \geq 0$. All of these values are in the domain of f, so we have

$$(g \circ f)(x) = g(f(x)) = 2\sqrt{1 - \frac{1}{(x+1)^2}},$$

with domain $D = \{x : x \leq -2 \text{ or } x \geq 0\}$. ■

EXAMPLE 8 Using the same functions f and g, find the evaluation formula and the domain of acceptable inputs for $f \circ g$.

Solution To find the formula for $f \circ g$, we substitute $\sqrt{4-x^2}$ for each instance of x in the expression $2/(x+1)$ to obtain

$$(f \circ g)(x) = f(g(x)) = \frac{2}{\sqrt{4-x^2}+1}.$$

The domain D of $f \circ g$ is the set of all real values x in the domain of g (in other words, $-2 \le x \le 2$) which are also acceptable inputs for this formula. Because of the division involved, we must have

$$\sqrt{4-x^2}+1 \neq 0.$$

This means we must have

$$\sqrt{4-x^2} \neq -1,$$

but the $\sqrt{}$ symbol indicates the nonnegative square root, so this does not present an added restriction.

Hence, the domain is $D = \{x : -2 \le x \le 2\}$. ■

Notice that in this case, the functions $f \circ g$ and $g \circ f$ are different.

▶▶▶ **The order of composition can definitely make a difference in the final resulting function formula and its domain.**

Diagramming compositions and finding domains

To analyze a function with a complicated formula, it can be extremely helpful to think of it as a composition of simpler functions. For example, if we are trying to evaluate a function using the built-in functions on a computer or calculator, we may need to perform the evaluation in steps corresponding to the composition.

Finding the domain of acceptable inputs for a function can also be made easier if we can break down the function into its component parts and follow the path of the evaluation process. This allows us to avoid inputs that would result in a division by zero, a square root (or other even root) of a negative value, or any other unacceptable real number evaluation.

We can diagram a composition of functions by starting with a general input x and connecting the chain of compositions with arrows.

▶▶▶ **When analyzing a chain of compositions, ask yourself to identify the order in which you should perform the computations when evaluating the function.**

EXAMPLE 9 Diagram the chain of composition for the function p such that $p(x) = (\sin(5x))^2$ and analyze which functions are being composed.

Solution Suppose that we were to evaluate this function at, say, $x = \pi$. First we would have to compute $5 \cdot \pi$, plug this into the sin function to get $\sin(5\pi) = 0$, and finally square this number to get our final output of $(0)^2 = 0$. This chain of evaluations would take place for any input x, so we diagram the composition as

$$x \longmapsto 5x \longmapsto \sin(5x) \longmapsto (\sin(5x))^2.$$

At the first step we are taking the input x and multiplying it by 5. At the second step we are taking the result from the first step and applying the sine function. At the third and final step, we take the result from the second step and square it. If we had three functions f, g, and h such that

$$f(x) = 5x,$$

$$g(x) = \sin x,$$

$$h(x) = x^2,$$

then
$$(h \circ g \circ f)(x) = h(g(f(x))) = \sin^2(5x) = p(x),$$

so $h \circ g \circ f$ represents our original function p. ■

EXAMPLE 10 Diagram the chain of composition for the function q such that $q(x) = 5\sin(x^2)$ and analyze it to identify the functions being composed.

Solution In this case, the same functions are being composed as in the previous example, but with a different order of composition. The chain is diagrammed as

$$x \longmapsto x^2 \longmapsto \sin(x^2) \longmapsto 5\sin(x^2).$$

With the same f, g, and h as in Example 13, we have

$$(f \circ g \circ h)(x) = f(g(h(x))) = 5\sin(x^2) = q(x),$$

so $f \circ g \circ h$ represents our original function q. ■

EXAMPLE 11 Find the domain of acceptable real inputs for the function f such that

$$f(x) = \frac{\sqrt{7-2x}}{9-x^2}.$$

Solution Evaluation of the numerator takes x through the chain

$$x \longmapsto (7-2x) \longmapsto \sqrt{7-2x}.$$

There are no restrictions on evaluating $7-2x$, but at the second step, we must not allow a negative result to be input to the square root function. This requires

$$7-2x \geq 0,$$

which requires

$$x \leq \frac{7}{2}.$$

Evaluation of the denominator $9-x^2$ itself requires no restrictions, but since we will be dividing by this quantity, we must have $9-x^2 \neq 0$, which requires

$$x \neq \pm 3.$$

Combining these restrictions, we see that the domain of our function is

$$\{x : x \leq \frac{7}{2} \text{ and } x \neq \pm 3\}.$$

■

EXAMPLE 12 Find the domain of acceptable real inputs for the function g such that $g(x) = \sqrt{\cot 2x}$.

Solution Evaluation of this function takes us through the chain

$$x \longmapsto 2x \longmapsto \cot 2x \longmapsto \sqrt{\cot 2x}.$$

There are no restrictions in evaluating $2x$, but we cannot feed an input that is any integer multiple of π to the cotangent function. This requires

$$2x \neq n\pi$$

for all integers n. So we must have

$$x \neq \frac{n\pi}{2}$$

for all integers n. The final step of the chain involves taking the square root of $\cot 2x$, so we also must have

$$\cot 2x \geq 0.$$

Examining the graph of the cotangent function reveals that we need

$$n\pi < 2x \leq n\pi + \frac{\pi}{2}$$

for any integer n. This already includes our previous restriction on x, so the domain D can be written as

$$D = \{x : \frac{n\pi}{2} < x \leq \frac{n\pi}{2} + \frac{\pi}{4} \text{ for any integer } n\}.$$

■

EXERCISES for Section 1.4

For exercises 1–6: For each function f specified by the formula for $f(x)$, determine the domain D of real number inputs x for which the output $f(x)$ produced is a real number.

1. $f(x) = \dfrac{2x - 1}{x^2 - 3}$
2. $f(x) = \sqrt{4 - 3x}$
3. $f(x) = \sqrt[3]{4 - 3x}$
4. $f(x) = \sec(\pi x)$
5. $f(x) = \sqrt{1 + x + x^2}$
6. $f(x) = \tan^2(x) - \sec^2(x)$

For exercises 7–12: Express each function formula below as a composition of the functions chosen from f, g, h, j, and k whose formulas are:

$$f(x) = x^2, \quad g(x) = 3x, \quad h(x) = \sin x, \quad j(x) = \frac{1}{x - 4}, \quad k(x) = \sqrt{x}.$$

7. $p(x) = 3\sin^2(\dfrac{1}{x - 4})$
8. $q(x) = \dfrac{1}{\sqrt{x} - 4}$
9. $s(x) = \dfrac{3}{\sqrt{x^2 - 4}}$
10. $u(x) = 27x^2$
11. $v(x) = \sin(9x^2)$
12. $w(x) = \dfrac{x - 4}{17 - 4x}$

For exercises 13–26: Given the tables of values of the two functions shown, find the values indicated.

Table for f

input	output
−1	3
0	4
1	−2
2	6
3	2
4	−1

Table for g

input	output
−1	3
0	1
1	−7
2	0
3	−1
4	2

For Exercises 13-26

13. $(f+g)(4)$

14. $(g-f)(-1)$

15. $3f(1)$

16. $(gf)(1)$

17. $(\frac{f}{g})(2)$

18. $(f \circ g)(-1)$

19. $(g \circ f)(4)$

20. $g^2(-1)$

21. $f((-1)^2)$

22. all x such that $f(x) = g(x)$

23. all x such that $(f-g)(x) = 3$

24. all x such that $(f \circ g)(x) = 2$

25. all x such that $(g \circ f)(x) = 2$

26. x such that $(f \circ f \circ f \circ f)(x) = 6$

For exercises 27–40: Given the graphs of the two functions f and g shown, graph the indicated functions.

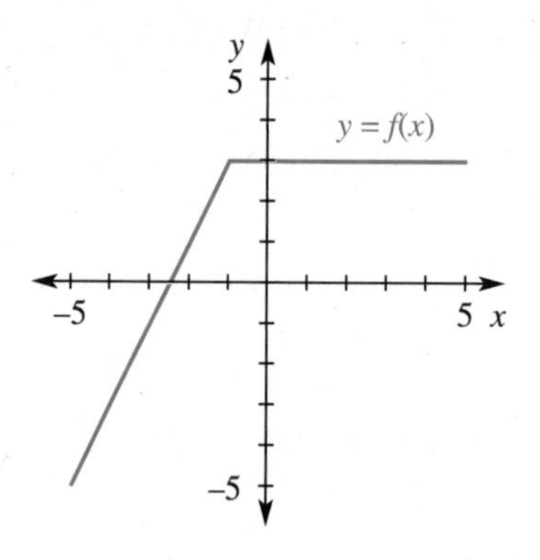

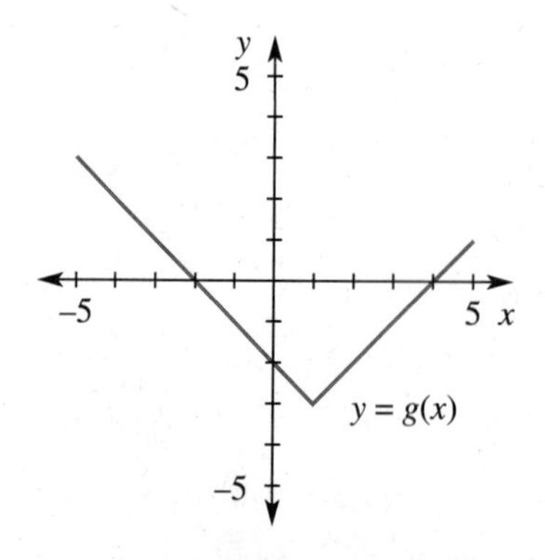

For Exercises 27-40

27. $f + g$
28. $g - f$
29. $3f$
30. $y = f(x^2)$
31. $y = f(2/x)$
32. $y = f(x - 2)$
33. $y = f(2x)$
34. $y = f(x + 2)$
35. $y = f(x) + 3$
36. f/g
37. $f \circ g$
38. $g \circ f$
39. g^2
40. gf

For exercises 41–48: The **hyperbolic functions** are defined in terms of the natural exponential function and are used in a variety of contexts, including the special theory of relativity. The two basic hyperbolic functions are the hyperbolic sine sinh (sometimes pronounced "sinch") and the hyperbolic cosine cosh (sometimes pronounced "coash"). These functions are defined by the formulas

$$\sinh(x) = \frac{e^x - e^{-x}}{2} \quad \text{and} \quad \cosh(x) = \frac{e^x + e^{-x}}{2}.$$

The hyperbolic tangent function tanh has the formula

$$\tanh(x) = \frac{\sinh(x)}{\cosh(x)} = \frac{e^x - e^{-x}}{e^x + e^{-x}}.$$

The other three hyperbolic functions (sech, csch, and coth) are defined in ways similar to those for the corresponding trigonometric functions:

$$\operatorname{sech}(x) = \frac{1}{\cosh(x)}, \qquad \operatorname{csch}(x) = \frac{1}{\sinh(x)}, \qquad \coth(x) = \frac{\cosh(x)}{\sinh(x)}.$$

41. Find the domain of acceptable inputs for each of the hyperbolic functions.

42. Graph $y = \sinh x$, $y = \cosh(x)$, and $y = \tanh(x)$.

43. Graph $y = \operatorname{sech} x$, $y = \operatorname{csch}(x)$, and $y = \coth(x)$.

44. Which of the hyperbolic functions are even?

45. Which of the hyperbolic functions are odd?

46. Which of the hyperbolic functions are bounded (in other words, all the outputs lie in a bounded interval of y-values)?

47. The trigonometric (circular) functions sin and cos satisfy the identity $\cos^2(x) + \sin^2(x) = 1$ by virtue of their definition in terms of the unit circle $x^2 + y^2 = 1$. The graph of $x^2 - y^2 = 1$ is a *hyperbola*. Show that the hyperbolic functions satisfy the identity

$$\cosh^2(x) - \sinh^2(x) = 1$$

for all real numbers x.

48. Show that $\cosh(x) + \sinh(x) = e^x$ and $\cosh(x) - \sinh(x) = e^{-x}$ for all real values x.

1.5 INVERSE FUNCTIONS

Sometimes we wish to *reverse* a function process. That is, starting with a function's output value, we would like to recover the original input value.

Definition 4

A function f has an **inverse** g, provided that

$$g(f(x)) = x \text{ and } f(g(y)) = y$$

for each x in the domain of f and for each y in the domain of g. If f has such an inverse, we usually write

$$g = f^{-1}.$$

Every function must produce a single output for each input. But to reverse the process, we need the additional guarantee that no two different inputs produce the same output. In other words, for a function to be invertible, its inputs and outputs must match up in a *one-to-one correspondence.*

What exactly are inverses?

The notion of an inverse occurs over and over again in mathematics. Keep in mind that the word *inverse* is always used in reference to (a) some operation and (b) some identity for that operation. For example, the *additive* inverse of any real number x is $-x$, since

$$x + (-x) = 0$$

and 0 is the identity for real number addition. The *multiplicative* inverse of a nonzero real number x is its reciprocal $1/x$, since

$$x \cdot (\frac{1}{x}) = 1$$

and 1 is the identity for real number multiplication.

The inverse function f^{-1} is really an inverse in this same sense. The operation is function composition, and the identity is the identity function ($i(x) = x$). Note that $(f \circ f^{-1})(x) = x$ and $(f^{-1} \circ f)(y) = y$.

Inverse functions from numeric, graphical, and symbolic perspectives

Let's examine the properties of inverse functions from the viewpoint of their numeric, graphical, and symbolic representations.

> Numerically, a function f has an inverse, provided that for any two different inputs $x_1 \neq x_2$ we must have $f(x_1) \neq f(x_2)$.

The function f defined by the formula $f(x) = x^2$ does not have an inverse, since $2 \neq -2$, but $f(2) = f(-2) = 4$.

The function g defined by the formula $g(x) = x^3$ does have an inverse, since $(x_1)^3 \neq (x_2)^3$ whenever $x_1 \neq x_2$.

> Symbolically, a function f has an inverse if we can solve $y = f(x)$ uniquely for x in terms of y. In other words, substituting any output value y in the equation $y = f(x)$ can result in at most one possible input x satisfying the equation.

For example, note that we can't solve $y = x^2$ uniquely for x, since $x = \pm\sqrt{y}$ gives two possible values for x, given any positive value y. On the other hand, we can solve $y = x^3$ uniquely for x, and thus write a formula for g^{-1}:

$$g^{-1}(y) = \sqrt[3]{y}.$$

EXAMPLE 13 Find f^{-1} if it exists, where $f : \mathbb{R} \longrightarrow \mathbb{R}$, and

$$f(x) = x^5 - 3.$$

Solution If f has an inverse, we must be able to solve the equation

$$y = x^5 - 3$$

for a single value of x, given any value y. After adding 3 to both sides and taking the fifth root, we obtain

$$x = \sqrt[5]{y+3}.$$

Thus,
$$f^{-1}(y) = \sqrt[5]{y+3}.$$

We check our inverse function by noting that

$$f^{-1}(f(x)) = \sqrt[5]{f(x)+3} = \sqrt[5]{(x^5-3)+3} = \sqrt[5]{x^5} = x$$

for each real value x, and

$$f(f^{-1}(y)) = (\sqrt[5]{y+3})^5 - 3 = (y+3) - 3 = y$$

for each real value y. ■

EXAMPLE 14 Find g^{-1} if it exists, where $g : \mathbb{R} \longrightarrow \mathbb{R}$, and

$$g(x) = |2x - 1|.$$

Solution If g has an inverse, we must be able to solve the equation

$$y = |2x - 1|$$

for a single value of x, given any value y. But this is not possible. When $y = 3$, for instance, we have either $x = 2$ or $x = -1$. So g has no inverse. ■

Every function has a graph passing the vertical line test, since each input must produce a single output. For a function to have an inverse, each output must be paired with only one input, so the function's graph must also pass the *horizontal line test:* any horizontal line intersects the graph in at most one point.

Since f^{-1} reverses the input-output process f, the graph of f^{-1} can be determined by simply switching the coordinates of the ordered pairs of f. If we graph both f and f^{-1}, the graphs will appear to be mirror images through the line $y = x$.

This fact allows us to graph an inverse function f^{-1} directly from the graph of the original function f, even if we are unable or it is impossible to compute a formula for the inverse function. In fact, some inverse functions are simply given new names when there is no algebraic way to describe them. The logarithmic functions, which are inverses of the exponential functions, can be thought of in this way.

To illustrate, note that the graph of $y = a^x$ ($a > 0$, $a \neq 1$) passes the horizontal line test. The inverse function is simply $\log_a$, and the graph of $y = \log_a(x)$ is the reflection of $y = a^x$ through the line $y = x$. Figure 1.11 illustrates this for $a = 2$ and $a = 2/3$.

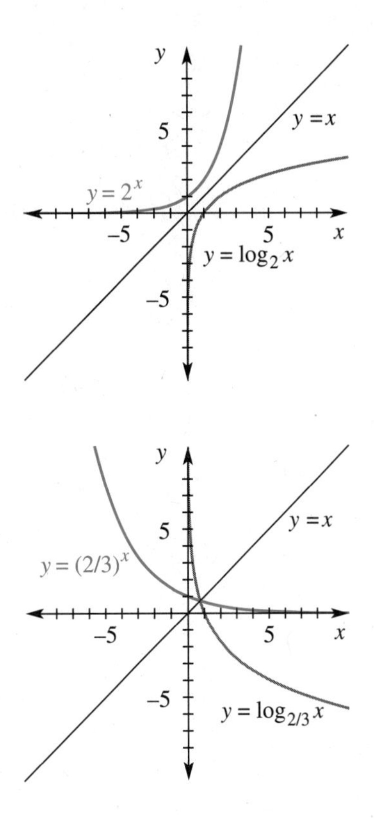

Figure 1.11 The graphs of $y = a^x$ and $y = \log_a x$ are symmetric with respect to $y = x$.

Restricted domains

Even in the case that a function is not one-to-one, we can obtain a partial inverse by suitably restricting the domain of the function. Remember, if we change the domain of a function, we have effectively created a new function.

For example, the function $f : \mathbb{R} \longrightarrow \mathbb{R}$ such that

$$f(x) = x^2$$

does not have an inverse because it is not one-to-one (the parabola $y = x^2$ fails the horizontal line test). If we define a new function g by restricting the domain to nonnegative real numbers, $g : \{x : x \geq 0\} \longrightarrow \mathbb{R}$, with $g(x) = x^2$, then this function does have an inverse, namely, $g^{-1} : \{x : x \geq 0\} \longrightarrow \mathbb{R}$, with

$$g^{-1}(x) = \sqrt{x}.$$

Figure 1.12 illustrates how restricting the domain allows the inverse to be defined in this case.

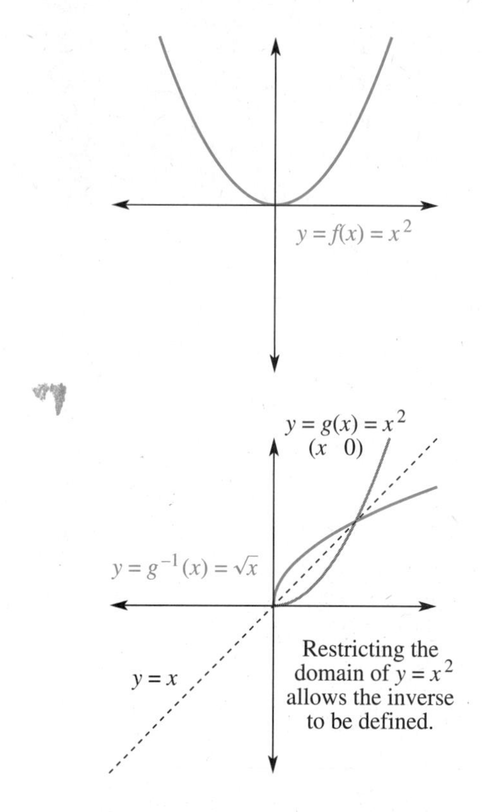

Figure 1.12 Restricting the domain of a function.

Inverse trigonometric functions

The inverse trigonometric functions are meant to reverse the trigonometric functions in much the same way that exponential and logarithmic functions reverse each other. In other words, if we feed the output of a trigonometric function into its inverse, we should obtain the original input angle back again. However, since each of the six trigonometric functions is periodic, there are infinitely many different input angles producing the same output. For example, asking for the missing value in

$$\sin(?) = 1/2$$

has infinitely many possible answers (either $\pi/6$, $5\pi/6$, or any other value differing by a multiple of 2π from these). If we want a *unique* answer, we must arbitrarily agree to restrict the choices to some set of possible values. In other words, if we restrict the domain of inputs for each trigonometric function so that each output possible value is produced exactly once, then we can talk about the inverses in a meaningful way. We'll remove this ambiguity by restricting the domain of inputs for each trigonometric function so that only one choice is possible.

The abbreviations for the inverse trigonometric functions are **arcsin, arccos, arctan, arccsc, arcsec,** and **arccot**. These names are meant to remind us that the *output* of an inverse trigonometric function will be an angle measured along the *arc* of the unit circle. In general, if trig is one of the trigonometric functions, then

$$\operatorname{arctrig}(y) = x$$

will mean the same as

$$y = \operatorname{trig}(x),$$

provided that x is in the appropriate range of values. The domains and specific restrictions on outputs for each inverse trigonometric function are given as follows:

$0 \leq \arccos(y) \leq \pi$	for $-1 \leq y \leq 1$
$-\frac{\pi}{2} \leq \arcsin(y) \leq \frac{\pi}{2}$	for $-1 \leq y \leq 1$
$-\frac{\pi}{2} < \arctan(y) < \frac{\pi}{2}$	for all real numbers y
$0 < \operatorname{arccot}(y) < \pi$	for all real numbers y
$0 \leq \operatorname{arcsec}(y) \leq \pi$ (and $\neq \frac{\pi}{2}$)	for $\lvert y\rvert \geq 1$
$-\frac{\pi}{2} \leq \operatorname{arccsc}(y) \leq \frac{\pi}{2}$ (and $\neq 0$)	for $\lvert y\rvert \geq 1$

EXAMPLE 15 Find $\arctan(-1)$ and $\operatorname{arcsec}(2)$.

Solution If $x = \arctan(-1)$, then $\tan x = 1$ and $-\pi/2 < x < \pi/2$. The only number satisfying these requirements is $x = \pi/4$.

If $x = \operatorname{arcsec}(2)$, then $\sec x = 2$ (or $\cos x = 1/2$), and $0 \leq x \leq \pi$, $x \neq \pi/2$. The only number satisfying these requirements is $x = \pi/3$.

Summarizing, $\arctan(1) = \pi/4$, and $\operatorname{arcsec}(2) = \pi/3$. ■

The graph of any of the inverse trigonometric functions can be obtained by first graphing the corresponding trigonometric function over the restricted domain and then reflecting the graph over the line $y = x$.

EXAMPLE 16 Graph the inverse sine function $y = \arcsin(x)$.

Solution Figure 1.13 shows the graph of $y = \sin(x)$ over the interval $[-\pi/2, \pi/2]$, along with the graph of $y = \arcsin(x)$ obtained by reflecting over the line $y = x$. ■

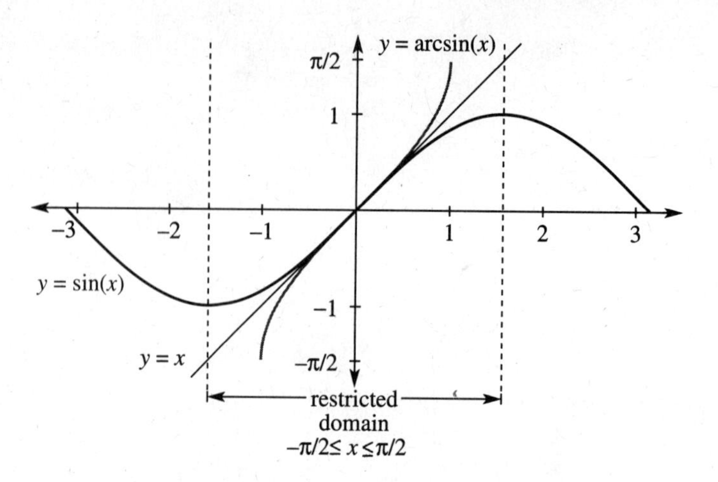

Figure 1.13 Graphs of $y = \sin(x)$ and $y = \arcsin(x)$.

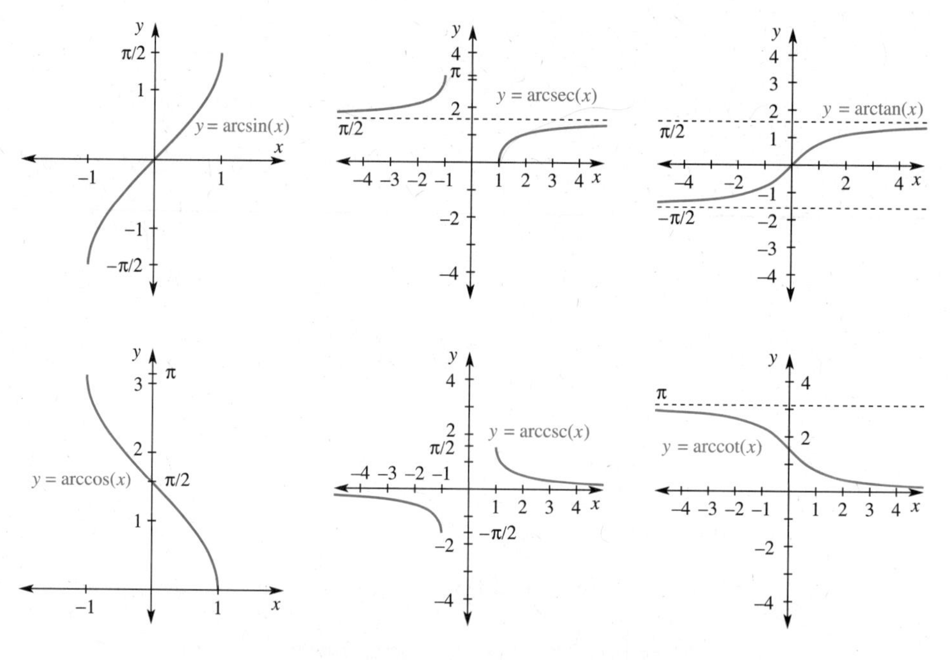

Figure 1.14 Graphs of the inverse trigonometric functions.

The trigonometric inverses are sometimes labelled $\sin^{-1}$, $\cos^{-1}$, $\tan^{-1}$, $\csc^{-1}$, $\sec^{-1}$, and $\cot^{-1}$, respectively.

▶▶▶ **BEWARE: The notation f^{-1} used for the *inverse* of the function f must not be confused with the similar notation a^{-1} used for the *reciprocal* $1/a$ of the real number a.**

We need to take special care with the trigonometric functions because of the common abbreviations used for powers of these functions. For example, $\sin^n x$ stands for $(\sin x)^n$ when n is any power *except* -1. The important exception is

$$\sin^{-1}(x) = \arcsin x,$$

where $\sin^{-1}$ refers to the inverse sine function. Note that when we need it, we already have a special name for the *reciprocal* of $\sin(x)$, namely

$$\frac{1}{\sin(x)} = \csc(x).$$

In this book we will usually use the notation arcsin rather than $\sin^{-1}$ in the interest of avoiding this source of confusion.

Figure 1.14 illustrates the graphs of the six inverse trigonometric functions.

EXERCISES for Section 1.5

For exercises 1–8: For each function, determine whether it has an inverse, and, if so, find and graph its inverse function.

1. $f : \mathbb{R} \longrightarrow \mathbb{R}$, where $f(x) = x^3 - x$

2. $g : \{x : x \neq 0\} \longrightarrow \mathbb{R}$, where $g(x) = 1/x$

3. $i : \mathbb{R} \longrightarrow \mathbb{R}$, where $i(x) = x$

4. $p : \mathbb{R} \longrightarrow \mathbb{R}$, where $p(x) = x^3 + x + 1$

5. $q : \mathbb{R} \longrightarrow \mathbb{R}$, where $q(x) = x^2 + x + 1$

6. $s : \{t : t \geq 1\} \longrightarrow \mathbb{R}$, where $s(t) = t^2 + t + 1$

7. $h : \mathbb{R} \longrightarrow \mathbb{R}$, $h(x) = \frac{9}{5}x + 32$.

8. $r : \mathbb{R} \longrightarrow \mathbb{R}$, $r(x) = 2^x$

For exercises 9–12: Suppose that the function f is linear, so that

$$f(x) = mx + b,$$

where m and b are real numbers.

9. Show that if $m = 0$, then f does not have an inverse f^{-1}.

10. Find a formula for $f^{-1}(x)$, when $m \neq 0$, and show that f^{-1} is also a linear function.

11. If $m \neq 0$, $m \neq 1$, and $m \neq -1$, find the intersection point for the graphs of $y = f(x)$ and $y = f^{-1}(x)$.

12. For what value of m are the graphs of $y = f(x)$ and $y = f^{-1}(x)$ perpendicular to each other?

For exercises 13–20: Given the table of values of the two functions f and g shown, find the values indicated.

Table for f

input	output
–1	3
0	4
1	–2
2	6
3	2
4	–1

Table for g

input	output
–1	3
0	1
1	–7
2	0
3	–1
4	2

For Exercises 13-20

13. $f^{-1}(2)$

14. $g^{-1}(0)$

15. $(g \circ f^{-1})(4)$

16. $(f(2))^{-1}$

17. $f^{-1}(g^{-1}(0))$

18. $f^{-1}(g(3))$

19. all x such that $f^{-1}(g^{-1}(x)) = 0$

20. all x such that $f^{-1}(x) = g^{-1}(x)$

For exercises 21–26: Find the indicated inverse trigonometric value.

21. $\arcsin(-1/2)$

22. $\arccos(-1)$

23. $\text{arcsec}(\sqrt{2})$

24. $\text{arccsc}(-2\sqrt{3})$

25. $\arctan(\sqrt{3})$

26. $\text{arccot}(-5)$

---

27. Is $\arcsin(\sin(x)) = x$ true for all real values x, true for some values x, or true for no values x?

28. Is $\tan(\arctan x) = x$ true for all real values x, true for some values x, or true for no values x?

29. If the graph of $y = f(x)$ and the graph of $y = f^{-1}(x)$ intersect at a point (a, b), what can you say about a and b?

30. Find the point of intersection of the graphs of $y = \log_{1/2}(x)$ and $y = (1/2)^x$. For what values a do the graphs of $y = \log_a x$ and $y = a^x$ intersect?

For exercises 31–36: Most calculators do not have keys for sec, csc, and cot, since one can evaluate each of these functions using the keys for sin, cos, and $1/x$. Similarly, most calculators do not have keys for arcsec, arccsc, and arccot. Graph each of the following, and determine which three could be used as alternatives for computing $y = \text{arcsec}(x)$, $y = \text{arccsc}(x)$, and $y = \text{arccot}(x)$, for $x > 0$.

31. $y = \frac{\pi}{2} - \arcsin(x)$

32. $y = \arcsin(1/x)$

33. $y = \frac{\pi}{2} - \arccos(x)$

34. $y = \arccos(1/x)$

35. $y = \frac{\pi}{2} - \arctan(x)$

36. $y = \arctan(1/x)$

---

37. Which of the inverse trigonometric functions are even?

38. Which of the inverse trigonometric functions are odd?

39. Which of the inverse trigonometric functions are bounded (that is, all of the outputs lie in a bounded interval of y-values)?

40. Which of the inverse trigonometric functions have the origin $(0, 0)$ as a point on their graphs?

For exercises 41–44: The six hyperbolic functions are defined in the exercises for Section 1.4.

41. The hyperbolic functions sinh, tanh, csch, and coth all have inverses. Sketch the graphs of the inverse hyperbolic functions

$$y = \sinh^{-1}(x), \quad y = \tanh^{-1}(x), \quad y = \operatorname{csch}^{-1}(x), \quad y = \coth^{-1}(x)$$

by reflecting the graphs of the corresponding hyperbolic functions over the graph of the line $y = x$.

42. Graph $y = \cosh x$ and $y = \operatorname{sech} x$ over the restricted domain $D = \{x : x \geq 0\}$.

43. If we restrict the domains of the hyperbolic functions cosh and sech to $D = \{x : x \geq 0\}$, then we can define the inverse functions $\cosh^{-1}$ and sech^{-1}. Sketch the graphs of the inverse hyperbolic functions

$$y = \cosh^{-1}(x) \qquad \text{and} \qquad y = \operatorname{sech}^{-1}(x)$$

by reflecting the graphs from the previous exercise over the graph of the line $y = x$.

44. What is the domain of each of the inverse hyperbolic functions?

For exercises 45–50: Many calculators and software packages do not have the inverse hyperbolic functions "built-in." The formulas in the exercises below can be used for computations involving the inverse hyperbolic functions. Graph each one, and match it with one of the inverse hyperbolic function graphs

$$y = \sinh^{-1} x, \quad y = \cosh^{-1} x, \quad y = \tanh^{-1} x,$$

$$y = \operatorname{csch}^{-1} x, \quad y = \operatorname{sech}^{-1} x, \quad y = \coth^{-1} x.$$

45. $y = \frac{1}{2} \ln\left(\frac{1+x}{1-x}\right)$, for $-1 < x < 1$

46. $y = \frac{1}{2} \ln\left(\frac{x+1}{x-1}\right)$, for $x < -1$ or $x > 1$

47. $y = \ln\left(\frac{1+\sqrt{1-x^2}}{x}\right)$, for $0 < x \leq 1$

48. $y = \ln\left(\frac{1}{x} + \frac{\sqrt{1+x^2}}{|x|}\right)$, for $x \neq 0$

49. $y = \ln(x + \sqrt{x^2+1})$, for all real numbers x

50. $y = \ln(x + \sqrt{x^2-1})$, for $x \geq 1$

1.6 MATHEMATICAL MODELING—FINDING THE FUNCTION

In order to use mathematics to solve real-world problems, the most important (and often the most difficult) step is to identify and describe a pattern or relationship in a way that allows us to take advantage of our mathematical tools. This activity is called *mathematical modeling*, and it is the bridge that enables us to use mathematics to solve applied problems in any discipline.

In modeling a functional relationship involving real number measurements, the analyst or researcher commonly follows three steps:

1. Gather paired data (inputs and outputs) in a table (numerical representation).

2. Graph these ordered pairs (graphical representation).

3. Describe the functional relationship (or an approximation of it) with a symbolic formula (symbolic representation).

The model can then be tested by using it to predict new number pairs or graph points and then checking these predictions against newly gathered data.

In general, this procedure of gathering data, looking for patterns and relationships, devising mathematical models and using them to make predictions, and checking those predictions against new data is a hallmark of scientific inquiry. Let's illustrate the procedure with a discussion of an experiment involving a functional relationship.

An experiment: dropping a ball from a tower

Suppose that we are in a tower and we drop a ball repeatedly from several different heights, each time recording the time it takes for the ball to hit

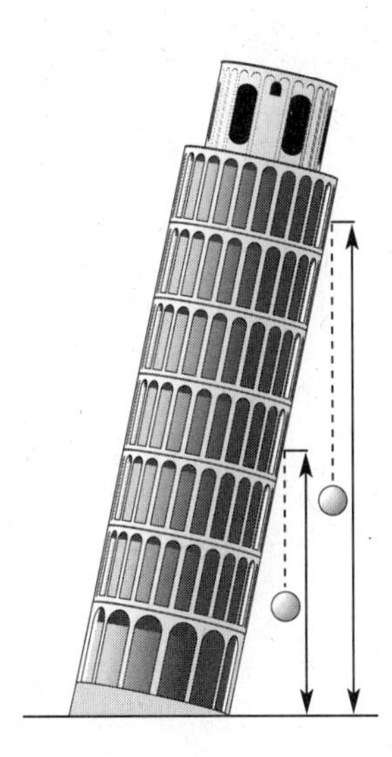

Figure 1.15 A ball-dropping experiment.

the ground (Figure 1.16). All other factors being equal (such as wind conditions), we hypothesize that the time it takes the ball to hit the ground depends entirely on the height from which it is dropped. In other words, *the ball's drop time is a function of the height.*

How could this functional relationship between height and time be evident from the data we record? If the drop time depends entirely on the height, then *for repeated drops from the same height, we should get the same time reading.* That is, on every occasion that we drop the ball from, say, 20 feet, we should observe the same drop time. In actually performing this experiment, it's likely that we might observe slightly different times for repeated drops from the same height. The source of this variation could be imprecision in measuring the height and/or time. If the variation in readings is small enough that we could legitimately attribute it to measurement imprecision, then our belief in the functional relationship between height and time is still reasonable. However, if we cannot adequately account for this variation, we need to reexamine our hypothesis regarding a functional relationship between height and time or look for additional variables that could explain our observations.

Now, suppose that we are satisfied that our experimental data supports our belief in a functional relationship between height and time. The next logical question is, "What's the nature of the relationship?" or, "Exactly what kind of function is it?" A good first step in answering this question is to arrange the data in a two-column table of numbers, with one column listing the different heights from which we dropped the ball and the second column listing the corresponding drop times. Table 1.3 shows some sample data from our ball-dropping activity.

height in feet	time in seconds
4	0.50
8	0.71
12	0.87
16	1.00
20	1.12
24	1.22
28	1.32
32	1.41
36	1.50
40	1.58
44	1.66
48	1.73
52	1.80
56	1.87
60	1.94
64	2.00

Table 1.3 Table of heights and drop times.

Each different height is recorded along with the corresponding time (or perhaps the average time, if we drop the ball several times from each height). Certainly, this table of values is not complete, for there are many other different heights from which we could drop the ball. We can look for patterns in the paired numbers, in the hope that we can describe some relationship that allows us to *predict* the time it would take the ball to drop from any given height. In particular, we seek a formula allowing us to simply compute the time t (in seconds) for any given height h in feet. That is, we are looking for a formula of the form

$$t = f(h),$$

where t represents the drop time in seconds and $f(h)$ represents some expression whose value is determined by the value of h, when h is measured in feet. If we see what we think is such a pattern, we can check our formula by repeating the experiment at some new heights.

Graphing the data—linear interpolation

A powerful aid in our search for a pattern is the visual display of the paired numbers representing the recorded heights and times. Figure 1.16 shows data from our table graphed as a set of points. The horizontal axis corresponds to the height in feet, and the vertical axis corresponds to the drop time in seconds. Each point corresponds to one of the pairs of numbers from our table.

The graph in Figure 1.17 has the same points connected with straight line segments. The "piece-wise linear" graph can be used to make predictions of expected drop times for heights that fall between our recorded data points. For a new height that lies between two recorded heights, a sensi-

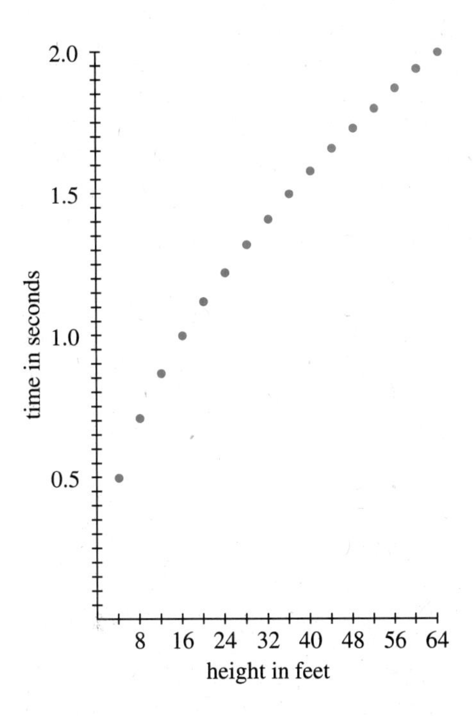

Figure 1.16 Graph of data points for the ball-dropping experiment.

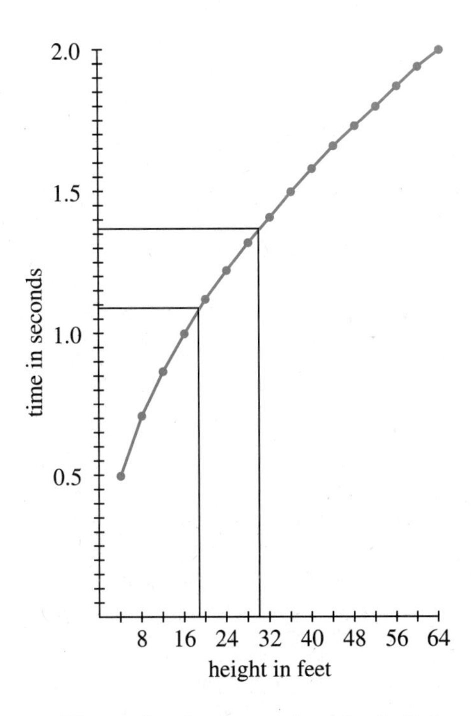

Figure 1.17 Piece-wise linear graph of the ball-dropping data.

ble strategy for predicting the corresponding drop time is to read the plotted value on the line segment connecting the recorded points. This technique of prediction is called *linear interpolation.*

EXAMPLE 17 Using linear interpolation and the recorded data, predict the corresponding drop times from 30 feet and from 19 feet.

Solution Since 30 feet is *halfway* between the recorded heights of 28 feet and 32 feet, the technique of linear interpolation predicts the expected drop time as approximately 1.365 seconds, which is *halfway* between the corresponding recorded drop times of 1.32 seconds and 1.41 seconds.

Similarly, 19 feet is 3/4 of the way between the recorded heights of 16 feet and 20 feet. So, by linear interpolation, we predict the corresponding drop time to be 1.09 seconds, which is 3/4 of the way between the corresponding drop times of 1.00 seconds and 1.12 seconds. Visually, these time predictions are made by locating the points on the piece-wise linear graph corresponding to 30 feet and 19 feet, respectively, and reading the time from the vertical axis. ■

We can generalize the procedure of linear interpolation for our example. Suppose h_1 and h_2 are two recorded heights with $h_1 < h_2$, and t_1 and t_2 are the corresponding drop times. If h_0 is an unrecorded height such that

$$h_1 < h_0 < h_2$$

and we want to use linear interpolation to predict the corresponding drop time t_0, then we choose t_0 so that

$$\frac{t_0 - t_1}{t_2 - t_1} = \frac{h_0 - h_1}{h_2 - h_1}.$$

An important assumption underlies the use of linear interpolation—we assume that between two inputs close together, the change in output is roughly proportional to the change in input.

Finding and testing a model

The piece-wise linear graph also gives us a visual approximation to a single smooth curve passing through all the points. If there is a simple formula $t = f(h)$ expressing drop time t (in seconds) as a function of the height h (in feet), then the shape of the piece-wise linear graph can provide a rough picture of the graph that formula generates. In turn, this picture can help us make an educated guess about a formula describing the relationship between time and height.

For example, based on our graph, we might reasonably rule out a *global* linear relationship between t and h, meaning that there is no *single* straight line that will pass through all our data points. Symbolically, this means that we cannot expect a functional relationship of the form

$$t = mh + b$$

to fit the data. Does the graph remind you of any other types of graphs you've seen before? For example, can we find part of a parabola that passes through the data points? This turns out to be a good guess (and somebody in history eventually made this guess). In fact, the upper half of the parabola with equation

$$16t^2 = h$$

does a very nice job of fitting our recorded data. (Try each recorded pair of values for t and h in the equation.) If we write this equation in the functional form $t = f(h)$, we have

$$t = \sqrt{\frac{h}{16}}.$$

To test our formula, we can drop the ball from some new heights. Additional drop times are recorded in Table 1.4.

height in feet	time in seconds
19	1.09
30	1.37
70	2.09
120	2.75

Table 1.4 Additional drop times.

If we check our formula with this new data by substituting the heights and comparing the computed results with the experimental results, we find that the formula gives us excellent predictions. Until we are presented with experimental data that conflicts with our computed results, we appear to have a formula that effectively describes the functional relationship between height and drop time, at least for heights in the range of those of our experiment.

EXERCISES for Section 1.6

For exercises 1–6: The table shown provides data on the population of a bacteria culture in the presence of limited nutrient supply. Use linear interpolation to predict the population of the bacteria culture at the times indicated.

time in hours	population
1	210
2	232
3	260
4	293
5	333
6	382
7	438
8	500
9	562
10	618
11	667
12	707
13	740
14	768
15	790
16	809
17	825
18	839
19	850
20	860

For Exercises 1-6

1. 3 hours and 30 minutes

2. 10 hours and 45 minutes

3. 15 hours and 15 minutes

4. 6 hours and 20 minutes

5. 19 hours and 54 minutes

6. 7 hours and 30 minutes

---

7. Use the model $f(h) = \sqrt{h/16}$ to predict how long it would take a ball to drop from a height of 100 miles (remember, h is measured in feet and $f(h)$ is measured in seconds).

8. Divide 100 miles by the time you found in exercise 7 to find the average speed of the ball (express your answer in miles per hour). Does this seem reasonable? What factors might make the model unreasonable for this value h?

For exercises 9–12: The illustration shows a graph of hours of daylight at a particular latitude as a function of time of year.

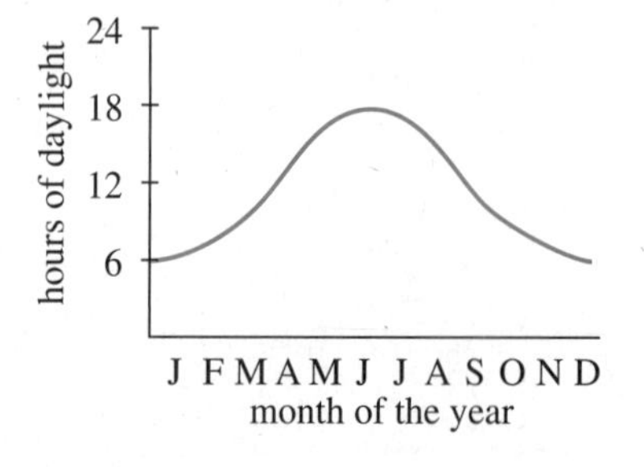

For Exercises 9-12

9. During what month are the hours of daylight increasing the fastest?

10. During what month are the hours of daylight decreasing the fastest?

11. Was the data in the graph gathered at a location in the Northern Hemisphere or the Southern Hemisphere?

12. Let t be the number of months passed, so that January represents $t = 1$, February represents $t = 2$, and so on, with December representing $t = 12$. Find suitable parameters A, B, C, and D, so that the graph of a function of the form

$$H(t) = A \sin B(t - C) + D$$

fits the data shown in the graph.

For exercises 13–24: The graphs lettered A through I represent models that fit certain phenomena quite well. The exercises that follow describe these phenomena. Match each description with its graph (some graphs may be used more than once; some not at all).

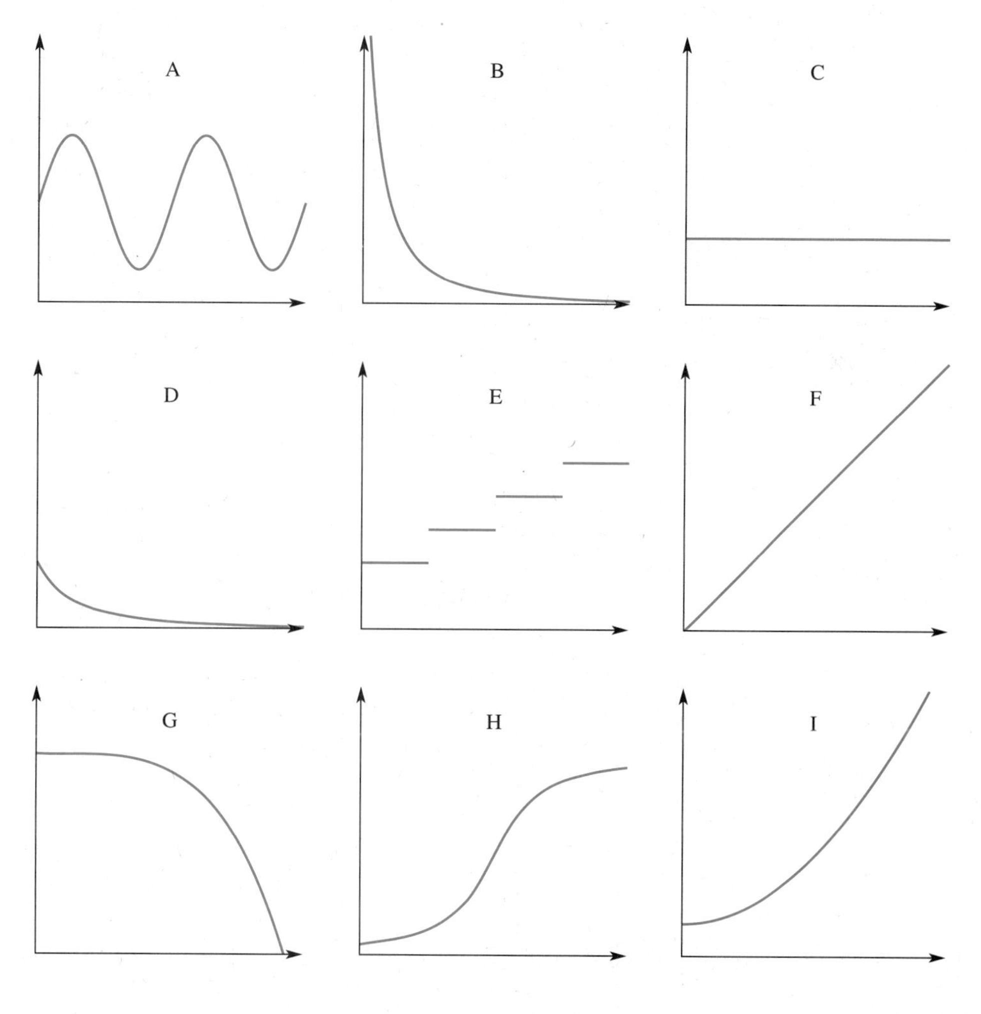

For Exercises 13-24

13. The balance of a mortgage on a house as a function of time.

14. The population of the bacteria culture in the presence of limited nutrients (see exercises 1-6) as a function of time.

15. The gravitational force exerted between two objects as a function of the distance between them. (See our discussion of power functions in Section 1.1.)

16. The amount of a decaying radioactive material as a function of time.

17. The population of a bacteria culture in the presence of unlimited nutrients as a function of time.

18. The height of the bob on a swinging pendulum as a function of time.

19. The number of representatives a state is apportioned as a function of its population.

20. The number of senators a state is apportioned as a function of its population.

21. The number of people who have heard a rumor as a function of time.

22. The cost of postage on a package, as a function of its weight.

23. The spread of a communicable disease through a population as a function of time.

24. The circumference of a planet as a function of its radius.

2

Limits—Local and Global Behavior of Functions

Much of calculus concerns the behavior of functions—that is, how the outputs act or change relative to the inputs. Limits provide an effective language for describing both a function's *local behavior* (over small intervals) as well as its *global behavior* (over large intervals).

In this chapter, we begin with an informal discussion of limits and a closely related concept called *continuity*. Then, we show how limits can be investigated numerically and how the local and global behavior of a function can be analyzed graphically. Along the way, we point out some important consequences of continuity for functions, and we show how these observations can be used to find approximate solutions to equations. Finally, we introduce a more formal definition of limit. We show how the definition can be understood numerically in terms of *error tolerances* and graphically in terms of the scaling of a viewing window for the function's graph.

The notion of limit also underlies the concept of derivative, as we see in the next chapter.

2.1 THE LANGUAGE OF LIMITS

Let's start out with a graphical example by considering the graph of $y = f(x)$ in Figure 2.1. Imagine that you are walking along the x-axis toward a particular value $x = a$. As you walk, you watch the graph very carefully, taking note of the output $f(x)$ for each input x you pass. Now, as you approach very near the value $x = a$, you are asked to make a prediction of the real number output value $f(a)$. You are not allowed to see the *actual* output value $f(a)$ (if there is one), but you may observe the graph over inputs as close to a as you please. Based on these nearby values, you are

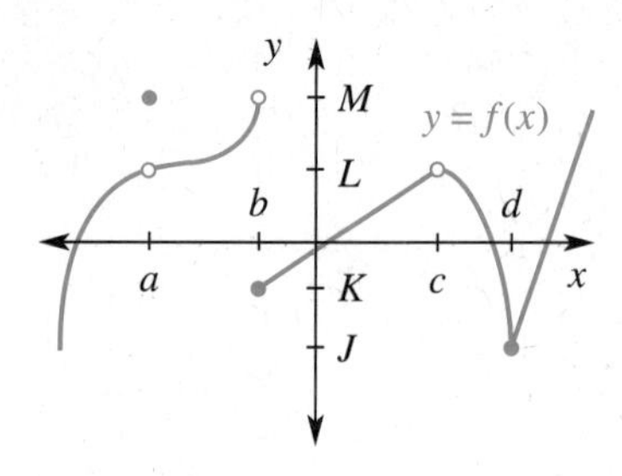

Figure 2.1 Predicting function outputs from a graph.

likely to predict the value L as the output $f(a)$, even though the actual output value is $f(a) = M$. This kind of output behavior is deserving of a special language:

In the mathematical notation of limits, we write

$$\lim_{x \to a} f(x) = L$$

and say that the number L is the **limit** of $f(x)$ as x approaches a.

The notation suggests that the output $f(x)$ gets near the value L as the input x gets near the value a. In other words, think of the limit L as the predicted output value for the function at $x = a$, which can be different from the actual output value $f(a) = M$. It is possible that your prediction depends on whether you approach from the left-hand side or the right-hand side.

$\lim\limits_{x \to a^-} f(x)$ is called the **left-hand limit of** $f(x)$ **as** x **approaches** a, and it represents the prediction from the left side, as you pass values $x < a$.

$\lim\limits_{x \to a^+} f(x)$ is called the **right-hand limit of** $f(x)$ **as** x **approaches** a, and it represents the prediction from the right side, as you pass values $x > a$.

▶▶▶ **Note that the positive and negative signs used on a^+ and a^- refer only to the *direction of approach* and have nothing to do with the *value* of a. If no sign is used as a superscript on a, then this denotes THE limit, meaning a common prediction from both sides.**

For the function in Figure 2.1, the prediction from the left is

$$\lim_{x \to a^-} f(x) = L$$

and the prediction from the right is

$$\lim_{x \to a^+} f(x) = L.$$

Note that neither prediction matches the *actual* output value $f(a) = M$, but the two predictions match each other. If the predictions do not match, or if it is impossible to even make a prediction, we say the limit *does not exist.*

EXAMPLE 1 For the function in Figure 2.1, determine visually the limits of $f(x)$ at $x = b$, c, and d, if the limits exist.

Solution For each value, we need to examine both one-sided limits.

For $x = b$, $\lim_{x \to b^-} f(x) = M$ and $\lim_{x \to b^+} f(x) = K$. Since the two one-sided limits do not match, we conclude that

$$\lim_{x \to b} f(x) \text{ does not exist.}$$

For $x = c$, $\lim_{x \to c^-} f(x) = L$ and $\lim_{x \to c^+} f(x) = L$. Since the two one-sided limits do match, we conclude that

$$\lim_{x \to c} f(x) = L.$$

For $x = d$, $\lim_{x \to d^-} f(x) = J$ and $\lim_{x \to d^+} f(x) = J$. Since the two one-sided limits do match, we conclude that

$$\lim_{x \to d} f(x) = J.$$

■

▶▶▶ **As you can see from this example, determining a limit at a point depends only on the left- and right-hand limits, and not on the *actual output* (if any) of the function at that point.**

Estimating limits graphically

With machine graphics, you might be able to estimate the value of a limit $\lim_{x \to a} f(x)$ by graphing $y = f(x)$ over an interval containing the target a and using a visual analysis. Indeed, we can visually approach $x = a$ by zooming in on the graph.

EXAMPLE 2 Estimate graphically

$$\lim_{x \to 0} \frac{\sin x}{x}.$$

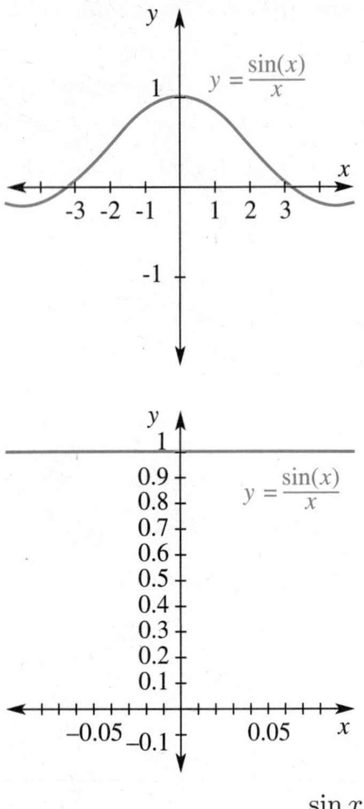

Figure 2.2 Graphs of $y = \dfrac{\sin x}{x}$.

Solution Figure 2.2 shows two machine-generated plots of the graph of $y = \dfrac{\sin x}{x}$. The first viewing window appears to indicate an output value of 1 at $x = 0$ (though we know that 0 is not in the domain of the function). To investigate this further, in the second viewing window we show a close-up of the graph with the horizontal range between $x = -0.1$ and $x = 0.1$. In this view, the graph of $y = \dfrac{\sin x}{x}$ resembles the horizontal line $y = 1$. This reinforces our first impression, so we could say that *graphically*,

$$\lim_{x \to 0} \frac{\sin x}{x} \text{ appears to be } 1. \qquad \blacksquare$$

Since a machine-generated graph is only a finite collection of pixels, a "hole" in a graph may or may not appear. For example, if the hole occurs *between* two adjacent plotted values, it may go undetected. In this example, we do not see the hole in the graph of $y = \dfrac{\sin x}{x}$ because the y-axis itself fills it in.

In general, a graph can be helpful in suggesting whether or not a limit exists at a particular point $x = a$, and it gives us a reasonable idea of the value of the limit when it does exist. However, a graph cannot provide definitive *proof* of the existence or value of the limit. In particular, if we use a machine to graph a function, the precision limitations of the machine may not allow us to look at function outputs $f(x)$ for inputs x arbitrarily close to a given number a. In fact, if we get *too close*, round-off errors may tempt us to draw some erroneous conclusions.

Continuity

We say that a function is **continuous** at a point where the limit of a function matches the output at that point. Using the notation of limits, we have the following definition.

Definition 1

The function f is **continuous at** $x = a$ if and only if

$$\lim_{x \to a} f(x) = f(a).$$

This definition requires three conditions for a function f to be continuous at $x = a$:

Requirement 1.	$\lim_{x \to a} f(x)$ must exist.
Requirement 2.	$f(a)$ must be defined.
Requirement 3.	These values must match.

Put informally, if the function f is continuous at $x = a$, then we can predict the *correct* output value $f(a)$ on the basis of the outputs $f(x)$ for x near a. The three requirements rule out breaks in the graph at $x = a$, hence the motivation for the term *continuous*.

EXAMPLE 3 Figure 2.3 shows the graph of a function f. At which of the points a, b, c, d is f continuous?

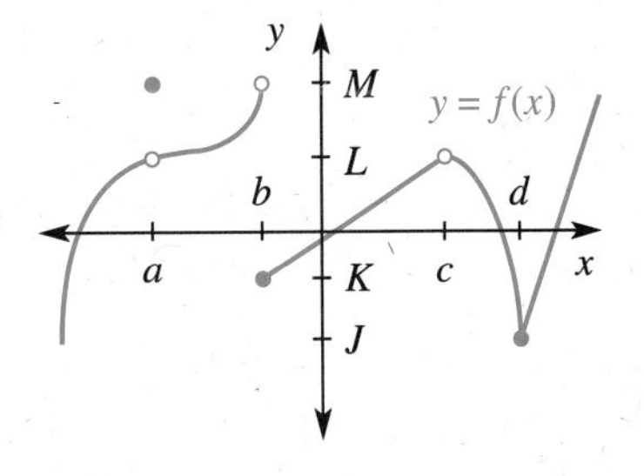

Figure 2.3 Where is f continuous?

Solution At each of the points a, b, c, and d we check each of the three requirements.

At $x = a$, f is not continuous, because $\lim_{x\to a} f(x) = L \neq M = f(a)$. (Requirements 1. and 2. are met, but not Requirement 3.)

At $x = b$, f is not continuous, because $\lim_{x\to b} f(x)$ does not exist. (Requirement 1. is not met.)

At $x = c$, f is not continuous, because $f(c)$ is not defined (Requirement 1. is met, but not Requirement 2.)

At $x = d$, f is continuous, because $\lim_{x\to d} f(x) = J = f(d)$. (All three requirements are met.) ■

We can talk about left-hand and right-hand continuity at a point according to whether the left-hand or right-hand limit of the function matches the actual output value there.

The function f is **continuous from the left** at $x = a$ if and only if

$$\lim_{x\to a^-} f(x) = f(a).$$

The function f is **continuous from the right** at $x = a$ if and only if

$$\lim_{x\to a^+} f(x) = f(a).$$

EXAMPLE 4 For the same function f illustrated in Figure 2.3, determine whether f is continuous from the left or right at $x = b$.

Solution The function f is continuous from the right at b because $\lim_{x\to b^+} f(x) = K = f(b)$, but f is not continuous from the left at b since $\lim_{x\to b^-} f(x) = M \neq f(b)$. ■

Note that the function f is continuous at $x = a$ if and only if f is continuous from both sides at $x = a$.

Check your graphical understanding of the language of limits and continuity with the following example.

EXAMPLE 5 For the function f illustrated in Figure 2.4, at which of the six points a_1, a_2, ..., a_6 is f continuous?

Solution Table 2.1 shows the limit and continuity information for each of the inputs a_1, a_2, ..., a_6. ■

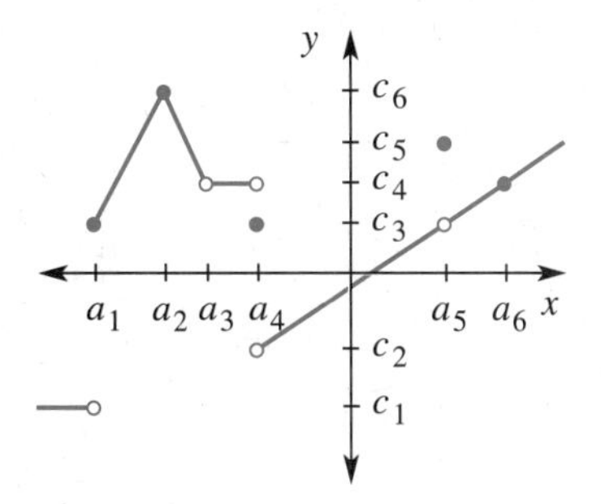

Figure 2.4 Where is the function continuous?

input $x=a$	output $f(a)$	left-hand limit $\lim_{x\to a^-} f(x)$	right-hand limit $\lim_{x\to a^+} f(x)$	limit $\lim_{x\to a} f(x)$	Is f continuous at $x=a$?
a_1	c_3	c_1	c_3	does not exist	no
a_2	c_6	c_6	c_6	c_6	yes
a_3	undefined	c_4	c_4	c_4	no
a_4	c_3	c_4	c_2	does not exist	no
a_5	c_5	c_3	c_3	c_3	no
a_6	c_4	c_4	c_4	c_4	yes

Table 2.1 Limit table for the function f.

EXERCISES for Section 2.1

For exercises 1–6: Sketch the graph of a function satisfying the stated requirements.

1. $\lim_{x\to 1^+} f(x) = 2$ $\lim_{x\to 1^-} f(x) = -1$ $f(1)$ is undefined.

2. $\lim_{x\to -2^-} g(x) = 0$ $\lim_{x\to -2^+} g(x) = 0$ $g(-2) = 1$

3. $\lim_{x\to 2^-} h(x) = -2$ $\lim_{x\to 2^+} h(x) = 2$ $h(2) = 0$

4. $\lim_{x\to 0^-} i(x) = -1$ $\lim_{x\to 0^+} i(x) = -2$ $i(0) = -1$

5. $\lim_{x\to -1^-} j(x) = 3$ $\lim_{x\to -1^+} j(x) = -2$ $j(-1) = -2$

6. $\lim_{x\to -3^-} k(x) = 1$ $\lim_{x\to -3^+} k(x) = 1$ $k(-3)$ is undefined.

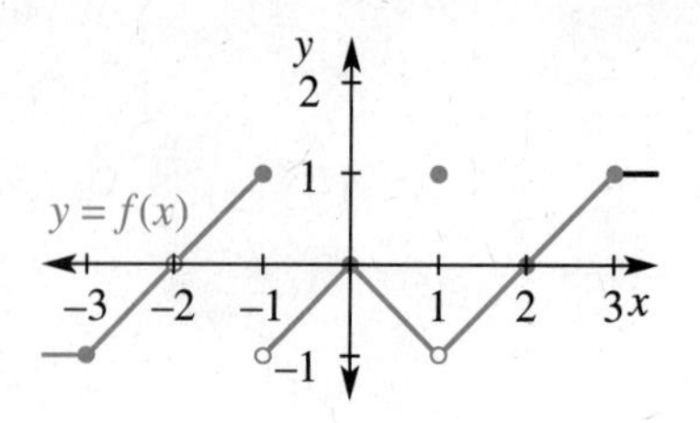

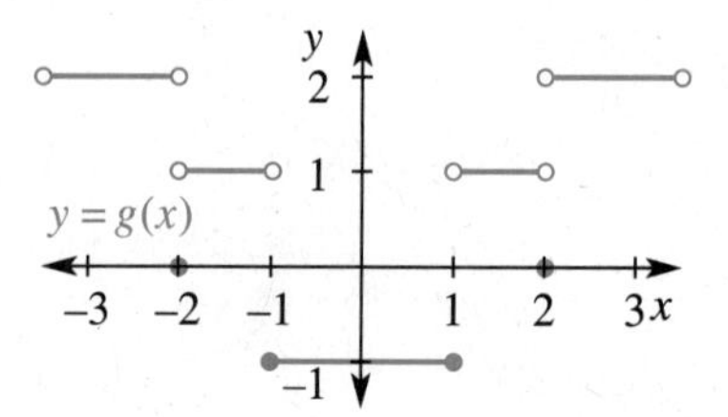

For Exercises 7–12

For exercises 7–12: The two functions f and g have the graphs shown. Use these to graph the following functions over the interval $[-3, 3]$.

7. $f + g$

8. $f - g$

9. fg

10. $2f$

11. $f \circ g$

12. $g \circ f$

For exercises 13–20: Using the graphs of f and g and your graphs from exercises 7-12, fill out a table like the one shown for each of the functions indicated.

input $x = a$	output $f(a)$	left-hand limit $\lim_{x \to a^-} f(x)$	right-hand limit $\lim_{x \to a^+} f(x)$	limit $\lim_{x \to a} f(x)$	Is f continuous at $x = a$? (yes or no)
–3					
–2					
–1					
0					
1					
2					
3					

For Exercises 13-20

13. f

14. g

15. $f + g$

16. $f - g$

17. fg

18. $2f$

19. $f \circ g$

20. $g \circ f$

For exercises 21–36: For the function f defined,

(a) Graph the function over the interval $[-5, 5]$. (Note: In some cases, $f(0)$ is not defined.)

(b) Graphically estimate the two one-sided limits:

$$\lim_{x\to 0^+} f(x) \qquad \lim_{x\to 0^-} f(x)$$

(c) Graphically estimate $\lim\limits_{x\to 0} f(x)$ if it exists.

21. $f(x) = |x|$
22. $f(x) = x/x$
23. $f(x) = |x|/x$
24. $f(x) = \dfrac{\sin(2x)}{5x}$
25. $f(x) = 1/x^2$
26. $f(x) = 1/x$
27. $f(x) = \sin(1/x)$
28. $f(x) = x\sin(1/x)$
29. $f(x) = \tan(x)$
30. $f(x) = \cot(x)$
31. $f(x) = \dfrac{1-\cos x}{x}$
32. $f(x) = \sin^2(x) + \cos^2(x)$
33. $f(x) = (1+x)^{1/x}$
34. $f(x) = \arctan(1/x)$
35.
$$f(x) = \begin{cases} x^2 \text{ if } x < 0 \\ 2x - 1 \text{ if } x \geq 0 \end{cases}$$
36.
$$f(x) = \begin{cases} 1 \text{ if } x > 0 \\ 0 \text{ if } x = 0 \\ -1 \text{ if } x < 0 \end{cases}$$

(How does this function differ from the function in exercise 23?)

2.2 EXPLORING LIMITS NUMERICALLY

The computational power made available by technology gives us a useful numerical tool for investigating limits. By computing $f(x)$ for a sequence of inputs approaching a from the left ($x < a$), and for another sequence approaching a from the right ($x > a$), we can gather evidence (but not proof) of whether or not $\lim\limits_{x\to a} f(x)$ exists and, if it exists, what the limiting value is. If both sequences seem to stabilize to the same value L, this is supporting evidence that the limit exists and

$$\lim_{x\to a} f(x) = L.$$

Examples of numerical investigations of limits

EXAMPLE 6 Numerically investigate

$$\lim_{x\to 0}\frac{\sin x}{x},$$

where x is understood to be measured in radians.

Solution $\dfrac{\sin x}{x}$ is not defined for $x = 0$, but we can sample the output values for any input $x \neq 0$. We can try sequences of inputs that approach 0 from different sides, say

$$0.1, 0.01, 0.001, \ldots$$

from the right of 0, and

$$-0.1, -0.01, -0.001, \ldots$$

from the left of 0.

The corresponding outputs appear to be getting very close to 1 from either direction, as shown by the first three inputs we try from either side (see Table 2.2). On the basis of this evidence, we could say that *numerically*

$$\lim_{x\to 0}\frac{\sin x}{x} \ \textit{appears to be}\ 1.$$

x	$\sin(x)/x$	x	$\sin(x)/x$
0.1	0.998334	–0.1	0.998334
0.01	0.999983	–0.01	0.999983
0.001	0.999998	–0.001	0.999998

Table 2.2 Values of $\sin(x)/x$ sampled near 0.

In fact, if we use machine computation of $\dfrac{\sin x_0}{x_0}$ for a value x_0 close enough to 0, the round-off precision of the machine actually may result in an output of 1. ■

EXAMPLE 7 Numerically investigate $\lim_{x\to 0} f(x)$ (if it exists) if

$$f(x) = \frac{\sqrt{|x|}}{|\sqrt{x+1}-1|}.$$

Solution We will investigate this limit by computing $f(x)$ for x sampled closer and closer to 0 (see Table 2.3). As the inputs x get closer and closer to 0 both from the left and from the right, the outputs $f(x)$ appear to become larger without stabilizing. This is *evidence* that the limit $\lim_{x\to 0} f(x)$ does not exist. ■

x	$f(x)$
0.1	6.478902473
0.01	20.04987607
0.001	63.26136854
0.0001	200.0040001
0.00001	632.4555320
0.000001	2000.000000

x	$f(x)$
−0.1	6.162277666
−0.01	19.94987434
−0.001	63.22973312
−0.0001	199.9948001
−0.00001	632.4555320
−0.000001	2000.000000

Table 2.3 $f(x) = \dfrac{\sqrt{|x|}}{|\sqrt{x+1}-1|}$ sampled near 0.

EXAMPLE 8 Numerically investigate $\lim_{x\to 0} f(x)$ (if it exists) if

$$f(x) = \frac{|x|}{|\sqrt{x+1}-1|}.$$

Solution Again, we explore the limit by computing $f(x)$ for x sampled closer and closer to 0 (see Table 2.4). From both directions, $x > 0$ and $x < 0$, the outputs $f(x)$ seem to be stabilizing to 2. This is evidence that $\lim_{x\to 0} f(x) = 2$. ■

x	$f(x)$
0.1	2.048808848
0.01	2.004987562
0.001	2.000499875
0.0001	2.000049999
0.00001	2.000005000
0.000001	2.000000500

x	$f(x)$
−0.1	1.948683298
−0.01	1.994987437
−0.001	1.999499875
−0.0001	1.999949999
−0.00001	1.999995000
−0.000001	1.999999500

Table 2.4 $f(x) = \dfrac{|x|}{|\sqrt{x+1}-1|}$ sampled near 0.

▶▶▶ **We examine a sequence of values in order to find evidence of a trend. Simply taking a single sample very near the limit point does *not* give very good evidence of whether the limit actually exists.**

EXAMPLE 9 Numerically investigate $\lim_{x\to 0} f(x)$ (if it exists) if

$$f(x) = \cos(\frac{1}{x}).$$

Solution We compute $f(x)$ for x sampled closer and closer to 0 (see Table 2.5). From both directions, $x > 0$ and $x < 0$, the values do not seem to stabilize at all, even though the outputs must be confined to values between -1 and 1. This suggests that the limit $\lim_{x\to 0} \cos(1/x)$ does not exist. ■

x	$f(x)$	x	$f(x)$
0.1	−0.839071529076	−0.1	−0.839071529076
0.01	0.862318872288	−0.01	0.862318872288
0.001	0.562379076291	−0.001	0.562379076291
0.0001	−0.952155368259	−0.0001	−0.952155368259
0.00001	−0.999360807438	−0.00001	−0.999360807438
0.000001	0.936752127533	−0.000001	0.936752127533
0.0000001	−0.907270386182	−0.0000001	−0.907270386182
0.00000001	−0.363385089356	−0.00000001	−0.363385089356

Table 2.5 $f(x) = \cos(1/x)$ sampled near 0.

EXAMPLE 10 Numerically investigate $\lim_{x\to 3} f(x)$ (if it exists) if

$$f(x) = \frac{2x-6}{\sqrt{x^2-6x+9}}.$$

Solution Now we must compute $f(x)$ for x sampled closer and closer to 3 (see Table 2.6). From the right ($x > 3$), the values seem to stabilize to 2. From the left ($x < 3$), the values seem to stabilize to -2. Although it appears that there is a limiting value both from the left and from the right, these one-sided limits are not the same. This is evidence that the limit does not exist. We could summarize this particular behavior with the notation

$$\lim_{x\to 3^-} f(x) = -2 \quad \text{and} \quad \lim_{x\to 3^+} f(x) = 2,$$

but we emphasize that $\lim_{x\to 3} f(x)$ does not exist. ■

x	$f(x)$	x	$f(x)$
3.1	2	2.9	−2
3.01	2	2.99	−2
3.001	2	2.999	−2
3.0001	2	2.9999	−2
3.00001	2	2.99999	−2
3.000001	2	2.999999	−2

Table 2.6 $f(x) = \dfrac{2x-6}{\sqrt{x^2-6x+9}}$ sampled near 3.

Machine precision and limits

The number of digits a machine allocates to represent a number is called the machine's **precision**. Whenever the machine completes one step of a computation, the result is rounded to this number of digits.

▶▶▶ **Since machine computation has limited precision, the accuracy of a computation actually may decrease as you sample inputs very close to the target value.**

EXAMPLE 11 Assuming 10-digit precision, numerically investigate $\lim_{x\to 3} \frac{f(x)-f(3)}{x-3}$, where $f(x) = \frac{x}{54321}$.

Solution To investigate

$$\lim_{x\to 3} \frac{\frac{x}{54321} - \frac{3}{54321}}{x-3},$$

we compute a sequence of sample values computed with 10-digit arithmetic, precision, as shown in Table 2.7. However, note that for any $x \neq 3$, we can simplify the expression as

$$\begin{aligned}
\frac{f(x)-f(3)}{x-3} &= \frac{\frac{x}{54321} - \frac{3}{54321}}{x-3} \\
&= \frac{\frac{x-3}{54321}}{x-3} \\
&= \frac{1}{54321} \qquad \text{for } x \neq 3 \\
&= 0.00001840908673 \qquad \text{to 10 digits of precision.}
\end{aligned}$$

x	$f(x)$
3.1	0.00001840908673
3.01	0.00001840908673
3.001	0.0000184090867
3.0001	0.000018409087
3.00001	0.00001840909
3.000001	0.0000184091
3.0000001	0.00001841
3.00000001	0.0000184

Table 2.7 Sampled values of $\frac{f(x)-f(3)}{x-3}$ for x near 3.

For this machine, the output values computed by the machine actually become less accurate as x approaches 3, due to the rounding of the values $f(x)$ and $f(3)$ at every intermediate step. ■

EXERCISES for Section 2.2

For exercises 1–24: Numerically investigate each limit. Indicate whether the evidence suggests that the limit exists or doesn't exist.

1. $\lim_{x\to 0} \left(2+\frac{(x+1)^3-(x+1)^2}{x}\right)$

2. $\lim_{x\to 0} \frac{(x+1)^6-(x+1)^4}{x}$

3. $\lim_{x\to 0} \frac{|x^2|}{|\sqrt{x^2+4}-2|}$

4. $\lim_{x\to 0} \frac{|x^2|}{|\sqrt{x+x^2+4}-2-0.25x|}$

5. $\lim_{x\to 0} x\ln(|x|)$

6. $\lim_{x\to 0} x\ln(|x|)^{10}$

7. $\lim_{x\to 0} x\cdot 2^{(1/|x|)}$

8. $\lim_{x\to 0} x^{10}\cdot 2^{(1/|x|)}$

9. $\lim_{x\to 0} \frac{\sqrt{1-x^4}}{1-x^2}$

10. $\lim_{x\to 0} \frac{\sin(x^2)}{x^2}$

11. $\lim_{x\to 0} \left(\frac{1}{x}-\frac{1}{\sin(x)}\right)$

12. $\lim_{x\to 1} \frac{|2x^2+x-1|}{3|x+1|-0.5}$

13. $\lim_{x\to 1} (x-1)^2\cdot\ln((x-1)^2)$

14. $\lim_{x\to 2} \left(\frac{1}{x-2}+\frac{x-1}{2-x}\right)$

15. $\lim_{x\to 4} \frac{4-x}{2-\sqrt{x}}$

16. $\lim_{x\to -3} \frac{(x+3)}{|x+3|}$

17. $\lim_{x\to -2} \frac{x^3-5x+8}{24x+48}$

18. $\lim_{x\to -1} \frac{x^3+10x^2+16x+7}{5x+5}$

19. $\lim_{x\to -3} \frac{x^4-12x^2+x-2}{30x-90}$

20. $\lim_{x\to 2} \frac{x^3-8}{x^2-4}$

21. $\lim_{x\to -3} \frac{|x+3|}{2x^2+6x+1}$

22. $\lim_{x\to 3} \frac{2x^3-x^2-12x-9}{16x^2-48x-32}$

23. $\lim_{x\to -1} \frac{x^2-x+1}{5x-5}$

24. $\lim_{x\to 2} \frac{2x^2-5x+2}{5x^2-7x-6}$

2.3 ANALYZING LOCAL BEHAVIOR GRAPHICALLY

If a function f is continuous at $x = a$, then it behaves predictably at that point in the sense that

$$\lim_{x\to a} f(x) = f(a).$$

When f is *not* continuous at a, then somehow the function's output has behaved unpredictably at that point.

A point a at which f is not continuous is called a **discontinuity** for f. The language of limits allows us to describe the local behavior of a function's outputs $f(x)$ near a discontinuity, and in this section we'll analyze graphically some of the kinds of local behavior one might encounter.

Removable and essential discontinuities

If
$$\lim_{x \to a} f(x) = L,$$
(satisfying one of the requirements of continuity), then the only things keeping f from being continuous at a are the possibilities that either:

1. $f(a)$ is undefined (leaving a "hole" in the graph), or
2. $f(a)$ is defined, but $f(a) \neq L$.

In either case, we could imagine "repairing" the function f in order to make it continuous at $x = a$ by simply defining or redefining the output to be L. In other words, we create a new function g such that:

$$g(x) = \begin{cases} f(x) \text{ if } x \neq a \\ L \text{ if } x = a \end{cases}$$

Now, g is continuous at $x = a$ and the graph of $y = g(x)$ is identical to the graph of $y = f(x)$ with the one difference that $g(a) = L$.

For this reason, whenever f actually has a limit at a discontinuity, we call it a **removable discontinuity**. To remove such a discontinuity at $x = a$, one must change the function by defining or redefining the output to match the limiting value.

If, however, $\lim_{x \to a} f(x)$ does not exist, then there is no way to "repair" the discontinuity. Such a nonremovable discontinuity is called an **essential discontinuity**. The following graphical example illustrates both types of discontinuities.

EXAMPLE 12 For the function f whose graph is illustrated in Figure 2.5, describe the local behavior near $x = a$, $x = b$, $x = c$, and $x = d$. In particular, describe whether a removable or essential discontinuity exists at each point.

Solution The function f has *removable discontinuities* at $x = a$ and $x = c$, since f does have a limit L at each of these points. Defining or changing the output of the function to be L at these points repairs the "holes" in the graph.

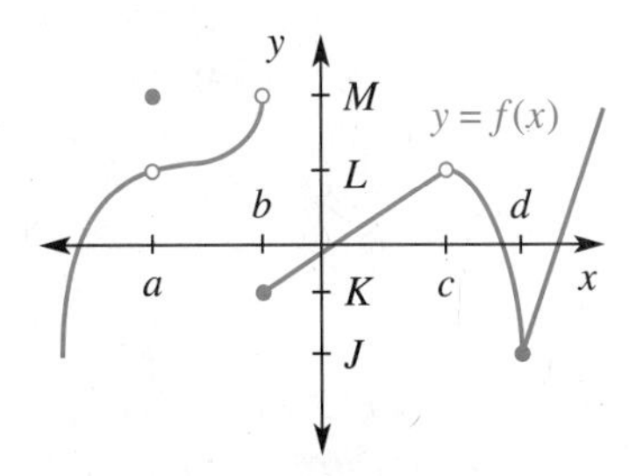

Figure 2.5 Which discontinuities are removable?

The function f has an *essential discontinuity* at $x = b$, since f does not have a limit at $x = b$.

The function f is *continuous* at $x = d$, even though the graph makes a sharp turn at that point. ■

The language of limits helps us describe the graphical behavior of a function at a point of discontinuity. Let's examine some common types of essential discontinuities.

Jump discontinuities

If the left-hand and right-hand limits of $f(x)$ exist, but do *not* match at $x = a$, then

$$\lim_{x \to a} f(x) \quad \text{does not exist.}$$

In this case, we say that the function f has a **jump discontinuity** at $x = a$. This type of essential discontinuity is exhibited graphically by a sudden jump at $x = a$.

EXAMPLE 13 Analyze the local behavior of f near $x = 0$, where:

$$f(x) = \begin{cases} x^2 \text{ if } x < 0 \\ 2x - 1 \text{ if } x \geq 0 \end{cases}$$

Solution For $x < 0$, the first line of the formula applies and $f(x) = x^2$. From this, we see that

$$\lim_{x \to 0^-} f(x) = 0.$$

For $x \geq 0$, the second line of the formula applies and $f(x) = 2x - 1$. From this, we see that

$$\lim_{x \to 0+} f(x) = -1.$$

Since the one-sided limits do not match, f has no limit at $x = 0$. Figure 2.6illustrates the graph of this function. ■

Vertical asymptotes

If the magnitude of the function values $f(x)$ grows without bound (in other words, $|f(x)|$ gets arbitrarily large) as x approaches a from either the left or

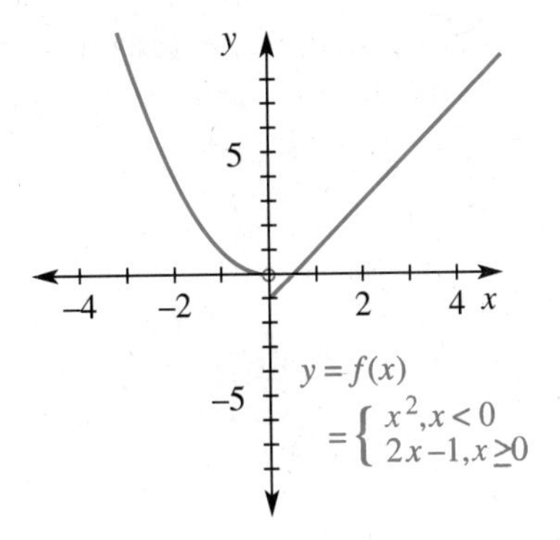

Figure 2.6 The function f has a jump discontinuity at $x = 0$.

the right, then

$$\lim_{x \to a} f(x) \quad \text{does not exist.}$$

In this case, the vertical line $x = a$ is called a **vertical asymptote** of the graph of $y = f(x)$.

EXAMPLE 14 Analyze the local behavior of $y = 1/x$ near $x = 0$.

Solution As x approaches 0 through positive values, the output $1/x$ is positive and grows larger without bound. As x approaches 0 through negative values, the output $1/x$ is negative and becomes larger in magnitude (in other words, $|1/x|$ grows larger) without bound.

The vertical line $x = 0$ (the y-axis in this case) is a vertical asymptote for the graph of $y = 1/x$ (see Figure 2.7). To describe this unbounded behavior near $x = 0$, we write

$$\lim_{x \to 0^-} \frac{1}{x} = -\infty \qquad \text{and} \qquad \lim_{x \to 0^+} \frac{1}{x} = \infty.$$

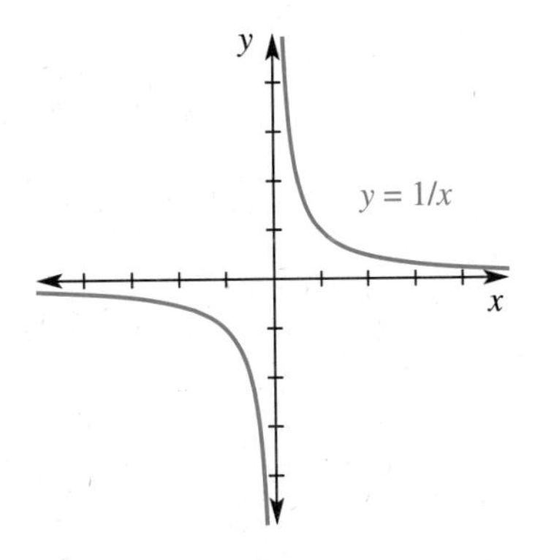

Figure 2.7 The graph of $y = 1/x$ has $x = 0$ as a vertical asymptote.

We must emphasize that neither of these one-sided limits exists. All we are saying with this notation is *why* the limits do not exist. Namely, the function outputs are growing in magnitude without bound in either the positive or negative direction. ■

▶▶▶ **BEWARE! The symbols ∞ and $-\infty$ do not represent real numbers. As used here, they are simply a convenient shorthand for describing the behavior of the function.**

EXAMPLE 15 Analyze the local behavior of the function

$$f(x) = \frac{1}{x^2}$$

near $x = 0$.

Solution The value of $1/x^2$ is positive and grows without bound as x approaches 0 from either side. Hence,

$$\lim_{x\to 0^-} \frac{1}{x^2} = \infty \quad \text{and} \quad \lim_{x\to 0^+} \frac{1}{x^2} = \infty.$$

In this case, we can write

$$\lim_{x\to 0} \frac{1}{x^2} = \infty,$$

but again we must emphasize that this notation is used to describe the function behavior and that

$$\lim_{x\to 0} \frac{1}{x^2} \text{ does not exist.}$$

The graph of $y = 1/x^2$ has $x = 0$ as a vertical asymptote (see Figure 2.8). ■

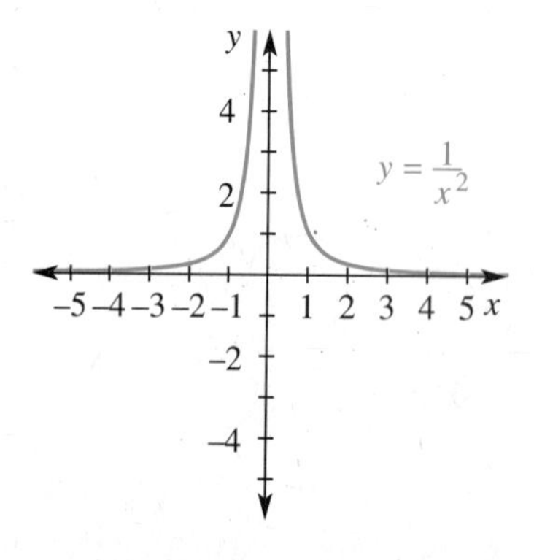

Figure 2.8 The graph of $y = 1/x^2$ has $x = 0$ as a vertical asymptote .

Using the language of limits, we can summarize by noting that the graph of $y = f(x)$ has a vertical asymptote $x = a$, provided that at least one of the following is true:

$$\lim_{x \to a^-} f(x) = \infty \qquad \lim_{x \to a^-} f(x) = -\infty$$

$$\lim_{x \to a^+} f(x) = \infty \qquad \lim_{x \to a^+} f(x) = -\infty$$

It is certainly possible for a function to have infinitely many different discontinuities, as shown in the following example.

EXAMPLE 16 Find all the discontinuities of f if $f(x) = \tan x$.

Solution The value of $\tan x$ is undefined at $x = \pi/2$ and, because of this function's periodic nature, a discontinuity exists at each value $x = \pi/2 + n\pi$ for any integer n. As x approaches $\pi/2$ from the left-hand side with $x < \pi/2$, the values of $\tan x$ grow larger without bound. As x approaches $\pi/2$ from the right-hand side with $x > \pi/2$, the values of $\tan x$ are negative and their magnitude grows larger without bound. Thus,

$$\lim_{x \to \frac{\pi}{2}^-} \tan x = \infty \quad \text{and} \quad \lim_{x \to \frac{\pi}{2}^+} \tan x = -\infty.$$

Since this behavior is repeated at every other discontinuity, we conclude that the graph of $y = \tan x$ has a vertical asymptote at every value $a = \frac{\pi}{2} + n\pi$, where n is any integer. ■

Another type of essential discontinuity

A limit also can fail to exist for a function that does not have any jump discontinuities or vertical asymptotes.

EXAMPLE 17 Analyze the local behavior of the function f near $x = 0$, where

$$f(x) = \sin\left(\frac{1}{x}\right).$$

Solution In this case, the outputs $f(x)$ wildly oscillate between $y = -1$ and $y = 1$ as x approaches 0 (see Figure 2.9). We are forced to conclude that

$$\lim_{x \to 0} \sin\left(\frac{1}{x}\right) \quad \text{does not exist,}$$

for $f(x)$ approaches no particular value as x approaches 0. Hence, f has an essential discontinuity at $x = 0$, but it is not a jump discontinuity or vertical asymptote. ■

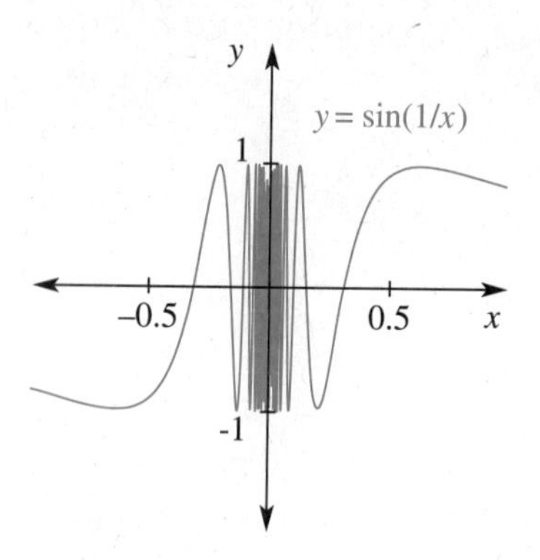

Figure 2.9 The graph of $y = \sin(1/x)$.

Discontinuities of rational functions

A rational function of the form $f(x) = p(x)/q(x)$ (where $p(x)$ and $q(x)$ are polynomials) has discontinuities precisely at those values a for which the denominator $q(a) = 0$, or equivalently, those values a for which $(x - a)$ is a factor of $q(x)$. Whether the discontinuity is removable or essential will depend on how often $(x - a)$ appears as a factor in the numerator $p(x)$.

> If $(x - a)$ appears as a factor in the denominator $q(x)$ *more times than* in the numerator $p(x)$, then the graph of the rational function has a vertical asymptote at $x = a$.
> If $(x - a)$ appears as a factor in the denominator $q(x)$ *the same times as or fewer times than* in the numerator $p(x)$, then the graph of the rational function has a removable discontinuity at $x = a$.

Let's illustrate this with a simple example.

EXAMPLE 18 Analyze the local behavior of the rational function $f(x) = \dfrac{x^3 - 8x^2 + 16x}{x^2 - 5x + 4}$ near its discontinuities.

Solution We factor both the numerator and denominator to find

$$\frac{x^3 - 8x^2 + 16x}{x^2 - 5x + 4} = \frac{x(x-4)(x-4)}{(x-4)(x-1)}.$$

The discontinuities occur at the zeroes of the denominator:

$$x = 4 \quad \text{and} \quad x = 1.$$

Since $(x-4)$ appears as a factor twice in the numerator and only once in the denominator, we can further simplify the expression to

$$\frac{x(x-4)(x-4)}{(x-4)(x-1)} = \frac{x(x-4)}{(x-1)} \qquad \text{for } x \neq 4.$$

There is a removable discontinuity at $x = 4$ (the graph will have a "hole" there), since

$$\lim_{x\to 4} \frac{x^3 - 8x^2 + 16x}{x^2 - 5x + 4} = \lim_{x\to 4} \frac{x(x-4)}{(x-1)} = 0.$$

Since $(x-1)$ appears as a factor in the denominator but not at all in the numerator, however, there is an essential discontinuity at $x = 1$ (the graph will have a vertical asymptote there).

The behavior of $f(x)$ near $x = 1$ is described using the language of limits. We have

$$\lim_{x\to 1^-} f(x) = +\infty \qquad \text{and} \qquad \lim_{x\to 1^+} f(x) = -\infty.$$

The graph of $y = f(x)$ shown in Figure 2.10 illustrates the behavior near both discontinuities. ■

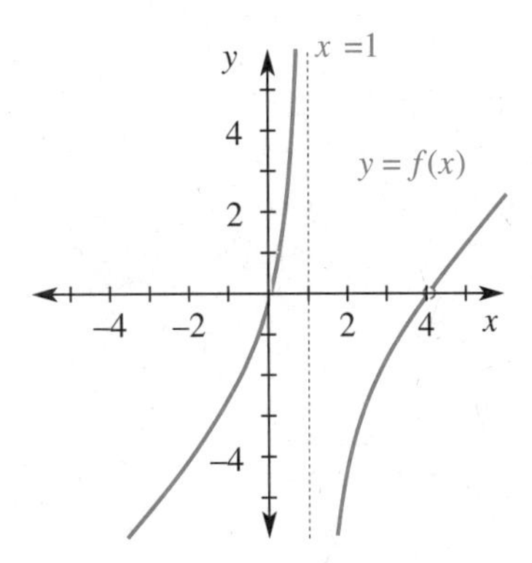

Figure 2.10 Discontinuities of the rational function $y = \dfrac{x^3 - 8x^2 + 16x}{x^2 - 5x + 4}$.

Machine graphics and vertical asymptotes

Consider the rational function g with

$$g(x) = \frac{-2x^3 - 3x + 5}{4x^2 + 6x - 7}.$$

The graph of $y = g(x)$ has vertical asymptotes at both zeroes of the denominator:

$$x = \frac{-3 \pm \sqrt{37}}{4}.$$

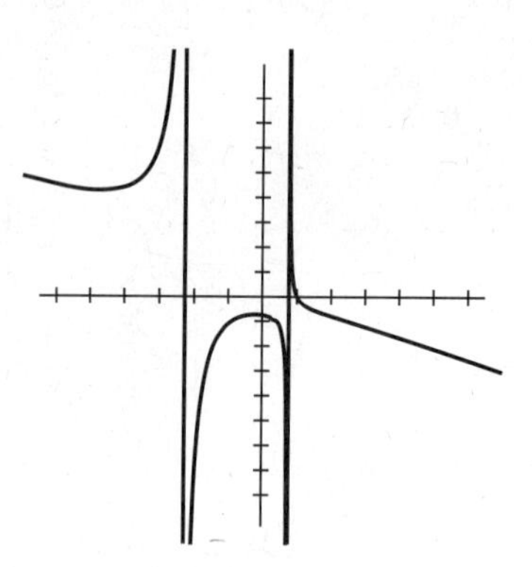

Figure 2.11 Machine plot of $y = \dfrac{-2x^3 - 3x + 5}{4x^2 + 6x - 7}$.

The zeroes are obtained by applying the quadratic formula to the equation $4x^2 + 6x - 7 = 0$.

Figure 2.11 shows a machine plot of the graph of $y = g(x)$. In this plot, two vertical lines appear in the graph. It might seem that the machine has been so kind as to draw the vertical asymptotes for us! However, the vertical asymptotes are located at *irrational* values of x, and they do not correspond to any pixel coordinate. What we are actually seeing is a phenomenon common to machine-generated graphs. If a computer graphing utility or calculator is set on "connected" mode, it assumes that the function being plotted is continuous. If a vertical asymptote is not detected because it lies between two adjacent plot values, then the machine may connect the graph across the vertical asymptote! Hence, we are seeing the machine's attempt to "connect the dots."

At a different scaling, a "spike" may occur near one of the vertical asymptotes of $y = g(x)$. Indeed, at very large scalings, one might not visually detect the local behavior near a vertical asymptote or other discontinuity at all!

EXERCISES for Section 2.3

For exercises 1–12: Determine whether the function is continuous at $x = 0$ and, if not, analyze the local behavior there.

1. $f(x) = |x|$
2. $f(x) = \dfrac{\sin 2x}{5x}$
3. $f(x) = \sin^2 x + \cos^2 x$
4. $f(x) = \cot x$
5. $f(x) = \dfrac{1 - \cos x}{x}$
6. $f(x) = x \sin(1/x)$
7. $f(x) = \arctan(1/x)$
8. $f(x) = (1 + x)^{1/x}$
9. $f(x) = \text{arccot}(1/x)$
10. $f(x) = \cos(1/x)$
11. $f(x) = \text{arcsec}(x)$
12. $f(x) = \text{arccsc}(x)$

For exercises 13–18: Find all the vertical asymptotes of the graphs of the functions.

13. $y = \csc x$

14. $y = \cot x$

15. $y = \sec x$

16. $y = \log_{10}(x)$

17. $y = 3^{1/x}$

18. $y = \dfrac{1}{1 + x + x^2}$

For exercises 19–24: Each function has a split formula. Graph each function and determine whether the function has a jump discontinuity.

19. $g(x) = \begin{cases} |x| \text{ if } x < -1 \\ x + 2 \text{ if } x \geq -1 \end{cases}$

20. $h(x) = \begin{cases} 4 - x^2 \text{ if } x \leq 2 \\ x^2 - 4 \text{ if } x > 2 \end{cases}$

21. $i(x) = \begin{cases} 0 \text{ if } x \leq -3 \\ (x + 3)^3 \text{ if } x > -3 \end{cases}$

22. $j(x) = \begin{cases} \dfrac{1}{x - 1} \text{ if } x < 1 \\ 2x - 1 \text{ if } x \geq 1 \end{cases}$

23. $k(x) = \begin{cases} \sin x \text{ if } x < \pi \\ x - 2\pi \text{ if } x \geq \pi \end{cases}$

24. $s(x) = \begin{cases} 2 \text{ if } x < -2 \\ x^2 \text{ if } x \geq -2 \end{cases}$

For exercises 25–40: For each rational function f described, find all discontinuities and analyze the local behavior of the function at each discontinuity.

In particular, if a discontinuity is removable, give the coordinates of the "hole" in the graph. If the graph has a vertical asymptote, describe the behavior on each side of the vertical asymptote. Sketch a graph of the function in a viewing window that includes all the discontinuities.

25. $f(x) = \dfrac{x^2 - 6x + 5}{x^2 - 5x + 6}$

26. $f(x) = \dfrac{x^2 + 2x - 3}{x^3 + 27}$

27. $f(x) = \dfrac{x^2 - 3x + 4}{x^2 + 2x - 3}$

28. $f(x) = \dfrac{x^3 - 4x + 7}{2x^2 - 5x + 1}$

29. $f(x) = \dfrac{x^2 + 3x + 2}{2x^2 + 3x - 2}$

30. $f(x) = \dfrac{7 + 4x - 2x^2}{3x^2 + 2x + 1}$

31. $f(x) = \dfrac{x^2 - 9}{x^2 - 6x + 9}$

32. $f(x) = \dfrac{4x^3 + 2x - 5}{8 - 9x^3}$

33. $f(x) = \dfrac{2x^3 - x^2 - 12x - 9}{16x^2 - 48x - 32}$

34. $f(x) = \dfrac{1}{x - 2} + \dfrac{x - 1}{2 - x}$

35. $f(x) = \dfrac{x^3 - 5x + 8}{24x + 48}$

36. $f(x) = \dfrac{x^3 + 10x^2 + 16x + 7}{5x + 5}$

37. $f(x) = \dfrac{x^4 - 12x^2 + x - 2}{30x - 90}$

38. $f(x) = \dfrac{x^3 - 8}{x^2 - 4}$

39. $f(x) = \dfrac{x^2 - x + 1}{5x - 5}$

40. $f(x) = \dfrac{2x^2 - 5x + 2}{5x^2 - 7x - 6}$

2.4 CONTINUITY AND ITS CONSEQUENCES

A function f is continuous at $x = a$ provided that

$$\lim_{x \to a} f(x) = f(a).$$

This definition of continuity rules out many "bad" function behaviors, including "holes," jump discontinuities, vertical asymptotes, wild oscillations, and other behaviors that do not fall into these categories.

Table 2.8 summarizes the limit and continuity information for several functions, each of which has a discontinuity at the point $x = 0$. These examples of discontinuous functions are good ones to keep in mind when thinking about the properties that continuous functions must have.

function $f(x)$	output $f(0)$	left-hand limit $\lim_{x \to 0^-} f(x)$	right-hand limit $\lim_{x \to 0^+} f(x)$	limit $\lim_{x \to 0} f(x)$	Is the discontinuity removable ?
x/x	undefined	1	1	1	yes
$\sin(x)/x$	undefined	1	1	1	yes
$\lvert x \rvert/x$	undefined	-1	1	does not exist	no
$1/x$	undefined	$-\infty$ (does not exist)	∞ (does not exist)	does not exist	no
$1/x^2$	undefined	∞ (does not exist)	∞ (does not exist)	∞ (does not exist)	no
$\sin(1/x)$	undefined	does not exist	does not exist	does not exist	no

Table 2.8 Examples of functions with discontinuities at $x = 0$.

Which functions are continuous?

If we know that a function f is continuous at $x = a$, then it's easy to compute its limit by simply evaluating the function:

$$\lim_{x \to a} f(x) = f(a).$$

Many of the functions in our dictionary enjoy the property of continuity at every input in their domains.

Every polynomial function p is continuous at every real number. In other words, for any real number a, it is true that

$$\lim_{x \to a} p(x) = p(a).$$

EXAMPLE 19 Find $\lim_{x \to -0.5} 8x^3 - 4x^2 + \sqrt{3}x - \pi$.

Solution Since $8x^3 - 4x^2 + \sqrt{3}x - \pi$ is a polynomial, we evaluate this limit by simply evaluating the polynomial at $x = -0.5$:

$$\lim_{x \to -0.5} 8x^3 - 4x^2 + \sqrt{3}x - \pi = 8(-0.5)^3 - 4(-0.5)^2 + \sqrt{3}(-0.5) - \pi = -2 - \frac{\sqrt{3}}{2} - \pi. \blacksquare$$

Similarly, a rational function f is continuous wherever it is defined. In other words, if

$$f(x) = \frac{p(x)}{q(x)},$$

where $p(x)$ and $q(x)$ are polynomials, then

$$\lim_{x \to a} \frac{p(x)}{q(x)} = \frac{p(a)}{q(a)} \qquad \text{provided } q(a) \neq 0.$$

A rational power function also is continuous at every point a in its domain, unless a happens to be the *endpoint* of the domain.

EXAMPLE 20 Where are each of the following rational power functions continuous?

$$f(x) = x^{2/3} \qquad g(x) = x^{1/2} \qquad h(x) = x^{-3} \qquad k(x) = x^{-2}$$

Solution The graphs of these four functions are shown in Figure 2.12. The function f is continuous at every real number including $x = 0$ where the cusp in the graph occurs.

The function g is continuous at every $x > 0$, but not at $x = 0$ (we cannot approach 0 from the left, so the limit does not exist there). We can only say that g is continuous from the right at 0.

The functions h and k are continuous at every $x \neq 0$. Neither function is defined at 0 (nor do their limits exist at 0.) ■

The *exponential, logarithmic, trigonometric, and inverse trigonometric functions* also are continuous at each point in their respective domains.

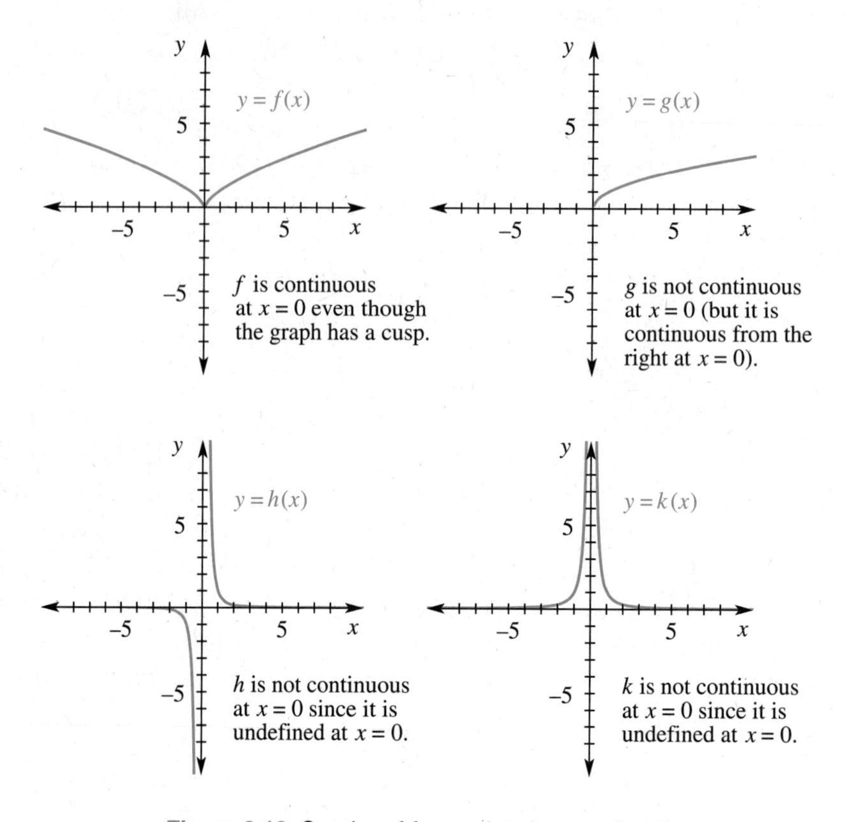

Figure 2.12 Graphs of four rational power functions.

EXAMPLE 21 Find the set of values at which the function f is continuous, if $f(x) = \tan x$.

Solution The set of values at which the f is continuous is

$$\{x : x \neq \frac{\pi}{2} + n\pi,\ n \text{ an integer}\},$$

the domain of the tangent function. ■

EXAMPLE 22 Find the set of values at which the function g is continuous, if $g(x) = \ln x$.

Solution The set of values at which the g is continuous is

$$\{x : x > 0, \},$$

the domain of the natural logarithmic function. ■

Consequences of continuity

Definition 2

A function f is **continuous on an open interval** (a, b), provided that f is continuous at every point of the interval. A function f is **continuous on a closed and bounded interval** $[a, b]$, provided that f is continuous at every point in the open interval (a, b) and continuous from the right at a and continuous from the left at b.

Intuitively, a function is continuous over an interval if its graph is "unbroken" over that entire interval. The idea of a continuous function having an unbroken graph seems simple and natural enough, but the property of continuity turns out to be crucial in the analysis of functions. Here, we want to point out some of the more profound consequences of continuity and illustrate graphically the reasoning behind them. The mathematical proofs of these statements require using the formal definitions of limit and continuity (see Section 2.6) along with fundamental properties of the real numbers. These proofs can be found in most books on real analysis.

Two important properties of a function that is continuous on a closed and bounded interval are stated as theorems.

Theorem 2.1

The Intermediate Value Theorem

Hypothesis: Suppose that f is continuous on the closed interval $[a, b]$.

Conclusion: For every real value y_0 between $f(a)$ and $f(b)$ inclusive, there is at least one input $a \le x_0 \le b$ such that $f(x_0) = y_0$.

□

Theorem 2.2

The Extreme Value Theorem

Hypothesis: Suppose that f is continuous on the closed interval $[a, b]$.

Conclusion: The function f produces definite minimum and maximum output values over the interval $[a, b]$. That is, there are inputs x_1 and x_2 between a and b inclusive such that for *any* input $a \le x \le b$ we have $f(x_1) \le f(x) \le f(x_2)$.

□

IVT: For each y_0 between $f(a)$ and $f(b)$ there exists x_0 between a and b such that $f(x_0) = y_0$.

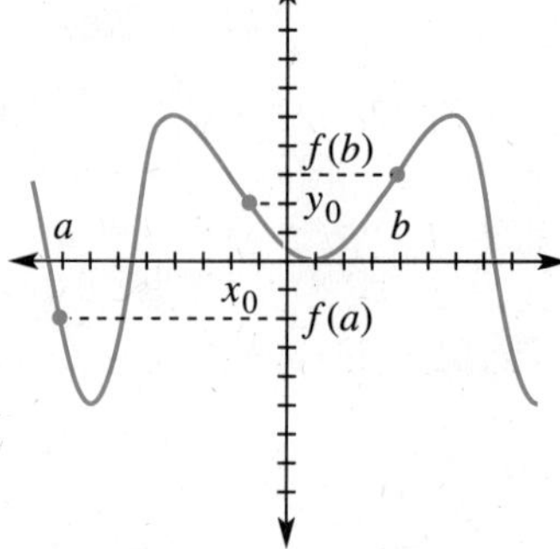

Figure 2.13 Illustration of the Intermediate Value Theorem.

EVT: There exists x_1 and x_2 between a and b such that for every x between a and b $f(x)$ is between $y_1 = f(x_1)$ and $y_2 = f(x_2)$.

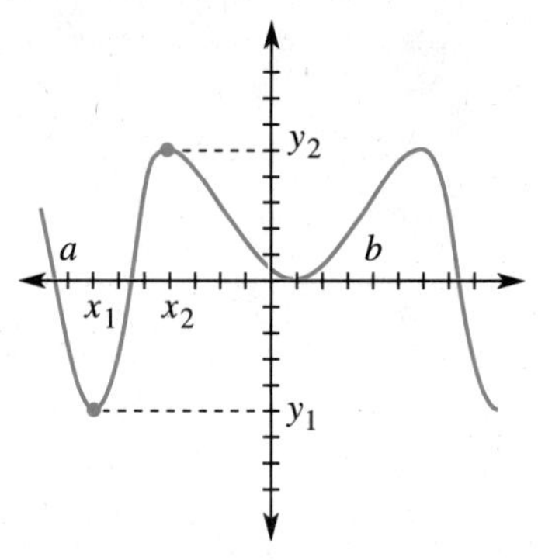

Figure 2.14 Illustration of the Extreme Value Theorem.

The hypothesis of a theorem states the requirements needed to guarantee the conclusion. The hypotheses of these two theorems are the same: we have a function f continuous on a closed interval $[a, b]$. If we reason graphically, this suggests that the graph of f must connect the points $(a, f(a))$ and $(b, f(b))$ with no holes, jumps, vertical asymptotes, or any other kinds of graphical breaks along the way. The conclusion of the intermediate value theorem is simply that such a graph must cross every horizontal line $y = y_0$ between $y = f(a)$ and $y = f(b)$ at least once (see Figure 2.13). The conclusion of the extreme value theorem is that we can find definite high and low extreme y-values on our graph between a and b (see Figure 2.14).

A *corollary* to a theorem is a proposition that builds on the theorem by adding some additional hypotheses or special cases of the hypotheses to make a special conclusion. For example, the following theorem is actually a corollary to the intermediate value theorem.

Theorem 2.3

Intermediate Zero Theorem

Hypothesis 1: f is continuous on the closed interval $[a, b]$.

Hypothesis 2: $f(a)$ and $f(b)$ have *opposite signs*.

Conclusion: f has at least one *zero* strictly between a and b.

Reasoning A *zero* of a function f is any input x_0 such that $f(x_0) = 0$. Since f satisfies the hypothesis of the intermediate value theorem and 0 is between $f(a)$ and $f(b)$, there must be at least one input $a \leq x_0 \leq b$ such that $f(x_0) = 0$. Since neither a nor b is a zero for f, we must have $a < x_0 < b$. □

The intermediate zero theorem is also known as the *location principle* or *Bolzano's theorem*, in honor of the mathematician Bernard Bolzano (1781-1848).

Roots of continuous functions—the bisection method

An equation involving a single (real number) unknown x can be expressed in the form $f(x) = 0$, where f is a real-valued function of x. In other words, finding the solution to such an equation is often equivalent to finding the *roots* or *zeroes* of a certain function f.

There are some numerical methods that can help us find approximate solutions to these equations in many cases. The **bisection method** is a procedure for finding or approximating a zero or root of a continuous function f. The idea behind the method is simple, and it relies on the observation we recorded as the intermediate zero theorem.

If f is continuous on the interval $[a, b]$, and if $f(a)$ and $f(b)$ have different signs (one is positive and the other is negative), then there must be at least one solution $x = r$ to the equation

$$f(x) = 0$$

such that $a < r < b$.

We outline the bisection method below:

Step 1. Express the equation in the form $f(x) = 0$, if it is not already in that form.

Step 2. Find two values $x = a$ and $x = b$ such that the function f is continuous on $[a, b]$ and $f(a)$ and $f(b)$ have different signs. (By the intermediate zero theorem, the equation must have at least one solution between a and b.)

Step 3. Choose the point x_1 *halfway between* a and b. We can compute the value of x_1 by simply averaging the endpoints: $x_1 = (a + b)/2$.

Step 4. Now, if $f(x_1) = 0$, then we've found a solution to our equation. If $f(x_1) \neq 0$, then $f(x_1)$ must be either positive or negative. This means that $f(x)$ changes sign over *one* of the two new intervals formed: $[a, x_1]$ and $[x_1, b]$.

Step 5. Repeat steps 3 and 4 to choose x_2 to be the midpoint of the new "half" interval over which f changes sign. If $f(x_2) = 0$, we're done. If $f(x_2) \neq 0$, we continue to repeat the procedure again to find $x_3, x_4, x_5, x_6, \ldots$.

The bisection method repeatedly bisects the interval of interest until we find an exact root x_n—that is, when we find

$$f(x_n) = 0.$$

However, it's conceivable that the bisection process could go on indefinitely without ever "hitting" an exact root. But we do have a firm way of telling how close to an exact root we must be at each step. By the nature of the bisection process, the length of the interval of possibilities is cut in half at each step. Since the original interval $[a, b]$ has a length $b - a$, this means that our nth choice x_n will be within $(b - a)/2^n$ of an actual root r. In other words, we can say that

$$x_n - \frac{b-a}{2^n} \leq r \leq x_n + \frac{b-a}{2^n}.$$

This gives us an effective way of predetermining the number of steps required to get within a given precision of an actual root.

EXAMPLE 23 Show that $x^3 + x - 3 = 0$ has at least one solution in the interval $[0, 2]$. Use the bisection method to find the first six approximations $x_1, x_2, \ldots, x_6$ to a solution, and find the largest possible error in the sixth approximation.

Solution Let $f(x) = x^3 + x - 3$ be a polynomial function. We know it is continuous, and, since

$$f(0) = 0^3 + 0 - 3 = -3 \quad \text{and} \quad f(2) = 2^3 + 2 - 3 = 7,$$

f has at least one zero in the interval $[0, 2]$.

We try $x_1 = 1$ (the midpoint of $[0, 2]$) as a possible root:

$$f(x_1) = f(1) = 1^3 + 1 - 3 = -1.$$

Of the two intervals $[0, 1]$ and $[1, 2]$, f changes sign on $[1, 2]$, so we next try $x_2 = 3/2$. (Note that we compute the midpoint of an interval by averaging the endpoints: $3/2 = (1 + 2)/2$.)

$$f(x_2) = f(1.5) = (1.5)^3 + 1.5 - 3 = 1.875$$

Now f changes sign on $[1, 1.5]$, so we try

$$x_3 = \frac{1 + 1.5}{2} = 1.25$$

and we get

$$f(x_3) = f(1.25) \approx 0.2.$$

Since $f(1)$ is negative and $f(1.25)$ is positive, we next try

$$x_4 = \frac{1 + 1.25}{2} = 1.125$$

and we get

$$f(x_4) = f(1.125) \approx -0.46.$$

This indicates that the next try should be

$$x_5 = \frac{1.125 + 1.25}{2} = 1.1875$$

and we get

$$f(x_5) = f(1.1875) \approx -0.14.$$

Using $x_6 = \dfrac{1.1875 + 1.25}{2} = 1.21875$, we have

$$f(x_6) = f(1.21875) \approx .03.$$

Now, an actual root must be between 1.21875 and 1.1875, so x_6 is no further away than

$$1.21875 - 1.1875 = .03125.$$

Note that we can tell in advance the precision of x_6 before we start the bisection method. Starting with x_1 as the midpoint of an interval $[a, b]$,

$$\text{the largest possible error in } x_n \text{ is } \frac{b - a}{2^n}.$$

In this case $a = 0$, $b = 2$, and $n = 6$, so

$$\frac{b-a}{2^n} = \frac{2-0}{2^6} = \frac{1}{32} = .03125$$

is the largest possible error in x_6 as an approximation to the solution of $x^3 + x - 3 = 0$. ■

EXAMPLE 24 Find a root, with an error of at most 0.001, of the equation $\sin(x) = 0.3$ by the bisection method.

Solution We define $f(x) = \sin(x) - 0.3$ and look for an interval over which $f(x)$ changes sign. By trial and error, we find $f(0) = -0.3 < 0$ and $f(1) \approx 0.54147 > 0$. Since f is continuous on $[0, 1]$ we have the conditions to apply the bisection method.

The midpoint is $x_1 = 0.5$ and $f(0.5) \approx 0.17943 > 0$, so our new interval is $[0, 0.5]$ and our error is at most 0.5. The next midpoint is $x_2 = 0.25$ and $f(0.25) \approx -0.052596 < 0$, so that the next interval is $[0.25, 0.5]$ and the error is at most 0.25.

Continuing in this way, we can collect our results in Table 2.9. The length of the final interval shown is less than 0.001, so either endpoint (or the midpoint, for that matter) provides an estimate of the root accurate to within 0.001. ■

left endpoint	midpoint	right endpoint	maximum error
$f(0.0) < 0$	$f(0.25) < 0$	$f(0.5) > 0$	0.5
$f(0.25) < 0$	$f(0.375) > 0$	$f(0.5) > 0$	0.25
$f(0.25) < 0$	$f(0.3125) > 0$	$f(0.375) > 0$	0.125
$f(0.25) < 0$	$f(0.28125) < 0$	$f(0.3125) > 0$	0.0625
$f(0.28125) < 0$	$f(0.296875) < 0$	$f(0.3125) > 0$	0.03125
$f(0.296875) < 0$	$f(0.3046875) < 0$	$f(0.3125) > 0$	0.015625
$f(0.3046875) < 0$	$f(0.3046875) < 0$	$f(0.3125) > 0$	0.0078125
$f(0.3046875) < 0$	$f(0.3046875) < 0$	$f(0.30859375) > 0$	0.00390625
$f(0.3046875) < 0$	$f(0.3046875) < 0$	$f(0.30859375) > 0$	0.001953125
$f(0.3046875) < 0$	$f(0.3046875) < 0$	$f(0.306640625) > 0$	0.0009765625

Table 2.9 Bisecting intervals in search of a solution to $\sin(x) - 0.3 = 0$.

The graphical estimation of roots discussed in Chapter 0 is essentially a visual version of the bisection method. First, we obtain a viewing window in which the graph crosses the x-axis. Then we repeatedly zoom in, all the while keeping the x-intercept in the viewing window. One measure of our accuracy at any step is simply the width of the window. (However, keep in mind that machine graphics are based on numerical computations of finite precision.)

What does it mean to solve an equation?

When working with equations, you may be used to thinking in terms of exact solutions. That is, to really solve an equation such as

$$f(x) = 0,$$

one must find the precise real values x making $f(x)$ exactly equal to 0.

However, if f is a function modeling some physical process, then it may well be based on physical measurements, all of which have some bounds on their accuracy. If an equation $f(x) = 0$ is derived from a function model based on incomplete or inaccurate data, then an exact solution to this equation may well represent an imprecise solution to the "true" equation. The point we are making is that in many real life applications, what we seek is not so much an exact solution but a sufficiently accurate solution for our purposes.

Furthermore, even if we had an equation based on complete and perfectly accurate data, we would be fortunate indeed if it could be solved exactly. For example, take a simple polynomial equation of the form

$$p(x) = 0.$$

If $p(x)$ happens to be linear (degree 1) or quadratic (degree 2), we're in luck, because we have a definite procedure for solving for x:

To solve $mx + b = 0$, with $m \neq 0$, take $x = -b/m$.

To solve $ax^2 + bx + c = 0$, with $a \neq 0$, take $x = \dfrac{-b \pm \sqrt{b^2 - 4ac}}{2a}$.

However, if $p(x)$ is a cubic polynomial (degree 3), we generally must hope that we can find its factors in order to find its exact roots. Artificially nice textbook examples may condition you to think that this is not so hard, but arbitrarily chosen cubic polynomials do not generally lend themselves to factorization "on sight."

There actually is a general, but relatively complicated, method for exactly solving cubic polynomial equations (as given by *Cardan's formulas*, named after Girolamo Cardan [1501–1576]) and an even more complicated method for quartic (fourth-degree) equations. These methods have been programmed into some computer algebra systems. One might think that we need only program the exact solution procedure for each degree polynomial equation for the machine to produce the exact solutions.

Alas, it has been shown that it is *mathematically impossible* to derive a general solution procedure like that of the quadratic formula or Cardan's formulas for polynomials of degree 5 and higher! (That does not mean it is impossible to solve *any* such equations; it just means that there is no general formula producing the solution to *every* fifth degree polynomial equation.)

Given the difficulty of solving polynomial equations exactly, imagine the challenge of exactly solving complicated equations involving trigonometric, exponential, and logarithmic functions. Even when it is possible to express the solution to such equations in terms of an exact formula, the evaluation of the result will almost certainly involve computing an approximation! Thus, numerical techniques such as the bisection method are exceedingly important tools for approximating solutions of real-world equations.

EXERCISES for Section 2.4

For exercises 1–6: Each function below has a split evaluation formula containing a parameter, A. In each exercise find a value for A that makes the function continuous at every value x.

1. $g(x) = \begin{cases} |x + A| \text{ if } x \leq 1 \\ 2x^2 \text{ if } x \geq 1 \end{cases}$

2. $h(x) = \begin{cases} 2x^2 + x - A \text{ if } x \leq 0 \\ x^3 + A \text{ if } x > 0 \end{cases}$

3. $i(x) = \begin{cases} A \text{ if } x \leq 0 \\ \arctan(1/x) \text{ if } x > 0 \end{cases}$

4. $j(x) = \begin{cases} (x + A)^2 \text{ if } x \leq 0 \\ (x - 2A)^4 \text{ if } x > 0 \end{cases}$

5. $k(x) = \begin{cases} Ax + 2 \text{ if } x \leq 3 \\ 1 - x \text{ if } x > 3 \end{cases}$

6. $s(x) = \begin{cases} A\dfrac{(x-2)^2(x-1)}{(x-1)(x-3)} \text{ if } x < 1 \\ 2x - 5 \text{ if } x \geq 1 \end{cases}$

---

7. Suppose that $f(x) = 1/x$. Then $f(-1) = -1$ and $f(1) = 1$, but there is no value $-1 < x_0 < 1$ such that $f(x_0) = 0$. Why isn't this a contradiction to the intermediate zero theorem?

8. Suppose that $f(x) = 1/x$. Then f is continuous on the closed interval $[1, \infty)$, but f has no definite minimum value on this interval. Why isn't this a contradiction to the extreme value theorem?

9. Suppose that $f(x) = 1/x$. Then f is continuous on the bounded interval $(0, 1]$, but f has no definite maximum value on this interval. Why isn't this a contradiction to the extreme value theorem?

A natural question to ask regarding a theorem is: to what extent can the hypothesis and conclusion be interchanged? This is called the **converse** of the original theorem.

10. Draw the graph of a function f such that $f(-2) = -1$, $f(2) = 1$, and for each value $-1 \leq y_0 \leq 1$ there is some value $-2 \leq x_0 \leq 2$ such that $f(x_0) = y_0$, but f is not continuous on the interval $[-2, 2]$. This shows that the converse of the intermediate value theorem does not hold.

11. Draw the graph of a function g such that g takes on definite extreme high and low values over the interval $[-2, 2]$, but g is not continuous over this interval. This shows that the converse of the extreme value theorem does not hold.

12. Suppose that you start to hike up a mountain path at 8 A.M., and reach the summit at 5 P.M. that afternoon. After camping for the night, you set out the next morning at 8 A.M.. and head back down the mountain along the same path. Suppose that you reach your original starting point at 5 P.M. Is there any place on the mountain path that you pass at exactly the same time of day going down as you did going up?

For exercises 13–22: Verify that the equation must have a root between the two values a and b. Then, using the midpoint of $[a, b]$ as a first approximation x_1, find three successive approximations x_2, x_3, and x_4 by the bisection method. Finally, determine how many total steps are required to guarantee an approximation within .01 of a root.

13. $x^2 = 3.2; \quad a = 1,\ b = 2$

14. $x^3 - 23 = 0; \quad a = 2,\ b = 3$

15. $\sin(x) = 0.7; \quad a = 0.7,\ b = 0.8$

16. $x^5 + 3.6x^4 - 2.51x^3 - 22.986x^2 - 28.24x = 10.4; \quad a = 2,\ b = 3$

17. $x + \sqrt{x} + \sqrt{x^3} = 7; \quad a = 1.8,\ b = 2.6$

18. $xe^{x^2} = \sqrt{x^2 + 1}; \quad a = 0.4,\ b = 1.$

19. $\ln(x^2 + \ln x) = 0; \quad a = 0.725,\ b = 1.25$

20. $x^3 - \sqrt{x^2 + 1} + x = 3; \quad a = 1.1,\ b = 1.6$

21. $3\cos(\cos(x)) = 2x; \quad a = 1.1,\ b = 2.2$

22. $\sqrt[4]{x} + x^3 = x + 0.5$; $a = 0.2$, $b = 1.2$

2.5 ANALYZING GLOBAL BEHAVIOR GRAPHICALLY

The global behavior of a function refers to the behavior of its outputs for negative and positive inputs of large magnitude (meaning $|x|$ is large). The language of limits is useful for discussing this global behavior.

If a function's outputs $f(x)$ stablize to a limit L_1 as we sample positive inputs of larger and larger magnitude, we write

$$\lim_{x\to\infty} f(x) = L_1.$$

We write $\lim_{x\to-\infty} f(x) = L_2$

if the outputs $f(x)$ approach L_2 for negative inputs x of larger and larger magnitude. For example, consider the function f such that

$$f(x) = \frac{1}{x}.$$

For large positive values x, the value of $1/x$ is a small positive number. For negative values x of large magnitude, $1/x$ is a negative number of small magnitude. We write

$$\lim_{x\to\infty} \frac{1}{x} = 0 \quad \text{and} \quad \lim_{x\to-\infty} \frac{1}{x} = 0.$$

In this case, the two limiting values are the same.

As another example, we note that

$$\lim_{x\to\infty} \arctan x = \frac{\pi}{2} \quad \text{and} \quad \lim_{x\to-\infty} \arctan x = -\frac{\pi}{2}.$$

Horizontal asymptotes

The limiting values

$$\lim_{x\to\infty} f(x) = L_1 \quad \text{and} \quad \lim_{x\to-\infty} f(x) = L_2$$

are represented graphically by the horizontal lines $y = L_1$ and $y = L_2$, which are the **horizontal asymptotes** of the graph of $y = f(x)$.

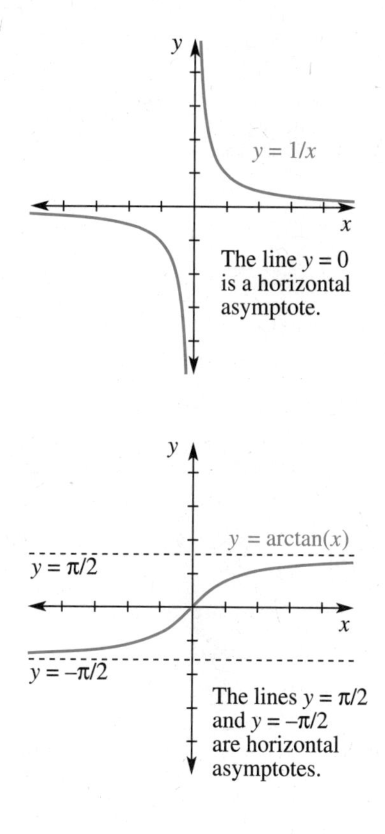

Figure 2.15 Asymptotes of the graphs of $y = 1/x$ and $y = \arctan x$.

Roughly speaking, a line is an asymptote of a curve if the farther the points on the curve are from the origin, the closer the points are to the line. For a vertical asymptote, the farther the point on the curve is vertically from the origin, the closer the point is to the vertical line. For a horizontal asymptote, the farther the point on the curve is horizontally from the origin, the closer the point is to the horizontal line.

For the graph of $y = 1/x$, the vertical line $x = 0$ (the y-axis) is a vertical asymptote, and the horizontal line $y = 0$ (the x-axis) is a horizontal asymptote. For the graph of $y = \arctan x$, the lines $y = \pi/2$ and $y = -\pi/2$ are horizontal asymptotes (and there are no vertical asymptotes). Figure 2.15 illustrates this behavior.

Analyzing the global behavior of rational functions

The global behavior of a rational function can be characterized either by a horizontal asymptote or by polynomial-like behavior. We'll illustrate this statement by means of examples, but first we make an important observation.

If n is any positive integer, then for *any* constant c we have

$$\lim_{x\to\infty} \frac{c}{x^n} = 0 = \lim_{x\to-\infty} \frac{c}{x^n}.$$

EXAMPLE 25 Analyze the global behavior of the rational function f, where

$$f(x) = \frac{-2x^2 - 3x + 5}{4x^3 + 6x^2 - 7}.$$

Solution We need to analyze the behavior of the outputs for inputs x of large magnitude. First, we factor out the largest common power of x occurring in the numerator and denominator:

$$f(x) = \frac{x^2}{x^2} \cdot \frac{-2 - \frac{3}{x} + \frac{5}{x^2}}{4x + 6 - \frac{7}{x^2}} = \frac{-2 - \frac{3}{x} + \frac{5}{x^2}}{4x + 6 - \frac{7}{x^2}} \quad \text{for } x \neq 0.$$

Now, every term in the numerator and denominator having the form c/x^n becomes small in magnitude as x grows large in magnitude. In other words, for $|x|$ large, we have

$$f(x) \approx \frac{-2}{4x + 6} = -\frac{1}{2x + 3},$$

and

$$\lim_{x\to\infty} f(x) = 0 = \lim_{x\to-\infty} f(x).$$

Hence, the graph of $y = f(x)$ has a horizontal asymptote $y = 0$ (see Figure 2.16). ■

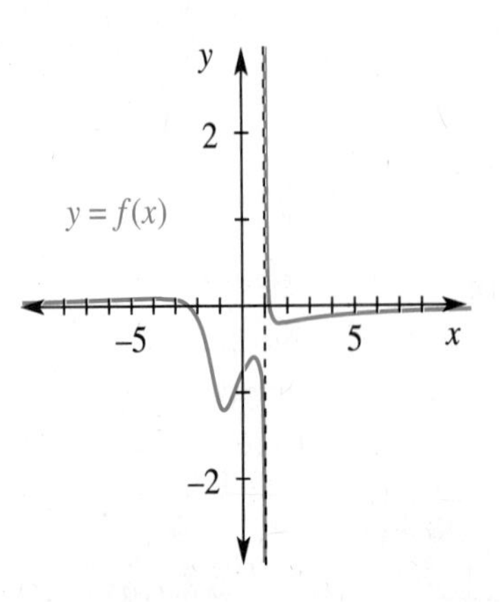

Figure 2.16 Graph of $y = f(x)$.

▶▶▶ **Beware of a common misconception. It *is possible* for the graph of a function to cross a horizontal asymptote, as is the case with $y = f(x)$.**

EXAMPLE 26 Analyze the global behavior of the rational function g, where

$$g(x) = \frac{-2x^3 - 3x + 5}{4x^2 + 6x - 7}.$$

Solution We need to analyze the behavior of the outputs for inputs x of large magnitude. First, we factor out the largest common power of x occurring in the numerator and denominator:

$$g(x) = \frac{x^2}{x^2} \cdot \frac{-2x - \frac{3}{x} + \frac{5}{x^2}}{4 + \frac{6}{x} - \frac{7}{x^2}} = \frac{-2x - \frac{3}{x} + \frac{5}{x^2}}{4 + \frac{6}{x} - \frac{7}{x^2}} \quad \text{for } x \neq 0.$$

For $|x|$ large, we have

$$g(x) \approx \frac{-2x}{4} = -\frac{x}{2}.$$

Thus, as $|x|$ grows, so does the magnitude of $g(x)$:

$$\lim_{x \to \infty} g(x) = -\infty \qquad \text{and} \qquad \lim_{x \to -\infty} g(x) = \infty.$$

The graph of $y = g(x)$ has no horizontal asymptotes.

Figure 2.17 shows the graphs of $y = g(x)$ at two different scalings. The second illustration also shows the line $y = -x/2$ so that you can see how well it approximates the graph of $y = g(x)$ for points farther from the origin. Such a line is sometimes called an **oblique asymptote**. ■

EXAMPLE 27 Analyze the global behavior of the rational function h, where

$$h(x) = \frac{-2x^3 - 3x + 5}{4x^3 + 6x^2 - 7}.$$

Solution We need to analyze the behavior of the outputs for inputs x of large magnitude. First, we factor out the largest common power of x occurring in the numerator and denominator:

$$h(x) = \frac{x^3}{x^3} \cdot \frac{-2 - \frac{3}{x^2} + \frac{5}{x^3}}{4 + \frac{6}{x} - \frac{7}{x^3}} = \frac{-2 - \frac{3}{x^2} + \frac{5}{x^3}}{4 + \frac{6}{x} - \frac{7}{x^3}} \quad \text{for } x \neq 0.$$

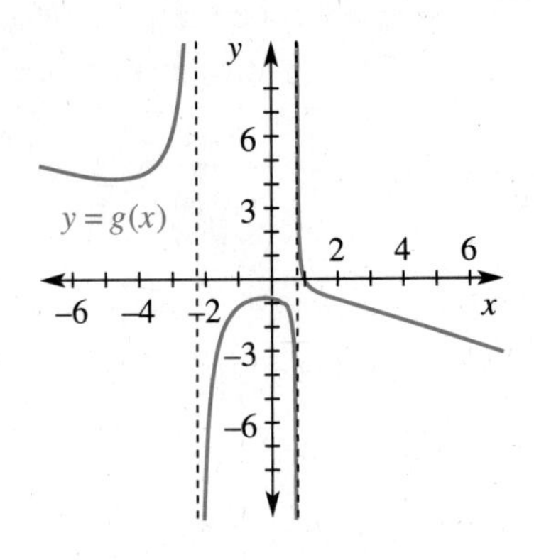

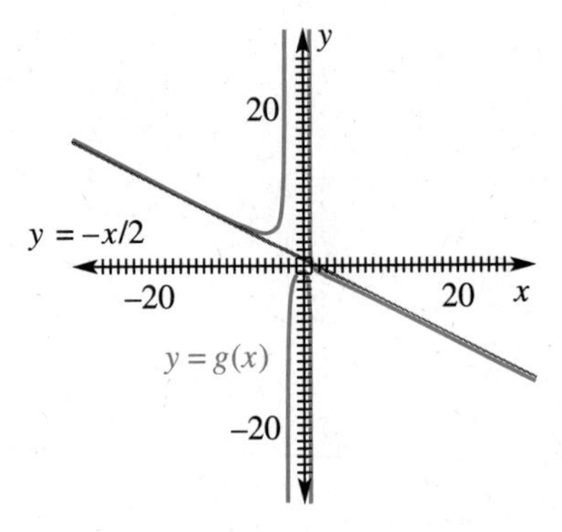

Figure 2.17 Two graphs of $y = g(x)$.

For $|x|$ large, we have $h(x) \approx \dfrac{-2}{4} = -\dfrac{1}{2}$, so

$$\lim_{x\to\infty} h(x) = -\frac{1}{2} = \lim_{x\to-\infty} h(x).$$

Hence, the graph of $y = h(x)$ has a horizontal asymptote $y = -1/2$ (see Figure 2.18). ■

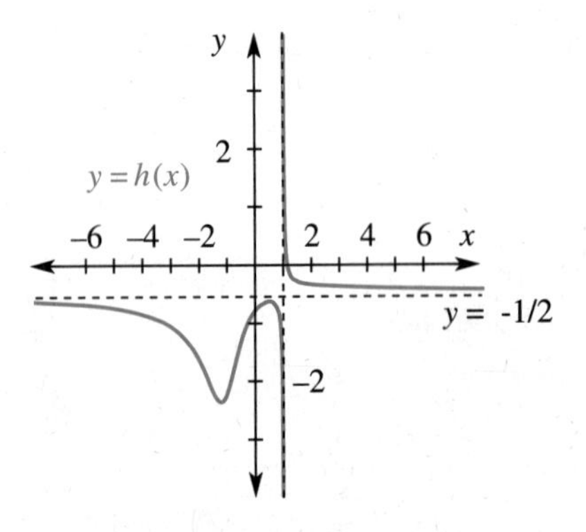

Figure 2.18 Graph of $y = h(x)$.

We can generalize the results of these three examples to analyze the global behavior of any rational function

$$f(x) = \frac{p(x)}{q(x)}.$$

Suppose the highest degree term of the numerator $p(x)$ is ax^n and the highest degree term of the denominator $q(x)$ is bx^m.

If $n < m$, then $y = 0$ is a horizontal asymptote of the graph of $y = \dfrac{p(x)}{q(x)}$.

If $n = m$, then $y = a/b$ is a horizontal asymptote of the graph of $y = \dfrac{p(x)}{q(x)}$.

If $n > m$, then there are no horizontal asymptotes of the graph of $y = f(x)$.

In this case,

$$\frac{p(x)}{q(x)} \approx \frac{ax^k}{b}$$

for large $|x|$, where $k = n - m$.

Using machine graphics to study global behavior

The global behavior of a rational function can be explored nicely with machine graphics. If the degree n of the numerator is less than or equal to the degree m of the denominator, then the graph of $y = \dfrac{p(x)}{q(x)}$ has some horizontal asymptote $y = c$. This also means that the graph of $y = \dfrac{p(x)}{q(x)}$ becomes indistinguishable from $y = c$ when we zoom out horizontally. In other words, if we set a horizontal x-range of $[-M, M]$ for M large enough, then the graph of $y = \dfrac{p(x)}{q(x)}$ has the appearance of a flat line.

If $n > m$, then for large $|x|$,

$$\frac{p(x)}{q(x)} \approx cx^k,$$

where $k = n - m$ is the difference of the degrees and where $c = a/b$ is the ratio of the leading coefficients a and b of $p(x)$ and $q(x)$, respectively. This means that for suitably large scalings, the graph of $y = \dfrac{p(x)}{q(x)}$ will look very much like the graph of the power function $y = cx^k$. What are these suitable scalings? If we set the horizontal x-range to $[-M, M]$ and the vertical y-range to $[-M^k, M^k]$ for M large enough, then the two graphs should be indistinguishable.

For example, consider the rational function $f(x) = \dfrac{2x^5 - 3x + 5}{4x^2 + 6x - 7}$. For $|x|$ large, we have

$$f(x) = \frac{2x^5 - 3x + 5}{4x^2 + 6x - 7} \approx \frac{x^3}{2}.$$

Figure 2.19 shows the graph of $y = f(x)$ at two different scalings. In the first plot, the graph is shown with an x-range and y-range of $[-3, 3]$. We can see the local behavior of $y = f(x)$ near two vertical asymptotes.

In the second plot, the graph is shown with an x-range of $[-100, 100]$ and a y-range of $[-1000000,\ 1000000]$ (note that $1000000 = (100)^3$). At this scaling, we can appreciate the similarity in the global behavior of $y = f(x)$ and $y = x^3/2$ (also shown), but the local behavior near the vertical asymptotes of $y = f(x)$ cannot be discerned.

Global behavior and machine precision

Numerically, we can investigate $\lim_{x\to\infty} f(x)$ or $\lim_{x\to-\infty} f(x)$ by sampling $f(x)$ for sequences of positive and negative inputs x of large magnitude.

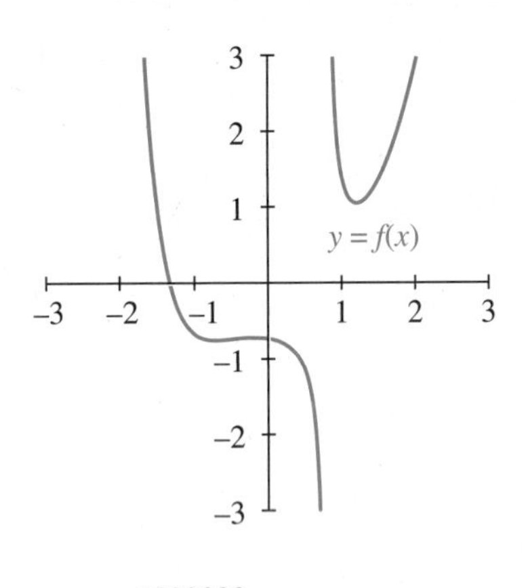

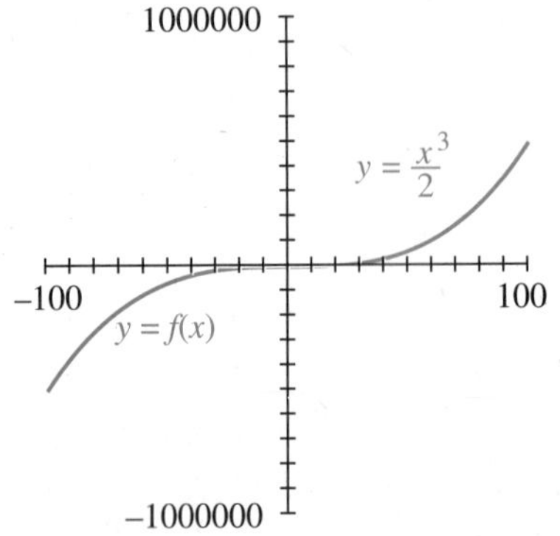

Figure 2.19 Graphs of $y = \dfrac{2x^5 - 3x + 5}{4x^2 + 6x - 7}$ at two different scalings.

EXAMPLE 28 Numerically investigate $\lim_{x\to\infty} f(x)$, where $f(x) = \left(1 + \frac{1}{x}\right)^x$.

Solution If we sample $f(x)$ for $x = 10$, $x = 100$, $x = 1000$, ..., $x = 1000000 = 10^6$, we obtain the results shown in Table 2.10. These outputs appear to be stabilizing, which suggests that the limit exists. In fact, the limit does exist, and

$$\lim_{x\to\infty} \left(1 + \frac{1}{x}\right)^x = e \approx 2.171828.$$

■

x	$(1 + \frac{1}{x})^x$
10	2.59374246010
100	2.70481382942
1000	2.71692393224
10000	2.71814592683
100000	2.71826823717
1000000	2.71828046932

Table 2.10 Sampling $(1 + (1/x))^x$ for large x.

However, recall that there are limitations on the magnitude of numbers we can represent with a machine. The precision limitations of a machine may make computations with large numbers inaccurate. Let's use the previous example to illustrate.

Suppose that we compute our sample outputs with a machine having 12 digits of precision. Table 2.11 shows the results as we continue to sample $f(x)$ for $x = 10^7$, $x = 10^8$, ..., $x = 10^{12}$. Note that this machine computes $f(10^{12}) = 1$. If we continue sampling for inputs $x = 10^n$ where $n > 12$, this machine computes $f(10^n) = 1$ each time. If we had started our sampling with such large values x, we might have concluded that the limiting value is 1, rather than the correct limiting value e. Why does the machine behave this way?

x	$(1 + \frac{1}{x})^x$
10^7	2.71828169254
10^8	2.71828181487
10^9	2.71828182710
10^{10}	2.71828182832
10^{11}	2.71828182845
10^{12}	1

Table 2.11 Sampling $(1 + (1/x))^x$ with 12-digit precision.

If we examine the computations involved, we see that

$$f(10^{12}) = (1.000000000001)^{1000000000000}.$$

The exponent requires only 1 digit of precision, but the base requires 13 digits of precision! This means that our machine must round the base to 12 digits, resulting in the computation

$$1^{1000000000000} = 1.$$

Thus, by sampling for inputs too large, we exceed the limitations of the machine's precision.

EXERCISES for Section 2.5

For exercises 1–14: Find $\lim_{x\to-\infty} f(x)$ and $\lim_{x\to\infty} f(x)$ for each function f described.

1. $f(x) = \cos(1/x)$
2. $f(x) = \sin(1/x)$
3. $f(x) = 2 + \ln(1 + 1/x)$
4. $f(x) = \text{arccot}(x)$
5. $f(x) = \text{arccsc}(x)$
6. $f(x) = \text{arcsec}(x)$
7. $f(x) = 2^x$
8. $f(x) = \log_{10}(x)$
9. $f(x) = (1 - 1/x)^x$
10. $f(x) = \sin(x)/x$
11. $f(x) = \tanh(x)$
12. $f(x) = \coth(x)$
13. $f(x) = 3^{-x}$
14. $f(x) = 4^{1/x}$

For exercises 15–30: Analyze the global behavior of each rational function f described.

If the graph has a horizontal asymptote, give its equation $y = c$. Give the horizontal x-range and vertical y-range for a viewing window in which the graph of $y = f(x)$ is indistinguishable from the graph of $y = c$.

If the graph has no horizontal asymptote, find cx^k such that $f(x) \approx cx^k$ for $|x|$ large. Give the horizontal x-range and vertical y-range for a viewing window in which the graph of $y = f(x)$ is indistinguishable from the graph of $y = cx^k$.

15. $f(x) = \dfrac{x^2 - 6x + 5}{x^2 - 5x + 6}$
16. $f(x) = \dfrac{x^2 + 2x - 3}{x^3 + 27}$
17. $f(x) = \dfrac{x^2 - 3x + 4}{x^2 + 2x - 3}$
18. $f(x) = \dfrac{x^3 - 4x + 7}{2x^2 - 5x + 1}$
19. $f(x) = \dfrac{x^2 + 3x + 2}{2x^2 + 3x - 2}$
20. $f(x) = \dfrac{7 + 4x - 2x^2}{3x^2 + 2x + 1}$
21. $f(x) = \dfrac{x^2 - 9}{x^2 - 6x + 9}$
22. $f(x) = \dfrac{4x^3 + 2x - 5}{8 - 9x^3}$
23. $f(x) = \dfrac{2x^3 - x^2 - 12x - 9}{16x^2 - 48x - 32}$
24. $f(x) = \dfrac{1}{x - 2} + \dfrac{x - 1}{2 - x}$
25. $f(x) = \dfrac{x^3 - 5x + 8}{24x + 48}$
26. $f(x) = \dfrac{x^3 + 10x^2 + 16x + 7}{5x + 5}$

27. $f(x) = \dfrac{x^4 - 12x^2 + x - 2}{30x - 90}$

28. $f(x) = \dfrac{x^3 - 8}{x^2 - 4}$

29. $f(x) = \dfrac{x^2 - x + 1}{5x - 5}$

30. $f(x) = \dfrac{2x^2 - 5x + 2}{5x^2 - 7x - 6}$

---

31. A "limit at infinity" can be investigated numerically or graphically by substituting $1/x$ for x and studying the equivalent one-sided limit at $x = 0$. We have

$$\lim_{x\to\infty} f(x) = \lim_{x\to 0+} f\left(\frac{1}{x}\right) \quad \text{and} \quad \lim_{x\to-\infty} f(x) = \lim_{x\to 0^-} f\left(\frac{1}{x}\right),$$

when they exist. Explain in your own words why these limits are equivalent.

32. For each function f in exercises 1-14, investigate the local behavior of $y = f(1/x)$ at $x = 0$. Compare your results with the global behavior of $y = f(x)$.

2.6 FORMAL DEFINITION OF LIMIT

If behavior of the function f we're analyzing is sufficiently simple, then we can often get a reasonable estimate of a limit value directly from the graph of $y = f(x)$ or by sampling the outputs $f(x)$ for appropriate inputs x. However, many functions can be very difficult or essentially impossible to graph accurately, even with sophisticated graphing calculators or computers. The numerical limitations of a machine effectively prevent us from sampling inputs x arbitrarily close to a given value a or of arbitrarily large magnitude. We really need a more precise definition of limit for these situations.

Mathematicians struggled for generations before coming up with a suitably precise definition of the concept of limit. That definition is presented below.

Definition 3

The real number L is the **limit** of $f(x)$ as x approaches a, written

$$\lim_{x \to a} f(x) = L,$$

if and only if the following condition holds: Given any $\epsilon > 0$, there is a $\delta > 0$ such that $|f(x) - L| < \epsilon$ whenever $0 < |x - a| < \delta$.

We'll interpret this definition both numerically in terms of error tolerances and graphically in terms of the scalings of a viewing window.

Error tolerances for inputs and outputs

Let's examine the "ϵ-δ" condition in the definition more closely. Think of the positive number ϵ (the Greek letter "epsilon") as a desired function *output error tolerance*. The statement $|f(x) - L| < \epsilon$ is just another way of saying that the function output $f(x)$ needs to be within ϵ of the number L:

$$L - \epsilon < f(x) < L + \epsilon.$$

Now, think of the positive number δ (the Greek delta) as the *input error tolerance* required to guarantee our desired output accuracy. The condition $0 < |x - a| < \delta$ means that x is within δ of a but $x \neq a$. Hence, if

$$a - \delta < x < a \quad \text{or} \quad a < x < a + \delta,$$

then we must be guaranteed that $L - \epsilon < f(x) < L + \epsilon$.

The formal limit definition says that this guarantee can always be made when the limit exists. In other words, given *any* positive output error tolerance ϵ, we can always find a corresponding positive input error tolerance δ that guarantees that degree of output accuracy. We can think of the definition as providing a universal error tolerance test that L must pass in order to be called the limit of $f(x)$ as x approaches a.

EXAMPLE 29 Given $\lim_{x \to 2} \dfrac{3x^2 - 3x - 6}{x - 2} = 9$, find a specific positive value δ for $\epsilon = .001$. That is, find a value $\delta > 0$ such that

$$\left|\frac{3x^2 - 3x - 6}{x - 2} - 9\right| < .001 \quad \text{whenever} \quad 0 < |x - 2| < \delta.$$

Solution Starting with the inequality

$$\left|\frac{3x^2 - 3x - 6}{x - 2} - 9\right| < .001,$$

we can rewrite the left-hand expression as

$$\left|\frac{3x^2-3x-6}{x-2}-\frac{9(x-2)}{x-2}\right| = \left|\frac{3x^2-3x-6-9(x-2)}{x-2}\right|$$

$$= \left|\frac{3x^2-12x+12}{x-2}\right|$$

$$= 3\left|\frac{(x-2)(x-2)}{x-2}\right|$$

$$= 3|x-2| \quad \text{for } x \neq 2.$$

This means that for $x \neq 2$, our desired inequality is equivalent to

$$3|x-2| < .001.$$

Hence, if we can just guarantee that

$$|x-2| < \frac{.001}{3},$$

the limit $L = 9$ passes the test. If we choose any value δ less than $(.001)/3$, such as $\delta = .0003$, as our input error tolerance, we will meet our output error tolerance requirement.

Written using inequalities, we have

$$8.999 < \frac{3x^2-3x-6}{x-2} < 9.001$$

whenever $$1.9997 < x < 2.0003, \quad x \neq 2.$$

Note that any smaller value of δ would also guarantee the same output error tolerance. ■

The ϵ's and δ's of scaling

Graphically, the formal requirements for

$$\lim_{x \to a} f(x) = L$$

correspond to the graph of $y = f(x)$ being forced to lie between the horizontal lines $y = L - \epsilon$ and $y = L + \epsilon$, provided the inputs x are between the vertical lines $x = a - \delta$ and $x = a + \delta$, with the possible exception of $x = a$ itself (see Figure 2.20).

We could restate the formal definition of limit in terms of the scaling of a viewing window for the graph. Suppose that we are given a value $\epsilon > 0$ as our output tolerance. First, we set the *vertical* y-range to $[L - \epsilon,\ L + \epsilon]$.

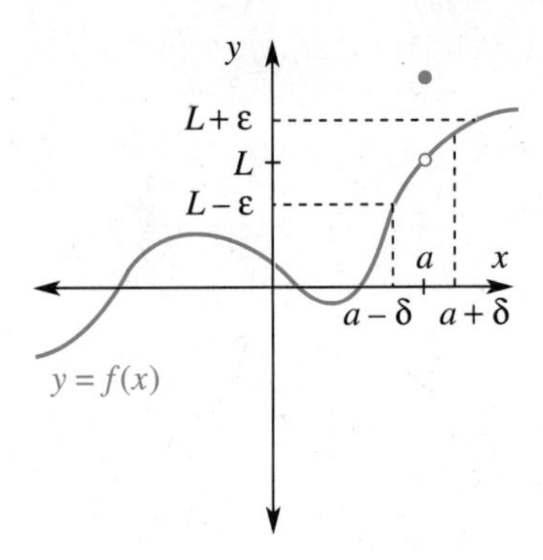

Figure 2.20 Graphical illustration of the limit definition.

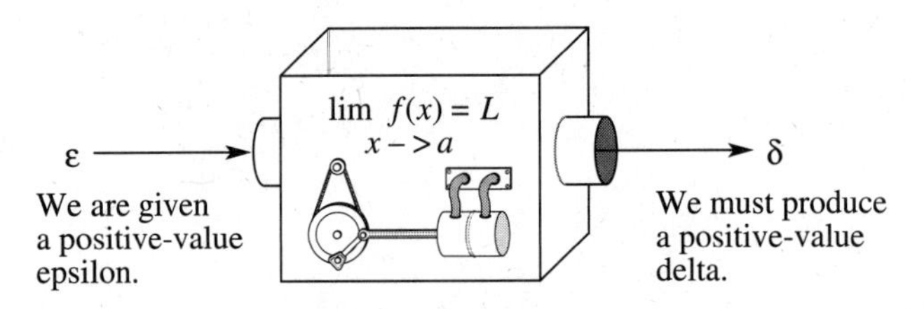

Figure 2.21 The ϵ-δ machine for limits.

Once this vertical scaling has been set, our challenge is to rescale the *horizontal* x-range to $[a-\delta,\ a+\delta]$ so that the graph of $y = f(x)$ enters from the left and leaves from the right, always staying in the viewing window (with the lone possible exception of $f(a)$ itself). We are not allowed to change the vertical scaling once it has been set; we must achieve this "well-behaved" graph through horizontal scaling only. If we are successful, then δ satisfies the requirement in the formal definition.

Limit proofs—the ϵ-δ machine

In the previous example, we found an appropriate value $\delta = .0003$ value for a specific value $\epsilon = .001$. To *prove* that

$$\lim_{x \to a} \frac{3x^2 - 3x - 6}{x - 2} = 9$$

requires demonstrating that such an appropriate δ-value exists for each possible given ϵ-value. There are infinitely many possible ϵ-values, so we cannot simply list a corresponding δ-value for each one. What we really need is to describe a *process* by which we can always produce the needed δ-value. In other words, we need an ϵ-δ machine taking the given ϵ and producing an appropriate δ (see Figure 2.21). Of course, in general, the δ-value also depends on the particular function f, the input target a, and the limit value L.

How does one write a so-called ϵ-δ limit proof? In general, one starts with the assumption that we already have some unspecified value $\epsilon > 0$. Then we must provide some means for producing or choosing $\delta > 0$ such that

$$|f(x) - L| < \epsilon \quad \text{whenever} \quad 0 < |x - a| < \delta.$$

A strategy for hunting down δ is to start with the inequality

$$|f(x) - L| < \epsilon$$

and use it to derive an inequality of the form

$$|x - a| < an\ expression\ in\ terms\ of\ \epsilon.$$

This expression describes exactly how to choose our δ for *any* ϵ.

EXAMPLE 30 Give an ϵ-δ proof that $\lim_{x \to 2} \frac{3x^2 - 3x - 6}{x - 2} = 9$.

Solution PROOF: Let $\epsilon > 0$ be given. We must find $\delta > 0$ such that

$$\left|\frac{3x^2 - 3x - 6}{x - 2} - 9\right| < \epsilon$$

whenever $0 < |x - a| < \delta$.

Now, we write the left-hand side of this inequality as

$$\begin{aligned} \left|\frac{3x^2 - 3x - 6}{x - 2} - 9\right| &= \left|\frac{3x^2 - 3x - 6 - 9(x - 2)}{x - 2}\right| \\ &= \left|\frac{3x^2 - 12x + 12}{x - 2}\right| \\ &= 3\left|\frac{(x - 2)(x - 2)}{x - 2}\right| \\ &= 3|x - 2| \qquad (\text{for } x \neq 2). \end{aligned}$$

To guarantee that $3|x - 2| < \epsilon$, we need $|x - 2| < \frac{\epsilon}{3}$. Thus, let $\delta = \frac{\epsilon}{3}$. Now, whenever

$$0 < |x - 2| < \delta = \frac{\epsilon}{3},$$

we have

$$\left|\frac{3x^2 - 3x - 6}{x - 2} - 9\right| < \epsilon.$$

(The formula $\delta = \epsilon/3$ serves as our ϵ-δ machine, and it provides a way of picking an appropriate δ for *any* given ϵ.) ∎

New limits from old

Once we know some particular limit values, we often can deduce other limit values directly. Suppose two functions f and g each have a limit at a particular point $x = a$, with

$$\lim_{x \to a} f(x) = L_1 \qquad \text{and} \qquad \lim_{x \to a} g(x) = L_2.$$

Going back to the definition of a limit, we know that for inputs x sufficiently close to a (but not equal to a), the values of $f(x)$ and $g(x)$ are guaranteed to be within any predetermined tolerance of the values L_1 and L_2, respectively. It seems natural to expect that we could guarantee that the value of $f(x) + g(x)$ will be close to $L_1 + L_2$, $f(x) - g(x)$ will be close to $L_1 - L_2$, $f(x)g(x)$ will be close to $L_1 L_2$, and $f(x)/g(x)$ will be close to L_1/L_2 (unless $L_2 = 0$). This indeed is the case, and we can formally state that

$$\lim_{x \to a} (f + g)(x) = L_1 + L_2,$$

$$\lim_{x \to a} (f - g)(x) = L_1 - L_2,$$

$$\lim_{x \to a} fg(x) = L_1 L_2,$$

$$\lim_{x \to a} \frac{f}{g}(x) = \frac{L_1}{L_2}, \quad \text{provided } L_2 \neq 0.$$

The key to these results is that the ϵ-δ machines for f and g can be used to make ϵ-δ machines for these new functions. For instance, given any positive output error tolerance $\epsilon > 0$, we could make sure that $f(x) + g(x)$ is within ϵ of $L_1 + L_2$ by choosing an input tolerance δ small enough so that as long as $0 < |x - a| < \delta$, *simultaneously* $f(x)$ is within $\epsilon/2$ of L_1 and $g(x)$ is within $\epsilon/2$ of L_2 . Since $L_1 + L_2$ passes the limit test, we conclude that

$$\lim_{x \to a} (f + g)(x) = L_1 + L_2.$$

The other three results can be shown in a similar way (though the choice of δ is trickier for the limits of $fg(x)$ and $(f/g)(x)$).

Formal definition of continuity

The formal definition of continuity is sometimes expressed using ϵ's and δ's directly instead of the limit requirement.

Definition 4 The function f is **continuous** at $x = a$ if and only if given any $\epsilon > 0$, there is a $\delta > 0$ such that $|f(x) - f(a)| < \epsilon$ whenever $|x - a| < \delta$.

Numerically, this means that the outputs $f(x)$ cannot be changing drastically near $x = a$. In other words, if x is close to a and f is continuous at a, then the output $f(x)$ must be relatively close to $f(a)$. Recall that if we are given any output error tolerance $\epsilon > 0$, we can always specify an input error tolerance $\delta > 0$ so that

$$f(a) - \epsilon < f(x) < f(a) + \epsilon \quad \text{whenever} \quad a - \delta < x < a + \delta.$$

Graphically, this means that for any vertical scaling of a viewing window centered at $(a, f(a))$, we can rescale the horizontal axis so that the graph of $y = f(x)$ enters the window from the left and leaves to the right, always staying within the window.

EXAMPLE 31 Prove that any constant function h (that is, $h(x) = c$ for all x, where c is a constant) is continuous at every real number $x = a$.

Solution We need to show that h is continuous at every point $x = a$. Using the definition, this means that for any real number a we must show

$$\lim_{x \to a} h(x) = h(a) = c.$$

PROOF: Let $\epsilon > 0$. Let $\delta = 1$ (or let δ be *any* positive number, for that matter). Then, whenever $|x - a| < \delta$, we have $|h(x) - c| = |c - c| = 0 < \epsilon$. ■

EXAMPLE 32 Prove that the identity function ($i(x) = x$ for all x) is continuous at every real number $x = a$.

Solution We need to show that if a is any real number, then

$$\lim_{x \to a} i(x) = i(a) = a.$$

PROOF: Let $\epsilon > 0$ be given. Let $\delta = \epsilon$. Then, whenever

$$|x - a| < \delta = \epsilon,$$

we have

$$|i(x) - a| = |x - a| < \epsilon.$$

■

Combining continuous functions

If f and g are continuous at a, they have limit values that match their outputs $f(a)$ and $g(a)$. This means that the limits of $f+g$, $f-g$, and fg will also match their output values at $x=a$, so these functions are all continuous at a. The function f/g is also continuous at a (provided $g(a) \neq 0$ so that division by zero does not occur).

As for composition, suppose g is continuous at b and $g(b) = L$. Now suppose that

$$\lim_{x \to a} f(x) = b.$$

Since we can guarantee the output $f(x)$ to be as close as we want to b when x is close enough to a, we can also guarantee that $g(f(x))$ is close to L for x close enough to a. In other words,

$$\lim_{x \to a} g(f(x)) = L.$$

If f also happens to be continuous at a so that $b = f(a)$ and $L = g(b) = g(f(a))$, then

$$\lim_{x \to a} g(f(x)) = g(f(a))$$

and $g \circ f$ must be continuous at $x = a$.

Summarizing,

> If functions f and g are continuous at every real number $x = a$, then
>
> $$f+g \qquad f-g \qquad fg \qquad f \circ g$$
>
> are also continuous at every real number $x = a$. Furthermore, f/g is continuous at every point a such that $g(a) \neq 0$.

The squeezing principle

Another way of deducing a limit value is through comparison with known limit values. The **squeezing principle** is an example of such a comparison technique.

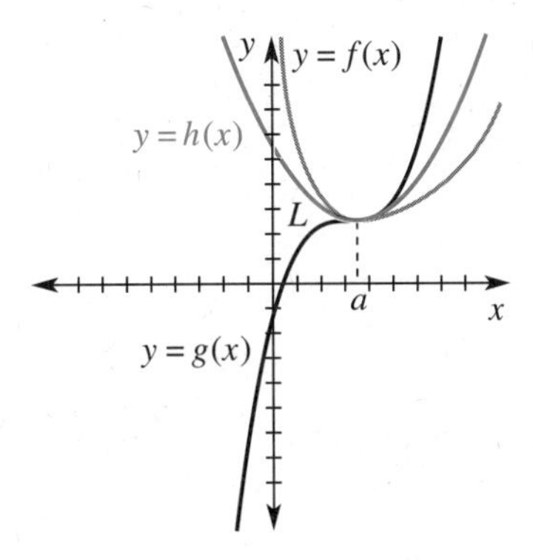

Figure 2.22 Illustration of the squeezing principle.

Theorem 2.4

The Squeezing Principle for Limits

Hypothesis 1: Two functions f and g have the same limit L at $x = a$:

$$\lim_{x\to a} f(x) = L = \lim_{x\to a} g(x).$$

Hypothesis 2: A third function h always has its output $h(x)$ sandwiched between $f(x)$ and $g(x)$ whenever x is sufficiently close but not equal to a. That is, for some $c > 0$ we have either

$$f(x) \leq h(x) \leq g(x) \qquad \text{or} \qquad g(x) \leq h(x) \leq f(x)$$

whenever $0 < |x - a| < c$.

Conclusion: We must also have $\lim_{x\to a} h(x) = L$.

Reasoning Suppose that $\epsilon > 0$ is given. By the hypotheses, we can choose a positive δ small enough so that $\delta < c$ and so that *both* $f(x)$ and $g(x)$ are between $L - \epsilon$ and $L + \epsilon$ whenever $0 < |x - a| < \delta$. Since $h(x)$ is "squeezed" between $f(x)$ and $g(x)$ for these values of x (by Hypothesis 2), we must have $h(x)$ between $L - \epsilon$ and $L + \epsilon$ also. Thus, $\lim_{x\to a} h(x) = L$. □

When you analyze a theorem such as this, try to visualize a typical situation where the hypotheses are satisfied. Figure 2.22 illustrates graphically an example of three functions satisfying the hypotheses of the squeezing principle. Note that the graph of $y = h(x)$ does not always lie between the graphs of f and g, but it must be sandwiched between them in some neighborhood of a. (The squeezing principle is also known as the sandwich theorem.)

Next, look at the conclusion of the theorem and try to get a feeling for how the hypotheses force this conclusion to be true. Near a, the graphs of f and g form a corridor that narrows to a single point (a, L). Since the graph of h must eventually stay within that corridor, its graph is also forced toward this point.

For the vertical scaling $[L - \epsilon, L + \epsilon]$ of a viewing window, if we set the horizontal scaling $[a - \delta, a + \delta]$ so that the graphs of $y = f(x)$ and $y = g(x)$ are in view, then the graph of $y = h(x)$ must also stay within the viewing window.

EXAMPLE 33 It can be shown using a geometric argument that for $-\pi/2 < x < \pi/2$ ($x \neq 0$), we have

$$\cos x < \frac{\sin x}{x} < \sec x.$$

Use this fact and the squeezing principle to show that

$$\lim_{x \to 0} \frac{\sin x}{x} = 1.$$

Solution If $f(x) = \cos x$ and $g(x) = \sec x$, then f and g are continuous at $x = 0$, with

$$\lim_{x \to 0} \cos x = \cos 0 = 1 \qquad \text{and} \qquad \lim_{x \to 0} \sec x = \sec 0 = 1.$$

Since $\frac{\sin x}{x}$ lies between $\cos x$ and $\sec x$ for all x near 0, we must have

$$\lim_{x \to 0} \frac{\sin x}{x} = 1$$

by the squeezing principle. ■

EXERCISES for Section 2.6

For exercises 1–6: You are given a limit of the form $\lim_{x \to a} f(x) = L$.

(a) Find a suitable positive value δ that would guarantee

$$|f(x) - L| < .01 \qquad \text{whenever} \qquad 0 < |x - a| < \delta.$$

Illustrate by graphing $y = f(x)$ with vertical y-range $[L - .01,\ L + .01]$ and with your chosen x-range $[a - \delta,\ a + \delta]$.

(b) Verify the stated limit using an ϵ-δ proof.

1. $\lim_{x \to 1} (x - 7) = -6$

2. $\lim_{x \to 3} \frac{x^2 - 9}{x - 3} = 6$

3. $\lim_{x \to -\frac{1}{2}} \frac{4x^3 + 4x^2 + x}{2x^2 + x} = 0$

4. $\lim_{x \to -2} |x + 1| = 1$

5. $\lim_{x \to 2} 1000x = 2000$

6. $\lim_{x \to -93.2} 14.83 = 14.83$

For exercises 7–22: For each function f defined, determine whether or not $\lim_{x \to 0} f(x)$ exists.

If a limit L exists, then set the vertical scaling of a viewing window to $[L - .01,\ L + .01]$ and find a horizontal scaling $[-\delta, \delta]$ such that the graph of the function enters the viewing window from the left, exits to the right, and stays within the window (with the possible exception at $x = 0$).

7. $f(x) = |x|$

8. $f(x) = x/x$

9. $f(x) = |x|/x$

10. $f(x) = \dfrac{\sin(2x)}{5x}$

11. $f(x) = 1/x^2$

12. $f(x) = 1/x$

13. $f(x) = \sin(1/x)$

14. $f(x) = x\sin(1/x)$

15. $f(x) = \tan(x)$

16. $f(x) = \cot(x)$

17. $f(x) = \dfrac{1 - \cos x}{x}$

18. $f(x) = \sin^2(x) + \cos^2(x)$

19. $f(x) = (1 + x)^{1/x}$

20. $f(x) = \arctan(1/x)$

21.

$$f(x) = \begin{cases} x^2 \text{ if } x < 0 \\ 2x - 1 \text{ if } x \geq 0. \end{cases}$$

22.

$$f(x) = \begin{cases} 1 \text{ if } x > 0 \\ 0 \text{ if } x = 0 \\ -1 \text{ if } x < 0. \end{cases}$$

---

23. Prove directly, using an ϵ-δ proof, that the function $f : x \longmapsto 2x + 1$ is continuous at every real number $x = a$.

24. Prove directly, using an ϵ-δ proof, that any linear function of the form $f(x) = mx + b$ is continuous at every real number $x = a$.

25. If $f(x) = x^2$, prove directly, using an ϵ-δ proof, that the function f is continuous at $x = 3$. (Hint: split your proof up into two cases, depending on the size of ϵ. First, find a δ that would work for any $\epsilon \geq 1$. Then, for $0 < \epsilon < 1$, find δ in terms of ϵ.)

26. Is it possible that the product of two functions fg is continuous at $x = a$ even if neither function f nor g is continuous at $x = a$? If so, describe an example. If not, explain why.

---

27. Use the squeezing principle to show that

$$\lim_{x \to 0} \quad x\sin\left(\frac{1}{x}\right) = 0.$$

(Hint: $-1 \leq \sin(1/x) \leq 1$ for all values $x \neq 0$.)

28. For $-\pi/2 \leq x \leq \pi/2$, show that

$$0 \leq 1 - \cos(x) \leq \sin^2(x).$$

(Hint: $\sin^2(x) = 1 - \cos^2(x) = (1 + \cos(x))(1 - \cos(x))$ and $\cos(x) \geq 0$ for the values x given.)

29. For $0 < x < \pi/2$, show that

$$0 < \frac{1 - \cos(x)}{x} < \frac{\sin^2(x)}{x}$$

and that for $-\pi/2 < x < 0$,

$$\frac{\sin^2(x)}{x} < \frac{1 - \cos(x)}{x} < 0.$$

30. Use the results of the previous exercise along with the squeezing principle to show that

$$\lim_{x \to 0} \frac{1 - \cos(x)}{x} = 0.$$

3

The Derivative

The derivative is one of the most useful and powerful concepts in all of calculus. To motivate the definition of a derivative, we'll examine two closely related ideas—slope and rate of change—by using the example of a car's motion. In this case, the graphical interpretation of derivative is represented by the *slope* of the car's distance vs. time graph. The physical interpretation of derivative is represented by the car's *speed*—that is, the rate of change of distance relative to time. Keeping these two interpretations of derivative in mind can be helpful in understanding and using the information the derivative provides.

The slope of a line can be thought of as the rate of change of a linear function's output relative to change in input (rise/run), and therein lies the key connection between the two interpretations of derivative. The derivative allows us to measure the slopes of more general, nonlinear function graphs. While a linear function has a single slope value associated with its entire graph, the slope of the graph of a more general function will vary from point to point. In this chapter, we review some of the key properties of linear functions and then extend these ideas to include *locally linear* functions, whose graphs may be made up of pieces of straight lines of different slopes. Remarkably, many functions are *approximately* locally linear. This fact allows the wide use of the derivative as a tool.

We will see that the formal definition of derivative is based on a limit of slope values, and we use this idea directly to both approximate and compute derivative values. Then we turn to the physical interpretation of derivative as a rate of change. Finally, we establish some general formulas and rules that can make finding derivatives a mechanical process for many functions. In the next two chapters, we use the derivative to analyze function behavior and apply the derivative as a tool for solving a variety of problems.

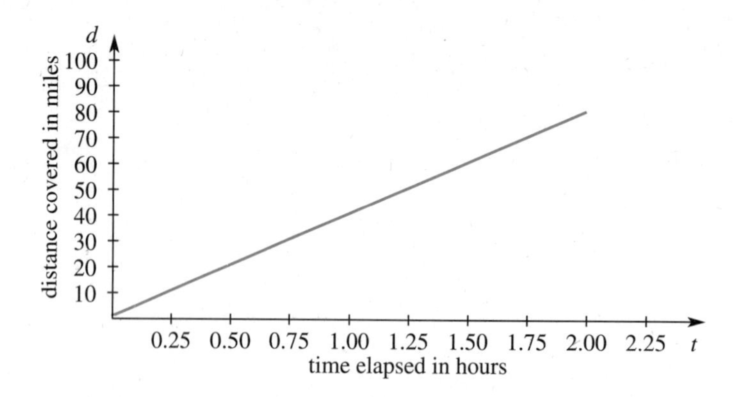

Figure 3.1 Graph of distance vs. time for a car traveling at a constant rate of 40 mph.

3.1 WHAT IS A DERIVATIVE?—SLOPES AND RATES OF CHANGE

When one variable quantity is a function of another, a central question we want to ask is, "How fast do the outputs (values of the dependent variable) change relative to change in the inputs (values of the independent variable)?" The *derivative* of a function provides us with a measure of this rate of change.

The word *rate* brings to mind a familiar formula from algebra:

$$d = rt,$$

where d represents *distance* covered, t represents elapsed *time*, and r represents the rate or speed.

For example, an automobile traveling at a constant rate of 40 mph (miles per hour) for a time of 2 hours will cover a distance of 80 miles. Graphically, we can represent the relationship between d, t, and r with a straight line, as in Figure 3.1. Here the vertical axis represents d, the distance covered in miles, and the horizontal axis represents t, the time elapsed in hours.

But what represents r, the rate? The answer is the slope of the line. The slope describes the relationship between d and t. We have an increase in the value of d of 40 miles for every unit increase (1 hour) of t. Graphically, r simply represents the rise/run of the line. With units attached, we have

$$r = \frac{d}{t} = \frac{40 \text{ miles}}{1 \text{ hour}} = 40 \text{ mph}.$$

Rates of change—constant, average and instantaneous

The situation we have just described is very unrealistic. How often have you been in a car that was able to maintain a speed of exactly 40 mph for two solid hours? Unless the setting was one under artificial control (like

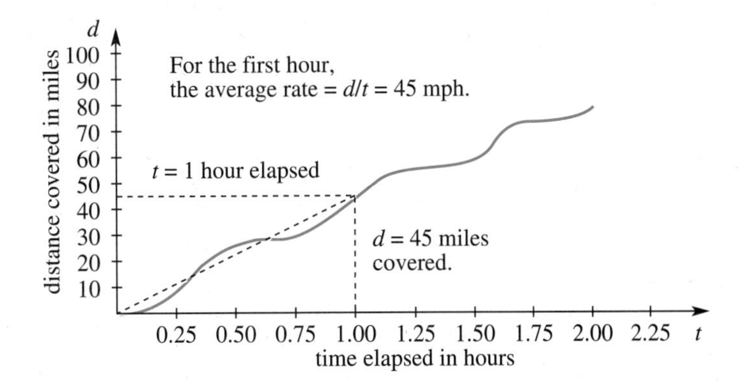

Figure 3.2 The graph of distance vs. time for a car traveling at varying speeds.

an automobile alone on a deserted racetrack), attempting such a feat is not advisable. In Figure 3.2 we have a graph of a more realistic car ride, where the speed of the car fluctuates over the course of the trip. Here, again, the total distance covered by the car over 2 hours is 80 miles, but the graph of distance versus time is not a straight line.

We see that the slope of the graph starts out flat, representing that the car began the trip from a stopped position. The slope of the graph becomes gradually steeper, corresponding to the increase in speed of the car. Subsequent changes in the slope of the graph occur at times when the car is slowing down or speeding up. Steeper portions of the graph represent faster speeds, while flatter portions of the graph correspond to slower speeds.

The rate, or speed, of the first car is *constant*: the car travels at 40 mph for the entire duration of the trip. The second car travels the same distance over the same elapsed time, but now we have to speak of 40 mph as being the *average* speed for the trip. If we examine just the first hour of the trip, we note that the second car has traveled 45 miles, so for the first hour, this car has an average speed of 45 miles per hour. For the second hour of the trip, this car has an average speed of 35 miles per hour. The formulas $d = rt$ and $r = d/t$ both still hold for the interpretation of r as an average rate. In other words,

$$\text{average rate} = \frac{\text{total distance covered}}{\text{total elapsed time}}.$$

Take care to note that the average rate of the second car depends on the *specific* time interval under consideration.

The *instantaneous* rate refers to the speed of our car at a particular instant. Graphically, we could think of instantaneous rate as corresponding to the slope of our distance vs. time graph at a single point in time.

Speedometers, odometers, and clocks

Each of the three variables d, t, and r can be thought of as representing instrument readings from inside our car. An *odometer* measures d, the distance covered. A *clock* measures t, the time elapsed. The *speedometer* measures r, the speed of our car at any particular instant.

Together, an odometer and a clock can be used to calculate the *average* speed of our car over any time interval $t_0 \leq t \leq t_1$. If $d(t)$ represents the position of the car at time t, then the average speed over this time interval is given by

$$\text{average speed} = \frac{\text{total distance}}{\text{total elapsed time}} = \frac{d(t_1) - d(t_0)}{t_1 - t_0}.$$

The difference $d(t_1) - d(t_0)$ is the distance covered between our starting position $d(t_0)$ and our final position $d(t_1)$, while the difference $t_1 - t_0$ provides the elapsed time between our initial and end times. The quotient of these differences is the average speed over the time interval. Graphically, this average speed corresponds to the slope of the line connecting the two points $(t_0, d(t_0))$ and $(t_1, d(t_1))$.

Measuring instantaneous speed

In contrast, the speedometer reading provides the instantaneous speed of our car at a single point in time, and it corresponds to the slope of the graph at a single point. How could you get a reading of the instantaneous speed of a car without seeing its speedometer? Barring a drastic change in speed while we take the measurements, it would be reasonable to approximate the instantaneous speed of the car by measuring its average speed over a very short time interval.

EXAMPLE 1 Estimate the speedometer reading if your car covers 0.1 miles in 5 seconds.

Solution Your average speed over that time is

$$r = \frac{d}{t} = \frac{0.1 \text{ miles}}{5 \text{ seconds}} = \frac{1.2 \text{ miles}}{60 \text{ seconds}} = 72 \text{ miles per hour.}$$

This should be a good approximation of the speedometer reading during those 5 seconds. ■

In Example 1, we are not directly measuring the speed at a particular time. Rather, we are measuring the total distance covered over a very small interval of time and calculating the average speed from this measurement. This will be a good approximation if the speed doesn't change abruptly while we are trying to measure it—that is, if the graph of distance covered is very nearly *linear* with respect to time. If we had an extremely accurate odometer (measuring thousandths of a mile) and a stopwatch that could measure tenths of a second, we could possibly obtain an even better estimate of instantaneous speed by using a smaller time interval to calculate average speed.

This is precisely the principle by which police radar determines the speed of a car on the highway. By calculating the time it takes for the radar beam to bounce off a car and return, the radar device can measure the distance to an approaching car. If two beams are bounced off the car separated by a very small (known) time difference, then the device can take the difference in distance measurements and calculate the average speed. Since the time interval is so tiny, the radar reading is essentially identical to the car's speedometer reading.

Visually, if we magnify this graph at a single point until it appears linear, the apparent slope may be a good approximation of the slope at that point.

EXAMPLE 2 Figure 3.3 shows a magnified view of the graph of our second car at the time $t = 1$ hour. Approximate the slope (speed of the car) at this instant.

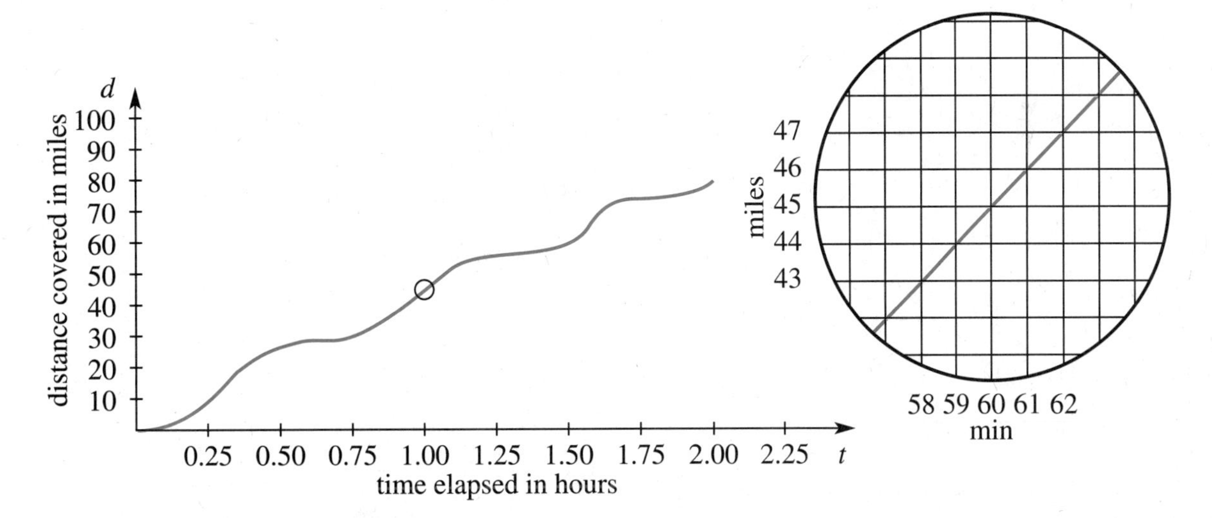

Figure 3.3 The car's speed appears to be 60 mph at $t = 1$ hour.

Solution The graph looks approximately linear in the close-up view. The rise/run between $t = 60$ minutes (1 hour) and $t = 61$ minutes appears to be 1 mile per minute, or 60 miles per hour. ■

If, however, the speed changes considerably while we are measuring it, our approximation may not be a good one. In particular, if we remeasured over a smaller time interval that includes our point of interest, we might come up with a very different speed. What we need is a precise way of calculating the instantaneous rate of change or, equivalently, the slope of the graph at a single point. In a nutshell, calculating the derivative gives us this information. In other words, you can think of a derivative as connecting a *speedometer* to a function process or as providing a *slope machine* for reading the slope of the function graph at any single point.

EXERCISES for Section 3.1

For exercises 1–8: A graph of the distance travelled by a car over the first hour of a trip is shown.

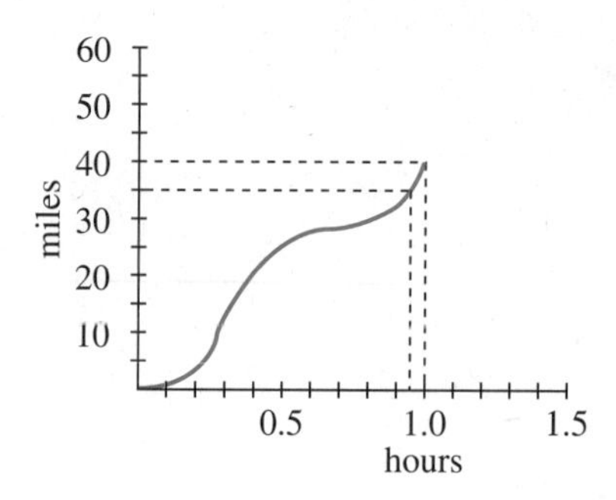

For Exercises 1–8

1. Find the average speed of the car for the entire first hour.

2. Find the average speed of the car for the 3-minute interval represented by the dashed lines.

3. Is the car speeding up or slowing down over the first fifteen minutes of the trip?

4. When is the car moving the fastest in the first half hour? When is the car moving slowest in the second half hour?

5. Assuming that the car maintains its speed beyond the last recorded point, estimate graphically when it will cross the 50-mile mark.

6. Assuming that the car maintains its speed beyond the last recorded point, estimate graphically where the car will be at $t = 1.5$ hours. (You are *extrapolating* information not on the original graph.)

7. Estimate the instantaneous speed of the car at $t = 0.5$ hours and at $t = 1.0$ hours.

8. Estimate graphically when the speedometer of the car reads exactly the same as the average speed for the first hour of the trip.

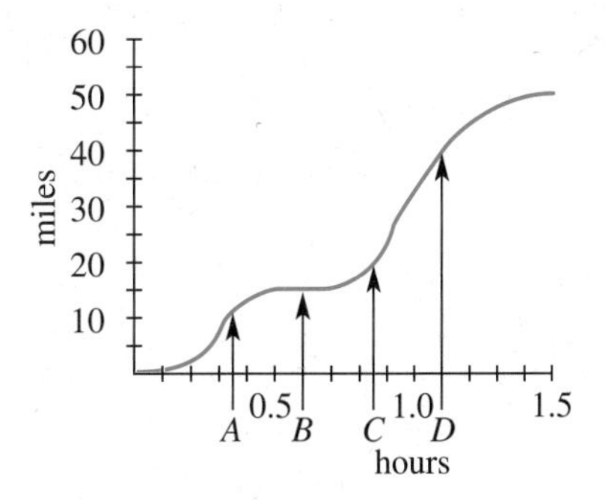

For Exercises 9–15

For exercises 9–15: Another graph of the distance travelled by a car over time is shown.

9. At which of the times A,B,C, or D is the car travelling the fastest?

10. At which of the times A,B,C, or D is the car stopped?

11. At which of the times A,B,C, or D is the car gaining speed the fastest?

12. At which of the times A,B,C, or D is the car losing speed the fastest?

13. Find the average speed for the entire trip, the average speed between times A and D, the average speed between B and D, and the average speed between C and D.

14. Estimate the speedometer reading at each of the times A,B,C, and D.

15. At which of the times A,B,C,or D is the car's instantaneous speed the closest to its average speed for the entire trip?

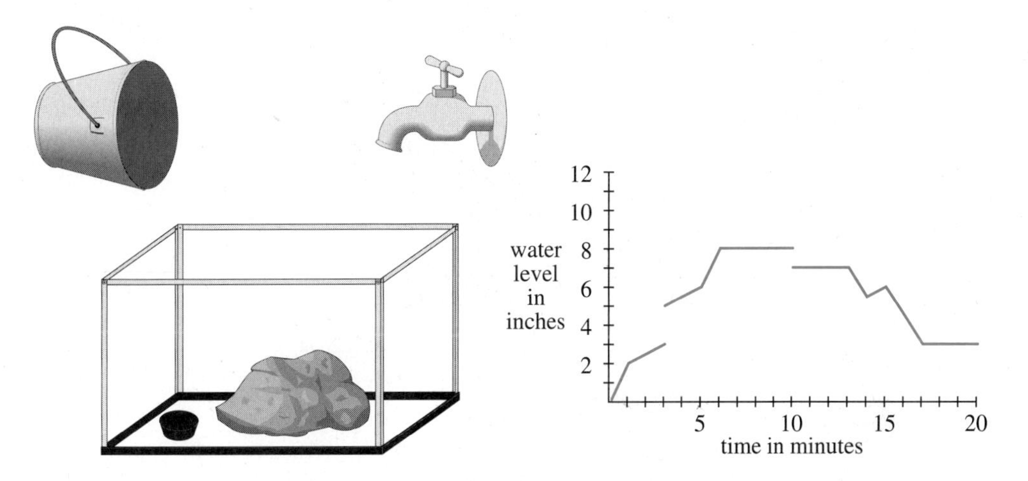

For Exercises 16–25

For exercises 16–25: An illustration of an aquarium and a graph of its water level as a function of time is shown. When the faucet is on, the water level rises at a steady rate. Similarly, when the plug is pulled out, the water level falls at a steady rate (but slower than the faucet's rate). At various times, some events happen that affect the water level and/or the rate at which the water level changes. In the exercises below, you are asked to identify at exactly what time the given event occurred.

16. The plug is pulled out with the faucet turned off.

17. A large rock is pulled out of the aquarium.

18. The plug is pulled out with the faucet turned on.

19. The plug is put in with the faucet turned off.

20. The plug is put in with the faucet turned on.

21. The faucet is turned on with the plug in.

22. The faucet is turned on with the plug out.

23. A bucket of water is dumped into the aquarium all at once.

24. The faucet is turned off with the plug in.

25. The faucet is turned off with the plug out.

---

26. Now, assume that the rock is placed back in the aquarium at $t = 20$ minutes and the faucet is turned back on at the same time. Suppose that the aquarium is 12 inches deep; when will it overflow?

3.2 LINEAR AND LOCALLY LINEAR FUNCTIONS

Linear functions occupy much of the study of algebra, but they gain a new importance in the study of calculus. A linear function has a straight line $y = mx + b$ for a graph, and the slope m of that line tells us the rate of change of the function—that is, how fast (and in what direction) the y-values (outputs) change as the x-values (inputs) increase.

While linear functions are extremely important in their own right, there are real-world processes that are simply not described well by linear models. Amazingly, however, many of these same processes behave almost linearly if we focus our attention over very small intervals of inputs. Calculus provides the tool for studying these processes. Physically, a derivative provides us with a measure of the *instantaneous rate of change* of a function's outputs; geometrically, it provides the slope of the function's graph *at each point.* To understand how to calculate derivatives, let's first review how slope is measured for linear functions.

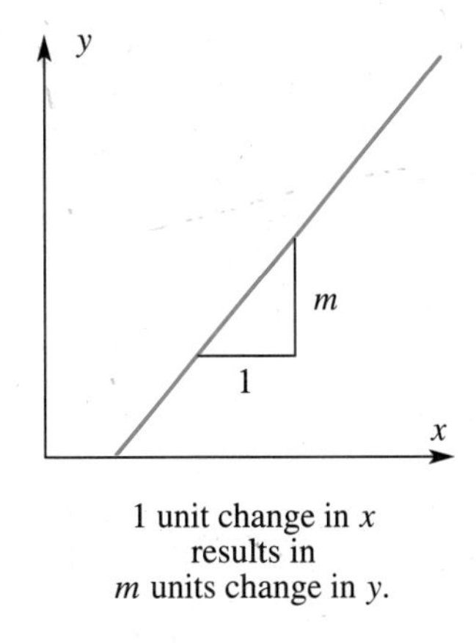

Figure 3.4 Slope measures rise/run.

If we have any two distinct points (x_1, y_1) and (x_2, y_2) from the graph of a linear function, we can compute the slope by using the **two-point formula**

$$m = \frac{y_2 - y_1}{x_2 - x_1}.$$

If we call the linear function f, we can write this as

$$m = \frac{f(x_2) - f(x_1)}{x_2 - x_1}.$$

Given a point on a line, the slope m allows us to obtain other points on the line by stepping off m units in the y-direction for every unit we step right in the x-direction (see Figure 3.4). That is, the slope of a linear function measures the rise/run of the function graph. As we move one unit to the right in the x-direction, the graph will rise m units in the y-direction (a negative *rise* represents a *fall*).

Lines

The formula for a linear function can be expressed in a variety of different forms, each having its own advantages. The most general form of the equation for a line is

$$Ax + By + C = 0,$$

where A, B, and C are real numbers.

If $B = 0$, then the equation can be rewritten in the form $x = -C/A$, and the graph is a *vertical* line. (Conversely, any vertical line has an equation of the form $x = a$ for some constant a.) A vertical line does not represent the graph of y as a function of x, and it has *undefined slope.*

If $B \neq 0$, we can solve for y as a function of x:

$$y = -\frac{A}{B}x - \frac{C}{B}.$$

This line has slope $m = -A/B$. Any function f whose formula can be written as

$$f(x) = mx + b$$

for all x is a linear function.

The **slope-intercept form** of a line is

$$y = mx + b.$$

When it is written in this form, we can directly read off the slope m and the *y-intercept* $(0, b)$—that is, the point where the graph crosses the y-axis.

A horizontal line with an equation of the form

$$y = b$$

represents a *constant* function, and this line has slope $m = 0$.

The value of the slope of a linear function tells us instantly whether the function outputs $f(x)$ are increasing (positive slope), decreasing (negative slope), or constant (zero slope) as we increase the inputs x (see Figure 3.5).

▶▶▶ **Beware of the distinction between a line having 0 slope and *no* slope (undefined). Horizontal lines have slope $m = 0$, while vertical lines have no defined slope.**

Geometric properties of lines are often easily described in terms of their slopes.

Two distinct lines in the Cartesian plane with the same slope m must be *parallel.* Conversely, if two such lines are parallel, then either they have the same slope or both are vertical.

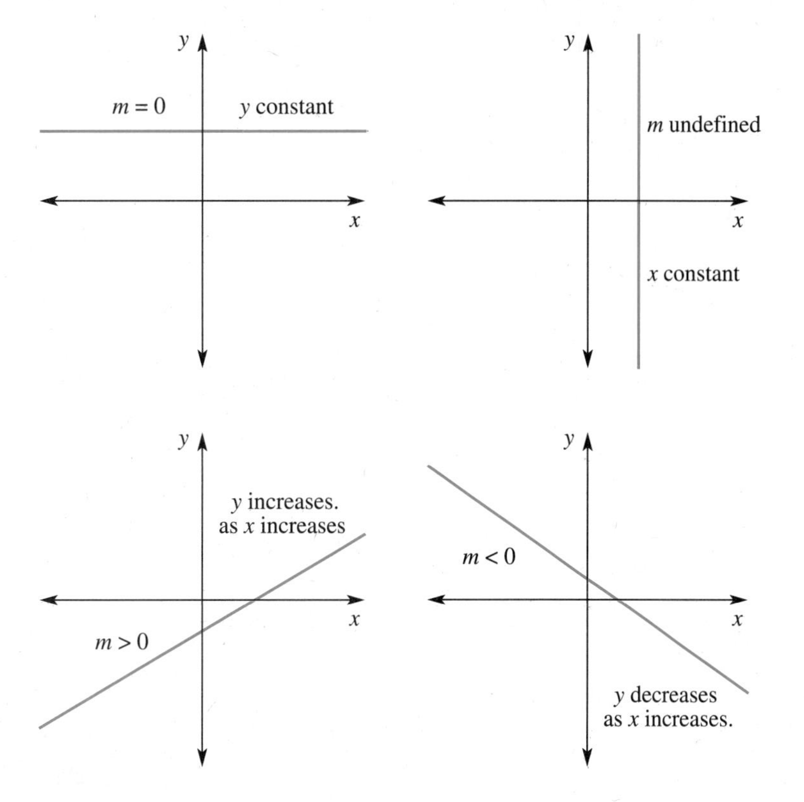

Figure 3.5 Interpreting slope values.

> If a line has slope $m \neq 0$, then a perpendicular line has slope $-1/m$. Conversely, two perpendicular lines must satisfy this slope property, unless one is horizontal (slope 0) and the other is vertical (undefined slope).

Point-slope and Taylor forms

A linear function is completely determined by its slope m and a single point on its graph.

> Given a line with slope m and a particular point (x_0, y_0) on the line, the equation of the line can be expressed in **point-slope form**:
>
> $$y - y_0 = m(x - x_0).$$

If we start with the point-slope form for a linear function f whose graph $y = f(x)$ passes through $(x_0, f(x_0))$ with slope m, we obtain

$$f(x) - f(x_0) = m(x - x_0).$$

(We have just written $f(x)$ for y and $f(x_0)$ for y_0.) Now, if we add $f(x_0)$ to both sides of this equation, we obtain another form that we will find useful.

> The **Taylor form** of a linear function f at $x = x_0$ is
> $$f(x) = f(x_0) + m(x - x_0).$$

The Taylor form, named after the English mathematician Brook Taylor (1685-1731), can be thought of as emphasizing a specific starting point $(x_0, f(x_0))$ from which we locate other points on the line.

EXAMPLE 3 A line has an equation $2x - 3y + 6 = 0$. Find its equation in slope-intercept form, its point-slope form at the point $(3, 4)$, and its Taylor form at $x_0 = -4$.

Solution Solving the equation for y gives us the slope-intercept form:

$$y = \frac{2}{3}x + 2.$$

Now we know the slope $m = 2/3$, so we can write down the point-slope form at $(3, 4)$:

$$y - 4 = \frac{2}{3}(x - 3).$$

When $x_0 = -4$, $y_0 = f(x_0) = \frac{2}{3}(-4) + 2 = -\frac{2}{3}$. Hence,

$$f(x) = -\frac{2}{3} + \frac{2}{3}(x - (-4)) = -\frac{2}{3} + \frac{2}{3}(x + 4)$$

is the Taylor form at $x_0 = -4$. ■

All these forms are equivalent, but they emphasize different information about the line.

EXAMPLE 4 The graph of a certain linear function f has slope 2 and passes through the point $(3, 7)$. Find its Taylor form at $x_0 = 3$.

Solution Using $x_0 = 3$, $f(x_0) = 7$, and $m = 2$, we have

$$f(x) = 7 + 2(x - 3).$$ ■

EXAMPLE 5 The linear function g is such that $g(0) = 3$ and $g(2) = 2$. What is its Taylor form at $x_0 = 5$?

Solution If we let $x_1 = 0$ and $x_2 = 2$ as given, then

$$m = \frac{g(2) - g(0)}{2 - 0} = \frac{2 - 3}{2} = -\frac{1}{2}.$$

We have $x_0 = 5$, so the only missing information is the value of $g(5)$. Since g is assumed to be linear, we must have (using the point-slope form)

$$g(5) - g(0) = -\frac{1}{2}(5 - 0) = -\frac{5}{2},$$

and substituting $g(0) = 3$ shows that $g(5) = 1/2$. Now we can write the Taylor form of g at $x_0 = 5$ as

$$g(x) = \frac{1}{2} - \frac{1}{2}(x - 5).$$

You can verify that $g(0) = 3$ and $g(2) = 2$ using the Taylor form. ■

EXAMPLE 6 The slope-intercept form of a linear function

$$f(x) = mx + b$$

is the Taylor form at what point?

Solution Since $x = (x - 0)$ and $f(0) = b$, we can consider the slope-intercept form to be simply the Taylor form at $x_0 = 0$:

$$f(x) = mx + b = f(0) + m(x - 0).$$ ■

The important idea: change in output is proportional to change in input

For a linear function, the change in output is always proportional to the change in input. In other words, there is a constant m such that

$$f(x_2) - f(x_1) = m(x_2 - x_1)$$

for any two inputs x_1 and x_2.

On the surface, all we have done here is rewrite the slope formula in a way that holds true even when $x_1 = x_2$. But, the real importance lies in the notion of *proportional change*. Here, *proportional* means that if we multiply the change in input by any factor, then the change in output will be multiplied by the same factor. We could call m the *constant of proportionality*, relating the change in output to the change in input. For example, for any linear function with any slope m, *twice as big a change in input produces twice as big a change in output.*

EXAMPLE 7 Suppose that the function g is linear and $g(9) - g(4) = 7$. Find $g(5) - g(3)$.

Solution We are told that a change in input of 5 units ($5 = 9 - 4$) produces a change in output of 7 units. For a linear function, this means that for every 1 unit change in input, we'll have a $7/5$ units change in output. To find the change in output $g(5) - g(3)$, we find the change in input and multiply by $7/5$:

$$g(5) - g(3) = \frac{7}{5}(5 - 3) = \frac{14}{5}.$$

■

Let's be careful here. Note that we're talking about the *change* in inputs and outputs rather than the *values* of inputs and outputs themselves. In Example 7, note that we don't actually know the output $g(x)$ for any specific input x, but we are able to find the change in output given a change in input. This frees the notion of linearity from the units of measurement we use for the dependent and independent variables.

If one says today's temperature is twice as high as yesterday's, this represents very different physical situations, depending on whether the Fahrenheit or Celsius temperature scale is used. For example, suppose that yesterday's temperature was $41°F = 5°C$. If the reference is to the Fahrenheit scale, it is quite warm today ($82°F$). If we are using the Celsius scale instead ($10°C = 59°F$), then the today's weather is not nearly so warm! But, if one says that the temperature *rise* from Tuesday to Wednesday was twice the *rise* from Monday to Tuesday, then the physical situation is exactly the same, regardless of the temperature scale.

Lines and angles of inclination, incidence, and reflection

Assuming that x and y are measured in the same units of distance, we can use trigonometry to relate the slope m of the graph of a line $y = mx + b$ to its **angle of inclination** θ:

$$m = \tan\theta.$$

The angle of inclination is measured counterclockwise from any horizontal line (the x-axis, for instance), and we always have $0 \leq \theta < \pi$ (see Figure 3.6). For example, the angle of inclination of the line $y = x$ is $\theta = \pi/4$ (45°). If a line has angle of inclination $\theta = \pi/2$, then the line is vertical and the slope is undefined.

When a light ray hits a flat reflective surface (like that of a mirror), the **angle of incidence** α is equal to the **angle of reflection** β (see Figure 3.7). By changing the position of the surface, we can use this principle to redirect a light ray (or radar beam) emitted from a fixed source toward a target of our choosing. For example, assume that a light ray is directed down vertically and we can control the angle of inclination θ of our mirror. In the exercises, you will establish the precise direction of the reflected light ray in terms of θ.

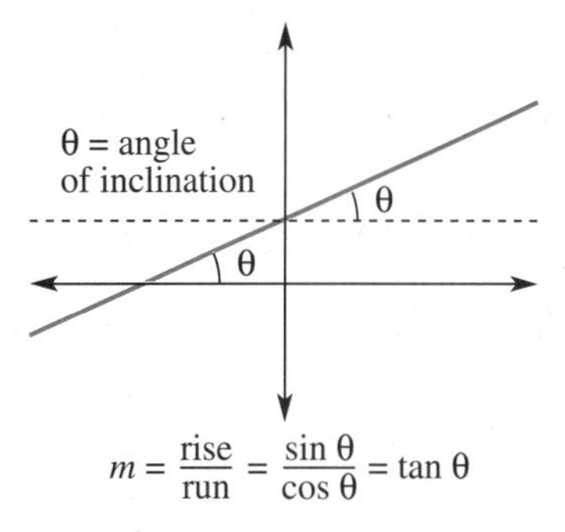

Figure 3.6 Angle of inclination.

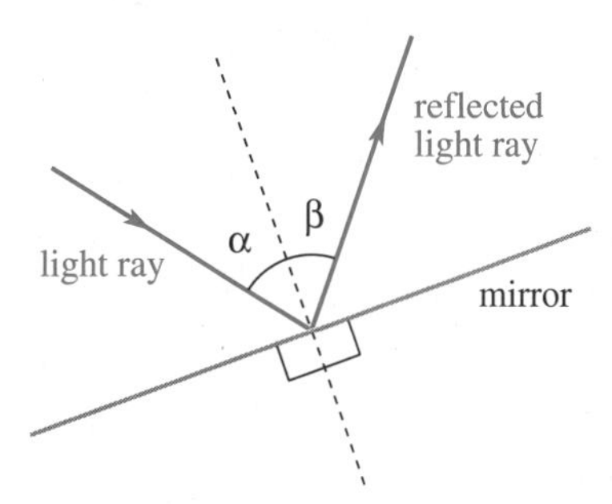

Figure 3.7 Angles of incidence and reflection.

Local linearity

Figure 3.8 illustrates a *line graph* representing a stock's price over a nine-month period. In essence, line graphs *interpolate* the values between the given data points, and we might use such a graph to approximate output values for inputs falling between two known points. Line graphs are often used to spot trends or patterns in the output values gathered over time.

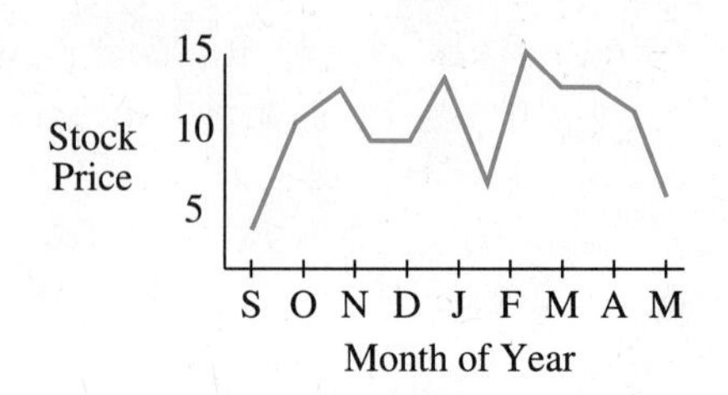

Figure 3.8 A line graph of a stock's price.

If we focus our attention on a small piece of the graph between two consecutive corners, we are unable to distinguish it from the graph of an ordinary linear function. Indeed, we call the function represented by this graph **piece-wise linear**. The slope of the graph of a piece-wise linear function depends on the particular piece of the graph we examine. When we pass a corner, the slope suddenly changes. This leads us naturally to say that the function is *locally linear* except at those points at which there are corners or breaks in the graph.

Recall that an open interval containing the point x_0 is called a *neighborhood* of x_0. Using the language of neighborhoods, we can give a graphical definition of local linearity.

Definition 1 A function f is **locally linear** at x_0 if the graph of $y = f(x)$ coincides with a straight line over a neighborhood of x_0.The slope m of this line is called the **slope at the input** x_0.

EXAMPLE 8 Suppose that f is the piece-wise linear function corresponding to the table and graph in Figure 3.9. Find the slope at $x_0 = 1.4$. Then use linear interpolation to find $f(1.4)$. Find a formula valid for evaluating $f(x)$ between $x = 1$ and $x = 2$.

Solution The graph of the function between $x = 1$ and $x = 2$ is the straight line segment connecting the points $(1, 2)$ and $(2, -2)$. The slope of the segment is given by

$$m = \frac{f(2) - f(1)}{2 - 1} = \frac{-2 - 2}{1} = -4.$$

Now we can determine $f(1.4)$ by noting that

$$\frac{f(1.4) - 2}{1.4 - 1} = -4,$$

so

$$f(1.4) = (-4)(0.4) + 2 = 0.4.$$

input	output
0	0
1	2
2	–2
3	0

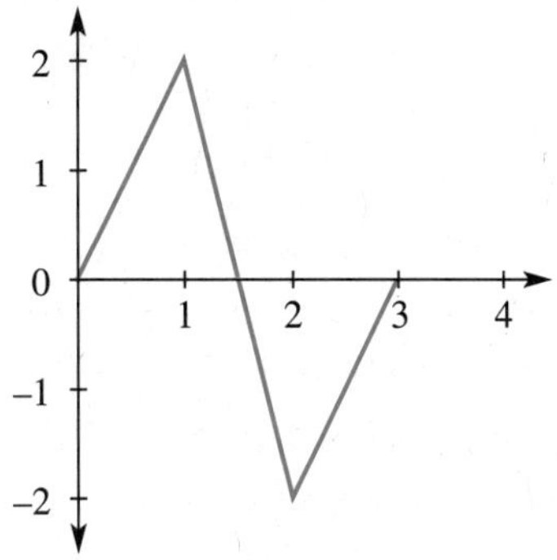

Figure 3.9 Data table and graph of a piece-wise linear function.

The formula

$$f(x) = 0.4 - 4(x - 1.4)$$

is valid for evaluating $f(x)$ whenever $1 \leq x \leq 2$. ■

An important special case of a piece-wise linear function is a **step function**. Step functions are piece-wise *constant*. They get their name from their graphs, which resemble a set of stairs. An example of a step function is the postage due on a parcel as a function of its weight (see Figure 3.10). The postage is constant for different intervals of weight, jumping up at specific weights.

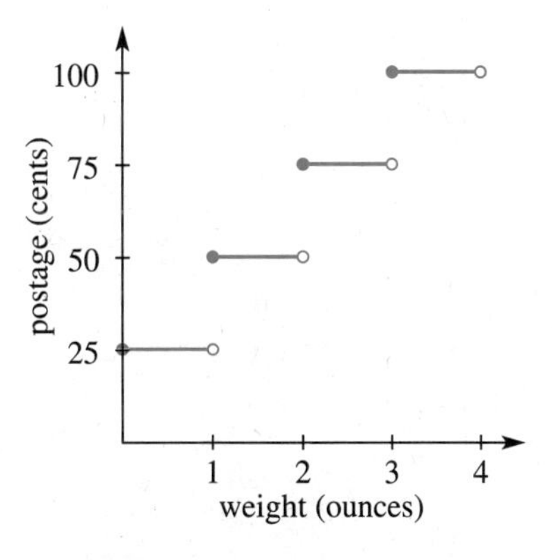

Figure 3.10 Postage is a step function of weight.

EXERCISES for Section 3.2

For exercises 1–12: Suppose f and g are linear functions. The graph of $y = f(x)$ has slope 3 and passes through the point $(-4, 1)$. The graph of $y = g(x)$ passes through the two points $(-1, -2)$ and $(1, -3)$.

1. Find the slope-intercept form of f.

2. Find the Taylor form of f at $x_0 = 2$.

3. Find the slope-intercept form of g.

4. Find the slope-intercept form of the line passing through the origin and parallel to the graph of g.

5. Find the Taylor form of g at $x_0 = -1.5$.

6. Find the Taylor form at $x_0 = 4$ for the line perpendicular to the graph of f at the point $(4, f(4))$.

7. Find the constant function whose graph passes through the intersection of the graphs of f and g.

8. Find the slope-intercept form for g^{-1}.

9. Find the Taylor form of f^{-1} where the graphs of f and f^{-1} intersect.

10. Find the slope-intercept forms for $f + g$, $f - g$, $f \circ g$. Relate the slopes of each of these functions to the slopes of f and g.

11. Do $f \circ g$ and $g \circ f$ have the same slope? Are their graphs the same line?

12. What change in input is required to produce a 1 unit change in output for each of the functions f, g, $f + g$, $f - g$, and $f \circ g$?

For exercises 13–18: For each function,

(a) verify that the function is linear by graphing the function,

(b) find the slope-intercept form,

(c) find the Taylor form at $x_0 = 1$, and

(d) determine the slope directly by calculating the two-point formula using $x_0 = 1$ as one input and using each of the following values as the second input:

$$x_1 = .9, \quad x_2 = .99, \quad x_3 = .999, \quad x_4 = .9999, \quad \text{and} \quad x_5 = .99999.$$

(e) Using a calculator, find which of the inputs $x_1, \ldots, x_5$ gives the most accurate slope value.

13. $y = \dfrac{x}{12345}$

14. $y = \dfrac{5 - x}{7}$

15. $y = \dfrac{(x-5)^2 - (x+3)^2}{9}$

16. $y = 1 + 0.12345678(x - 1)$

17. $y = \dfrac{x^3 + x^2 + x + 1}{3x^2 + 3}$

18. $y = \dfrac{2(x + 3(x + 4(x + 5)))}{29}$

19. The table shows some input-output data pairs. Using linear interpolation, estimate $f(0.5)$, $f(1.6)$, and $f(2.25)$.

input	output
0	5.32
1	6.11
2	2.20
3	4.07

For Exercise 19

20. Does this data come from a linear process?

For exercises 21–30: Use the graphs of $y = f(x)$ and $y = g(x)$ to answer the following exercises.

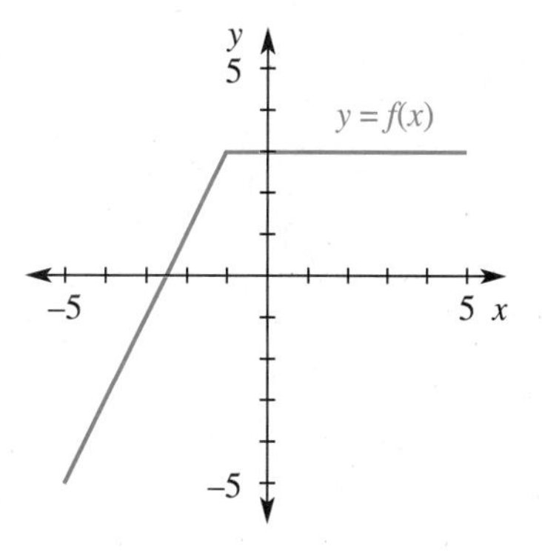

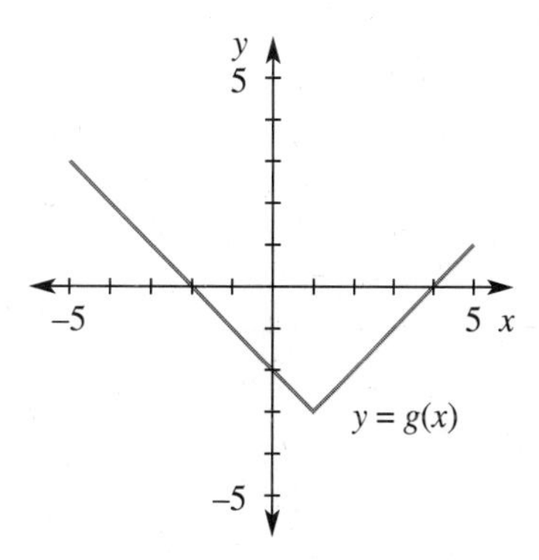

For Exercises 21–30

21. What is the slope of $y = f(x)$ at $x = -4$?

22. What is the slope of $y = g(x)$ at $x = 1$?

23. What is the slope of $y = f(x) + g(x)$ at $x = 4$?

24. What is the slope of $y = f(x) - g(x)$ at $x = 0$?

25. What is the slope of $y = f(g(x))$ at $x = 3$?

26. What is the slope of $y = g(f(x))$ at $x = -2$?

27. What is the slope of $y = 2f(x)$ at $x = 2$?

28. What is the slope of $y = g(x)/3$ at $x = 3$?

29. Graph $y = f(x)g(x)$. Over what intervals is fg linear?

30. Graph $y = f(x)/g(x)$. Over what intervals is f/g linear?

---

31. Find the angle of inclination of the line $y = \sqrt{3}x - 1$.

32. Find the slope-intercept form of a line passing through the point $(-3, 0)$ and having angle of inclination $3\pi/4$.

For exercises 33–40: A mirror is inclined at an angle θ to the horizontal. A light ray directed vertically downward to the mirror is reflected from the surface. In these exercises, establish the direction of the reflected light ray.

You may find the illustration helpful. We have extended the path of the light ray and its reflection through the mirror to the horizontal and labeled some relevant angles. Assume that $0 < \theta < \pi/4$.

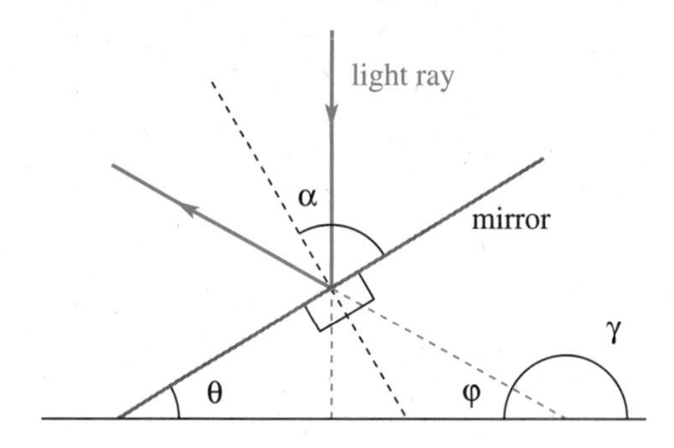

For Exercises 33–40

33. Show that $\alpha = \theta$. (Hint: find a complementary angle to both α and θ.)

34. Show that $\phi = \dfrac{\pi}{2} - 2\theta$. (Hint: remember that the angle of reflection is equal to the angle of incidence, and use the previous exercise.)

35. Show that $\gamma = \dfrac{\pi}{2} + 2\theta$.

36. If we use the x-axis to represent the horizontal line in the illustration, then the slope of the mirror is $m = \tan\theta$ and the slope of the line perpendicular to the mirror is

$$\frac{-1}{m} = \frac{-1}{\tan\theta}.$$

Show that the slope of the reflected light ray is the *average* of these two slopes. In other words, show that

$$\tan\gamma = \frac{1}{2}\left(m - \frac{1}{m}\right).$$

(Hint: we know that $\tan\gamma = \tan(\frac{\pi}{2} + 2\theta)$. Show that

$$\tan\left(\frac{\pi}{2} + 2\theta\right) = \frac{1}{2}\left(\tan\theta - \frac{1}{\tan\theta}\right)$$

by using trigonometric identities.)

37. The result you established for $0 < \theta < \pi/4$ is:

For a light ray projected vertically downward on an inclined mirror of slope m, the slope of the reflected light ray is

$$\frac{1}{2}\left(m - \frac{1}{m}\right).$$

Draw a similar diagram for each of the cases where

$$(a)\ \frac{\pi}{4} < \theta < \frac{\pi}{2} \qquad (b)\ \frac{\pi}{2} < \theta < \frac{3\pi}{4} \qquad (c)\ \frac{\pi}{2} < \theta < \pi.$$

Show that the same result holds in each of these cases.

38. What happens if the mirror is inclined at an angle of $\theta = \pi/4$ or $3\pi/4$ ($m = \pm 1$)? Does the result still hold?

39. What happens if the mirror is horizontal ($\theta = 0$ and $m = 0$)?

40. What happens if the mirror is vertical ($\theta = \pi/2$ and m is undefined)?

Two step functions worthy of special names are the **floor** and **ceiling** functions, whose graphs are illustrated in the figure. The "floor of x" is denoted $\lfloor x \rfloor$, and it is the largest integer n such that $n \le x$. For example,

$$\lfloor 1.2 \rfloor = 1, \quad \lfloor 7 \rfloor = 7, \quad \lfloor -3.4 \rfloor = -4, \quad \lfloor -2 \rfloor = -2.$$

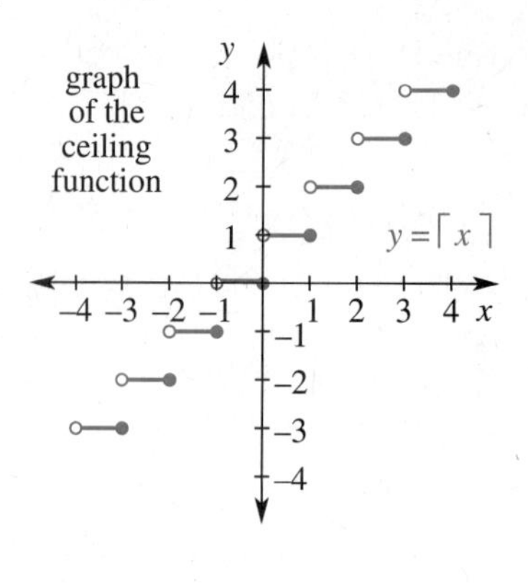

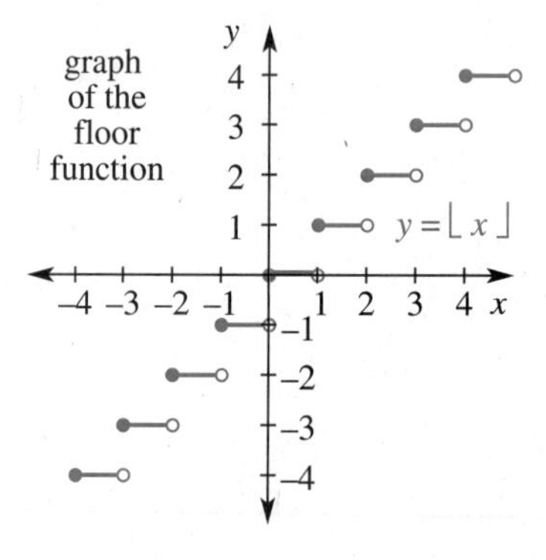

For Exercises 41–50

The floor function is sometimes called the **greatest integer function**, since its output $\lfloor x \rfloor$ is the greatest integer less than or equal to the input x. (The older notation for greatest integer of x is $[x]$.)

The "ceiling of x" is denoted $\lceil x \rceil$ and is the smallest integer n such that $n \geq x$. For example,

$$\lceil 1.2 \rceil = 2, \quad \lceil 7 \rceil = 7, \quad \lceil -3.4 \rceil = -3, \quad \lceil -2 \rceil = -2.$$

The floor and ceiling functions are often used when a real number result is computed but a whole number result is needed. For example, suppose you determined that 17.54 workers are needed to complete a job by a certain deadline. Thus, you actually need $18 = \lceil 17.54 \rceil$ workers to complete the job on schedule.

For exercises 41–48: Graph each of the functions indicated below over the interval $[-5, 5]$.

41. $y = (\lfloor x \rfloor + \lceil x \rceil)/2$

42. $y = \lceil x \rceil - \lfloor x \rfloor$

43. $y = 2\lfloor x \rfloor$

44. $y = \lfloor 2x \rfloor$

45. $y = \lceil -x \rceil$

46. $y = -\lceil x \rceil$

47. $y = \lceil x \rceil - x$

48. $y = x - \lfloor x \rfloor$

49. For what values x is $\lfloor x \rfloor = \lceil x \rceil$?

50. For what values x is $\lceil x \rceil = \lfloor x \rfloor + 1$?

3.3 DEFINING AND COMPUTING THE DERIVATIVE

We opened this chapter by considering the problem of measuring the instantaneous speed of a car. We found that this problem corresponds to measuring the slope of a distance vs. time graph at a single point. We can generalize this problem to that of measuring the slope of any function's graph $y = f(x)$ at a single point (x_0, y_0).

For some functions, the problem is easy to solve. A linear function has a straight line for a graph, and the slope m is the same at all points. To measure the slope at (x_0, y_0), we just choose any other distinct point (x, y) on the line and divide the change in output (the rise) by the change in input (the run):

$$m = \frac{y - y_0}{x - x_0}.$$

This method can also be used to find the slope at a point (x_0, y_0) on the graph of a locally linear function, provided that (x_0, y_0) is not a corner in the graph and we choose the second point (x, y) close enough to be within the neighborhood where the graph is a straight line.

Alas, most functions are not linear, or even locally linear. If the graph of $y = f(x)$ is a curve, then how can we talk about the slope at a point (x_0, y_0)?

Fortunately—and remarkably—many functions are *approximately* locally linear. That is, over a sufficiently *small* interval of inputs, a function may behave almost like a linear function, and its graph will appear almost straight!

For example, the graph of $y = \sin x$ is a curve and is not straight over any interval of inputs. However, if we magnify the graph of $y = \sin x$ at $x = 0$, we find that it looks virtually identical to the straight line $y = x$ with slope 1 (see Figure 3.11). This picture strongly suggests that it may be reasonable to say that the slope of the graph of $y = \sin(x)$ at $x = 0$ is 1.

The difference quotient

How can we make more mathematically precise our visual observation of the slope of the sine curve at $x = 0$? Using the two-point formula for the slope of a line as a guide, we can first define the *difference quotient*.

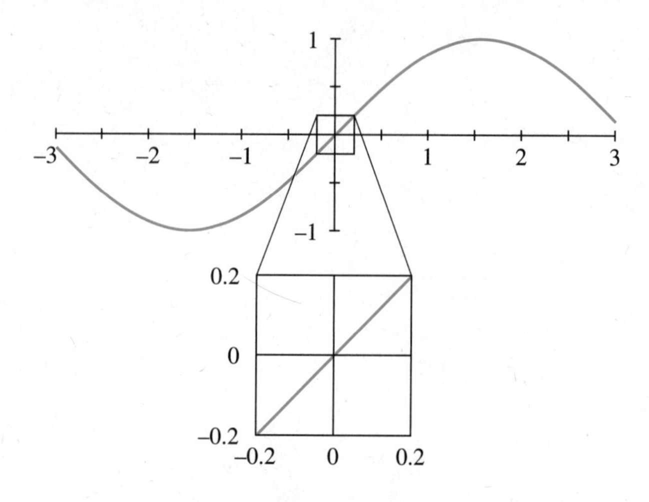

Figure 3.11 Zooming in on the graph of $y = \sin(x)$ near $(0, 0)$.

Definition 2

The **difference quotient** for a function f between two distinct inputs x_1 and x_2 is defined to be

$$\frac{\Delta f}{\Delta x} = \frac{f(x_2) - f(x_1)}{x_2 - x_1}.$$

If we use y to denote $f(x)$, with $y_1 = f(x_1)$ and $y_2 = f(x_2)$, then we may also write this difference quotient as

$$\frac{\Delta y}{\Delta x} = \frac{y_2 - y_1}{x_2 - x_1}.$$

The symbol Δ is the capital Greek letter "delta." We read Δy as the *change in* y and Δx as the *change in* x. These symbols are sometimes called the **increments** in y and x, respectively.

For a linear function, the difference quotient $\frac{\Delta y}{\Delta x}$ simply gives us the slope m. For a nonlinear function, the value of the difference quotient will depend on the two particular inputs we choose. We can interpret the value of the difference quotient of a general function as the slope of a line passing through the points $(x_1, f(x_1))$ and $(x_2, f(x_2))$. Such a line is called a **secant line** to the graph of $y = f(x)$. Figure 3.12 shows this graphical interpretation of the difference quotient.

▶▶▶ **In geometry, a secant line to a circle passes through exactly two points of the circle. Note that a secant line to a function graph $y = f(x)$ could possibly pass through more than two points of the graph.**

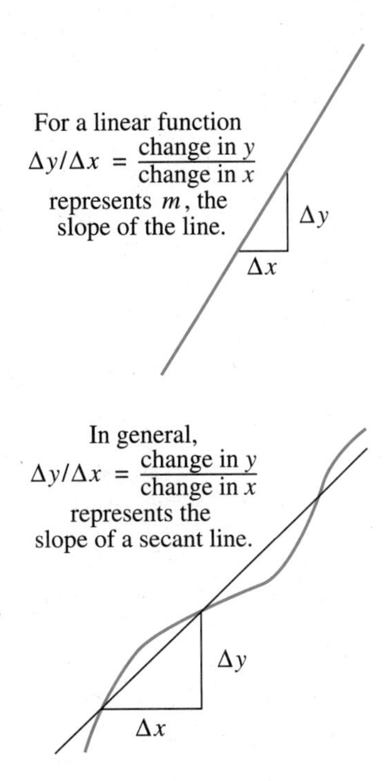

Figure 3.12 Graphical interpretation of the difference quotient.

EXAMPLE 9 Suppose that $f(x) = x^2$ for all x. Calculate $\dfrac{\Delta f}{\Delta x}$ between $x_1 = 2$ and $x_2 = 4$, and between $x_1 = 3$ and $x_2 = 5$.

Solution Between $x_1 = 2$ and $x_2 = 4$, we have

$$\frac{\Delta f}{\Delta x} = \frac{f(x_2) - f(x_1)}{x_2 - x_1} = \frac{4^2 - 2^2}{4 - 2} = \frac{12}{2} = 6.$$

Between $x_1 = 3$ and $x_2 = 5$, we have

$$\frac{\Delta f}{\Delta x} = \frac{f(x_2) - f(x_1)}{x_2 - x_1} = \frac{5^2 - 3^2}{5 - 3} = \frac{16}{2} = 8.$$

The fact that the difference quotient is different for these two pairs of points shows that f is definitely *not* linear, a fact also evident from the graph of $y = x^2$. ■

Let's return to our example of the sine curve. Using $(x_0, y_0) = (0, 0)$, we can compute the difference quotient using a nearby second point (x, y) on the graph of $y = \sin x$. At $x = 0.2$, we have $y = \sin(0.2) \approx 0.19867$. For this choice, we have

$$\frac{\Delta y}{\Delta x} = \frac{y - y_0}{x - x_0} \approx \frac{0.19867 - 0}{0.2 - 0} = 0.99335.$$

If we choose another input even closer to 0, such as $x = -0.1$, we have $y = \sin(-0.1) \approx -0.0998334$, and the difference quotient is

$$\frac{\Delta y}{\Delta x} = \frac{y - y_0}{x - x_0} \approx \frac{-0.0998334 - 0}{-0.1 - 0} = 0.99834,$$

which is even closer to 1. For $x = .01$, we have $y = \sin(.01) = 0.00999983$, and

$$\frac{\Delta y}{\Delta x} = \frac{y - y_0}{x - x_0} \approx \frac{0.00999983 - 0}{.01 - 0} = 0.999983.$$

It appears that the values of the difference quotients approach 1 as the second input x is chosen closer and closer to 0. Indeed, using the language of limits, we have

$$\lim_{x \to 0} \frac{\sin x - 0}{x - 0} = \lim_{x \to 0} \frac{\sin x}{x} = 1$$

(as noted in Chapter 2). Hence, while the graph of $y = \sin x$ is not linear, it seems sensible to say the slope is 1 at $x = 0$, since the difference quotients tend toward that single limiting value.

Definition of the derivative

The example above shows how we can formulate a solution to the slope measurement problem for a general function f and a particular input x_0. If the difference quotients

$$\frac{\Delta f}{\Delta x} = \frac{f(x) - f(x_0)}{x - x_0}$$

approach a limit m_0 as inputs x approach x_0, then we call m_0 the slope of the graph of $y = f(x)$ at $(x_0, f(x_0))$.

▶▶▶ **Keep in mind that for two points chosen *too close* together, the limitations on the precision of machine computation could result in *worse* rather than better accuracy in the calculation of a difference quotient.**

Graphically, the difference quotient is the slope of the (secant) line passing through the points $(x_0, f(x_0))$ and $(x, f(x))$. Now, imagine a sequence of inputs x_1, x_2, x_3, x_4, ..., chosen closer and closer to x_0. If the slopes of the corresponding secant lines approach a single value m_0 (see

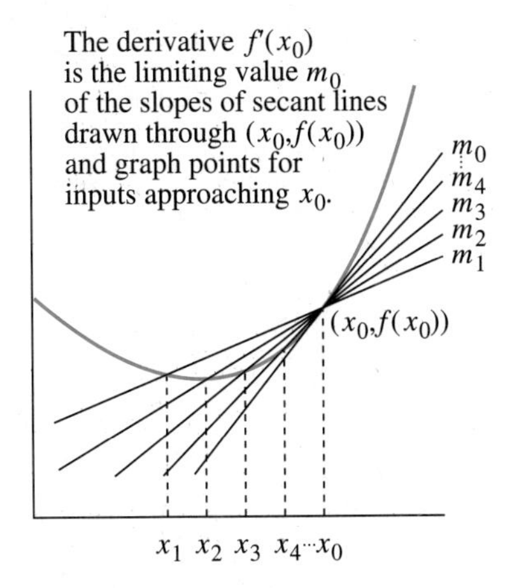

Figure 3.13 The derivative as the limit of the slopes of secant lines.

Figure 3.13), we call m_0 the slope of the graph of $y = f(x)$ at the point $(x_0, f(x_0))$.

If, however, a limiting value for the difference quotients does not exist, then we say the slope of the graph is *undefined.* This is precisely the motivation for the definition of derivative.

Definition 3

Suppose that $f : D \longrightarrow \mathbb{R}$ and $x_0 \in D$, the domain of f. We say f is **differentiable at** $x = x_0$ provided that

$$f'(x_0) = \lim_{x \to x_0} \frac{f(x) - f(x_0)}{x - x_0}$$

exists. If f is differentiable at $x = x_0$, we call this limit $f'(x_0)$ the **derivative of** f **at** $x = x_0$ (with respect to the independent variable x).

Note: The notation $f'(x_0)$ is read "f prime of x_0."

EXAMPLE 10 If $f(x) = \sin x$, is f differentiable at $x = 0$? If so, find $f'(0)$.

Solution Previously, we verified that

$$\lim_{x \to 0} \frac{f(x) - f(0)}{x - 0} = \lim_{x \to 0} \frac{\sin x}{x} = 1,$$

so f is differentiable at $x = 0$, and $f'(0) = 1$. ■

If f is differentiable at x_0, this tells us that f is approximately locally linear in a neighborhood of x_0. If we examine the graph of $y = f(x)$ near $x = x_0$ under sufficiently high magnification, it should look like a straight line.

Using machine graphics, if we zoom in far enough with *equal scale factors* vertically and horizontally on the graph of $y = f(x)$, with a viewing window centered at the point $(x_0, f(x_0))$, then the graph should eventually appear to be a straight line with slope equal to the derivative $f'(x_0)$.

Being differentiable at a point has profound implications, for it means that the important property of linearity holds (or almost holds) in a neighborhood of the point. We noted that if we could measure the average speed of a car over a very small time interval, this value would approximate the true *instantaneous speed* (speedometer reading). On a distance vs. time graph, the average speed over a time interval is represented by the slope of the secant line passing through two points. The problem of measuring instantaneous speed corresponds to finding a limiting value for these slopes as one point moves closer to the other. In general, the derivative represents the instantaneous rate of change of output relative to change in input.

Alternative forms of the derivative definition

The definition of derivative expresses $f'(x_0)$ as a limit.

$$f'(x_0) = \lim_{x \to x_0} \frac{f(x) - f(x_0)}{x - x_0}.$$

There are several ways this limit may be written. If we let $\Delta x = x - x_0$ in the definition, we rewrite x as

$$x = x_0 + (x - x_0) = x_0 + \Delta x.$$

As x approaches x_0, Δx approaches 0, so we rewrite the definition as

$$f'(x_0) = \lim_{\Delta x \to 0} \frac{f(x_0 + \Delta x) - f(x_0)}{\Delta x}.$$

Sometimes it is convenient to use the letter h to represent Δx:

$$f'(x_0) = \lim_{h \to 0} \frac{f(x_0 + h) - f(x_0)}{h}.$$

Definition 4

The **left-hand derivative** of f at $x = x_0$ is denoted

$$f'_-(x_0) = \lim_{x \to x_0^-} \frac{f(x) - f(x_0)}{x - x_0},$$

provided that x_0 is in the domain of f and this left-hand limit exists. The **right-hand derivative** of f at $x = x_0$ is denoted

$$f'_+(x_0) = \lim_{x \to x_0^+} \frac{f(x) - f(x_0)}{x - x_0},$$

provided that x_0 is in the domain of f and this right-hand limit exists.

We can see from the definition that the derivative $f'(x_0)$ exists if and only if both $f'_-(x_0)$ and $f'_+(x_0)$ exist and $f'_-(x_0) = f'_+(x_0)$.

EXAMPLE 17 Find $f'_-(0)$ and $f'_+(0)$ (if they exist) for $f(x) = |x|$.

Solution For the left-hand derivative:

$$\begin{aligned} f'_-(0) = \lim_{x \to 0^-} \frac{f(x) - f(0)}{x - 0} &= \lim_{x \to 0^-} \frac{|x| - |0|}{x - 0} \\ &= \lim_{x \to 0^-} \frac{-x}{x} \qquad (|x| = -x \text{ since } x < 0) \\ &= -1. \end{aligned}$$

For the right-hand derivative:

$$\begin{aligned} f'_+(0) = \lim_{x \to 0^+} \frac{f(x) - f(0)}{x - 0} &= \lim_{x \to 0^+} \frac{|x| - |0|}{x - 0} \\ &= \lim_{x \to 0^+} \frac{x}{x} \qquad (|x| = x \text{ since } x > 0) \\ &= 1. \end{aligned}$$

Both the left- and right-hand derivatives at $x = 0$ exist, but they do not match. The derivative $f'(x_0)$ is undefined. ■

EXAMPLE 18 Find $g'_-(2)$ and $g'_+(2)$ (if they exist) for $g(x) = (x - 2)^{3/2}$.

Solution Since $g(x) = (x - 2)^{3/2} = \sqrt{(x - 2)^3}$ is undefined when $x < 2$, the left-hand derivative $g'_-(2)$ does not exist. (We cannot even approach $x = 2$ from the left-hand side.) On the other hand,

$$g'_+(2) = \lim_{x\to 2^+} \frac{g(x)-g(2)}{x-2} = \lim_{x\to 2^+} \frac{(x-2)^{3/2}-0}{x-2}$$
$$= \lim_{x\to 2^+} (x-2)^{1/2}$$
$$= 0.$$

Since there is no left-hand derivative, the derivative $g'(2)$ does not exist. ■

EXERCISES for Section 3.3

For exercises 1–10: Zoom in (with the same factor both horizontally and vertically) on the graph of the indicated function $y = f(x)$ to estimate $f'(1)$ graphically.

1. $f(x) = x^{2/3}$
2. $f(x) = x^{3/2}$
3. $f(x) = x^{4/3}$
4. $f(x) = x^{3/4}$
5. $f(x) = x^{-1/2}$
6. $f(x) = x^{-3}$
7. $f(x) = \arctan(x)$
8. $f(x) = \operatorname{arccot}(x)$
9. $f(x) = 2^x$
10. $f(x) = \log_{10} x$

For exercises 11–20: Zoom in (with the same factor both horizontally and vertically) on the graph of the indicated function $y = f(x)$ to estimate its derivative graphically at $x = 0$.

11. $f(x) = \sin x$
12. $f(x) = \cos x$
13. $f(x) = \tan x$
14. $f(x) = \sec x$
15. $f(x) = \csc x$
16. $f(x) = \cot x$
17. $f(x) = \sin x^2$
18. $f(x) = \sin^2 x$
19. $f(x) = \sin^2 x + \cos^2 x$
20. $f(x) = \sin 6x$

For exercises 21–28: Approximate the indicated derivative numerically by computing the difference quotient using $h = \pm.001$, and averaging the results.

21. $f'(1.25)$ where $f(x) = 4x + 1$
22. $f'(-2)$ where $f(x) = x^2 + x + 1$
23. $f'(-1.5)$ where $f(x) = \dfrac{1}{2x+1}$
24. $f'(3)$ where $f(x) = \sqrt{2x+3}$
25. $f'(2.9)$ where $f(x) = -3.5$
26. $f'(1.5)$ where $f(x) = \dfrac{|-2x+3|}{5}$
27. $f'(6)$ where $f(x) = \dfrac{x-1}{4}$
28. $f'(1)$ where $f(x) = x^3$

For exercises 29–36: Calculate the derivative by computing the appropriate limit of difference quotients. Compare the accuracy of your numerical estimates in exercises 21-28 with the actual value of the derivative.

29. $f'(1.25)$ where $f(x) = 4x + 1$
30. $f'(-2)$ where $f(x) = x^2 + x + 1$
31. $f'(-1.5)$ where $f(x) = \dfrac{1}{2x+1}$
32. $f'(3)$ where $f(x) = \sqrt{2x+3}$

33. $f'(2.9)$ where $f(x) = -3.5$

34. $f'(1.5)$ where $f(x) = \dfrac{|-2x+3|}{5}$

35. $f'(6)$ where $f(x) = \dfrac{x-1}{4}$

36. $f'(1)$ where $f(x) = x^3$

For exercises 37–40: Find left-hand and right-hand derivatives $f'_-(x_0)$ and $f'_+(x_0)$, if they exist, at the indicated point for the function f.

37. $f(x) = \dfrac{|-2x+3|}{5}$; $x_0 = 1.5$

38. $f(x) = \sqrt{x^2-1}$; $x_0 = -1$

39. $f(x) = |\sin x|$; $x_0 = 0$

40. $f(x) = \sqrt{1-x^2}$; $x_0 = 1$

A numerical technique for estimating the value of a derivative $f'(x_0)$ is the use of the **symmetric difference quotient**

$$f'(x_0) \approx \frac{f(x_0+h) - f(x_0-h)}{2h}$$

for small values h.

41. Show that the symmetric difference quotient is just the average of the two difference quotients

$$\frac{f(x_0+h) - f(x_0)}{h} \quad \text{and} \quad \frac{f(x_0) - f(x_0-h)}{h}.$$

(This is the technique used in exercises 21–28.)

42. There are cases, however, where the symmetric difference quotient can give a misleading estimate of the derivative. For example, if $f(x) = |x|$, show that any nonzero value h used in the symmetric difference quotient to approximate $f'(0)$ gives us the erroneous estimate $f'(0) \approx 0$, even though the derivative does not exist at $x = 0$.

3.4 THE DERIVATIVE FUNCTION

We have seen how to compute the derivative of a given function f *at a particular point* x_0:

$$f'(x_0) = \lim_{h \to 0} \frac{f(x_0+h) - f(x_0)}{h}.$$

Now, imagine performing this process at every possible input x for which the limit

$$f'(x) = \lim_{h \to 0} \frac{f(x+h) - f(x)}{h}$$

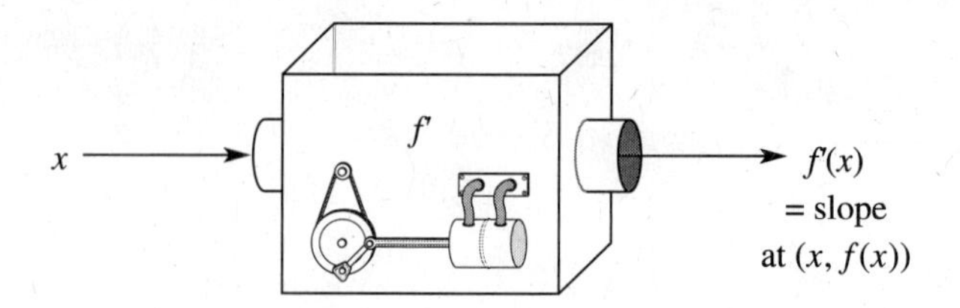

Figure 3.15 The derivative as a slope machine.

exists. What we have is a new *function* "derived" from our original function f. We could illustrate this process as a slope machine (or speedometer) as in Figure 3.16. Given any input x, the machine outputs the instantaneous rate of change $f'(x)$, which provides the slope of the graph of the original function at $(x, f(x))$.

Sketching the graph of the derivative function

By applying the idea of a local slope to several points along the graph of a function, we can sketch approximately how the graph of the derivative function must look. The idea is to estimate the slope at each point on the graph of the original function and then to plot *this value* as the output of the derivative function.

EXAMPLE 19 Sketch the graph of the derivative $y = f'(x)$, if f is the function with formula $f(x) = x^2$.

Solution Figure 3.16 shows the graph of $y = x^2$ and close-ups of the graph for the inputs $x = -3, -2, -1, 0, 1, 2,$ and 3. The slopes at each of these points, respectively, appear to be approximately $-6, -4, -2, 0, 2, 4,$ and 6.

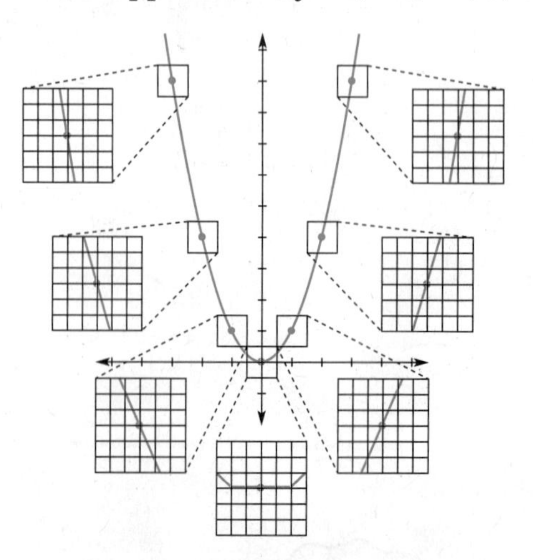

Figure 3.16 Estimating slope values from the graph $y = x^2$.

If we pair each input with the corresponding *slope value* and then plot these ordered pairs, we can get a good sketch of the graph of the derivative function (Figure 3.17).

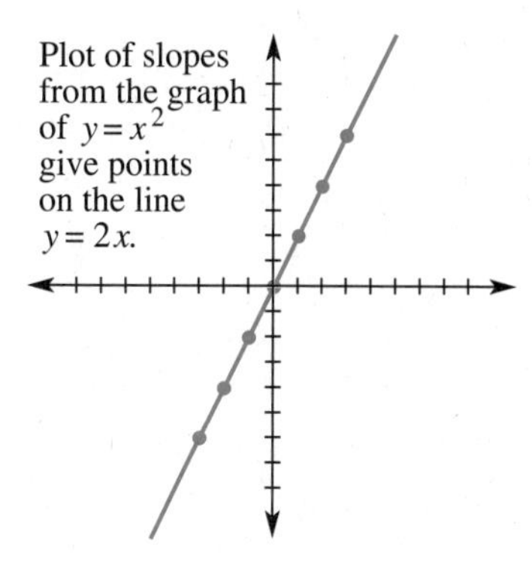

Figure 3.17 Sketch of the derivative's graph $y = f'(x)$ for $f(x) = x^2$.

In this case, the graph of the derivative function appears to coincide with the graph of $y = 2x$. ■

Calculating the derivative function

To obtain a derivative function, we must obtain the precise derivative value at each point in the domain at which the limit of the difference quotients exists. Certainly it is impossible to carry out a separate limit calculation at every possible input. But, if we have a formula for the function f, we can often summarize all the derivative computations in a single formula. This formula represents the symbolic form of the derivative, and it shortcuts the work of re-computing the limit of the difference quotient at each point.

EXAMPLE 20 Find the formula for the derivative $f'(x)$ for $f(x) = x^2$.

Solution The general limit of difference quotients for f is

$$\begin{aligned}
\lim_{h \to 0} \frac{f(x+h) - f(x)}{h} &= \lim_{h \to 0} \frac{(x+h)^2 - x^2}{h} \\
&= \lim_{h \to 0} \frac{(x^2 + 2xh + h^2) - x^2}{h} \\
&= \lim_{h \to 0} \frac{2xh + h^2}{h} \\
&= \lim_{h \to 0} \frac{h \cdot (2x + h)}{h}.
\end{aligned}$$

For any $h \neq 0$, the difference quotient has the value $2x + h$ (we can cancel the h's), and so

$$f'(x) = \lim_{h \to 0} (2x + h) = 2x. \quad \blacksquare$$

Our sketch from the Example 19 is verified. We now have a formula to calculate the derivative of the function $f(x) = x^2$ at any point x. For example, the slope of the graph $y = x^2$ at $x = -5$ is

$$f'(-5) = 2(-5) = -10.$$

Fortunately, almost all of the basic functions we encountered in Chapter 1 have simple formulas for their derivatives. In the remainder of this section, we derive the formulas for the derivatives of a few of the most commonly used functions.

If f is a function with domain D, then the derivative function by f' has as its domain

$$D' = \{x \in D : f \text{ is differentiable at } x\}.$$

(The acceptable inputs for f' are those inputs for f where the derivative exists.) The output value $f'(x)$ at any $x \in D'$ is the derivative of the original function f at x.

To find the limit of a difference quotient at a general input value x, we'll find it most convenient to write the difference quotient as

$$f'(x) = \lim_{h \to 0} \frac{f(x+h) - f(x)}{h}.$$

Derivatives of linear functions

First on our list of basic functions are the linear ones, since the derivative is so easy to compute. The derivative of a linear function is a constant whose value is simply the slope of the line.

> If $f(x) = mx + b$ where m and b are constants, then $f'(x) = m$.

EXAMPLE 21 Find a formula for $f'(x)$ when f has the formula $f(x) = 3x - 17$.

Solution Since f is a linear function, its graph has the same slope everywhere—namely, $m = 3$. Therefore $f'(x) = 3$ for all x. ■

This derivative formula for a linear function $f(x) = mx + b$ follows from calculating the limit of difference quotients

$$\lim_{h\to 0}\frac{f(x+h)-f(x)}{h}=\lim_{h\to 0}\frac{(m(x+h)+b)-(mx+b)}{h}=\lim_{h\to 0}\frac{mh}{h}=m.$$

EXAMPLE 22 Find the derivative of the identity function. $i(x)=x$.

Solution If $i(x)=x$ for all x, then $i'(x)=1$. ■

Derivatives of constant functions

Constant functions are just a special case of linear functions, but it is worthwhile drawing special attention to them.

If $f(x)=c$ for all x, then $f'(x)=0$.

EXAMPLE 23 If $g(x)=3$ for all x, find $g'(x)$.

Solution Since g is a constant function, $g'(x)=0$. This simply says that the rate of change of the outputs of a constant function is 0. ■

Derivatives of monomial functions

Suppose that $f(x)=x^n$ (n a nonnegative integer). Monomial functions like these can be viewed as building blocks for polynomial and rational functions. Once we know the derivatives of these monomial functions, this information will help us find the derivatives of any polynomial or rational function, as we will see later in this chapter. Let's look at a specific example.

EXAMPLE 24 Find the formula for $f'(x)$, if $f(x)=x^3$ for all x.

Solution The general limit of the difference quotient for f is

$$\begin{aligned}\lim_{h\to 0}\frac{f(x+h)-f(x)}{h}&=\lim_{h\to 0}\frac{(x+h)^3-(x^3)}{h}\\&=\lim_{h\to 0}\frac{(x^3+3x^2h+3xh^2+h^3)-x^3}{h}\\&=\lim_{h\to 0}\frac{3x^2h+3xh^2+h^3}{h}\\&=\lim_{h\to 0}\frac{h\cdot(3x^2+3xh+h^2)}{h}\\&=\lim_{h\to 0}(3x^2+3xh+h^2)=3x^2.\end{aligned}$$

Thus, if $f(x)=x^3$, then $f'(x)=3x^2$. ■

We now have calculated the derivatives of several monomial functions. Let's arrange the results systematically.

If $f(x) = 1 = x^0$	then $f'(x) = 0$
If $f(x) = x = x^1$	then $f'(x) = 1$
If $f(x) = x^2$	then $f'(x) = 2x$
If $f(x) = x^3$	then $f'(x) = 3x^2$

Do you see a pattern emerging? In every case so far ($n = 0, 1, 2, 3$), we can note that

$$\text{if} \quad f(x) = x^n, \qquad \text{then} \quad f'(x) = nx^{n-1}.$$

Does this pattern hold for all nonnegative integers n? The answer is yes! To see why, we need to note that when expanded,

$$(x+h)^n = x^n + nhx^{n-1} + h^2 \cdot \text{(other terms)}.$$

When we form the limit of a difference quotient for $f(x) = x^n$, we obtain

$$f'(x) = \lim_{h \to 0} \frac{(x+h)^n - x^n}{h} = \lim_{h \to 0} \frac{x^n + nhx^{n-1} + h^2 \cdot \text{(other terms)} - x^n}{h}.$$

After canceling $x^n - x^n$ in the numerator and factoring out h/h, we are left with

$$f'(x) = \lim_{h \to 0} \frac{h}{h} \cdot (nx^{n-1} + h \cdot \text{(other terms)}) = nx^{n-1}.$$

(For $h \neq 0$, the factor $h/h = 1$, and as h approaches 0, $h \cdot$(other terms) vanishes, leaving only nx^{n-1}.)

> If $f(x) = x^n$, where n is a nonnegative integer, then
> $$f'(x) = nx^{n-1}.$$

EXAMPLE 25 Find $f'(x)$ when $f(x) = x^{1000}$.

Solution $f'(x) = 1000x^{999}$. ■

Derivative of the sine function

Before we start finding the derivative of the sine function through the limit of a difference quotient, let's take a look at the graph of $y = \sin x$ (x measured in radians). If we zoom in on the graph at several points and note the slopes, we can sketch the graph of the derivative (see Figure 3.18). Does this derivative graph look familiar to you?

Another way to approximate the graph of the derivative $y = f'(x)$ using a machine is to simply plot the difference quotient

$$y = \frac{f(x+h) - f(x)}{h}$$

for a small value h. For example, the graph of the derivative of $\sin x$ can be approximated by plotting the difference quotient for $h = .01$:

$$y = \frac{\sin(x + .01) - \sin(x)}{.01}.$$

(Try it!)

To compute the precise derivative, we must find the limit of the general difference quotient for the sine function. To do this, we use the addition

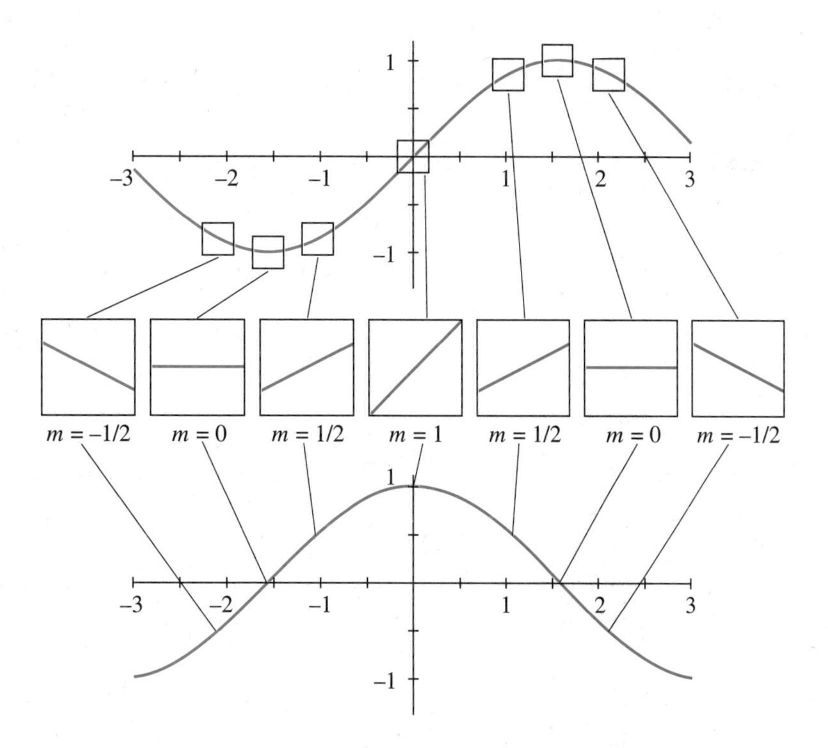

Figure 3.18 Sketching the graph of the derivative of $\sin x$.

formula for sine and some algebra to obtain

$$\begin{aligned}\lim_{h\to 0}\frac{\sin(x+h)-\sin x}{h} &= \lim_{h\to 0}\frac{\sin x\cos h+\cos x\sin h-\sin x}{h}\\ &= \lim_{h\to 0}\left(\sin x\cdot\frac{\cos h-1}{h}+\cos x\cdot\frac{\sin h}{h}\right).\end{aligned}$$

We noted earlier (see Section 2.6) that

$$\lim_{x\to 0}\frac{\sin x}{x}=1 \qquad \text{and} \qquad \lim_{x\to 0}\frac{\cos x-1}{x}=0.$$

These same limits appear here with h in place of x. Hence, as h approaches 0, we have

$$\lim_{h\to 0}\left(\sin x\cdot\frac{\cos h-1}{h}+\cos x\cdot\frac{\sin h}{h}\right)=\sin x\cdot 0+\cos x\cdot 1=\cos x.$$

Did you guess this result from the sketch of the derivative?

If $f(x)=\sin x$, then $f'(x)=\cos x$.

Derivative of the cosine function

Given that the derivative of the sine function is the cosine function, one might be tempted to guess that the opposite also holds. However, take some time to check the graph of $y=\cos x$ and you will see that as x increases from 0, the slope of the graph is *negative*, while the value of $\sin x$ for the same inputs is *positive*. If we visually analyze the graph of $y=\cos x$, however, we are soon led to a different conclusion.

If $f(x)=\cos x$, then $f'(x)=-\sin x$.

To verify this result, we take the limit of the difference quotient and make use of the addition formula for cosine:

$$\begin{aligned}\lim_{h\to 0}\frac{\cos(x+h)-\cos x}{h} &= \lim_{h\to 0}\frac{\cos x\cos h-\sin x\sin h-\cos x}{h}\\ &= \lim_{h\to 0}\left(\cos x\cdot\frac{\cos h-1}{h}-\sin x\cdot\frac{\sin h}{h}\right)\\ &= \cos x\cdot 0-\sin x\cdot 1=-\sin x.\end{aligned}$$

Derivatives of exponential functions

An exponential function f has the formula $f(x) = a^x$ for some base $a > 0$. Here is a limit fact that we will need to find the derivative of an exponential function.

$$\text{If } a > 0, \text{ then } \lim_{h \to 0} \frac{a^h - 1}{h} = \ln a.$$

If $f(x) = a^x$, then we use this limit along with the properties of exponents to calculate

$$\begin{aligned} f'(x) &= \lim_{h \to 0} \frac{f(x+h) - f(x)}{h} \\ &= \lim_{h \to 0} \frac{a^{x+h} - a^x}{h} \\ &= \lim_{h \to 0} \frac{a^x a^h - a^x}{h} \\ &= \lim_{h \to 0} a^x \left(\frac{a^h - 1}{h} \right) = a^x (\ln a). \end{aligned}$$

EXAMPLE 26 Suppose that $f(x) = 2^x$ and $g(x) = 3^x$. Find $f'(0)$, $f'(5)$, $g'(0)$, and $g'(-2)$.

Solution We have $f'(x) = 2^x(\ln 2)$ and $g'(x) = 3^x(\ln 3)$. Using these formulas, we have

$$f'(0) = 2^0(\ln 2) = \ln 2 \approx 0.6931471806,$$

$$f'(5) = 2^5(\ln 2) = 32 \ln 2 \approx 22.18070978,$$

$$g'(0) = 3^0(\ln 3) = \ln 3 \approx 1.098612289, \text{ and}$$

$$g'(-2) = 3^{-2}(\ln 3) = \frac{\ln 3}{9} \approx 0.1221680321.$$

■

Compare the values of $f'(0)$ and $g'(0)$ with the approximations we found in the previous section:

$$f'(0) \approx 0.693147 \quad \text{and} \quad g'(0) \approx 1.0986125.$$

EXAMPLE 27 Suppose that $f(x) = e^x$. Find a formula for $f'(x)$.

Solution $f'(x) = e^x(\ln e) = e^x \cdot 1 = e^x$. ■

This is quite remarkable! The derivative of the natural exponential function is itself!

EXERCISES for Section 3.4

You can use a machine grapher to approximate the graph of the derivative of a function by simply plotting the difference quotient

$$y = \frac{f(x+h) - f(x)}{h}$$

for a suitably small h.

For exercises 1–20:

(a) Graph the function over the interval $(0, 2)$ using a machine grapher. (The function may not be defined for some values in this interval.)

(b) On paper, make a rough sketch of the derivative of the function by visually estimating the slope at several points of your graph from part (a). Then plot the difference quotient function

$$y = \frac{f(x+.01) - f(x)}{.01}$$

using $h = .01$ and compare this graph with your sketch.

(c) Try to find another function g whose graph $y = g(x)$ resembles the difference quotient graph in part (b).

1. $f(x) = x^{2/3}$
2. $f(x) = x^{3/2}$
3. $f(x) = x^{4/3}$
4. $f(x) = x^{3/4}$
5. $f(x) = x^{-1/2}$
6. $f(x) = x^{-3}$
7. $f(x) = \arctan(x)$
8. $f(x) = \operatorname{arccot}(x)$
9. $f(x) = \ln x$
10. $f(x) = e^x$
11. $f(x) = \sin x$
12. $f(x) = \cos x$
13. $f(x) = \tan x$
14. $f(x) = \sec x$
15. $f(x) = \csc x$
16. $f(x) = \cot x$
17. $f(x) = \sin x^2$
18. $f(x) = \sin^2 x$
19. $f(x) = \sin^2 x + \cos^2 x$
20. $f(x) = \sin 2x$

For exercises 21–28: You are given the graph of a function on a grid. Assuming that the grid lines are spaced 1 unit apart both horizontally and vertically, sketch the graph of the derivative of each function over the same interval.

21.

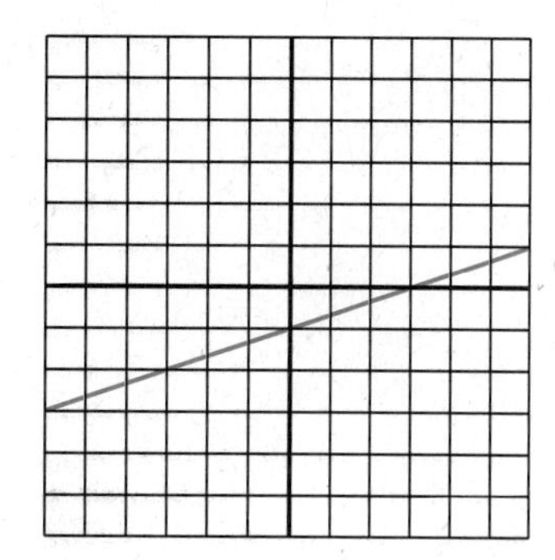

22.

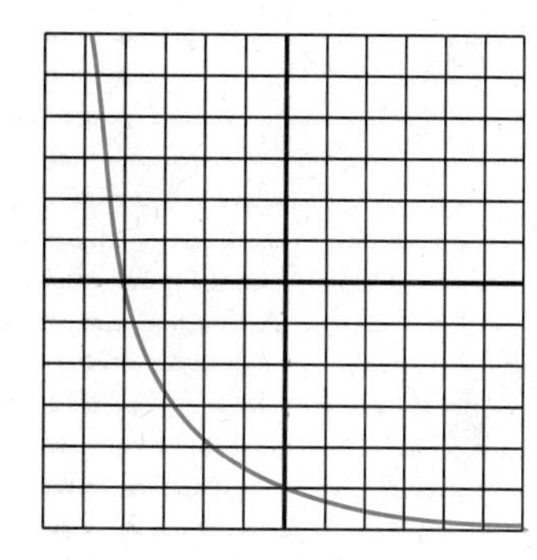

23.

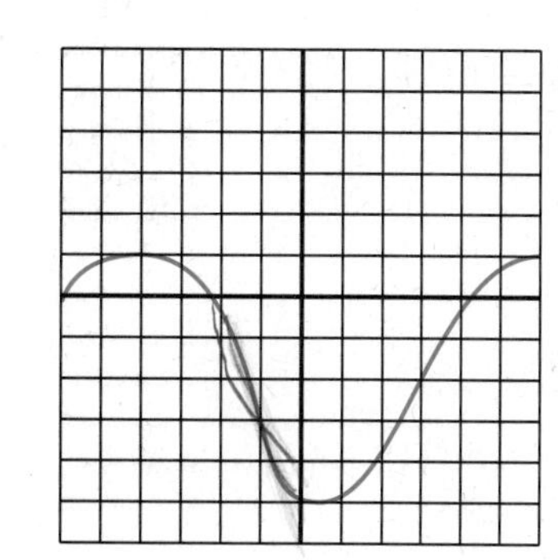

24.

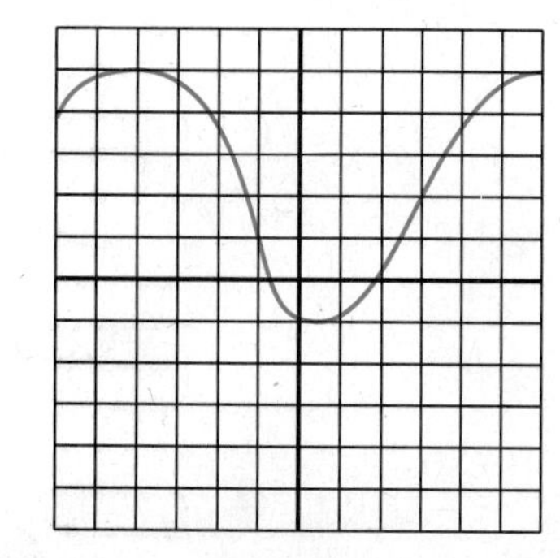

25.

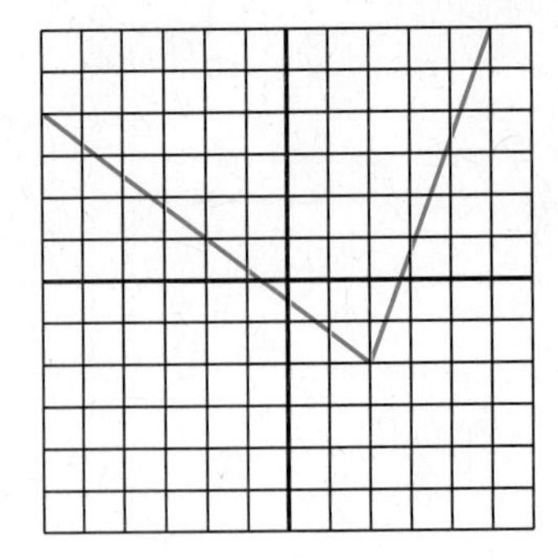

26.

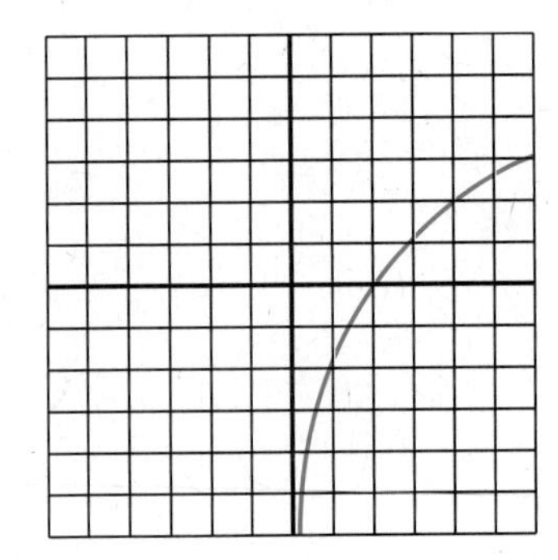

27.

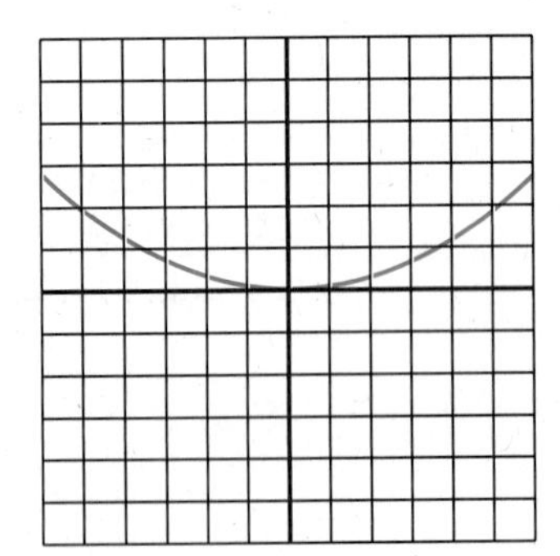

28.

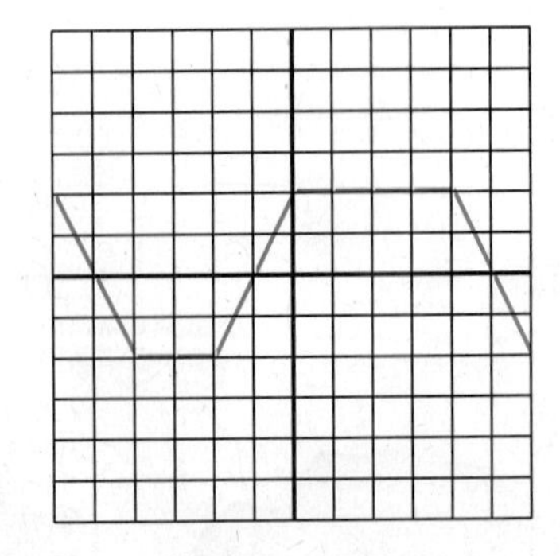

29. Which two functions in exercises 21–28 have exactly the same derivative graph?

30. If two different functions have exactly the same derivative, then explain in your own words how their graphs are alike and how they could be different.

For exercises 31–34: Find the derivative $f'(x)$ by calculating

$$f'(x) = \lim_{h \to 0} \frac{f(x+h) - f(x)}{h}.$$

31. $f(x) = \frac{1}{x}$

32. $f(x) = \sqrt{x}$

33. $f(x) = x^{-2}$

34. $f(x) = \frac{x^2}{4}$

We made use of a limit fact to find the derivative of an exponential function:

$$\lim_{h \to 0} \frac{a^h - 1}{h} = \ln a.$$

35. Investigate the limit numerically for $a = 10$. How small must h be for $\frac{10^h - 1}{h}$ to agree with $\ln 10$ to 5 decimal places?

36. Investigate the limit numerically for $a = 1/2$. How small must h be for $\frac{(1/2)^h - 1}{h}$ to agree with $\ln(1/2) = -\ln 2$ to 5 decimal places?

For exercises 37–40: Consider the functions f and g having formulas

$$f(x) = 10^x \quad \text{and} \quad g(x) = x^{10}.$$

37. Graph $y = f(x)$ and $y = g(x)$.

38. Show that $f(0) > g(0)$, $f(2) < g(2)$, and $f(10) = g(10)$. Find a value $0 < a < 2$ such that $f(a) = g(a)$ to 5 decimal places.

39. Calculate $f'(x)$ and $g'(x)$ using the formulas from this section.

40. Find a value b such that $f'(b) = g'(b)$ to 5 decimal places. What can you say about the graphs of $y = f(x)$ and $y = g(x)$ at $x = b$?

3.5 PHYSICAL INTERPRETATIONS OF THE DERIVATIVE

Leibniz notation for the derivative

There is another notation for derivative that emphasizes the connection to difference quotients:

Leibniz notation for the derivative If $y = f(x)$, then we write

$$\frac{dy}{dx} = f'(x) = y'.$$

The symbol $\frac{dy}{dx}$ is read simply as "dee-why-dee-ex" and was developed by Gottfried Leibniz (1646-1716). Along with Isaac Newton (1642-1727), Leibniz is generally credited as one of the inventors or discoverers of calculus. The appeal of this notation is the close symbolic similarity to the difference quotient. Indeed, if we use Δy and Δx to represent the change in function output and input, then we can rewrite the definition of the derivative using Leibniz notation.

Definition of derivative (in Leibniz notation)

$$\frac{dy}{dx} = \lim_{\Delta x \to 0} \frac{\Delta y}{\Delta x}.$$

The *single* quantity $\frac{dy}{dx}$ is the limit of the ratios $\frac{\Delta y}{\Delta x}$ as Δx approaches 0. Another way of thinking of the Leibniz notation is in terms of an *operator* acting on the function represented by y. That is, think of $\frac{dy}{dx}$ as

$$\frac{dy}{dx} = \frac{d}{dx}(y) = y'(x),$$

where $\frac{d}{dx}$ is read as "the derivative with respect to x of " and operates on the function expressed by y to produce the derivative y'.

This does not mean that you will never encounter the symbols dy and dx separately. For example, we could think of dx and dy as new variables related by the equation

$$dy = y'(x) \cdot dx.$$

Written this way, dy and dx are called **differentials**. Historically, the early users of calculus thought of dx and dy as infinitesimally small increments in input and output, respectively.

The prime notation makes it easy to distinguish between a derivative *function* f' and the specific numerical *value* of the derivative at a particular point $f'(x_0)$. The symbol dy/dx by itself does not tell us at which point x_0 we are measuring the slope or rate of change. To remedy this, we can use a long vertical bar with a subscript specifying this point.

Leibniz notation for the derivative at $x = x_0$

$$\left.\frac{dy}{dx}\right|_{x=x_0} = y'(x_0).$$

Now all the essential information to communicate a derivative at a specific point is present: the original dependent variable y, the derivative operator d/dx (which also tells us the independent variable), and the specific point x_0. The Leibniz notation

$$\frac{dy}{dx}$$

should be used to refer to the derivative *function*, while

$$\left.\frac{dy}{dx}\right|_{x=x_0}$$

should be used for the derivative's *value* at $x = x_0$. This notation using the vertical bar is read, "the value of $\frac{dy}{dx}$ where $x = x_0$."

EXAMPLE 28 If $y = x^5$, find $\frac{dy}{dx}$ and $\left.\frac{dy}{dx}\right|_{x=2}$.

Solution The derivative function is $\frac{dy}{dx} = 5x^4$, and its value at $x = 2$ is

$$\left.\frac{dy}{dx}\right|_{x=2} = 5 \cdot 2^4 = 5 \cdot 16 = 80.$$

■

We will see that the Leibniz notation for derivatives has a few advantages. Many properties and rules about derivatives resemble simple algebraic facts involving differentials when written in Leibniz notation. That can help us as an aid to remember these derivative facts. If a particular function name or dependent variable label is not important, then the Leibniz notation can be used with the function formula itself. For example,

$$\frac{d}{dx}(x^3)\bigg|_{x=5} = (3x^2)\bigg|_{x=5} = 3 \cdot 5^2 = 3 \cdot 25 = 75.$$

So far, we have been using y to represent the dependent variable (output) and x to represent the independent variable (input). There are many situations where other letters may be used, particularly for their mnemonic value. For example, if we are investigating the change in atmospheric pressure over time, then we might use p (for pressure) to represent the dependent variable and t (for time) to represent the independent variable. The instantaneous rate of change of pressure with respect to time can be denoted

$$p'(t) = \frac{dp}{dt}.$$

EXAMPLE 29 The area A of a circle of radius r is given by the formula

$$A = \pi r^2.$$

Find $A'(r) = \dfrac{dA}{dr}$ using the definition of derivative.

Solution In this case, our independent variable is r and the dependent variable is A. Using ΔA and Δr to represent increments in these variables, we have

$$\begin{aligned}
A'(r) = \frac{dA}{dr} &= \lim_{\Delta r \to 0} \frac{\Delta A}{\Delta r} \\
&= \lim_{\Delta r \to 0} \frac{A(r + \Delta r) - A(r)}{\Delta r} \\
&= \lim_{\Delta r \to 0} \frac{\pi(r + \Delta r)^2 - \pi r^2}{\Delta r} \\
&= \lim_{\Delta r \to 0} \frac{\pi(r^2 + 2r\Delta r + \Delta r^2) - \pi r^2}{\Delta r} \\
&= \lim_{\Delta r \to 0} \frac{\pi r^2 + 2\pi r\Delta r + \pi\Delta r^2 - \pi r^2}{\Delta r} \\
&= \lim_{\Delta r \to 0} \frac{2\pi r\Delta r + \pi\Delta r^2}{\Delta r} \\
&= \lim_{\Delta r \to 0} (2\pi r + \pi\Delta r) \\
&= 2\pi r.
\end{aligned}$$

Hence, $A'(r) = \dfrac{dA}{dr} = 2\pi r$. ■

Other notations for derivative

There are other notations for derivative that enjoy quite a bit of use, particularly in the study of differential equations. One of these, called *operator notation*, is denoted by a D prefixed to the function name. In operator notation, we can write

$$Df \qquad \text{or} \qquad Dy$$

to denote the derivative of a function $y = f(x)$.

We can add a subscript to D to indicate the independent variable. The notation $D_x y$ means the derivative of y with respect to x, and $D_t p$ means the derivative of p with respect to t.

Newtonian notation for the derivative (named after Newton) employs a dot over the function name instead of the prime symbol. In Newtonian notation, we can write

$$\dot{f} \qquad \text{or} \qquad \dot{y}$$

to denote the derivative of a function $y = f(x)$.

The fact that there are so many different notations for derivatives is testimony to their widespread use. The preferred notation depends on the context, but in this book we will use the prime notation and the Leibniz notation almost exclusively.

Derivative as rate of change

When we consider the derivative as rate of change, we should be aware of the units describing a function's inputs and outputs. We can interpret the derivative as measuring the number of units change in the dependent variable per unit change in the independent variable. For example, if $y = f(x)$ is measured in centimeters (cm) and x is measured in grams (g), then the values of the derivative dy/dx will have units of centimeters per gram (cm/g).

The idea of a derivative as measuring rate of change is extremely important to keep in mind and helps us identify when the derivative is the right mathematical tool to use. In each of the examples below, we'll examine the reasonableness of this idea by comparing the value of the derivative (instantaneous rate) with the value of the difference quotient (average rate) over a very small change in the independent variable.

EXAMPLE 30 Computer chips are manufactured by etching circuits on square wafers of silicon. The error tolerance acceptable in the production of these chips is very small. You operate a machine that cuts out wafers of side length

5 centimeters, and you need to know how much the area A of the wafer changes if the actual side length x differs from the 5 cm setting. Find dA/dx and interpret it as a rate of change of A with respect to the length of its side x when $x = 5$ cm.

Solution As a function of its side length x, the area A of a square wafer is given by the formula

$$A = x^2.$$

We compute $\frac{dA}{dx} = 2x$. Since x is measured in *centimeters*, A is measured in *square centimeters*. The units of $\frac{dA}{dx}$ are *square centimeters per centimeter*. When $x = 5$ cm, the rate of change of A with respect to x is

$$\left.\frac{dA}{dx}\right|_{x=5\text{ cm}} = 10\ \frac{\text{cm}^2}{\text{cm}}.$$

In this example, it's tempting to reduce the units $\frac{\text{cm}^2}{\text{cm}}$ to simply cm, but that would disguise the true nature of $\frac{dA}{dx}$ as a rate of change of one quantity relative to another. When the length of a side of a square wafer is 5 cm, the rate of change of its area is 10 square centimeters increase per centimeter increase in length of the side. ■

The reasonableness of the derivative formula $\frac{dA}{dx} = 2x$ can be seen geometrically if we approximate the difference quotient $\frac{\Delta A}{\Delta x}$ for a small change Δx in the length of the side. Figure 3.19 illustrates that when we increase the length of the side by a small amount Δx, most of the change in area ΔA is accounted for by the sum of the areas of two thin rectangles $2x\Delta x$.

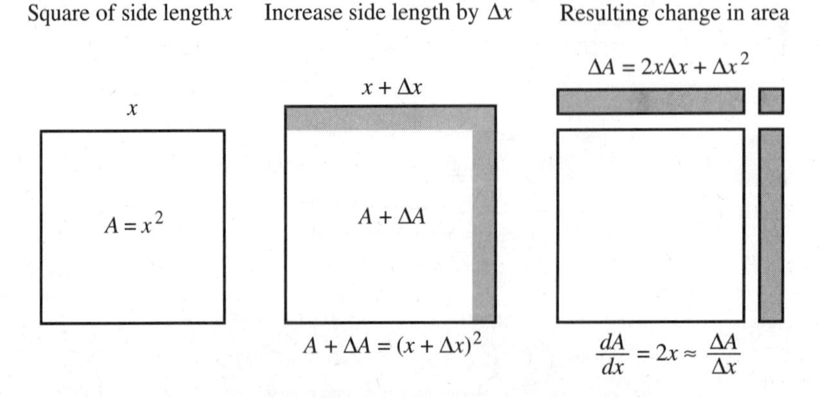

Figure 3.19 Rate of change in area of the square.

If we use this approximation of ΔA to compute the difference quotient, we have

$$\frac{\Delta A}{\Delta x} \approx \frac{2x\Delta x}{\Delta x} = 2x = \frac{dA}{dx}.$$

The error between this approximate difference quotient and the true difference quotient is simply $(\Delta x)^2/\Delta x = \Delta x$. (We're missing the area of the small square in the numerator ΔA.) As Δx approaches 0, the relative contribution of this error vanishes.

EXAMPLE 31 You are growing crystals having the shape of cubes. When the side of a crystal grows beyond a length of 2 mm, you harvest the material by "shaving" the substance from the surface of the crystal. You want to know how much the volume V of the crystalline substance increases as the length of the side x increases beyond 2 mm. Compute $\dfrac{dV}{dx}$ and interpret it as a rate of change when $x = 2$ mm.

Solution As a function of the length of its side x, the volume V of a cube is given by the formula

$$V = x^3.$$

We calculate $\dfrac{dV}{dx} = 3x^2$. Since x is measured in *millimeters*, V is measured in *cubic millimeters*. The units of $\dfrac{dV}{dx}$ are cubic mm per mm. When $x = 2$ mm, the rate of change of V with respect to x is

$$\left.\frac{dV}{dx}\right|_{x=2\text{ mm}} = 3 \cdot 2^2 = 12\ \frac{\text{mm}^3}{\text{mm}}.$$

■

Figure 3.20 illustrates that most of the change in volume ΔV after a small increase Δx in the length of the side is accounted for by the three flat square "slabs," whose total volume is $3x^2\Delta x$ (using $length \cdot width \cdot thickness$ and adding the results). Using this as an approximation for ΔV gives us

$$\frac{\Delta V}{\Delta x} \approx \frac{3x^2\Delta x}{\Delta x} = 3x^2 = \frac{dV}{dx}.$$

The error in our approximation to $\dfrac{\Delta V}{\Delta x}$ is

$$\frac{3x(\Delta x)^2 + (\Delta x)^3}{\Delta x} = 3x\Delta x + (\Delta x)^2.$$

Again, the smaller Δx is, the more insignificant this error.

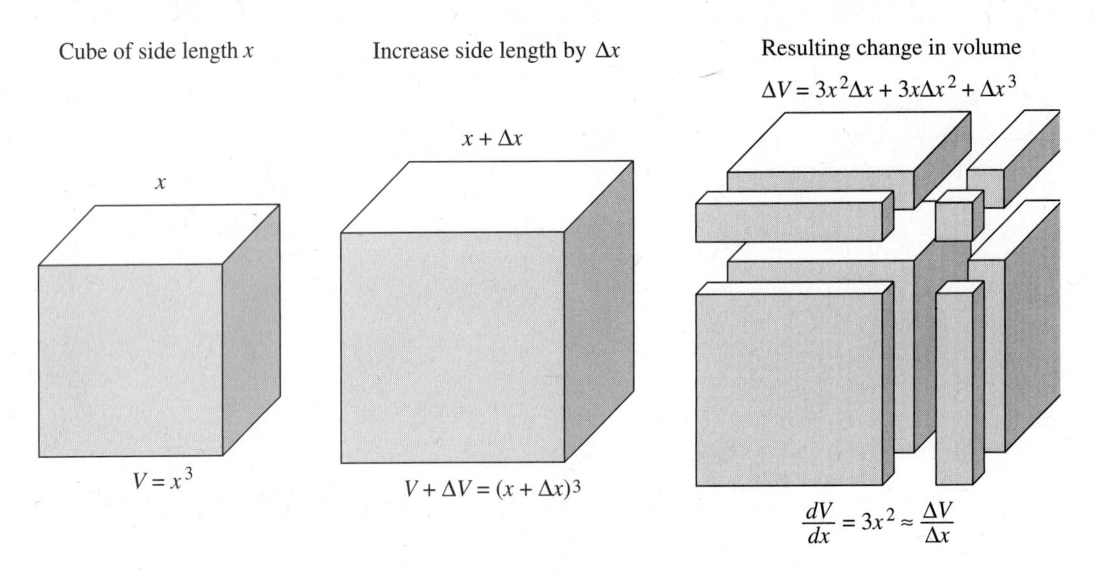

Figure 3.20 Rate of change in volume of the cube.

EXAMPLE 32 An oil spill spreads out as a circular slick on the surface of the ocean. After two days, the radius of the slick is 7 km. You want to know how the contaminated area A will grow if the radius r of the slick continues to spread beyond 7 km. Compute $\frac{dA}{dr}$ and interpret it as a rate of change of A with respect to the radius r when $r = 7$ km.

Solution As a function of its radius r, the area A of a circle is given by the formula $A = \pi r^2$. We calculate $\frac{dA}{dr} = 2\pi r$. (Remember, π is a *constant.*) Since r is measured in kilometers, A is measured in square kilometers. The units of $\frac{dA}{dr}$ are km^2 per km. When $r = 7$ km, the rate of change of A with respect to r is

$$\left.\frac{dA}{dr}\right|_{r=7\text{ km}} = 14\pi\ \frac{\text{km}^2}{\text{km}}.$$

■

The change in area ΔA corresponding to a small change in radius Δr corresponds to the area of a thin *annulus*, or band, as shown in Figure 3.21.

If we imagine "snipping" the band and straightening it out to a long strip, we can see that the area of the band should be reasonably close to the product of its length ($\approx 2\pi r$, the circumference of the original circle) and its thickness Δr. Using this as our approximation for ΔA gives us

$$\frac{\Delta A}{\Delta r} \approx \frac{2\pi r \Delta r}{\Delta r} = 2\pi r = \frac{dA}{dr}.$$

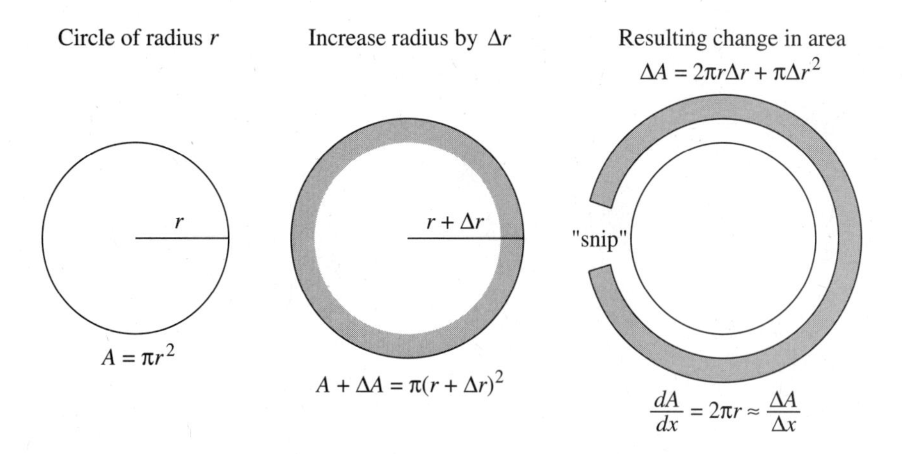

Figure 3.21 Rate of change in area of the circle.

Position and velocity

One of the most important uses of differential calculus is in the study of motion and force in physics. Indeed, we used the motion of a car as our motivating example of a derivative as a speedometer reading. Let's resume that discussion now.

To avoid confusion with the Leibniz notation's d, we'll use s to denote the *position of the car as a function of time* t . Now, if s is a differentiable function of t, then its derivative gives us the **velocity**, or instantaneous rate of change of position, with respect to t. We write v for velocity, so that

$$v(t) = \frac{ds}{dt} = s'(t).$$

In our initial discussion of the car's motion, we used the term *speed* instead of *velocity* . Velocity is really a more accurate term for our purposes, since speed refers to how fast the car is moving, while velocity also tells us the *direction of motion*. If our car travels in a straight line, we can interpret a *positive* velocity $v = 40$ mph as *forward* motion, while a *negative* velocity $v = -40$ mph should be interpreted as *reverse* motion at the same speed. In other words, speed gives us the *magnitude* (absolute value) of velocity, or

$$\text{speed} = |\text{velocity}|.$$

For vertical motion, positive and negative velocity will correspond to upward and downward movement, but exactly which will depend on how we choose to measure the position. In one setting, we might measure the depth of a canyon as a positive distance. In another setting, we might choose to measure height above sea level, so that the same canyon floor might be considered to be at a negative height.

EXAMPLE 33 The vertical height s (in feet) of a ball thrown upwards from a tall building is described by the position function

$$s(t) = -16t^2 + 96t + 640,$$

where t is measured in seconds.

Calculate the velocity $v(t) = s'(t)$ and use this to answer the following questions:

(a) What is the initial velocity (at time $t = 0$)?

(b) What is the height of the ball when the velocity is 0?

(c) What is the velocity of the ball when it returns to earth ($s = 0$)?

Solution The velocity is

$$\begin{aligned} v(t) &= \frac{ds}{dt} = s'(t) \\ &= \lim_{h\to 0} \frac{s(t+h) - s(t)}{h} \\ &= \lim_{h\to 0} \frac{(-16(t+h)^2 + 96(t+h) + 640) - (-16t^2 + 96t + 640)}{h} \\ &= \lim_{h\to 0} \frac{-16t^2 - 32th - 16h^2 + 96t + 96h + 640 + 16t^2 - 96t - 640}{h} \\ &= \lim_{h\to 0} \frac{h(-16h - 32t + 96)}{h} \\ &= \lim_{h\to 0} (-16h - 32t + 96) \\ &= -32t + 96. \end{aligned}$$

The units of the velocity $v(t)$ are feet per second.

(a) The initial velocity is

$$v(0) = f'(0) = -32 \cdot 0 + 96 = 96 \text{ feet per sec.}$$

(b) The velocity is 0 when $-32t + 96 = 0$. Solving for t, we have $t = 3$ seconds. Now, substituting $t = 3$ back into the original position function to find the ball's height, we have

$$s(3) = -16 \cdot 3^2 + 96 \cdot 3 + 640 = 784 \text{ feet.}$$

(c) $s = 0$ when $-16t^2 + 96t + 640 = 0$. Dividing both sides by -16 yields

$$t^2 - 6t - 40 = 0.$$

The solutions to this quadratic equation are

$$t = 10 \text{ sec} \qquad \text{and} \qquad t = -4 \text{ sec}.$$

The second solution satisfies the quadratic equation but does not make sense in this particular physical setting. (We assume that we cannot go back in time.) Using $t = 10$ in our expression for velocity gives us

$$v(10) = -32 \cdot 10 + 96 = -224 \text{ feet per sec}.$$

The negative value for the velocity indicates that the ball was heading downward (naturally) when it hit the ground. ■

EXERCISES for Section 3.5

For exercises 1–6: A spherical weather balloon is being inflated with helium. You are interested in keeping the balloon aloft as long as possible, but you must also be sensitive to overinflating the balloon.

As a function of its radius r, the volume of a sphere is given by the formula

$$V = \frac{4}{3}\pi r^3.$$

An illustration of a sphere of radius r and a sphere of slightly larger radius $r + \Delta r$ is shown. The change in volume is the volume of the shell.

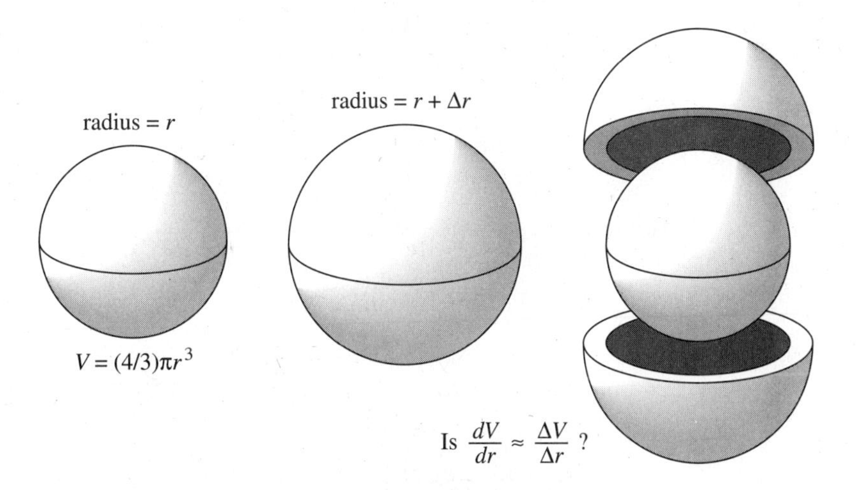

For Exercises 1–6

1. If the radius of the balloon is 36 inches and the balloon expands in radius by 3 inches, how much does the volume of the balloon change? What is the average rate of change of the volume of the balloon per inch change in radius?

2. If the radius of the balloon is 48 inches and the balloon expands in radius by 2 inches, how much does the volume of the balloon change? What is the average rate of change of the volume of the balloon per inch change in radius?

3. If the radius of the balloon is r inches and the balloon expands in radius by Δr inches, find ΔV, the change in volume of the balloon. What is the average rate of change of the volume of the balloon per inch change in radius?

4. For a small change in radius Δr, we can approximate the change in volume ΔV by taking the product of the surface area of the original sphere ($4\pi r^2$) and the thickness of the shell Δr. Use this idea to approximate the difference quotient $\dfrac{\Delta V}{\Delta r}$.

5. Find $\dfrac{dV}{dr}$ and compare it with the approximation in exercise 4.

6. Interpret $\dfrac{dV}{dr}$ as a rate of change when $r = 36$ inches and when $r = 48$ inches.

---

7. The perimeter P of a square computer chip must be coated with a special substance for handling. You need to know how much this perimeter changes as length of the side x differs from a 5 cm setting. Calculate $\dfrac{dP}{dx}$ and interpret it as a rate of change of P with respect to the length of the side x when $x = 5$ cm.

8. The length of the side of a second type of chip requires a setting of 3.6 cm. Again, you need to know how much the area A and the perimeter P change as the length of the side x varies from its 3.6 cm setting. Calculate and interpret $\dfrac{dA}{dx}$ and $\dfrac{dP}{dx}$ as rates of change with respect to the length x when $x = 3.6$ cm.

9. These computer chips are handled by robots. The "claw" of the robot's hand must be open wide enough to grip the chip from corner to opposite corner. If y represents the diagonal length of the square computer chip, you want to know how this grip distance changes as the side length of the chip x differs from a 3.6 cm setting. Calculate $\dfrac{dy}{dx}$ and interpret it as a rate of change of y with respect to the length x of its side when $x = 5$ cm and when $x = 3.6$ cm.

10. To harvest a substance from cubic crystals, you find a better method than scraping the substance off the surface. Instead, you soak the crystals in a special acid solution that strips the substance from all sides of the crystal at once. To know how much of the solution to use, you need to know how the surface area S of the cube changes as a function of the length x of its side. Calculate $\dfrac{dS}{dx}$ and interpret it as a rate of change of S with respect to x when x is 2 mm.

11. Once these cubic crystals have been harvested, they will be sucked out of the acid solution through a small glass pipe so that they can continue to grow. The main diagonal z of a cube (from corner to far opposite corner) determines the minimal diameter of the pipe you'll need. You need to know how z changes as a function of the length of the side x. Calculate $\frac{dz}{dx}$ and interpret it as a rate of change of z with respect to x when x is 2 mm.

12. A ship must drop several warning buoys around the circumference of a circular oil slick to alert fishing boats of its presence. If the radius r of the slick continues to grow, the captain wants to know how much the circumference C will increase. Find $\frac{dC}{dr}$ and interpret it as a rate of change with respect to the radius r when $r = 7$ km.

For exercises 13–27: A falling object released from a height of 15 meters has the position function

$$s(t) = (15 - 6.729 \cdot t^2)$$

describing its height as a function of elapsed time. Here t is measured in seconds and $s(t)$ is measured in meters.

13. Find $s(0)$. (How high is the object when it is released?)

14. Find when the object is exactly two meters off the ground.

15. Find how high the object is at $t = 0.3$ seconds.

16. Find when the object hits the ground. (For what value of t is $s(t) = 0$ meters?)

17. How far off the ground is the object exactly 0.5 seconds before it hits the ground?

18. Graph $y = s(t)$ for the time interval from the object's initial release to the time it hits the ground.

19. Find the average velocity (in meters per second) of the object over the time from release until it hits the ground.

20. Find the average velocity of the object between $t = 0.3$ seconds and $t = 0.4$ seconds.

21. Find the average velocity of the object between $t = 0.29$ seconds and $t = 0.3$ seconds.

22. Find the average velocity of the object between $t = 0.3$ seconds and $t = 0.301$ seconds.

23. Compute the instantaneous speed (in meters per second) of the object (by computing a limit of difference quotients) at $t = 0.3$ seconds.

24. Compute the velocity $v(t)$ of the object at any time t.

25. What is the velocity of the object at the instant it hits the ground?

26. At what moment is the instantaneous velocity of the object the same as its average velocity over the entire drop time (exercise 19)?

27. Graph $y = v(t)$ for the time interval from the object's initial release to the time it hits the ground. Calculate $\frac{dv}{dt}$ and interpret it graphically. What are the units of measurement for $\frac{dv}{dt}$?

For exercises 28–30: An open cone is manufactured by cutting a sector (piece of pie) of angle θ out of a circular sheet of radius $R = 6$ inches and then connecting the edges of the remaining piece of material.

28. Express the area A of the cut-out sector of the circle as a function of the sector angle θ (measured in radians). Calculate $\frac{dA}{d\theta}$ and interpret it as a rate of change when θ is $\pi/4$ radians.

29. Express the circumference C of the opening of the cone as a function of θ. Calculate $\frac{dC}{d\theta}$ and interpret it as a rate of change when θ is $\pi/3$ radians.

30. Express the external surface area S of the open cone as a function of θ. Calculate $\frac{dS}{d\theta}$ and interpret it as a rate of change when θ is $\pi/2$ radians.

3.6 NEW DERIVATIVES FROM OLD—RULES OF DIFFERENTIATION

Given two functions f and g, we can build several new functions:

$$f + g, \qquad f - g, \qquad fg, \qquad \frac{f}{g}.$$

The domains of these new functions depend on the domains of f and g. When f and g are differentiable, we'd like to have some way of determining if these new functions are also differentiable and how their derivatives are related to f' and g'. In this section we discuss the basic rules governing how to find these new derivatives without the need to resort to the formal definition.

The linearity rule

Keep in mind that the derivative of a function measures the slope of its graph, provided that the function is differentiable (meaning that it is approximately *locally* linear). We might ask what happens when we combine two *globally* linear functions. For example, if

$$f(x) = m_1 x + b_1 \qquad \text{and} \qquad g(x) = m_2 x + b_2,$$

then the formulas for $f + g$ and $f - g$ are

$$(f + g)(x) = (m_1 + m_2)x + (b_1 + b_2)$$
$$(f - g)(x) = (m_1 - m_2)x + (b_1 - b_2).$$

We can see that $f + g$ and $f - g$ are also linear and that their graphs have slopes $m_1 + m_2$ and $m_1 - m_2$, respectively. If we multiply a linear function by a constant, the new function is also linear. For example, if $f(x) = mx + b$ and c is a constant, then $cf(x) = cmx + cb$ and the slope is cm.

The results are similar for locally linear functions. If f and g are both locally linear, then $f + g$, $f - g$, and cf will also be locally linear. Moreover, at any point where both slopes exist, the slope of the sum function is the sum of the slopes, and the slope of the difference function is the difference in the slopes. If we multiple a locally linear function by a constant, the slope at each point is multiplied by the same constant.

It is perhaps not so suprising that properties that hold for globally and locally linear functions also hold for differentiable functions that are approximately locally linear.

> For two differentiable functions f and g:
>
> $$(f + g)' = f' + g' \qquad (f - g)' = f' - g'.$$
>
> If we use u to represent $f(x)$ and v to represent $g(x)$, then in Leibniz notation we have:
>
> $$\frac{d(u + v)}{dx} = \frac{du}{dx} + \frac{dv}{dx} \qquad \frac{d(u - v)}{dx} = \frac{du}{dx} - \frac{dv}{dx}.$$

These sum and difference rules for derivatives follow from the algebra of limits applied to the difference quotients. For the sum rule,

$$(f+g)'(x) = \lim_{h\to 0} \frac{(f+g)(x+h)-(f+g)(x)}{h}$$
$$= \lim_{h\to 0} \frac{[f(x+h)+g(x+h)]-[f(x)+g(x)]}{h}$$
$$= \lim_{h\to 0} \frac{[f(x+h)-f(x)]+[g(x+h)-g(x)]}{h}$$
$$= \lim_{h\to 0} \left(\frac{f(x+h)-f(x)}{h} + \frac{g(x+h)-g(x)}{h}\right)$$
$$= f'(x)+g'(x).$$

(The difference property is verified in a similar way.)

EXAMPLE 34 Find $f'(x)$ if $f(x) = x^2 + 5x$.

Solution $f'(x) = \dfrac{d}{dx}(x^2) + \dfrac{d}{dx}(5x) = 2x + 5.$ ■

EXAMPLE 35 Find $\dfrac{dy}{dx}$ if $y = x^3 - \sin x$.

Solution $\dfrac{dy}{dx} = \dfrac{d}{dx}(x^3 - \sin x) = 3x^2 - \cos x.$ ■

If f is a differentiable function and c is a constant, then

$$(cf)' = cf'.$$

In Leibniz notation,

$$\frac{d(cy)}{dx} = c\frac{dy}{dx}.$$

EXAMPLE 36 Find $\dfrac{d}{dx}(5\sin x)$.

Solution $\dfrac{d}{dx}(5\sin x) = 5 \cdot \dfrac{d}{dx}(\sin x) = 5\cos x.$ ■

The constant multiple property holds because we can factor the constant out of the difference quotient:

$$(cf)'(x) = \lim_{h\to 0} \frac{cf(x+h)-cf(x)}{h} = \lim_{h\to 0} c\left[\frac{f(x+h)-f(x)}{h}\right] = cf'(x).$$

Taking all these properties together, we can summarize the *linearity rule*.

Linearity rule for differentiation

If f and g are differentiable and a and b are constants, then

$$(af + bg)' = af' + bg'.$$

In Leibniz notation, if u and v are differentiable functions of x, then

$$\frac{d}{dx}(au + bv) = a\frac{du}{dx} + b\frac{dv}{dx}.$$

The linearity rule allows us to take the derivative of any polynomial function easily.

EXAMPLE 37 Find $f'(x)$ if $f(x) = 3x^4 - 5x^2 + \frac{x}{3} - \sqrt{2}$.

Solution $f'(x) = 3(4x^3) - 5(2x) + \frac{1}{3} \cdot 1 = 12x^3 - 10x + \frac{1}{3}$. ■

EXAMPLE 38 Find $\frac{dy}{dx}$ when $y = \frac{4x - 2x^5}{7}$.

Solution Since $\frac{4x - 2x^5}{7} = \frac{4}{7}x - \frac{2}{7}x^5$, we have $\frac{dy}{dx} = \frac{4}{7} - \frac{10}{7}x^4 = \frac{4 - 10x^4}{7}$. ■

EXAMPLE 39 Find $\frac{ds}{dt}$ when $s(t) = -16t^2 + 96t + 640$.

Solution $s'(t) = -16(2t) + 96 + 0 = -32t + 96$. ■

The product rule and quotient rule

The linearity rule for derivatives is very natural. What happens when we differentiate the *product* or *quotient* of two functions? First, let's note that even if f and g are *linear*, fg and f/g are *not* linear in general, as we can see from their formulas:

$$(fg)(x) = (m_1 m_2)x^2 + (m_1 b_2 + m_2 b_1)x + b_1 b_2$$

$$\frac{f}{g}(x) = \frac{m_1 x + b_1}{m_2 x + b_2}.$$

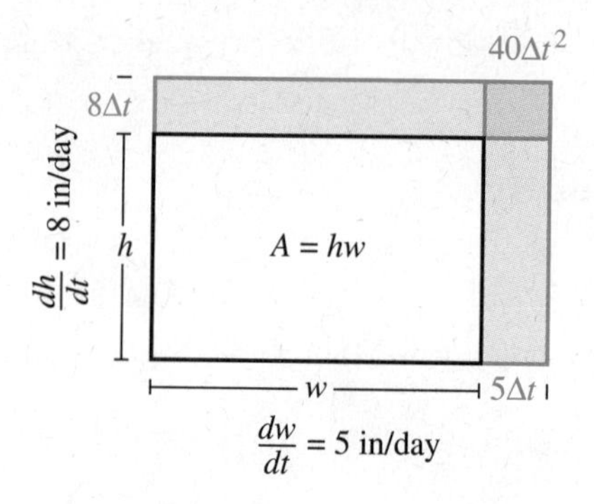

Figure 3.22 Rate of area change for a growing rectangular plot of vegetation.

This tells us at once that we should not expect the rules for products and quotients to be quite as simple as for sums and differences. Let's look at a concrete example to reason what the product rule for derivatives should be.

A rectangular plot of vegetation (weeds) is free to grow in two directions. Due to differences in the availability of sunlight, the plot grows faster in one direction than the other. The width w of the plot grows at a rate of $\frac{dw}{dt} = 5$ inches per day, and the length h of the plot grows at a rate of $\frac{dh}{dt} = 8$ inches per day.

Figure 3.22 depicts what our rectangle of width w and length h might look like one day, and then a few days later. At what rate is the *area* A of the vegetation growing? If we use Δt to represent elapsed time (in days), then

$$\text{new width } \approx w + 5\Delta t \qquad \text{and} \qquad \text{new length } \approx h + 8\Delta t.$$

The change in area ΔA is represented by the sum of the areas of the three shaded rectangles in the illustration:

$$\Delta A = h \cdot 5\Delta t + w \cdot 8\Delta t + (5\Delta t) \cdot (8\Delta t).$$

If we form the difference quotient $\frac{\Delta A}{\Delta t}$, then

$$\frac{\Delta A}{\Delta t} = 5h + 8w + 40\Delta t.$$

As the elapsed time Δt approaches 0, so does the last term $40\Delta t$, and we have

$$\frac{dA}{dt} = 5h + 8w = \frac{dw}{dt} \cdot h + \frac{dh}{dt} \cdot w.$$

This example illustrates how the product of two quantities changes when the two quantities change at different *constant rates*. The same relationship holds even when the rates are not constant. This result is known as the *product rule*.

Product rule for differentiation
If f and g are differentiable functions, then

$$(fg)' = f'g + fg'.$$

In Leibniz notation,

$$\frac{d(uv)}{dx} = \frac{du}{dx}v + u\frac{dv}{dx}.$$

The product rule can be verified formally by using a little clever algebra on the difference quotient for the product:

$$\begin{aligned}
(fg)'(x) &= \lim_{h\to 0} \frac{(fg)(x+h) - (fg)(x)}{h} \\
&= \lim_{h\to 0} \frac{f(x+h)g(x+h) - f(x)g(x)}{h} \\
&= \lim_{h\to 0} \left(\frac{f(x+h)g(x+h) - f(x)g(x+h) + f(x)g(x+h) - f(x)g(x)}{h} \right) \\
&= \lim_{h\to 0} g(x+h)\frac{f(x+h) - f(x)}{h} + \lim_{h\to 0} f(x)\frac{g(x+h) - g(x)}{h} \\
&= g(x)f'(x) + f(x)g'(x).
\end{aligned}$$

Some commentary is in order. Note that in the third line, we subtracted the new expression $f(x)g(x+h)$ in the numerator and then added it right back, resulting in no change in the value of the quotient. In the fourth line, we broke this complicated quotient into two terms. Look! The usual difference quotient we use for computing $f'(x)$ is a factor of the first term and the difference quotient for computing $g'(x)$ is a factor of the second term. As h approaches 0, $g(x+h)$ approaches $g(x)$, and the two difference quotients approach $f'(x)$ and $g'(x)$, respectively.

EXAMPLE 40 Find $\frac{dy}{dx}$ when $y = (5x^2 - 3)(2x^3 + 7x)$, using the product rule.

Solution We can consider y to be the product of

$$u = 5x^2 - 3 \qquad \text{and} \qquad v = 2x^3 + 7x.$$

Using the product rule, we have

$$\begin{aligned}\frac{dy}{dx} = \frac{d}{dx}(uv) &= \frac{du}{dx}\cdot v + u\cdot\frac{dv}{dx}\\ &= (10x)(2x^3+7x) + (5x^2-3)(6x^2+7)\\ &= 20x^4 + 70x^2 + 30x^4 - 18x^2 + 35x^2 - 21\\ &= 50x^4 + 87x^2 - 21.\end{aligned}$$

■

EXAMPLE 41 Find $\frac{dy}{dx}$ when $y = (5x^2-3)(2x^3+7x)$ by first expanding the product and then taking the derivative.

Solution Since $y = (5x^2-3)(2x^3+7x) = 10x^5 + 29x^3 - 21x$, we have

$$\frac{dy}{dx} = 50x^4 + 87x^2 - 21.$$

■

When taking the derivative of a product of polynomials, we see that we now have an alternative. For products of other functions, we may have no choice but to use the product rule.

EXAMPLE 42 Find $\frac{df}{dx}$ when $f(x) = x^3 \sin x$.

Solution $\frac{df}{dx} = \frac{d}{dx}(x^3)\cdot\sin x + x^3\cdot\frac{d}{dx}(\sin x) = 3x^2\sin x + x^3\cos x.$ ■

For a product of three or more functions, we need to apply the product rule more than once.

EXAMPLE 43 Find y' when $y = 4x^2 \sin x \cos x$.

Solution We see that y is the product of three functions:

$$u = 4x^2 \qquad v = \sin x \qquad w = \cos x.$$

To use the product rule on $y = uvw$, we think of y first as the product $u\cdot(vw)$, so that

$$\begin{aligned}\frac{dy}{dx} &= \frac{d(4x^2)}{dx}(\sin x\cos x) + 4x^2\frac{d(\sin x\cos x)}{dx}\\ &= 8x\sin x\cos x + 4x^2\cdot\left[\frac{d(\sin x)}{dx}\cos x + \sin x\frac{d(\cos x)}{dx}\right]\\ &= 8x\sin x\cos x + 4x^2\cos^2 x - 4x^2\sin^2 x.\end{aligned}$$

■

Note that we had to apply the product rule a second time in this example. In general, if $y = uvw$, then

$$y' = u'vw + uv'w + uvw'.$$

The constant multiple rule is just a special case of the product rule. If we think of cf as the product of a constant function c (meaning $x \longmapsto c$ for each x) and the function f, then applying the product rule, we have

$$(cf)' = 0 \cdot f + c \cdot f' = cf'.$$

Quotient rule

Suppose that k, g, and f are differentiable functions such that

$$f = kg.$$

If we take the derivative of f using the product rule, then

$$f' = k'g + kg'.$$

Now, if we substitute $k = f/g$ and solve for k', we get the *quotient rule*:

Quotient rule for differentiation

If f and g are differentiable, and $k(x) = \dfrac{f(x)}{g(x)}$, then

$$k' = \left(\frac{f}{g}\right)' = \frac{f'g - fg'}{g^2},$$

which is valid for any value x at which $g(x) \neq 0$.

In Leibniz notation, if $y = u/v$, then

$$\frac{dy}{dx} = \frac{\frac{du}{dx} \cdot v - u \cdot \frac{dv}{dx}}{v^2}.$$

The quotient rule allows us to take the derivative of any rational function (quotient of two polynomial functions).

EXAMPLE 44 Find $\dfrac{dy}{dx}$ when $y = \dfrac{2x^3 - 5x + 7}{x^2 - 3x}$.

Solution Letting $u = 2x^3 - 5x + 7$ and $v = x^2 - 3x$, we have

$$\begin{aligned}\frac{dy}{dx} &= \frac{\frac{du}{dx} \cdot v - u \cdot \frac{dv}{dx}}{v^2} \\ &= \frac{(6x^2 - 5)(x^2 - 3x) - (2x^3 - 5x + 7)(2x - 3)}{(x^2 - 3x)^2} \\ &= \frac{6x^4 - 18x^3 - 5x^2 + 15x - 4x^4 + 6x^3 + 10x^2 - 15x - 14x + 21}{x^4 - 6x^3 + 9x^2} \\ &= \frac{2x^4 - 12x^3 + 5x^2 - 14x + 21}{x^4 - 6x^3 + 9x^2}.\end{aligned}$$

■

More derivative formulas

The product and quotient rules can now be used to develop some new derivative formulas.

EXAMPLE 45 Find the derivative formula for $\frac{d}{dx}(\tan x)$.

Solution Since $\tan x = \frac{\sin x}{\cos x}$, we have

$$\begin{aligned}\frac{d}{dx}(\tan x) &= \frac{\frac{d}{dx}(\sin x) \cdot \cos x - \sin x \cdot \frac{d}{dx}(\cos x)}{\cos^2 x} \\ &= \frac{\cos^2 x + \sin^2 x}{\cos^2 x} = \frac{1}{\cos^2 x} = \sec^2 x.\end{aligned}$$

In the second line we've used $\cos^2 x + \sin^2 x = 1$ and $\sec x = \frac{1}{\cos x}$. ■

EXAMPLE 46 Find the derivative formula for $\frac{d}{dx}(\csc x)$.

Solution Since $\csc x = \frac{1}{\sin x}$, we have

$$\begin{aligned}\frac{d}{dx}(\csc x) &= \frac{0 \cdot \sin x - 1 \cdot \cos x}{\sin^2 x} \\ &= \frac{-\cos x}{\sin^2 x} = \frac{-1}{\sin x}\,\frac{\cos x}{\sin x} = -\csc x \cot x.\end{aligned}$$

■

Our two new trigonometric derivative formulas are as follows.

$$\frac{d}{dx}(\tan x) = \sec^2 x \qquad \frac{d}{dx}(\csc x) = -\csc x \cot x.$$

In the exercises, you are asked to verify the formulas for the derivatives of the other two trigonometric functions.

$$\frac{d}{dx}(\sec x) = \sec x \tan x \qquad \frac{d}{dx}(\cot x) = -\csc^2 x.$$

We can now extend our derivative formula for monomial functions to include negative integer exponents.

If n is a positive integer and $f(x) = x^{-n}$, then $f'(x) = -nx^{-n-1}$.

We can verify this using the quotient rule:

$$\begin{aligned}\frac{d(x^{-n})}{dx} &= \frac{d(\frac{1}{x^n})}{dx}\\ &= \frac{\frac{d(1)}{dx}\cdot x^n - 1\cdot\frac{d(x^n)}{dx}}{(x^n)^2}\\ &= \frac{0\cdot x^n - nx^{n-1}}{x^{2n}}\\ &= -nx^{n-1-2n} = -nx^{-n-1}.\end{aligned}$$

EXAMPLE 47 Find $\frac{df}{dw}$, if $f(w) = \frac{1}{w^3}$.

Solution Since $\frac{1}{w^3} = 1w^{-3}$, we have $\frac{df}{dw} = -3w^{-4} = -\frac{3}{w^4}$. ■

Letters can be used to represent a variety of quantities—variables, constants, parameters, functions, etc. When several letters appear in a single functional expression, then the question "What is the derivative?" makes no sense unless we know exactly which letter represents the independent variable. Certainly a machine cannot be expected to guess this information correctly unless we specify the independent variable.

For example, suppose that

$$y = 3x^2 + 2t^4.$$

Is y a function of variable x (with t constant), a function of variable t (with x constant) or possibly a function of both variables x and t? We really have no way of knowing the right interpretation of the letters x and t without some context. The denominator of the Leibniz notation for derivative specifies the independent variable.

EXAMPLE 48 Find $\frac{dy}{dx}$ and $\frac{dy}{dt}$ for $y = 3x^2 + 2t^4$.

Solution Letters other than the specified independent variable are assumed to represent constants:

$$\frac{dy}{dx} = \text{derivative of } y \text{ with respect to } x$$
$$= 6x \text{ (since we assume } t \text{ is constant)}$$
$$\frac{dy}{dt} = \text{derivative of } y \text{ with respect to } t$$
$$= 8t^3 \text{ (since we assume } x \text{ is constant)}$$

■

When using the prime notation, we should mention the independent variable if there is any doubt as to what it is.

EXERCISES for Section 3.6

For exercises 1–10: Find the indicated derivatives.

1. Find $\frac{dy}{dx}$ when $y = (x^3 + 3x^2 + 1)(2x^2 + 8x - 5)$.
2. Find $\frac{dy}{dx}$ when $y = (8x^2 - 5x)(13x^2 + 4)$.
3. Find $\frac{dx}{dy}$ when $x = (y^5 - 2y^3)(7y^2 + y - 8)$.
4. Find $\frac{dA}{ds}$ when $A = (2s^2 - 3s + 1)(9s - 1)$.
5. Find $\frac{dy}{dw}$ when $y = (w - 1)(w - 3)$.
6. Find $\frac{dy}{dx}$ when $y = (x^2 - 6)(2x^{-1} - \frac{1}{3}x^{-3} - 7)$.
7. Find $\frac{dy}{dx}$ when $y = (x^2 - 6)(3x^3 - x + 1)$.

8. Find $\dfrac{dy}{dx}$ when $y = (x^2+1)(x^2+2)(x^3+3)$.

9. Find $\dfrac{dy}{dz}$ when $y = z(2z^3 - 5z + 1)(6z^2 + 7)$.

10. Find $\dfrac{dy}{dx}$ when $y = x(x+1)(x+2)(x+3)$.

For exercises 11–20: Find the indicated derivatives.

11. Find $\dfrac{ds}{dt}$ when $s = t^2 + t^{-2}$.

12. Find $\dfrac{dV}{dz}$ when $V = z^2 - z^{-2}$.

13. Find $\dfrac{dy}{dx}$ when $y = 1 + x^{-1} + x^{-2} + x^{-3}$.

14. Find $\dfrac{dy}{dx}$ when $y = x + x^{-1}$.

15. Find $\dfrac{ds}{dt}$ when $s = t^6 + t^{-6}$.

16. Find $\dfrac{dy}{dx}$ when $y = 2x^{-4} + 3x^{-2} + 2$.

17. Find $\dfrac{dT}{dv}$ when $T = v^{-1} - 2v^{-2}$.

18. Find $\dfrac{dy}{dx}$ when $y = 3 + 2x^{-2} + 4x^{-3}$.

19. Find $\dfrac{dy}{dx}$ when $y = 2x^{-1} - \dfrac{1}{3}x^{-3} - 7$.

20. Find $\dfrac{dy}{dt}$ when $y = 1 + t^{-1}$.

For exercises 21–30: Find the indicated derivatives.

21. Find $\dfrac{dy}{dx}$ when $y = \dfrac{3x^2 - x + 2}{4x^2 + 5}$.

22. Find $\dfrac{dA}{dv}$ when $A = \dfrac{v^3 - 1}{v^2 + 1}$.

23. Find $\dfrac{ds}{dt}$ when $s = \dfrac{8t + 15}{t^2 - 2t + 3}$.

24. Find $\dfrac{dy}{dx}$ when $y = \dfrac{3x^3 - 7x^2 + 4x + 3}{x^2 + 2}$.

25. Find $\dfrac{dy}{dx}$ when $y = \dfrac{3x - 1}{x^2}$.

26. Find $\dfrac{ds}{dt}$ when $s = \dfrac{3t + 4}{6t - 7}$.

27. Find $\dfrac{dy}{dx}$ when $y = \dfrac{3x^2 - 5}{2x^2 + 7}$.

28. Find $\dfrac{dV}{ds}$ when $V = \dfrac{8s^2 - 4}{1 - 9s^2}$.

29. Find $\dfrac{dy}{dx}$ when $y = \dfrac{x}{x + 1}$.

30. Find $\frac{dQ}{dw}$ when $Q = \frac{2w+5}{7w-9}$.

For exercises 31–40: For each function whose formula $f(x)$ is given, find $f'(x)$.

31. $f(x) = \frac{2^x + 3^x}{5^x}$

32. $f(x) = \csc x$

33. $f(x) = \cot x$

34. $f(x) = \frac{1}{\sec x}$

35. $f(x) = 2\sin x - 7\cos x$

36. $f(x) = \sin x \cos x$

37. $f(x) = \tan x \cot x$

38. $f(x) = x^2 2^x$

39. $f(x) = \cosh(x) = \frac{e^x + \frac{1}{e^x}}{2}$

40. $f(x) = \sinh(x) = \frac{e^x - \frac{1}{e^x}}{2}$

3.7 THE CHAIN RULE

In this section, we expand our dictionary of derivative formulas considerably through the use of the most important rule of differentiation.

The chain rule defined

The **chain rule** describes the relationship between the derivative of the *composition* of two functions and the derivatives of the individual functions. In considering the composition of two *linear* functions, note that if $f(x) = m_1x + b_1$ and $g(x) = m_2x + b_2$, we have

$$(f \circ g)(x) = m_1m_2x + (m_1b_2 + b_1).$$

This shows that $f \circ g$ is also linear and that the slope is the *product* m_1m_2.

The same is true for locally linear functions. If g is linear at the particular point x_0 (with slope m_2), and f is linear at the particular point $y_0 = g(x_0)$ (with slope m_1), then $f \circ g$ is linear at x_0, with slope m_1m_2.

The *chain rule* says that the same situation holds for derivatives. As a physical illustration of the chain rule, consider two gears A and B meshed. As gear A rotates, it causes gear B to rotate also. Now suppose that gear B rotates 6 times for every rotation of gear A, and suppose that gear A rotates 5 times per minute. How fast does gear B rotate relative to time? The answer is clearly 30 times per minute, the *product* of B's rate relative to A and A's rate relative to time.

Chain rule for differentiation

If g is differentiable at x_0 (with derivative $g'(x_0)$) and f is differentiable at $y_0 = g(x_0)$ (with derivative $f'(y_0)$), then $f \circ g$ is differentiable at x_0 with derivative

$$(f \circ g)'(x_0) = f'(y_0)g'(x_0) = f'(g(x_0))g'(x_0).$$

In Leibniz notation, if y is a differentiable function of u and u is a differentiable function of x, then

$$\frac{dy}{dx} = \frac{dy}{du}\frac{du}{dx}.$$

To be more precise, the Leibniz form for the chain rule should include the crucial information regarding where the various derivatives are to be evaluated:

$$\left.\frac{dy}{dx}\right|_{x=x_0} = \left.\frac{dy}{du}\right|_{u=u(x_0)} \left.\frac{du}{dx}\right|_{x=x_0}.$$

Thought of in this way, the chain rule seems natural. If y is a function of u, and u is a function of x, then the rate of change of y with respect to x is the product of the rate of change of y with respect to u and the rate of change of u with respect to x.

The chain rule in Leibniz notation suggests a simple cancellation of the du's in fraction multiplication, but it is really a statement of the relationship between the derivatives of two functions composed together. We should point out, however, that the formal proof of the chain rule has some subtleties we will not go into here.

EXAMPLE 49 If $f(x) = \sin^3 x$, find $f'(x)$.

Solution Let $u = \sin x$ and $y = u^3$. Considered as a function of x, we have

$$y = u^3 = (\sin x)^3 = \sin^3 x = f(x).$$

Using the chain rule, we have

$$f'(x) = \frac{dy}{dx} = \frac{dy}{du}\frac{du}{dx} = 3u^2 \cdot \cos x.$$

Substitute $u = \sin x$ to write the expression entirely in terms of x:

$$f'(x) = 3\sin^2 x \cos x.$$

■

EXAMPLE 50 If $g(x) = \sin(x^3)$, find $g'(x)$.

Solution This time let $u = x^3$ and $y = \sin u$. Then $y = \sin(x^3)$ and

$$g'(x) = \frac{dy}{dx} = \frac{dy}{du}\frac{du}{dx} = \cos u \cdot (3x^2) = \cos(x^3) \cdot (3x^2).$$ ■

Rational power functions

Suppose that p is an integer, q is a positive integer, and $u = x^{p/q}$. Then

$$u^q = x^p.$$

Now, if we let $y = u^q$, then on one hand the chain rule gives us

$$\frac{dy}{dx} = qu^{q-1}\frac{du}{dx}.$$

On the other hand $y = x^p$, so we know that

$$\frac{dy}{dx} = px^{p-1}.$$

Setting these two expressions for $\frac{dy}{dx}$ equal to each other, we have

$$qu^{q-1}\frac{du}{dx} = px^{p-1}.$$

If we now solve for $\frac{du}{dx}$, we find

$$\frac{du}{dx} = \frac{px^{p-1}}{qu^{q-1}} = \frac{px^{p-1}}{q(x^{p/q})^{q-1}} = \frac{px^{p-1}}{qx^{p-(p/q)}} = \frac{p}{q}x^{(p/q)-1}.$$

Assuming that $u = x^{p/q}$ is differentiable, the chain rule shows that the derivative formula for power functions is wonderfully consistent.

> If r is any rational power in lowest terms (including positive and negative integers), then
>
> $$\frac{d}{dx}(x^r) = rx^{r-1}.$$

To make use of this rule, function formulas involving radicals should be rewritten with rational exponents for purposes of differentiation.

EXAMPLE 51 Find $\frac{d}{dx}(\sqrt[3]{x^2})$.

Solution $\frac{d}{dx}(\sqrt[3]{x^2}) = \frac{d}{dx}(x^{2/3}) = \frac{2}{3} \cdot x^{-1/3} = \frac{2}{3\sqrt[3]{x}}$. ■

A special case of the chain rule is sometimes given a special name.

Power rule for differentiation

If u is a differentiable function of x and r is any rational number in lowest terms, then

$$\frac{d(u^r)}{dx} = ru^{r-1} \cdot \frac{du}{dx}.$$

EXAMPLE 52 Find $\frac{dw}{dz}$ if $w = (3z^2 - z)^5$.

Solution Let $u = 3z^2 - z$. Then $w = u^5$ and

$$\frac{dw}{dz} = 5u^4 \frac{du}{dz} = 5(3z^2 - z)^4(6z - 1).$$ ■

EXAMPLE 53 Find $\frac{dp}{d\theta}$ if $p = \sqrt{\sin \theta^3}$.

Solution Let $u = \sin \theta^3$. Then $p = u^{1/2}$ and

$$\frac{dp}{d\theta} = \frac{1}{2} u^{-1/2} \frac{du}{d\theta}$$

$$= \frac{1}{2\sqrt{\sin \theta^3}} (\cos \theta^3)(3\theta^2).$$

Note that we essentially used the chain rule twice, for the function $u = \sin \theta^3$ is also a composition of functions. ■

A dictionary of derivative formulas and rules

We now have derivatives of many of the basic functions mentioned in Chapter 1. Let's summarize them below in Leibniz notation.

DICTIONARY OF DERIVATIVE FORMULAS

$y = x^r$ (r rational)	$\dfrac{dy}{dx} = rx^{r-1}$
$y = a^x \ (a > 0, \ a \neq 1)$	$\dfrac{dy}{dx} = a^x (\ln a)$
$y = \sin x$	$\dfrac{dy}{dx} = \cos x$
$y = \cos x$	$\dfrac{dy}{dx} = -\sin x$
$y = \tan x$	$\dfrac{dy}{dx} = \sec^2 x$
$y = \csc x$	$\dfrac{dy}{dx} = -\csc x \cot x$
$y = \sec x$	$\dfrac{dy}{dx} = \sec x \tan x$
$y = \cot x$	$\dfrac{dy}{dx} = -\csc^2 x$

Our dictionary of derivative rules is summarized using the prime notation.

DICTIONARY OF DERIVATIVE RULES

If f, g are differentiable, a, b are constants and x_0 is a specific input.

Linearity rule:	$(af + bg)'(x_0) = af'(x_0) + bg'(x_0)$
Product rule:	$(fg)'(x_0) = f'(x_0)g(x_0) + f(x_0)g'(x_0)$
Quotient rule:	$(f/g)'(x_0) = \dfrac{f'(x_0)g(x_0) - f(x_0)g'(x_0)}{g^2(x_0)}$
Chain rule:	$(f \circ g)'(x_0) = f'(g(x_0)) \cdot g'(x_0)$
Power rule:	$(f^r)'(x_0) = rf^{r-1}(x_0) \cdot f'(x_0)$

The power rule is actually the application of the chain rule and the formula for the derivative of a power function. Similarly, we could write down a chain rule version of each of the basic derivative formulas. If u is a differentiable function of x, we can write these rules in Leibniz notation.

$y = u^r$ (r rational)	$\dfrac{dy}{dx} = ru^{r-1}\dfrac{du}{dx}$
$y = a^u \ (a > 0, \ a \neq 1)$	$\dfrac{dy}{dx} = a^u (\ln a)\dfrac{du}{dx}$

$$y = \sin u \qquad \frac{dy}{dx} = \cos u \frac{du}{dx}$$

$$y = \cos u \qquad \frac{dy}{dx} = -\sin u \frac{du}{dx}$$

$$y = \tan u \qquad \frac{dy}{dx} = \sec^2 u \frac{du}{dx}$$

$$y = \csc u \qquad \frac{dy}{dx} = -\csc u \cot u \frac{du}{dx}$$

$$y = \sec u \qquad \frac{dy}{dx} = \sec u \tan u \frac{du}{dx}$$

$$y = \cot u \qquad \frac{dy}{dx} = -\csc^2 u \frac{du}{dx}$$

The basic formulas and rules allow us to differentiate very complicated functions. Indeed, you can see how a machine with only the basic formulas stored and the basic rules programmed can completely automate the differentiation process, at least for functions built out of the basic ones. For functions not built out of these basic functions, we can always resort to the definition of derivative as a limit of difference quotients to find, or at least to approximate, the derivative.

EXAMPLE 54 Find $\frac{dy}{dx}$ when $y = x^2 \sin\left(\frac{5x^3 - 4}{12x + \pi}\right) - \tan^2(\sqrt[5]{x^2})$.

Solution For a function this complicated, it can be useful to make some intermediate substitutions. Here, let $u = \frac{5x^3 - 4}{12x + \pi}$ and $v = \sqrt[5]{x^2} = x^{2/5}$.

Then $y = x^2 \sin u - \tan^2 v$

and

$$\frac{dy}{dx} = \left(2x \sin u + x^2 \cos u \frac{du}{dx}\right) - 2 \tan v \cdot \sec^2 v \frac{dv}{dx}.$$

Now we can compute $\frac{du}{dx}$ and $\frac{dv}{dx}$ and substitute into this expression. We have

$$\frac{du}{dx} = \frac{15x^2(12x + \pi) - (5x^3 - 4) \cdot 12}{(12x + \pi)^2} \quad \text{and} \quad \frac{dv}{dx} = \frac{2}{5} x^{-3/5} = \frac{2}{5\sqrt[5]{x^3}},$$

so our final expression for $\frac{dy}{dx}$ is

$$\begin{aligned}\frac{dy}{dx} =& 2x \sin\left(\frac{5x^3 - 4}{12x + \pi}\right) \\ &+ x^2 \cdot \cos\left(\frac{5x^3 - 4}{12x + \pi}\right) \cdot \left(\frac{15x^2(12x + \pi) - (5x^3 - 4) \cdot 12}{(12x + \pi)^2}\right) \\ &- 2 \tan(\sqrt[5]{x^2}) \cdot \sec^2(\sqrt[5]{x^2}) \cdot \frac{2}{5\sqrt[5]{x^3}}.\end{aligned}$$

■

The point is that when applied to compositions and algebraic combinations of basic functions, differentiation is a quite mechanical (although sometimes tedious) process. Finding the *right* function that describes a real-world process and then analyzing and interpreting the information produced by the derivative are far more important activities.

EXERCISES for Section 3.7

For exercises 1–20: Below are shown the outputs that the functions f,g, and h and their derivatives assign to certain inputs. Use this information to compute the derivatives indicated.

$f(1) = 4$	$g(1) = 3$	$h(1) = 1$
$f(2) = 3$	$g(2) = 2$	$h(2) = 4$
$f(3) = 2$	$g(3) = 1.9$	$h(3) = 7$
$f(4) = 5$	$g(4) = 1.3$	$h(4) = 12$
$f(5) = 1$	$g(5) = 1$	$h(5) = 18$

$f'(1) = -7.2$	$g'(1) = -0.7$	$h'(1) = 5$
$f'(2) = 0.5$	$g'(2) = -0.3$	$h'(2) = 6$
$f'(3) = -0.5$	$g'(3) = -0.85$	$h'(3) = 7$
$f'(4) = -4$	$g'(4) = -0.6$	$h'(4) = 8$
$f'(5) = 1$	$g'(5) = -0.23$	$h'(5) = 9$

1. $F'(3)$; $F(x) = 7.1 \cdot f(x)$
2. $F'(1)$; $F(x) = g(x)/2$
3. $F'(2)$; $F(x) = 2.3 + h(x)$
4. $F'(1)$; $F(x) = (0.6)f(x) + 5g(x)$
5. $F'(6)$; $F(x) = h(3x - 16)$
6. $F'(2)$; $F(x) = f(x^2)$
7. $F'(1)$; $F(x) = g(x) - f(x)$
8. $F'(3)$; $F(x) = \dfrac{5}{h(x)}$
9. $F'(2)$; $F(x) = (2f(x) + 3h(x))^2$
10. $F'(1)$; $F(x) = -f(g(x))$
11. $F'(3)$; $F(x) = h(x - f(x))$
12. $F'(1)$; $F(x) = h(h(h(x)))$
13. $F'(2)$; $F(x) = f((g(x))^2)$
14. $F'(1)$; $F(x) = \dfrac{f(x)}{f(g(x))}$
15. $F'(2)$; $F(x) = f(x)g(x)h(x)$
16. $F'(5)$; $F(x) = g(x)/h(x)$
17. $F'(4)$; $F(x) = f(x)^2$
18. $F'(-5)$; $F(x) = f(-x)h(2x + 12)$
19. $F'(2)$; $F(x) = e^{g(x)}$
20. $F'(2)$; $F(x) = g(f(h(x)))$

For exercises 21–30: Using the graphs of $y = f(x)$ and $y = g(x)$, compute the derivatives indicated.

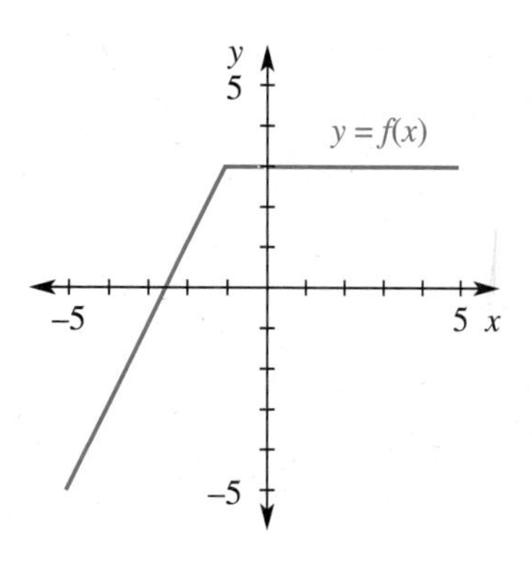

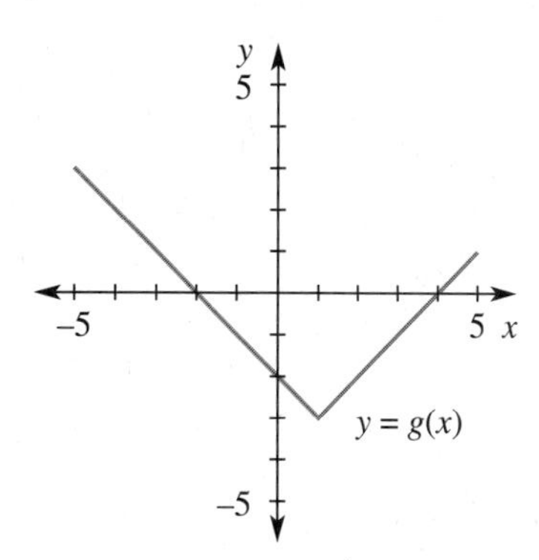

For Exercises 21–30

21. $F'(4)$; $F(x) = f(x) + g(x)$

22. $F'(-4)$; $F(x) = f(x) - g(x)$

23. $F'(1)$; $F(x) = f(x) \cdot g(x)$

24. $F'(1)$; $F(x) = \frac{f(x)}{g(x)}$

25. $F'(3)$; $F(x) = 2f(x) - 3g(x)$

26. $F'(-3)$; $F(x) = \dfrac{1}{f(x)}$

27. $F'(-2)$; $F(x) = g(x^2)$

28. $F'(1)$; $F(x) = g(2x - 3)$

29. $F'(-3)$; $F(x) = f(g(x))$

30. $F'(1)$; $F(x) = g(f(x))$

For exercises 31–40: Determine the numerical value of the derivative, if it exists.

31. $f'(27)$ where $f(x) = \sqrt[3]{x}$

32. $g'(8)$ where $g(x) = \sqrt{1 + \sqrt{1 + x}}$

33. $k'(\sqrt{\pi})$ where $k(x) = \sin(x^2)$

34. $y'(1)$ where $y = \sqrt{\frac{x+3}{x+5}}$

35. $f'(\pi/6)$ where $f(x) = 1 - (\sin(x))^2$

36. $\left.\dfrac{dy}{dx}\right|_{x=-36}$ where $y = \sqrt{x^2}$

37. $\left.\dfrac{d(x^{-5})}{dx}\right|_{x=1}$

38. $f'(0.81)$ where $f(x) = \dfrac{\sqrt{x}}{1 + \sqrt{x}}$

39. $f'(2)$ where $f(x) = 1 + \cfrac{1}{1 + \cfrac{1}{1 + \cfrac{1}{x}}}$

40. $f'(1)$ where $f(x) = \sqrt{x^2 - 2x + 1}$

For exercises 41–54: Find the derivative $f'(x)$.

41. $f(x) = (x^2 - x - 2)(x^2 + 2x - 8)$
42. $f(x) = \dfrac{x^2 - 3x + 2}{x^3 + 8}$
43. $f(x) = (4x^3 + 2x - 5)(8 - 9x^3)$
44. $f(x) = \dfrac{2x^2 - x - 3}{x^2 + 3x + 2}$
45. $f(x) = (x^2 - 6x + 5)^4$
46. $f(x) = (x^3 + 27)\sin(x^2 + 2x - 3)$
47. $f(x) = \cos(x^2 - 3x + 4)$
48. $f(x) = \tan(2x^2 - 5x + 1)$
49. $f(x) = \sec(x^2 + 6x + 8)$
50. $f(x) = \sin^2(6 - 4x - 2x^2)$
51. $f(x) = (2x^2 + 3x - 2)^{2/3}$
52. $f(x) = \sqrt[4]{7 + 4x - 2x^2}$
53. $f(x) = \dfrac{\sqrt{x^2 - 25}}{x^2 + 6x + 5}$
54. $f(x) = \dfrac{(11x^2 - 10x + 1)^{3/2}}{(3x^2 + 5x + 7)^{4/3}}$

---

55. Find $\dfrac{d}{dx}((x^2 + 1)^4)$.
56. Find $\dfrac{d}{dx}(\sin^3(x))$.
57. Find $\dfrac{d}{dx}(\sqrt[3]{5x^2 - 17x})$.
58. Find $\dfrac{d}{dx}(\sin^2 x + \cos^2 x)$.
59. Find $\dfrac{d}{dx}(\sin(\sin(x)))$.
60. Find $\dfrac{d}{dx}(1/\cos^3(x))$.

For exercises 61–66: Each limit of the difference quotient represents $f'(x_0)$ for some function f and some input x_0. Find f and x_0.

61. $\lim_{h \to 0} \dfrac{(5 + h)^2 - (5)^2}{h}$
62. $\lim_{\Delta x \to 0} \dfrac{\frac{1}{(2+\Delta x)} - \frac{1}{(2)}}{\Delta x}$
63. $\lim_{\Delta x \to 0} \dfrac{(-1 + \Delta x)^3 - (-1)^3}{\Delta x}$
64. $\lim_{x \to 4} \dfrac{\sqrt{x} - 2}{x - 4}$
65. $\lim_{h \to 0} \dfrac{\frac{1}{\sqrt{2+h}} - \frac{1}{\sqrt{2}}}{h}$
66. $\lim_{h \to 0} \dfrac{81 \cdot 3^h - 81}{h}$

---

67. Find $\dfrac{d}{dx}(\sin(x))$ when x is measured in degrees, given that

$$x^\circ = x \cdot \frac{\pi}{180} \textit{ radians}.$$

68. Let $f(x) = 10^x$, $g(x) = 2^x$, and $h(x) = 5^x$. Find $f'(x)$, $g'(x)$ and $h'(x)$ and verify that the quotient rule holds when applied to $h(x) = f(x)/g(x)$.

69. Suppose that $f(0) = b$ and $f'(0) = m$. You decide to plot $y = f(x)$ and $y = mx + b$ in the same viewing window. Explain what happens if you zoom in with equal scale factors horizontally and vertically on the point $(0, b)$.

70. Suppose that your car's tires have a 13-inch radius and are spinning at 1000 revolutions per minute. What is your speedometer reading in miles per hour?

4

The Derivative as a Tool for Analysis

In Chapter 3 we noted several interpretations of the derivative. While all the interpretations are closely related, each has its own unique flavor to add to our understanding of derivatives.

Symbolically, the derivative f' may have a formula that can be *derived* directly from the formula for the original function f.

Graphically, f' provides a *slope* machine for the graph of the function f.

Numerically, f' provides a *limiting value* of difference quotients of the function f at each input.

Physically, f' acts as a *speedometer* for the function f, providing a reading of the instantaneous rate of change of the dependent variable with respect to the independent variable.

Is one interpretation more useful than another? It depends very much on the context and specific use of the derivative. Whenever it is appropriate, assigning multiple interpretations to the derivative can help you check the reasonableness of your computations as well as shed new light on what those computations mean.

In this chapter, we take a closer look at how the derivative can be used as a powerful tool for analyzing the behavior of a function. We'll examine in detail how we can use the derivative to find linear approximations of functions, to find the roots of a function, to analyze the increasing and decreasing behavior of the function outputs, and to find the maximum and minimum output values of the function.

To use the derivative as a tool for solving real world problems requires us to find the "right" function. We'll examine how some functions arise naturally under constraints, a situation that can be exploited to effectively use the derivative to maximize or minimize a quantity of interest. Finally, we'll examine some theorems regarding derivatives that have both important graphical and physical interpretations.

4.1 LINEAR APPROXIMATIONS—TANGENT AND NORMAL LINES

When it is possible to find the derivative f' directly, we can use it to *predict* the output of the function f, even when no formula exists. In the case of a moving car, for example, we can use the speedometer reading together with the car's position to predict where the car will be a short time in the future.

EXAMPLE 1 Suppose that the time it takes you to get your foot off the gas pedal when you see someone's brake lights come on is 0.5 seconds. What is a safe distance to leave between your car and the car in front of you at 60 mph?

Solution Assuming that your brakes work at least as well as those of the car in front of you, you won't collide as long as your car doesn't cover the entire distance separating your cars in the 0.5 seconds it takes you to react.

If you are traveling at approximately constant velocity during this short time interval, the car will travel approximately

$$60\frac{\text{miles}}{\text{hours}} \cdot (0.5 \text{ sec}) \cdot \frac{1 \text{ hour}}{60 \cdot 60 \text{ sec}} = \frac{1}{120} \text{ miles} = 44 \text{ feet}.$$

So, if you leave more than 44 feet between the cars, you should avoid a collision. ■

Assuming that the velocity is approximately constant during the reaction time is equivalent to assuming that the position function of the car is approximately a *linear* function of time during this interval. The slope of this linear approximation function is represented by the velocity 60 mph.

Best linear approximations

A linear function is determined by the slope of its graph and the output value at one particular input. We can use this to find a linear approximation function for any differentiable function at a particular point. That is, for a differentiable function f and an input x_0, we can use the derivative $f'(x_0)$ as the slope of a line passing through the point $(x_0, f(x_0))$. The function g whose graph is this line is a linear approximation function for the original function f. In fact, this linear approximation function g is called the *best* linear approximation function.

Definition 1

> The **best linear approximation** to a differentiable function f at the point x_0 is a linear function g of the form
>
> $$g(x) = f(x_0) + m(x - x_0)$$
>
> where the slope is $m = f'(x_0)$. Note that $g(x_0) = f(x_0)$.

Note that the formula for g has been written in *Taylor form.* Sometimes this best linear approximation g is called the *linear Taylor approximation* of the function f. This linear function g can be thought of as a *local* approximation for f. For values x close to x_0, we have

$$f(x) \approx g(x) = f(x_0) + m(x - x_0).$$

The anatomy of this best linear approximation can be dissected in terms of the instrument readings in our car example (Figure 4.1). Here we used the instantaneous velocity (speedometer reading) as the slope. The function output $f(x_0)$ (odometer reading) is the original position of the car when we see the brakes come on at time x_0 (clock reading). Our goal was to approximate the new position $f(x)$ at time x only 0.5 seconds later (perhaps measured by a stopwatch). Since both the odometer reading and the speedometer reading depend on the point at which the readings are taken, the best linear approximation makes sense only as the best linear approximation *at some particular point.*

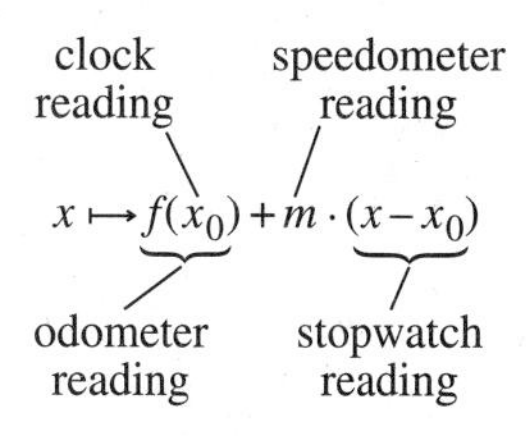

Figure 4.1 Anatomy of the best linear approximation g.

In general, the relative accuracy of the best linear approximation gets better the closer we are to the point at which we computed the slope (speedometer reading). Exactly what do we mean by "best" here? Of all the *linear* functions we might choose to approximate the actual distance covered, this one is the best in the sense that not only does the prediction become more accurate as we focus our attention on smaller elapsed times but also *it becomes more accurate faster than any other possible choice.*

EXAMPLE 2 Suppose that the actual position of the car could be modeled by the function

$$s(t) = 58t + t^2,$$

where t is measured in hours and s is measured in miles. Find the best linear approximation function for the distance traveled at the instant $t = 1$, then compare the error between the actual position function and that linear approximation for the times $t = 1.5$ hours and $t = 1$ hour and 0.5 seconds.

Solution The instantaneous velocity of the car at time t is

$$s'(t) = 58 + 2t$$

(units of mph). At $t = 1$ we have $s'(1) = 60$. We use this as the slope m of our linear approximation. The actual position of the car at $t = 1$ would be $s(1) = 59$, so we can write the linear approximation as

$$s(t) \approx 59 + 60(t - 1) = 60t - 1.$$

For $t = 1.5$ the actual position function gives us (in miles)

$$s(1.5) = 58(1.5) + (1.5)^2 = 89.25.$$

Using the best linear approximation we have (in miles),

$$s(1.5) \approx 59 + 60(1.5 - 1) = 59 + 30 = 89.$$

Hence, the error is -0.25 miles. For $t = 1$ hour and 0.5 seconds (≈ 1.000014 hours), we find that the error is about -0.0075 miles. ■

EXAMPLE 3 Find the best linear approximation and the derivative of f at $x = 1$ if $f(x) = 2^x$.

Solution We have $f(1) = 2^1 = 2$, and since $f'(x) = (\ln 2)2^x$, the slope is

$$m = f'(1) = (\ln 2)2 \approx 1.3863.$$

The formula for the best linear approximation to f at $x = 1$ is

$$g(x) = f(1) + f'(1)(x - 1) = 2 + 1.3863(x - 1).$$ ■

EXAMPLE 4 Find the best linear approximation and the derivative of f at $x = 5.7$ if $f(x) = x^2 - 3$.

Solution The derivative is $f'(x) = 2x$. We have

$$f(5.7) = (5.7)^2 - 3 = 32.49 - 3 = 29.49 \quad \text{and} \quad f'(5.7) = 2(5.7) = 11.4.$$

Thus, the best linear approximation for f at $x = 5.7$ is

$$g(x) = 29.49 + 11.4(x - 5.7).$$ ■

Tangent and normal lines

Once we have found the best linear approximation to a function f at a particular input x_0, we can graph it as the line with slope $f'(x_0)$ and passing through the point $(x_0, f(x_0))$.

Graphically, this line will often appear to "kiss" the graph of the original function at the point $(x_0, f(x_0))$, much like a tangent line to a circle. For this reason, the **tangent line** to the graph of a function f at the point $(x_0, f(x_0))$ is *defined* to be the graph of this best linear approximation.

Unlike the tangent line to a circle, the tangent line to a graph could well intersect the graph at other points (see Figure 4.2). If you graphed both the tangent line and the original function $y = f(x)$ using machine graphics and then zoomed in on the point of tangency far enough, it would become impossible to distinguish the two graphs from one another (unless you zoomed in so far as to have round-off precision errors take effect). This suggests a way to check visually the reasonableness of a tangent line equation.

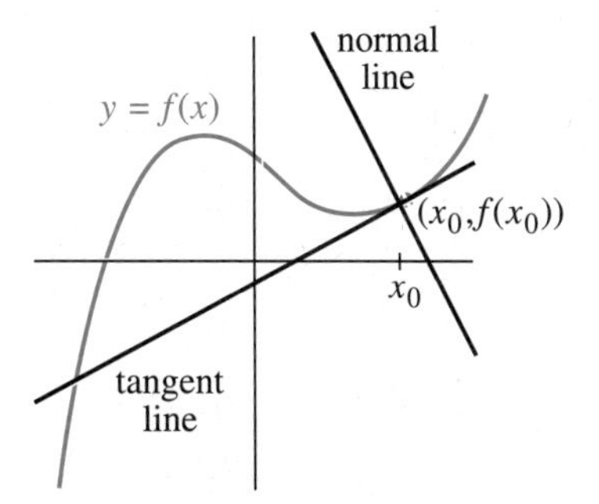

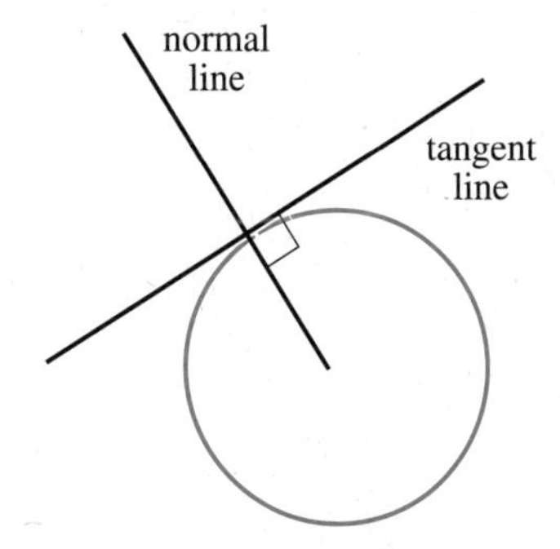

Figure 4.2 Tangent and normal lines to a graph and a circle.

A **normal line** to the graph of a function f at the point $(x_0, f(x_0))$ is defined to be the *line perpendicular to the tangent line at that point*. (If $m \neq 0$ is the slope of a line, then $-1/m$ is the slope of a line perpendicular to it.) A well-known property of the normal line to a circle is that it must pass through the center of the circle. As related to the graph of a function $y = f(x)$, we can think of the normal line as providing the direction to move if we want to move away from the graph as quickly as possible.

EXAMPLE 5 Find the equation of the tangent line to the graph of $y = x^2$ at the point $(3, 9)$.

Solution Since $\dfrac{dy}{dx} = 2x$, the slope of the tangent line is given by

$$\left.\frac{dy}{dx}\right|_{x=3} = 6,$$

and the equation of the tangent line at $(3, 9)$ is $y = 6(x - 3) + 9$. ■

EXAMPLE 6 Suppose that $f(x) = 2/x^3$. Find the equation of the tangent line to the graph of $y = f(x)$ at the input $x_0 = -2$.

Solution Since $f(x) = 2x^{-3}$, we have $f'(x) = -6x^{-4}$. The tangent line must pass through the point

$$(x_0, f(x_0)) = (-2, 2/(-2)^3) = (-2, -1/4)$$

and the slope of the tangent line must be

$$m = f'(-2) = -6(-2)^{-4} = -6/16 = -3/8.$$

Hence, the equation of the tangent line is

$$y = -\frac{3}{8}(x + 2) - \frac{1}{4}.$$ ■

EXAMPLE 7 Find the equation of the normal line to the graph of $y = x^{2/3}$ at the point $(-8, 4)$.

Solution Since $\dfrac{dy}{dx} = \dfrac{2}{3}x^{-1/3}$, the slope of the tangent line is given by

$$m = \left.\frac{dy}{dx}\right|_{x=-8} = \frac{2}{3} \cdot \frac{1}{(-8)^{1/3}} = -\frac{1}{3}.$$

The slope of the normal line would be the *negative reciprocal*

$$\frac{-1}{m} = \frac{-1}{-1/3} = 3.$$

Hence the equation of the normal line at $(-8, 4)$ is $y = 3(x + 8) + 4$. ■

EXAMPLE 8 Suppose that $g(x) = \cos(x)$. Find the equation of the normal line to the graph of $y = g(x)$ at $x_0 = 0$.

Solution Our line must pass through the point $(x_0, g(x_0)) = (0, \cos(0)) = (0, 1)$. Since $g(x) = \cos(x)$, we have

$$g'(x) = -\sin(x),$$

so the slope of the tangent line at $x_0 = 0$ is

$$m = -\sin(0) = 0.$$

This means that the tangent line is *horizontal*, requiring the normal line to be *vertical*. Since the normal line passes through $(0, 1)$, we conclude that its equation is $x = 0$. ■

Application—reflection from curved surfaces

When a light ray hits a flat reflective surface (such as a mirror), it is known that the *angle of incidence* α is equal to the *angle of reflection* β (see Figure 4.3). Note that these angles are measured relative to a line perpendicular to the surface.

When the mirror is curved, a light ray striking at a particular point will be reflected in the same direction as if it struck the tangent line at that point. In other words, the angle of incidence and reflection are measured relative to the normal line to the mirror at that point.

By carefully constructing the shape of a curved mirror, it is possible to "gather" all reflected light rays to a single point, or to reflect all the light rays from a single source in the same direction. For example, the headlights on a car generally have two bulbs. The reflective surface of the headlight is shaped so that all the light rays from one of these bulbs are reflected straight forward. Your "brights" are on when this bulb is lit (along with the other bulb). When this bulb is turned off, you are left with "low beams" from the remaining bulb (these light rays are reflected down and away from the oncoming traffic).

Another example is a satellite dish constructed in the same way to gather incoming communication beams to a single point to boost reception.

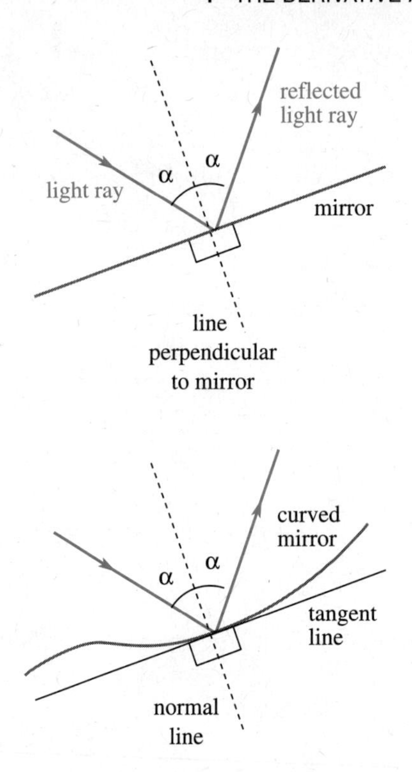

Figure 4.3 Reflection from a curved surface.

The inside surface of rocket exhausts are shaped so that the outward force of the exploding fuel is all directed downward as it bounces off the walls of the exhaust. The shape having this useful reflective property in these examples is amazingly easy to describe: a simple parabola rotated about its axis! In the exercises, you will establish this property of parabolas by the use of calculus.

EXERCISES for Section 4.1 **1.** Find the equation(s) of the tangent lines to $y = x^3 + 2x^2 - 4x + 5$ that are parallel to the line $2y + 8x - 5 = 0$.

2. Find the equation(s) of the tangent lines to $y = x^2 - 6x + 2$ that are perpendicular to the line $y = 6x - 2$.

3. Find the equation(s) of the tangent lines to $y = x^3 - x^2 - 5x + 2$ that are parallel to the line passing through $(-3, 2)$ and $(1, 4)$.

4. Find the equation(s) of the tangent lines to $y = \cos x$ that are horizontal.

5. Find all points where the normal line to $y = 3x^2 + 4x - 6$ has slope $-\frac{1}{10}$.

6. Find the equations of the normal lines to $y = 3x^2 + 4x - 9$ that are parallel to the line $2x + 5y = 1$.

7. Find the equation of the normal line to the graph of $y = (x - 8)^{2/3} + 1$ through the point $(0, 5)$.

8. Find the equation of the normal line to the graph of $y = \sqrt{4 - x^2}$ at the point $(2, 0)$.

9. Find the equation of the tangent line to the graph of $y = \sqrt{8x^2 + 5x + 7}$ at the point $(2, 7)$.

10. Find all points where the slope of the tangent line to the graph of $y = \tan x$ is 1.

For exercises 11–20: Find the equations of the tangent and normal lines to the graph of $y = f(x)$ at the specified input.

11. $f(x) = x^2 + x + 1; \quad x_0 = 1.6$

12. $f(x) = 2x^2 - 7x + 3; \quad x_0 = 3/2$

13. $f(x) = x^3 - 12x; \quad x_0 = -2$

14. $f(x) = \dfrac{3x - 17}{5}; \quad x_0 = 4$

15. $f(x) = x^5; \quad x_0 = 1$

16. $f(x) = 3; \quad x_0 = 2$

17. $f(x) = \sin^2 x; \quad x_0 = \pi/3$

18. $f(x) = \tan x; \quad x_0 = 3\pi/4$

19. $f(x) = \sin x^2; \quad x_0 = 0$

20. $f(x) = \sqrt{a^2 - x^2}; \quad x_0 = b$

(Note: In exercise 20, a and b are positive constants with $-a < b < a$.)

For exercises 21–30: This activity requires a machine grapher.

(a) Find the best linear approximation of the given function at the specified input x_0.

(b) Use the best linear approximation to predict the function's output value at $x_0 + 1$, $x_0 - 1$, $x_0 + .001$, and $x_0 - .001$.

(c) Compare the predicted values with the actual function value at each of these points and calculate the error.

(d) Finally, graph both the original function and its best linear approximation over the interval $[x_0 - .1, x_0 + .1]$.

21. $f(x) = x^2; \quad x_0 = -3$

22. $f(x) = \sqrt{x}; \quad x_0 = 9$

23. $f(x) = x^{2/3}; \quad x_0 = -8$

24. $f(x) = x^3 - 4x; \quad x_0 = -1.5$

25. $f(x) = \sin x; \quad x_0 = \pi/3$

26. $f(x) = \cos x; \quad x_0 = 0$

27. $f(x) = \tan x; \quad x_0 = \pi/4$

28. $f(x) = 1/x; \quad x_0 = -2$

29. $f(x) = x; \quad x_0 = 0$

30. $f(x) = 5.42; \quad x_0 = 132.78$

Reflective property of a parabolic surface

Consider a reflective surface generated by rotating a parabola about its axis. (You'll need a sheet of graph paper with quarter-inch rulings for this activity.) Every radial cross-section (sliced through the center) of this "dish" has the shape of the original parabola. In the following exercises, you'll establish the extremely important reflective property of this dish.

31. Suppose that we can represent the radial cross-section by the graph of the parabola $y = x^2/4$. On a sheet of graph paper (using 1 inch as a unit), carefully plot the parabola and mark the points:

$$A = (-3, 2.25) \qquad B = (-1, 0.25) \qquad C = (0, 0) \qquad D = (2, 1) \qquad E = (4, 4)$$

32. Find the equation of the tangent line to the curve at each of the 5 points.

33. Find the equation of the normal line to the curve at each of the 5 points.

34. Through each of the 5 points, draw a short segment of the tangent line and a short segment of the normal line.

35. Suppose that light rays directed vertically downward strike the parabola. Using a protractor, determine where a vertical light ray is reflected at each of the 5 points. (Remember, the vertical ray and the reflected ray make the same angle with the normal line.) Extend the reflected line until it meets the y-axis.

36. All of the drawn reflected lines should meet at the same point on the y-axis. What point is it?

37. Show that if $(a, a^2/4)$ is any point on the parabola with $a \neq 0$, then the slope of the tangent line is $m = a/2$ and the slope of the normal line is $-2/a$.

38. In the exercises for Section 3.2, it is shown that if a vertical light ray strikes a reflective surface of slope m, the reflected light ray travels along a line whose slope is the average of m and $-1/m$. Use this fact to show that the slope of the reflected ray to the parabola at $(a, a^2/4)$ is $\dfrac{a^2-4}{4a}$.

39. Find the equation of the line through $(a, a^2/4)$ with slope $\dfrac{a^2-4}{4a}$. Show that the y-intercept of any such line is $(0, 1)$.

The point $(0, 1)$ is called the *focus* of this parabola. Every parabola has a focus that possesses this special reflective property, which is why the parabolic reflector is such an important design.

40. By a suitable choice of coordinate axes, *any* parabola fits the graph of $y = \dfrac{x^2}{4p}$ for some constant p. Show that the focus of this parabola is the point $(0, p)$.

4.2 FINDING ROOTS—NEWTON'S METHOD

An especially important application of the best linear approximation is called **Newton's method**, named after Isaac Newton. Newton's method, like the bisection method, is used to approximate roots of functions. While it is not as widely applicable as the bisection method (discussed in Chapter 2), Newton's method tends to be much more efficient.

To solve an equation $f(x) = 0$ by Newton's method, we need:

1. a "seed" x_0 (our first guess or rough estimate of the root), and
2. the iterating function $g(x) = x - \dfrac{f(x)}{f'(x)}$.

A sequence of approximations is found by feeding the seed x_0 as an input into the iterating function g, and then continuing to feed the output result back into the iterating function:

$$\begin{aligned}
x_1 &= x_0 - \frac{f(x_0)}{f'(x_0)}\\
x_2 &= x_1 - \frac{f(x_1)}{f'(x_1)}\\
x_3 &= x_2 - \frac{f(x_2)}{f'(x_2)}\\
x_4 &= x_3 - \frac{f(x_3)}{f'(x_3)}\\
&\vdots\\
x_{n+1} &= x_n - \frac{f(x_n)}{f'(x_n)}\\
&\vdots
\end{aligned}$$

This process is continued until the sequence of results stabilizes toward some limiting value r. The process of repeatedly feeding the output of a function back in as the next input is called **iteration**. For Newton's method, the iterating function has been chosen to produce a sequence of approximations that we hope approaches a root of our original function f.

How Newton's method works

To see how Newton's method works in a simple case, suppose first that our original function f is linear (but not constant). Then $f(x) = mx + b$, with slope $m \neq 0$. In this case $f'(x) = m$, and the iterating function is

$$g(x) = x - \frac{mx + b}{m} = -\frac{b}{m}.$$

This constant function takes any input x and produces $-b/m$ as the output. Note that $-b/m$ is the root of our original linear function f!

Now, in general, suppose that we have a differentiable function f. Then the iterating function finds the root of the best linear approximation at any input x where the first derivative $f'(x) \neq 0$. For example, the best linear approximation to f at $x = x_0$ is

$$y = f(x_0) + f'(x_0)(x - x_0).$$

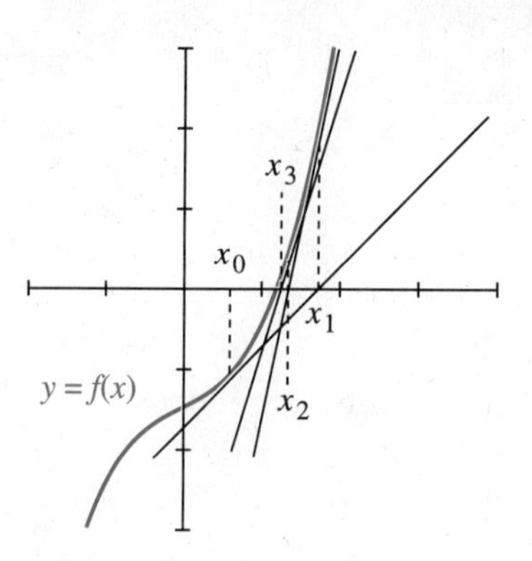

Figure 4.4 Newton's method produces roots of best linear approximations to f.

If we find the root x_1 of this best linear approximation (the value x_1 making $y = 0$), we obtain

$$x_1 = x_0 - \frac{f(x_0)}{f'(x_0)}.$$

We then repeat the process by finding x_2, the root of the best linear approximation to f at $x = x_1$, and so on.

Figure 4.4 illustrates Newton's method graphically. Starting with x_0, we find the tangent line to the graph of $y = f(x)$ at the point $(x_0, f(x_0))$. Our next input x_1 is where this tangent line crosses the x-axis. Then we find the tangent line at the point $(x_1, f(x_1))$ and the input x_2 where it crosses the x-axis. The input x_3 in this illustration almost coincides with the root, showing how quickly Newton's method can converge.

EXAMPLE 9 Find the third iterate x_3 to approximate a solution of $x^2 = 3$ by Newton's method with an initial seed $x_0 = 5$.

Solution Rewriting this equation in the form $f(x) = 0$, where $f(x) = x^2 - 3$, we have $f'(x) = 2x$, and our iterating function is

$$g(x) = x - \frac{f(x)}{f'(x)} = x - \frac{x^2 - 3}{2x} = \frac{2x^2}{2x} - \frac{x^2 - 3}{2x} = \frac{x^2 + 3}{2x}.$$

Using $x_0 = 5$, we obtain

$$x_1 = \frac{5^2 + 3}{2 \cdot 5} = \frac{28}{10} = 2.8,$$

$$x_2 = \frac{(2.8)^2 + 3}{2(2.8)} = \frac{1084}{560} \approx 1.93571,$$

$$x_3 \approx \frac{(1.93571)^2 + 3}{2(1.93571)} \approx 1.74276.$$

Since $\sqrt{3}$ is a root of f, this third iterate x_3 is an approximation to $\sqrt{3} \approx 1.73205$. ■

There is more than one solution to the equation $x^2 = 3$ $(x = \pm\sqrt{3})$. The initial choice of the seed x_0 affects which root, if any, that Newton's method "seeks out."

EXAMPLE 10 Find the third iterate x_3 to approximate a solution of $x^2 = 3$ by Newton's method, with an initial seed $x_0 = -1$.

Solution Using $f(x) = x^2 - 3$, our iterating function is the same as before:

$$g(x) = x - \frac{f(x)}{f'(x)} = \frac{x^2 + 3}{2x}.$$

Using $x_0 = -1$, we obtain

$$x_1 = \frac{(-1)^2 + 3}{2 \cdot (-1)} = -2,$$

$$x_2 = \frac{(-2)^2 + 3}{2(-2)} = -1.75,$$

$$x_3 = \frac{(-1.75)^2 + 3}{2(-1.75)} \approx -1.73214.$$

Starting with a new seed $x_0 = -1$ resulted in our third iterate x_3 approximating $-\sqrt{3} \approx -1.73205$, the other solution of the equation $x^2 = 3$. ■

Error in approximation

How can we judge the accuracy of our approximation? One criterion may seem obvious: How close is our approximation to the value we seek?

In the case of approximating roots of the equation $f(x) = 0$, this criterion judges an approximation x_n by the error $|x_n - r|$, where r is a true root. The smaller $|x_n - r|$ is, the closer x_n is to a root of the original equation. In our first example, $x_3 \approx 1.74276$, while $\sqrt{3} \approx 1.73205$. Hence,

$$|x_3 - \sqrt{3}| \approx |1.74276 - 1.73205| \approx 0.01071.$$

In our second example, $x_3 \approx -1.73214$, and

$$|x_3 - (-\sqrt{3})| \approx |-1.73214 - (-1.73205)| \approx 0.00009.$$

(It is not insignificant that the initial seed x_0 started out closer to a root in the second example than in the first.)

At this point, you may be asking yourself, "If I already know the value that I am trying to approximate, why am I bothering to approximate it in the first place?" Certainly, it is more often the case that one uses approximation techniques such as Newton's method when the value of the root is unknown. There is, however, another criterion that may be far more important for our purposes: How well does the approximation satisfy our original requirements?

This criterion judges an approximation x_n by measuring $|f(x_n)|$. The smaller $|f(x_n)|$ is, the closer x_n *behaves* like a root of the original equation. Note that this criterion does not depend on us knowing any target value in advance.

In our first example, we can check that

$$|x_3^2 - 3| \approx |(1.74276)^2 - 3| \approx 0.03723,$$

while in our second example we have

$$|x_3^2 - 3| \approx |(-1.73214)^2 - 3| \approx 0.00032.$$

You can see that this criterion still gives us a way of comparing approximations without directly measuring the errors.

Where to start and when to stop

The two main decisions that must be made when using Newton's method are:

1. What seed x_0 do we start with?
2. When do we stop iterating?

Graphing can give us good visual clues to the general vicinity of a root and thus help us make a good guess for our initial seed x_0.

As far as knowing when to stop, we could test each of our approximations $x_1, x_2, x_3, \ldots$ against some criterion and stop when the test is passed. For example, if we are searching for a root to $f(x) = 0$, we might decide to stop with x_n when $|f(x_n)| < .0001$.

Another criterion is often used for Newton's method, as well as other iterative procedures. We may decide to halt the procedure when the approximations stabilize to some limiting value. Note that if x_n is a root of f (so that $f(x_n) = 0$), then the next iterate is

$$x_{n+1} = x_n - \frac{f(x_n)}{f'(x_n)} = x_n - 0 = x_n.$$

When the approximations become fixed on a single value, this is evidence that we have found a root.

EXAMPLE 11 The equation $3^x = x^3$ has another positive solution besides $x = 3$. Graphing both $y = 3^x$ and $y = x^3$ reveals another intersection point near $x = 2.5$. Use Newton's method with $x_0 = 2.5$ as an initial seed and iterate until the approximations are fixed to 10 decimal places.

Solution We rewrite the equation as $f(x) = 3^x - x^3 = 0$. The derivative is

$$f'(x) = (\ln 3)3^x - 3x^2$$

and the iterating function is

$$g(x) = x - \frac{f(x)}{f'(x)} = x - \frac{3^x - x^3}{(\ln 3)3^x - 3x^2}.$$

Using $x_0 = 2.5$, we find (rounding each approximation to 11 decimal places):

$$x_1 \approx 2.47750287933$$

$$x_2 \approx 2.47805237090$$

$$x_3 \approx 2.47805268031$$

$$x_4 \approx 2.47805268031$$

After only 4 iterations, the process seems to have stabilized to 10 decimal places. If we substitute $x = 2.47805268031$ into both sides of the original equation, we find

$$3^{(2.47805268031)} \approx 15.2170898204 \quad \text{and} \quad (2.47805268031)^3 \approx 15.2170898204,$$

where both results are rounded to 10 decimal places. ■

When does Newton's method fail?

We have just seen how quickly Newton's method can "home in" on a root of an equation,

$$f(x) = 0.$$

However, there are instances where the method can fail. If we look at the iterating function,

$$g(x) = x - \frac{f(x)}{f'(x)},$$

we can see what difficulties might arise:

1. If at any step, our approximation x_n fails to be in the domain of f, then our next approximation is undefined.

2. Similarly, if our approximation x_n fails to be in the domain of f', then our next approximation is undefined.

3. If $f'(x_n) = 0$, then our next approximation is undefined.

EXAMPLE 12 Why does Newton's method fail with $f(x) = \sqrt{x}$ and initial seed $x_0 = 1$?

Solution The derivative is $f'(x) = \dfrac{1}{2\sqrt{x}}$, so the iterating function is

$$g(x) = x - \frac{\sqrt{x}}{1/(2\sqrt{x})}.$$

With $x_0 = 1$, we obtain

$$x_1 = g(1) = 1 - \frac{\sqrt{1}}{1/(2\sqrt{1})} = 1 - 2 = -1.$$

The value $x_1 = -1$ is not in the domain of our original function f, and thus we are unable to continue the process. ■

Sometimes slightly changing the initial seed overcomes the difficulty. In this particular example, however, any other positive initial seed x_0 also produces a negative value for x_1, halting the process.

Graphically, we can see why Newton's method will fail if the approximation term x_n produces a first derivative value $f'(x_n) = 0$: the tangent line in this case is *horizontal*, and hence does not cross the x-axis (unless x_n is already the root we seek).

EXAMPLE 13 Why does Newton's method fail with $f(x) = 4x^3 + 1$ and initial seed $x_0 = 0.5$?

Solution The derivative is $f'(x) = 12x^2$, so the iterating function is

$$g(x) = x - \frac{4x^3 + 1}{12x^2} = \frac{12x^3}{12x^2} - \frac{4x^3 + 1}{12x^2} = \frac{8x^3 - 1}{12x^2}.$$

With $x_0 = 0.5$, we obtain

$$x_1 = g(0.5) = \frac{8(0.5)^3 - 1}{12(0.5)^2} = \frac{1 - 1}{3} = 0.$$

On the next iteration, we find that $x_2 = g(0)$ is undefined, since $f'(0) = 12(0)^2 = 0$. ■

In this case, changing the initial seed to another value can yield better results.

Another situation where Newton's method may fail is when the approximations oscillate or cycle periodically through the same set of values.

EXAMPLE 14 Investigate the behavior of Newton's method in solving $x^4 - 10x^2 = 8$ using the initial seed $x_0 = 2$ and the initial seed $x_0 = 3$.

Solution We need to find a root of the function $f(x) = x^4 - 10x^2 - 8$. Since $f'(x) = 4x^3 - 20x$, we have

$$g(x) = x - \frac{x^4 - 10x^2 - 8}{4x^3 - 20x}$$

as our iterating function.

First, with $x_0 = 2$, we have

$$x_1 = 2 - \frac{2^4 - 10(2)^2 - 8}{4(2)^3 - 20(2)} = -2,$$

and

$$x_2 = -2 - \frac{(-2)^4 - 10(-2)^2) - 8}{4(-2)^3 - 20(-2)} = 2.$$

We've bounced back to our original seed $x_0 = 2$. If we continue, our approximations will never stabilize, but simply oscillate forever between 2 and -2.

In contrast, if we start out with $x_0 = 3$, the iterating function produces a sequence that stabilizes quickly to a value $x \approx 3.27789$ after only four steps. If we substitute this back into the original equation, we find

$$(3.27789)^4 - 10(3.27789)^2 \approx 8.00000.$$

In this case, changing the seed brought better fruit to our efforts. ■

It also is possible for Newton's method to diverge away from a root. For example, the function $f(x) = x^{1/3}$ certainly has a root $x = 0$. However, if we form the iterating function, we obtain

$$g(x) = x - \frac{x^{1/3}}{(1/3)x^{-2/3}}.$$

For any $x \neq 0$, the iterating function simplifies to $g(x) = -2x$. This means that for any seed $x_0 \neq 0$, the iterating function will produce

$$x_1 = -2x_0, \quad x_2 = -2x_1 = 4x_0, \quad x_3 = -2x_2 = -8x_0, \quad \ldots.$$

Unless we hit the root with our very first guess, Newton's method will take us farther and farther away from the true root!

Which technique is better—Newton's method or the bisection method? Newton's method has the advantage of very rapid convergence (when it does indeed converge). However, as some of the examples above show, it can sometimes fail miserably. The bisection method is slower, but it has the advantage of keeping the root trapped in smaller and smaller intervals.

A strategy of some machine root-finders is to use a combination of both methods. For example, if the machine detects that $f(a)$ and $f(b)$ have different signs, then it may apply Newton's method using the midpoint of the interval as a seed but not allow the approximations to stray outside the interval $[a, b]$.

EXERCISES for Section 4.2

For exercises 1–10: Use Newton's method to find five successive approximations to a root of the given equation in the given interval. Use the midpoint of the interval as your initial seed x_0.

1. $x^2 - 3.2 = 0; \quad [1, 2]$
2. $x^3 - 23 = 0; \quad [2, 3]$
3. $\sin(x) - 0.7 = 0; \quad [0.7, 0.8]$
4. $x^5 + 3.6x^4 - 2.51x^3 - 22.986x^2 - 28.24x - 10.4 = 0; \quad [2, 3]$
5. $x + \sqrt{x} + \sqrt{x^3} - 7 = 0; \quad [1.8, 2.6]$
6. $xe^{x^2} - \sqrt{x^2 + 1} = 0; \quad [0.4, 1]$
7. $\ln(x^2 + \ln(x)) = 0; \quad [0.625, 1.35]$
8. $x^3 - \sqrt{x^2 + 1} + x - 3 = 0; \quad [1.1, 1.6]$
9. $3\cos(\cos(x)) - 2x = 0; \quad [1.1, 2.2]$
10. $\sqrt[4]{x} + x^3 - x - 0.5 = 0; \quad [0.2, 1.2]$

For exercises 11–17: Suppose that $f(x) = \sqrt[7b]{1 - \dfrac{7}{x}}$ with $b > 0$.

11. Find a root of $f(x)$ by using algebra.
12. Show that the iterating function for Newton's method applied to f is

$$g(x) = x + bx(7 - x).$$

13. Find two values for b for which the Newton's method approximations with $x_0 = 1$ converges to 7.

14. Find a value for b for which the Newton's method approximations with $x_0 = 1$ diverge to ∞, or show that there aren't any.

15. Find a value for b for which the Newton's method approximations with $x_0 = 1$ diverge to $-\infty$, or show that there aren't any.

16. Find a value for $b \neq 0$ for which $1 = x_0 = x_2$. Will the Newton's method approximations converge in this case?

17. Find two values for b for which the Newton's method approximations with $x_0 = 1$ oscillate chaotically.

---

18. Approximate the root of $x^3 + x - 3$ that lies in the interval $[0, 2]$ using Newton's method, starting with $x_0 = 1$. Compare the speed of convergence of the first six approximations with that of the bisection method applied to the same interval.

19. Use Newton's method to find the three smallest positive roots of the equation $x + \tan(x) = 0$ (to 10 decimal places).

20. Why does Newton's method fail with $f(x) = \sqrt{x}$ and *any* positive initial seed x_0?

21. Find a "bad seed" for Newton's method applied to $f(x) = 4x^3 - 3x$.

The **golden ratio** is the positive root of the equation

$$x^2 = x + 1.$$

22. Find the golden ratio using the quadratic formula.

23. Use Newton's method with an initial seed $x_0 = 1$ applied to $f(x) = x^2 - x - 1$ to find the golden ratio accurate to 10 decimal places. How many iterations does it take?

24. The Fibonacci ratios are

$$\frac{1}{1}, \quad \frac{2}{1}, \quad \frac{3}{2}, \quad \frac{5}{3}, \quad \frac{8}{5}, \quad \frac{13}{8}, \quad \frac{21}{13}, \quad \frac{34}{21}, \quad \ldots.$$

Note that the numerator of any term in the sequence is the denominator of the next term, and that the *sum* of the numerator and denominator of any term is the numerator of the next term. What are the next five terms of the sequence?

25. Convert your decimal approximations of the iterates from exercise 23 to rational form. Show that each of the approximations is a Fibonnaci ratio!

4.3 ANALYZING FUNCTION BEHAVIOR—CRITICAL VALUES

The old saying that "a picture is worth a thousand words" is truly an understatement in mathematics. Graphs are extremely powerful tools for analyzing a function, and many types of function behavior translate directly to easily visualized characteristics of the graph of the function. In this section, we'll see how the interpretation of derivative as slope can be exploited in analyzing a function's behavior.

Differentiability means smooth behavior

Knowing that a function f is *continuous* at a point a guarantees that the graph of f can have no "hole" or break at that point. Knowing that a function f is *differentiable* at a point a automatically means that f is continuous at $x = x_0$, because the limit of difference quotients

$$\lim_{x \to x_0} \frac{f(x) - f(x_0)}{x - x_0}$$

could not possibly exist unless $\lim_{x \to x_0} f(x) = f(x_0)$. So a "hole," jump, vertical asymptote, or other discontinuous behavior cannot occur at a point where the function has a derivative.

But differentiability at a point means more: the graph of the function cannot have a sharp corner or cusp at that point. Figure 4.5 shows the graph of $g(x) = x^{2/3}$. The slope is undefined at $x = 0$ ($g'(x) = \frac{2}{3}x^{-1/3}$). Thus, g is not differentiable at $x = 0$; this is shown by the sharp cusp in the graph there. Similarly, the absolute value function is not differentiable at $x = 0$, as evidenced by the sharp corner in its graph at $x = 0$. Both of these functions, however, are continuous at $x = 0$.

Could a function be not differentiable even at a point where its graph is smooth? The graph of the function $f(x) = x^{1/3}$ is illustrated in Figure 4.6. The graph certainly looks smooth at $x = 0$, but the tangent line there is vertical and the graph has undefined slope at $x = 0$. (Note that $f'(x) = \dfrac{1}{3}x^{-2/3}$ is undefined when $x = 0$.)

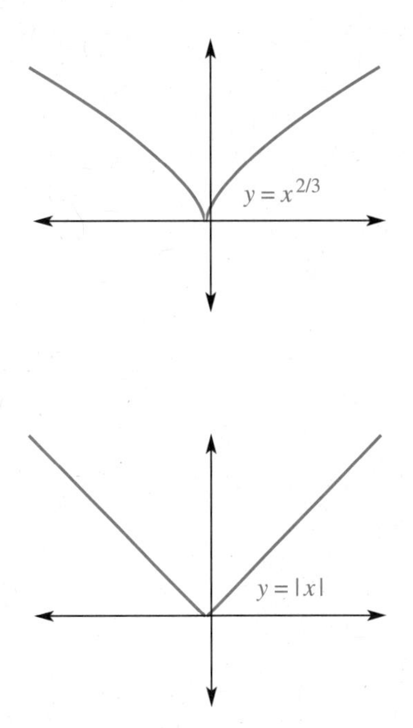

Figure 4.5 Derivative does not exist at a cusp or sharp corner.

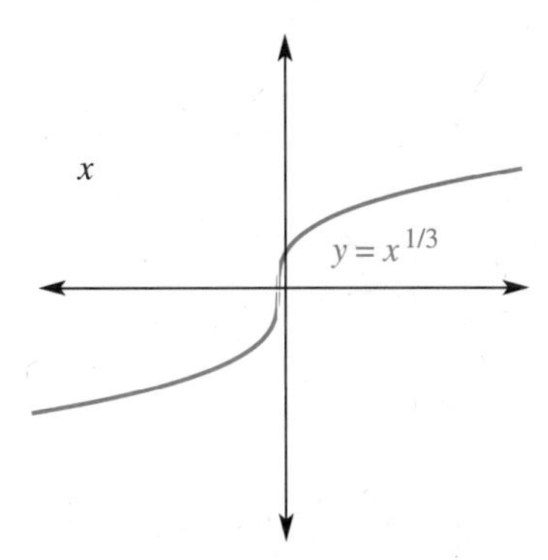

Figure 4.6 The derivative is undefined when the tangent line is vertical (graph has an undefined slope at $x = 0$.

Summarizing what we have noted so far:

> The existence of $f'(x_0)$ requires that the graph of $y = f(x)$ can have no "hole," jump discontinuity, vertical asymptote, sharp corner, cusp, or vertical tangent at $(x_0, f(x_0))$.

Increasing and decreasing function behavior

In general, a function is said to be *increasing* or *decreasing* depending on whether its outputs increase or decrease as the inputs increase. Let's make this more precise mathematically.

Definition 2

Suppose that the function f is defined on an interval containing x_1 and x_2. The function f is **increasing** over the interval if, whenever $x_1 < x_2$, then

$$f(x_1) \leq f(x_2).$$

The function f is **strictly increasing** over the interval if, whenever $x_1 < x_2$, then

$$f(x_1) < f(x_2).$$

The function f is **decreasing** over the interval if, whenever $x_1 < x_2$, then

$$f(x_1) \geq f(x_2).$$

The function f is **strictly decreasing** over the interval if, whenever $x_1 < x_2$, then

$$f(x_1) > f(x_2).$$

If f is either increasing or decreasing over an interval, we say that f is **monotonic** over the interval. If f is either strictly increasing or strictly decreasing on an interval, then we say that f is **strictly monotonic** over the interval.

The slope of the graph of a linear or a piece-wise linear function tells us instantly whether the function is strictly increasing (positive slope), strictly decreasing (negative slope), or constant (zero slope). The derivative of a differentiable function gives us similar information.

▶▶▶ **If $f'(x) > 0$ on an interval (a, b), then the original function f is strictly *increasing* on that interval.**

▶▶▶ **If $f'(x) < 0$ on an interval (a, b), then the original function f is strictly *decreasing* on that interval.**

Critical values

Now, what happens at a value x_0 (*in the domain of* f) where $f'(x_0)$ is neither positive nor negative? There are only two possibilities: either $f'(x_0) = 0$ or $f'(x_0)$ is not even defined. In either case, we call x_0 a *critical value* for the function f.

Definition 3

A **critical value** x_0 for a function f is an input *in the domain* of f such that either $f'(x_0) = 0$ or $f'(x_0)$ is *undefined*.

Graphically, a critical value is indicated where the graph of $y = f(x)$ is either flat (slope 0) or has a sharp corner, cusp, vertical tangent, or other such behavior making the slope *undefined*.

For example, the input $x = 0$ is a critical value for each of the functions $y = x^{2/3}$, $y = x^{1/3}$, and $y = |x|$, since in each case, the derivative $\frac{dy}{dx}$ is undefined for $x = 0$. Note carefully that $x = 0$ is *not* a critical value for $y = 1/x$, because it is not even in the domain of the function.

▶▶▶ **Critical values must be in the domain of the function.**

Figure 4.7 illustrates the graph of a function with nine different critical values indicated: $x_1, x_2, \ldots, x_9$. The inputs x_1, x_2, x_8, and x_9 are critical values because a sudden change in the direction of the graph occurs. (The derivative value is undefined at these points.) The inputs x_4 and x_6 are critical values because the tangent to the graph at those points is vertical. (Again, the derivative value is undefined.) The inputs x_3, x_5, and x_7 are critical values because the tangent is horizontal. (The derivative value is 0.)

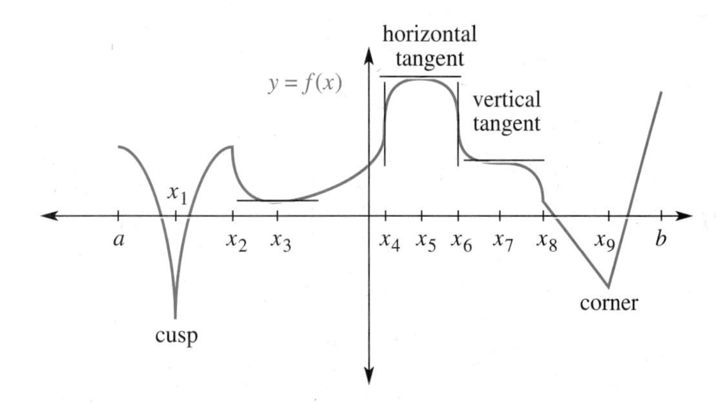

Figure 4.7 Critical values occur where $f'(x)$ is zero or undefined.

EXAMPLE 15 Find the critical values of the function f if $f(x) = \frac{1}{x} + x^2$.

Solution The derivative is

$$f'(x) = -\frac{1}{x^2} + 2x.$$

The derivative f' is undefined at $x = 0$, but this is *not* a critical value, because 0 is not in the domain of the original function. If we set $f'(x) = 0$,

$$-\frac{1}{x^2} + 2x = 0$$

and solve for nonzero values x, we obtain

$$-1 + 2x^3 = 0.$$

(Multiply both sides of the equation by x^2.) We conclude that $x = 1/\sqrt[3]{2}$ is the *only* critical value of f. ■

Local extrema and the critical value theorem

Critical values deserve special attention in the analysis of a function, because they are potential locations for extreme values of the function. Here, we mean extreme in a *local* sense. Let's make that more clear with the following definition.

Definition 4

A **local maximum** of a function f occurs at a point x_0, if $f(x_0) \geq f(x)$ for all x in some neighborhood of x_0.
A **local minimum** of a function f occurs at a point x_0, if $f(x_0) \leq f(x)$ for all x in some neighborhood of x_0.

The point x_0 is a local maximum (or local minimum) if there is an open interval containing x_0 such that $f(x_0)$ is the maximum (or the minimum) output value over that interval. If either a local minimum or local maximum for f occurs at x_0, we say that a **local extremum** occurs there. Some books use the term *relative* in place of the term *local.*

▶▶▶ **Be careful to distinguish between a *local extremum* and its *location.* On the one hand, a local minimum or local maximum refers to the *output* $f(x_0)$ of the function. On the other hand, the location is the *input* $x = x_0$.**

Figure 4.8 illustrates the locations of the local extrema for the function whose graph is shown in Figure 4.7. Note that every local minimum and local maximum occurred at a critical value. That is the conclusion of the *critical value theorem.*

Theorem 4.1

Critical value theorem
Hypothesis: f has a local extremum at x_0.
Conclusion: Either $f'(x_0) = 0$ or $f'(x_0)$ is undefined.

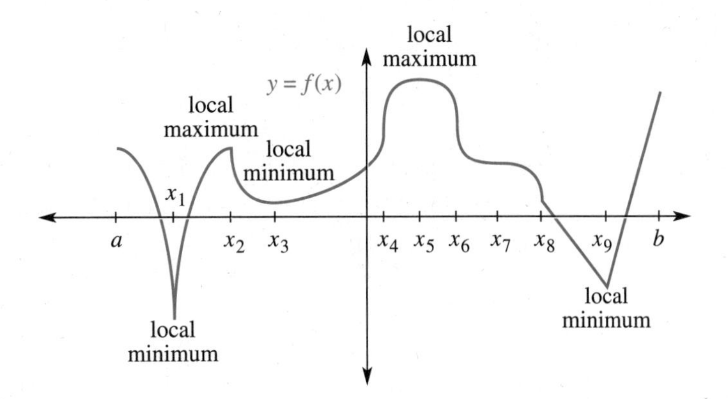

Figure 4.8 Local extrema occur at critical values.

Reasoning Let's think about the situation of a local maximum first. (Think of x_0 as being x_2 or x_5 in Figure 4.8.) In some neighborhood of x_0, $f(x_0) \geq f(x)$ for all inputs x in the neighborhood. That means that if $x < x_0$, then

$$\frac{f(x) - f(x_0)}{x - x_0} \geq 0,$$

and if $x > x_0$, then

$$\frac{f(x) - f(x_0)}{x - x_0} \leq 0.$$

So, as x approaches x_0 from the left, all the difference quotients are greater than or equal to 0, and as x approaches x_0 from the right, all the difference quotients are less than or equal to 0. If there is a *limit* of these difference quotients, it *must be* 0. If there is *not* a limit, then the derivative doesn't even exist at that point. In either case, we can conclude that x_0 is a critical value of f.

The situation of a local minimum is similar. (Think of x_0 as being x_1, x_3, or x_9 in Figure 4.8.) Now the difference quotients from the left are less than or equal to 0, and the difference quotients from the right are greater than or equal to 0. If f has a derivative at the local minimum, then $f'(x_0) = 0$. Otherwise $f'(x_0)$ is undefined. □

▶▶▶ **Be careful how you read this theorem, for its *converse* is not true.**

The theorem says that if f has any local extrema, they must occur at critical values. It *does not say* that if f has a critical value, then an extremum must occur there. Figure 4.8 shows that x_4, x_6, x_7, and x_8 are all critical values, but not a single one is the location of a local extremum.

Modeling rates of change from data

Even when we have gathered and plotted data from a process, but do not have a symbolic formula that fits the data, we can still explore the rate of change of the process. Table 4.1 shows the population of a bacteria culture at one-hour intervals, along with the increases in population computed by finding the successive hourly differences. Figure 4.9 illustrates a plot of the data. When we fit a curve to the data, we see a graph with a shape characteristic of many populations.

time in hours	population	growth rate (cells per hour)
1	210	
		22
2	232	
		28
3	260	
		33
4	293	
		40
5	333	
		49
6	382	
		56
7	438	
		62
8	500	
		62
9	562	
		56
10	618	
		49
11	667	
		40
12	707	
		33
13	740	
		28
14	768	
		22
15	790	
		19
16	809	
		16
17	825	
		14
18	839	
		11
19	850	
		10
20	860	

Table 4.1 Computing population growth rate for each hour.

Population growth can be influenced by many factors, including the size of the existing population and the available resources (such as food and light). When the population is small, the bacteria population's growth rate is slow. As its size increases, so does its growth rate, until the population approaches the limit that can be supported by the available resources.

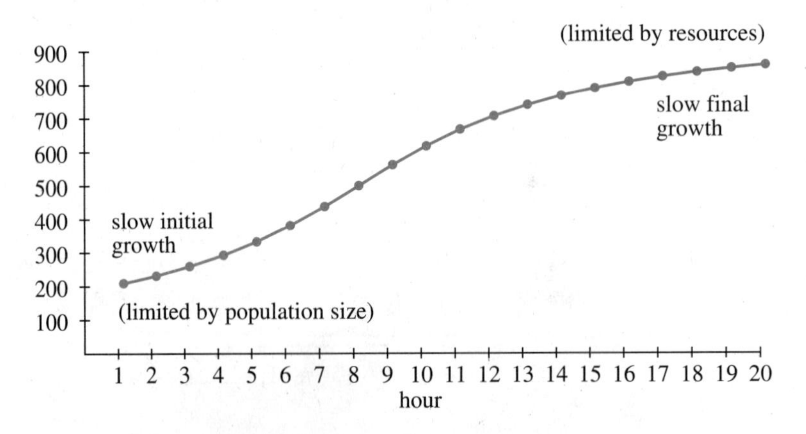

Figure 4.9 Population growth of a bacteria culture.

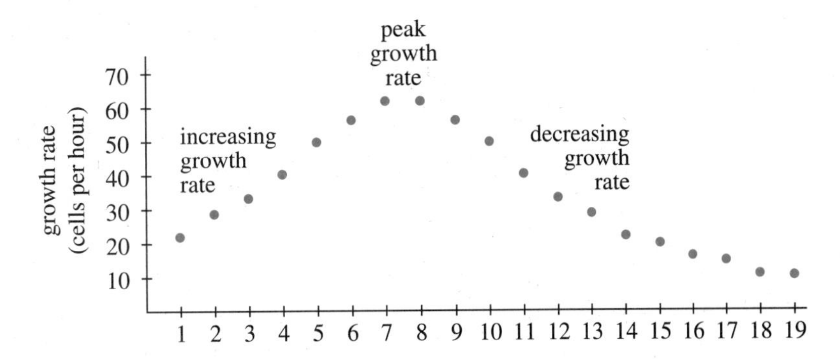

Figure 4.10 Population growth rate as a function of time.

We can visually approximate the growth rate at a particular time by estimating the slope of the graph at that point. We can also measure the *average* rate of change in population over each hour. If we plot the average growth rate for each elapsed hour as a function of *time*, we obtain the plot in Figure 4.10.

Since the independent variable again is time, we can think of this plot as providing approximate values of the derivative for the population function graph in Figure 4.9. In other words, if we use P for population and t for time in hours, then Figure 4.10 gives us approximate values for $\frac{dP}{dt}$. This graph not only tells us that the rate of population growth is always positive but also gives a better idea when that rate is greatest.

EXERCISES for Section 4.3

For exercises 1–20: For each function below:

(a) graph the function f over the interval $[-6, 6]$ (not all points in the interval may be in the domain).

(b) identify the intervals over which f is increasing and the intervals over which f is decreasing.

(c) graph the derivative f' over the interval $[-6, 6]$.

(d) identify the intervals over which f' is positive and the intervals over which f' is negative.

(e) record the critical values of f in the interval $[-6, 6]$.

(f) record which of the critical values represent a local minimum and which represent a local maximum.

1. $f(x) = x^2$

2. $f(x) = \sqrt{x}$

3. $f(x) = x^{2/3}$

4. $f(x) = x^3 - 4x$

5. $f(x) = \sin x$

6. $f(x) = \cos x$

7. $f(x) = \tan x$

8. $f(x) = 1/x$

9. $f(x) = x^{1/5}$

10. $f(x) = 5(3 - x)^3$

11. $f(x) = x^2 + x + 1$

12. $f(x) = 2x^2 - 7x + 3$

13. $f(x) = x^3 - 12x$

14. $f(x) = \dfrac{3x - 17}{5}$

15. $f(x) = x^5$

16. $f(x) = 3$

17. $f(x) = \sin^2 x$

18. $f(x) = 2^x - x^2$

19. $f(x) = \sin x^2$

20. $f(x) = \sqrt{25 - x^2}$

21. Using the information you gathered in exercises 1–20, find those critical values at which $f'(x)$ changes sign from positive to negative. What kind of local extremum (maximum or minimum) occurs at these values?

22. Using the information you gathered in exercises 1–20, find those critical values at which $f'(x)$ changes sign from negative to positive. What kind of local extremum (maximum or minimum) occurs at these values?

23. Using the information you gathered in exercises 1–20, find those critical values at which $f'(x)$ does not change sign. What kind of local extremum (maximum or minimum) occurs at these values?

24. Now, on the basis of your answers to exercises 21–23, use the sign of the derivative to devise criteria that relate critical values to the local maxima and minima of a function.

For exercises 25–28: Refer to the data for the ball-dropping experiment supplied in Table 4.2 and plotted in the illustration shown.

height in feet	time in seconds
4	0.50
8	0.71
12	0.87
16	1.00
20	1.12
24	1.22
28	1.32
32	1.41
36	1.50
40	1.58
44	1.66
48	1.73
52	1.80
56	1.87
60	1.94
64	2.00

Table 4.2 Table of heights and drop times.

25. If t is the time it takes for the ball to drop from height h, interpret $\dfrac{dt}{dh}$ as a rate of change with appropriate units.

26. Calculate the average time increase per foot for each interval determined by the measured heights. For example, for the first interval from 4 ft to 8 ft, the drop time increased from 0.5 sec to 0.71 sec for an average time increase per foot of $\dfrac{0.71 - 0.5}{8 - 4} = .0525$ sec per foot.

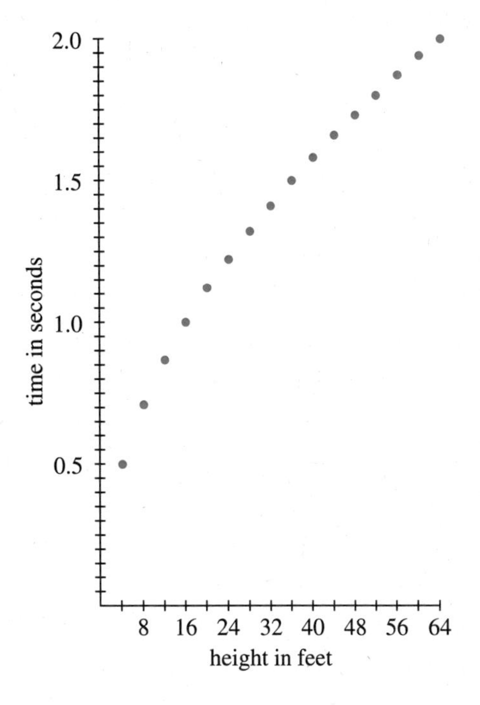

For Exercises 25–28

27. Plot the computed values from exercise 26 as a function g of the height. For example, $g(4) = .0525$. How would you describe what the resulting graph looks like? Can you find a symbolic formula that generates the graph?

28. Calculate $\frac{dt}{dh} = f'(h)$ where $f(h) = \sqrt{h/16}$ and compare the graph of f' to the graph of g from the previous exercise.

For exercises 29–32: A graph of hours of daylight as a function of time of year is shown.

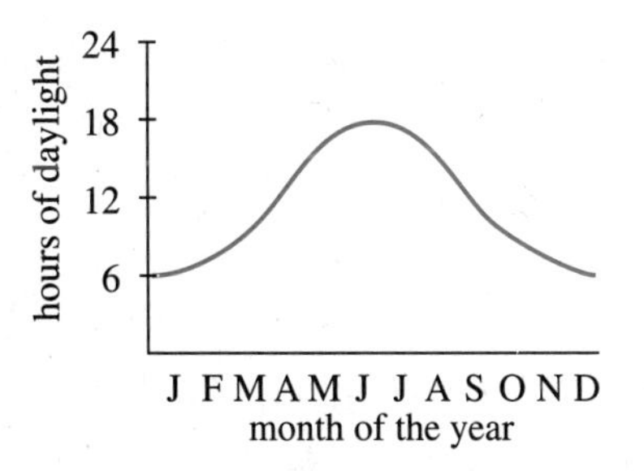

For Exercises 29–32

29. What is the *date* of the local maximum?

30. Is the derivative positive or negative during: winter? spring? summer? fall?

31. The vernal and autumnal equinoxes refer to the first day of spring and fall, respectively. If you plotted the *rate of change* of hours of daylight as a function of time, describe how the vernal and autumnal equinoxes could be spotted from this graph.

32. Elaborate stone formations used to find the summer and winter solstices are considered wonders of ancient civilizations. Why do you think it is so much more difficult to pinpoint the first day of winter and summer than it is to pinpoint the vernal and autumnal equinoxes?

For exercises 33–40: Table 4.3 gives the level y (in centimeters) of fluid in a tank of industrial chemical reactants at time t (in minutes). Our purpose is to learn about the rate at which this level changes with passing time.

time t	level y
0.0	0.525
0.8	4.927
1.2	6.011
1.6	6.506
2.0	6.525
2.4	6.184
2.8	5.599
3.2	4.883
3.6	4.154
4.0	3.525
4.4	3.112
4.8	3.031
5.2	3.395
6.0	5.925
6.4	8.320

Table 4.3 Level of chemical reactants over time.

33. What are the lowest and highest levels? When do they occur?

34. Are there times when the liquid is relatively or temporarily at a high or low level (even if not the overall highest or lowest)? Identify these times and levels.

35. Give time intervals during which the level is rising. Do the same for time intervals during which the level is falling. How would you describe the times of transition between these two behaviors?

36. Make a careful graph of y as a function of t, approximating a smooth curve through the points. Assuming that y is differentiable, describe the sign of $\frac{dy}{dt}$ over the time intervals you found in exercise 35.

37. When is the level rising most rapidly? (Try adding a column to the table to give the differences or changes in level.)

38. When does it decrease most quickly? How can you deal with unequal time intervals?

39. Explore the use of a graph of the differences or changes against t to explain and interpret your answers to exercise 38.

40. Create a fourth column by tabulating the changes in the changes (differences for the third column). What kind of information do these numbers give? Is there a useful graphical interpretation?

4.4 FINDING EXTREMA—THE DERIVATIVE TEST

If the derivative f' of a continuous function f is defined in a neighborhood of a critical value (except possibly at the critical value itself), then we can use f' to determine whether the critical value is the location of a local minimum, a local maximum, or neither. This **derivative test** for local extrema is simple, and we can reason graphically as follows:

As we move past the location x_0 of a local maximum from left to right, the function's graph must change from rising *uphill* (positive slope) to the peak to falling *downhill* (negative slope) past the peak. More precisely, if $f'(x)$ is positive on an interval (a, x_0), and $f'(x)$ is negative on an interval (x_0, b), then $f(x_0)$ is a local maximum.

Similarly, if we move past the location of a local minimum from left to right, the function's graph must change from falling downhill to rising uphill. Or, in terms of the derivative, if $f'(x)$ is negative on an interval (a, x_0) and $f'(x)$ is positive on an interval (x_0, b), then $f(x_0)$ is a local minimum.

Let's summarize these observations.

The derivative test for local extrema
Suppose that x_0 is a critical value of f.
If $f'(x)$ changes sign from positive to negative at x_0, then a local maximum occurs at x_0.
If $f'(x)$ changes sign from negative to positive at x_0, then a local minimum occurs at x_0.
If $f'(x)$ does not change sign at x_0, then the critical value is the location of neither a local minimum nor a local maximum.

You can check the derivative test for yourself on each of the nine critical values in Figure 4.7.

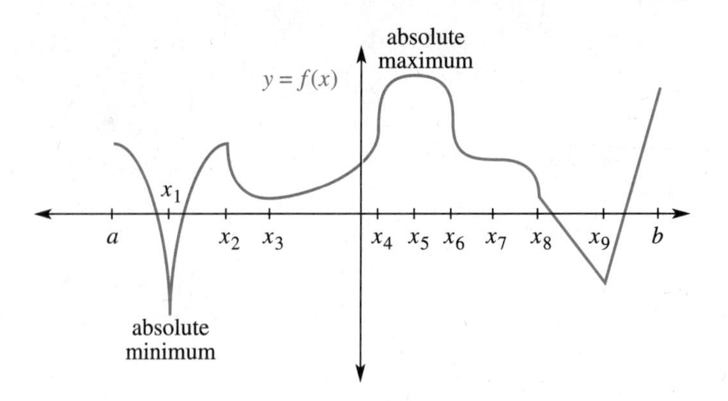

Figure 4.11 Absolute extrema of f over $[a, b]$.

Absolute extrema

By an **absolute maximum** or **absolute minimum**, we mean the highest or the lowest output value achieved by the function (see Figure 4.11). Certainly, a function does not necessarily have either an absolute maximum or an absolute minimum output value. For example, the function $y = 1/x$ takes on *arbitrarily* high and low output values for inputs near $x = 0$. However, if a continuous function is *defined* on a closed interval $[a, b]$, then we must have absolute maximum and minimum output values over that interval (by the extreme value theorem). These extreme values could occur either at the critical values in that interval or, possibly, at one or more of the endpoints.

In any case, we can outline a step-by-step strategy for locating the absolute extrema of a continuous function f over a closed interval $[a, b]$:

Strategy for Finding Absolute Extrema of f over $[a, b]$

Step 1. *Find the derivative f'.*

Step 2. *Find the critical values of f that lie in the interval $[a, b]$.*

This requires finding each of those values $a < x_0 < b$ such that $f'(x_0) = 0$ or $f'(x_0)$ is undefined.

Step 3. *Identify which critical values are locations of local minima and which are locations of local maxima.*

Step 4. *Evaluate $f(x_0)$ for each local extremum and evaluate $f(a)$ and $f(b)$ for comparison to identify the absolute minimum and maximum output values.*

For each critical value x_0 in the interval, we can use the derivative test to identify x_0 as the location of a local minimum, local maximum, or neither. We examine the sign of $f'(x)$ to the left and to the right of the critical value x_0. If $f'(x)$ changes sign from positive (+) to negative (−), then $f(x_0)$ is a local maximum value. If $f'(x)$ changes sign from negative (−) to positive (+), then $f(x_0)$ is a local minimum value. (If $f'(x)$ does not change sign, then $f'(x_0)$ is neither a maximum nor minimum.)

It is easiest to remember these criteria if you visualize the graphical behavior associated with the slope: as we move from left to right, a change from uphill to downhill represents a peak (local maximum) and a change from downhill to uphill represents a valley (local minimum). (See Figure 4.12.)

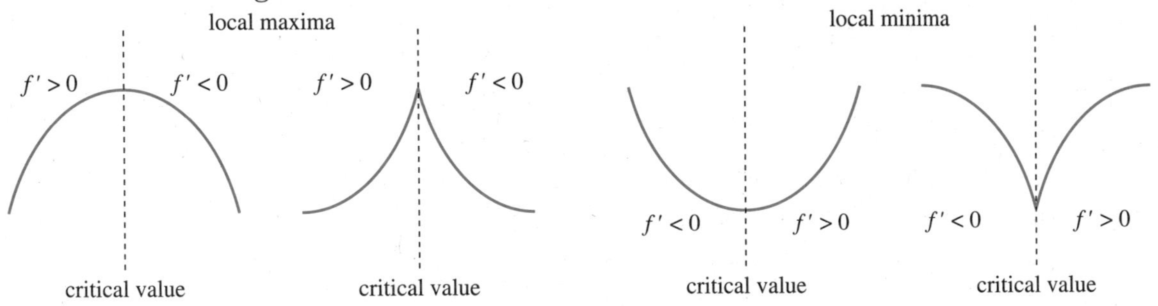

Figure 4.12 Visualizing the derivative test.

▶▶▶ **When finding absolute extrema of a function over a closed interval $[a, b]$, don't forget to compare the function outputs at the critical values to the function outputs $f(a)$ and $f(b)$ at the endpoints of the interval.**

EXAMPLE 16 Find the absolute maximum and minimum of $f(x) = x^3 - 12x$ on the closed interval $[-1, 3]$.

Solution **Step 1.** The derivative is $f'(x) = 3x^2 - 12$.

Step 2. The derivative is defined over the entire interval. $f'(x) = 3x^2 - 12 = 0$ when $x^2 = 4$—that is, when $x = \pm 2$. Only one of these two critical values is in the given interval $[-1, 3]$: $x = 2$.

Step 3. $3x^2 - 12 < 0$ for $x < 2$ (provided x is reasonably close to 2) and $3x^2 - 12 > 0$ for $x > 2$. This means that f has a *local minimum* at $x = 2$.

Step 4. Finally, we check the actual output values at the one local minimum we found ($x = 2$) and at the endpoints ($x = -1$ and $x = 3$):

$$f(2) = 2^3 - 12 \cdot 2 = -16, \quad f(-1) = (-1)^3 - 12 \cdot (-1) = 11, \quad f(3) = 3^3 - 12 \cdot 3 = -9.$$

From these values, we can see that $f(2) = -16$ is the absolute minimum of f over $[-1, 3]$ and $f(-1) = 11$ is the absolute maximum. ■

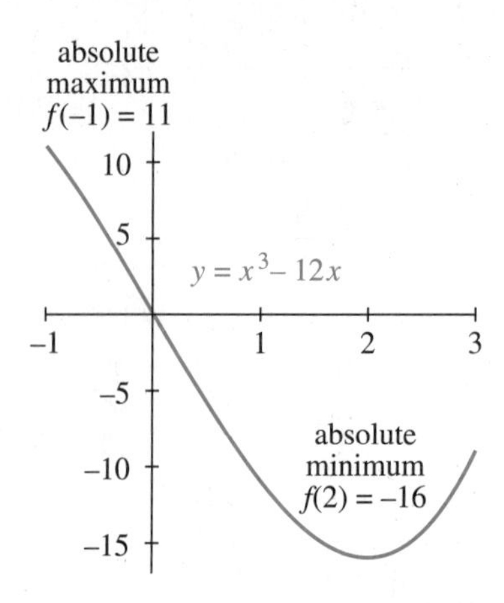

Figure 4.13 Setting the vertical range of the viewing window using the absolute extrema.

We note that knowing this information allows us to specify a vertical range for graphing the function over this interval so that the entire graph fits in our viewing window. Figure 4.13 shows a graph of $y = x^3 - 12x$, using $[-1, 3]$ as the horizontal range and $[-16, 11]$ as the vertical range.

Of course, with machine graphics we can often get a good estimate of the absolute minimum and maximum function outputs over an interval by simply graphing the function over that interval. We may need to experiment a while to find a vertical scaling that shows us approximate locations of the maximum and minimum. Even if our grapher has *autoscaling* (meaning that the machine automatically tries out some inputs from the interval first to determine a reasonable vertical scaling for graphing), we still may need to adjust the scaling to see the approximate value of a minimum with one view and the approximate maximum value with another view.

Because a machine grapher ultimately graphs only finitely many values, it's possible that important function behavior is missed between the plotted points. Analyzing the function with the derivative gives us a more definitive way of locating the extrema. We could even use the grapher to aid in our analysis of the derivative. For example, if we graphed *the derivative* over the same interval, the locations where the derivative's graph crosses over the x-axis indicate local minima or local maxima of the original function (see exercises 21-28).

EXERCISES for Section 4.4

For exercises 1–10: Find *all* the critical values and classify each as a local minimum, local maximum, or neither using the derivative test.

1. $f(x) = x^3 - x$
2. $f(x) = \dfrac{1}{x}$
3. $f(x) = -\frac{4}{(x+1)^2}$
4. $f(x) = 3$
5. $f(x) = \tan x$
6. $f(x) = \csc x$
7. $f(x) = \sec x$
8. $f(x) = \cot x$
9. $f(x) = |2x - 3|$
10. $f(x) = \sin^2(x) + \cos^2(x)$

For exercises 11–16: Find the absolute maximum and absolute minimum of each function over the indicated closed interval.

11. $f(x) = 2x^2 + 3x - 1 \quad [-2, 1]$
12. $f(x) = -4x^3 + 5 \quad [1, -1]$
13. $f(x) = -x^2 - 3x + 6 \quad [1, 2]$
14. $f(x) = x^2 - 3x + 1 \quad [-4, -2]$
15. $f(x) = -2x^2 + 3x - 1 \quad [-1, 4]$
16. $f(x) = |\sin(x/3)| \quad [\pi/4, \pi/3]$

For exercises 17–20: You are given the formula for the vertical position $s(t)$ of some object over the time interval $0 \leq t \leq 60$ (s measured in feet and t measured in seconds). Find the maximum and minimum heights attained over the interval $[0, 60]$.

17. $s(t) = -16t^2 + 64000$
18. $s(t) = .002t^3 - 0.27t^2 + 12t + 10$
19. $s(t) = |90 - t^2/30|$
20. $s(t) = 2\sin \pi t/20$

For exercises 21–28: You are given the graphs of the *derivatives* of eight functions (grid lines spaced one unit apart both horizontally and vertically). For each, indicate the locations of the local maxima and local minima (if any) of the original function.

21.

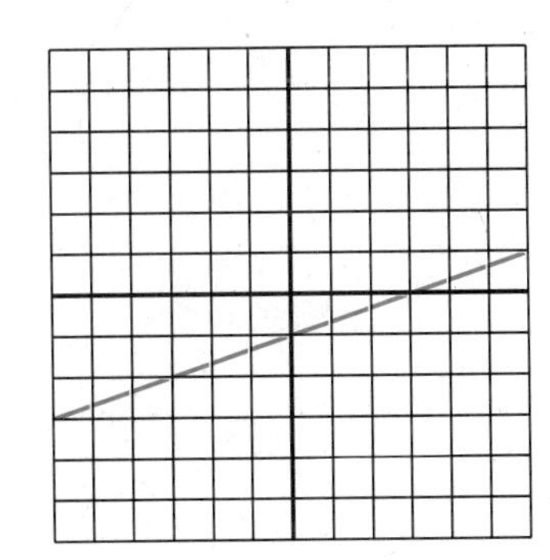

22.

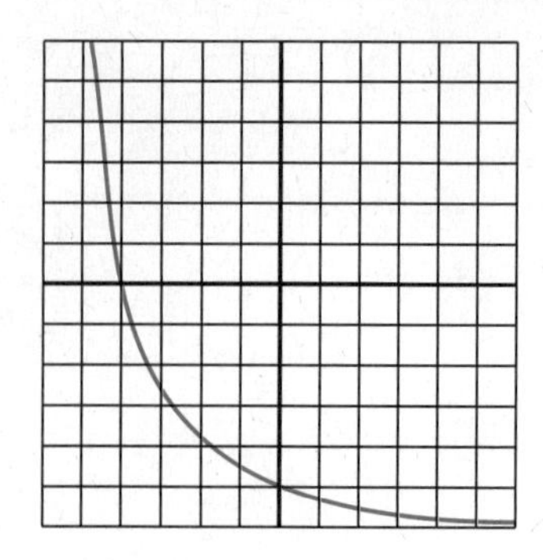

23.

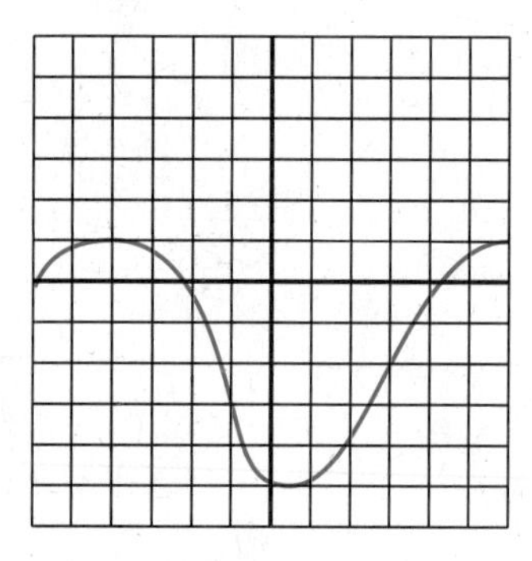

24.

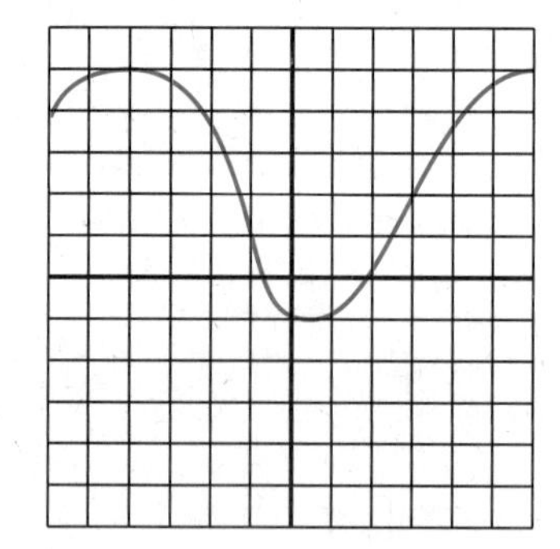

25.

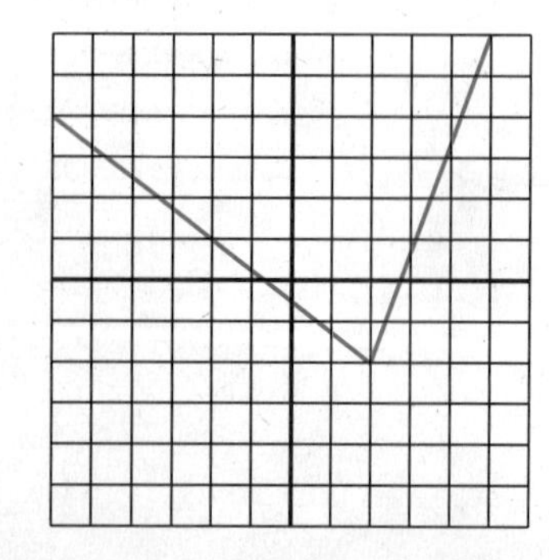

26.

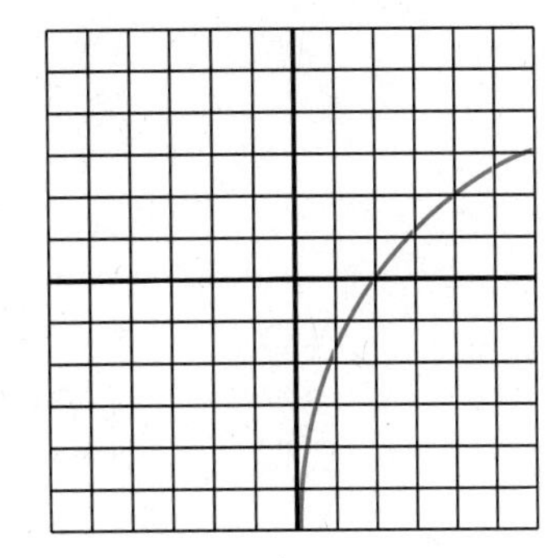

27.

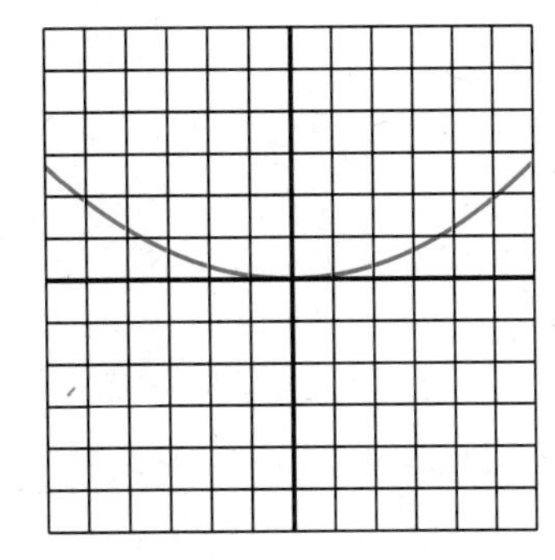

28.

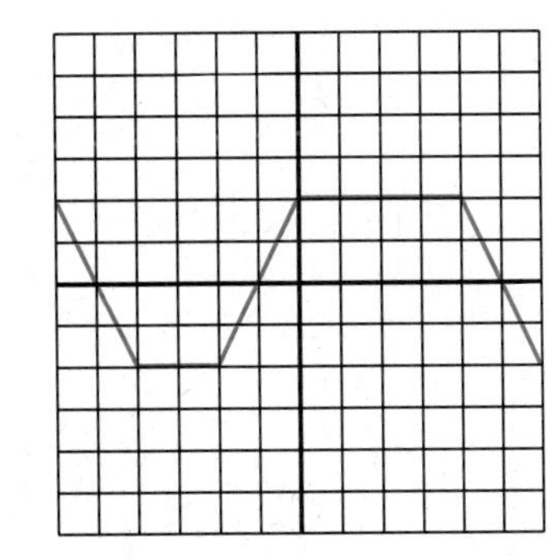

4.5 FINDING EXTREMA UNDER CONSTRAINTS

In many applications, the inputs and outputs of a function process may play the role of *causes* and *effects*. Keep in mind that any process that produces an output completely determined by the input can be called a function, even if it is unreasonable to attribute a cause-and-effect connection. It might sound awkward to refer to the radius as "causing" the area of the circle, yet we still say that the area is a function of the radius, since the area is completely determined by the radius by the formula $A = \pi r^2$.

Modeling a function defined by a constraint

A worker at a factory is given the task of designing two locking metal parts. One is to be made from a metal ball of 5 centimeters radius, so that it can rotate easily in all directions. The other part comes to a conical point (like the sharpened end of a pencil). A conical hole of the same size will be bored from the ball so that the two parts fit together snugly.

In researching the problem, the worker finds that she can purchase spherical ball bearings of the correct size (radius 5 cm). The volume of material to be bored out of each bearing is of critical concern, for it not only affects the strength of the first part but also determines the expense necessary in constructing the second part.

The worker knows that the volume V of a cone depends both on the height h and the radius r of its base from the formula

$$V = \frac{1}{3}\pi r^2 h.$$

However, she finds from trial and error that the constraint of fitting the conical piece in the ball makes the height and radius interdependent (that is, the value of one determines the other). The worker poses the following problem to you:

Problem: Given a sphere of radius 5 cm, express the volume V of a cone inscribed in the sphere as a function of only the cone's height h. Figure 4.14 shows two typical cones inscribed in a sphere of radius 5 cm.

Let's agree to use the same units (cm) for the radius and height of the cone and for the radius of the sphere, so the volume of the cone will be expressed in cubic cm. The volume of a cone is given by the formula

$$V = \frac{1}{3}\pi r^2 h,$$

where V is the volume of the cone, r is the radius of the cone's base, and

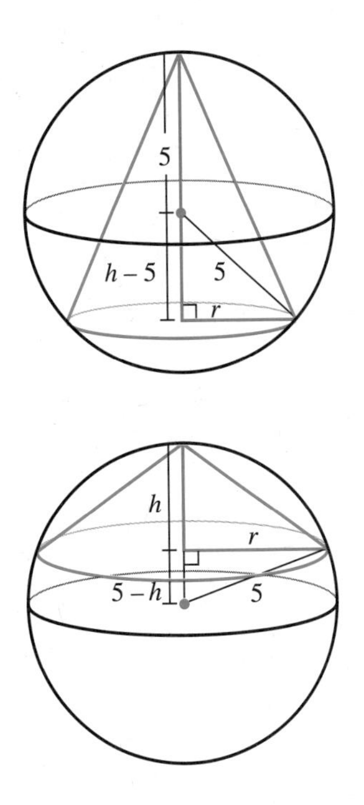

Figure 4.14 Cones inscribed in spheres of radius 5 cm.

h is the height of the cone. In general, the volume of a cone is a function of both its height and radius, but in this situation our cone is constrained to be inscribed in a sphere of radius 5 cm. This constraint will force the values of r and h to be related. A very tall or very short cone will have a small radius, while the medium cone (with its base at the equator of the sphere) will have the largest radius—5 cm, the radius of the sphere.

We could try several different values h for the height of the cone and compute the corresponding volume V for each value of h. For instance, a cone with a height $h = 5$ cm will have its base at the equator of the sphere, so the radius r of the cone is also 5 cm. The volume of this particular cone is $V = \frac{1}{3}\pi 5^3 = \frac{125}{3}\pi$ cubic cm. If we repeat this process for several different heights h and compute the resulting volumes V, we can arrange the pairs of values (h, V) in a table and plot them in an attempt to find a relationship, or pattern, in the values.

Another way to find a functional relationship between V and h is to express r in terms of h and then substitute this expression for r in the volume formula to get a functional expression solely in terms of h.

Since we are not going to consider "degenerate" cones (those collapsing to a single point or line segment), we know that the height h must be strictly greater than 0 cm and strictly less than 10 cm. Hence, the physical constraints on the problem also provide us with a natural *domain* for the possible heights h.

The illustration shows the geometry of two typical cones, one with a height greater than the sphere's radius 5 cm and one with a height smaller than 5 cm, showing the relationship between the dimensions of the cone and the radius of the sphere. For a cone that is more than 5 cm tall, we can draw a right triangle having legs of r and $h - 5$ cm, respectively, and a hypotenuse of 5 cm (the radius of the sphere). In this case, the Pythagorean theorem gives us

$$(h-5)^2 + r^2 = 5^2,$$

or

$$\begin{aligned} r^2 &= 5^2 - (h-5)^2 \\ &= 25 - (h^2 - 10h + 25) \\ &= 10h - h^2. \end{aligned}$$

Since r^2 appears in the volume formula, we can simply substitute $(10h - h^2)$ directly for r^2 to obtain

$$\begin{aligned} V &= \frac{1}{3}\pi(10h - h^2)h \\ &= \frac{1}{3}\pi(10h^2 - h^3) \end{aligned}$$

whenever $5 \text{ cm} < h < 10 \text{ cm}$.

For a cone that is less than 5 cm tall, we can draw a right triangle having legs of r and $5 - h$ cm, respectively, and a hypotenuse of 5 cm. Now we have

$$(5-h)^2 + r^2 = 5^2,$$

or

$$\begin{aligned} r^2 &= 5^2 - (5-h)^2 \\ &= 25 - (25 - 10h + h^2) \\ &= 10h - h^2. \end{aligned}$$

This is exactly the same substitution value for r^2 that we obtained in the previous case, so we also have

$$V = \frac{1}{3}\pi(10h^2 - h^3)$$

whenever $0 \text{ cm} < h < 5 \text{ cm}$.

Since our formula $V = \frac{1}{3}\pi(10h^2 - h^3)$ worked for all other possible values of h, we might try it for $h = 5\ cm$ also:

$$\begin{aligned} V &= \frac{1}{3}\pi(10(5^2) - 5^3) \\ &= \frac{125}{3}\pi \text{ cubic cm.} \end{aligned}$$

Since this cone has a radius $r = 5$ cm, we note that its volume is, indeed,

$$\frac{1}{3}\pi r^2 h = \frac{125}{3}\pi \text{ cubic cm.}$$

Thus, the formula works for all possible values of h, and

$$V(h) = \frac{1}{3}\pi(10h^2 - h^3)$$

for any h such that $0 < h < 10$, where V is in cubic cm and h is in cm. We have found an equation in h that represents the volume V of the inscribed cone.

Finding an extremum

Once a quantity has been expressed as a function of a single variable, we can use the derivative to help us find how to the maximize or minimize the value of the quantity. The worker wishes to maximize the volume of the conical part. Hence, the problem she must solve is how to find exactly what height to make the cone to realize this maximum volume.

Problem: Given a sphere of radius 5 cm, find the height of the cone of maximum volume V that can be inscribed in the sphere. With a formula in hand that describes the volume explicitly in terms of h, the solution is a straightforward application of calculus. Since

$$V(h) = \frac{1}{3}\pi(10h^2 - h^3),$$

we have

$$V'(h) = \tfrac{1}{3}\pi(20h - 3h^2).$$

This expression is defined for all values in the relevant domain ($0 < h < 10$), so the only critical values h are those such that

$$\frac{1}{3}\pi(20h - 3h^2) = 0.$$

After multiplying both sides by $3/\pi$ and factoring, we have

$$h(20 - 3h) = 0.$$

The value $h = 0$ is not relevant (it is not in the domain), so

$$h = \frac{20}{3} \approx 6.667 \text{ cm}$$

is the only critical value of interest.

We can check that $V'(h) = \frac{1}{3}\pi h(20 - 3h)$ is positive for $h < 20/3$ and negative for $h > 20/3$. Hence, the derivative test verifies that this is precisely the height h that achieves the maximum cone volume.

To find the actual maximum volume of the cone, we can substitute $h = 20/3$ into our formula for V:

$$V(\frac{20}{3})= \frac{1}{3}\pi(10(\frac{20}{3})^2 - (\frac{20}{3})^3) = \frac{4000\pi}{81} \approx 155.14 \text{ cm}^3.$$

In Chapter 5, you will see how problems of optimization can often be posed as problems of finding extrema under constraints.

EXERCISES for Section 4.5

For exercises 1–10: The following exercises describe geometric objects under various constraints. Find the domain and formula for the indicated function.

1. The surface area S of a cylinder inscribed in a sphere of radius 5 cm as a function of the height h of the cylinder.

2. The area A of a rectangle inscribed in a circle of radius 12 inches as a function of the width w of the rectangle.

3. The volume of a box with square base inscribed in a sphere of diameter 12 ft as a function of the box's height h.

4. The surface area S of a box with square base inscribed in a sphere of diameter 12 ft as a function of its height h.

5. The volume V of a cone circumscribed about a sphere of radius 6 m as a function of its own radius r.

6. The area A of an isosceles triangle inscribed in a circle of diameter 8 cm as a function of its vertex angle θ.

7. The area A of an isosceles triangle circumscribed about a circle of diameter 8 cm as a function of its vertex angle θ.

8. The perimeter P of an isosceles triangle inscribed in a circle of diameter 8 cm as a function of its base length b.

9. The diagonal ℓ of a rectangle inscribed in a circle of radius 12 inches as a function of the width w of the rectangle.

10. An open cone is manufactured by cutting a sector (piece of pie) of angle θ out of a circle of radius $R = 6$ inches and then connecting the edges of the remaining piece. Express the volume V of the cone as a function of θ. (Hint: calculate the radius r of the opening of the cone as a function of θ. Then use this and the Pythagorean theorem to calculate the height h of the cone as a function of θ. Finally, use formula $V = \pi r^2 h/3$ to find V as a function of θ.)

For exercises 11–20: Find the indicated extremum of the quantities described. (Hint: your answers to exercises 1–10 will be needed here.)

11. Find the maximum of the surface area S of a cylinder inscribed in a sphere of radius 5 cm. (See exercise 1.)

12. Find the maximum of the area A of a rectangle inscribed in a circle of radius 12 inches. (See exercise 2.)

13. Find the maximum of the volume of a box with square base inscribed in a sphere of diameter 12 ft. (See exercise 3.)

14. Find the maximum of the surface area S of a box with square base inscribed in a sphere of diameter 12 ft. (See exercise 4.)

15. Find the minimum of the volume V of a cone circumscribed about a sphere of radius 6 m. (See exercise 5.)

16. Find the maximum of the area A of an isosceles triangle inscribed in a circle of diameter 8 cm. (See exercise 6.)

17. Find the minimum of the area A of an isosceles triangle circumscribed about a circle of diameter 8 cm. (See exercise 7.)

18. Find the maximum of the perimeter P of an isosceles triangle inscribed in a circle of diameter 8 cm. (See exercise 8.)

19. Find the maximum of the diagonal ℓ of a rectangle inscribed in a circle of radius 12 inches. (See exercise 9.)

20. An open cone is manufactured by cutting a sector (piece of pie) of angle θ out of a circle of radius $R = 6$ inches and then connecting the edges of the remaining piece. Find the maxmimum volume V of the cone that can be constructed in this way. (See exercise 10.)

4.6 THE MEAN VALUE THEOREM

The mean value theorem is one of the most important results regarding the derivative of a function. It is a wellspring of information, even though its main idea is fairly simple.

The word *mean* here is used in the sense of *average*, and we can think of the mean value theorem as pointing out an important connection between average and instantaneous rate of change. To illustrate the idea of the theorem, let's go back to our example of the car traveling at varying speeds. Suppose that you drive a car for two hours and travel exactly 80 miles. We already know that this means that the *average* velocity for the trip is

$$\frac{\textit{total distance}}{\textit{total time}} = \frac{80 \text{ miles}}{2 \text{ hours}} = 40 \text{ mph}.$$

Now, the question: Did there have to be some instant during the two hours when your instantaneous velocity (speedometer reading) was exactly 40 mph?

The answer is *yes*. To understand why, suppose for the sake of argument that your speedometer *never* read 40 mph for even a single instant. Then either your car's velocity was always less than 40 mph or always over 40 mph for the entire trip. In the first case, if you always travel at a velocity less than 40 mph for two hours, you cannot possibly cover the entire distance of 80 miles. In the second case, if you always travel at a velocity of more than 40 mph for two hours, you will undoubtedly cover *more* than 80 miles. Since you covered *exactly* 80 miles on the trip, by process of elimination we must conclude that there is at least one instant at which you are traveling at a velocity of *exactly* 40 mph.

This is the principle by which a police officer at a toll booth may write a speeding ticket. If your toll ticket has a time stamp, your average speed for the trip between toll booths can be computed. If this average speed is in excess of the speed limit, then the police officer may conclude that you broke the speed limit at least once during the trip.

Rolle's theorem and the mean value theorem

Now we'll turn to a graphical interpretation of this theorem and the reasoning behind it. First, let's look at a closely related theorem.

Theorem 4.2

Rolle's theorem
Hypothesis 1: f is continuous on $[a, b]$.
Hypothesis 2: f is differentiable on (a, b).
Hypothesis 3: $f(a) = f(b)$.
Conclusion: There is at least one point $a < x_0 < b$ such that $f'(x_0) = 0$.

Reasoning Geometrically, the hypotheses require the graph of f to connect two points with the same y-coordinate (Hypothesis 3) with an unbroken, smooth curve (Hypotheses 1 and 2). (See Figure 4.15.) The conclusion of the theorem states that there must be at least one point between a and b where the slope of the graph is $m = 0$. In the illustration shown, we actually see three such points.

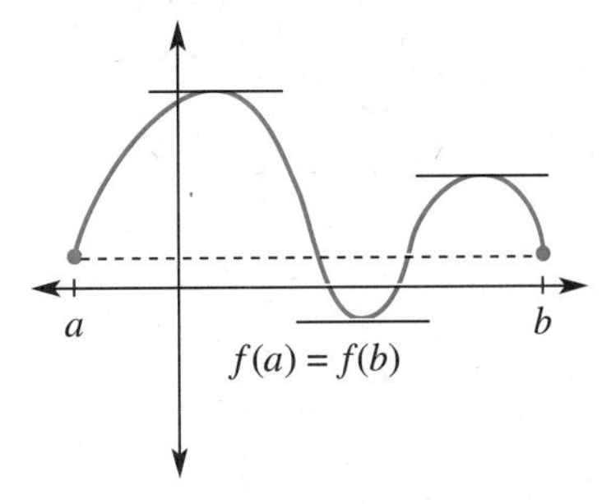

Figure 4.15 Illustration of Rolle's theorem.

Recall the extreme value theorem: *a continuous function must have definite minimum and maximum output values over a closed interval.* So, Hypothesis 1 guarantees that f must have definite minimum and maximum values on $[a, b]$. If *both* the minimum and maximum happen to occur at the two endpoints, then f must actually be a *constant* function (since $f(a) = f(b)$ by Hypothesis 3). In that case, the conclusion of Rolle's theorem is easily satisfied, since $f'(x_0) = 0$ for *any* choice of x_0 between a and b (the graph is horizontal between a and b).

If f is not constant, then either the minimum or maximum (or both) occur somewhere strictly between a and b. If x_0 is a point where this extremum occurs, then the critical value theorem (Theorem 4.1) requires that x_0 be a critical value, which means that $f'(x_0) = 0$ or is undefined. Now Hypothesis 2 is important. Since the derivative is defined for all such values between a and b, we must have $f'(x_0) = 0$. □

Rolle's theorem can be used to prove the mean value theorem, which we now state formally.

Theorem 4.3

Mean value theorem

Hypothesis 1: f is continuous on $[a, b]$.

Hypothesis 2: f is differentiable on (a, b).

Conclusion: $f'(x_0) = \dfrac{f(b) - f(a)}{b - a}$ for at least one input $a < x_0 < b$.

Note that the hypotheses are the same as Rolle's theorem except that we've dropped the hypothesis requiring $f(a) = f(b)$. The function f may take on different values at the endpoints of the interval. Geometrically, the conclusion states that there must be at least one point x_0 between a

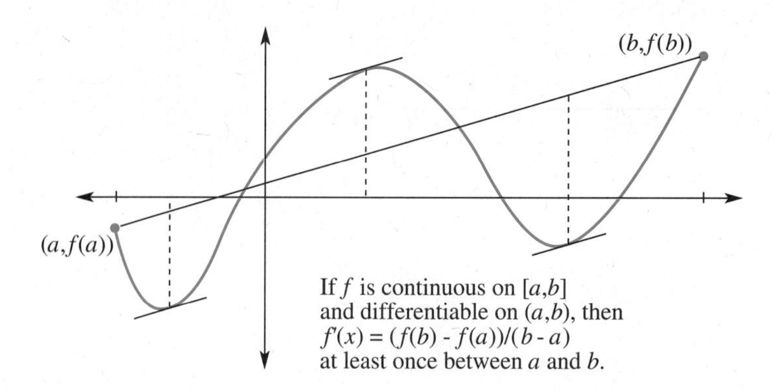

Figure 4.16 Illustration of the mean value theorem.

and b where the slope $f'(x_0)$ matches the slope of the secant line connecting the two points $(a, f(a))$ and $(b, f(b))$.

Such a situation is shown in Figure 4.16. Note that this illustration looks like a "tilted" version of our illustration for Rolle's theorem. If $f(a) = f(b)$, the secant line is horizontal and has slope 0. In this case, the conclusion of the mean value theorem is the same as Rolle's theorem: there is at least one point between a and b where the slope is 0. In fact, we can use Rolle's theorem to prove the mean value theorem.

Reasoning

Suppose we let g represent the linear function whose graph is the secant line. Then

$$g(a) = f(a) \qquad \text{and} \qquad g(b) = f(b),$$

and the slope of the graph of $y = g(x)$ can be found by using the two-point formula with $(a, f(a))$ and $(b, f(b))$:

$$m = \frac{f(b) - f(a)}{b - a}.$$

Now we can apply Rolle's theorem to the function difference $f - g$, because $f - g$ still satisfies our first two hypotheses and we have

$$f(a) - g(a) = 0 = f(b) - g(b).$$

By Rolle's theorem, there must be at least one point x_0 such that

$$(f - g)'(x_0) = f'(x_0) - g'(x_0) = 0 \qquad \text{or} \qquad f'(x_0) = g'(x_0).$$

But g is a linear function, so its derivative $g'(x_0)$ is just the slope m of the line passing through the two points $(a, f(a))$ and $(b, f(b))$. We can conclude that

$$f'(x_0) = \frac{f(b) - f(a)}{b - a}.$$

□

Rolle's theorem and the mean value theorem (as well as the intermediate value theorem and the extreme value theorem) can be classified as *existence* theorems. The conclusion of each theorem guarantees the *existence* of one or more real numbers satisfying a particular property or equation. They do not, however, provide us with a recipe or procedure for actually finding these numbers. For that, we are left to our own devices. (For example, the critical value theorem tells us exactly *where* to look for local extrema of a function.) Existence theorems are useful in a couple of ways. For one, they can confirm that we are not wasting our time looking for a solution to an equation. For another, simply knowing that a solution to an equation exists may be far more important information than the value of the actual solution.

Equal derivatives mean vertically parallel graphs

Suppose you know that for all x such that $a < x < b$,

$$f'(x) = 0.$$

Must f be *constant* over the interval (a, b)?

Surely, the derivative of a constant function will be zero over the interval, but we're asking whether or not the *converse* must be true. In other words, could it be possible for the derivative to be zero at every point in the interval without the graph being a continuous flat line over the interval?

We can use the mean value theorem to argue that f must, indeed, be a constant function over (a, b) by showing that any two inputs x_1 and x_2 in the interval must produce the same output values $f(x_1) = f(x_2)$. First, note that the slope of the line through the two points $(x_1, f(x_1))$ and $(x_2, f(x_2))$ is

$$m = \frac{f(x_2) - f(x_1)}{x_2 - x_1}.$$

If we apply the mean value theorem to our function f over the interval $[x_1, x_2]$, there exists at least one point x_0 between x_1 and x_2 such that $f'(x_0) = m$. But we already know that the derivative $f'(x) = 0$ over the whole interval, so $m = 0$ and the numerator $f(x_2) - f(x_1) = 0$. This means that $f(x_2) = f(x_1)$ for any x_1 and x_2 in the interval (a, b). Let's highlight a generalization of this conclusion as a theorem.

Theorem 4.4

Hypothesis: Suppose that two functions f and g have the same derivative over (a, b). That is, $f'(x) = g'(x)$ for $a < x < b$.
Conclusion: f and g differ only by a constant function over (a, b). In other words, there is some constant C such that $f(x) = g(x) + C$ for $a < x < b$.

Reasoning Since the derivative of $f - g$ is $f' - g'$, the hypothesis means that the derivative of $f - g$ is zero (0) over the whole interval (a, b). From our discussion above, we can conclude that $f(x) - g(x)$ is constant. That is, for some real number C, we have

$$f(x) - g(x) = C \qquad \text{for} \qquad a < x < b.$$

Adding $g(x)$ to both sides of the equation gives us the conclusion of the theorem. □

Graphically, just as two lines with the same slope are parallel, two functions with the same derivative have "vertically parallel" graphs, in the sense that the vertical distance (the constant C) between them is always the same (see Figure 4.17).

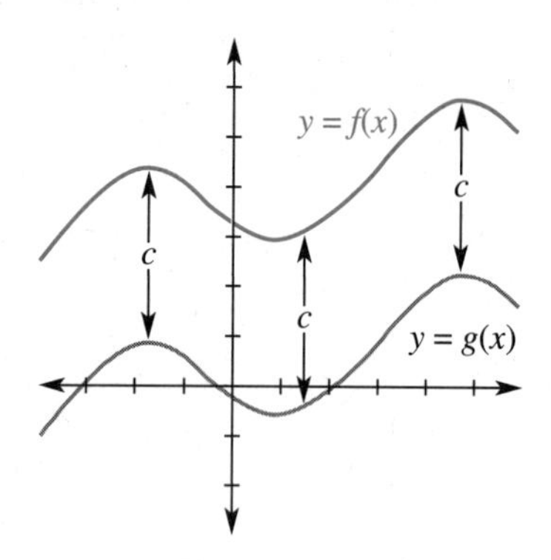

Figure 4.17 Functions with equal derivatives.

EXERCISES for Section 4.6

For exercises 1–20:

(a) Graph $y = f(x)$ over the indicated interval $[a, b]$.

(b) Graph the line passing through the points $(a, f(a))$ and $(b, f(b))$.

(c) Find at least one point $a < x_0 < b$ satisfying the conclusion of the mean value theorem, or explain what hypothesis of the mean value theorem is violated by the function f.

1. $f(x) = x^2, \quad [1, 2]$
2. $f(x) = \sqrt{x}, \quad [1, 4]$
3. $f(x) = x^{2/3}, \quad [-8, 8]$
4. $f(x) = x^3 - 4x, \quad [-2, 3]$
5. $f(x) = \sin x, \quad [-\pi/2, 0]$
6. $f(x) = \cos x, \quad [\pi/6, \pi/3]$
7. $f(x) = \tan x, \quad [-\pi/4, \pi/4]$
8. $f(x) = 1/x, \quad [-3, 2]$
9. $f(x) = x^{1/5}, \quad [-1, 1]$
10. $f(x) = 5(3 - x)^3, \quad [0, 3]$
11. $f(x) = x^2 + x + 1, \quad [-1, 0]$
12. $f(x) = 2x^2 - 7x + 3, \quad [-6, 6]$
13. $f(x) = x^3 - 12x, \quad [-2, 2]$
14. $f(x) = \dfrac{3x - 17}{5}, \quad [-10, 7]$
15. $f(x) = x^5, \quad [-1, 2]$
16. $f(x) = 3, \quad [-7, 10]$
17. $f(x) = \sin^2 x, \quad [0, \pi/2]$
18. $f(x) = 2^x - x^2, \quad [0, 4]$
19. $f(x) = \sin x^2, \quad [0, \pi/2]$
20. $f(x) = \sqrt{25 - x^2}, \quad [-3, 4]$

For exercises 21–28: For each of the function graphs shown, the grid lines are spaced 1 unit apart both horizontally and vertically. Approximate the slope of the secant line connecting the leftmost and rightmost points visible on the graph. If possible, locate at least one point at which the slope of the tangent line is the same as the slope of this secant line.

21.

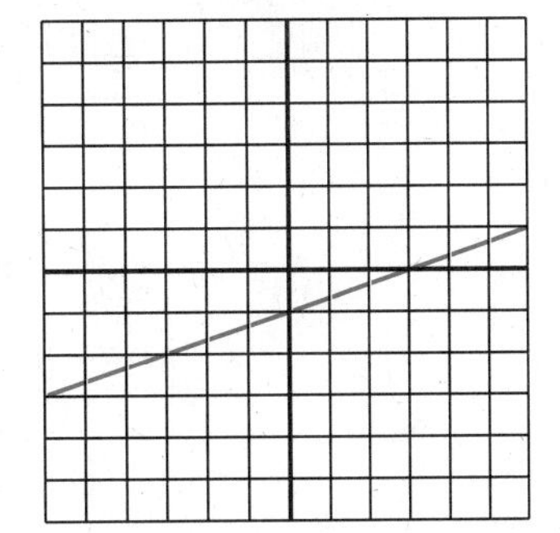

22.

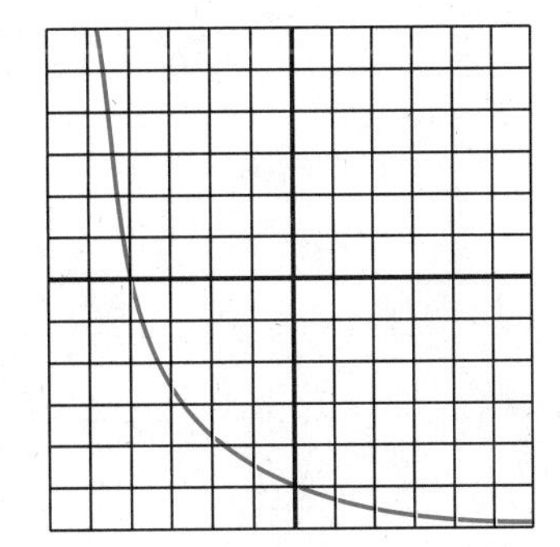

23.

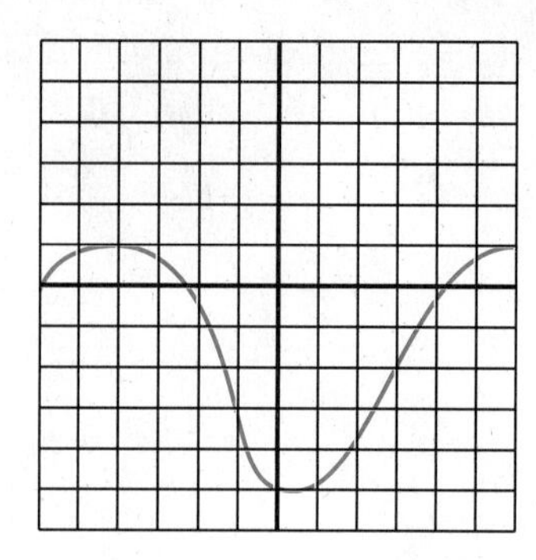

24.

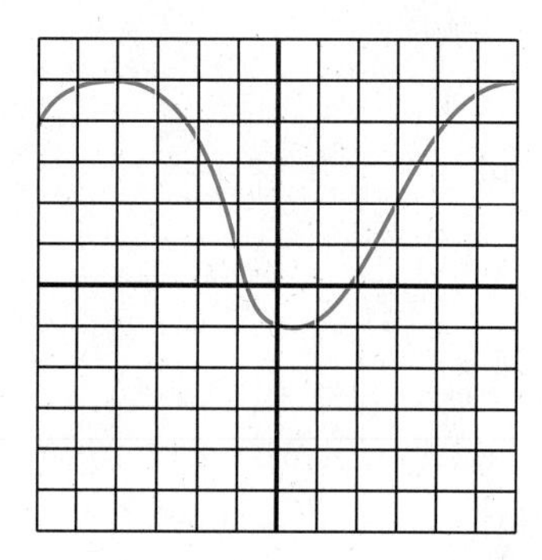

25.

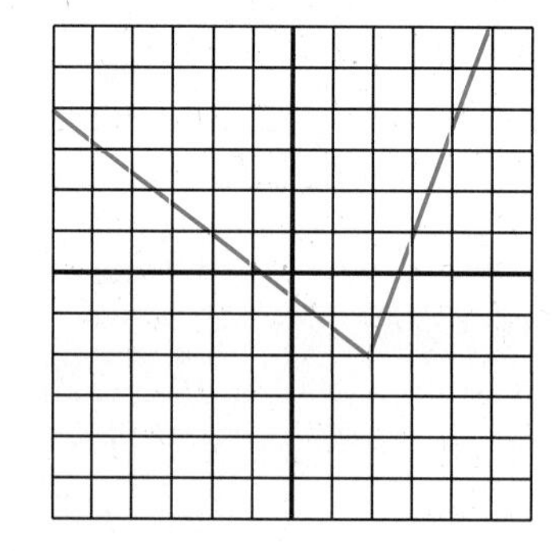

26.

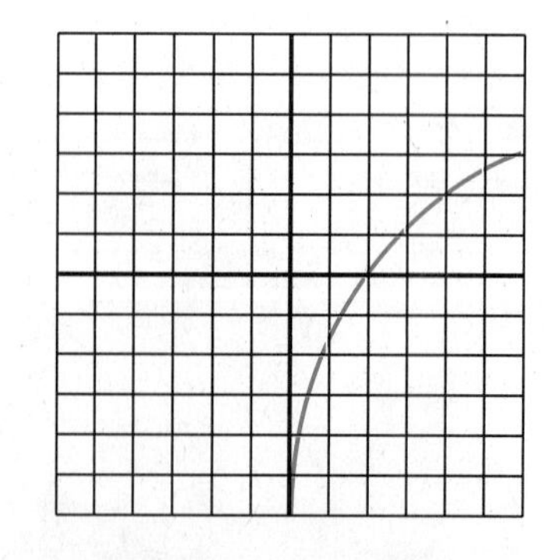

27.

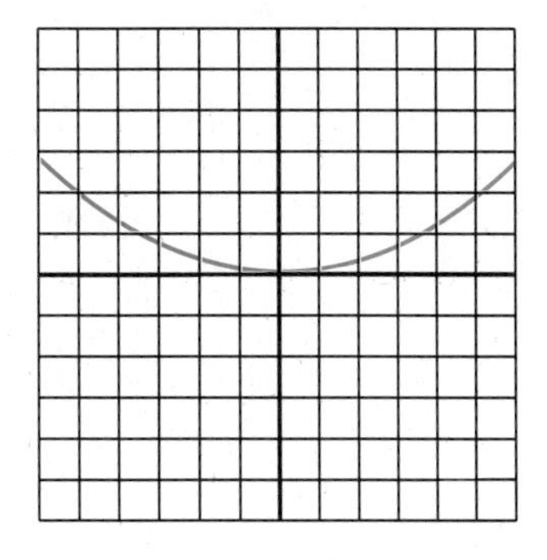

28.

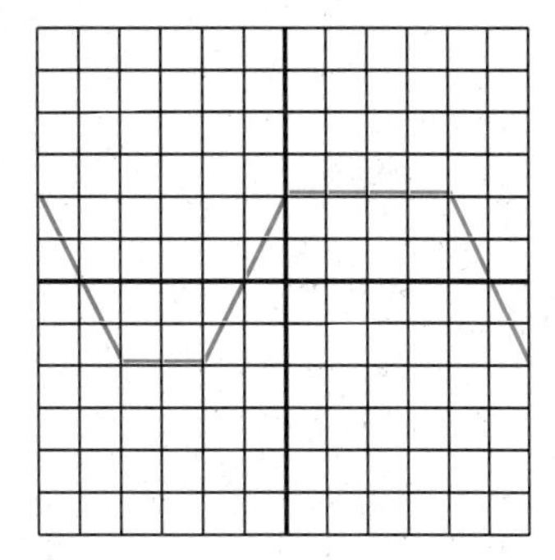

29. For which graphs above were you unable to locate a point where the tangent line is parallel to the secant line? For each graph, explain which hypothesis of the mean value theorem was violated.

30. Verify that $f(x) = (\sin(x) + \cos(x))^2$ and $g(x) = \sin(2x)$ have the same derivative. Graph both functions to see that the graphs are parallel. What is the constant difference C in this case?

New tax regulations require the Platypus Company to maintain more complete travel records. For this reason, the company decides to install trip-meters in each of the company vehicles. These meters graphically record the distance travelled over time by each vehicle.

When a new employee, Ed, returns from a delivery trip to a neighboring town, fellow workers comment that the trip seemed to take a long time. Ed replies "Shortly after I got on the freeway, I ran into road construction, and this kept my speed down to about 10 mph for nearly an hour. I drove the remaining 20 miles on the freeway at 55 mph. By then it was time for lunch, so I stopped for a 30-minute lunch break. After another 10 minutes at the local speed limit (25 mph), I made the delivery. It took about 15 minutes of paperwork to complete the delivery and I came back by the same route. There were no construction delays in this direction."

31. Shown is the recording from Ed's trip-meter. Point out the ways in which the recording supports Ed's recounting of the trip and the ways in which it does not.

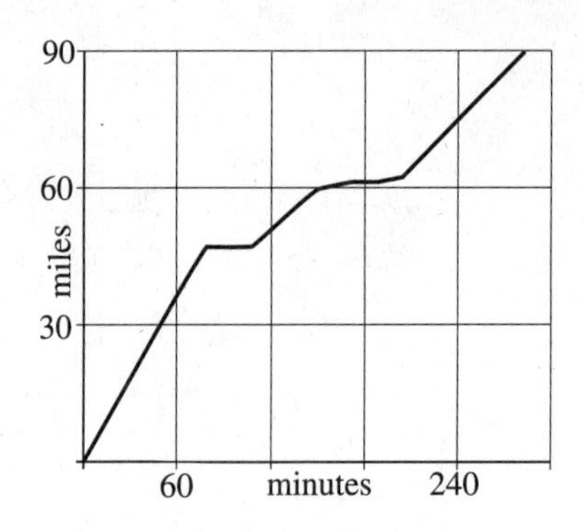

For Exercise 31

32. Draw what Ed's recording should have looked like if the trip was as he described.

33. It is company policy that no one using a company vehicle should exceed a 45-mph average speed over any one-hour segment of a trip. Did Ed comply with this policy?

34. Is it possible to comply with this policy and yet violate a 45-mph speed limit at some time during the trip? If so, how? If not, why not?

35. Is it possible to comply with this policy and yet have an average speed of 50 mph over a two-hour period? If so, how? If not, why not?

36. Another company policy states that drivers must take a rest stop at least once an hour. Adrian wants to travel at the freeway speed limit of 65 mph, adhere to all company policies, and yet make the travel time as short as possible. How long should the rest stops be? (Model this two ways: one in which the car can stop or attain full speed instantly, and another where it takes 1 minute to come to a stop or reach full speed.)

One day, Sue is complaining to her friend, Jamal, about her least-favorite delivery route. "I really hate that route. I manage to get every traffic light. I get to the intersection just as the light turns red and take off as soon as it turns green but I still get every light!" "I know," says Jamal,"I was one light behind you on your last trip!" Fred overhears the conversation and says "Don't you know that those traffic lights are timed? If you drive at the right speed, you can miss every light. Get out your trip records and I'll show you." When they superimpose their trip records, they see the situation shown in the illustration.

37. Locate the positions on the recording likely to correspond to traffic lights.

38. At what speed, or range of speeds, can they travel after stopping for the first light and miss all the others (assume that the lights are red approximately half the time and green the other half)?

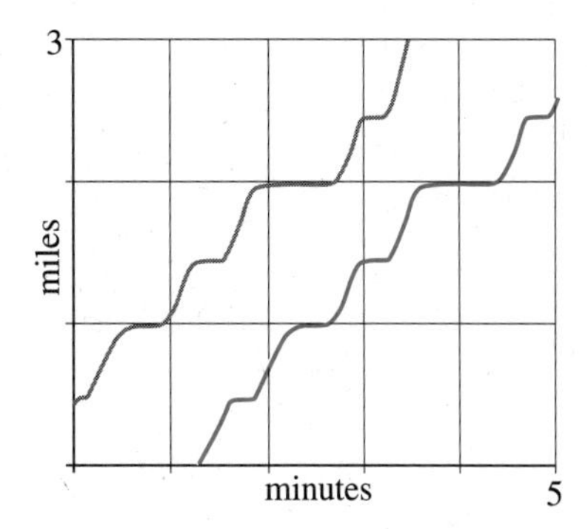

For Exercises 37–40

39. Can they travel at half the speed range you indicated above (ignoring traffic constraints) and still miss all the lights? If so, why? If not, why not?

40. How does Sue and Jamal's average speed compare with the fastest non-stop speed you found?

5

Applications and Extensions of the Derivative

Calculus originated in an effort to solve particular problems. In this chapter, we examine some of the many applications of derivatives and consider how the idea of derivative can be extended beyond functions of a single variable.

Perhaps the most important of these problems deal with *optimization*—that is, problems requiring us to find the "best" value of some quantity. This often translates to finding when a quantity achieves an extreme value under constraints. As we already saw in the last chapter, the derivative is a powerful tool for finding such extrema.

In this chapter we also discuss *higher order* derivatives (that is, derivatives of derivatives) and interpret the information they can provide both graphically and physically. *Implicit differentiation* allows us to find the slopes of curves and rates of change described in ways other than as function graphs. We apply this information to the problem of measuring rates of change of several related quantities. Calculus can be used to solve problems involving particle motion described by *parametric equations*.

5.1 OPTIMIZATION

In quantitative terms, optimization most often means to maximize or minimize some variable quantity. For instance, a business strives to maximize profits and minimize costs. Manufacturers seek to maximize yields while minimizing resources used. In economics, engineering, and the physical, biological, and social sciences, we can identify many problems of optimization.

If the variable quantity we want to maximize or minimize can be modeled as a function of other variables, then calculus can provide a powerful tool for solving the optimization problem. In Chapter 4, we noted how the absolute extrema of a function of one variable must occur either at a critical value x_0 (an input in the domain of the function such that $f'(x_0) = 0$ or $f'(x_0)$ is undefined) or at an endpoint in the domain of the function. With that knowledge in hand, we can outline a step-by-step strategy for solving applied optimization problems with calculus.

Strategy for Solving Optimization Problems

Step 1. *Identify the dependent variable. Express it in terms of the other variables in the process.*

What variable quantity are we trying to maximize or minimize? Label it and the other variables appropriately. A picture may be helpful.

Step 2. *Identify the constraints.*

The constraints are the boundaries and restrictions on the process. A constraint might be in the form of a particular interval of possible values for a variable or in the form of some relationship or connection that must hold between the variables.

Step 3. *Express the dependent variable as a function of a single independent variable. Identify the domain of the independent variable.*

Start with the expression (in terms of possibly several variables) from Step 1. Examine your constraints from Step 2 and use them to reformulate the expression in terms of one variable. The goal is to arrive at a relationship such as

$$y = f(x),$$

where y represents the quantity to be maximized or minimized and x is the single independent variable. Find the domain of acceptable values for x. This domain may take the form of some interval of real numbers. Take special note of whether or not the endpoints of such an interval are acceptable values.

Step 4. *If you can graph the dependent variable as a function of the independent variable,* ***do it!***

You should insure that your graph contains all acceptable values of the independent variable.

One reason you might not be able to draw the graph is that the functional relationship you have derived involves unspecified constants (parameters). In this case, you should make a sample graph (or graphs) with some reasonable values chosen for these parameters. While you will not be able to use this graph to actually determine the maximum or minimum, it will still be useful as a "reality check" when you have found the maximum or minimum.

Step 5. *Identify the locations and values of the absolute maximum and/or minimum.*

If you have made a graph, it often will give you a pretty good estimate on the location of the maximum and/or minimum. The maximum occurs where the graph reaches its highest point, and the minimum occurs where the graph reaches its lowest point.

To "home in" on the maximum or minimum, make a list containing all the candidates for maxima and minima. This will include all the endpoints (if there are any) and critical values in the acceptable domain, together with their function values. (When you determine the acceptable region, you determine the end points.) Finding the critical values requires finding those x in the acceptable region where $f'(x) = 0$ or $f'(x)$ is *undefined.*

The derivative test can be used to identify which critical values are local maxima, local minima, or neither. The function can be evaluated at the appropriate critical values and the endpoints to find the absolute extrema.

Step 6. *Interpret the results and use them to answer the particular questions posed by the problem.*

What exactly is being asked for in the problem? If we need to know the maximum or minimum value of the quantity, we must report the function value $f(x)$. If we need to know under what conditions this extremum occurs, we must report one or more of the values of the other variables involved in the process.

Interpreting the result includes *checking its reasonableness.* Graphically, we can use a plot of the function obtained in Step 4 over the appropriate domain and check visually the reasonableness of either the function values $f(x)$ or the locations of the extrema. We should also ask ourselves whether these values make sense in terms of the physical setting of the problem. Any conflict between our computations and this graphical or physical information must be resolved.

Optimization examples and problems—a metalworks plant

The Platypus Metalworks Corporation makes and sells a large line of metal products. The company's plant, located on the banks of a river, consists of three buildings—one for manufacturing, one for warehousing, and one as a business office. In one part of the manufacturing facility, sheets of metal of various sizes and rolls of wire of various thicknesses are produced. In another part of the facility, these metal sheets and wire are trimmed, folded, and welded in various configurations to make different products. The finished products are warehoused until they are shipped out to customers.

The examples in the remainder of this section and many of the exercises that follow provide a variety of optimization problems that might arise in the activities and operations of this metalworks plant. The intent is to provide a suitable real-world context for a wide range of practical optimization problems, while making clear the power of calculus to solve such problems.

EXAMPLE 1 Platypus is famous for its cookie sheets (which last a lifetime and longer, according to the ads). The cookie sheets come in a variety of sizes, and a special trim is applied to the perimeter of each. To standardize the trim length, all the rectangular cookie sheets have a perimeter of 60 inches. For what dimensions is the area of the sheet the greatest?

Solution **Step 1.** Identify the dependent variable.

We want to maximize the area of the sheet. If we label the area A, then we can write A in terms of the width w and the length ℓ of the sheet:

$$A = w\ell.$$

Step 2. Identify the constraints.

The sheet must have a perimeter of 60 inches. In terms of the width and length of the sheet, we must have

$$2w + 2\ell = 60.$$

Step 3. Express the dependent variable as a function of a single independent variable and identify its domain.

We can use the constraint to solve for either w or ℓ in terms of the other variable. Solving for ℓ, we have $2\ell = 60 - 2w$, so that

$$\ell = 30 - w.$$

Now we can substitute this expression for ℓ in our functional expression for the area that we wish to maximize:

$$A = w(30 - w) = 30w - w^2.$$

We have now written A as a function of w. What is the domain of acceptable values for w? The algebraic expression $30w - w^2$ is certainly defined for any real number w, but the physical situation would require w to be a positive number ($w > 0$). How large can w be? If the perimeter is 60 inches, then the width must be strictly less than 30 inches. Hence, the acceptable values for w are

$$0 < w < 30.$$

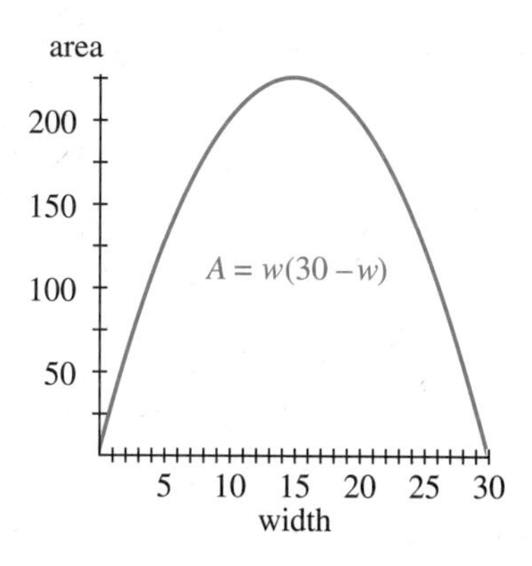

Figure 5.1 Graph of area A as a function of width w.

Step 4. Graph the dependent variable as a function of the independent variable.

In this case, we graph A as a function of w. The acceptable values for w are between (but not including) 0 and 30. It is clear from the graph in Figure 5.1 that the maximum area occurs near the middle of the interval ($w \approx 15$.)

Step 5. Identify the locations and values of the absolute maximum and/or minimum.

The domain $(0, 30)$ is an *open* interval and does not include its endpoints. (Note that if we had included the endpoints, $w = 0$ and $w = 30$ each would result in $A = 0$).

To find the critical values, we take the derivative with respect to w:

$$A'(w) = 30 - 2w.$$

This derivative is never undefined for any value of w. Setting

$$A'(w) = 30 - 2w = 0$$

and solving for w, we have

$$w = 15.$$

This value $w = 15$ is in the domain of the function, so $w = 15$ is the only critical value. This, then, is the only value on our list, and the area corresponding to $w = 15$ is $w(30 - w) = 225$. It is pretty clear from the graph that this is a maximum, but for insurance we'll apply the derivative test to this critical value. For $w < 15$, the derivative $A'(w) = 30 - 2w > 0$ and for $w > 15$, the derivative $A'(w) = 30 - 2w < 0$. Since the derivative's value changes from positive to negative, $A(15) = 30 \cdot 15 - 15^2 = 225$ is a *local maximum* value for the function, and it must be the *absolute maximum*.

Step 6. Interpret the results and answer the question posed.

We have found that the width $w = 15$ corresponds to the maximum area. We are asked to find the *dimensions* of the rectangle. To find the length ℓ, we can go back to Step 3 and substitute $w = 15$ to find

$$\ell = 30 - w = 30 - 15 = 15.$$

Therefore, the rectangle of perimeter 60 inches having maximum area is a *square* 15 inches by 15 inches. ■

Certainly the maximum was evident from the graph in Example 1. The power of calculus comes into full play when we need to generalize the solution to an optimization problem. This is often the case when we replace a specific constant in the problem with a parameter (unspecified constant).

EXAMPLE 2 The Platypus cookie sheet custom shop is equally famous for its cookie sheets. They take a customer's special trim and make a custom cookie sheet with the trim wrapped around the perimeter. If the length of the customer's trim is P inches, for what dimensions (expressed in terms of P) is the area of the sheet going to be the greatest?

Solution **Step 1.** Identify the dependent variable.

We want to maximize the area of the sheet. If we label the area A, then we can write A in terms of the width w and the length ℓ of the sheet:

$$A = w\ell.$$

Step 2. Identify the constraints.

The sheet must have a perimeter of P inches. In terms of the width and length of the sheet we must have

$$2w + 2\ell = P.$$

Step 3. Express the dependent variable as a function of a single independent variable and identify its domain.

We can use the constraint to solve for either w or ℓ in terms of the other variable. Solving for ℓ, we have $2\ell = P - 2w$, so that

$$\ell = \frac{P}{2} - w.$$

Now we can substitute this expression for ℓ in our functional expression for area

$$A = w(\frac{P}{2} - w) = \frac{P}{2}w - w^2.$$

We have now written A as a function of w. What is the domain of acceptable values for w? The algebraic expression $P/2w - w^2$ is certainly defined for any real numbers w and P, but the physical situation requires w and P to be positive numbers ($w > 0$ and $P > 0$). Since the customer is in control of the length of the trim P, it is a parameter rather than an independent variable. How large can w be? If the perimeter is P inches, then the width must be strictly less than $P/2$ inches. Hence, the acceptable values for w are

$$0 < w < \frac{P}{2}.$$

Step 4. Graph the dependent variable as a function of the independent variable.

In this case, we can't directly graph A as a function of w since we don't know in advance the value of P. However, we already have a sample graph for one reasonable value of P, namely $P = 60$. In that case, the maximum occurred in the middle of the graph ($w = \frac{P/2}{2}$). Is this true for any positive P, or was our example a fluke?

Step 5. Identify the locations and values of the absolute maximum and/or minimum.

The domain $(0, \frac{P}{2})$ is an *open* interval and does not include its endpoints. (Note that if we had included the endpoints, $w = 0$ and $w = \frac{P}{2}$ each result in $A = 0$).

To find the critical values, we take the derivative with respect to w:

$$A'(w) = \frac{P}{2} - 2w.$$

This derivative is never undefined for any value of w or P. Setting $A'(w) = \frac{P}{2} - 2w = 0$ and solving for w, we have

$$w = \frac{P}{4}.$$

This value $w = \frac{P}{4}$ is in the domain of the function, so $w = \frac{P}{4}$ is the only critical value. This is the only value on our list, and in this case we'll need to apply the derivative test to this critical value. For $w < \frac{P}{4}$, the derivative $A'(w) = \frac{P}{2} - 2w > 0$, and for $w > \frac{P}{4}$, the derivative $A'(w) = \frac{P}{2} - 2w < 0$. By the derivative test, $A(\frac{P}{4}) = \frac{P}{4}(\frac{P}{2} - \frac{P}{4}) = \frac{P^2}{16}$ is a *local maximum* value for the function, and it must be the absolute maximum.

Step 6. Interpret the results and answer the question posed.

We have found that the width $w = \frac{P}{4}$ corresponds to the maximum area. We are asked to find the dimensions of the rectangle in terms of P. To find the length ℓ, we can go back to Step 3 and substitute $w = \frac{P}{4}$ to find

$$\ell = \frac{P}{2} - w = \frac{P}{2} - \frac{P}{4} = \frac{P}{4}.$$

In other words, the rectangular cookie sheet of maximum area is always a square. ■

EXAMPLE 3 A rectangular tin box with closed bottom and open top is to be constructed out of 54 square inches of material. The length of the box is to be twice the width. If w, ℓ, and h are the width, length, and height, respectively, of the box, find the maximum possible volume of the box and the dimensions of the box.

Solution **Step 1.** Identify the dependent variable.

We want to maximize the *volume* of the box. If we label the volume V, then we can write V in terms of the box's three dimensions:

$$V = w\ell h.$$

Step 2. Identify the constraints.

We have two constraints on our box. First, we know that the material of the box must have a total area of 54 in^2. This means that the area of the four sides and the area of the bottom must total 54 in^2. That is, we must have

$$2wh + 2\ell h + wl = 54 \text{ in}^2.$$

Second, we know that the length must be twice the width ($\ell = 2w$). Figure 5.2 shows an illustration of the box with these constraints.

Step 3. Express the dependent variable as a function of a single independent variable, and identify its domain.

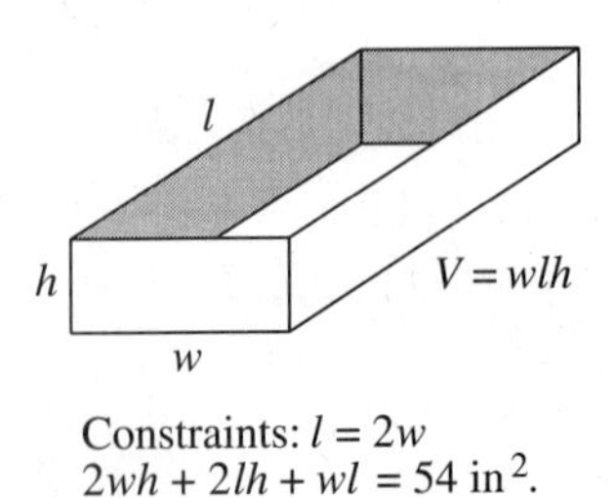

Figure 5.2 Maximizing the volume of an open box.

We substitute $2w$ for ℓ to rewrite the volume as

$$V = 2w^2h,$$

and we also rewrite the other constraint as

$$2wh + 4wh + 2w^2 = 6wh + 2w^2 = 54.$$

If we solve this for h, we obtain

$$h = \frac{54 - 2w^2}{6w}.$$

Now we substitute $\frac{54 - 2w^2}{6w}$ for h in the volume formula:

$$V = 2w^2 \cdot \frac{54 - 2w^2}{6w} = \frac{108w^2 - 4w^4}{6w} = 18w - \frac{2w^3}{3}.$$

Now we have written V as a function of w alone. What is the domain of possible values for w? Certainly, $w > 0$. The larger w becomes, the shallower the box must be because of the constraint on our materials. The extreme of a flat sheet with no sides ($h = 0$) would leave only the bottom of the box taking up all the available material ($wl = 2w^2 = 54$). For this extreme, $w = \sqrt{27} \approx 5.2$. Of course, this box has 0 volume and is not of interest for our optimization purposes, but we now know that our possible values for w are

$$0 < w < \sqrt{27} \approx 5.2.$$

Step 4. Graph the dependent variable as a function of the independent variable.

We graph $V = \frac{18w - 2w^3}{3}$ over the w-interval $[0, 5.2]$ to give us some idea of where the maximum value occurs (see Figure 5.3). On the basis of this picture, the maximum volume appears to be between 35 and 40 cubic inches, and it corresponds to a width $w \approx 3$ inches. We can use this information to monitor the reasonableness of our results using calculus.

Step 5. Identify the locations and values of the absolute maximum and/or minimum.

The endpoints of the domain $(0, \sqrt{27})$ are not included. (Even if they were, they would result in a minimum 0 volume instead of a maximum volume for the box.)

To find the critical values, we take the derivative $V'(w)$:

$$V'(w) = 18 - \frac{6w^2}{3} = 18 - 2w^2.$$

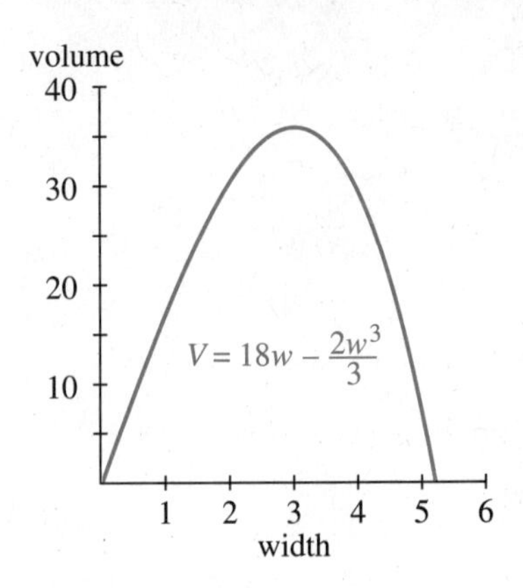

Figure 5.3 Graph of volume V as a function of width w.

This derivative is never undefined for any value of w. If we set $V'(w) = 0$, we have

$$18 - 2w^2 = 0, \qquad \text{so that} \qquad w = \pm 3.$$

The value $w = -3$ is not acceptable, since we must have a positive width for the box, so the only valid critical value is $w = 3$. Let's apply the derivative test to this critical value. For $w < 3$, the derivative $V'(w) = 18 - 2w^2 > 0$ and for $w > 3$, the derivative $V'(w) = 18 - 2w^2 < 0$. By the derivative test, $V(3) = 18 \cdot 3 - (2 \cdot 3^3)/3 = 54 - 18 = 36$ is a *local maximum* for the function and must be the *absolute maximum* in our domain.

Step 6. Interpret the results and answer the question posed.

We have found the width $w = 3$ that produced the maximum volume of 36 in^3. We also are asked to find the dimensions of the box. From the constraints, we have $\ell = 2w = 6$ in, and $h = \dfrac{54 - 2w^2}{6w} = \dfrac{36}{18} = 2$ in. Hence, the box of maximum volume has dimensions

$$3 \text{ in} \times 6 \text{ in} \times 2 \text{ in}$$

and a total volume of 36 in^3. ■

EXAMPLE 4 A small rectangular sheet of metal 10 cm wide and 20 cm long is folded down the middle and triangles are glued to the ends to produce a V-shaped feed or water trough for a pet cage. What should the angle of the bend be to maximize the amount the trough can hold?

Solution **Step 1.** Identify the dependent variable.

Figure 5.4 shows a picture of the piece used for the trough. The volume of the trough is determined by taking the area of its cross section and multiplying by its length. Since the length is fixed at 20 cm, maximizing the volume is equivalent to maximizing the area of the cross section. From

Figure 5.4, we can see that the cross section will be an isosceles triangle with legs of 5 cm and a vertex angle of θ (the angle of the fold).

If we let C be the area of the triangular cross section, then

$$C = bh/2.$$

Step 2. Identify the constraints.

To find the optimal angle θ, we need to express C as a function of the single variable θ. The constraints in this problem are defined by the side length of the triangle. Figure 5.4 shows how half the base ($b/2$) and the height h of the triangle can be viewed as legs of a right triangle with angle $\theta/2$. The hypotenuse is fixed at 5 cm by the problem constraints.

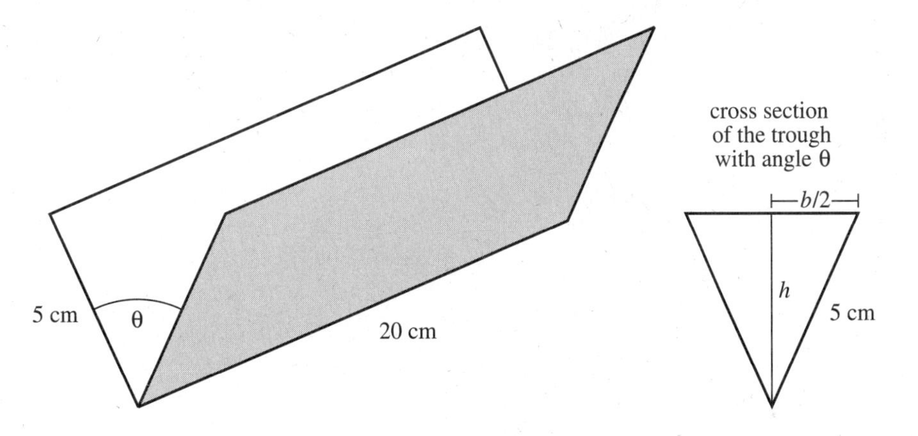

Figure 5.4 A trough made by folding a sheet of metal.

Step 3. Express the dependent variable as a function of a single independent variable and identify its domain.

Using this information and some trigonometry, we write

$$\sin\frac{\theta}{2} = \frac{\textit{opposite}}{\textit{hypotenuse}} = \frac{b/2}{5} \qquad \text{and} \qquad \cos\frac{\theta}{2} = \frac{\textit{adjacent}}{\textit{hypotenuse}} = \frac{h}{5}.$$

If we solve for b and h and substitute these quantities into our cross-sectional area formula, we obtain C entirely in terms of θ:

$$C = 25\sin\frac{\theta}{2}\cos\frac{\theta}{2}.$$

The domain of possible values for θ are between $0°$ and $180°$, or in terms of radians:

$$0 < \theta < \pi.$$

The endpoints of the interval correspond to a flat sheet ($\theta = \pi$) or a completely folded sheet ($\theta = 0$), both of which result in a cross section having no area.

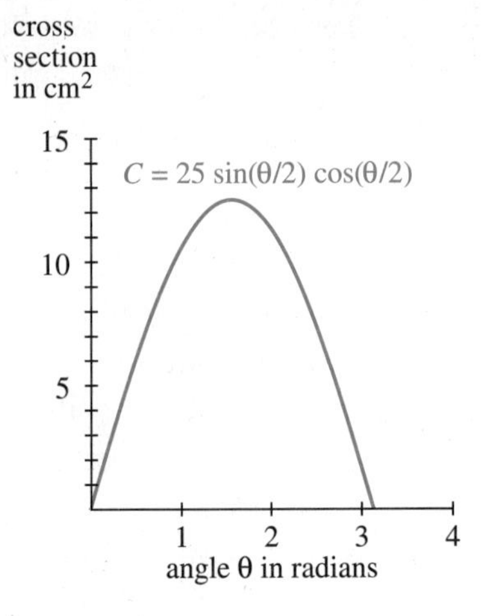

Figure 5.5 Graph of the area C of the cross section as a function of angle θ.

Step 4. Graph the dependent variable as a function of the independent variable.

In this case we want to graph $C = 25 \sin \frac{\theta}{2} \cos \frac{\theta}{2}$ for $0 < \theta < \pi$ radians. The graph in Figure 5.5 indicates that the maximum value occurs about midway between the endpoints of the interval, or at $\theta \approx \frac{\pi}{2}$.

Step 5. Identify the locations and values of the absolute maximum and/or minimum.

Since $\sin \theta = 2 \sin \frac{\theta}{2} \cos \frac{\theta}{2}$, we rewrite our expression for C as

$$C = \frac{25}{2} \sin \theta.$$

Differentiating C with respect to θ gives us

$$\frac{dC}{d\theta} = \frac{25}{2} \cos \theta.$$

If we set $\frac{dC}{d\theta} = 0$, we can see that the critical values will occur exactly when

$$\cos \theta = 0.$$

The only value θ in our domain satisfying this equation is

$$\theta = \pi/2 \qquad \text{or} \qquad 90^\circ.$$

Since $\cos(\theta) > 0$ for $\theta < \pi/2$ and $\cos(\theta) < 0$ for $\theta > \pi/2$, the derivative test tells us that $\theta = \pi/2$ will produce a local maximum for the area of the cross section. (You can check the second derivative test to see the same result.)

Step 6. Interpret the results and answer the question posed.

Folding the sheet at a 90° angle is optimal to maximize the volume of the trough. ■

EXAMPLE 5 A cylindrical can with closed bottom and closed top is to be constructed to have a volume of 1 gallon (approximately 231 cubic inches). The material used to make the bottom and top costs \$0.06 per square inch, and the material used to make the curved surface costs \$0.03 per square inch. Find the dimensions of the can (diameter and height) that minimize the total cost and determine what that minimum cost is.

Solution **Step 1.** Identify the dependent variable.

We want to minimize the total cost C of the materials used to make the can. Figure 5.6 illustrates the three component surfaces of the can (top, bottom, and curved surface). The curved surface can be unrolled to form a rectangle having the same height as the can and a length equal to the circumference of the can. The top and bottom are circles with the same diameter as the can.

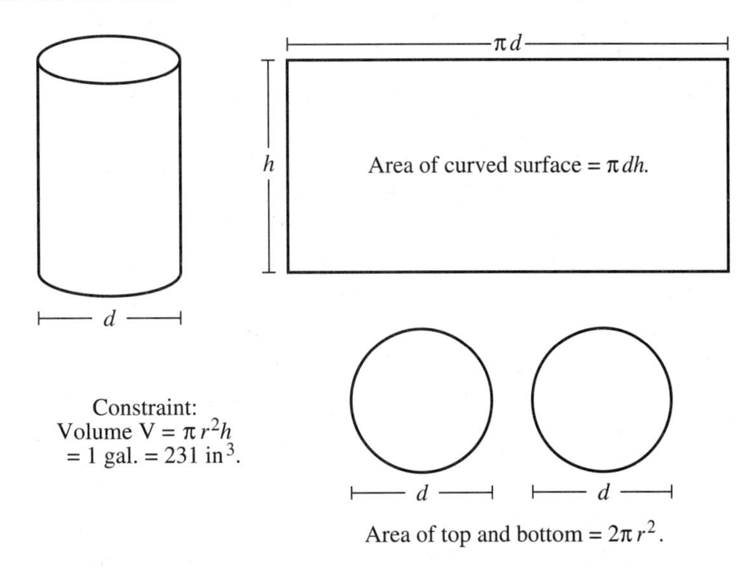

Figure 5.6 Minimizing the cost of a cylindrical can.

If the diameter d and height h of the can are measured in inches, then we need to compute the area of each part of the can, multiply each area by the corresponding cost per square inch, and total the results:

$$C = (.03)\pi dh + (.06)2\pi r^2,$$

where r is the radius ($d = 2r$) and C is the cost in dollars.

Step 2. Identify the constraints.

The can must hold exactly 1 gallon. Since we are measuring the dimensions of the can in inches, we need to convert the volume measurement to in^3. In this case, 1 gallon is equivalent to 231 cubic inches. Using the volume formula for a cylinder, we can now write the constraint as

$$V = \pi r^2 h = 231 \text{ in}^3.$$

Step 3. Express the dependent variable as a function of a single independent variable, and identify its domain.

The constraint equation from Step 2 allows us to solve for h in terms of r,

$$h = \frac{231}{\pi r^2},$$

and since $d = 2r$, we can write the cost C entirely in terms of r:

$$C = (.03)\pi(2r)\frac{231}{\pi r^2} + (.06)2\pi r^2 = \frac{13.86}{r} + (.12)\pi r^2.$$

To determine the domain of our independent variable r, we see that $r > 0$. We could theoretically (though certainly not practically) make the radius of the can as large as we want by making the can extremely short (h close to zero). So, r could be any positive real number.

Step 4. Graph the dependent variable as a function of the independent variable.

In this case, we want to graph $C = \dfrac{13.86}{r} + (.12)\pi r^2$ for all positive values of r. Since we cannot graph the function over its entire domain, we will graph it for some reasonable values of r—say, over the interval $0 < r < 5$. This will at least give us some idea of the shape of the graph. The result is shown in Figure 5.7. The graph appears to have a *local* minimum at $r \approx 2.5$, but we can't tell directly from it what happens for large values of r.

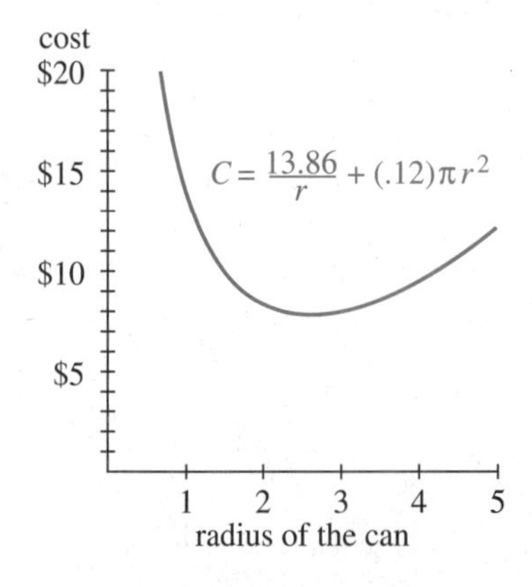

Figure 5.7 Graph of the cost function.

Step 5. Identify the locations and values of the absolute maximum and/or minimum.

Since our region of acceptable values has no endpoints, we need only consider the critical values.

Finding $\frac{dC}{dr}$, we have

$$\frac{dC}{dr} = -\frac{13.86}{r^2} + (.24)\pi r.$$

This expression is undefined when $r = 0$, but that value is not in the domain. The only critical values will occur when $\frac{dC}{dr} = 0$:

$$-\frac{13.86}{r^2} + (.24)\pi r = 0 \qquad \text{or} \qquad r^3 = \frac{13.86}{.24\pi}.$$

If we use $\pi \approx 3.1416$ as an approximation and take the cube root of both sides of this equation, we find

$$r \approx 2.64 \text{ in.}$$

This corroborates the conclusion we reached by looking at the graph. If we had chosen a region to graph that had not included this critical value, we would regraph now to insure that we included this point in the graph.

The derivative test verifies that $r \approx 2.64$ represents a *minimum* for our cost function. Substituting $r = 2.64$ into our cost function, we find

$$C \approx \frac{13.86}{2.64} + (.12)(3.1416)(2.64)^2 \approx \$7.88.$$

Step 6. Interpret the results and answer the question posed.

We have found that the minimum cost of the gallon can is approximately $\$7.88$. We were also asked to find the dimensions of this can. Since $r \approx 2.64$ in, we have

$$d = 2r \approx 5.28 \text{ in} \qquad \text{and} \qquad h = \frac{231}{\pi r^2} \approx 10.55 \text{ in}$$

as the diameter and height of the can, respectively. ■

We close by again summarizing the steps essential to solving an optimization problem with calculus.

Step 1. Identify the dependent variable.
Step 2. Identify the constraints.
Step 3. Express the dependent variable as a function of a single independent variable and identify its domain.
Step 4. Graph the function over its domain if you can.
Step 5. Identify the locations and values of the absolute maximum and/or minimum. Examine endpoints (if any) and critical values of the domain.
Step 6. Interpret the results and answer the question posed.

EXERCISES for Section 5.1

The following exercises continue to describe optimization problems involving the operations of the Platypus Metalworks Corporation. Suppose that you have been hired by Platypus to help solve their optimization problems because of your knowledge of calculus.

1. To prevent animals from harming themselves on sharp pieces of scrap metal, Platypus wants to fence off a rectangular scrap yard. You are given 100 meters of fencing to enclose the yard. Since the company is near the river, you decide to fence a rectangular plot along the river so that you need fence only three sides (see the illustration). What should be the dimensions of the yard to maximize the area enclosed?

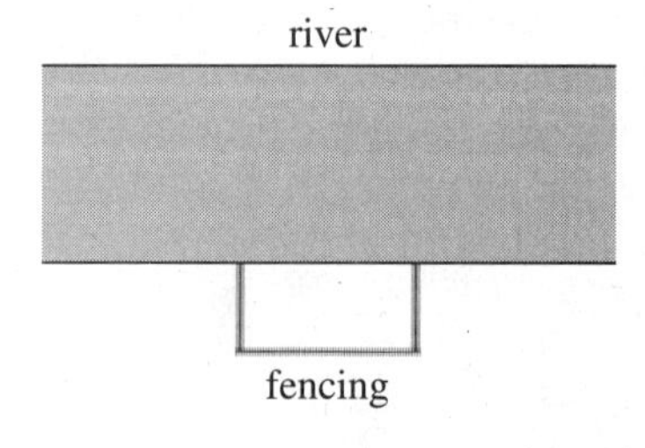

For Exercise 1

2. The managers are concerned that the fence will be unsightly to passers-by. You are now told that the yard must have at least 500 square meters of area, but you must use decorative fencing along the front (parallel to the river). The decorative fencing costs \$25 per meter, while the standard fencing costs \$15 per meter. What dimensions will you use to enclose 500 square meters to minimize the cost to the company?

3. Upon contacting the decorative fence supplier, you find that the \$25 price is not firm and may fluctuate. Determine in terms of D, the decorative fencing's eventual cost per meter, the dimensions you will use to enclose 500 square meters to minimize the cost to the company.

4. A rectangular box with square base and open top is constructed to have a volume of 270 cubic inches. The material used to make the bottom of the box costs \$.06 per square inch; the material used to make the rest of the box costs \$.03 per square inch. Find the dimensions of the box that minimize the total cost.

5. Your rectangular box project was so successful that you are now to make a series of boxes with the same construction, but with varying volumes. Determine the dimensions that minimize the total cost in terms of V, the specified volume of the box in cubic inches.

---

6. Hundreds of thousands of copies of a page of advertising information are to be mailed worldwide. The page contains 24 square inches of printed material with margins of 1.5 inches at the top and bottom of the page and 1 inch at the sides. What should be the overall dimensions (length and width, from edge to edge of the paper) to minimize the overall area of the page?

7. The ad agency tells you that the margin sizes they provided are wrong, but they haven't figured out the new ones yet. Find the overall dimensions of the page in terms of T and S, the top/bottom and left/right margins, respectively, that minimize the area.

---

8. A rectangular tin box with square base is constructed to have a volume of 96 cubic inches. The top of the box costs \$.06 per square inch to paint; the rest of the box, including the bottom, costs only \$.03 per square inch to paint. Find the dimensions of the box that minimize the total cost of painting.

9. A cylindrical can with closed bottom and closed top is made from two kinds of material. The material used to make the bottom and top of the can costs \$.06 per square inch, and the material used to make the curved surface of the can costs \$.03 per square inch. The total cost of the can is \$1.44. If r is the radius and h is the height of the can, find the value of r that maximizes the volume.

10. A rectangular box with square base and open top is constructed from two types of material. The material used to make the bottom of the box costs \$.10 per square inch; the material used to make the rest of the box costs \$.06 per square inch. The total cost of the box is \$3.00. If s is one side of the base of the box and h is the height, find the value of s that maximizes V.

11. Platypus makes lengths of rain gutter by taking a 12-inch-wide strip of metal and folding it up at equal angles four inches from the edges into a trapezoidal shape (see illustration). What should the angle be to maximize the capacity of the rain gutter?

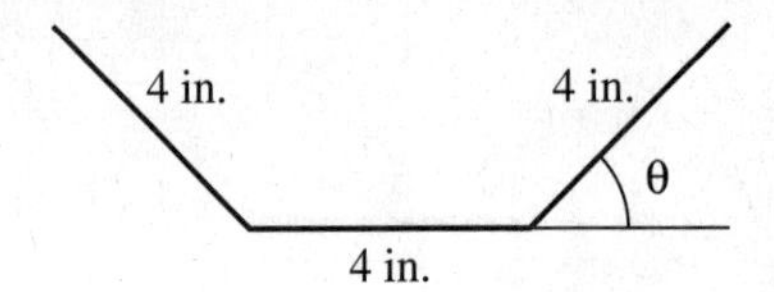

For Exercise 11

12. The boss tells you that she wants a sample of piece of pipe (6 inches in diameter) brought to the business office as an exhibit for an important shareholders' meeting. The instructions are clear: the bigger, the better. However, you are thinking ahead and realize that the business office has hallways that are only 8 feet across and that there is a corner you will need to negotiate along the way. What is the longest piece of pipe that you will be able to slide around the corner (assuming that the pipe cannot be tilted in the vertical direction)?

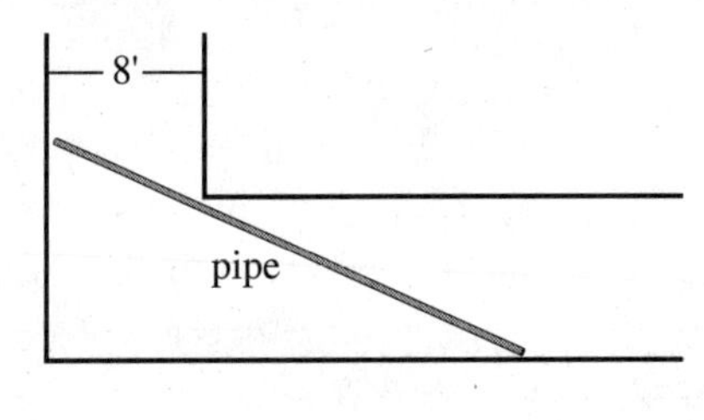

For Exercise 12

---

13. Platypus makes a variety of open-top boxes from a 20 cm by 30 cm rectangular flat sheet by cutting equal-sized squares off of each corner of the sheet and folding up the four sides (so that the depth of the box is the same as the side length of the square). How big should the squares be to produce a box of maximum volume?

14. Platypus's sheet metal supplier makes it attractive for them to accept rectangular sheets with the same 20-cm width, but varying lengths. Determine in terms of L, the length of the sheet, how big the squares should be to produce boxes of maximum volume.

15. Platypus also makes open-top and open-front trays from the same 20 cm by 30 cm rectangular flat sheet by cutting squares off the corners on only one end of the sheet and folding up three sides. How big should the squares be to produce a tray of maximum volume? (The illustration shows one way to make the tray. You should also check the other way.)

---

16. A cylindrical can with closed bottom and open top is made from two kinds of material. The material used to make the bottom of the can costs

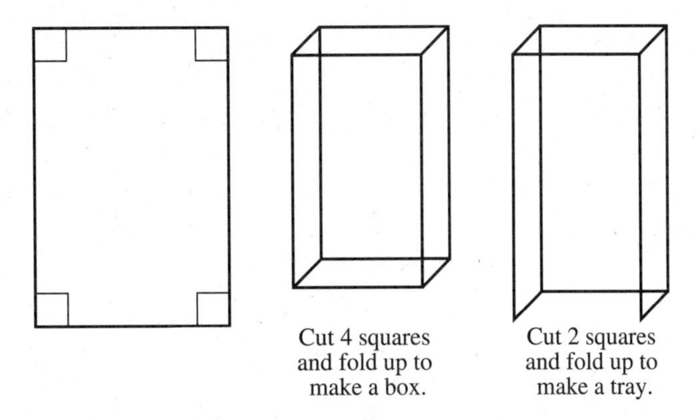

For Exercise 15

$.05 per square inch, and the material used to make the curved surface of the can costs $.03 per square inch. The total cost of the can is no more than $7.35. Find the dimensions of the can with greatest volume.

17. The business office wants to put in Norman windows, which are windows in the shape of rectangles capped by a semicircle (see illustration). These windows will have special decorative trim purchased by length, so it will pay to get the most light for the least perimeter of window. If 10 feet of trim is alloted for each Norman window (including the segment between the semicircle and the rectangle), what dimensions maximize their area?

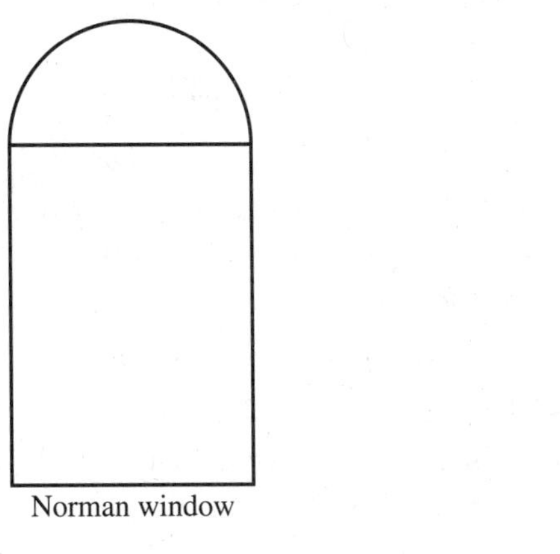

Norman window

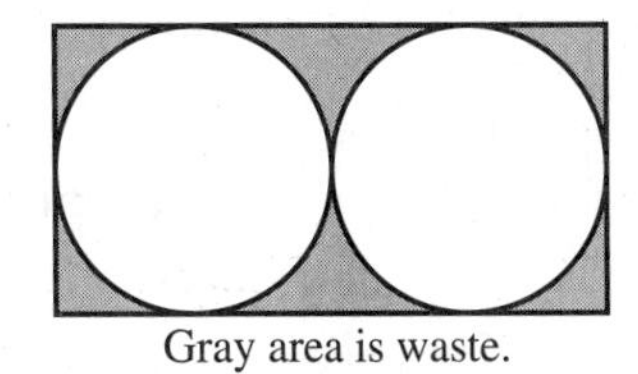

Gray area is waste.

For Exercise 17

For Exercise 18

18. Suppose that the top and bottom of the gallon can of Example 5 must be cut out of a rectangular piece of metal as shown, and the leftover material must be discarded. In other words, the cost of the bottom and top is now represented by the cost of this entire rectangle. What are the dimensions of the gallon can that now minimize the cost?

19. Platypus wants the power company to run a special line to the plant. The power company is located 3000 meters down the river on the opposite bank. Ground lines cost \$20 per meter. The river is 500 meters wide and underwater line will cost four times as much per meter as the above ground line. Since Platypus owns the riverfront property on both sides of the river all the way to the power plant, you may choose where and how the line should cross the river. What path will minimize the cost?

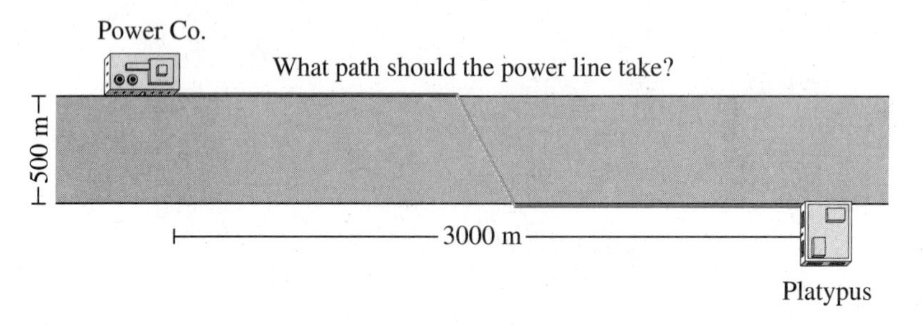

For Exercise 19

20. The water company hears about your success in minimizing the cost of the power line and hires you as a consultant. It seems that a new water-processing plant must be built to serve the towns of Alfa and Betaville, which are respectively 16 and 9 miles from the river and on the same side. The distance as the crow flies between the two towns is 25 miles. Determine the point on the shore at which a water-processing plant should be built to minimize the total length of pipeline needed to connect the plant to the two towns.

---

21. A wire 2 meters long is cut into two pieces. One piece is bent into a square for a stained glass frame, while the other piece is bent into a circle for a TV antenna. To cut down on storage space, where should the wire be cut to minimize the total area of both figures? Where should the wire be cut to maximize the total area?

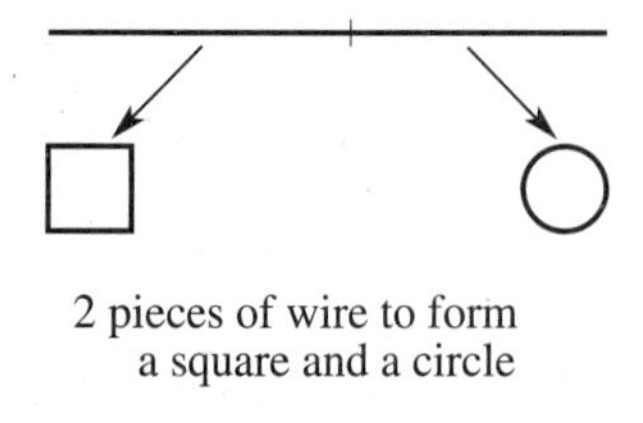

2 pieces of wire to form
a square and a circle

For Exercise 21

22. A wire 6 meters long is cut into twelve pieces, eight of one length and four of another. These pieces are welded together at right angles to form the frame of a box with a square base. Where should the cuts be made to maximize the volume of the box? Where should the cuts be made to maximize the *total surface area* of the box?

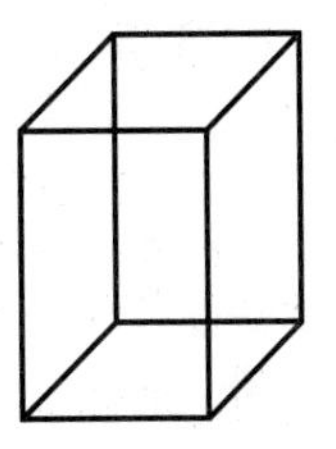

12 pieces of wire to frame a box

For Exercise 22

23. The first steps in making a metal funnel are to take a circular piece of metal, cut out a sector (piece of pie), and connect the two radial edges to make an open cone. What should the angle of the sector be to maximize the volume of this cone?

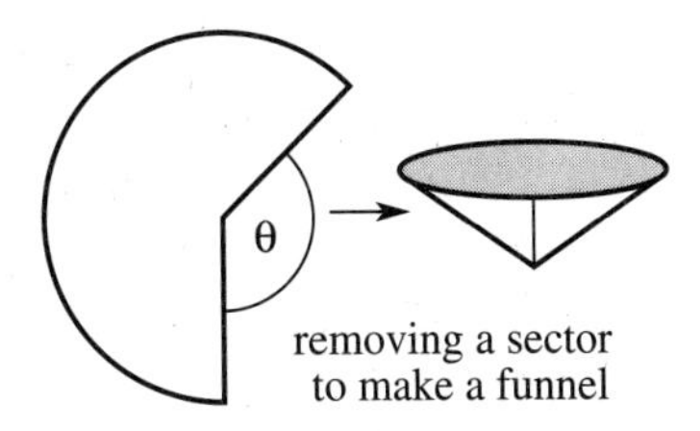

removing a sector to make a funnel

For Exercise 23

24. There is a circular path around the open space between the warehouse and business office. Since Platypus has added a night shift, there is a need for better lighting of the path. You have decided to erect a light pole in the middle of the circular area that has a radius of 20 meters. You want to place the light at a height that will maximize the light intensity on the path, so you consult some reference books and find that for this light,

$$I = \frac{10\sin(\theta)}{d^2},$$

where I is the light intensity at a point on the ground, d is the straight line distance from the light to the point, and θ is the angle this line makes with the ground. How high should the light be to maximize I?

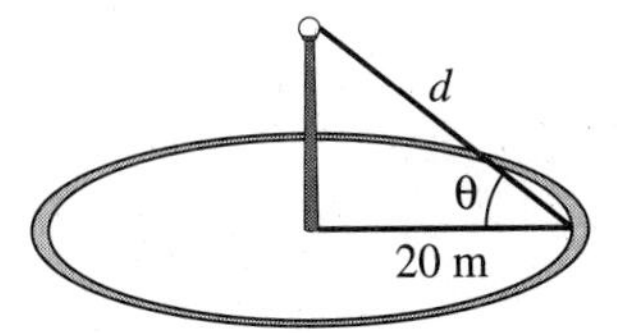

How high should the light be?

For Exercise 24

25. You find that additional lighting will be needed near one of the buildings. You decide to place some lights at ground level 50 feet apart. In a physics book, you find that the illumination I from a single light source is directly proportional to the strength S of the source and inversely proportional to the square of the distance d from the source. If two adjacent lights are rated at 200 and 300 units of strength, respectively, where between them is the total illumination the least?

26. In case of a power outage, a backup battery system is in place for the lighting system. You find that by Ohm's law, the current I in the circuit is given by

$$I = \frac{V}{R+r},$$

where V is the battery voltage, R is the variable resistance (you can set), and r is the constant internal resistance of the battery. The power output of the battery is

$$P = I^2 R.$$

Show that the maximum power occurs if $R = r$.

27. After working with these batteries, you get curious about your own car battery. You find that its power output is given by

$$P = VI - I^2 r.$$

What current corresponds to the maximum power in this battery?

---

28. Platypus has just landed a big contract for steel wool. Because steel wool is relatively light, the shipping department wants to pack as much as possible into each box sent out to cut down on handling charges. The trucking company allows boxes to have a combined length and girth (the distance measured around the box perpendicular to its length) of no more than 108 inches. If the shipping department uses boxes with square ends, what box dimensions will maximize the volume the box can hold?

29. Now suppose that the shipping dock uses cylindrical containers. What height and radius maximize the volume? Which, box or cylinder, is the best choice?

---

30. A chemical used by Platypus in treating metal is consumed at a constant rate of 1200 gallons per year. Any number of gallons can be ordered from the chemical company, but there is a set extra handling charge of \$100 for any order, no matter what the size. However, it costs Platypus an average of \$1 per gallon per year just to store the chemical. You are given instructions that the chemical should be reordered whenever the stock on hand gets down to 200 gallons. This means that if you order g gallons each time, you'll need to order $1200/g$ times a year and the company will be storing on average $g/2 + 200$ gallons throughout the year. How many gallons g should you order each time to minimize the extra handling and storage charges?

---

31. Platypus owns some land for future expansion. In the meantime they rent the land as plots to gardeners. They find that when the rent is $250 per season, they are able to rent all 200 lots, but for every $10 increase in rent, 5 of the plots go unrented. What rent should Platypus charge to obtain the largest gross income?

32. One of the gardeners, who plants apple trees, estimates that if 24 trees are planted per acre, each tree will yield 600 apples per year. For each additional tree planted per acre, the yield decreases by 12 apples per tree. What is the optimal number of trees to plant per acre?

33. Oil is discovered on some of the land Platypus owns. After 8 wells are drilled, the production level is 200 barrels per day by each well. For each additional well, the production drops off by 10 barrels per day for each well. How many additional wells should Platypus drill to realize the maximum production level?

34. Platypus is making arrangements for their annual shareholders' meeting. A local hotel charges $80 per day for rooms, but gives special rates to companies that reserve between 30 and 60 rooms. For each reservation over 30, the daily room rate is decreased by $1. How many rooms will result in the best room rate for Platypus? How many rooms will result in the most income per day for the hotel?

35. Platypus sells their cookie sheets for $2 each to retailers if less than 25 are ordered. If 25 or more are ordered (up to 100), then the price per sheet is reduced by 1 cent times the number ordered. What size order under 100 sheets brings in the most money for Platypus?

---

36. From a 9- by 12-inch piece of material, small squares are to be cut from two corners so that three edges can be bent up and fastened to manufacture a scoop (a rectangular box with no top and no front). What strategy (that is, location and length of the side of the small squares) maximizes the volume?

37. Suppose that for these scoops (see Exercise 36), Platypus realizes a return of $3.00 plus 6 cents per in^3 of volume. Also assume fixed labor cost of $2.40, material cost of $5.40 (5 cents/in^2), and a rebate of 2 cents/in^2 on scrap returned. You pay 1.5 cents/in for welding the seams. Now what strategy maximizes the profit?

Suppose that a rectangular box is to be constructed containing 200 in^3. The base is to be made of material that costs 43 cents per square inch, while the material for top and sides costs only 29 cents per square inch. The base is to be 4 times as long as it is wide. The cost of joining the base and sides together is 2 cents for each inch of edge, while the cost of hinging the top along its side is $1.15 per inch.

38. Decide on one dimension of the box to use as an independent variable and express the other two dimensions of the box in terms of it.

39. What is the domain of your independent variable? Describe three or four possible sets of dimensions for your box.

40. Write expressions in terms of your variable for the costs associated with the various edges.

41. Repeat exercise 40 for the areas and associated costs of the various faces of the box.

42. Collect your information to create a function that calculates the total cost of the box as a function of your variable.

43. Use a graph to estimate the most cost-efficient strategy (that is, the most economical shape) for constructing the box. Approximate the cost of the cheapest box.

A metal can is to be manufactured in cylindrical shape. The top and bottom will be cut from two squares and the corner scrap discarded (but paid for). The cost includes a vertical side seam to make the lateral portion and seams around top and bottom to attach those parts. The can holds 450 cm^3. The metal for the sides costs 0.1 cents/cm^2 (one tenth of a cent per square centimeter), while the materials cost for the bases (top and bottom) is 0.15 cents/cm^2. Allow 0.5 cents/cm for the vertical or side seam and 0.6 cents/cm for the seams joining top and bottom to the sides.

44. With the given figures, determine the strategy (measurements of the can) that minimize the cost. Give the dimensions to the nearest thousandth of a centimeter. Determine the corresponding cost to the nearest hundredth of a cent.

45. Repeat exercise 44 under the additional restriction that both materials come in rolls that are 12.5 cm wide. Hence, the pieces from which the bases and side are cut can be at most 12.5 cm wide, but can be any length. Does the strategy change? How much does the cost change?

46. A famous designer decides to save material in cutting out the bases. Instead of cutting them in the obvious way from a double square as in Plan A, he hopes to cut them from a shorter (though wider) rectangle as in

Plan B. Can savings be achieved this way? What shape rectangle should be used?

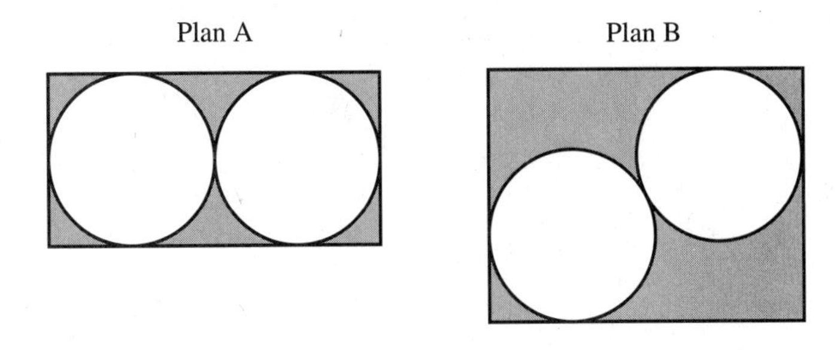

For Exercise 46

---

47. Sheet metal is bent into a gutter having for its cross section an isosceles trapezoid as shown in the illustration. The carrying capacity of the gutter is proportional to the area of the cross section, so it is desirable to maximize that area. If $b = 4.3$ inches and $s = 3$ inches, compute the bending angle θ that gives maximum area and the value of that area. Give your angular answer to the nearest hundredth of a degree, your area answer to the nearest tenth of a square inch.

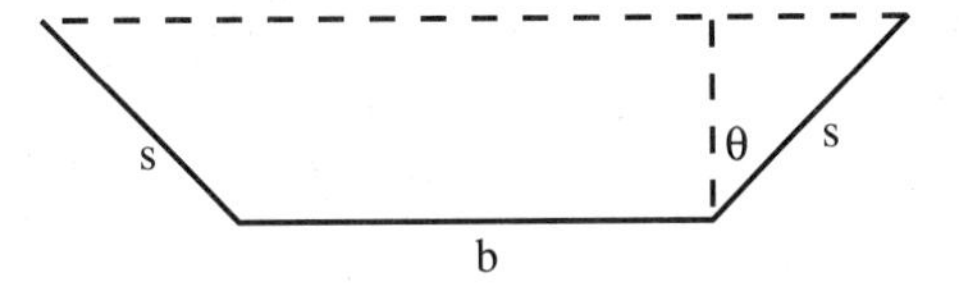

For Exercise 47

48. Long pieces of tubing needed by technicians in remodeling a lab must be moved through corridors of a research center. At one point they must be carried around a corner from a 4-foot-wide passage into an 11-foot-wide corridor as shown in the illustration. The ceilings are 8 feet high. What is the longest piece of tubing that can make the turn? Give your answer to the nearest tenth of a foot. (Yes, you can tilt the tubing vertically.)

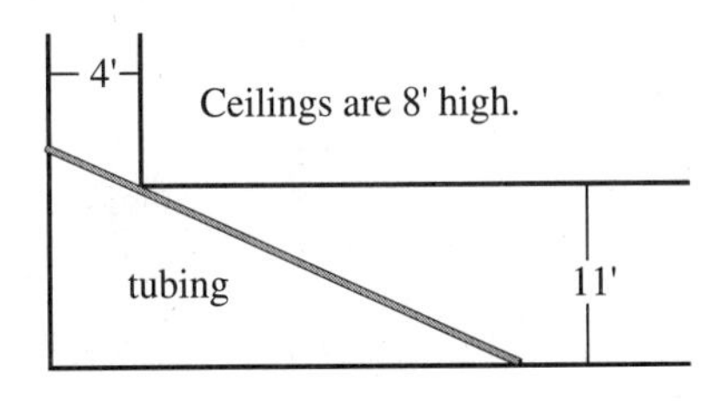

For Exercise 48

---

49. A large sign is located on top of the Platypus main office building. The sign is 10 feet tall, and its lower edge is 30 feet above eye level (for a person standing on the ground). How far from the point directly below the sign should a viewer stand to maximize the angle θ between the lines of sight of the top and bottom of the sign? (This determines the best view).

50. The company realizes that the best view should be from a distance of 60 feet from the building, where the public sidewalk runs. How high should the bottom of the sign be above eye level for someone standing on the sidewalk?

5.2 HIGHER ORDER DERIVATIVES

The derivative of a function f is a new function f'. We could, in turn, find *its* derivative $(f')'$ or simply f''. This derivative of the derivative is known as the *second* derivative of the original function f.

EXAMPLE 6 Find $f''(x)$ if $f(x) = x^3 - 5x^2 + 4x - 1$.

Solution The derivative is $f'(x) = 3x^2 - 10x + 4$. The second derivative is the derivative of the derivative, $f''(x) = 6x - 10$. ■

If y is used to denote the output of f, then we can denote the second derivative by y''. The Leibniz notation for the second derivative is written

$$\frac{d^2y}{dx^2} \quad \text{or} \quad \frac{d^2f}{dx^2}.$$

If you are wondering about the placement of the "exponents" on the Leibniz notation for derivative, note that

$$\frac{d^2y}{dx^2} \quad \text{represents} \quad \frac{d}{dx}\left(\frac{dy}{dx}\right),$$

and we can see the logic behind the locations of the superscripts. (Note that the "powers" here stand for repeated differentiation, not repeated multiplication.)

We can continue this process to find higher order derivatives. The third derivative (derivative of the second derivative) is denoted f''' or y'''. In Leibniz notation:

$$\frac{d^3y}{dx^3} \quad \text{or} \quad \frac{d^3f}{dx^3}.$$

For fourth and higher derivatives, the prime notation becomes unwieldy. We replace the prime marks by a superscript in parentheses:

$$f^{(4)}, \quad f^{(5)}, \quad f^{(6)}, \ldots$$

represent the fourth, fifth, sixth, and so on derivatives of f. The parentheses serve to distinguish between the derivative and a power of the function. Note the distinction:

$$y^4 = y \cdot y \cdot y \cdot y \qquad \text{and} \qquad y^{(4)} = y''''.$$

(Some books use square brackets for high-ordered derivatives, such as $y^{[4]}$.)

Physical interpretation of the second derivative—acceleration

What exactly does the second derivative y'' tell us? First, since it is the derivative of y', it tells us how fast the first derivative is changing with respect to change in the independent variable. If we think back to our automobile example, the first derivative of distance with respect to time ds/dt was the velocity of the car. How fast this velocity changes is referred to as the *acceleration*. For example, when someone says a car can go from 0 to 60 mph in 10 seconds, we have been given the data needed to compute the *average acceleration* of the car.

$$\textit{average acceleration} = \frac{\textit{total change in speed}}{\textit{total elapsed time}} = \frac{60 \text{ miles/hour}}{10 \text{ seconds}} = 8.8 \text{ ft/sec}^2.$$

What exactly is a "square second," the sec^2 in the denominator of the units? Note that in this context, the shorthand abbreviation ft/sec^2 is best interpreted as $\dfrac{\text{ft/sec}}{\text{sec}}$ (feet per second per second).

Just as the instantaneous velocity is given by the first derivative of position, the *instantaneous acceleration* is given by the first derivative of velocity, or equivalently, the second derivative of position:

$$a(t) = \frac{dv}{dt} = \frac{d^2s}{dt^2}.$$

EXAMPLE 7 The vertical position of an object thrown from the top of a building is given by

$$s(t) = -16t^2 + 96t + 640,$$

where s is measured in feet and t is measured in seconds. Find the object's position, velocity, and acceleration at $t = 5$ seconds.

Solution The position at time $t = 5$ seconds is

$$s(5) = -16 \cdot 5^2 + 96 \cdot 5 + 640 = 720 \text{ feet above the ground.}$$

Since the velocity $v(t) = \dfrac{ds}{dt} = -32t + 96$, we have

$$v(5) = -32 \cdot 5 + 96 = -64 \ \frac{\text{ft}}{\text{sec}} \ \text{(feet per second).}$$

The negative sign means that the object is falling toward the ground at this instant. Finally, the acceleration $a(t) = \dfrac{dv}{dt} = \dfrac{d^2s}{dt^2} = -32$, so

$$a(5) = -32 \ \frac{\text{ft}}{\text{sec}^2} \ \text{(feet per second per second).}$$

Note that for this example, the acceleration function is constant. In fact, this is exactly the acceleration due to the force of gravity. The negative sign indicates that the acceleration is also directed downward. ■

Graphical interpretation—concavity

While the second derivative f'' can be interpreted in a physical sense as acceleration, its graphical interpretations relate to both the graph of the original function and the graph of the first derivative.

Certainly, we can use the second derivative f'' to analyze the behavior of the first derivative f' in exactly the same way we use the first derivative to analyze the behavior of the original function f. In other words,

> If $f''(x) > 0$ on an interval (a, b), then $f'(x)$ is strictly *increasing* on that interval.
> If $f''(x) < 0$ on an interval (a, b), then $f'(x)$ is strictly *decreasing* on that interval.

Definition 1

> When the *slope* of a graph is strictly increasing, we say that the graph is **concave up**. When the *slope* of a graph is strictly decreasing, we say that the graph is **concave down**.

In terms of the original function's graph, the sign of the second derivative is an indicator of the *concavity*. Figure 5.8 illustrates the visual appearance of concavity in the graph of a function $y = f(x)$. As suggested by this picture, you can use the visual idea of a cup turned up or down to remind you of the graphical meanings of *concave up* and *concave down*. There is a geometrical way of thinking about concavity in terms of the tangent line to the graph of $y = f(x)$.

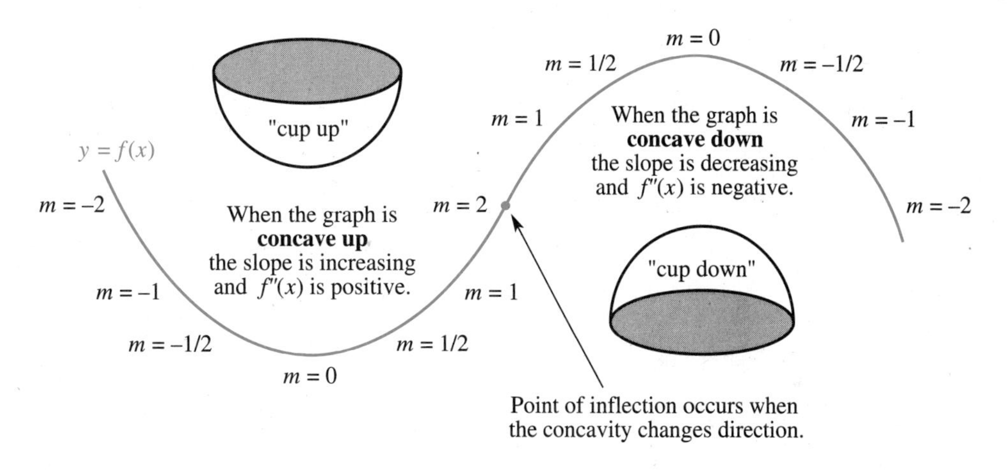

Figure 5.8 Graphical interpretation of concavity.

> If the function graph $y = f(x)$ is concave up at x_0 ($f''(x_0) > 0$), then locally the tangent line lies *below* the graph at $(x_0, f(x_0))$.
> If the function graph $y = f(x)$ is concave down at x_0 ($f''(x_0) < 0$), then locally the tangent line lies *above* the graph at $(x_0, f(x_0))$.

Figure 5.9 illustrates the relationship between concavity and the tangent lines to the graph.

Taken together, the signs of the first and second derivatives give us useful graphical information. Figure 5.10 illustrates four general shapes indicated by the different combinations of positive and negative first and second derivatives.

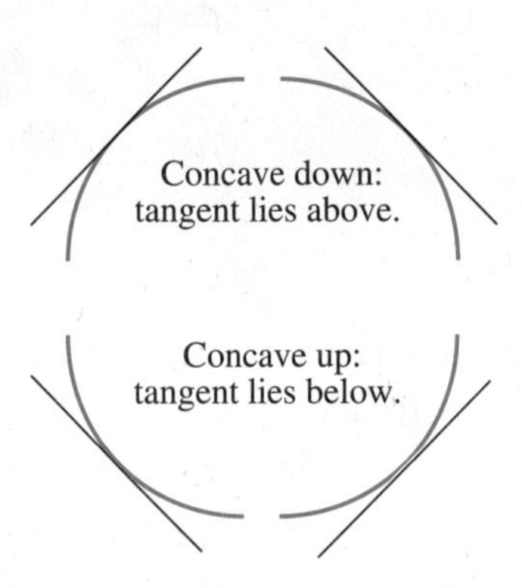

Figure 5.9 Concavity and tangent lines.

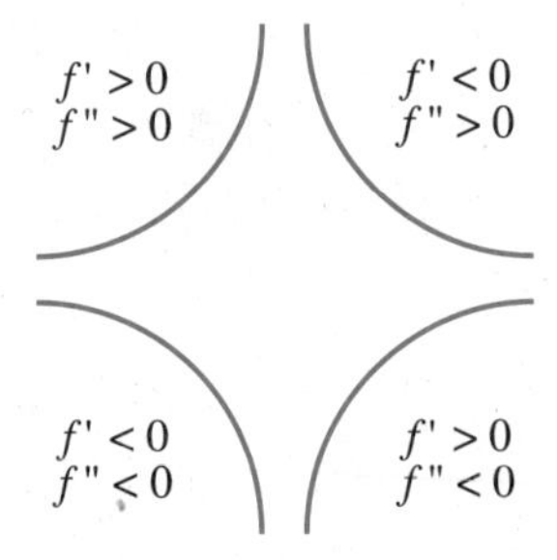

Figure 5.10 Graphical behavior indicated by the signs of f' and f''.

Inflection points

A point on the graph where the curve changes concavity is called a *point of inflection*. A point of inflection for the curve is indicated in the illustration above. We define a point of inflection using the second derivative.

Definition 2 A point $(x_0, f(x_0))$ is called a **point of inflection** for the graph $y = f(x)$ if there is a neighborhood of x_0 over which $f''(x)$ is positive on one side of x_0 and negative on the other side (f'' changes sign at x_0).

Note that an inflection point must occur at a critical value for the first derivative, and in fact may correspond to either a local minimum or maximum *slope*. For example, examine Figure 5.8 once again to see that the slope at the inflection point is locally the greatest. Therein lies an observation worth emphasizing:

▶▶▶ **For a differentiable function, the location of an inflection point is also the location of a local extremum of the *rate of change* of the function.**

To find the potential locations of inflection points, we need to check the critical values of the derivative—that is, those values x_0 in the domain of the function such that $f''(x_0) = 0$ or is *undefined*. Keep in mind that these are *potential* locations of points of inflection, just as critical values (where f' is zero or undefined) are potential locations of maxima and minima. To test for an inflection point, we must also determine whether the concavity of the graph changes direction.

▶▶▶ **At a point of inflection, the second derivative must change sign.**

Figure 5.11 illustrates the intervals over which the graph of f is concave up, concave down, or neither.

EXAMPLE 8 Using Figure 5.11, describe the behavior of the second derivative f'' over the interval (a, b).

Solution For $a < x < x_1$ and $x_1 < x < x_2$ the second derivative value $f''(x)$ is *negative*. The second derivative value $f''(x)$ is also negative for $x_4 < x < x_6$ and $x_7 < x < x_8$.

For $x_2 < x < x_4$ and $x_6 < x < x_7$, $f''(x)$ is *positive*.

The function appears to be linear for $x_8 < x < x_9$ and for $x_9 < x < b$. Since the first derivative is *constant* over these intervals, we have $f''(x) = 0$ over these intervals.

We note that at $x = x_1$, x_2, x_4, x_6, x_8, and x_9, the second derivative is definitely undefined (since even the first derivative is undefined at these points). The points of inflection for the graph are $(x_2, f(x_2))$, $(x_4, f(x_4))$, $(x_6, f(x_6))$, $(x_7, f(x_7))$. As we have noted, f'' is undefined at $x = x_2$, x_4, and x_6. As for x_7, it appears that $f'(x_7) = 0$ (the graph is flat), but we cannot tell visually whether $f''(x_7)$ is zero or undefined. ■

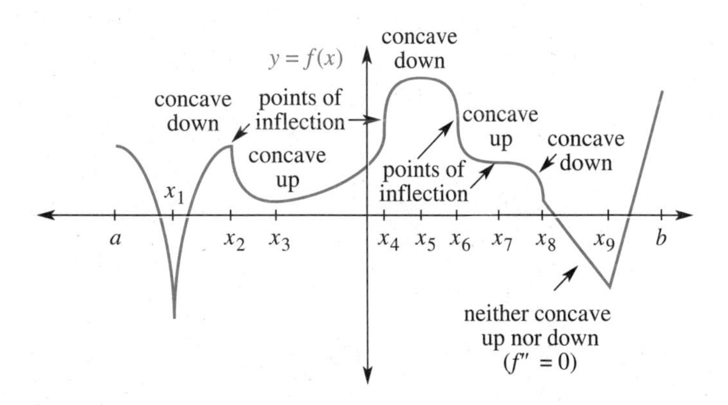

Figure 5.11 Concavity and points of inflection.

Visually, the location of an inflection point can be difficult to determine directly from a graph. The second derivative provides a tool for precisely locating inflection points.

EXAMPLE 9 Find all inflection points of the graph $y = x^3 - 5x^2 + 4x - 1$ and indicate the slope of the curve at these points.

Solution In Example 6, we found that

$$\frac{dy}{dx} = 3x^2 - 10x + 4 \quad \text{and} \quad \frac{d^2y}{dx^2} = 6x - 10.$$

Since the second derivative is defined for all values x, we need only look at the case $\frac{d^2y}{dx^2} = 0$. Setting

$$\frac{d^2y}{dx^2} = 6x - 10 = 0,$$

we find that

$$x = \frac{5}{3}$$

is a potential location of an inflection point. Checking the sign of the second derivative, we note that

$$\frac{d^2y}{dx^2} = 6x - 10 < 0 \quad \text{for} \quad x < \frac{5}{3} \quad \text{and} \quad \frac{d^2y}{dx^2} = 6x - 10 > 0 \quad \text{for} \quad x > \frac{5}{3}.$$

Since the second derivative changes sign, we know that $x = 5/3$ is the location of an inflection point. The y-coordinate of the inflection point is

$$y = (\frac{5}{3})^3 - 5(\frac{5}{3})^2 + 4(\frac{5}{3}) - 1 = \frac{-97}{27}.$$

The single point of inflection on the graph is $(\frac{5}{3}, \frac{-97}{27}) \approx (1.6667, -3.5926)$.

The graph of $y = f(x)$ is concave down to the left of the inflection point and concave up to the right of the inflection point. To find the slope at the inflection point, we evaluate the first derivative at $x = 5/3$:

$$\left.\frac{dy}{dx}\right|_{x=5/3} = 3(5/3)^2 - 10(5/3) + 4 = -13/3 \approx -4.6667.$$

(Graph $y = x^3 - 5x^2 + 4x - 1$ over the interval $[0, 3]$ to check the reasonableness of these answers.) ■

EXERCISES for Section 5.2

For exercises 1–10: Graph each function. Match the given description with the function or functions that fit that description. The word *always* should be interpreted to mean "for all inputs in the domain."

$y = 1/x$	$y = 1/x^2$	$y = \sqrt{x}$
$y = \arcsin(x)$	$y = \arccos(x)$	$y = \arctan(x)$
$y = \ln(x)$	$y = \log_{10}(x)$	$y = \log_{1/2}(x)$
$y = 2^x$	$y = 3^{-x}$	$y = e^{-x^2}$

1. The value of the function is always positive.

2. The value of the function is always negative.

3. The value of the first derivative is always positive.

4. The value of the first derivative is always negative.

5. The value of the second derivative is always positive.

6. The value of the second derivative is always negative.

7. The graph has an inflection point at $x = 0$.

8. The function has a critical value at $x = 0$.

9. The function has an absolute minimum at $x = 0$.

10. The function has an absolute maximum at $x = 0$.

For exercises 11–20: These power functions provide a good set of examples of different kinds of graphical behavior. Graph each function over the interval $[-5, 5]$. Each of your graphs should pass through the origin $(0, 0)$. Using your graphs and analyzing the first and second derivatives, answer the questions.

$y = x$	$y = x^{1/3}$
$y = \lvert x \rvert$	$y = x^{2/3}$
$y = -x^4$	$y = x^{5/3}$
$y = x^{4/3}$	$y = x^{7/3}$
$y = x^4$	$y = x^3$

11. Which functions have a critical value at $x = 0$?

12. Which of the graphs have a point of inflection at $(0, 0)$?

13. Which of the graphs have a horizontal tangent at $x = 0$?

14. Which of the graphs have a vertical tangent at $x = 0$?

15. Which of the graphs have a cusp at $x = 0$?

16. For which of these functions does $f'(0) = 0$, yet f has neither a local minimum nor a local maximum at $x = 0$?

17. For which of these functions does $f''(0) = 0$, yet f does not have $(0, 0)$ as a point of inflection?

18. For which of these functions is $f'(0)$ undefined, yet f has neither a local minimum nor a local maximum at $x = 0$?

19. For which of these functions is $f'(0) = 0$, but $f''(0)$ is undefined?

20. For which of these functions is $f''(0)$ undefined, yet f does not have $(0, 0)$ as a point of inflection?

For exercises 21–28: You are given the graphs of the *derivatives* $y = f'(x)$ of eight functions (grid lines are spaced one unit apart both horizontally and vertically). For each, indicate the locations of the points of inflection for the graphs of the original function $y = f(x)$. Where is the original function graph concave up or concave down?

21.

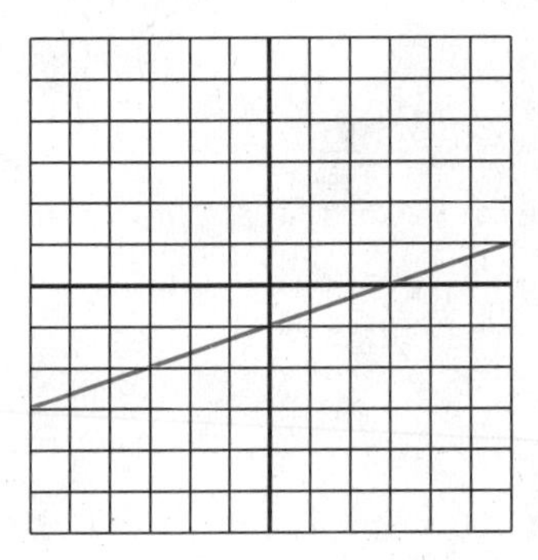

22.

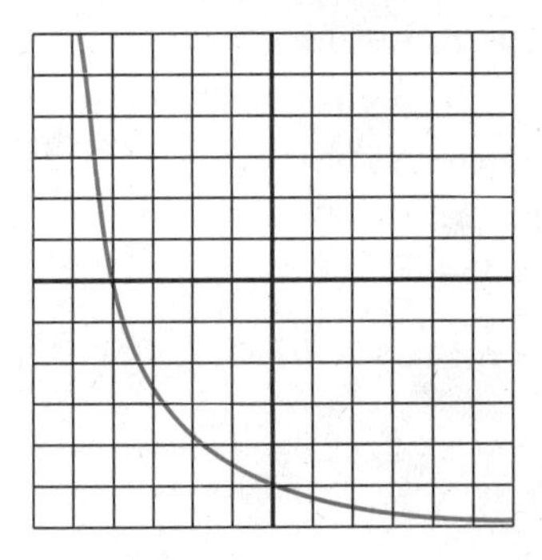

23.

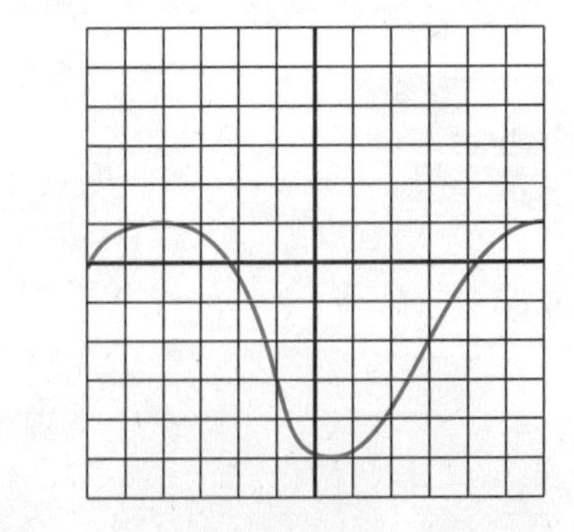

24.

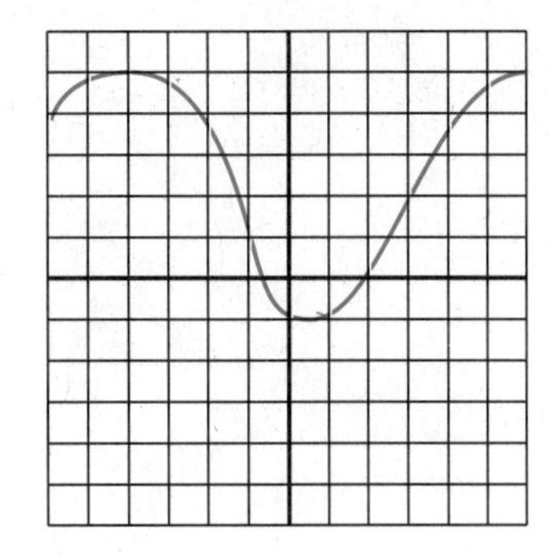

25.

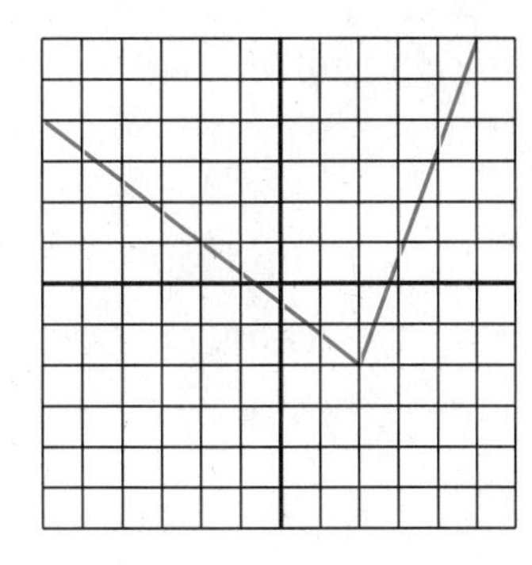

26.

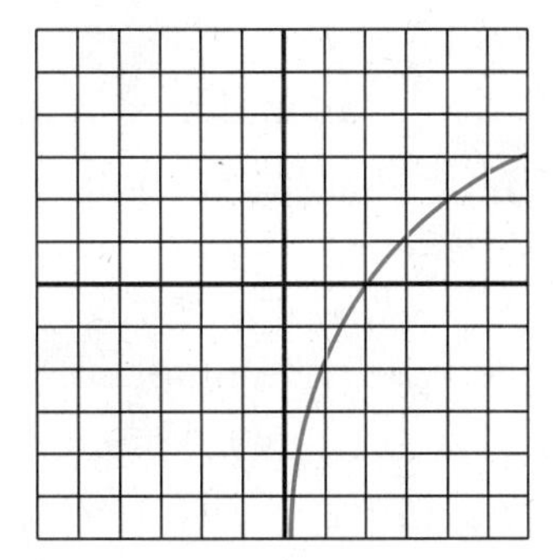

27.

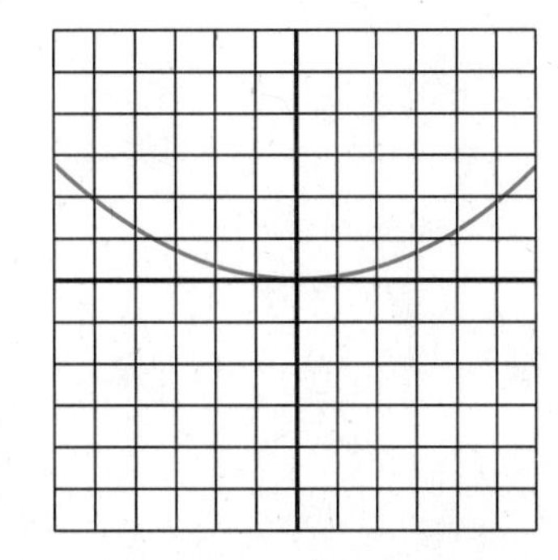

28.

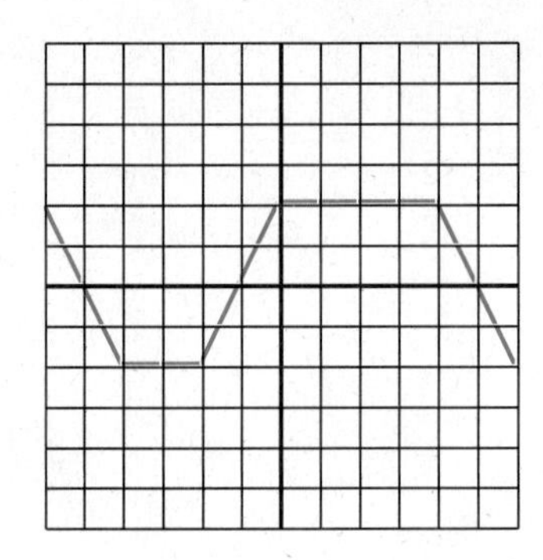

---

29. Each of the trigonometric functions is periodic, so any points of inflection for their graphs will appear periodically. Where do the points of inflection occur for each of the trigonometric functions:

$y = \sin(x)$	$y = \cos(x)$	$y = \tan(x)$
$y = \sec(x)$	$y = \csc(x)$	$y = \cot(x)$

30. Find the third and fourth derivatives of $f(x) = x^3 - 5x^2 + 4x - 1$.

31. If $p(x)$ is a polynomial of degree n, what is $p^{(n+1)}(x)$? Explain why.

32. Find the 1000th derivative of each of the following functions:

$$f(x) = \sin x \qquad g(x) = \cos x \qquad k(x) = e^x \qquad q(x) = 2^x.$$

(Hint: find the first through fifth derivatives and look for a pattern.)

33. If $f(x) = 1/x$, show that $f''(x) < 0$ for $x < 0$ and $f''(x) > 0$ for $x > 0$. Why isn't there a point of inflection at $x = 0$?

34. A student claims that every point on the graph of $y = x$ must be a point of inflection, since $\dfrac{d^2y}{dx^2} = 0$ for all x. Is the student correct?

For exercises 35–38: You are given the formula for the position $s(t)$ of some object over the time interval $0 \le t \le 60$ (s is measured in feet and t is measured in seconds). For each function s, find the following:

(a) its initial acceleration (at time $t = 0$);

(b) the times t in the interval $[0, 60]$ for which the acceleration is 0;

(c) the positions s for which the magnitude of the velocity is at its greatest;

(d) the times t in the interval $[0, 60]$ for which the magnitude of the acceleration is at its greatest; and

(e) the graph of the acceleration $y = a(t)$ over the interval $[0, 60]$.

35. $s(t) = -16t^2 + 64000$

36. $s(t) = .002t^3 - 0.27t^2 + 12t + 10$

37. $s(t) = |90 - t^2/30|$

38. $s(t) = 2\sin(\pi t/20)$

39. Draw a graph with a point $(x_0, f(x_0))$ such that $f'(x_0) = 0$ and $f''(x_0)$ is positive. What can you say about x_0?

40. Draw a graph with a point $(x_0, f(x_0))$ such that $f'(x_0) = 0$ and $f''(x_0)$ is negative. What can you say about x_0?

41. Draw a graph with a point $(x_0, f(x_0))$ such that $f'(x_0) = 0$ and $f''(x_0) = 0$. What can you say about x_0? (Be careful!)

42. Now, on the basis of your answers to these questions, what criteria can you devise that relate the value of the second derivative at a critical value to the local maxima and minima of a function? (These criteria are often called the **Second Derivative Test for Local Extrema**.)

For exercises 43–50:

(a) Find all critical values of f.

(b) Apply the second derivative test to each critical value to determine whether a local minimum or local maximum occurs there. (If the second derivative test fails, use the first derivative test.)

(c) Find the point(s) of inflection for the graph of $y = f(x)$.

(d) Find the interval(s) where the graph of $y = f(x)$ is concave up.

(e) Find the interval(s) where the graph of $y = f(x)$ is concave down.

43. $f(x) = -3x^4 + 4x^3$

44. $f(x) = x^3 + 3x^2 - 9x - 2$

45. $f(x) = -x^4 + 8x^3 - 18x^2 + 1$

46. $f(x) = 5x^3 - x^2 - x + 2$

47. $f(x) = 2x^3 + 2x^2 - 2x - 1$

48. $f(x) = -3x^4 - 8x^3 - 6x^2 + 3$

49. $f(x) = \dfrac{x^2}{x^2 - 4}$

50. $f(x) = \dfrac{1}{x^3 - x}$

5.3 IMPLICIT FUNCTIONS AND IMPLICIT DIFFERENTIATION

In this section we see how the derivative can be used to measure the slope of more general curves than function graphs.

Implicit functions

A curve in the Cartesian plane can often be represented as the graph of a function f with domain D. In other words, the curve is the set of points

$$\{(x, y) : x \in D, y = f(x)\}.$$

The slope of the curve at a single point (x_0, y_0) is given by the derivative

$$f'(x_0) = \left.\frac{dy}{dx}\right|_{x=x_0}.$$

This slope also represents the instantaneous rate of change of the variable y with respect to x.

Not all curves in the plane can be described as the graph of a function $y = f(x)$. Nevertheless, it may still be possible to use calculus to calculate the slope at a point on such a curve.

An equation in two unknowns x and y has associated with it a set or **locus** of points satisfying the equation. For instance, the locus of the equation

$$x^2 + y^2 = 9$$

is a circle with radius 3 and center at the origin (Figure 5.12). Now, this relation $x^2 + y^2 = 9$ does not describe y as a function of x. (The circle fails the vertical line test for function graphs.) However, if we restrict our attention to only a part of the circle, we can find a function whose graph *does* exactly match that part of the circle.

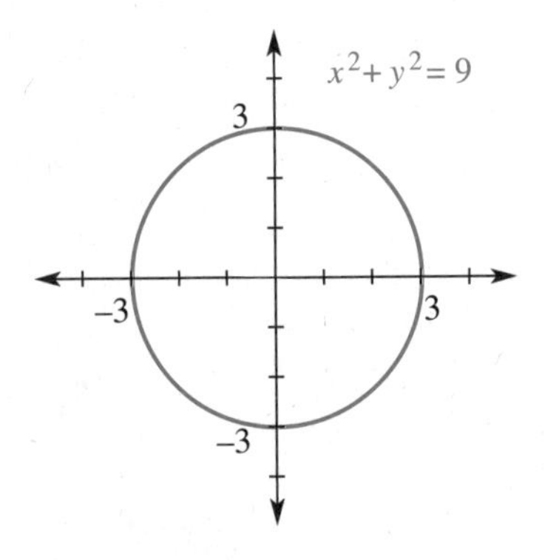

Figure 5.12 The circle $x^2 + y^2 = 9$.

EXAMPLE 10 Find functions f and g whose graphs match the top and bottom halves of the circle $x^2 + y^2 = 9$.

Solution If we solve $x^2 + y^2 = 9$ for y, we find

$$y = \pm\sqrt{9 - x^2}.$$

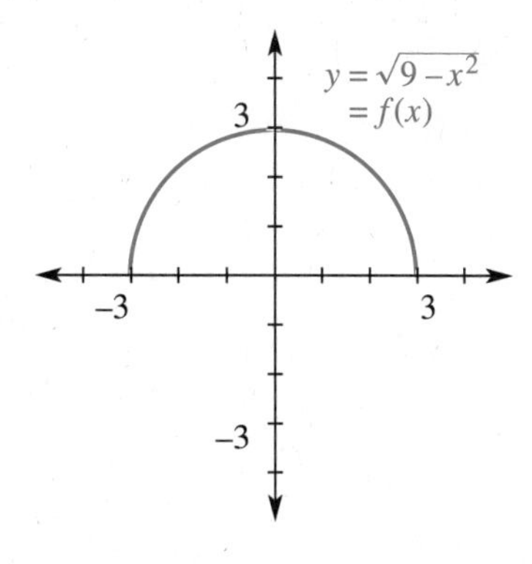

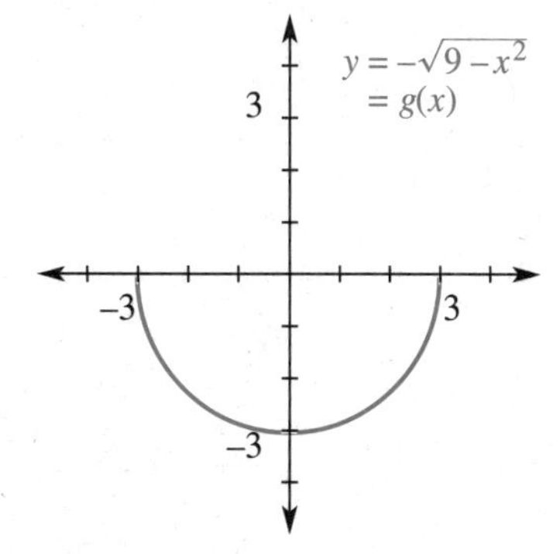

Figure 5.13 The graphs of f and g are semicircles.

Note that this does not describe a single function, because for $-3 < x < 3$, two values y are determined. Let f and g be defined by the formulas

$$f(x) = \sqrt{9 - x^2} \qquad \text{and} \qquad g(x) = -\sqrt{9 - x^2}.$$

Then the graphs of functions f and g are the top and bottom halves of the circle $x^2 + y^2 = 9$, as shown in Figure 5.13. ■

This is only one of infinitely many ways we could have broken the circle up into function graphs. For instance, we could have defined *four* functions corresponding to the quarter circles bounded by the coordinate axes.

We can think of the original equation

$$x^2 + y^2 = 9$$

as *implicitly* defining y as a function of x. This means that by suitably restricting our attention to only part of the equation's locus, we can find a *functional* relationship between y and x whose graph matches the locus in that region. The particular function may change as we move to different parts of the locus.

This suggests a strategy for computing $y' = \dfrac{dy}{dx}$ (if it exists) at any point (x_0, y_0) on the circle. First, we find a suitable function f whose graph coincides with the circle in a region containing (x_0, y_0), and then we compute $f'(x_0)$.

EXAMPLE 11 Find the slope of the tangent line to the circle $x^2 + y^2 = 9$ at the point $(1.8, 2.4)$.

Solution The point $(1.8, 2.4)$ is on the graph of $f(x) = \sqrt{9 - x^2}$ since it lies on the top half of the circle. Hence, we can find the slope of the tangent line by computing $f'(1.8)$. Since

$$f(x) = (9 - x^2)^{1/2},$$

we have

$$f'(x) = \frac{1}{2}(9 - x^2)^{-1/2}(-2x) = \frac{-x}{\sqrt{9 - x^2}},$$

using the chain rule. Substituting $x = 1.8$ gives us

$$f'(1.8) = \frac{-1.8}{\sqrt{9 - (1.8)^2}} = -0.75.$$

So the slope of the tangent line at $(1.8, 2.4)$ is -0.75.

Since we are dealing with a circle, we have a nice way of checking the reasonableness of this slope value. From geometry, we know that a line perpendicular to a tangent line to the circle at the point of tangency must pass through the center of the circle. Since the center of the circle is $(0, 0)$ and the point of tangency is $(1.8, 2.4)$, we can calculate directly the slope m of the normal line as $(2.4 - 0)/(1.8 - 0) = 2.4/1.8 = 4/3$. The slope of the tangent line should be the negative reciprocal $-1/m = -3/4 = -0.75$, just as we found using the derivative. ■

The approach described above is fine, but it depends on our ability to find a suitable function whose graph coincides with a part of the locus including the point in question. For a simple relation between x and y like the equation of a circle, this is not too difficult. In a more complicated relation, such as

$$\sin(xy) = 2x\cos^2(y),$$

it may be extremely difficult to find a suitable function.

Fortunately, there is a way to find the derivative value dy/dx at a point (x_0, y_0) without having to explicitly solve for y as a function of x.

Implicit differentiation

Given an equation in x and y, how can we find dy/dx at (x_0, y_0) without solving for y as a function of x? Let's assume for the moment that we have found such a function. That is, we assume that in an appropriate region including the point (x_0, y_0), a part of the equation's graph matches that of $y = f(x)$, where f is a differentiable function of x. Now, the original relationship between x and y still must hold, so we can differentiate both sides of the equation *with respect to* x while treating y as if it were a function of x. This process is called **implicit differentiation**, and it results in a relationship between x, y, and dy/dx. We can either attempt to solve this new equation for dy/dx in general, or we may substitute the specific values $x = x_0$ and $y = y_0$ and solve for the value of dy/dx at the particular point (x_0, y_0).

EXAMPLE 12 Use implicit differentiation to find dy/dx for the relation $x^2 + y^2 = 9$, and use it to calculate the slope of the tangent line at the point $(1.8, 2.4)$.

Solution If we assume that y is a function of x and differentiate both sides of

$$x^2 + y^2 = 9$$

with respect to x, we obtain

$$2x + 2y\frac{dy}{dx} = 0.$$

Note that on the left-hand side, we have by the chain rule $\dfrac{d(y^2)}{dx} = 2y \cdot \dfrac{dy}{dx}$, since the power rule applies to the *function* y raised to the second power.

We can solve for dy/dx to obtain

$$\frac{dy}{dx} = -\frac{x}{y},$$

and substituting the specific values $x = 1.8$ and $y = 2.4$ gives us

$$\left.\frac{dy}{dx}\right|_{(1.8,2.4)} = -\frac{1.8}{2.4} = -0.75$$

as the slope of the tangent line to the circle at that point. This matches the value we obtained by explicitly solving for y as a function of x. ■

In fact, our derivative formula

$$\frac{dy}{dx} = -\frac{x}{y}$$

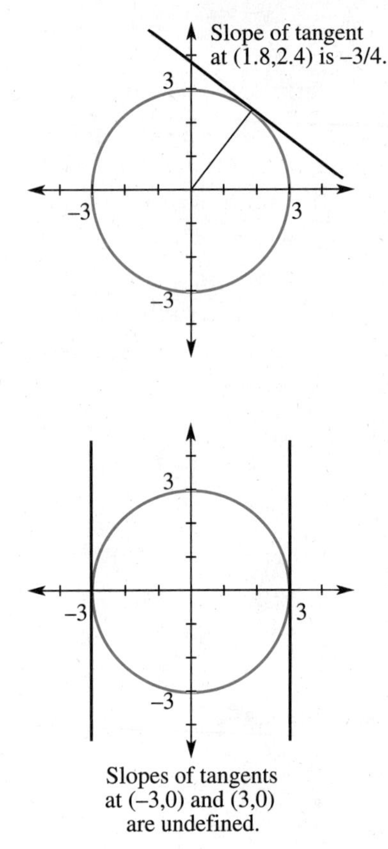

Figure 5.14 $\frac{dy}{dx} = -\frac{x}{y}$ is the slope of the tangent line to the circle.

applies to every point on the circle for which $-x/y$ is defined. If $y = 0$, then the slope of the tangent line to the circle is undefined. Figure 5.14 shows that this reflects the fact that the tangent lines to the circle at $(3, 0)$ and $(-3, 0)$ are vertical.

Implicit differentiation relies heavily on the chain rule. Let's summarize the procedure.

Implicit Differentiation Procedure

Given an equation in terms of x and y, we find dy/dx by implicit differentiation as follows:

Step 1. Assume that y is a differentiable function of x.

Step 2. Differentiate both sides of the equation with respect to x.

Step 3. Solve for dy/dx.

▶▶▶ **When using implicit differentiation to find dy/dx, always remember the chain rule when treating y as a function of x.**

In step 3, if the derivative value is desired at a particular point (x_0, y_0), one can substitute x_0 for x and y_0 for y either before or after solving for dy/dx.

EXAMPLE 13 Find $\left.\frac{dy}{dx}\right|_{(-4,2)}$ if $x^2y^2 - \frac{y^3}{x} = 66$.

Solution We might start by noting that the point $(-4, 2)$ is indeed on the curve defined by this equation, since

$$(-4)^2 \cdot 2^2 - \frac{2^3}{-4} = 64 + 2 = 66.$$

Taking the derivative of both sides of the original equation with respect to x gives us

$$(2x \cdot y^2 + x^2 \cdot 2y\frac{dy}{dx}) - \frac{3y^2(\frac{dy}{dx}) \cdot x - y^3 \cdot 1}{x^2} = 0,$$

where we have applied the product rule for the first term and the quotient rule for the second term. If we substitute $x = -4$ and $y = 2$ into this equation, we obtain

$$-32 + 64\frac{dy}{dx} - \frac{-48(\frac{dy}{dx}) - 8}{16} = 0.$$

Solving for $\frac{dy}{dx}$ gives us $\frac{dy}{dx} = \frac{63}{134}$. ■

EXAMPLE 14 Find a general formula for $y' = \frac{dy}{dx}$ when $\sin(xy) = 2x\cos^2(y)$.

Solution Differentiating both sides with respect to x (and writing y' for $\frac{dy}{dx}$):

$$\cos(xy) \cdot (1 \cdot y + x \cdot y') = 2\cos^2(y) + 2x \cdot (2\cos(y)(-\sin(y)) \cdot y').$$

After expanding,

$$y\cos(xy) + (x\cos(xy))y' = 2\cos^2(y) - (4x\cos(y)\sin(y))y',$$

and collecting terms involving y',

$$y'(x\cos(xy) + 4x\cos(y)\sin(y)) = 2\cos^2(y) - y\cos(xy),$$

we solve for y' to find

$$y' = \frac{2\cos^2(y) - y\cos(xy)}{x\cos(xy) + 4x\cos(y)\sin(y)}.$$ ■

We can repeat the process of implicit differentiation to find higher-order derivatives.

EXAMPLE 15 Find $y'' = \dfrac{d^2y}{dx^2}$ at $(1, -1)$ if $x^4 - y^3 = 2$.

Solution First, we find the value of $y' = \dfrac{dy}{dx}$ at $(1, -1)$ by implicitly differentiating $x^4 - y^3 = 2$ to obtain

$$4x^3 - 3y^2\frac{dy}{dx} = 0.$$

Substituting $x = 1$ and $y = -1$ yields

$$\left.\frac{dy}{dx}\right|_{(1,-1)} = \frac{4}{3}$$

as the value of the first derivative y' at the point $(1, -1)$. Now, if we implicitly differentiate a second time, considering both y *and* $\dfrac{dy}{dx}$ as functions of x, we get

$$12x^2 - 6y\frac{dy}{dx}\cdot\frac{dy}{dx} - 3y^2\frac{d^2y}{dx^2} = 0.$$

To find the value of the second derivative $y'' = \dfrac{d^2y}{dx^2}$ at $(1, -1)$, we can substitute $x = 1$, $y = -1$, and $dy/dx = 4/3$ to obtain

$$12 + \frac{32}{3} - 3\left.\frac{d^2y}{dx^2}\right|_{(1,-1)} = 0$$

and solve to find $\left.\dfrac{d^2y}{dx^2}\right|_{(1,-1)} = \dfrac{68}{9}$. ■

Finding derivatives of inverse functions

We can use implicit differentiation to extend our dictionary of derivative formulas by applying it to the logarithmic and inverse trigonometric functions. In general, if f is a differentiable function with an inverse f^{-1}, we can write

$$x = f^{-1}(y).$$

Now, using implicit differentiation with respect to x, we have

$$1 = (f^{-1})'(y)\frac{dy}{dx}.$$

Solving for $(f^{-1})'(y)$, we have

$$(f^{-1})'(y) = \frac{1}{\frac{dy}{dx}}.$$

Let's restate this result for emphasis:

Derivative of an inverse function.
If f is differentiable and f^{-1} is the inverse of f, then

$$(f^{-1})'(y) = \frac{1}{f'(x)}.$$

▶▶▶ **Since $x = f^{-1}(y)$, in Leibniz notation we have $\frac{dx}{dy} = (f^{-1})'(y)$, which leads to the highly suggestive notation**

$$\frac{dx}{dy} = \frac{1}{\frac{dy}{dx}}.$$

Let's apply this now to find the derivatives of logarithmic functions.

EXAMPLE 16 Find dy/dx if $y = \log_a x \quad (a > 0,\ a \neq 1)$.

Solution We rewrite $y = \log_a x$ as $x = a^y$. Using implicit differentiation yields

$$1 = a^y(\ln a) \cdot \frac{dy}{dx} = x \ln a \cdot \frac{dy}{dx}.$$

(We substituted x back in for a^y.) Solving for dy/dx, we have

$$\frac{dy}{dx} = \frac{1}{x \ln a}.$$ ■

EXAMPLE 17 Using the formula just obtained, find $f'(x)$ and $g'(x)$ if $f(x) = \log_2 x$ and $g(x) = \ln x$.

Solution $f'(x) = \frac{1}{x \ln 2}$. Recall that $\ln x = \log_e x$, so

$$g'(x) = \frac{1}{x \ln e} = \frac{1}{x}.$$ ■

The derivatives of the inverse trigonometric functions can also be obtained by implicit differentiation.

EXAMPLE 18 Find the derivative of $y = \arctan(x)$ by implicit differentiation.

Solution If $y = \arctan(x)$, then y satisfies

$$\tan y = x.$$

If we differentiate both sides with respect to x, we obtain

$$\sec^2 y \cdot \frac{dy}{dx} = 1.$$

Solving for dy/dx gives us

$$\frac{dy}{dx} = \frac{1}{\sec^2 y}.$$

Can we write $\sec^2 y$ in terms of x? Since we know $\tan y = x$, we have

$$\tan^2 y = x^2.$$

Substituting into the trigonometric identity $1 + \tan^2 y = \sec^2 y$ means that

$$\sec^2 y = 1 + x^2,$$

so we can write

$$\frac{dy}{dx} = \frac{1}{1 + x^2}.$$

■

EXAMPLE 19 Find the derivative of $y = \arcsin(x)$ by implicit differentiation.

Solution If $y = \arcsin(x)$, then y satisfies

$$\sin y = x.$$

If we differentiate both sides with respect to x, we obtain

$$\cos y \frac{dy}{dx} = 1.$$

Solving for dy/dx gives us

$$\frac{dy}{dx} = \frac{1}{\cos y}.$$

Now, if $y = \arcsin(x)$, then $-\pi/2 \leq y \leq \pi/2$, and $\cos y \geq 0$. Using the identity

$$\cos^2 y + \sin^2 y = 1,$$

we can write

$$\cos y = \sqrt{1 - \sin^2 y} = \sqrt{1 - x^2}.$$

(We can be sure of the positive square root, since $\cos y \geq 0$ and we have substituted x for $\sin y$.) Thus,

$$\frac{dy}{dx} = \frac{1}{\sqrt{1 - x^2}}.$$ ■

The derivatives of the other inverse trigonometric functions can be found in a similar manner. We include our new differentiation formulas below.

$y = \log_a(x)(a > 0,\ a \neq 1)$	$\frac{dy}{dx} = \frac{1}{x \ln(a)}$
$y = \arcsin(x)$	$\frac{dy}{dx} = \frac{1}{\sqrt{1 - x^2}}$
$y = \arccos(x)$	$\frac{dy}{dx} = \frac{-1}{\sqrt{1 - x^2}}$
$y = \arctan(x)$	$\frac{dy}{dx} = \frac{1}{1 + x^2}$
$y = \text{arccsc}(x)$	$\frac{dy}{dx} = \frac{-1}{\lvert x \rvert \sqrt{x^2 - 1}}$
$y = \text{arcsec}(x)$	$\frac{dy}{dx} = \frac{1}{\lvert x \rvert \sqrt{x^2 - 1}}$
$y = \text{arccot}(x)$	$\frac{dy}{dx} = \frac{-1}{1 + x^2}$

EXERCISES for Section 5.3

For exercises 1–12: You are given an equation in two variables, x and y, and a specific point on the locus of the equation. Find dy/dx in terms of x and y and evaluate dy/dx at the point indicated. Use that information to find the equations of the tangent line and the normal line at that point.

1. $4x^2 + 9y^2 = 36;\quad (-3/2, \sqrt{3})$
2. $xy = 1;\quad (-0.25, -4)$
3. $x^3 = y^2;\quad (4, 8)$
4. $x^{2/3} + y^{2/3} = 13;\quad (-27, -8)$
5. $(x + y)^2 = 9;\quad (1, 2)$
6. $x = \sqrt{y} + \sqrt[3]{y};\quad (12, 64)$
7. $e^x + e^y = 2 - xy;\quad (0, 0)$
8. $y^2 - 4x^2 = 5;\quad (-1, 3)$
9. $x^2 y - y^3 = 8;\quad (-3, 1)$
10. $\frac{1}{x} + \frac{3}{y} = 1;\quad (2, 6)$
11. $2^{xy} = 64;\quad (2, 3)$
12. $\cos(xy) + y^2 = 5;\quad (0, 2)$

For exercises 13–16: Find d^2y/dx^2 at the point indicated.

13. $x^2y^2 = x^2 + y^2$; $(0,0)$

14. $(x-y)/(x+y+1) = xy$; $(0,0)$

15. $xy + 16 = 0$; $(-2,8)$

16. $x^2 - 2xy + y^2 = 4$; $(2,0)$

---

17. Find the derivative of $y = \operatorname{arccos} x$ by implicit differentiation.

18. Find the derivative of $y = \operatorname{arccot} x$ by implicit differentiation.

19. Find the derivative of $y = \operatorname{arcsec} x$ by implicit differentiation.

20. Find the derivative of $y = \operatorname{arccsc} x$ by implicit differentiation.

For exercises 21–28: A vertical tangent line to the graph of $y = f(x)$ occurs where $\frac{dx}{dy} = 0$. Find the points on the following graphs where the tangent line is vertical.

21. $y = (x-8)^{2/3} + 1$

22. $y = x(x+2)^{3/5}$

23. $y = \sqrt{x+2}$

24. $y = \sqrt{16 - 9x^2}$

25. $y = \sqrt[3]{x-5}$

26. $y = (x^2 + 3x + 2)^{1/3}$

27. $y = \sqrt{4 - x^2}$

28. $y = |x^3 - x|$

For exercises 29–32: Find the slope of the tangent line to the given curve at any point (x_0, y_0) on the curve. At which points is the tangent line vertical?

29. $x^{1/3} + y^{1/3} = a^{1/3}$ (a constant)

30. $x^3 + y^3 = a^3$ (a constant)

31. A general hyperbola centered at the origin $\frac{x^2}{a^2} - \frac{y^2}{b^2} = 1$

32. A general ellipse centered at the origin $\frac{x^2}{a^2} + \frac{y^2}{b^2} = 1$

For exercises 33–46: For each function f, find $f'(x)$.

33. $f(x) = [\arctan(e^x)]^3$

34. $f(x) = \ln(\tan(\sqrt{x}))$

35. $f(x) = \tan(\ln(\sqrt{x}))$

36. $f(x) = \ln(\ln(x))$

37. $f(x) = \ln(3x^2 + e^{-3x})$

38. $f(x) = \cot^2(\ln(x))$

39. $f(x) = x^2 \ln(\sin(x))$

40. $f(x) = \arcsin(2x)\sin(2x)$

41. $f(x) = e^{-3x}\tan(\ln(x))$

42. $f(x) = \ln(x)\tan(x^{1/2})$

43. $f(x) = \log_2\left(\frac{2-x}{2+x}\right)^{1/2}$

44. $f(x) = \ln\left[\frac{(2x+1)^{1/2}}{(3x-1)^3}\right]$

45. $f(x) = \frac{5^{-x}}{\log_3(3x+2)}$

46. $f(x) = \arctan\sqrt{x}$

5.4 RELATED RATES

One of the most common uses of derivatives is in analyzing processes that change with time. In other words, time t is the independent variable. The interpretation of a derivative as a rate of change is particularly appropriate when the independent variable is time.

Often several quantities may be changing simultaneously with time. If these quantities are related to each other in some way, then clearly their rates of change will also be related.

EXAMPLE 20 Find df/dt, if x and y are functions of t (time) and

$$f(t) = x^3 + e^y.$$

Solution We use the chain rule to find df/dt, noting that x and y are functions of time t:

$$\frac{df}{dt} = 3x^2\frac{dx}{dt} + e^y\frac{dy}{dt}.$$

This expression relates the rate of change of f with respect to t to the rates of change of x and y with respect to t. Note that we can use this expression to determine the value of df/dt at any specific time t, provided that we know the values of x, y, dx/dt, and dy/dt at that time. ■

As an illustration of a physical situation involving related rates, consider a balloon being inflated. Simultaneously, its geometric attributes of volume, surface area, radius, diameter, and circumference are all changing, as well as other physical attributes such as weight, internal pressure, and even temperature. All of these variables are changing as an outcome of the single act of inflating the balloon. Since many of these variables are closely related to one other by geometric formulas or by physical laws, knowing the rates of change of some of them may allow us to determine the rates of change of other variables.

EXAMPLE 21 Suppose that an inflating balloon is a sphere and that its radius is changing at the rate of 3 cm/sec. How fast is the volume of the balloon changing when the radius is 20 cm?

Solution The relationship between the balloon's radius r and its volume V is given by the formula for the volume of a sphere:

$$V = \frac{4}{3}\pi r^3.$$

In this situation, both the radius r and the volume V are functions of time. We might express this fact by writing

$$V(t) = \frac{4}{3}\pi r(t)^3.$$

If we differentiate both sides of the relationship with respect to t, we arrive at

$$V'(t) = \frac{4}{3}\pi \cdot 3r(t)^2 r'(t) = 4\pi r(t)^2 r'(t).$$

(Note that we used the chain rule in differentiating the right-hand side.) We are interested in finding the rate of change of the volume (namely, $V'(t)$) at the particular instant that the radius $r(t) = 20$ cm. Since $r'(t)$ represents the rate of change of the radius of the balloon, we know that

$$r'(t) = 3 \text{ cm/sec}.$$

Substituting these known values above, we have

$$V'(t) = 4\pi \cdot (20 \text{ cm})^2 \cdot 3 \text{ cm/sec} = 4800\pi \text{ cm}^3/\text{sec}.$$

Note that carrying the units through our computation leads to the units for our final result. The units cm^3/sec make perfect sense, because $V'(t)$ represents change in volume cm^3 per (/) unit of time (sec). ■

This example illustrates the solution of what is commonly called a *related rates problem.* A related rates problem generally refers to the task of determining the rate of change (with respect to time) of some variables based on their relationship to other variables whose rates of change are known.

Strategy for Solving Related Rates Problems

Step 1. *Identify the variable and constant quantities involved in the process, along with any rates of change.*

What quantities change value with time? These will be variables, and they should be labeled appropriately. What quantities keep a fixed value? These are treated as constants (even though the particular fixed value may be unknown). What rates of change are given? The units of measurement can be extremely helpful in identifying rates of change. For example, units like miles per hour or gallons per second tell us the rate of change (d/dt) of other quantities measured in units of miles and gallons, respectively.

Step 2. *Find a relationship between the variables.*

How are the variable quantities related? Is there a formula or equation that involves the relevant variables? Do NOT substitute the numerical value of any variable at a specific time into the relationship (until Step 4).

Step 3. *Differentiate with respect to time to find a relationship between the variables and their rates of change.*

This means differentiating both sides of the equation from Step 2 with respect to time t. Be sure to treat those variables that change with time as functions of time, observing the chain rule and other rules of differentiation.

Step 4. *Substitute all known variable and rate values for the specific instant of time in question, and determine the unknown rates of change.*

This may merely be a matter of solving the resulting equation or may require using that information in some other way to determine the unknown rate(s) of change.

Step 5. *Interpret the results and use them to answer the particular questions posed by the problem.*

What exactly is being asked for in the problem? If we need to know a particular rate of change, this may be given by Step 4. Analyzing both the *sign* (positive or negative) and the *units* ("something" per unit of time) can be helpful in judging the reasonableness of our answer.

EXAMPLE 22 An empty underground storage tank has the shape of a cone (vertex down) 20 feet deep and 40 feet in diameter. If we start pumping into the tank at the constant rate of 100 gallons per minute, how fast is the depth of the fluid in the tank changing 10 minutes after we start pumping? (For future reference, we note that the conversion for gallons to cubic feet is 1 gal ≈ 0.13368 ft^3.)

Solution **Step 1.** Identify the variable and constant quantities involved in the process, along with any given rates of change.

During the process of pumping fluid into the tank, the volume, the depth, and the radius of the circular surface of the fluid in the tank will all be changing. These are the variables in the process. Let's label them as follows:

$$V = \text{volume at time } t, \qquad h = \text{depth at time } t, \qquad r = \text{radius at time } t.$$

Figure 5.15 illustrates the problem.

Given the dimensions of the tank, it appears that a suitable unit of measurement for r and h would be *feet*, in which case we should measure

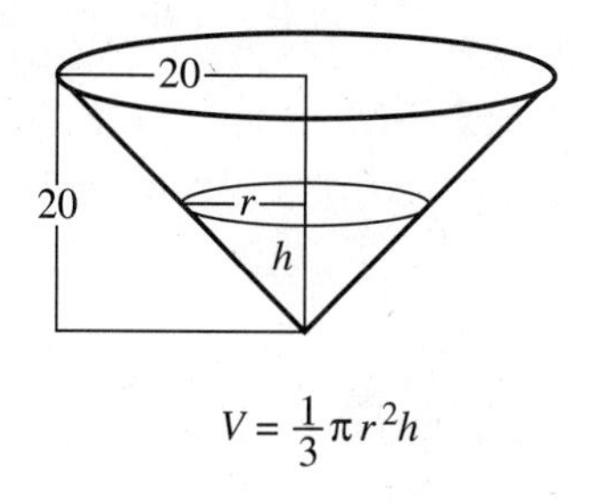

Figure 5.15 The conical underground storage tank.

V in *cubic feet*. The constant quantities in this problem are the dimensions of the tank—its total depth of 20 feet and its diameter of 40 feet.

The other information given in this problem tells us that $dV/dt = 100$ gal/min ≈ 13.368 ft^3/min at all times t. We wish to use this information to find dh/dt when $t = 10$ minutes.

Step 2. Find a relationship between the variables.

We can relate the volume V of the fluid to the radius and height by the formula for the volume of a cone.

$$V = \frac{1}{3}\pi r^2 h.$$

From the illustration, we also note that r and h can be considered legs of a triangle that is similar to a larger triangle with equal legs of length 20 feet (the full radius and height of the tank). Thus, the ratios of these lengths must be the same:

$$\frac{r}{h} = \frac{20}{20} = 1, \qquad \text{so that} \qquad r = h.$$

With this information, we can relate V and h as functions of time.

$$V(t) = \frac{1}{3}\pi (h(t))^3.$$

Step 3. Differentiate with respect to time to find a relationship between the variables and their rates of change:

$$\frac{dV}{dt} = \frac{1}{3}\pi(3h(t)^2)\frac{dh}{dt} = \pi h(t)^2 \frac{dh}{dt}.$$

Step 4. Substitute all known variable and rate values for the specific instant of time in question and determine the unknown rate(s) of change.

Since fluid is being pumped in at a constant rate of 100 gallons per minute, we know that

$$\left.\frac{dV}{dt}\right|_{t=10} = 100 \text{ gal/min}.$$

After 10 minutes we will have pumped in 1000 gallons, so

$$V(10) = 1000 \text{ gallons.}$$

From $V = \dfrac{1}{3}\pi h(t)^3$, we can compute $h(10)$: first, since 1 gallon ≈ 0.13368 ft^3, we have

$$1000 \text{ gal} \approx 133.68 \text{ ft}^3 \approx \frac{3.14159}{3}(h(10))^3,$$

from which we find that

$$h(10) \approx \sqrt[3]{\frac{401.4}{3.14159}} \approx 5.04 \text{ ft.}$$

We substitute

$$h(10) \approx 5.04 \text{ ft} \qquad \text{and} \qquad \left.\frac{dV}{dt}\right|_{t=10} = 100 \text{ gal/min} \approx 13.368 \text{ ft}^3\text{/min}$$

into the equation for $\dfrac{dV}{dt}$:

$$\left.\frac{dV}{dt}\right|_{t=10} = \pi(h(10))^2 \left.\frac{dh}{dt}\right|_{t=10},$$

to obtain

$$13.368 \text{ ft}^3\text{/min} \approx (3.14159)(5.04 \text{ ft})^2 \cdot \left.\frac{dh}{dt}\right|_{t=10}.$$

Solving for the unknown rate, we have

$$\left.\frac{dh}{dt}\right|_{t=10} \approx 0.1675 \text{ ft/min.}$$

Step 5. Interpret the results and use them to answer the particular questions posed by the problem.

After 10 minutes of pumping, the fluid is rising at a rate of approximately 0.1675 ft/min (a little over two inches each minute). ■

EXAMPLE 23 Two roads intersect at right angles. Two cars travel through the intersection simultaneously (barely missing a collision). The first car travels at a speed of 30 mph, traveling due north. The other car travels at a speed of 40 mph, traveling due east. How fast is the distance between them changing 30 minutes later?

Solution **Step 1.** Identify the variable and constant quantities involved in the process, along with any given rates of change.

The distance each car travels from the starting point is changing with time, as is the distance between the two cars. If we label the distance

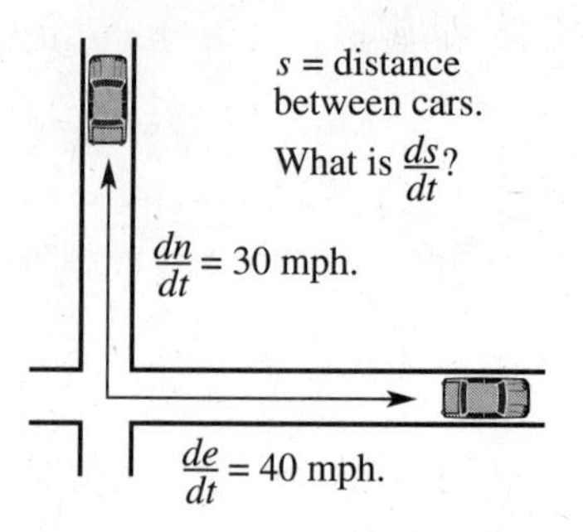

Figure 5.16 How fast is the distance between the two cars changing?

traveled north by the first car as n, and the distance traveled east by the second car as e, then we know that

$$\frac{dn}{dt} = 30 \text{ mph} \qquad \text{and} \qquad \frac{de}{dt} = 40 \text{ mph}.$$

If we label the distance between the two cars as s, then we need to find ds/dt when $t = 0.5$ hours. Figure 5.16 shows an illustration of the situation.

Step 2. Find a relationship between the variables. The three variables n, e, and s are related by the Pythagorean theorem:

$$n^2 + e^2 = s^2.$$

Step 3. Differentiate with respect to time to find a relationship between the variables and their rates of change:

$$2n\frac{dn}{dt} + 2e\frac{de}{dt} = 2s\frac{ds}{dt}.$$

Step 4. Substitute all known variable and rate values for the specific instant of time in question and determine the unknown rate(s) of change.

After 30 minutes (0.5 hours), the northbound car will have travelled 15 miles and the eastbound car will have travelled 20 miles. In other words,

$$n(0.5) = 15 \text{ miles} \qquad \text{and} \qquad e(0.5) = 20 \text{ miles}.$$

Using this and the Pythagorean theorem, we can compute

$$s(0.5) = \sqrt{15^2 + 20^2} = 25 \text{ miles}.$$

We substitute these and the known rates into the equation from Step 3 to obtain

$$2(15)(30) + 2(20)(40) = 2(25)\left.\frac{ds}{dt}\right|_{t=0.5}$$

and solve to find

$$\left.\frac{ds}{dt}\right|_{t=0.5} = \frac{900+1600}{50} = 50 \text{ miles per hour.}$$

Step 5. Interpret the results and use them to answer the particular questions posed by the problem.

Thirty minutes after the cars leave the intersection, the distance between them is increasing at a rate of 50 mph. ■

▶▶▶ **WARNING! A common error in solving related rates problems is to substitute a particular value for t before differentiating with respect to time t.**

Doing so effectively changes the variable quantities to constants. (What do you think will happen when you differentiate?)

EXERCISES for Section 5.4

For exercises 1–4: Consider the inflating balloon described in this section. Find the rates of change indicated.

1. How fast is the circumference of the balloon changing when the radius is 5 cm?

2. How fast is the surface area of the balloon changing when the radius is 10 cm?

3. Suppose that the elasticity of the balloon at room temperature is given by the equation $E = 100 - \sqrt{V}$. The balloon explodes when the elasticity reaches 0. How fast is the volume of the balloon changing at the moment of explosion?

4. How fast was the elasticity changing at the moment of explosion?

For exercises 5–10: Find df/dt if x, y, and θ are functions of t (time) and f is the function indicated.

5. $f(t) = x^4 + 6\sin(\theta)$

6. $f(t) = 4x^3 + 10\cos(\theta)$

7. $f(t) = 5x^3 - 4\arcsin(y)$

8. $f(t) = 2x^3 - 5\arctan(y)$

9. $f(t) = \pi\sin(x^2\arcsin(y))$

10. $f(t) = \pi\cdot\sin^2(\theta) + \pi\cdot\cos^2(\theta)$

---

11. Two roads intersect at right angles. An eastbound car leaves the intersection traveling at a speed of 40 mph. Two hours later, a northbound car leaves the same intersection at a speed of 30 mph. How fast is the distance between them changing five hours after the eastbound car leaves?

12. Suppose now that the eastbound road is actually elevated 30 feet above the northbound road. How fast is the distance between the two cars changing four hours later, if they leave the intersection at the same moment?

13. At the end of one of the assembly lines at the Platypus corporation, metal shavings are emptied into a conical pile whose height is always the same as its diameter. If the shavings are spilled onto the pile at the rate of 10 cm^3/sec, how fast is the radius of the pile increasing when the height is 5 cm?

14. A weather balloon is tethered so that it stays at a constant height of 250 meters. The wind blows it horizontally at a rate of 5 meters/sec away from its original position. If the line is spooled out so that the altitude remains constant, how fast must the line be let out when the balloon lies over a point on the ground 300 meters from the spool?

15. A rectangular swimming pool has a depth ranging from 1 meter at the shallow end to 4 meters deep at the diving end. The pool is 50 meters long and 25 meters wide. The bottom slopes from the edge of the shallow area (10 meters long) to the diving area (also 10 meters long) as shown in the illustration. If water is pumped out of a full pool at the rate of 250 gallons per minute, how fast is the water level dropping when the depth at the diving end is 1 meters? 2 meters? 3 meters?

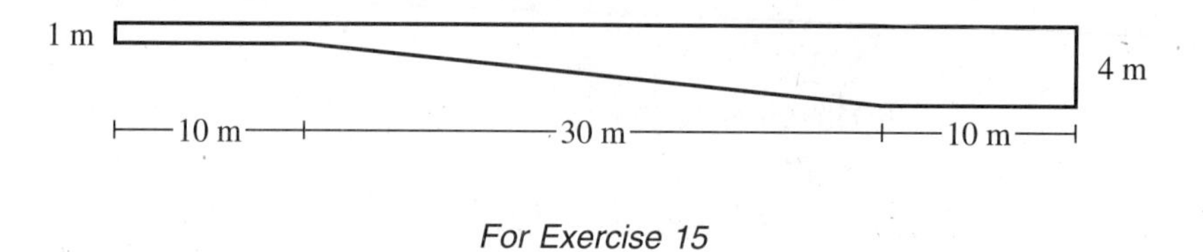

For Exercise 15

16. Platypus has accidentally spilled 30 ft^3 of chemicals into the river, causing a circular slick whose area is expanding while its thickness is decreasing. If the radius of the slick expands at the rate of 1 foot per hour, how fast is the thickness of the slick decreasing when the area is 100 ft^2?

17. A woman standing on the bank of a river is reeling in a fish. The tip of her fishing rod is 5 feet above the water's surface at the bank's edge. How fast is the fish approaching shore when there are 30 feet of line out from the tip of the rod and the woman is reeling in 3 inches per second?

18. A baseball diamond is 90 feet square and the pitcher's mound is 60 feet 6 inches from home plate. If a pitcher throws a baseball at 100 miles per hour, how fast is the distance between the ball and first base changing as the ball crosses home plate?

A trough has ends shaped like isosceles trapezoids: 11 feet wide at the top, 5 feet wide at the bottom, and 4 feet in (perpendicular) height. The trough is 12 feet long. Water is pumped in at the steady rate of 15 ft^3 per minute.

19. How long will it take to fill the trough?

20. How deep is the water after 5 minutes?

21. How fast is the water rising 5 minutes after pumping begins?

22. What are the depth and rate of rising after 10 minutes?

A spherical balloon is being inflated at the uniform rate of 10 ft^3 per minute.

23. At what rate is its circumference increasing when its radius is 3 feet?

24. At what rate is the surface area increasing 7 minutes after inflation begins?

When gravel is deposited from a conveyor, it assumes the shape of an inverted right circular cone. The steepness of the pile depends on the average size and roughness of the pieces of gravel. For one particular grade of gravel, the ratio of the height of the cone to its radius is $3:2$. The conveyor delivers 20 ft^3/min. to the pile.

25. How fast is the height of the pile increasing when its radius is 10 ft?

26. How fast is the radius increasing 15 minutes after the operation begins?

Oil is leaking from an ocean tanker at the rate of 5000 liters per second, resulting in a circular oil slick of (average) depth 4 cm. (Note: 1 liter = 1000 cm^3.)

27. How fast is the radius of the slick increasing when the radius is 300 meters?

28. How fast is the radius increasing 4 hours after the leaking began? Give your answers to the nearest hundredth of a centimeter per second.

A tank in the shape of a right circular cone with its point downward has an altitude of 11 feet and a radius at the top of 4 feet. It is filled at the rate of 15 ft^3/min.

29. How long does it take to fill?

30. What are the depth and rate of rising of the water after 10 minutes?

31. What are the time and rate of rising of the water level when the depth is 5 feet?

32. Find the rising rate at any time t (where $0 < t < T$ and T is the time it takes to completely fill the tank).

5.5 PARAMETRIC EQUATIONS AND PARTICLE MOTION

Another way that a curve in the Cartesian plane may be described is through the use of **parametric equations**. Parametric equations describe both coordinates x and y as functions of a third variable t over some common domain D. A curve described in such a way is called a **parametrized curve**, and the shared independent variable t is called the **parameter** for the curve. This is a different use for the word *parameter* than in earlier chapters. In this case, the parameter t really is the *independent variable*, while x and y are both *dependent variables*.

The choice of the letter t is not accidental. Parametric equations are particularly suited to describing the path of a moving particle or object over time. The outputs $x(t)$ and $y(t)$ give us the precise coordinates of the moving particle at time t.

EXAMPLE 24 Graph the curve described by the parametric equations

$$x = t^2 \quad \text{and} \quad y = t^3 \quad \text{for} \quad 0 \leq t \leq 2.$$

Solution For each value t in the interval $[0, 2]$ we plot

$$(x(t), y(t)) = (t^2, t^3).$$

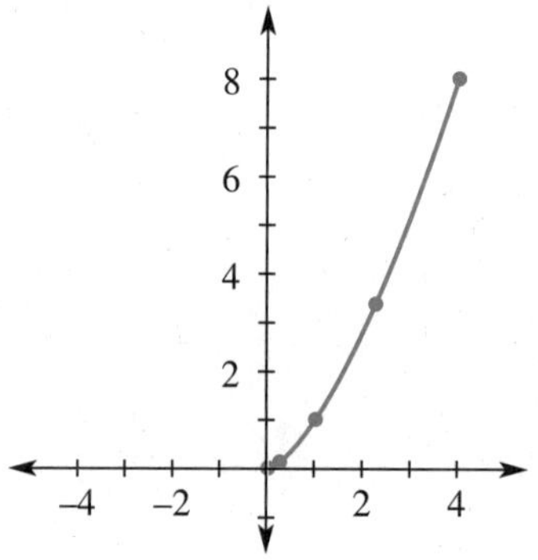

t	x	y
0	0	0
0.5	0.25	0.125
1	1	1
1.5	2.25	3.375
2	4	8

Figure 5.17 Table of values and graph of $(x(t), y(t)) = (t^2, t^3)$.

In Figure 5.17 we show a selected table of values for t, x, and y and the graph of the resulting parametrized curve. If we look only at the graph, note that we cannot extract the value of t that corresponds to a point on the curve. All we see are the paired outputs $(x(t), y(t))$. The choice of the letter t is not accidental; it is meant to suggest an independent variable measured in units of *time*. A parametrized curve is often thought of as the path that a moving object traces out through time. The parametric equations giving us $x(t)$ and $y(t)$ tell us the coordinates of the position of the object. The path by itself cannot tell us *when* the object is at a certain point, since the curve is just a set of points. In fact, a completely different pair of parametric equations could give us exactly the same curve. ■

EXAMPLE 25 Graph the curve corresponding to the parametric equations

$$x = t^2 - 4t + 4 \qquad \text{and} \qquad y = t^3 - 6t^2 + 12t - 8 \qquad \text{for} \qquad 2 \leq t \leq 4.$$

Solution Even though the parametric equations have changed (as well as the interval of values t), the graph consists of exactly the same points as before, as shown in Figure 5.18. ■

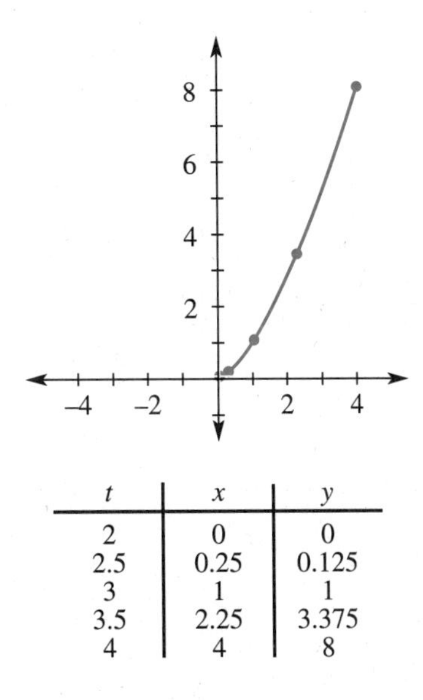

t	x	y
2	0	0
2.5	0.25	0.125
3	1	1
3.5	2.25	3.375
4	4	8

Figure 5.18 Table of values and graph of $(x(t), y(t)) = (t^2 - 4t + 4, t^3 - 6t^2 + 12t - 8)$.

EXAMPLE 26 Using the parametric equations

$$x = t^2 \qquad \text{and} \qquad y = t^3 \qquad \text{for} \qquad 0 \leq t \leq 2,$$

express y as a function of x. Then use this to find

$$\left.\frac{dy}{dx}\right|_{t=0.5}.$$

Solution Since $x = t^2$ and $t \geq 0$ on the interval $[0, 2]$, we can write $t = \sqrt{x}$ and substitute for t in the expression for y:

$$y = t^3 = (\sqrt{x})^3 = x^{3/2}.$$

From this, we compute

$$\frac{dy}{dx} = \frac{3}{2}x^{1/2} = \frac{3\sqrt{x}}{2}.$$

When $t = 0.5$, we have $x = t^2 = (0.5)^2 = 0.25$. Substituting into dy/dx yields

$$\left.\frac{dy}{dx}\right|_{t=0.5} = \frac{3\sqrt{0.25}}{2} = \frac{3(0.5)}{2} = 0.75,$$

the slope of the curve at the point $(0.25, 0.125)$. ■

Finding the slope of a parametrized curve

This method of finding dy/dx is fine as long as we are successful in writing y as a function of x. (Or, if we could just find some relationship solely in terms of x and y, we might find dy/dx using implicit differentiation.) This may be quite difficult to do, even for fairly simple parametric equations. However, it is possible to find dy/dx directly in terms of t using the parametric equations for x and y. The reasoning is based on the chain rule. If we could write

$$y = f(x),$$

then substituting x as a function of t gives us

$$y = f(x(t)).$$

If we take the derivative with respect to t, we have (in Leibniz notation)

$$\frac{dy}{dt} = \frac{dy}{dx}\frac{dx}{dt}.$$

Algebraically, we can solve for dy/dx as

$$\frac{dy}{dx} = \frac{\frac{dy}{dt}}{\frac{dx}{dt}},$$

provided $dx/dt \neq 0$. This means we can compute dy/dx directly in terms of t, by taking the quotient of dy/dt and dx/dt. If we think of the curve as the path of a moving object, then the derivatives dx/dt and dy/dt tell us how fast the position of the object changes in the horizontal and vertical directions, respectively. The derivative dy/dx then gives us a rate of change of the y-coordinate relative to change in the x-coordinate.

EXAMPLE 27 Using the parametric equations

$$x = t^2 - 4t + 4 \qquad \text{and} \qquad y = t^3 - 6t^2 + 12t - 8 \qquad \text{for} \qquad 2 \le t \le 4,$$

calculate

$$\left.\frac{dy}{dx}\right|_{t=2.5}.$$

Solution $\dfrac{dy}{dx} = \dfrac{\frac{dy}{dt}}{\frac{dx}{dt}} = \dfrac{3t^2 - 12t + 12}{2t - 4}$, so we can compute

$$\left.\frac{dy}{dx}\right|_{t=2.5} = \frac{3(2.5)^2 - 12(2.5) + 12}{2(2.5) - 4} = 0.75.$$

This represents the slope of the parametrized curve at the point

$$(x(2.5), y(2.5)) = (0.25, 0.125).$$

■

Note that even though this parametrization was different, we calculated the same slope for the same curve at the same point. The slope dy/dx at a point depends only on the curve itself, and not on a particular parametrization of that curve. Hence, if we use a graphing calculator or software to plot a curve given parametric equations, we will not be able to judge visually the values of dx/dt and dy/dt at a specific point from the graph alone, but we can certainly estimate their ratio dy/dx.

EXAMPLE 28 Suppose that we parametrize the circle $x^2 + y^2 = 9$ using parametric equations

$$x = 3\cos(t) \qquad \text{and} \qquad y = 3\sin(t) \qquad \text{for} \qquad 0 \le t \le 2\pi.$$

Find the equations of the tangent line and of the normal line at $t = 2\pi/3$.

Solution $\dfrac{dy}{dx} = \dfrac{\frac{dy}{dt}}{\frac{dx}{dt}} = \dfrac{3\cos t}{-3\sin t} = -\cot(t)$. So,

$$\left.\frac{dy}{dx}\right|_{t=\frac{2\pi}{3}} = -\cot(\frac{2\pi}{3}) = \frac{1}{\sqrt{3}}.$$

The slope m of the tangent line is $1/\sqrt{3}$ and the slope $-1/m$ of the normal line is $-\sqrt{3}$. The point of tangency is

$$(x(t), y(t)) = (3\cos(\frac{2\pi}{3}), 3\sin(\frac{2\pi}{3})) = (-\frac{3}{2}, \frac{3\sqrt{3}}{2}).$$

From this information we can write down the equation of the tangent line

$$y = \frac{1}{\sqrt{3}}(x + \frac{3}{2}) + \frac{3\sqrt{3}}{2},$$

and

$$y = -\sqrt{3}(x + \frac{3}{2}) + \frac{3\sqrt{3}}{2}$$

is the equation of the normal line. ■

The use of the parametrization gives us an additional way to solve this problem.

EXAMPLE 29 If we set up an appropriate coordinate system for the plane of the orbit of a satellite, then the parametric equations can be expressed as

$$x(t) = a\cos t \qquad y(t) = b\sin t.$$

Show that the path of the satellite is the ellipse

$$\frac{x^2}{a^2} + \frac{y^2}{b^2} = 1$$

and calculate the velocities $x'(t)$ and $y'(t)$.

Solution If we substitute $x(t) = a\cos t$ and $y(t) = b\sin t$ into the equation of the ellipse, we can verify that

$$\frac{x(t)^2}{a^2} + \frac{y(t)^2}{b^2} = \frac{a^2\cos^2 t}{a^2} + \frac{b^2\sin^2 t}{b^2} = \cos^2 t + \sin^2 t = 1.$$

The velocities are

$$x'(t) = -a\sin t \qquad y'(t) = b\cos t.$$ ■

Note that any function graph of the form $y = f(x)$ can be considered a parametrized curve by simply substituting t for x:

$$x(t) = t \qquad y(t) = f(t).$$

If f has an inverse function, we can obtain its graph parametrically by simply interchanging the parametric equations, so that

$$x(t) = f(t) \qquad y(t) = t.$$

For example, if you plot the parametrized curve described by

$$x(t) = \sin t \qquad y(t) = t \qquad \text{for } -\frac{\pi}{2} \le t \le \frac{\pi}{2},$$

it matches the graph of $y = \arcsin x$.

Intersections vs. collisions

If we have two parametrized curves (two pairs of parametric equations), we should distinguish between an intersection point and a "collision" point. An intersection point is any point that lies on both curves. If this intersection point corresponds to the same value of t for both curves, we could call it a collision point. (An intersection of two roads may or may not be the site of a collision between two cars travelling on those roads.)

EXAMPLE 30 Consider two objects in motion over the time interval $0 \leq t \leq 2\pi$. The position (x_1, y_1) of the first object is described by the parametric equations

$$x_1(t) = 2\cos t \qquad y_1(t) = 3\sin t.$$

The position of the second object (x_2, y_2) is described by the parametric equations

$$x_2(t) = 1 + \sin t \qquad y_2(t) = \cos t - 3.$$

At what time(s) do the objects collide?

Solution Figure 5.19 illustrates the paths of the two objects. We can see that there are two intersection points of these paths. To collide, the objects must be at the same position *at the same time*. In other words, we must have

$$x_1(t) = 2\cos t = 1 + \sin t = x_2(t)$$

$$y_1(t) = 3\sin t = \cos t - 3 = y_2(t).$$

By adding 3 to both sides of the second equation, we can see that $\cos t = 3\sin t + 3$. If we substitute $3\sin t + 3$ for $\cos t$ in the first equation, we have

$$2(3\sin t + 3) = 1 + \sin t.$$

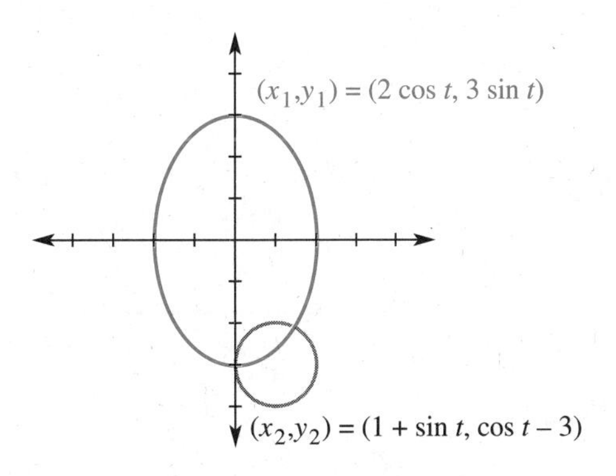

Figure 5.19 Paths of two objects.

Solving for $\sin t$, we have $\sin t = -1$, so $t = 3\pi/2$ is the only time that both objects occupy the same spot simultaneously. We can check that

$$(x_1(\frac{3\pi}{2}), y_1(\frac{3\pi}{2})) = (2\cos(\frac{3\pi}{2}), 3\sin(\frac{3\pi}{2})) = (0, -3)$$

and

$$(x_2(\frac{3\pi}{2}), y_2(\frac{3\pi}{2})) = (1 + \sin(\frac{3\pi}{2}), \cos(\frac{3\pi}{2}) - 3) = (0, -3).$$ ■

Parametric equations of a projectile

Suppose that a projectile is launched at an initial velocity v_0 ft/sec at an angle of inclination θ to the ground. (A projectile might be anything from a thrown ball to a rocket.) If the projectile is subject to no other force than gravity, we want to describe its flight path in terms of parametric equations

$x(t) =$ horizontal position of the projectile at time t

$y(t) =$ horizontal position of the projectile at time t.

Figure 5.20 illustrates the situation. Using trigonometry with the right triangle shown, we can see that the initial horizontal velocity is $v_0 \cos\theta$ and the initial vertical velocity is $v_0 \sin\theta$. There are no other horizontal forces acting on the object, so the horizontal position of the projectile is given by

$$x(t) = v_0 t \cos\theta + x_0,$$

where x_0 is the initial horizontal position of the projectile.

Vertically, the downward acceleration due to gravity gives us a vertical position of the projectile as

$$y(t) = v_0 t \sin\theta - 16t^2 + y_0,$$

where y_0 is the initial vertical position of the projectile.

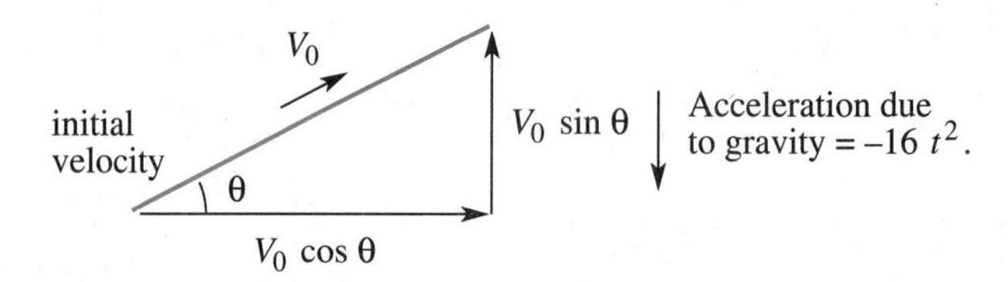

Figure 5.20 Launch of a projectile.

EXAMPLE 31 A rocket is launched from ground level with an initial velocity $v_0 = 1200$ mph at an angle of inclination $\theta = 32°$. Find:

(a) its maximum height,

(b) the time it takes to return to earth,

(c) the distance it travels horizontally from the launch site during that time, and

d) its horizontal and vertical velocities at the time of impact.

Solution We'll take the initial position of the rocket to be $(x_0, y_0) = (0, 0)$. First, we need to convert the initial velocity v_0 to ft/sec:

$$1200 \cdot \frac{\text{miles}}{\text{hours}} = 1200 \cdot \frac{5280 \text{ feet}}{3600 \text{ sec}} = 1760 \frac{\text{feet}}{\text{sec}}.$$

Since $\sin 32° \approx 0.530$ and $\cos 32° \approx 0.848$, we can write the parametric equations for the horizontal and vertical positions of the rocket as

$$x(t) \approx 1760(0.848)t = (1492.5)t \text{ feet}$$

and

$$y(t) \approx 1760(0.530)t - 16t^2 = ((932.8)t - 16t^2) \text{ feet}.$$

(a) To find the maximum height of the rocket, we need to maximize its vertical distance from the earth. To find the critical value, we set

$$\frac{dy}{dt} = 932.8 - 32t = 0$$

and find

$$t = \frac{932.8}{32} = 29.15 \text{ seconds}.$$

You can check that dy/dt changes from positive to negative at this critical value, so the maximum height does occur at this time. The actual height achieved by the rocket is

$$y(29.15) = 932.8(29.15) - 16(29.15)^2 = 13{,}595.6 \text{ feet} \approx 2.575 \text{ miles}.$$

(b) The rocket returns to earth when

$$y(t) = (932.8)t - 16t^2 = t(932.8 - 16t) = 0.$$

Launch time is represented by $t = 0$, while the return time is

$$t = \frac{932.8}{16} = 58.3 \text{ seconds}.$$

(c) The horizontal position of the rocket at the time it strikes the earth is

$$x(58.3) = (1492.5)(58.3) = 87,012.75 \text{ feet} \approx 16.48 \text{ miles}.$$

(d) The horizontal velocity is constant ($\frac{dx}{dt} = 1492.5$), so the horizontal and vertical velocities at $t = 58.3$ seconds are:

$$\left.\frac{dx}{dt}\right|_{t=58.3} = 1492.5 \text{ ft/sec} \qquad \left.\frac{dy}{dt}\right|_{t=58.3} = 932.8 - 32(58.3) = -932.8 \text{ ft/sec}.$$

The negative vertical velocity indicates that the direction is downward. ■

EXERCISES for Section 5.5

For exercises 1–10: For each pair of parametric equations given:

(a) Graph the curve for the interval $0 \le t \le 2\pi$.

(b) Find dy/dx in terms of t by first calculating dx/dt and dy/dt.

(c) Find the equations of the tangent line and the normal line to the path of the object at the time t_0 given.

1. $x(t) = 2\cos(t)$, $y(t) = 3\sin(t)$ $\quad t_0 = \pi/3$
2. $x(t) = -3\cos(t)$, $y(t) = 2\sin(t)$ $\quad t_0 = \pi/6$
3. $x(t) = 5 - t$, $y(t) = 25 - 10t + t^2$ $\quad t_0 = 3$
4. $x(t) = 2t + 3$, $y(t) = 3t + 2$ $\quad t_0 = 5$
5. $x(t) = t\cos(t)$, $y(t) = t\sin(t)$ $\quad t_0 = 2\pi/3$
6. $x(t) = \arctan(t)$, $y(t) = t$ $\quad t_0 = 1$
7. $x(t) = |5 - t|$, $y(t) = t$ $\quad t_0 = 4$
8. $x(t) = \sqrt{40 - t^2}$, $y(t) = t$ $\quad t_0 = 2$
9. $x(t) = \cosh t = \dfrac{e^t + e^{-t}}{2}$, $y(t) = \sinh t = \dfrac{e^t - e^{-t}}{2}$ $\quad t_0 = 2$
10. $x(t) = 3\cos(2t)\cos t$, $y(t) = 3\cos(2t)\sin t$ $\quad t_0 = \pi/4$

---

11. Suppose that $x(t)$ and $y(t)$ determine the coordinates of an object travelling around the unit circle. If dx/dt is positive when the object is in the third quadrant, is dy/dt positive, negative, or zero? Is the object travelling clockwise or counterclockwise?

12. Consider two objects in motion over the time interval $0 \le t \le 2\pi$. The position (x_1, y_1) of the first object is described by the parametric equations

$$x_1(t) = 2\cos t \qquad y_1(t) = 3\sin t.$$

The position of the second object (x_2, y_2) is described by the parametric equations

$$x_2(t) = 1 + \sin t \qquad y_2(t) = \cos t - 3.$$

Find the intersection point of the paths of the two objects that is *not* a collision point.

13. Find all the intersection points for the pair of curves

$$x_1(t) = t^3 - 2t^2 + t; \quad y_1(t) = t \qquad \text{and} \qquad x_2(t) = 5t; \quad y_2(t) = t^3$$

and indicate which intersection points are true collision points.

14. Find a function graph that matches the parametrized curve

$$x(t) = \log_2 t \qquad y(t) = 2t \qquad \text{for all } t.$$

For exercises 15–24: Using only t, $\sin t$, and $\cos t$, describe a pair of parametric equations $x(t)$ and $y(t)$ and an appropriate interval of values for t such that the parametrized curve matches the given graph.

15. $y = \arcsin x$

16. $y = \operatorname{arcsec} x$

17. $y = \arctan x$

18. $y = \operatorname{arccot} x$

19. $y = \operatorname{arccsc} x$

20. $y = \arccos x$

21. the unit circle $x^2 + y^2 = 1$

22. the ellipse $4x^2 + 9y^2 = 36$

23. the line segment connecting $(-1, 1)$ and $(1, -1)$

24. the graph of $y = \sin 2x$ for $-\pi \leq x \leq \pi$

For exercises 25–28: A rocket is launched from ground level with a given initial velocity v_0 at an angle of inclination θ. Find:

(a) its maximum height,

(b) the time it takes to return to earth,

(c) how far it travels horizontally from the launch site during that time,

and

(d) its horizontal and vertical velocities at the time of impact.

25. $v_0 = 1200$ mph at an angle of inclination $\theta = 49°$

26. $v_0 = 1500$ mph at an angle of inclination $5°$

27. $v_0 = 1100$ ft/sec at an angle of inclination $72°$

28. $v_0 = 1$ mile/sec at an angle of inclination $90°$

---

29. Suppose that a rocket is launched from ground level with a given initial velocity of 1000 ft/sec at an angle of inclination θ. What angle θ will result in the greatest horizontal distance traveled by the rocket? What angle will result in the greatest vertical distance?

30. Suppose that a rocket is launched from ground level with a given initial velocity of 1000 ft/sec at an angle of inclination $30°$. After 20 seconds, a booster rocket imparts an additional acceleration that keeps the rocket traveling in a straight path in the same direction it was heading that instant (in other words, along the tangent line to the curve of its original path). What angle does this straight line path make with the horizontal?

---

31. A baseball player hits a fastball at 100 mph from shoulder height (5 feet) at an angle of inclination $15°$ to the horizontal. The horizontal direction of the ball is directly toward a fence 10 feet high and 400 feet away. Does the ball clear the fence?

32. What is the downward velocity of the ball when it hits the ground?

33. At what angle of inclination θ should the ball be hit to land precisely at the base of the fence?

34. At what angle of inclination θ should the ball be hit to land precisely on top of the fence?

35. If the player hits a shoulder-height line drive 100 mph at $0°$ inclination to the horizontal, how far will the ball travel before it hits the ground?

36. The top of the upper deck of the baseball stadium is at a distance of 500 feet from the player and at a height of 105 feet. If the player hits the ball at 100 mph and at angle of inclination $45°$, will the ball leave the stadium?

6

The Integral

So far, our attention has been on the branch of calculus known as the *differential calculus*. In this chapter we turn to the other major branch, the **integral calculus**, including both types of integrals: *definite* integrals and *indefinite* integrals.

The idea of a definite integral has its origins in problems of area measurement, and the *definite integral* of a function f is closely related geometrically to the area of the region between the graph of the function and the x-axis. More generally, the definite integral provides a powerful tool for measuring accumulated change.

The problem of finding an *indefinite integral* of a function is equivalent to the problem of finding an *antiderivative* for that function. In other words, given a function f, we seek another function F such that $F' = f$. Geometrically, you can think of *antidifferentiation* as recovering a function from the slope(s) of its graph.

In this chapter, we examine both definite and indefinite integrals, their properties, and numerical, graphical, and symbolic methods for computing them. At first glance, it seems unlikely that the problem of measuring area would be related to the problem of finding an antiderivative. In the late 1600s, Newton and Leibniz first realized the true nature of the close connection between accumulated change (definite integrals) and antiderivatives (indefinite integrals). Their discovery marked not only the birth of modern calculus but also the dawn of a new age of scientific and technological advancement. The theorems that establish that connection are rightfully called the *fundamental theorems of calculus*, and they are the cornerstones of calculus. The highlight of the chapter is that marvelous connection established by the fundamental theorems of calculus.

6.1 WHAT IS A DEFINITE INTEGRAL? AREA AND ACCUMULATED CHANGE

Our interest in the method of exhaustion goes far beyond historical interest. The notion of computing the limiting value for an infinite sequence of approximations is at the heart of calculus. We have seen this idea before in the definition of a derivative as a limiting value of difference quotients.

Speedometers, odometers, and clocks—reversing the problem

We introduced the idea of derivative by using the example of a car's odometer, speedometer, and clock. The speedometer reading corresponds to a *derivative* reading: it gives us the instantaneous rate of change of distance (odometer reading) with respect to time (clock reading). One could approximate the speedometer reading from the odometer and clock by computing the ratio of the distance traveled to the length of a sufficiently small time interval (the difference quotient of change in distance over change in time). Graphically, the speedometer reading corresponds to the *slope* on a graph of distance traveled as a function of time.

Let's go back to the illustration of a moving car to motivate the idea of a *definite integral.* Consider reversing the problem of determining velocity from distance and time readings; our interest now is in determining the distance traveled by the car (odometer reading) from the car's velocity over time. Instead of plotting distance versus time, we now plot *velocity* versus time. For a car traveling at a *constant* rate of 40 mph over a two-hour period, the velocity graph is a horizontal line (see Figure 6.1).

The distance traveled over any elapsed time interval is

$$d = rt,$$

where r is the rate (the height of the constant velocity graph) and t is the elapsed time (the length of the time interval). For example, from $t = 1$ hour to $t = 1.5$ hours we have an elapsed time interval of 0.5 hours, so the car travels

$$d = rt = (40 \text{ mph})(0.5 \text{ hours}) = 20 \text{ miles}.$$

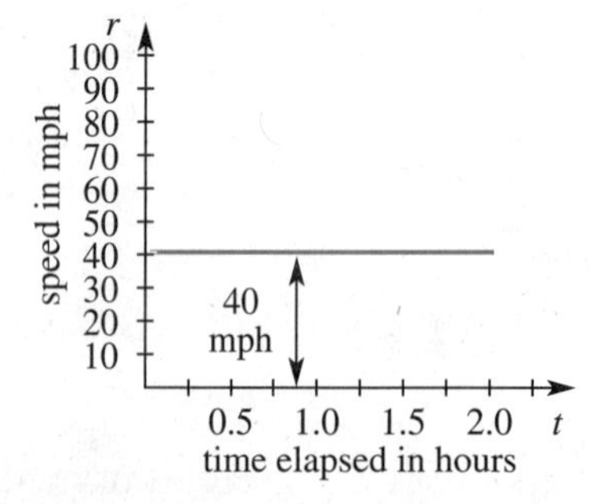

Figure 6.1 Constant rate vs. time for a car traveling 40 mph.

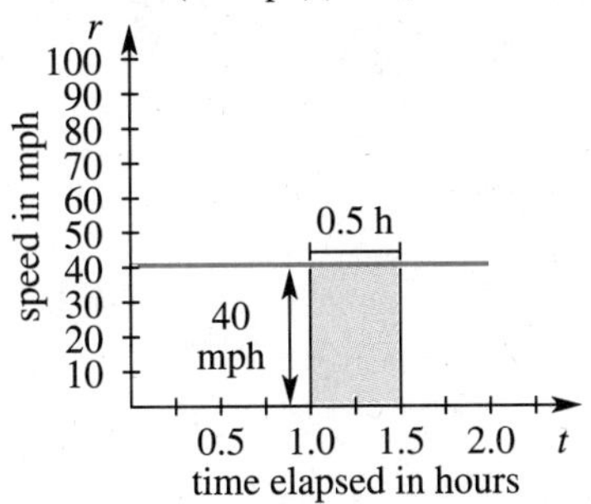

Figure 6.2 The area under a constant velocity graph represents distance traveled.

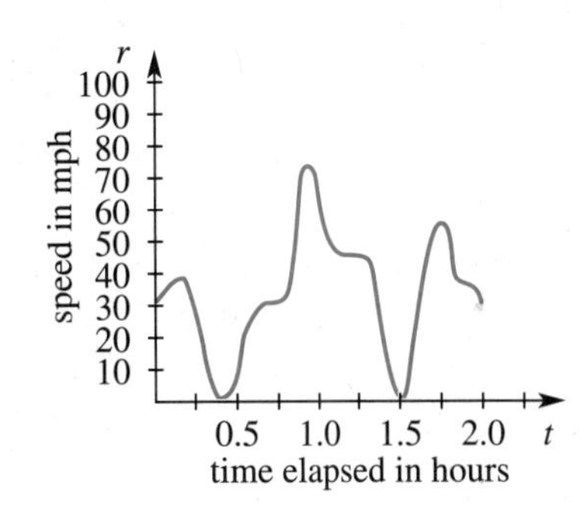

Figure 6.3 The velocity graph for a car with varying speeds.

Figure 6.2 illustrates this distance traveled as the area under the velocity graph (and above the t-axis) between $t = 1$ hour and $t = 1.5$ hours. This is the area of the shaded rectangle in Figure 6.2.

We can see that d, the distance traveled by the car, is graphically represented by the area of the shaded rectangle. The total area under the graph over the two-hour time interval represents the total distance of 80 miles traveled.

Finding distance traveled—area under the velocity graph

Of course, the formula $d = rt$ is not valid if the rate r changes or varies over the time interval. Figure 6.3 shows the graph of speedometer readings for a second car traveling at varying speeds. The *height* of this graph over any particular value t represents the *velocity* of the car at time t. How can we use this velocity graph to find the distance traveled by this car over a time interval?

EXAMPLE 1 Approximate the distance traveled by the second car over the first 15 minutes ($t = 0$ to $t = 0.25$ hours).

Solution It appears that the car is traveling at a velocity between 30 and 40 mph during most of the first 15 minutes. If we estimate that the average velocity over this time interval is about 35 mph, then our distance approximation is

$$d = rt \approx (35 \text{ mph})(0.25 \text{ hours}) = 8.75 \text{ miles}.$$

Graphically, we have approximated the area under the velocity graph with the area of a rectangle of "height" 35 mph and "length" 0.25 hours. ■

This approximation strategy can be refined. Suppose we *partition* our time interval into several shorter time intervals—say, 1 minute each in length. We can then approximate the area under the velocity graph for each minute and add the results to obtain a better total approximation.

EXAMPLE 2 Approximate the distance traveled by the second car during the first 15 minutes of the trip, given the minute-by-minute velocity readings gathered in Table 6.1.

time t in minutes	speed V in mph
0	30
1	31
2	32
3	33
4	34
5	35
6	36
7	36.5
8	37
9	37.5
10	38
11	38
12	37
13	34
14	31
15	28

Table 6.1 Minute-by-minute velocity readings.

Solution Our strategy is to approximate the distance the car travels for each minute of the trip and then add those results to approximate the *accumulated* distance traveled. We'll assume that the car's velocity is *approximately constant* over each minute. Starting with the first minute of the trip, we read the initial velocity of the car from the table to be 30 mph at $t = 0$. If the car does not change velocity drastically during this minute, the car will travel approximately

$$30\frac{\text{miles}}{\text{hour}} \cdot 1 \text{ minute} = 30\ \frac{\text{miles}}{\text{hour}} \cdot \frac{1}{60} \text{ hours} = 0.5 \text{ miles.}$$

To calculate the distance traveled during the second minute of the trip, we note the velocity at $t = 1$ minute (31 mph) and treat this as the car's approximate constant velocity for the second minute of the trip. Thus, the car travels approximately

$$31\ \frac{\text{miles}}{\text{hour}} \cdot 1 \text{ minute} = 31\ \frac{\text{miles}}{\text{hour}} \cdot \frac{1}{60} \text{ hours} \approx 0.5017 \text{ miles.}$$

If we continue in this way for each minute of the trip, we obtain the approximate distance traveled during each of the first 15 minutes. These results along with the approximate total distance traveled by the car are shown in Table 6.2. We can see that the car has traveled a distance

$$d \approx 8.667 \text{ miles}$$

during the first 15 minutes of the trip. ■

minute of trip	approximate distance (mi)
1	0.5000
2	0.5167
3	0.5333
4	0.5500
5	0.5667
6	0.5833
7	0.6000
8	0.6083
9	0.6167
10	0.6250
11	0.6333
12	0.6333
13	0.6167
14	0.5667
15	0.5167
total	8.6667

Table 6.2 Approximate distance traveled minute-by-minute.

The distance traveled by the car was approximated by assuming that the car's velocity was approximately constant during each minute. We used the velocity $v(t)$ at the *beginning* of each minute ($t = 0, 1, 2, \ldots, 14$ minutes) and multiplied by the length of a short time interval $\Delta t = 1$ minute ($1/60$ of an hour) to obtain the approximate distance traveled over each minute. (Since we used the velocity reading at the *beginning* of each minute, note that we did not make use of the velocity reading for $t = 15$ minutes.) Each of these approximate distance readings can be thought of graphically as the area of a thin rectangle (see Figure 6.4).

Some of our minute-by-minute distance readings are overestimates of the actual distance traveled and others are underestimates. Graphically,

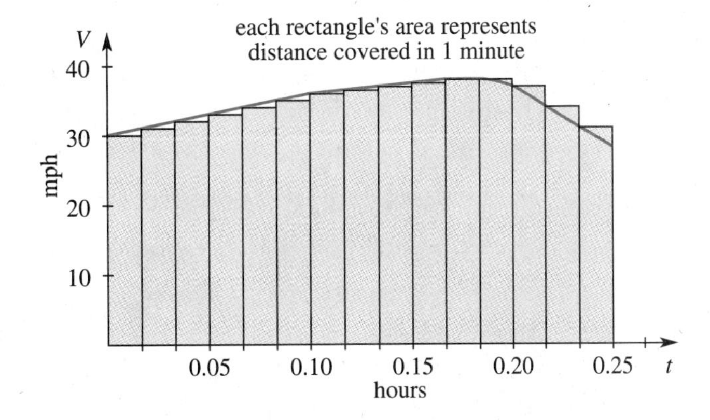

Figure 6.4 Approximating the area under the velocity graph.

this can be seen by observing whether the corresponding rectangle has more or less area than the area under the velocity graph. The sum of the distance readings (sum of the areas of the rectangles) provides a fairly reasonable approximation of the total distance traveled during the first 15 minutes of the trip.

We could imagine refining this process even further. Suppose we are able to get *second-by-second* velocity readings for the car over the first 15 minutes (= 900 seconds). We could use these to calculate the approximate distance traveled by the car over each second and add the results to obtain an even better approximation of the total distance. Of course, carrying out this calculation is tedious, and we would be well advised to use a computer or calculator to help with such a task.

Finding the area under a function graph

We have just seen how the area under a velocity graph over a time interval yields the distance traveled. Velocity represents the instantaneous rate of change in position with respect to time, while the distance traveled represents the accumulated change in position over that time interval. In general, if a function represents some rate of change or other physical quantity, then the area under the function's graph over an interval represents some accumulated change or effect over that interval. This relationship between area and accumulated change or effect provides the motivation for the *definite integral* of a function, which can be thought of intuitively as the "area under the function graph." The essential idea behind computing a definite integral is based directly on the process we used to approximate the area under the velocity graph.

In the next section, we will formally define a definite integral, but for the time being, let us just consider the general problem of finding the area under a function graph $y = f(x)$ over an interval $[a, b]$. First, let's make two assumptions regarding the function f:

1. $f(x) \geq 0$ for $a \leq x \leq b$, and
2. f is continuous on the interval $[a, b]$.

The problem can be stated more precisely: what is the area of the region bounded by the graph of $y = f(x)$, the x-axis, and the vertical lines $x = a$ and $x = b$? A typical region is illustrated in Figure 6.5. For some functions, simple geometry will suffice to answer the question.

EXAMPLE 3 Find the area of the region bounded by $y = 3$, the x-axis, $x = -1$, and $x = 4$.

Solution The region in question is the rectangle shown in Figure 6.6. This rectangle has height 3 and length $4 - (-1) = 5$. Hence, the area is 15. ■

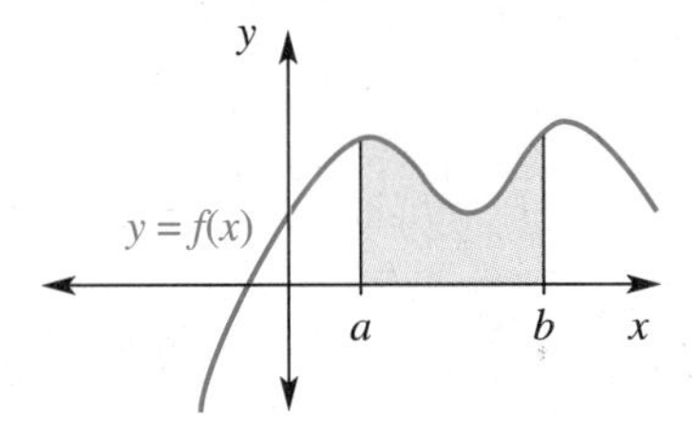

Figure 6.5 Problem: find the area of the shaded region.

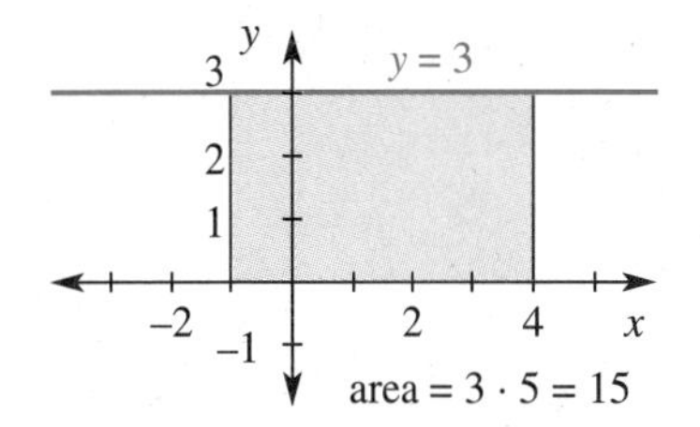

Figure 6.6 Area under a constant function's graph.

EXAMPLE 4 Find the area of the region bounded by the graph of $y = \dfrac{x+2}{3}$, the x-axis, and (a) $x = -2$ and $x = 1$; (b) $x = 0$ and $x = 4$.

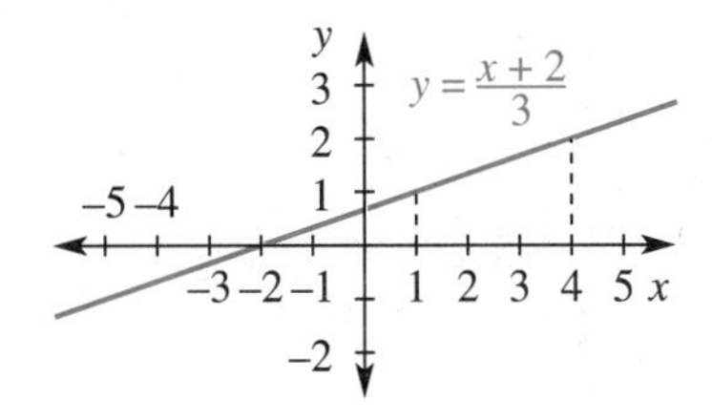

Figure 6.7 Graph of $y = \dfrac{x+2}{3}$.

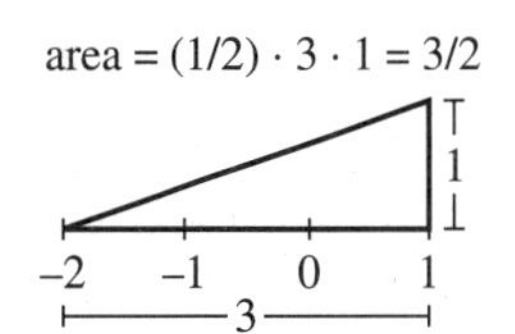

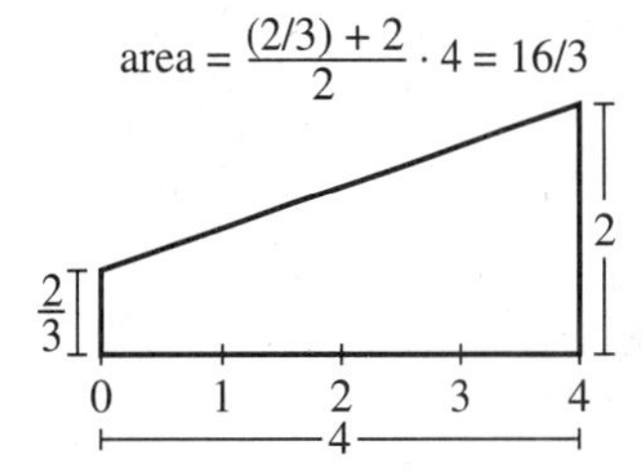

Figure 6.8 Two regions bounded between $y = \dfrac{x+2}{3}$ and the x-axis.

Solution Figure 6.7 shows the graph of $y = \dfrac{x+2}{3}$ over the two intervals in question. The boundaries of these two regions are a triangle and trapezoid, respectively. From Figure 6.8 we can see that:

(a) the area of the triangle is $\frac{3}{2}$, and

(b) the area of the trapezoid is $\frac{16}{3}$. ■

We can compute the area under a constant or linear function's graph using simple formulas from geometry. Now let's consider a function that is neither constant nor linear.

Problem: Find the area of the region bounded by $y = x^2$, the x-axis, $x = 1$, and $x = 2$. The top boundary of this region is the curve (part of a

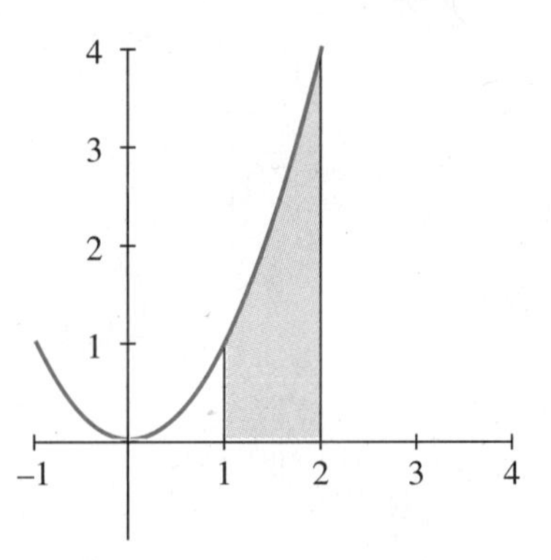

Figure 6.9 Region bounded by $y = x^2$, the x-axis, $x = 1$ and $x = 2$.

parabola) illustrated in Figure 6.9. Let's call the area of this region P (for parabola). Our strategy is to find lower and upper bounds for P by using the areas of *inscribed* and *circumscribed* rectangles.

First, we can get very rough lower and upper bounds on the area by noting that because $y = x^2$ is strictly increasing over the interval $[1, 2]$, its minimum value is $y = 1$ at the left endpoint ($x = 1$) and its maximum value is $y = 4$ at the right endpoint ($x = 2$). Geometrically, this means that we can *inscribe* a rectangle of height 1 within the region and *circumscribe* a rectangle of height 4 about the region, as shown in Figure 6.10A.

Let L_1 and U_1 stand for the lower and upper approximations we obtain from the areas of the inscribed and circumscribed rectangles, respectively. Since the width of each of these two rectangles is 1 (the length of the interval $[1, 2]$), the area P of our region must be between $L_1 = 1 \cdot 1 = 1$ and $U_1 = 4 \cdot 1 = 4$:

$$1 < P < 4.$$

We could average these two approximations to find a single estimate:

$$P \approx \frac{L_1 + U_1}{2} = \frac{1 + 4}{2} = 2.5.$$

To improve on our approximation, we can partition the interval $[1, 2]$ into two subintervals $[1, 1.5]$ and $[1.5, 2]$, each having length 0.5. Now we inscribe and circumscribe rectangles for each subinterval as shown in the Figure 6.10B.

Let L_2 represent the sum of the areas of the two inscribed rectangles and U_2 the sum of the areas of the two circumscribed rectangles. The height of the first inscribed rectangle is $1 = 1^2$, and the height of the second inscribed rectangle is found by evaluating $y = (1.5)^2 = 2.25$. Since the width of each rectangle is 0.5, we have

$$L_2 = 1 \cdot (0.5) + (2.25)(0.5) = 0.5 + 1.125 = 1.625.$$

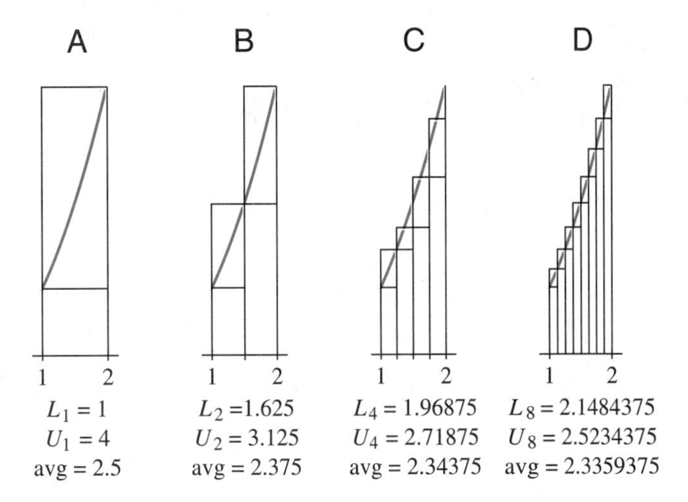

Figure 6.10 Approximating the area with inscribed and circumscribed rectangles.

The height of the first circumscribed rectangle is also 2.25 and the height of the second circumscribed rectangle is 4, so we have

$$U_2 = (2.25)(0.5) + (4) \cdot (0.5) = 1.125 + 2 = 3.125.$$

Now we can write

$$1.625 < P < 3.125,$$

and if we average the lower and upper approximations,

$$P \approx \frac{L_2 + U_2}{2} = \frac{1.625 + 3.125}{2} = 2.375.$$

We can try to improve the approximation even further by subdividing the interval into a greater number of equal-sized subintervals and again calculating the areas of the inscribed and circumscribed rectangles.

Figures 6.10C and 6.10D show that the difference between the lower and upper bounds we obtain using 4 and 8 subintervals, respectively, is narrowing. If we continue to increase the number of inscribed and circumscribed rectangles, the lower and upper approximations (and their averages) converge on a single limiting value. Since the true area of the region is always trapped between the lower and upper approximations, we reason that it must be that single value. In fact, in the next section we'll show that the limiting value is precisely

$$P = \frac{7}{3} = 2.3333333\ldots.$$

This value P is the *definite integral* of x^2 with respect to x over the interval $[1, 2]$. (Note that the average of L_8 and U_8 is already within .003 of the limiting value P.)

As you can see, the idea of a limit is essential to both branches of calculus. The value of a derivative at a point (slope of the tangent line) can be considered the limiting slope value of a sequence of secant lines.

Similarly, the value of a definite integral over an interval (area under the graph) can be considered the limiting total area value of inscribed and circumscribed rectangles.

Summation notation

Our strategy for approximating the area under the graph of $y = x^2$ between $x = 1$ and $x = 2$ made heavy use of *sums*, namely those of the areas of the inscribed and circumscribed rectangles. **Summation notation** is a very convenient mathematical notation for sums. An example of this notation is

$$\sum_{n=1}^{4} n^2.$$

The capital Greek letter "sigma" $\sum$ corresponds to the letter S and stands for a sum. The letter n is called an **index variable**, and it serves to label the individual terms in the sum. In this case, the notation tells us that the starting value of the index is $n = 1$ and the ending value is $n = 4$. Each integer n from 1 through 4 corresponds to a separate term of the sum. In this case, each term is given by the expression n^2, and the notation is really shorthand for the sum of four squares:

$$\sum_{n=1}^{4} n^2 = 1^2 + 2^2 + 3^2 + 4^2 = 1 + 4 + 9 + 16 = 30.$$

The index n is sometimes referred to as a *dummy* index, because the letter plays no other role than to label the terms. Any other letter can serve this purpose just as well.

Note that $\sum_{i=1}^{4} i^2 = 1^2 + 2^2 + 3^2 + 4^2 = 1 + 4 + 9 + 16 = 30$.

The index may not even be involved in the expression for the nth term. For example, $\sum_{n=1}^{5} 3 = 3 + 3 + 3 + 3 + 3 = 15$.

Sometimes it is convenient to start the index value at $n = 0$. For example,

$$\sum_{n=0}^{3} 2^n = 2^0 + 2^1 + 2^2 + 2^3 = 1 + 2 + 4 + 8 = 15.$$

EXAMPLE 5 Expand and calculate $\sum_{n=5}^{14}(8-n)$.

Solution This represents the sum of 10 consecutive integers (in descending order):

$$(8-5)+(8-6)+(8-7)+\cdots+(8-12)+(8-13)+(8-14)$$

$$=3+2+1+0+(-1)+(-2)+(-3)+(-4)+(-5)+(-6)=-15.$$ ■

In all these examples, it was not difficult to write down all the terms of the sum explicitly. The convenience of the summation notation is most evident when we have many terms to sum or perhaps an unspecified number of terms to sum. For example,

$$\sum_{n=1}^{100}(2n-1)$$

represents the sum of the first 100 odd positive integers:

$$1+3+5+7+\cdots+195+197+199=10000.$$

As another example,

$$\sum_{n=1}^{N}2n$$

represents the sum of the first N even positive integers:

$$2+4+6+\cdots+2(N-2)+2(N-1)+2N.$$

EXAMPLE 6 Express U_4 from Figure 6.10C using summation notation.

Solution We partition the interval $[1, 2]$ into 4 subintervals $[1, 1.25]$, $[1.25, 1.5]$, $[1.5, 1.75]$, $[1.75, 2]$, each of length 0.25. The areas of the four circumscribed rectangles sum to

$$U_4=(1.25)^2(0.25)+(1.5)^2(0.25)+(1.75)^2(0.25)+2^2(0.25).$$

Note that each of the four terms has a common factor (0.25). The other factors are $(1+1(0.25))^2$, $(1+2(0.25))^2$, $(1+3(0.25))^2$, and $(1+4(0.25))^2$, respectively. Thus, we can write U_4 in summation notation as

$$U_4=\sum_{n=1}^{4}(1+n(0.25))^2(0.25).$$ ■

EXERCISES for Section 6.1

For exercises 1–20: Use the velocity graph shown. Estimate the distance the car travels during each of the time intervals given.

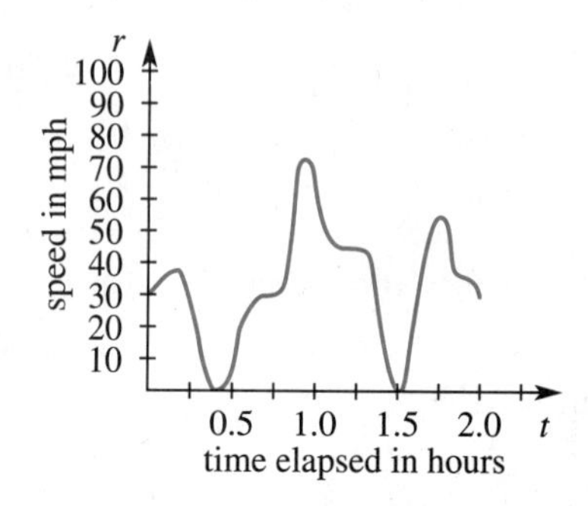

For Exercises 1–20

1. $t = 0.25$ hours to $t = 0.5$ hours

2. $t = 0.5$ hours to $t = 0.75$ hours

3. $t = 0.75$ hours to $t = 1.0$ hours

4. $t = 1.0$ hours to $t = 1.25$ hours

5. $t = 1.25$ hours to $t = 1.5$ hours

6. $t = 1.5$ hours to $t = 1.75$ hours

7. $t = 1.75$ hours to $t = 2.0$ hours

8. $t = 0$ hours to $t = 2$ hours

9. Here are the minute-by-minute velocity readings for the car during the second 15 minutes of the trip. Use these to approximate the distance traveled by the car during this time interval. Compare with your estimate from exercise 1.

time t in minutes	speed V in mph
15	28
16	24
17	20
18	16
19	12
20	9
21	6
22	3
23	0
24	1
25	1
26	2
27	3
28	4
29	6
30	8

10. Using these readings as well as the readings from the first 15 minutes, determine when the car has traveled exactly 10 miles (to the nearest minute).

Suppose that the graph represents the velocity of the car during two hours on a circular test track that is 2 miles in circumference.

11. How many laps (trips around the track) does the car complete during the two hours?

12. How many laps does the car complete during the first hour?

13. At what time does the car complete its tenth lap?

14. On which laps does the car make a "pit stop?"

15. On which lap does the car achieve its maximum speed?

Now suppose that another car traveling at a constant velocity of 40 mph starts at the same time.

16. At which times are the two cars traveling at exactly the same speed?

17. How far ahead does this car (the one traveling at 40 mph) get before the other car starts to catch up?

18. When does the other car catch up?

19. Find all the times at which the car traveling at 40 mph passes the other. (Remember, they are on a circular track.)

20. Find all the times at which the car traveling at 40 mph is passed by the other. (Remember, they are on a circular track.)

For exercises 21–30: It will be helpful to make a sketch of the region described.

21. Find the area of the region bounded by $y = (2x + 3)$, the x-axis, $x = 1$, and $x = 4$.

22. Find the area of the region bounded by $y = (3 - 2x)$, the x-axis, and the y-axis.

23. Find the area of the region bounded by $y = x$, the x-axis, $x = 3$, and $x = 7$.

24. Find the area of the region bounded by $y = |x|$, the x-axis, $x = -3$, and $x = 2$.

25. Find the area of the region bounded by $y = |3x + 2|$, the x-axis, $x = -5$, and $x = 1$.

26. Find the area of the region bounded by $y = |2 - 3x|$, the x-axis, $x = -2$, and $x = 3$.

27. Find the area of the region bounded by $y = \sqrt{4 - x^2}$, the x-axis, $x = -2$, and $x = 2$.

28. Find the area of the region bounded by $y = \sqrt{9 - (x - 1)^2}$, the x-axis, $x = -2$, and $x = 1$.

29. Find the area of the region bounded by $y = 2$, the x-axis, $x = -8$, and $x = -3$.

30. Find the area of the region bounded by $y = 2 - |x|$, the x-axis, $x = -2$, and $x = 2$.

For exercises 31–36: Using the graphs of functions f and g shown, find the areas described.

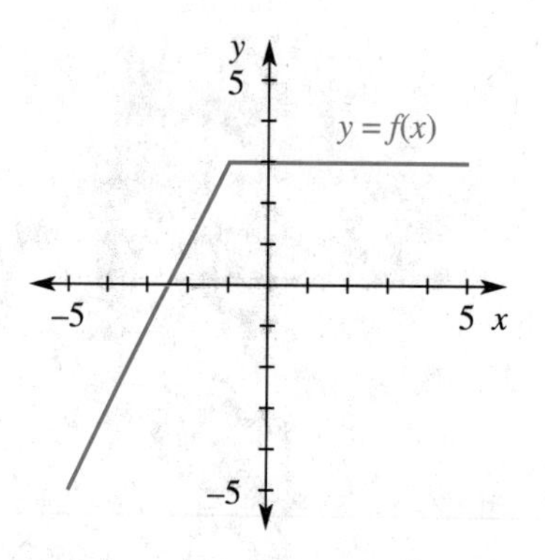

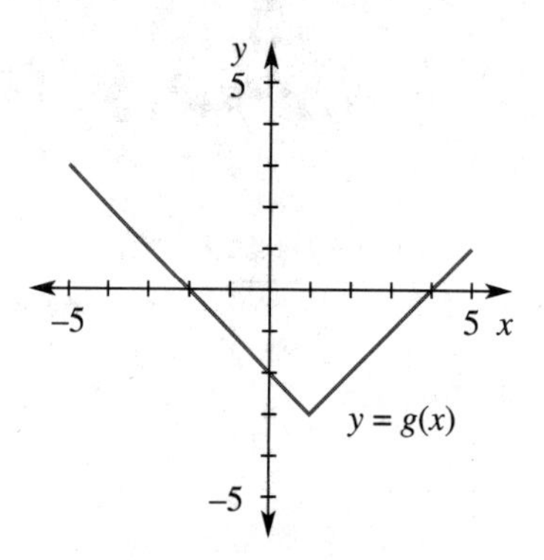

For Exercises 31–36

31. Find the area of the region bounded by $y = f(x)$, the x-axis, $x = -1$, and $x = 4$.

32. Find the area of the region bounded by $y = g(x)$, the x-axis, $x = -5$, and $x = -2$.

33. Find the area of the region bounded by $y = f(x)$, the x-axis, and the y-axis.

34. Find the area of the region bounded by $y = g(x)$ and the x-axis.

35. Find the area of the region bounded by $y = f(x)$, $y = g(x)$, and the y-axis.

36. Find the area of the region bounded by $y = f(x)$, $y = g(x)$, and the x-axis.

For exercises 37–46: Calculate the sums indicated.

37. $\sum_{n=3}^{7}(2n-5)$

38. $\sum_{n=1}^{5} 2^{-n}$

39. $\sum_{n=1}^{10} 2^n$

40. $\sum_{n=0}^{5}(2n^2-3n+1)$

41. $\sum_{i=1}^{4} i^i$

42. $\sum_{k=0}^{5}(2k^2-3k+k^3)$

43. $\sum_{n=0}^{100}(-1)^n$

44. $\sum_{i=0}^{5}(2i^2-3i+i^3)$

45. $\sum_{n=1}^{17} 5$

46. $\sum_{n=1}^{1000} n$

(Hint: $1+1000=1001$, $2+999=1001$, $3+998=1001$, $\ldots$)

For exercises 47–50: Refer back to Figure 6.10.

47. Express L_4 from Figure 6.10C using summation notation.

48. Express L_8 and U_8 from Figure 6.10D using summation notation.

49. Find L_{10} and U_{10} and express each of them using summation notation.

50. Average L_{10} and U_{10}. How far off of the true area of $7/3$ is it?

Historical notes: What exactly is π?—the method of exhaustion

The irrational number π appears in many formulas from geometry. Two familiar formulas are

$$C = 2\pi r \qquad \text{and} \qquad A = \pi r^2,$$

relating the circumference C and the area A of a circle to its radius r. The number π also appears in formulas for area and volume of cones, cylinders, and spheres. The history of π dates to the ancient Greek empire, and people's fascination with its properties continues to this day. Super computers have recently computed decimal approximations of π accurate to over a billion digits!

One of the important early mathematical discoveries about circles was that the ratio of the circumference to the diameter is constant, no matter what the size of the circle. The number π can be defined as

$$\pi = \frac{C}{d},$$

where C represents the circumference of the circle and d $(=2r)$ represents the diameter. If we compare this definition with the formula for the circumference of a circle, we can see that it is truly circular (pun intended) in the sense that we are no closer to knowing the value of π than before. We could also define π with the formula

$$\pi = \frac{A}{r^2},$$

but that is of no more help than the first definition.

We could *empirically* estimate π by drawing a circle, measuring its diameter with a ruler, wrapping string snugly around the boundary of the circle, then measuring the string's length and dividing by the diameter. (Perhaps a similar activity was the source of the Biblical estimate $\pi \approx 3$.) This method of determining π is subject to unavoidable errors of measurement. What we seek is a mathematical method for determining π to any degree of precision we desire.

Archimedes (287-212 B.C.) used the **method of exhaustion** to calculate an approximation of π. The idea of the technique is fairly simple, and it captures the key idea behind definite integrals in calculus. We will illustrate the method by applying it to the problem of estimating π, much as Archimedes himself did.

Suppose that we have a *unit circle* (the radius $r = 1$ unit). If we can determine the area A of this circle, then we will have determined π, since

$$A = \pi \cdot (1)^2 = \pi.$$

Our strategy is to obtain a sequence of better and better approximations to π by measuring the areas of regular polygons inscribed in and circumscribed around this unit circle. Because the polygons can be triangulated, we can mathematically determine their exact areas. Figure 6.11 illustrates the situation for inscribed and circumscribed squares, regular octagons, and regular 16-sided polygons.

Let a_n represent the area of an inscribed regular polygon having n sides and A_n represent the area of a circumscribed regular polygon with n sides. Since an inscribed polygon fits inside the circle, its area must be less than π. Since the circle fits inside a circumscribed polygon, however, the polygon must have an area greater than π. Hence, the areas a_n and A_n provide a lower and an upper bound for the value of π:

$$a_n < \pi < A_n.$$

Now, let's compute a_n and A_n for the specific values $n = 4$, 8, and 16.

In the case of $n = 4$ (inscribed and circumscribed squares), we see that the diagonal of the inscribed square is a diameter of the circle and has length 2. A side of this square must have length $\sqrt{2}$ (use the Pythagorean theorem) and so the area is $a_4 = (\sqrt{2})^2 = 2$. A square circumscribed about the circle will have *sides* of length 2, hence an area $A_4 = 2^2 = 4$. The areas

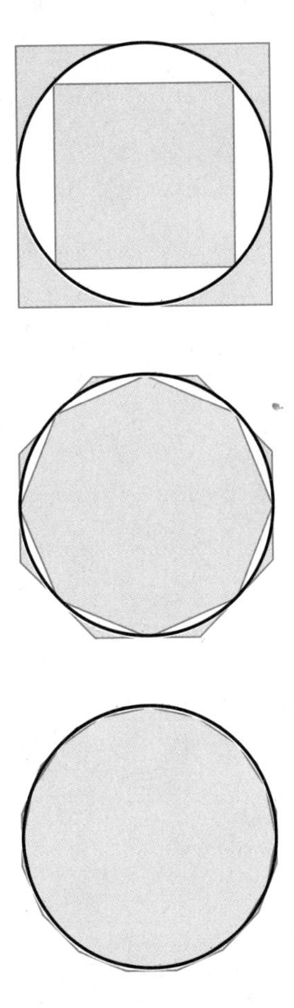

Figure 6.11 Approximating the area of a circle with regular polygons.

of the two squares trap the number π between them:

$$a_4 = 2 < \pi < 4 = A_4.$$

We can improve our approximations of π by using inscribed and circumscribed regular octagons ($n = 8$). We can calculate the area of a regular octagon by first subdividing it into eight congruent isosceles triangles (Figure 6.12) and summing their areas. The area of one of the inscribed octagon's triangles is $\sqrt{2}/4$, and the area of one of the circumscribed octagon's triangles is $\sqrt{2} - 1$. Summing these areas, we obtain the following improved lower and upper bounds on the value of π:

$$2.8284 \approx a_8 = 2\sqrt{2} < \pi < 8(\sqrt{2} - 1) = A_8 \approx 3.3137.$$

Continuing, the estimates are even better with the inscribed and circumscribed 16-sided regular polygons, and their areas narrow the distance between the lower and upper bounds:

$$3.0614 \approx a_{16} < \pi < A_{16} \approx 3.1826.$$

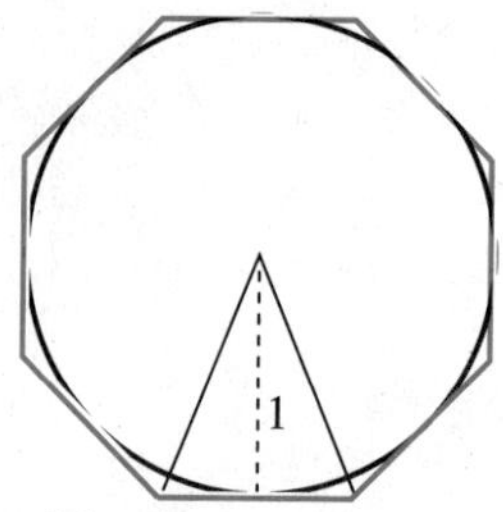

Area of the circumscribed octagon is
8 × the area of the isosceles triangle
(height = radius = 1 unit)

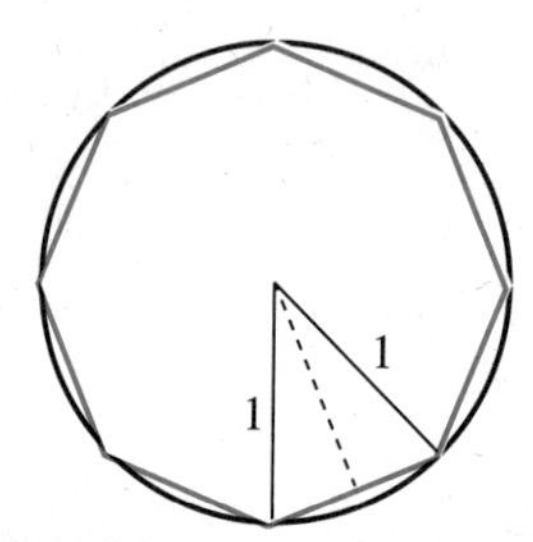

Area of the inscribed octagon is
8 × the area of the isosceles triangle
(leg length = radius = 1 unit)

Figure 6.12 Triangulating the octagon to find its area.

If you are wondering why we have doubled the number of sides of the polygons we use at each step, it is because we can compute the areas of the new polygons using information from the polygons at the previous step (and without using trigonometry, which Archimedes did *not* have at his disposal). Archimedes himself started with regular inscribed and circumscribed *hexagons* and doubled the number of sides at each step until he obtained the approximations

$$3\frac{10}{71} \approx a_{96} < \pi < A_{96} \approx 3\frac{1}{7}.$$

One of these estimates, $\pi \approx 3\frac{1}{7}$, is still in common usage to this day. Known, appropriately enough, as the Archimedean estimate of π, it is actually more accurate than the common decimal approximation to two places, $\pi \approx 3.14$.

In the case of the area of the circle, we can view the method of exhaustion as producing an infinite sequence of lower bound approximations and an infinite sequence of upper bound approximations. Both sequences converge on a single limiting value which we define as π. While we cannot write down the entire decimal expansion of π, we have a definite means of obtaining as close an approximation as we like.

Even though the ideas of limit and infinite process were totally foreign to Archimedes, the method of exhaustion applied to inscribed and circumscribed polygons can rightfully lay claim as one of the earliest uses of calculus.

6.2 DEFINING AND COMPUTING DEFINITE INTEGRALS

There are a variety of ways to define the definite integral of a function. We will present the *Riemann integral*, named after the mathematician Bernhard Riemann (1826-1866). It is general enough to allow a definite integral value to be defined for many functions, including every continuous function on a closed interval $[a, b]$. A key ingredient in the definition is the notion of a **Riemann sum**.

Figure 6.13 illustrates the geometrical interpretation of a Riemann sum. The interval $[a, b]$ has been partitioned into several subintervals of equal length Δx, and a point x_i has been selected from each subinterval. For each subinterval, we can associate a rectangle with a base on the x-axis. The subinterval length Δx corresponds to the common base length of each rectangle. The function outputs $f(x_i)$ correspond to the "heights" of these rectangles. Each product $f(x_i)\Delta x$ gives us a number corresponding to either the area of that rectangle or its negative (depending on whether $f(x_i)$ is *positive* or *negative*). The Riemann sum is the sum of these signed (positive or negative) rectangle areas.

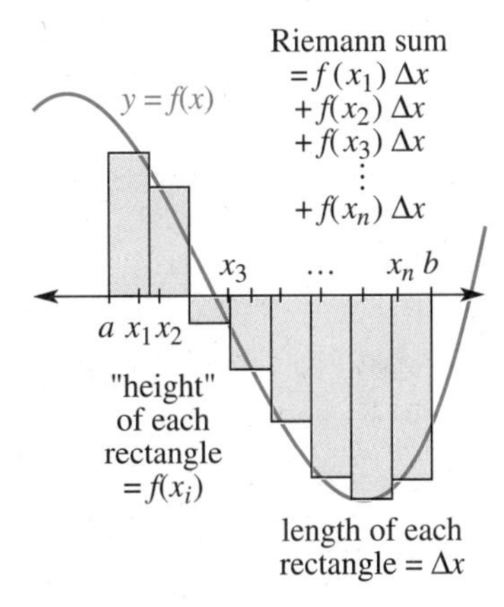

Figure 6.13 Geometrical meaning of a Riemann sum.

Procedure for forming a Riemann sum

Here are the steps for producing a Riemann sum for a function f on an interval $[a, b]$.

Step 1. For some positive integer n, subdivide the interval $[a, b]$ into n subintervals of equal length. This forms what is called a **regular partition** of $[a, b]$ of size n. If we denote the subinterval length as Δx, then

$$\Delta x = \frac{b-a}{n}.$$

We can mark off the subdivision points by starting at a and stepping off lengths of Δx until we reach b. If we label our starting point $a_0 = a$ and label the subdivision points successively, we have

$$a_0 = a, \quad a_1 = a + \Delta x, \quad a_2 = a + 2\Delta x, \quad a_3 = a + 3\Delta x, \quad \ldots, \quad a_n = b = a + n\Delta x$$

as our partition points.

EXAMPLE 7 Find the subinterval length Δx and the partition points for a regular partition of size 4 for the interval $[0, 3]$.

Solution With $n = 4$, $a = 0$, and $b = 3$, we have a subinterval length

$$\Delta x = \frac{b-a}{n} = \frac{3-0}{4} = 0.75.$$

The partition points are

$$0, \ 0.75, \ 1.5, \ 2.25, \ 3.$$

■

Step 2. Choose one point x_i ($i = 1, 2, \ldots, n$) from each of the n subintervals. So,

$$x_1 \in [a_0, a_1], \quad x_2 \in [a_1, a_2], \quad \ldots, \quad x_n \in [a_{n-1}, a_n].$$

Each point may be chosen from anywhere in its subinterval, including the endpoints.

EXAMPLE 8 Find the points x_1, x_2, x_3, x_4 for the regular partition of size 4 of $[0, 3]$ that correspond to:

(a) the left endpoint of each subinterval

(b) the right endpoint of each subinterval

(c) the midpoint of each subinterval

Solution The subintervals are

$$[0, 0.75], \qquad [0.75, 1.5], \qquad [1.5, 2.25], \qquad [2.25, 3].$$

(a) The left endpoints are $x_1 = 0$, $x_2 = 0.75$, $x_3 = 1.5$, and $x_4 = 2.25$.

(b) The right endpoints are $x_1 = 0.75$, $x_2 = 1.5$, $x_3 = 2.25$, and $x_4 = 3$.

(c) The midpoints are $x_1 = 0.375$, $x_2 = 1.125$, $x_3 = 1.875$, and $x_4 = 2.625$. ■

There are infinitely many acceptable choices of points for a given partition. Here is another choice for the partition of this example:

$$x_1 = 0.5, \qquad x_2 = 1.0, \qquad x_3 = 2.0, \qquad \text{and} \qquad x_4 = 2.7.$$

Step 3. Calculate $f(x_i)$ for each x_i chosen, multiply each function output by Δx, and sum the results:

$$f(x_1) \cdot \Delta x \quad + \quad f(x_2) \cdot \Delta x \quad + \quad \ldots \quad + \quad f(x_n) \cdot \Delta x.$$

▶▶▶ **This is the value of the Riemann sum for f over $[a, b]$ for this partition and choice of points.**

EXAMPLE 9 Find the particular Riemann sum value for the function $f(x) = x^2$ over the interval $[0, 3]$ with a regular partition of $n = 4$ subintervals and with chosen points $x_1 = 0.5$, $x_2 = 1.0$, $x_3 = 2.0$, and $x_4 = 2.7$.

Solution Using $\Delta x = (3 - 0)/4 = 0.75$ and the given points, we have

$$(0.5)^2(0.75) + (1.0)^2(0.75) + (2.0)^2(0.75) + (2.7)^2(0.75) = 9.405$$

as the value of this particular Riemann sum. ■

For any given function defined on an interval $[a, b]$, there are infinitely many possible Riemann sums that can be formed and evaluated. First, there are infinitely many partition sizes (the number n of subintervals could be any positive integer). And, for each partition, there are infinitely many possible choices of points $x_1, x_2, \ldots, x_n$ to make.

Summation notation is particularly convenient for denoting a Riemann sum.

Given a regular partition of the interval $[a, b]$ into n subintervals,

$$\sum_{i=1}^{n} f(x_i)\Delta x$$

is a *Riemann sum* for f over $[a, b]$, where one input x_i ($i = 1, 2, \ldots, n$) is chosen from each subinterval.

Upper and lower Riemann sums

By the extreme value theorem, a continuous function f always attains a minimum and maximum value over any closed interval. Given a regular partition of $[a, b]$ into n subintervals, we can apply that fact to form two special Riemann sums for a continuous function f.

> If we choose the points x_i ($i = 1, 2, \ldots, n$) so that $f(x_i)$ is the smallest output for each subinterval, then the resulting Riemann sum is called the **lower Riemann sum** for that partition and is denoted L_n.

For a positive function f, the lower Riemann sum corresponds to the sum of the areas of the inscribed rectangles.

> If we choose the points x_i so that $f(x_i)$ is the greatest output for each subinterval, then the resulting Riemann sum is called the **upper Riemann sum** for that partition and is denoted U_n.

For a positive function f, the upper Riemann sum corresponds to the sum of the areas of the circumscribed rectangles. The lower and upper Riemann sums L_n and U_n represent the two extreme values that all the possible Riemann sums could take for a partition of given size n.

▶▶▶ **If a continuous function is monotonically increasing or decreasing over $[a, b]$, it is easy to find the lower and upper Riemann sums for a partition of $[a, b]$. The minimum and maximum output values always occur at the *endpoints of each subinterval.***

EXAMPLE 10 Find the lower and upper Riemann sum values for the function $f(x) = x^2$ over the interval $[0, 3]$ with a regular partition of $n = 4$ subintervals.

Solution Again $\Delta x = 0.75$, and the subintervals are

$$[0, 0.75], \qquad [0.75, 1.5], \qquad [1.5, 2.25], \qquad [2.25, 3].$$

Since $f(x) = x^2 \geq 0$ over $[0, 3]$ and f is monotonically increasing, the left endpoints provide the inputs for the lower Riemann sum:

$$L_4 = 0^2(0.75) + (0.75)^2(0.75) + (1.5)^2(0.75) + (2.25)^2(0.75) = 5.90625.$$

The right endpoints provide the inputs for the upper Riemann sum:

$$U_4 = (0.75)^2(0.75) + (1.5)^2(0.75) + (2.25)^2(0.75) + 3^2(0.75) = 12.65625.$$

We can conclude that *any* Riemann sum for the function $f(x) = x^2$ over $[0, 3]$ with a regular partition of $n = 4$ subintervals must have a value between 5.90625 and 12.65625. ■

Formal definition of a definite integral

If these lower and upper extreme approximations close in on a single limiting value as the partition gets finer and finer (that is, as n gets larger and larger), then all the Riemann sums trapped between them must also close in on that same limiting value. That becomes the criterion for the formal definition of a definite integral.

Definition 1

Let f be a function defined on a closed interval $[a, b]$. If the Riemann sums for f over $[a, b]$ converge on a single limiting value A as the partition gets finer and finer, then we write

$$A = \lim_{n\to\infty} \sum_{i=1}^{n} f(x_i)\Delta x = \int_a^b f(x)\,dx$$

and say that f is **Riemann integrable** over the interval $[a, b]$.

The elongated "S" is the integral sign $\int$. This notation is due to Leibniz (who was also responsible for the d/dx notation for the derivative) and was meant to suggest a sum. We call $f(x)$ the **integrand**, and a and b the **limits of integration**, and dx denotes that the **variable of integration** is x. We call the real number $A = \int_a^b f(x)\,dx$ the *definite integral of f with respect to x from a to b.*

Computing definite integrals

EXAMPLE 11 Compute $\int_1^2 x^2\,dx$ as a limit of lower and upper Riemann sums.

Solution If we partition $[1, 2]$ into n subintervals of length $\Delta x = 1/n$, then the lower Riemann sum is

$$L_n = 1^2(\frac{1}{n}) + (1 + \frac{1}{n})^2(\frac{1}{n}) + (1 + \frac{2}{n})^2(\frac{1}{n}) + (1 + \frac{3}{n})^2(\frac{1}{n}) + \cdots + (1 + \frac{n-1}{n})^2(\frac{1}{n})$$

and the upper Riemann sum is

$$U_n = (1 + \frac{1}{n})^2(\frac{1}{n}) + (1 + \frac{2}{n})^2(\frac{1}{n}) + (1 + \frac{3}{n})^2(\frac{1}{n}) + \cdots + (1 + \frac{n}{n})^2(\frac{1}{n}).$$

With some algebraic effort, these expressions can be simplified to

$$L_n = \frac{14n^3 - 9n^2 + n}{6n^3} = \frac{7}{3} - \frac{3}{2n} + \frac{1}{6n^2}$$

and

$$U_n = \frac{14n^3 + 9n^2 + n}{6n^3} = \frac{7}{3} + \frac{3}{2n} + \frac{1}{6n^2}.$$

(You can check that these formulas give the lower and upper Riemann sums for $n = 1, 2, 4$, and 8 we found in the last section.) Now, as the partition becomes finer and finer (n grows larger and larger), the terms $3/2n$ and $1/6n^2$ grow smaller and smaller. In other words,

$$\lim_{n\to\infty} L_n = \frac{7}{3} = \lim_{n\to\infty} U_n,$$

and we can conclude that

$$\int_1^2 x^2\,dx = \frac{7}{3}.$$

■

Every continuous function f is Riemann integrable, but finding the limiting value A can be quite challenging. For many purposes, the approximations afforded by the Riemann sums may suit our needs.

EXAMPLE 12 Approximate $\int_{-2}^{1} \frac{1}{2^x}\,dx$ by averaging the upper and lower Riemann sum approximations using a regular partition of size $n = 5$.

Solution $\Delta x = \frac{1-(-2)}{5} = \frac{3}{5} = 0.6$ and the set of partition points is

$$\{-2.0, \ -1.4, \ -0.8, \ -0.2, \ 0.4, \ 1.0\}.$$

Figure 6.14 shows the graph of $y = \frac{1}{2^x}$ over the interval $[-2, 1]$.

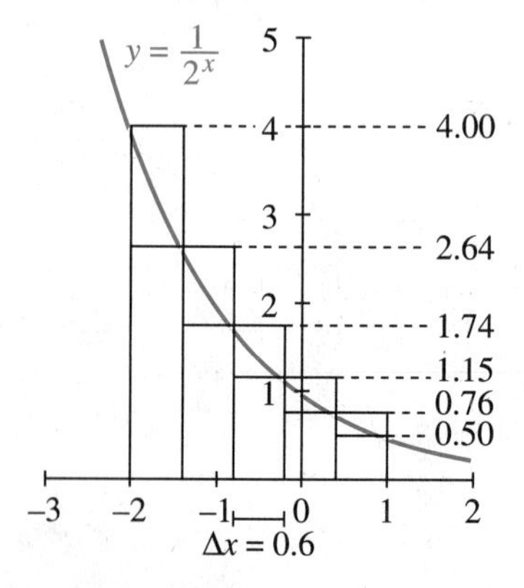

Figure 6.14 Graph of $y = \frac{1}{2^x}$ over $[-2, 1]$.

Because the function is strictly *decreasing* and positive over the interval, we find our maximum output values occurring at the left endpoints and the minimum output values occurring at the right endpoints of each subinterval. We calculate these endpoint output values rounded to two decimal places,

$$L_5 \approx 2.64(0.6) + 1.74(0.6) + 1.15(0.6) + 0.76(0.6) + (0.50)(0.6) = 4.074$$

and

$$U_5 \approx 4.00(0.6) + 2.64(0.6) + 1.74(0.6) + 1.15(0.6) + 0.76(0.6) = 6.174,$$

and we conclude that

$$4.074 \leq \int_{-2}^{1} \frac{1}{2^x}\,dx \leq 6.174.$$

If we average these lower and upper approximations, we have

$$\int_{-2}^{1} \frac{1}{2^x}\,dx \approx 5.124.$$

■

▶▶▶ **Understand that the average of the lower and upper approximations is not automatically a better estimate. It is possible that the true area of the region is very close to either the upper or the lower approximation.**

How do we know how good our approximation is? Since we know that the true area of the region is trapped between the lower and upper approximations, then the average cannot be off by more than half their difference.

For example, our approximation of 5.124 for $\int_{-2}^{1} \frac{1}{2^x}\,dx$ is the midpoint between the lower bound of 4.074 and the upper bound of 6.174. Therefore,

$$\text{largest possible error} = \frac{6.174 - 4.074}{2} = 1.05.$$

Actually, the approximation is much closer than this. The point is that we can quantify the largest possible error without knowing the limiting value.

The approximation process we have outlined is simple but increasingly tedious as n grows larger. Many calculators or computers with definite integration capabilities approximate the values of a definite integral in a way very similar to this. Later in this chapter we discuss some of the numerical techniques that exist for approximating the value of a definite integral.

Properties of the definite integral—graphical interpretations

The key properties of definite integrals follow directly from the Riemann sum definition:

$$\int_a^b f(x)\,dx = \lim_{n\to\infty} \sum_{i=1}^{n} f(x_i)\Delta x.$$

This limit of Riemann sums always exists if the function f is continuous over the interval $[a, b]$. If you keep in mind that the term $f(x_i)\Delta x$ represents the positive or negative area of a rectangle having height $f(x_i)$ and length Δx, then many of properties of definite integrals have natural geometric interpretations.

For example, if $f(x) \geq 0$ for $a \leq x \leq b$, we can interpret the definite integral $\int_a^b f(x)\,dx$ as the "area under the graph" of $y = f(x)$ between $x = a$ and $x = b$.

In the case that $f(x) < 0$ over the interval (so that the graph of f dips below the x-axis), the terms in the Riemann sum

$$\sum_{i=1}^{n} f(x_i)\Delta x$$

are all negative. Hence, the definite integral has a value equal to the *negative* of the area between the graph and the x-axis (see Figure 6.15).

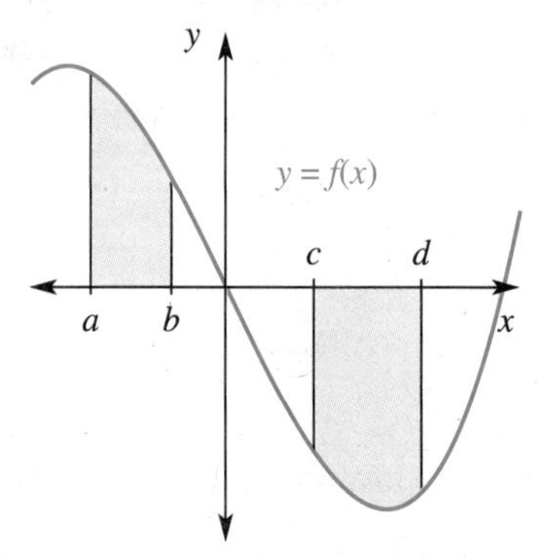

Figure 6.15 $\int_a^b f(x)\,dx$ is positive and $\int_c^d f(x)\,dx$ is negative.

If two intervals $[a, b]$ and $[b, c]$ are adjacent, we can combine the definite integrals of f over these intervals into a single definite integral over $[a, c]$.

Additivity over intervals

If $a < b < c$, then $\displaystyle\int_a^b f(x)\,dx + \int_b^c f(x)\,dx = \int_a^c f(x)\,dx.$

For example,

$$\int_0^2 \arctan(x)\,dx + \int_2^6 \arctan(x)\,dx = \int_0^6 \arctan(x)\,dx.$$

When a function takes on both negative and positive values over an interval, we can think of splitting the definite integral into its negative and positive components and adding the results.

EXAMPLE 13 Find $\int_{-5}^{4} \frac{x+2}{3}\,dx$.

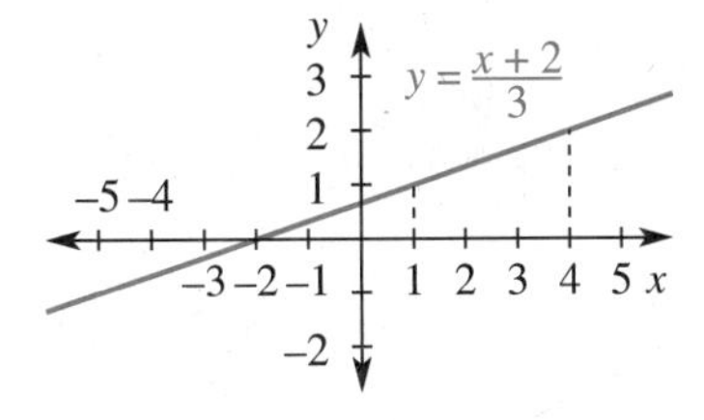

Figure 6.16 Graph of $y = \dfrac{x+2}{3}$.

Solution Using the graph in Figure 6.17 as a guide, we can write this definite integral as the sum of two definite integrals:

$$\int_{-5}^{4} \frac{x+2}{3}\,dx = \int_{-5}^{-2} \frac{x+2}{3}\,dx + \int_{-2}^{4} \frac{x+2}{3}\,dx.$$

The first definite integral represents the *negative* of the area of a triangle with base 3 and height 1. So,

$$\int_{-5}^{-2} \frac{x+2}{3}\,dx = -\frac{3}{2}.$$

The second definite integral represents the *positive* area of a triangle with base 6 and height 2. So,

$$\int_{-2}^{4} \frac{x+2}{3}\,dx = 6.$$

Our final result is

$$\int_{-5}^{4} \frac{x+2}{3}\,dx = -\frac{3}{2} + 6 = \frac{9}{2}.$$

■

If $a = b$, then we can consider the definite integral as measuring the area of a single line segment, which is zero. In other words,

$$\int_a^a f(x)\,dx = 0.$$

If $b < a$, then $\Delta x = \dfrac{b-a}{n}$ is negative, and all the terms in the Riemann sum change sign. In other words,

$$\int_a^b f(x)\,dx = -\int_b^a f(x)\,dx.$$

EXAMPLE 14 Find $\int_3^3 \frac{x+3}{2}\,dx$ and $\int_4^{-5} \frac{x+3}{2}\,dx$.

Solution $\int_3^3 \frac{x+3}{2}\,dx = 0$ and $\int_4^{-5} \frac{x+3}{2}\,dx = -\int_{-5}^4 \frac{x+3}{2}\,dx = -\frac{9}{2}$. ■

▶▶▶ **We can estimate the value of a definite integral or check the reasonableness of a definite integral computation by graphing the function $y = f(x)$ over the interval $[a, b]$ and using the graph to visually estimate the area.**

Constant multiple property

If c is a constant, then

$$\int_a^b cf(x)\,dx = c\int_a^b f(x)\,dx.$$

In other words, we can factor a *constant* through the definite integral sign. In terms of the Riemann sum,

$$\begin{aligned}\sum_{i=1}^n cf(x_i)\Delta x &= cf(x_1)\Delta x + cf(x_2)\Delta x + \cdots + cf(x_n)\Delta x \\ &= c(f(x_1)\Delta x + f(x_2)\Delta x + \cdots + f(x_n)\Delta x) \\ &= c\sum_{i=1}^n f(x_i)\Delta x.\end{aligned}$$

(The height of each rectangle is multiplied by the same constant c, so the total signed area is multiplied by the same constant c.)

For example, $\int_{-1}^4 2\sin(x)\,dx = 2\int_{-1}^4 \sin(x)\,dx$.

▶▶▶ **CAUTION! Don't abuse this property. Only constants can be safely factored through the integral sign. Do not factor variable quantities in or out of an integral expression.**

Additive function property

$$\int_a^b (f(x)+g(x))\,dx = \int_a^b f(x)\,dx + \int_a^b g(x)\,dx.$$

In other words, the definite integral of a sum of two continuous functions is the sum of their definite integrals. In terms of the Riemann sum,

$$\begin{aligned}
&\sum_{i=1}^{n}(f(x_i)+g(x_i))\Delta x\\
&=(f(x_1)+g(x_1))\Delta x + (f(x_2)+g(x_2))\Delta x + \cdots + (f(x_n)+g(x_n))\Delta x\\
&=(f(x_1)\Delta x + f(x_2)\Delta x + \cdots + f(x_n)\Delta x) + (g(x_1)\Delta x + g(x_2)\Delta x + \cdots + g(x_n)\Delta x)\\
&=\sum_{i=1}^{n} f(x_i)\Delta x + \sum_{i=1}^{n} g(x_i)\Delta x.
\end{aligned}$$

(You can think of "stacking" the rectangles for f and g to obtain the rectangles for $f+g$.)

For example, $\int_{-3}^{2}(\sin(x)+\cos(x))\,dx = \int_{-3}^{2}\sin(x)\,dx + \int_{-3}^{2}\cos(x)\,dx$.

These properties are sometimes combined and simply referred to as the *linearity property of the definite integral.*

Linearity property
If f and g are continuous over the interval $[a,b]$ and c_1 and c_2 are constants, then

$$\int_a^b (c_1 f(x) + c_2 g(x))\,dx = c_1\int_a^b f(x)\,dx + c_2\int_a^b g(x)\,dx.$$

The next property follows from noting that if $f(x) \le g(x)$ for $a \le x \le b$, then given any partition of any size n and any choice of points x_i, we are guaranteed to have

$$\sum_{i=1}^{n} f(x_i)\Delta x \le \sum_{i=1}^{n} g(x_i)\Delta x.$$

Comparison property
If $f(x) \leq g(x)$ for every $x \in [a, b]$, then

$$\int_a^b f(x)\,dx \leq \int_a^b g(x)\,dx.$$

When does the definite integral $\int_a^b f(x)\,dx$ exist?

Can we find the definite integral of a function that is not continuous? It depends on how *many* discontinuities there are and how *bad* they are. If there are only finitely many discontinuities and they are *removable* (such as those representing holes in the graph of the function), then the definite integral exists. The reasoning is as follows: if we "fixed" the function by changing its values at a finite number of points to remove the discontinuities, then this has no effect on the total signed area (since the area of each of the finitely many line segments is 0).

In fact, even if there were finitely many *jump* discontinuities, we could still find the definite integral by splitting the interval at the points where the jumps occur. One consequence of this is that we can find the definite integral of any step function.

EXAMPLE 15 Find $\int_{-1}^4 f(x)\,dx$ where the function f is the step function whose graph is shown in Figure 6.17.

Solution If we divide the interval of integration $[-1, 4]$ at the points where the jumps occur, we have

$$\begin{aligned}\int_{-1}^4 f(x)\,dx &= \int_{-1}^1 f(x)\,dx + \int_1^3 f(x)\,dx + \int_3^4 f(x)\,dx \\ &= 2(1-(-1)) + (-1)(3-1) + 1(4-3) \\ &= 4 - 2 + 1 = 3.\end{aligned}$$

■

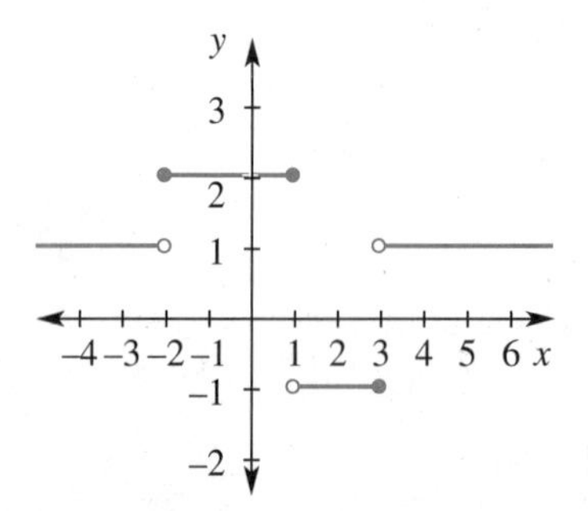

Figure 6.17 A step function.

However, if a function has infinitely many discontinuities over the interval $[a, b]$, then the definite integral may not exist (see exercises 37-40). Also, even a single discontinuity, such as at a vertical asymptote, may make it impossible to find the definite integral of a function. We examine this situation in more detail when we consider the subject of *improper integrals* in Chapter 7.

EXERCISES for Section 6.2

For exercises 1–4: For each given interval $[a, b]$, find Δx and the partition points $a_0, a_1, \ldots, a_n$ for a regular partition of the specified size n. Then indicate the choice of points $x_1, x_2, \ldots, x_n$ corresponding to:

(a) left endpoints of each subinterval

(b) right endpoints of each subinterval

(c) midpoints of each subinterval.

1. $[a, b] = [-2, 10]$; partition of size $n = 6$.

2. $[a, b] = [-3, 4]$; partition of size $n = 5$.

3. $[a, b] = [7, 12]$; partition of size $n = 8$.

4. $[a, b] = [-1, 3]$; partition of size $n = 10$.

For exercises 5–8: Using a partition of size $n = 5$, find the lower and upper Riemann sums for the definite integrals. Then find their average and the largest possible error in this approximation.

5. $\int_0^1 \sqrt{1 + x^2}\, dx$

6. $\int_{-1}^0 3^x\, dx$

7. $\int_{-1}^1 \arctan(x)\, dx$

8. $\int_1^4 \log_2(x)\, dx$

For exercises 9–16: Use the information below to find the values of the integrals.

$$\int_a^b f(x)\, dx = 2.5 \qquad \int_b^c f(x)\, dx = -5.0 \qquad \int_c^d f(x)\, dx = 1.5$$

9. $\int_b^a f(x)\, dx$

10. $\int_a^c f(x)\, dx$

11. $\int_b^d f(x)\, dx$

12. $\int_a^d f(x)\, dx$

13. $\int_a^c 2f(x)\, dx$

14. $\int_c^a f(x)\, dx$

15. $\int_d^a f(x)\, dx$

16. $\int_c^c f(x)\, dx$

For exercises 17–20: Consider the definite integral

$$\int_0^4 x(x-1)(x-2)(x-3)(x-4)\,dx.$$

17. Find the Riemann sum corresponding to the regular partitions of size $n = 1, 2, 4,$ and 8, using the left endpoint of each subinterval.

18. Find the Riemann sum corresponding to the regular partitions of size $n = 1, 2, 4,$ and 8, using the right endpoint of each subinterval.

19. Find the Riemann sum corresponding to the regular partitions of size $n = 1, 2, 4,$ and 8, using the midpoint of each subinterval.

20. Graph $y = x(x-1)(x-2)(x-3)(x-4)$ over the interval $[0, 4]$ and use the graph to explain the results of exercises 17-19.

For exercises 21–28: You are given the graph of a function f on a grid. Assuming that the grid lines are spaced 1 unit apart both horizontally and vertically, estimate the value of each of the following definite integrals by using $\Delta x = 1$ unit and counting "square units."

$$\int_1^5 f(x)\,dx, \qquad \int_{-3}^3 f(x)\,dx, \quad \text{and} \quad \int_6^{-2} f(x)\,dx.$$

If one or more of these definite integrals cannot be estimated for a particular graph, explain why.

21.

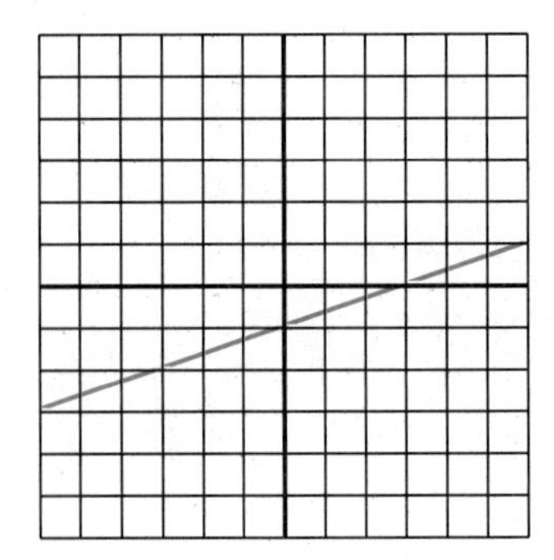

22.

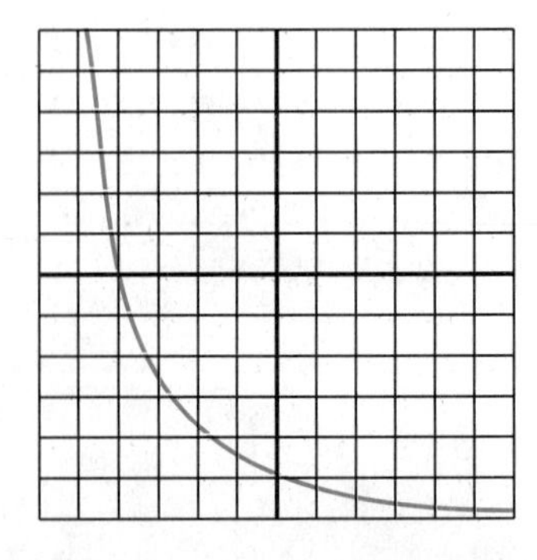

23.

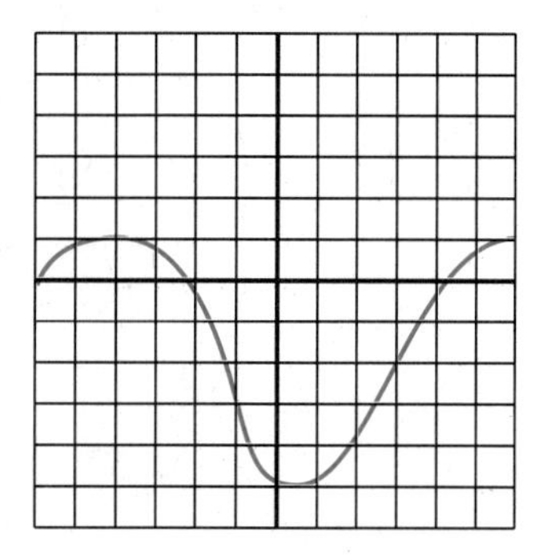

24.

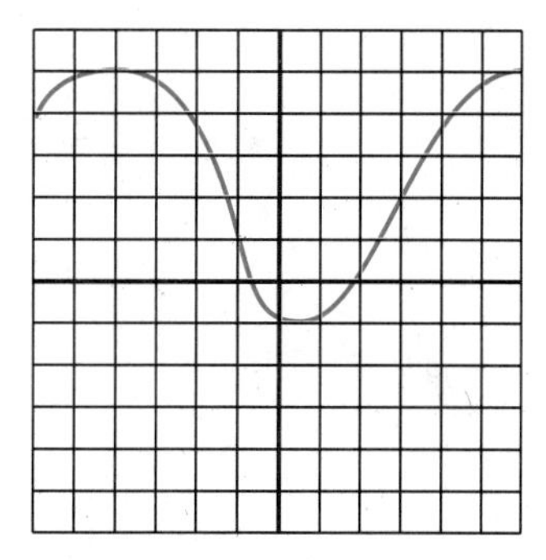

25.

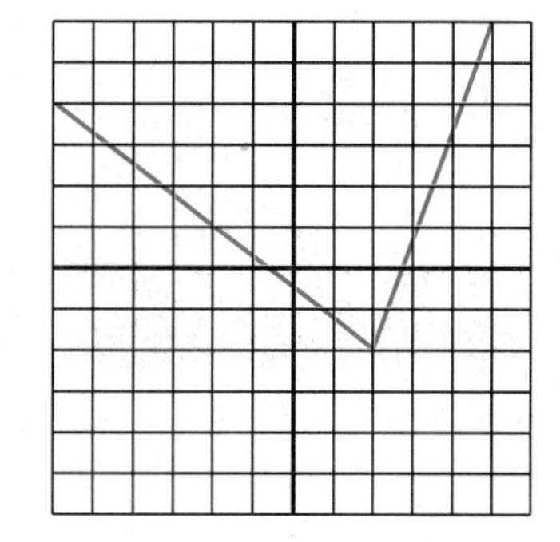

26.

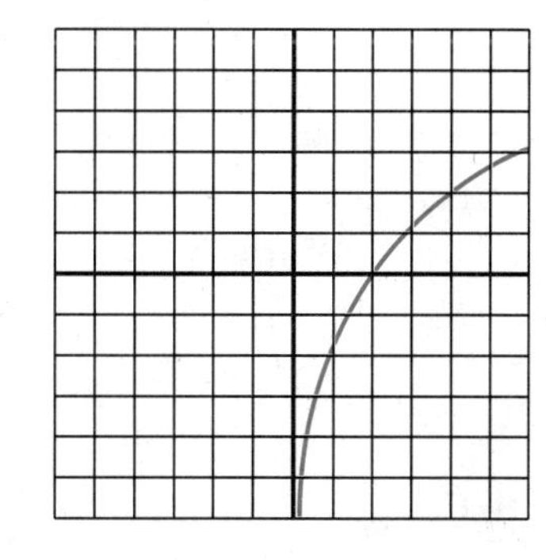

27.

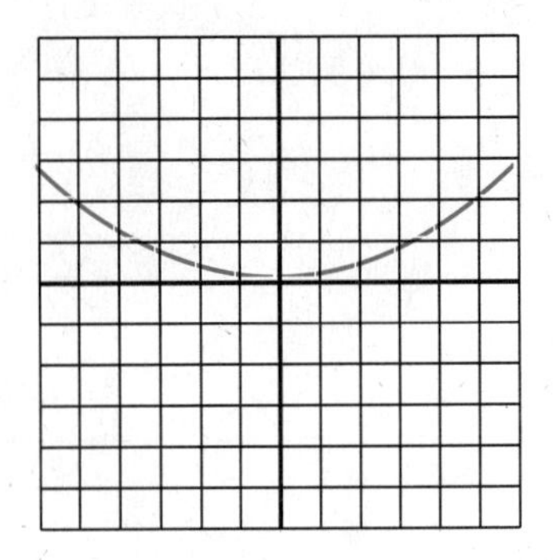

28.

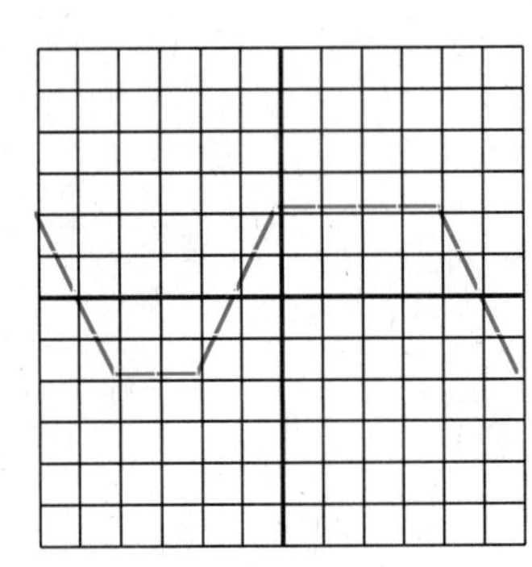

29. Compute the definite integral $\int_0^3 x^2\,dx$ as a limit of Riemann sums.

30. Find $\int_{-2}^{5} \frac{|x-3|-4}{2}\,dx$.

For exercises 31–36: Using the graphs of functions f and g shown on the next page, calculate the following definite integrals.

31. $\int_{-3}^{5} f(x)\,dx$

32. $\int_{1}^{4} g(x)\,dx$

33. $\int_{-2}^{2} (f(x)-3)\,dx$

34. $\int_{-3}^{4} (2g(x)+f(x))\,dx$

35. $\int_{0}^{-3} f(x)\,dx$

36. $\int_{-4}^{1} -3g(x)\,dx$

For exercises 37–40: Suppose that $f(x) = 1$ whenever x is an irrational number and $f(x) = 0$ whenever x is a rational number. Note that given any interval of real numbers $[a, b]$ $(a < b)$, it is always possible to choose rational and irrational numbers belonging to the interval.

37. Suppose that we form a regular partition of $[0, 1]$ of size n, where we choose all the points $x_1, x_2, \ldots, x_n$ to be rational. What is the value of the resulting Riemann sum for f over $[0, 1]$?

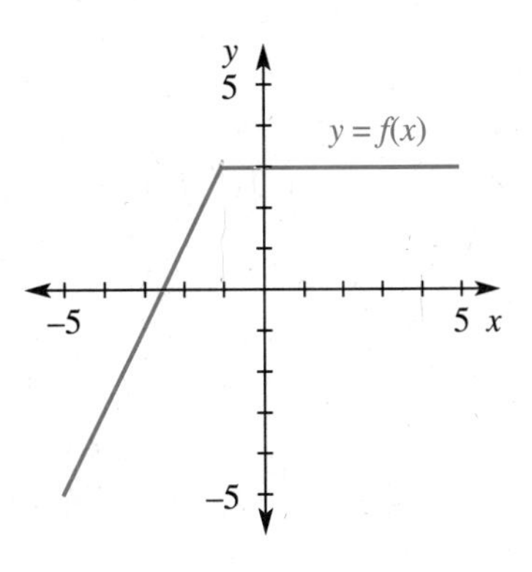

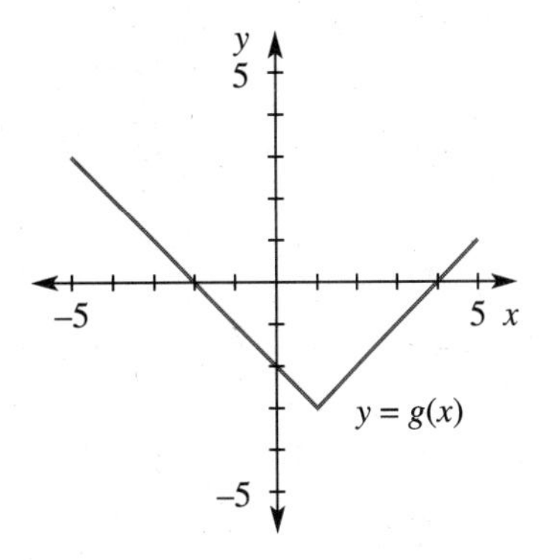

For Exercises 31–36

38. Suppose that we form a regular partition of $[0, 1]$ of size n, where we choose all the points x_1, x_2, $\ldots$, x_n to be irrational. What is the value of the resulting Riemann sum for f over $[0, 1]$?

39. If we form a regular partition of $[0, 1]$ and always choose either an endpoint or midpoint of each subinterval, what is the value of the Riemann sum?

40. Considering your results from exercises 37 and 38, does the definite integral

$$\int_0^1 f(x)\,dx$$

exist? Will the lower and upper Riemann sums ever close in on the same value?)

6.3 WHAT IS AN ANTIDERIVATIVE? SLOPE FIELDS

A differential equation is an equation involving a function and its derivatives. The simplest type of differential equation is of the form

$$\frac{dy}{dx} = f(x).$$

To solve this kind of differential equation means finding a function $y = F(x)$ such that $F'(x) = f(x)$. This reverse process of differentiation is known, naturally enough, as **antidifferentiation**.

Definition 2

Given a function f, we say that F is an **antiderivative** of f provided that $F' = f$.

Slope fields

The problem of finding an antiderivative can be posed graphically: How do we recover a function's graph from its slope?

The simplest case of such a problem is to find a function whose graph has constant slope m. In this case, we already know that the function must be linear,

$$f(x) = y_0 + m(x - x_0),$$

since constant slope is the defining property of a linear function. In fact, we have not one solution, but infinitely many of them corresponding to all the parallel lines with slope m (see Figure 6.18).

We need more information to pick out a single answer to the question. Knowing that some specific point (x_0, y_0) is on the graph of f does completely determine the solution of the original differential equation. This is called an *initial condition* (see Figure 6.19).

Now, suppose that we are given a more complicated problem: Find a function given the slope of its graph at each point, where the slope may change from point to point. For example, suppose we are given that

$$\frac{dy}{dx} = f(x) = x^2 + 1$$

for every x. Our task is to find an antiderivative $y = F(x)$ satisfying this equation. Again, there will be infinitely many solutions. (The graphs will form a family of curves, all having the same slope $\frac{dy}{dx} = x^2 + 1$ at each input x. An unique solution will be determined by specifying single point (x_0, y_0) on the curve (an initial condition.)

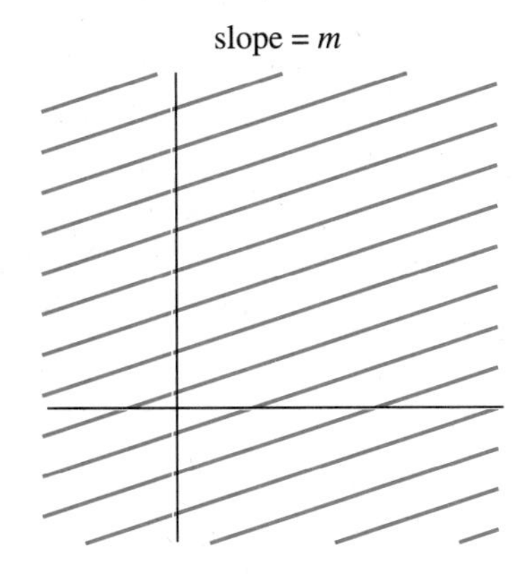

Figure 6.18 Infinitely many lines have a given slope m.

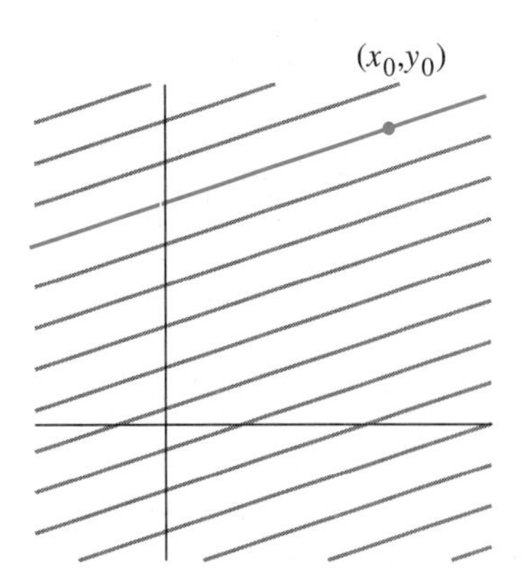

Figure 6.19 A given point (x_0, y_0) determines an unique line with slope m.

A nice way to graphically represent the slope information provided by $\frac{dy}{dx} = f(x)$ is by a **slope field** or **direction field**. In a slope field, a sample of points is chosen (usually arranged as a lattice or grid) and the slope at each point is represented by a short line segment through the sample point, with slope $f(x)$ determined by the slope function.

EXAMPLE 16 Suppose that we have the following function values: $f(-4.5) = -5$,

$$f(-3) = -2, \quad f(-1.5) = -\frac{1}{3}, \quad f(0) = 2, \quad f(1.5) = 3, \quad f(3) = 3, \quad f(4.5) = 2.$$

Use these to sketch a slope field for the antiderivatives of f, then sketch the graphs of some possible antiderivatives of f.

Solution The given function values $f(x)$ tell us the slope of any antiderivative's graph at the same input x. For example, since $f(0) = 2$, the graph of any antiderivative of f must have slope 2 at the point $x = 0$. We draw a family of small parallel tangent segments with common slope $m = 2$ above the input $x = 0$ to aid us. With each input x is associated such a family of parallel tangent segments whose common slope is determined by the value $f(x)$. This gives us the *slope field* for the antiderivatives of f. Figure 6.20 illustrates the part of the slope field we can determine from the given function values.

We can use the slope field to sketch the graphs of some of the antiderivatives of f. We simply pick a starting point and follow the directions indicated by the tangent segments. (This is why a slope field is sometimes called a direction field.) Figure 6.21 illustrates several such curves, each obtained by using a different starting point. If you take any two of these curves, the *vertical distance* between them will be the same for any input value x. ■

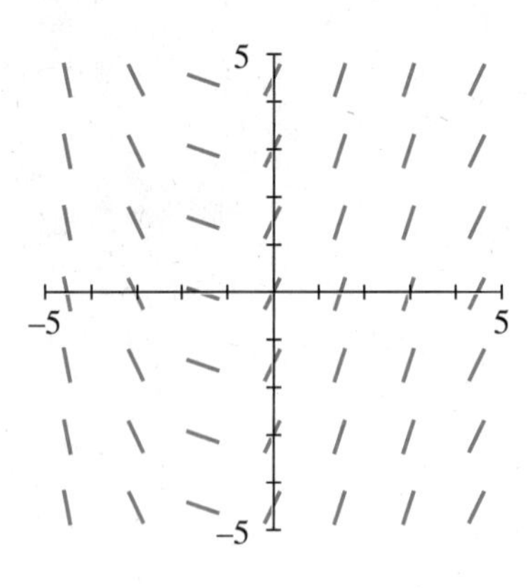

Figure 6.20 A slope field.

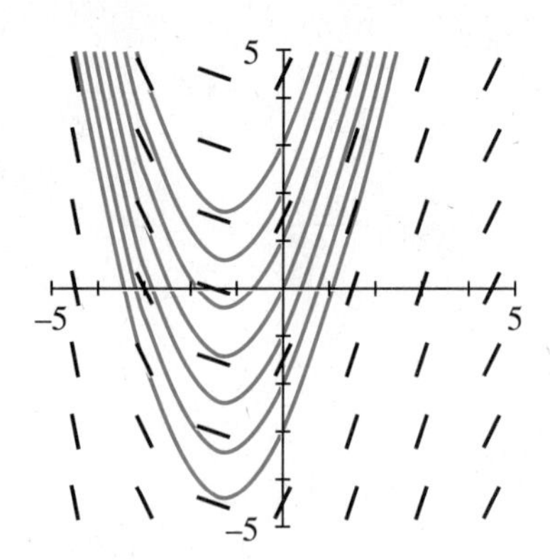

Figure 6.21 Family of antiderivative graphs.

If F is one of the antiderivatives of f and an initial value $F(x_0)$ is specified, this initial condition stipulates a starting point $(x_0, F(x_0))$ that "selects" one of these curves. For example, if we were given the initial value $F(0) = 1$, then the third graph from the top pictured in the illustration is an approximation of the graph of our desired antiderivative.

EXAMPLE 17 Using a slope field, approximate the graph of a solution to the differential equation $\dfrac{dy}{dx} = x^2 + 1$, with initial condition $y(1.5) = 2.5$.

Solution By plotting representative line segments at all the points with integer coordinates (x, y) such that $-3 \leq x \leq 3$ and $-3 \leq y \leq 3$, we obtain the slope field shown in Figure 6.22. From this picture we can almost "see" the family of antiderivatives and we can sketch a solution corresponding to the specific initial condition. Figure 6.23 illustrates the solution curve satisfying the initial condition $y(1.5) = 2.5$ obtained by sketching the solution curve passing through the point $(1.5, 2.5)$ and tangent to the line segments at each point. ■

In general, the graphs of the set of antiderivatives for a given function form an infinite family of *curves*. The graphs all have the same shape, since their local slopes are identical for every input x (they all have the same derivative f). If we don't have an initial condition, then we can still visualize the *shape* of the graph of an antiderivative, even though we cannot tell what its vertical position should be.

Speedometers, odometers, and clocks—reversing the problem

Let's reverse the problem of determining velocity from distance and time readings: our interest now is in determining the values of the distance

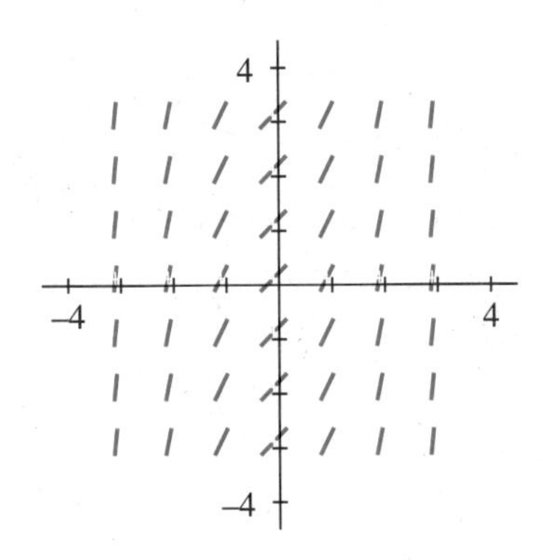

Figure 6.22 Slope field for $\frac{dy}{dx} = x^2 + 1$.

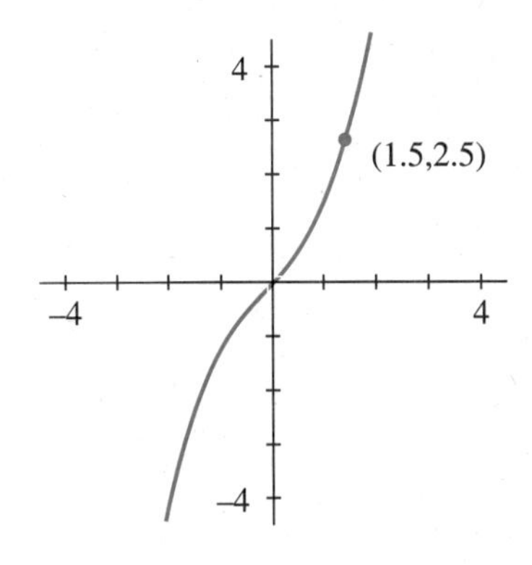

Figure 6.23 Graph of a function satisfying the initial condition $y(1.5) = 2.5$.

function (odometer readings) from the car's velocity over time. Instead of plotting distance versus time, we now plot *velocity* versus time. For a car traveling at a *constant* rate of 40 mph over a two-hour period, the graph would be a horizontal line (Figure 6.24).

Now, the vertical height of this horizontal line represents the *slope* of the original graph of distance versus time. If we assume that the car's initial position (at $t = 0$) represents 0 distance covered, then we can reconstruct the distance graph by using 40 mph as the slope of the line (Figure 6.25).

Of course, if the car had already traveled a certain distance before the start of our time interval, our distance graph would still have the same slope of 40 mph, but it would have a different d-intercept. For example, suppose that the car had already traveled 15 miles at the time we started our stopwatch or clock at $t = 0$. If it travels at a constant rate of 40 mph, then we can reconstruct its distance graph as shown in the illus-

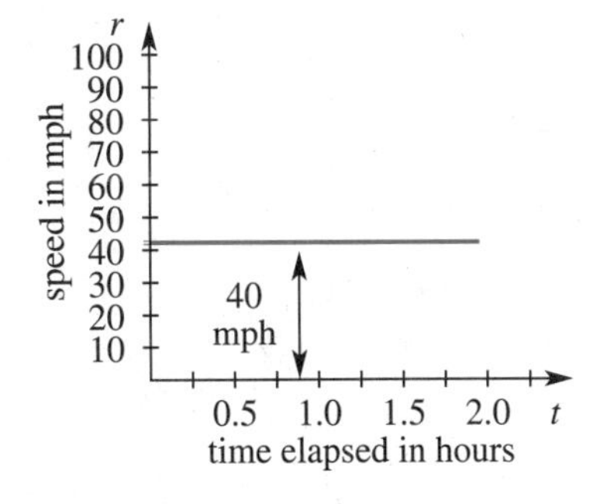

Figure 6.24 Constant rate vs. time for a car traveling 40 mph.

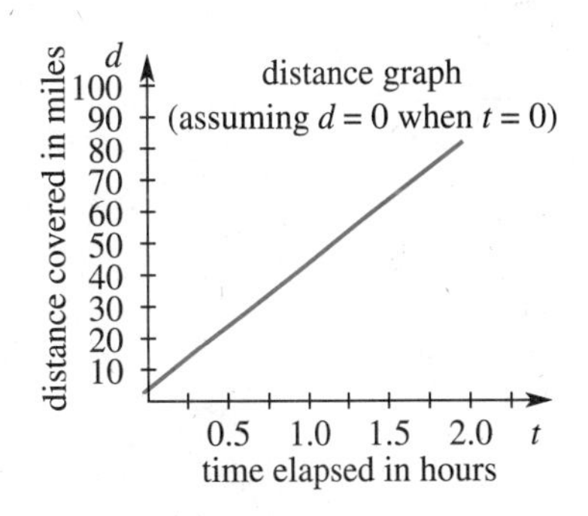

Figure 6.25 The distance graph for a car with initial position $d = 0$ miles.

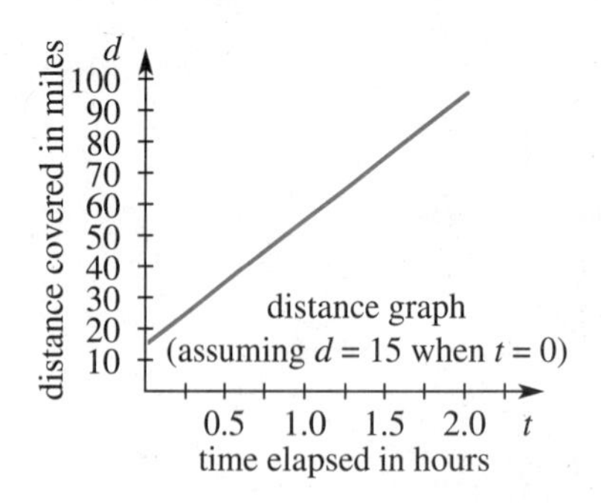

Figure 6.26 The distance graph for a car with initial position $d = 15$ miles.

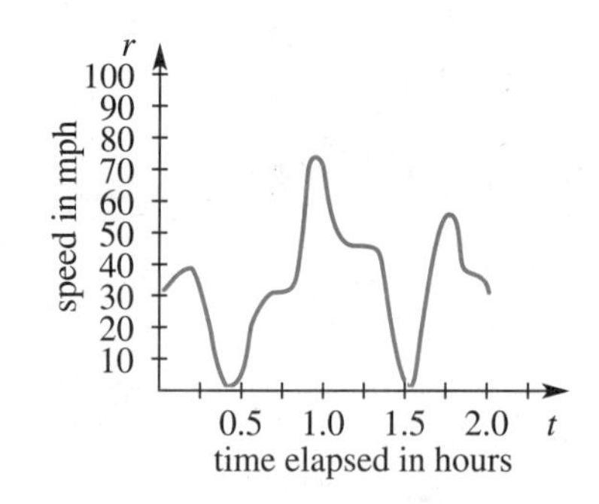

Figure 6.27 The velocity graph for a car with varying speeds.

tration in Figure 6.26. This corresponds to the fact that the equation of a line (the graph of the distance function),

$$y = mx + b,$$

cannot be determined by the slope m alone. We also need the y-intercept b (or some other point on the line that allows us to determine b). Knowing that our car travels at a constant rate of 40 mph is equivalent to knowing only the slope m of the distance graph. Additionally, knowing the initial position of the car is equivalent to knowing the y-intercept b of the line.

Now, let's suppose that our car travels at varying velocities over the trip. Figure 6.27 shows the graph of speedometer readings for a second car. If we assume that the initial position of the car is $d = 0$, how can we use this velocity graph to find the position of the car at any particular time t? One approximation strategy is outlined in the following example.

EXAMPLE 18 Assuming that the initial position of the car is $d = 0$, approximate the plot of the position function of the car over the first 15 minutes of trip, using the minute-by-minute velocity readings from Table 6.3.

Solution Earlier we computed the minute-by-minute running totals of the distance traveled by the car as shown in Table 6.4. If we plot these running totals of the distance traveled after each minute of the trip and connect the points with a smooth curve, we can obtain an approximate graph of the position function for this car. Of course, if the initial position (at time $t = 0$) of the car is not $d = 0$, then we must add the distance the car has already traveled to each of our measurements. Figure 6.28 shows plots of the position functions for an initial position of $d = 0$ and $d = 15$ miles, respectively. You can see that the initial position does not change the shape of the curve, but simply changes its vertical height.

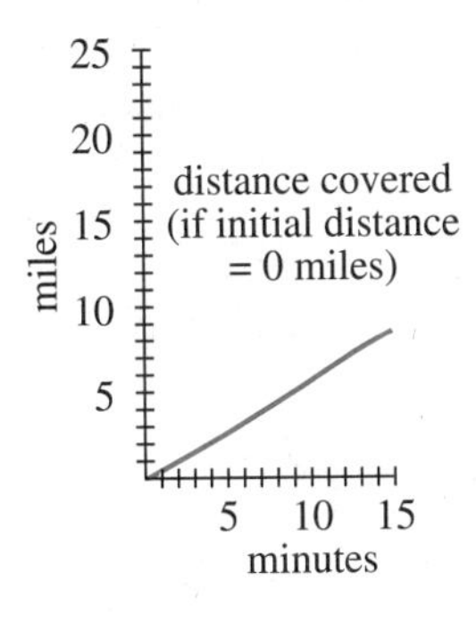

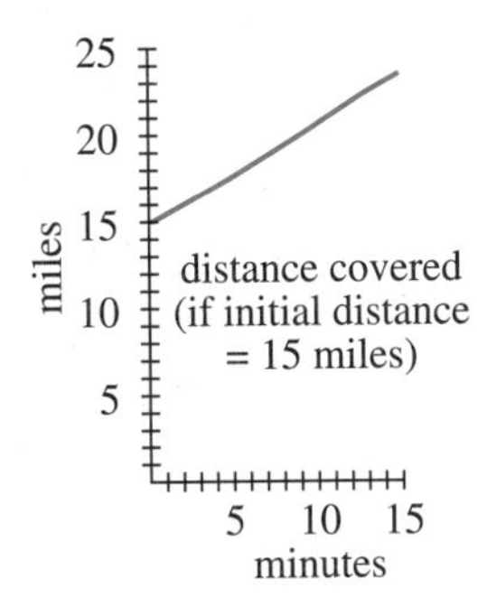

Figure 6.28 Position plots for initial positions of $d = 0$ and $d = 15$ miles.

time t in minutes	speed V in mph
0	30
1	31
2	32
3	33
4	34
5	35
6	36
7	36.5
8	37
9	37.5
10	38
11	38
12	37
13	34
14	31
15	28

Table 6.3 Minute-by-minute velocity readings.

Provided that we know the initial position of a car, we can estimate the values and sketch the graph of the original position function of a car from knowledge of its velocity function (the derivative of the position function). The position function is the *antiderivative* of the velocity function.

EXERCISES for Section 6.3

For exercises 1–4: Table 6.5 shows the minute-by-minute velocity readings of a car over the second 15 minutes of its trip.

1. Estimate the distance covered over the interval $[15 \text{ min}, 30 \text{ min}]$.

2. Plot the cumulative total distance covered after each minute of the interval $[15, 30]$, assuming that the car has already traveled 8.667 miles at $t = 15$ minutes.

3. Are there any inflection points in your graph from exercise 2? If so, at what time or times t?

4. Are there any local extrema in your graph from exercise 2? If so, at what time or times t?

minute of trip	approximate distance (mi)
1	0.5000
2	0.5167
3	0.5333
4	0.5500
5	0.5667
6	0.5833
7	0.6000
8	0.6083
9	0.6167
10	0.6250
11	0.6333
12	0.6333
13	0.6167
14	0.5667
15	0.5167
total	8.6667

Table 6.4 Approximate distance covered minute-by-minute.

time t in minutes	speed V in mph
15	28
16	24
17	20
18	16
19	12
20	9
21	6
22	3
23	0
24	1
25	1
26	2
27	3
28	4
29	6
30	8

Table 6.5

For exercises 5–20: Generate a slope field for each function over the indicated interval and sketch the graphs of three antiderivatives of the function over this interval.

5. $f(x) = 1/x, \quad [1, 5]$

6. $f(x) = 1/x, \quad [-5, -1]$

7. $f(x) = \tan(x), \quad (-\pi/2, \pi/2)$

8. $f(x) = \cot(x), \quad (0, \pi)$

9. $f(x) = \sec(x), \quad (-\pi/2, \pi/2)$

10. $f(x) = \csc(x), \quad (0, \pi)$

11. $f(x) = \arctan(x), \quad [0, 4]$

12. $f(x) = \operatorname{arccot}(x), \quad [0, 4]$

13. $f(x) = \arcsin(x), \quad [-1, 1]$

14. $f(x) = \arccos(x), \quad [-1, 1]$

15. $f(x) = \operatorname{arcsec}(x), \quad [1, 2]$

16. $f(x) = \operatorname{arcsec}(x), \quad [-2, 1]$

17. $f(x) = \operatorname{arccsc}(x), \quad [1, 2]$

18. $f(x) = \operatorname{arccsc}(x), \quad [-2, 1]$

19. $f(x) = \log_4(x), \quad [0.5, 2]$

20. $f(x) = e^{-x^2}, \quad [-2, 2]$

For exercises 21–28: You are given the graph of a function $y = f(x)$ on a grid. Assuming that the grid lines are spaced 1 unit apart both horizontally and vertically, sketch the slope field for the antiderivatives of f. Then use this slope field to sketch the graph of an antiderivative F of f over the interval $[0, 5]$, assuming $F(1) = -2$.

21.

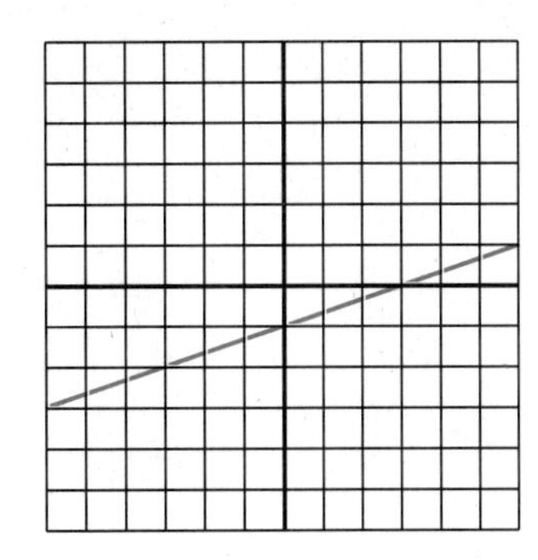

22.

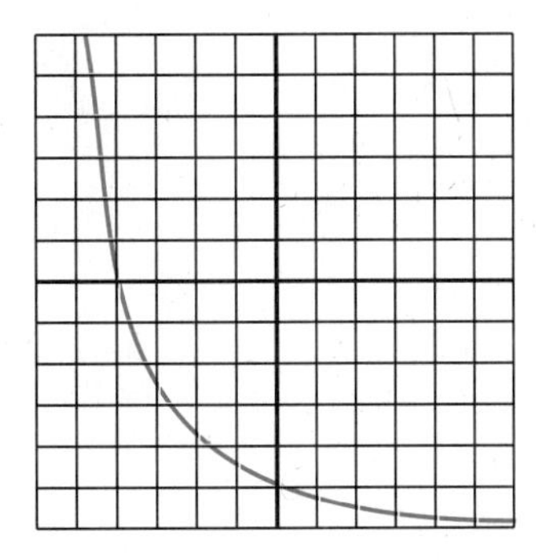

23.

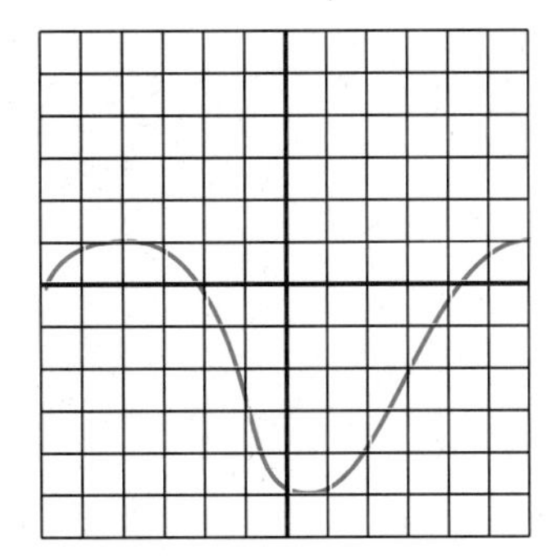

24.

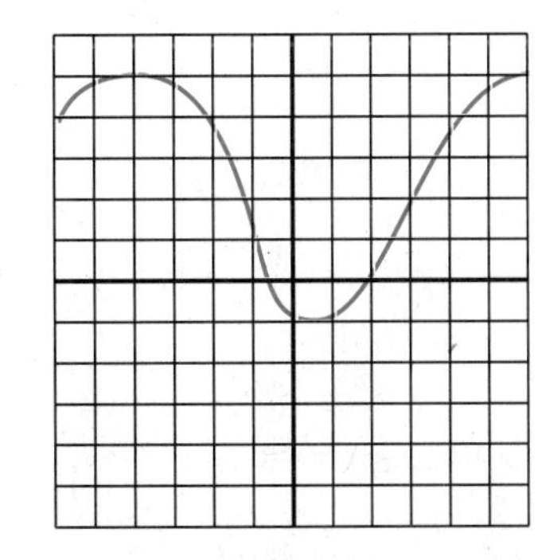

25.

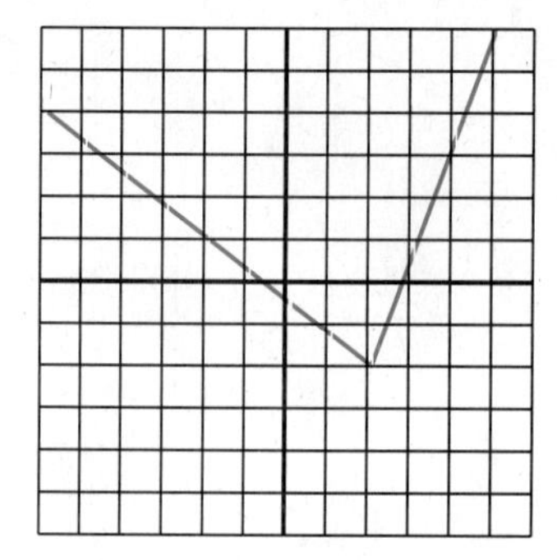

26.

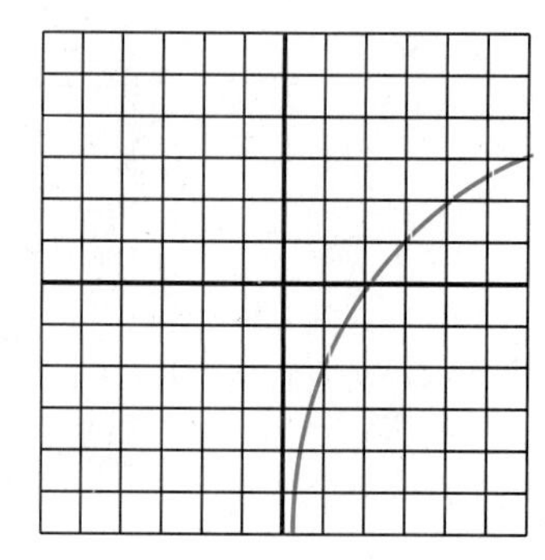

27.

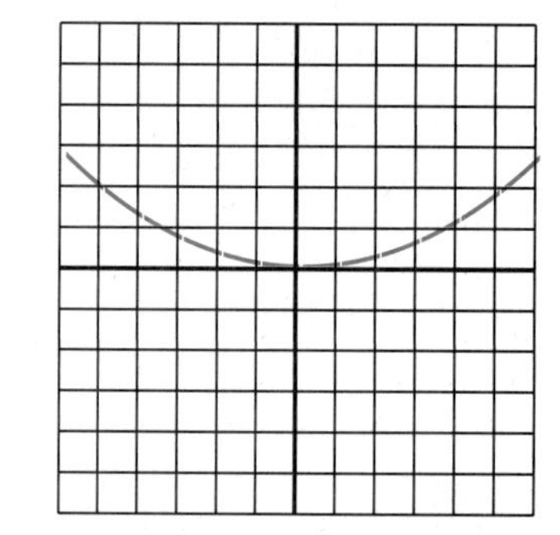

28.

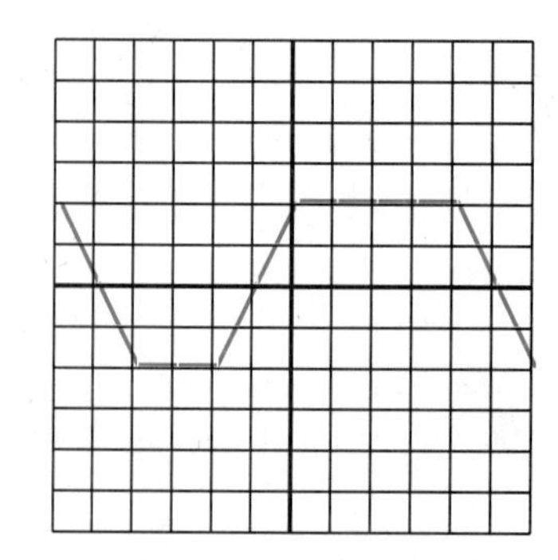

6.4 COMPUTING INDEFINITE INTEGRALS

Given a function f, slope fields provide us with a means of visualizing the shape of the graph of its family of antiderivatives. To find a symbolic formula for an antiderivative F, we must find a formula $F(x)$ satisfying

$$F'(x) = f(x).$$

EXAMPLE 19 Find an antiderivative of $f(x) = 2x$.

Solution Since $\frac{d}{dx}(x^2) = 2x$, we can see that $F(x) = x^2$ is an antiderivative of f. ■

Note that we have referred to "*an* antiderivative," and not "*the* antiderivative" of a function, since a function can have infinitely many different antiderivatives. For example, consider the functions F, G, H, and K defined by

$$F(x) = x^2 \qquad G(x) = x^2 + 3 \qquad H(x) = x^2 - \pi \qquad K(x) = x^2 + \sqrt{17}.$$

All of these functions are antiderivatives of f, since the derivatives of each of these functions is $2x$.

These functions all have something in common, however. All the functional expressions are of the form

$$x^2 + C,$$

where C is some constant ($C = 0,\ 3,\ -\pi$, and $\sqrt{17}$ in the examples given). Certainly, *any* other arbitrary numerical value of the constant C will produce a perfectly good antiderivative of f.

Is it possible that f also has other antiderivatives which are not of this particular form? The answer is NO! Recall that one of the consequences of the mean value theorem was that any two functions that have the same derivative over an interval (a, b) can differ only by a constant function. If F is any function with a derivative $F'(x) = 2x$ for all real numbers x, then it *must* be of the form $F(x) = x^2 + C$ for some constant C.

The integral symbol $\int$ used without any limits of integration denotes the general *antiderivative* of a function. When used in this way, we call it an **indefinite integral** to distinguish from its other use as a notation for *definite integrals*. We read

$$\int f(x)\,dx$$

as "the indefinite integral or general antiderivative of f with respect to x."

Given a continuous function f and any specific antiderivative F such that $F' = f$, we can write the general antiderivative of f as

$$\int f(x)\,dx = F(x) + C, \qquad C \text{ an arbitrary constant.}$$

This formula accounts for all the possible antiderivatives of the continuous function f. In other words, once we have found one antiderivative for f, we have essentially determined them *all* (up to the addition of the arbitrary constant).

Applying the notation to our example, we see that $\int 2x\,dx = x^2 + C$, where C is an arbitrary constant.

EXAMPLE 20 Find $\int \cos(x)\,dx$.

Solution Since $\frac{d}{dx}(\sin x) = \cos x$, we have

$$\int \cos(x)\,dx = \sin(x) + C,$$

where C is an arbitrary constant. ■

If we specify the output of the antiderivative at any particular input, this *initial condition* will determine a unique value C.

EXAMPLE 21 Find a function F with derivative $F'(x) = 3x^2$ and satisfying the initial condition $F(-2) = 5$.

Solution Since $\frac{d}{dx}(x^3) = 3x^2$, the antiderivative F must have the form

$$F(x) = x^3 + C$$

for some constant C. The initial condition specifies that

$$5 = F(-2) = (-2)^3 + C = (-8) + C,$$

from which we can see that $C = 13$. Hence,

$$F(x) = x^3 + 13$$

satisfies the requirements. ■

▶▶▶ **Be careful to distinguish the two uses of the $\int$ symbol:**

$$\int f(x)\,dx \text{ is an indefinite integral}$$

and represents any one of an entire family of antiderivatives of f.

$$\int_a^b f(x)\,dx \text{ is a definite integral}$$

and represents a specific real number $A = \lim_{n\to\infty} \sum_{i=1}^{n} f(x_i)\Delta x$, the limiting value of the Riemann sums.

Antiderivative formulas and properties

The derivative formula for any differentiable function provides us with a corresponding *antiderivative* formula.

EXAMPLE 22 Find $\int x^r\,dx$, where r is a *rational number* and $r \neq -1$.

Solution We know that $\frac{d}{dx}(x^{r+1}) = (r+1)x^r$ for any rational number r, and that for constants c, derivatives have the property

$$\frac{d(cf)}{dx} = c\frac{df}{dx}.$$

From this we see that for $r \neq -1$, we have

$$\frac{d}{dx}\left(\frac{x^{r+1}}{r+1}\right) = x^r.$$

(Note that this formula does not apply for $r = -1$ to avoid division by zero.) We conclude that

$$\int x^r\,dx = \frac{x^{r+1}}{r+1} + C,$$

where C is an arbitrary constant. ■

▶▶▶ **WARNING! The use of the arbitrary constant C in an indefinite integral formula**

$$\int f(x)\,dx = F(x) + C$$

assumes that the original function f is continuous. If f has any discontinuities, then its general antiderivative can involve a *different* constant for each interval over which f is continuous.

EXAMPLE 23 Find the general antiderivative F of $f(x) = \dfrac{1}{x^2}$, where $F(x)$ is defined for all $x \neq 0$.

Solution If we write $f(x) = \dfrac{1}{x^2} = x^{-2}$, we can see that the formula from the previous example can be applied:

$$\int x^{-2}\,dx = \frac{x^{-1}}{-1} + C = -\frac{1}{x} + C,$$

where C is an arbitrary constant.

However, since f is undefined at $x = 0$, the graph of its antiderivative could have a break at $x = 0$. Therefore, the most general antiderivative is:

$$F(x) = \begin{cases} -\dfrac{1}{x} + C_1 \text{ if } x < 0 \\ -\dfrac{1}{x} + C_2 \text{ if } x > 0 \end{cases}$$

Here C_1 and C_2 are two possibly different arbitrary constants. ■

For example, if $C_1 = 7$ and $C_2 = -3$, then

$$F(x) = \begin{cases} -\dfrac{1}{x} + 7 \text{ if } x < 0 \\ -\dfrac{1}{x} - 3 \text{ if } x > 0 \end{cases}$$

is a function certainly satisfying $F'(x) = \dfrac{1}{x^2}$ for all $x \neq 0$.

A way to visualize the necessity for different arbitrary constants is with a slope field. Figure 6.29 shows the slope field for the antiderivatives of $f(x) = \dfrac{1}{x^2}$ along with several potential graphs of antiderivatives. Note that $x = 0$ is a boundary that the curves do not cross. The graph of a particular antiderivative of $\dfrac{1}{x^2}$ can be obtained by choosing any one curve to the left of $x = 0$ and any other curve to the right of $x = 0$. Thus, C_1 and C_2 must satisfy these conditions.

The linearity rule for derivatives naturally implies a linearity rule for antiderivatives.

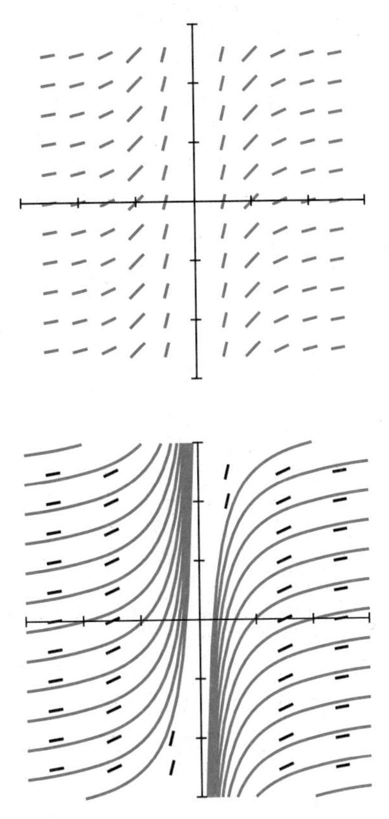

Figure 6.29 Slope field for antiderivatives of $\frac{1}{x^2}$.

Linearity rule for antiderivatives
If c is any constant, and f and g have antiderivatives, then

$$\int cf(x)\,dx = c\int f(x)\,dx$$

and

$$\int (f(x)+g(x))\,dx = \int f(x)\,dx + \int g(x)\,dx.$$

The linearity rule allows us to find the antiderivative of any polynomial function easily. Note that the term $\int dx = \int 1\,dx = x$, since $\frac{d}{dx}(x) = 1$.

EXAMPLE 24 Find $\int (5x^4 - 3x^3 + 7x^2 + x - 8)\,dx$.

Solution We simply *antidifferentiate* term by term factoring out the coefficients and using the formula $\int x^r\,dx = \dfrac{x^{r+1}}{r+1} + C$:

$$\begin{aligned}
&\int (5x^4 - 3x^3 + 7x^2 + x - 8)\, dx \\
=&5\int x^4\, dx - 3\int x^3\, dx + 7\int x^2\, dx + \int x\, dx - 8\int dx \\
=&5\cdot\frac{x^5}{5} - 3\cdot\frac{x^4}{4} + 7\cdot\frac{x^3}{3} + \frac{x^2}{2} - 8x + C \\
=&x^5 - \frac{3x^4}{4} + \frac{7x^3}{3} + \frac{x^2}{2} - 8x + C.
\end{aligned}$$

Note that we need only one arbitrary constant C in the final expression, since the arbitrary constants arising from each term will sum together as a single constant.

We can check our answer by taking the derivative and comparing it to the original integrand: $\frac{d}{dx}(x^5 - \frac{3x^4}{4} + \frac{7x^3}{3} + \frac{x^2}{2} - 8x + C) = 5x^4 - 3x^3 + 7x^2 + x - 8.$ ■

▶▶▶ **To check any antiderivative, differentiate and compare to the original function.**

EXAMPLE 25 Find $\int (\frac{4x^{2/3}}{\sqrt{7}} - 5\sqrt{x} + \frac{\pi}{3x^2})\, dx.$

Solution This becomes simpler if we write each term using rational exponents:

$$\begin{aligned}
\int (\frac{4x^{2/3}}{\sqrt{7}} - 5\sqrt{x} + \frac{\pi}{3x^2})\, dx &= \int (\frac{4}{\sqrt{7}}\cdot x^{2/3} - 5x^{1/2} + \frac{\pi}{3}x^{-2})\, dx \\
&= \frac{4}{\sqrt{7}}\cdot\frac{x^{5/3}}{5/3} - 5\cdot\frac{x^{3/2}}{3/2} + \frac{\pi}{3}\cdot\frac{x^{-1}}{-1} + C \\
&= \frac{12x^{5/3}}{5\sqrt{7}} - \frac{10x^{3/2}}{3} - \frac{\pi}{3x} + C.
\end{aligned}$$

■

Summary of antiderivative formulas

Other antiderivative formulas can be obtained directly by reversing the derivative formulas for the other basic functions. The antiderivative formulas for trigonometric functions are summarized below:

$$\int \cos(x)\, dx = \sin(x) + C \qquad \int -\sin(x)\, dx = \cos(x) + C$$

$$\int \sec^2(x)\, dx = \tan(x) + C \qquad \int -\csc(x)\cot(x)\, dx = \csc(x) + C$$

$$\int \sec(x)\tan(x)\,dx = \sec(x) + C \qquad \int -\csc^2(x)\,dx = \cot(x) + C$$

By reversing the differentiation formula for the natural exponential function, we obtain

$$\int e^x\,dx = e^x + C.$$

For exponentials of other bases $a > 0$ $(a \neq 1)$ we have

$$\int a^x\,dx = \frac{a^x}{\ln a} + C.$$

The natural logarithm fills a gap in our table of antiderivatives of powers of x. Recall that for $r \neq -1$,

$$\int x^r\,dx = \frac{x^{r+1}}{r+1} + C$$

on any interval where x^r is continuous. Since, on its domain of positive numbers, $\frac{d}{dx}\ln(x) = \frac{1}{x}$, it follows that

$$\int x^{-1}\,dx = \int \frac{1}{x}\,dx = \ln(x) + C$$

on the domain of positive numbers $x > 0$.

What happens when $x < 0$? We can examine this question by looking at the slope field for the differential equation $y' = \frac{1}{x}$ (see Figure 6.30). One solution of the differential equation (the one satisfying $y(1) = 0$) is $\ln(x)$. All other solutions on the right half-plane are $\ln(x) + C$ for various constants C. Note that the slope field on the left half-plane is simply the mirror image of that in the right half-plane. The graphs of the solutions in the left half-plane will also be mirror images of those in the right half-plane. In other words, any function of the form

$$y = \ln(-x) + C$$

will be a solution for $x < 0$:

$$\int x^{-1}\,dx = \int \frac{1}{x}\,dx = \ln(-x) + C$$

on the domain of negative numbers. We can combine this with the formula valid on the domain of positive numbers by using the absolute value notation

$$\int x^{-1}\,dx = \int \frac{1}{x}\,dx = \ln|x| + C$$

on any interval over which x^{-1} is continuous.

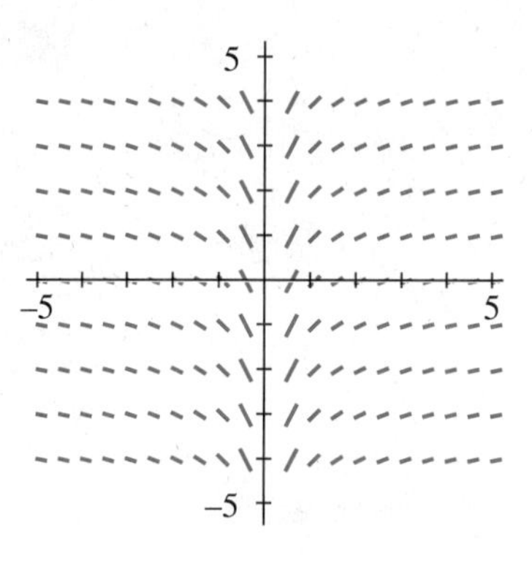

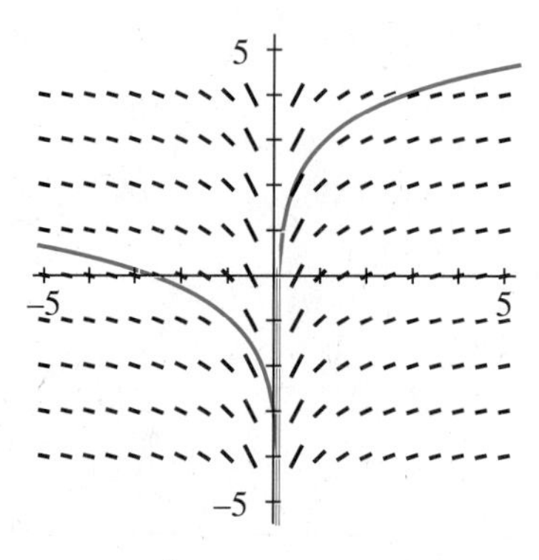

Figure 6.30 Slope field of $y' = \dfrac{1}{x}$ and solutions in the left and right half-plane.

We can reverse the differentiation formulas for the inverse trigonometric formulas to obtain

$$\int \frac{1}{\sqrt{1-x^2}}\,dx = \arcsin(x) + C \qquad \int \frac{-1}{\sqrt{1-x^2}}\,dx = \arccos(x) + C$$

$$\int \frac{1}{1+x^2}\,dx = \arctan(x) + C \qquad \int \frac{-1}{1+x^2}\,dx = \operatorname{arccot}(x) + C$$

$$\int \frac{1}{x\sqrt{x^2-1}}\,dx = \operatorname{arcsec}|x| + C \qquad \int \frac{-1}{x\sqrt{x^2-1}}\,dx = \operatorname{arccsc}|x| + C$$

The absolute value signs that appear in these last two antidifferentiation formulas serve a similar purpose as in the formula involving the natural logarithm.

For $x > 1$,

$$\int \frac{1}{x\sqrt{x^2-1}}\,dx = \operatorname{arcsec} x + C \qquad \int \frac{-1}{x\sqrt{x^2-1}}\,dx = \operatorname{arccsc} x + C.$$

For $x < -1$,

$$\int \frac{1}{x\sqrt{x^2-1}}\,dx = \operatorname{arcsec}(-x) + C \qquad \int \frac{-1}{x\sqrt{x^2-1}}\,dx = \operatorname{arccsc}(-x) + C.$$

Antidifferentiation as pattern matching

For differentiation, the linearity properties and the product, quotient, and chain rules allow us (or a machine) to differentiate virtually any function made up of the basic functions using algebra or composition. Unfortunately, while antiderivatives also enjoy the linearity property, there are no counterpart rules for indefinite integrals to allow us to mechanically antidifferentiate products, quotients, and compositions of basic functions.

Finding formulas for antiderivatives is often a matter of *pattern matching*. Given a function f, we attempt to recognize what function F would satisfy the requirement that $F' = f$. This can be a challenging task. While there are only a handful of basic derivative formulas needed along with the differentiation rules, there are entire books filled with indefinite integral formulas. Later in this chapter, we give some hints for recognizing antiderivatives and for using tables of integral formulas.

Some computer algebra systems have many indefinite integral formulas stored in their "libraries." When faced with an indefinite integral, a computer algebra system must search for the right pattern. In many cases, there simply are *no* explicit formulas to be found for the antiderivatives of some functions. For example, the function $f(x) = e^{-x^2}$ has no simple formula for its antiderivative. However, graphical strategies, like the use of a slope field, can give us valuable information about the behavior of the antiderivative.

EXERCISES for Section 6.4

For exercises 1–20: Find a formula of the form $F(x) + C$ for each of the indefinite integrals indicated.

1. $\int (x^2 + x + 1)\, dx$

2. $\int (3x^2 + 2x + 1)\, dx$

3. $\int \frac{x^4}{2}\, dx$

4. $\int \sqrt{17}\, dx$

5. $\int \sqrt{x}\, dx$

6. $\int \frac{2}{x^4}\, dx$

7. $\int \frac{3}{\sqrt{x}}\, dx$

8. $\int \pi x^{100}\, dx$

9. $\int \frac{x^3 - x^{-3}}{3}\, dx$

10. $\int \sqrt[5]{x}\, dx$

11. $\int x^{7/3}\, dx$

12. $\int (5\sin(x) - 3\cos(x))\, dx$

13. $\int (\sin^2(x) + \cos^2(x))\, dx$

14. $\int \frac{4}{\sqrt{1 - x^2}}\, dx$

15. $\int \frac{1}{4+4x^2}\,dx$

16. $\int \frac{1}{4x}\,dx$

17. $\int (e^x - 5x^2)\,dx$

18. $\int 2^x\,dx$

19. $\int (x - \sec x \tan x)\,dx$

20. $\int (\frac{1}{x} + \sec^2 x)\,dx$

This activity requires the use of a calculator or computer with numerical integration capabilities.

Graphing area functions

Suppose that we have a continuous function f, so that the definite integral $\int_a^b f(x)\,dx$ exists. We can define a new function by allowing the upper limit b to *vary*. That is, we fix the value a, but we treat b as our independent variable. Doing so gives us, in essence, an *area function*

$$A(b) = \int_a^b f(x)\,dx$$

that returns as an *output* the positive or negative area $A(b)$ "under the graph" of $y = f(x)$ between a and b, for any chosen *input* b.

For example, we can define an area function A for $f(x) = \dfrac{1}{1+x^2}$ by fixing the lower limit $a = 2$. Our area function is

$$A(b) = \int_2^b \frac{1}{1+x^2}\,dx.$$

For instance, $A(3) = \int_2^3 \frac{1}{1+x^2}\,dx \approx 0.1419$, and $A(0) = \int_2^0 \frac{1}{1+x^2}\,dx \approx -1.1071$. The graph of $y = 1/(1+x^2)$ lies entirely above the x-axis, but the value $A(0)$ is negative, since it represents area measured from *right to left* (see Figure 6.31).

Of course, if you had to compute by hand the approximate output value of an area function by a Riemann sum for a suitably fine partition, the

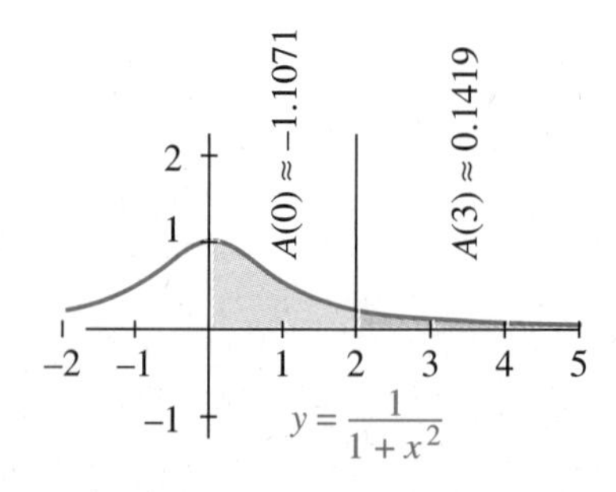

Figure 6.31 Calculating $A(b) = \int_2^b \frac{1}{1+x^2}\,dx$.

task would be exceedingly laborious, though not complicated. Numerical integration routines found on some calculators and software packages can replace these tedious area computations.

Now that we see how to make an area function A for a continuous function f and starting value a, our next question is: What is the derivative of A? The exercises that follow ask you to investigate this question.

21. Using a machine integrator, calculate

$$A(b) = \int_2^b \frac{1}{1+x^2}\,dx$$

to four decimal places for $b = 0,\ 0.1,\ 0.2,\ \ldots,\ 3.0$ (31 values in all; $A(0)$ and $A(3)$ have already been calculated for you). If you can program your calculator or computer to do this for you, all the better.

22. Use the results of exercise 21 to plot the graph of $y = A(b)$ for $0 \leq b \leq 3$. (In other words, the horizontal axis will represent b and the vertical axis will represent the area function value.)

23. Sketch the graph of the derivative $y = A'(b)$ by estimating the slope of this plot at several points.

24. Using your table of values for $A(b)$, calculate a table of values for the difference quotient function for A with $h = 0.1$. That is, calculate $G(b) = \dfrac{A(b+.1) - A(b)}{.1}$ for $b = 0,\ 0.2,\ 0.3,\ \ldots,\ 2.9$. Then plot $y = G(b)$. (It should look similar to your sketch of the derivative.)

25. Compare the graph of the derivative of the area function to that of the original function $y = f(x) = \dfrac{1}{1+x^2}$ over the interval $[0, 3]$. (If all has gone well, it should appear that $A' = f$.)

26. Repeat exercises 21-25 for the same function f, but this time change the starting value to $a = -2$ on the area function definition. What do you discover?

27. All the antiderivatives for a particular function differ only by a constant. Since $\arctan x$ is an antiderivative for $f(x) = 1/(1+x^2)$, can you find a starting value a such that the graph of the area function matches the graph of $y = \arctan(b)$?

28. Verify that $\arctan(3) - \arctan(2)$ gives us $A(3)$.

29. Verify that $\arctan(0) - \arctan(2)$ gives us $A(0)$.

30. Graph $y = \arctan(b) - \arctan(2)$ and compare it to your area function plot from exercise 22.

Many important functions can be defined as area functions. Consider the function

$$L(b) = \int_1^b \frac{1}{x}\, dx.$$

This area function is undefined for $b \leq 0$, since the function $f(x) = \dfrac{1}{x}$ is not continuous at $x = 0$.

31. Use a machine numerical integrator to calculate a table of values of $\int_1^b \frac{1}{x}\, dx$ for $b = 0.1, 0.2, 0.3, \ldots, 4.0$.

32. For what value b is $L(b) = 0$?

33. Graph $y = L(b)$ for $0.1 < b \leq 4$.

34. Use your graph to estimate the value b such that $L(b) = 1$.

35. Sketch the graph of the derivative $y = L'(b)$ for $0.1 < b \leq 4$. What should your graph look like?

36. Using your table of values, calculate the difference quotient function for L with $h = 0.1$, that is, calculate $G(b) = \dfrac{L(b+.1) - L(b)}{.1}$ for $0.1 \leq b \leq 3.9$ and graph $y = G(b)$.

(Note: The function L is better known as the *natural logarithm function* ln.)

6.5 THE FUNDAMENTAL THEOREMS OF CALCULUS

A *definite integral* is related geometrically to *area measurement*, and an *indefinite integral* defines a family of *antiderivatives* of a function. Except for a similarity in the notation, definite and indefinite integrals might seem to have little to do with each other.

If we examine the example of a car's motion, however, we can see that area measurement and antidifferentiation are intimately related. On the one hand, calculating the area under the velocity graph gives us the distance traveled by a car. On the other hand, by plotting running totals of distance traveled, we can antidifferentiate the velocity function and find the original position function! This connection between the two types of integration are the subject of the *fundamental theorems of calculus*.

The insight of Newton and Leibniz of this inverse relationship between the derivative and the definite integral is considered one of the greatest achievements in the history of mathematics and science, and is the central idea behind the fundamental theorems of calculus.

When a theorem is called "fundamental," it means that its statement is considered a cornerstone for the mathematical subject at hand. In number theory, the *fundamental theorem of arithmetic* states that every positive integer greater than 1 is either prime or can be factored as a product of primes in essentially only one way. (For example, $18 = 2 \cdot 3 \cdot 3$ is the only factorization of 18 into primes.) This property of positive integers is a key result in the foundations of number theory.

The fundamental theorems of calculus provide the tie between differential calculus and integral calculus. In some sense, these two branches of calculus developed quite separately from one another, but now we can see that area measurement problems such as those that Archimedes pondered and the multitude of physical problems involving rates of change turn out to be intimately related. When the connection between the two was discovered, it unleashed an avalanche of new results and applications for calculus. We now turn to the precise statements of and reasoning behind these two key theorems.

The first fundamental theorem of calculus

The derivative of a function f is the *slope function* for the graph of f. Now we use the definite integral to make an *area function* for the graph of f.

Suppose that $[a, b]$ is an interval and f is a continuous function such that the definite integral

$$\int_a^x f(t)\,dt$$

exists for every real number $a \leq x \leq b$. Note that we are using x as the upper limit of integration and t for the variable of integration. Figure 6.32 illustrates the graph of $y = f(t)$ and the region corresponding to a particular value x.

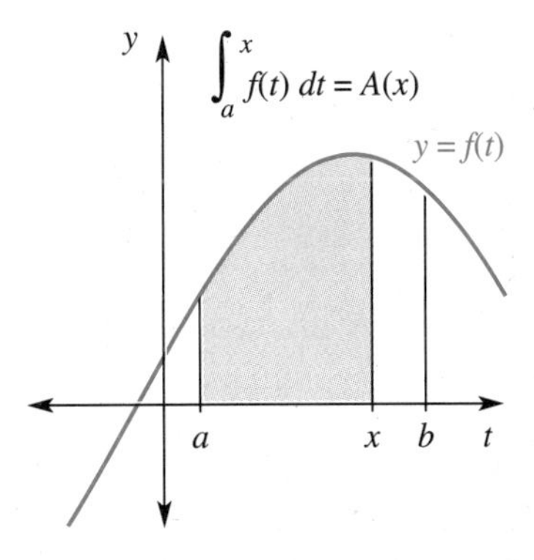

Figure 6.32 The value of the area function A depends on x.

This definite integral measures the (signed) area under the graph of $y = f(t)$ from a to x. If we keep a as a fixed reference point and vary the upper limit of integration x, then the value of this definite integral will also vary. In other words, we can think of this definite integral as describing a function of x. We'll call this function A for *area:*

$$A(x) = \int_a^x f(t)\,dt \qquad \text{for} \qquad a \le x \le b.$$

EXAMPLE 26 Set up and graph the area function A for $f(t) = \frac{1}{t}$ over the interval $[1, 3]$.

Solution The area function A in this case has as its formula the definite integral

$$A(x) = \int_1^x \frac{1}{t}\,dt \qquad \text{for} \qquad 1 \le x \le 3.$$

Using the definite integration capabilities of a calculator, we can compute $A(x)$ for several values of x (Table 6.6) and plot them (Figure 6.33).

x	$A(x)$
1.0	0.000
1.1	0.095
1.2	0.182
1.3	0.262
1.4	0.336
1.5	0.405
1.6	0.470
1.7	0.531
1.8	0.588
1.9	0.642
2.0	0.693
2.1	0.742
2.2	0.788
2.3	0.833
2.4	0.875
2.5	0.916
2.6	0.955
2.7	0.993
2.8	1.030
2.9	1.065
3.0	1.099

Table 6.6 Area under the graph of $y = \frac{1}{t}$ from 1 to x.

What's the rate of change of the area function? In other words, what is $A'(x)$? If we sketch the graph of the derivative A' using the graph of $y = A(x)$ as a guide, then we get a picture remarkably like that of the graph of $y = 1/x$ over the interval $[1, 3]$ (see Figure 6.34).

Is it a coincidence that we have come back to our original function f with x in place of t? In fact, the first fundamental theorem of calculus states that this will always be the case.

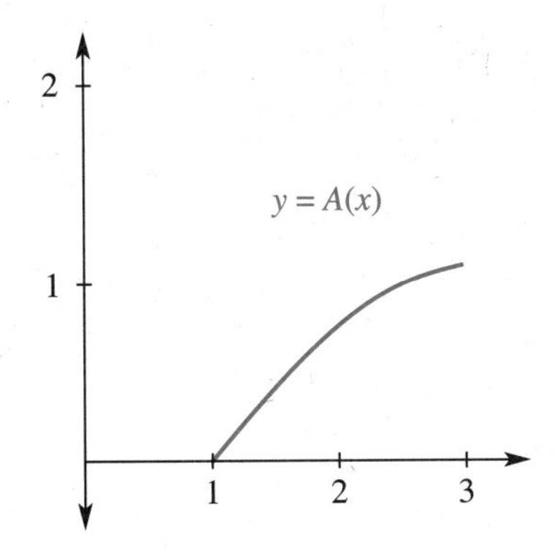

Figure 6.33 Plot of $y = A(x)$.

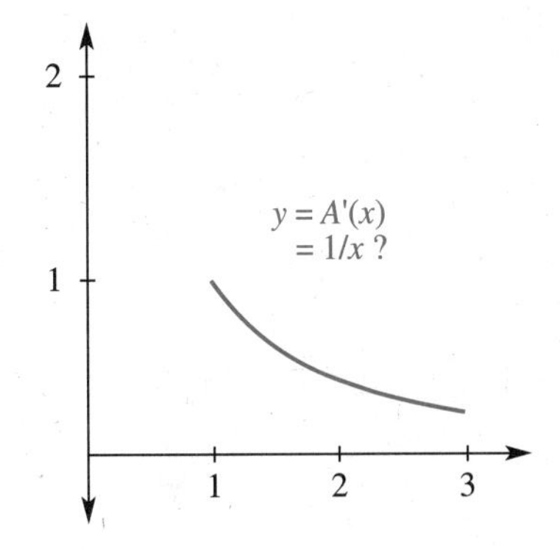

Figure 6.34 Plot of $y = A'(x)$.

Theorem 6.1

The first fundamental theorem of calculus

Hypothesis: Suppose that f is a continuous function such that

$$A(x) = \int_a^x f(t)\,dt$$

exists for every real number $a \leq x \leq b$.

Conclusion: If $a < x < b$, then $A'(x) = f(x)$.

Reasoning To estimate the derivative $A'(x)$ with a difference quotient, we need to examine

$$\frac{\Delta A}{\Delta x} = \frac{A(x + \Delta x) - A(x)}{\Delta x}$$

for a small change Δx.

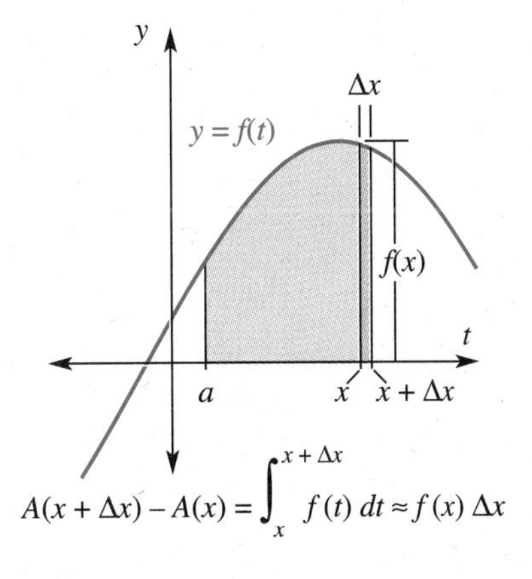

Figure 6.35 Finding the difference quotient of the area function.

The numerator of this difference quotient corresponds to the area of the dark strip in Figure 6.35 and is given by the definite integral

$$\int_{x}^{x+\Delta x} f(t)\,dt.$$

The area of this region is approximately the area of a tall, thin rectangle with width Δx and height $f(x)$. Hence,

$$A'(x) \approx \frac{A(x+\Delta x)-A(x)}{\Delta x} \approx \frac{f(x)\Delta x}{\Delta x} = f(x).$$

(This is assuming that the function value $f(x)$ and Δx are both positive, as suggested by the illustration. However, you can check that the product $f(x)\Delta x$ still gives us the correct sign of the approximate change in the value of the definite integral in case $f(x)$ and/or Δx are negative.)

To see that the derivative of the area function is, indeed, $A'(x) = f(x)$, we need to show

$$\lim_{\Delta x \to 0} \frac{\Delta A}{\Delta x} = f(x).$$

The true change ΔA lies between the areas of the inscribed and circumscribed rectangles over this small interval of length Δx. If L is the height of the inscribed rectangle and U is the height of the circumscribed rectangle, then we can say that ΔA lies between $L\Delta x$ and $U\Delta x$. Now, dividing through by Δx, we have

$$L \le \frac{\Delta A}{\Delta x} \le U.$$

As Δx approaches 0, our interval $[x, x+\Delta x]$ shrinks to a single point x. By hypothesis, the function f is continuous, so both the maximum function value U and the minimum function value L over this interval must approach $f(x)$.

Since $\dfrac{\Delta A}{\Delta x}$ is trapped between L and U, we must have

$$\lim_{\Delta x \to 0} \frac{\Delta A}{\Delta x} = f(x).$$

Thus, $A'(x) = f(x)$ as stated in the conclusion of the theorem. □

The first fundamental theorem says that we can produce an antiderivative for *any* continuous function f by finding an area function A for it. The choice of where to begin measuring the area (the reference point a) is entirely arbitrary. If we make a new choice of a, then we may be adding or subtracting some fixed amount from all our area function measurements. In other words, changing a may change the antiderivative by a constant.

EXAMPLE 27 Find an antiderivative for $f(x) = \dfrac{\cos(x)}{2^x}$.

Solution The area function defined by the formula

$$A(x) = \int_0^x \frac{\cos(t)}{2^t}\,dt$$

is an antiderivative of f by the first fundamental theorem of calculus. Hence, $A'(x) = \dfrac{\cos(x)}{2^x}$. We could have selected a different lower limit than 0:

$$F(x) = \int_{-\pi}^x \frac{\cos(t)}{2^t}\,dt$$

is another antiderivative of f. The functions A and F are both antiderivatives of f, and they differ by a constant. Specifically,

$$F(x) = A(x) + C,$$

where $C = \int_{-\pi}^0 \frac{\cos(t)}{2^t}\,dt$. (Note that *this* definite integral is a real number, not a function, because both limits of integration are constants.) ■

EXAMPLE 28 Find an antiderivative G for $g(x) = e^{-x^2}$ such that $G(3) = 0$.

Solution The first fundamental theorem of calculus tells us that any function G having a formula

$$G(x) = \int_a^x e^{-t^2}\,dt$$

will have a derivative

$$G'(x) = e^{-x^2} = g(x).$$

The initial condition will force us to make a particular choice of a. If we substitute $x = 3$, we have

$$0 = G(3) = \int_a^3 e^{-t^2}\,dt.$$

What value a makes this definite integral have value 0? Certainly, $a = 3$ does the job, so we have

$$G(x) = \int_3^x e^{-t^2}\, dt$$

as an antiderivative meeting the condition $G(3) = 0$. ■

Area functions are treated like any other differentiable functions when it comes to the rules of differentiation.

EXAMPLE 29 Suppose that $F(x) = \int_1^{x^3-7x} \cos^4(t)\, dt$. Find $F'(x)$.

Solution The function F can be thought of as a composition

$$F(x) = A(x^3 - 7x),$$

where A is the area function $A(x) = \int_1^x \cos^4(t)\, dt$. Using the chain rule, we have $F'(x) = A'(x^3 - 7x) \cdot (3x^2 - 7) = \cos^4(x^3 - 7x) \cdot (3x^2 - 7)$. ■

The second fundamental theorem of calculus

The second fundamental theorem of calculus is closely related to the first fundamental theorem. It gives us a powerful way of computing definite integrals, *provided* that we can find an antiderivative of the integrand.

Theorem 6.2

The second fundamental theorem of calculus
Hypothesis: F is any antiderivative of a continuous function f.
Conclusion: $\int_a^b f(x)\, dx = F(b) - F(a)$.

This theorem says that one way we can compute the definite integral of a function f over an interval $[a, b]$ is to first find an antiderivative F for the function, then simply take the difference of its value at the endpoints $F(b) - F(a)$.

EXAMPLE 30 Evaluate $\int_1^2 x^2\, dx$.

Solution One antiderivative of $f(x) = x^2$ is $F(x) = x^3/3$. The second fundamental theorem simply says that

$$\int_1^2 x^2\, dx = F(2) - F(1) = \frac{2^3}{3} - \frac{1^3}{3} = \frac{8}{3} - \frac{1}{3} = \frac{7}{3}.$$ ■

Note that any other antiderivative of f would have produced the same result. For instance, $G(x) = x^3/3 + 47$ is also an antiderivative of $f(x) = x^2$, but

$$G(2) - G(1) = (\frac{2^3}{3} + 47) - (\frac{1^3}{3} + 47) = \frac{8}{3} + 47 - \frac{1}{3} - 47 = \frac{7}{3}.$$

Since the constant 47 appears as a term in the evaluation of both $G(2)$ and $G(1)$, it simply cancels out when we take the difference. The same cancellation occurs if we replace 47 by any other arbitrary constant C.

A notation often used to denote the difference $F(b) - F(a)$ is:

$$F(x)\Big]_{x=a}^{x=b} \quad \text{or} \quad F(x)\Big]_a^b$$

We could write down the second fundamental theorem as

$$\int_a^b f(x)\,dx = \int f(x)\,dx\Big]_a^b.$$

In other words, the definite integral of f is the difference in the value of the indefinite integral at the limits of integration.

EXAMPLE 31 Find the area of the region bounded by the graph of $y = \frac{1}{1+x^2}$, the x-axis, $x = 0$, and $x = 1$.

Solution Since $y = \frac{1}{1+x^2}$ is positive, the desired area under its graph corresponds to the definite integral

$$\int_0^1 \frac{1}{1+x^2}\,dx.$$

Since $\frac{d}{dx}(\arctan x) = \frac{1}{1+x^2}$, we have

$$\int \frac{1}{1+x^2}\,dx\Big]_0^1 = \arctan(x)\Big]_0^1 = \arctan(1) - \arctan(0) = \frac{\pi}{4}.$$ ■

Let's see how the second fundamental theorem follows from the first fundamental theorem.

Reasoning Suppose that we have a continuous function f and any antiderivative F. We can set up an area function A such that

$$A(x) = \int_a^x f(t)\,dt.$$

From this we can see that $A(a) = 0$ and

$$A(b) = \int_a^b f(t)\,dt.$$

The first fundamental theorem of calculus tells us that A is also an antiderivative of f. Since two antiderivatives of the same continuous function can differ only by a constant, there must be some value C such that

$$A(x) = F(x) + C.$$

Let's try to find the value C. If we substitute $x = a$, we see that

$$A(a) = 0 = F(a) + C.$$

From this, we can conclude that $C = -F(a)$. Now we substitute $x = b$ to find

$$A(b) = \int_a^b f(t)\,dt = F(b) + C = F(b) - F(a),$$

as stated in the conclusion of the theorem. □

The first fundamental theorem gives a recipe for constructing an antiderivative of any continuous function f: we simply pick a point a and form the area function

$$A(x) = \int_a^x f(t)\,dt.$$

This function satisfies the requirement

$$A'(x) = f(x).$$

The second fundamental theorem gives a technique for computing definite integrals $\int_a^b f(x)\,dx$, provided that we can find an antiderivative F of the function f:

$$\int_a^b f(x)\,dx = F(b) - F(a).$$

Historical notes—a calculus controversy

The English mathematician Isaac Newton (1642-1727) is considered by many to be the greatest genius who ever lived. His three-volume work, *Principia Mathematica*, is lauded as the most influential scientific treatise in history. Legend would have us believe that Newton discovered the law of gravity on the occasion of an apple falling on his head. Whatever the truth of this anecdote, Newton and the German mathematician, Gottfried

Leibniz (1646-1716), are credited with being the first to comprehend the importance of the fundamental relationship between the slope of one graph (like that of distance versus time) and the area under the graph of those slopes (instantaneous speed versus time). There is strong evidence that Newton and Leibniz had essentially the same insight independently of each other. Their ideas were quickly recognized as ushering in a mathematical revolution. (It is a shame that these two men were drawn into a bitter plagiarism controversy over who discovered calculus. For one account of this "calculus controversy," see David Burton's *The History of Mathematics*.) Although Newton and Leibniz made their breakthrough observations in the seventeenth century, many of the key ideas of calculus can be traced back much further to Archimedes and the ancient Greeks. The insights of Newton and Leibniz were the culmination of centuries of development and refinement of those ideas. In recognition of his debt to Archimedes and other scientists who preceded him, Newton once said, "If I have seen farther than others, it is because I have stood on the shoulders of giants."

EXERCISES for Section 6.5

For exercises 1–6: Use the fundamental theorems of calculus to find an antiderivative F of the given function f having the specified initial value.

1. $f(x) = 2^{-x^2}$; $F(1) = 0$
2. $f(x) = \log_2(x)$; $F(2) = 0$
3. $f(x) = \cos^2(x)$; $F(-\pi) = 0$
4. $f(x) = \dfrac{1}{x^3+8}$; $F(-1) = 0$
5. $f(x) = \dfrac{1}{x}$; $F(\sqrt{17}) = 0$
6. $f(x) = \arctan(x)$; $F(-\sqrt{3}) = 0$

For exercises 7–12: Suppose that G is the area function with formula

$$G(x) = \int_2^x \frac{\sin(2t)}{1+t^2}\,dt.$$

In exercises 7–12, find $\dfrac{dy}{dx}$.

7. $y = G(x)$
8. $y = G(x^2)$
9. $y = x^2 G(x)$
10. $y = \dfrac{G(x)}{x^2}$
11. $y = (G(x))^2$
12. $y = G'(x)$

For exercises 13–20: Use the fundamental theorems of calculus to calculate each of the definite integrals given.

13. $\displaystyle\int_{-1}^{3} (x^2 + x + 1)\,dx$
14. $\displaystyle\int_{1}^{2.5} (3x^2 + 2x + 1)\,dx$
15. $\displaystyle\int_{4}^{9} \sqrt{x}\,dx$
16. $\displaystyle\int_{\pi/2}^{\pi} (5\sin(x) - 3\cos(x))\,dx$

17. $\int_{-2\pi}^{2\pi} (\sin^2(x) + \cos^2(x))\, dx$

18. $\int_{0}^{0.5} \frac{4}{\sqrt{1-x^2}}\, dx$

19. $\int_{0}^{1} \frac{1}{4+4x^2}\, dx$

20. $\int_{-4}^{-1} \frac{1}{x^2}\, dx$

For exercises 21–28: You are given the graph of a function f on a grid. Assuming that the grid lines are spaced 1 unit apart both horizontally and vertically, sketch the graph of the area function

$$A(x) = \int_{1}^{x} f(t)\, dt$$

over the interval $[1, 5]$ for each function. Then sketch the graphs of the derivative of each area function and compare it with the original function's graph.

21.

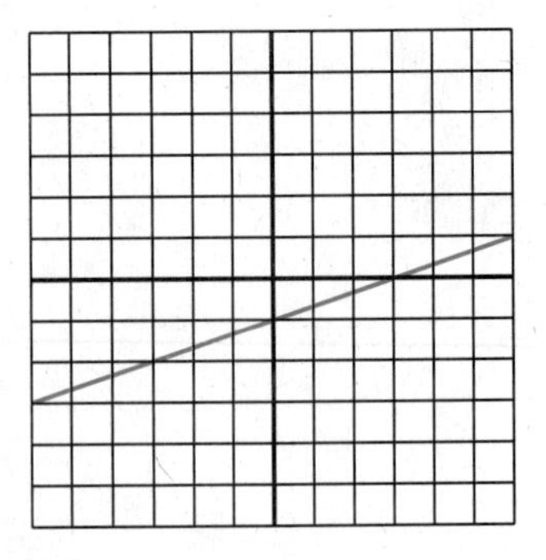

22.

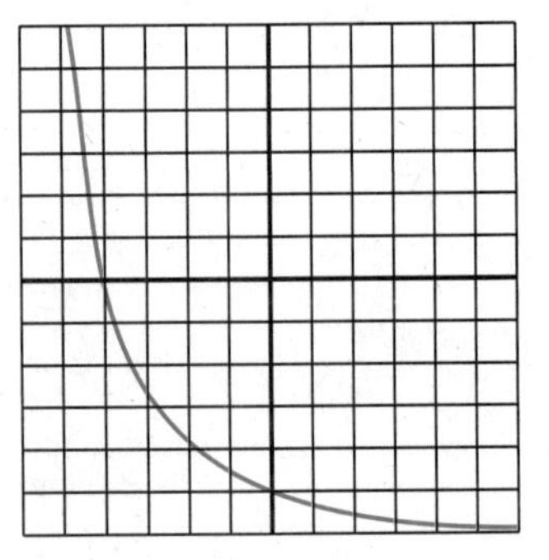

23.

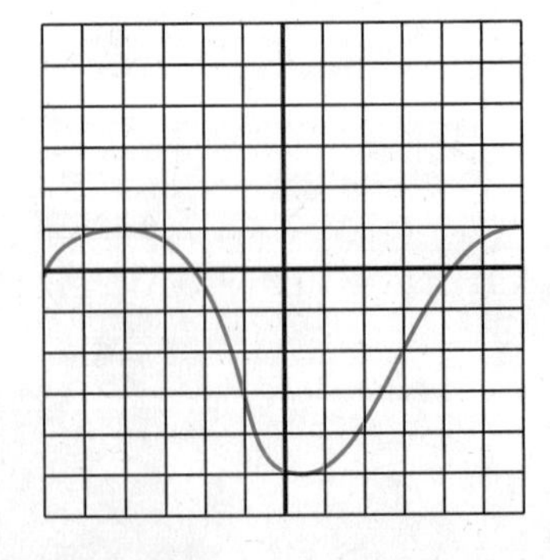

24.

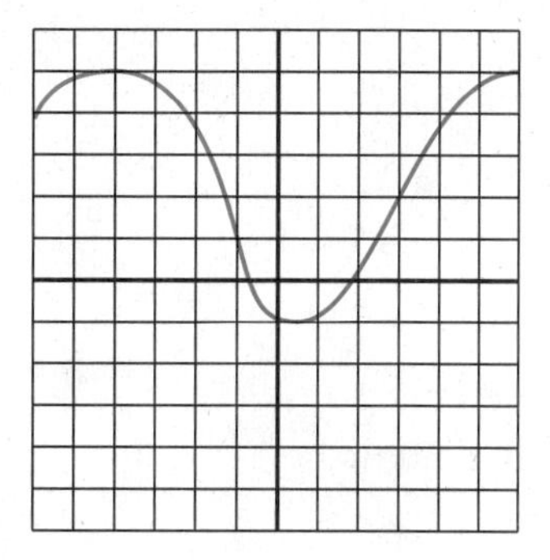

25.

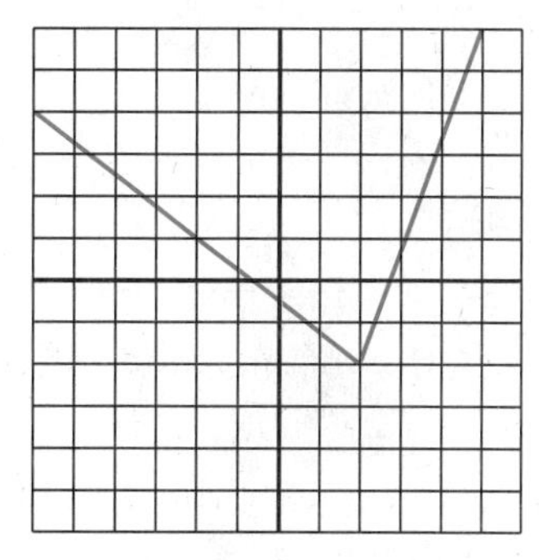

26.

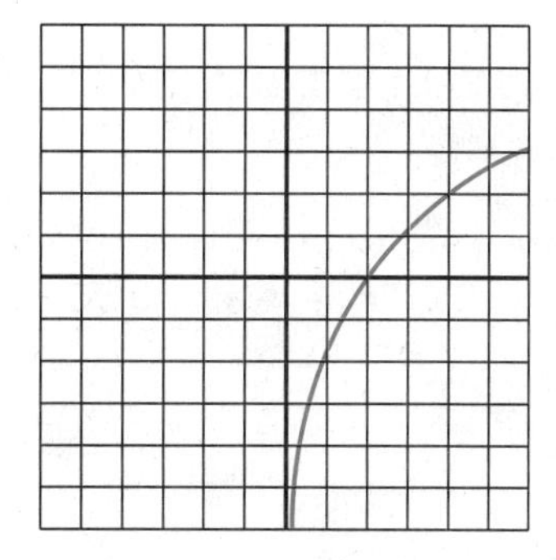

27.

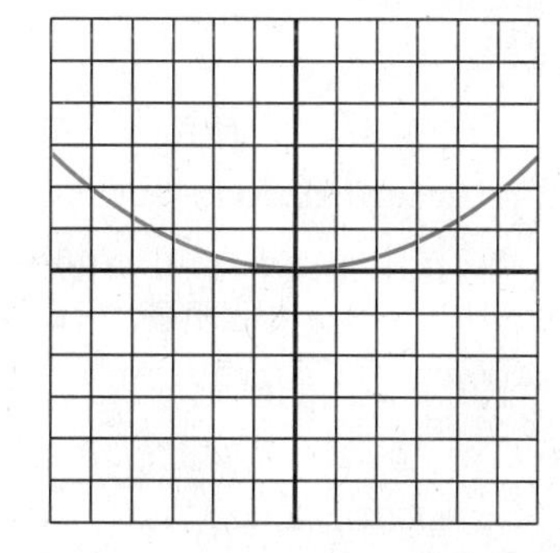

28.

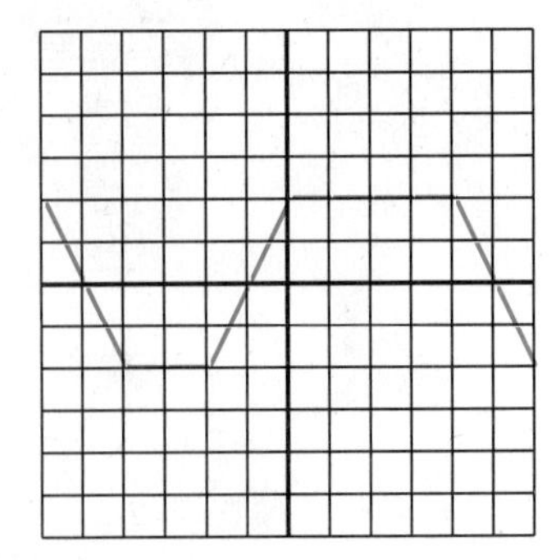

29. A student uses the fundamental theorems of calculus to calculate

$$\int_{-1}^{1} \frac{1}{x^2}\, dx = -\frac{1}{x}\bigg]_{-1}^{1} = -\frac{1}{1} - (-\frac{1}{-1}) = -2.$$

Graph $y = \dfrac{1}{x^2}$ and explain why this answer is unreasonable. Why isn't this a contradiction of the fundamental theorems of calculus?

30. Suppose that $F'(x) = f(x)$, where f is a continuous function. What initial condition must hold for $F(x) = \int_2^x f(t)\, dt$?

6.6 NUMERICAL INTEGRATION TECHNIQUES

The fundamental theorems of calculus allow us to evaluate a definite integral, provided that we can find an antiderivative for the integrand

$$\int_a^b f(x)\, dx = F(b) - F(a),$$

where $F' = f$.

If a calculator or computer is capable of finding an antiderivative F for the function f, it can use this antiderivative to evaluate the definite integral.

Sometimes it is difficult, or even impossible, to find an explicit formula for the antiderivative F. Of course, the fundamental theorems also guarantee that we can always find an antiderivative for a continuous function, but that puts us back where we started—trying to calculate a definite integral (the area function for the graph of $y = f(x)$).

In this section, we examine some of the numerical approximation techniques that can be used in evaluating definite integrals. The key idea to keep in mind is that a definite integral

$$\int_a^b f(x)\,dx$$

is *defined* to be the limiting value of Riemann sums

$$\lim_{n\to\infty} \sum_{i=1}^{n} f(x_i)\Delta x,$$

where the interval $[a, b]$ is partitioned into subintervals of length Δx, one input x_i is chosen from each subinterval, and we sum up the products $f(x_i)\Delta x$ for all the subintervals.

One way to approximate the value of a definite integral is to simply evaluate such a Riemann sum for a particular subinterval size Δx and a particular choice of inputs x_i from those subintervals. This is, indeed, the strategy in the first three methods of numerical integration we discuss. Other approximation techniques can be thought of as improvements achieved by averaging these Riemann sum results.

Left endpoint, right endpoint and midpoint rules

The left endpoint, right endpoint, and midpoint rules for approximating definite integrals are named for the choice of input we make from each subinterval. The advantage of making these particular selections is that they are easy to "automate." That is, it is not difficult to program a machine to make these selections and then carry out the computation. Let's make the procedures for carrying out these techniques explicit.

Step 1. Choose a number n of subintervals in the regular partition of $[a, b]$.

Step 2. Calculate $\Delta x = \dfrac{b-a}{n}$.

Step 3. Locate the n inputs $x_1, x_2, ..., x_n$.

Step 4. Evaluate f at each input x_i and find the Riemann sum:

$$\sum_{i=1}^{n} f(x_i)\Delta x = f(x_1)\Delta x + f(x_2)\Delta x + f(x_3)\Delta x + \cdots + f(x_n)\Delta x.$$

For the left endpoint rule, our inputs will be

$$x_1 = a, \quad x_2 = a + \Delta x, \quad x_3 = a + 2\Delta x, \quad \ldots, \quad x_n = a + (n-1)\Delta x.$$

For the right endpoint rule, our inputs will be

$$x_1 = a + \Delta x, \quad x_2 = a + 2\Delta x, \quad x_3 = a + 3\Delta x, \quad \ldots, \quad x_n = a + n\Delta x = b.$$

For the midpoint rule, our inputs will be

$$x_1 = a + \frac{\Delta x}{2}, \quad x_2 = a + \frac{3\Delta x}{2}, \quad x_3 = a + \frac{5\Delta x}{2}, \quad \ldots, \quad x_n = a + \frac{(2n-1)\Delta x}{2}.$$

Note that our inputs are equally spaced apart under all three rules, so that once we know the first input x_1, the rest are determined:

$$x_2 = x_1 + \Delta x, \quad x_3 = x_2 + \Delta x, \quad x_4 = x_3 + \Delta x, \quad \ldots, \quad x_n = x_{n-1} + \Delta x.$$

Using regular partitions makes it reasonably easy to program these techniques on a programmable calculator or computer. In fact, we could write a general program that handles all three of these techniques. The syntax of the program will, of course, depend on the particular programming language of your calculator or computer system, but the structure can be described by the flow chart outlined in Figure 6.36.

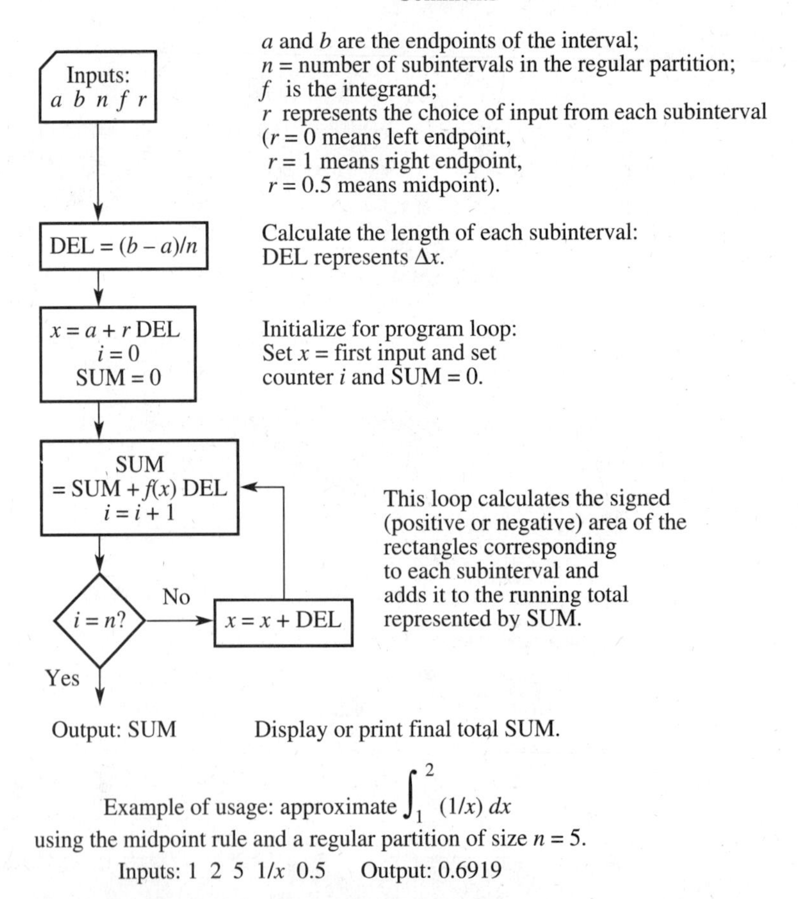

Figure 6.36 A program for computing Riemann sums.

EXAMPLE 32 Approximate $\int_{.5}^{3.5} \sin^3(x)\,dx$ using each of the three rules for a regular partition of size $n = 6$.

Solution Here $a = 0.5$, $b = 3.5$, $n = 6$, and $f(x) = \sin^3(x)$. The subinterval size is

$$\Delta x = \frac{b-a}{n} = \frac{3.5 - 0.5}{6} = 0.5.$$

If we calculate the output values of the function at each point of the partition, we find

$f(0.5) \approx 0.1102$ $f(1.0) \approx 0.5958$
$f(1.5) \approx 0.9925$ $f(2.0) \approx 0.7518$
$f(2.5) \approx 0.2144$ $f(3.0) \approx 0.0028$
$f(3.5) \approx -0.0432$

The left endpoint rule (use $r = 0$ in the RSUM program) leads to the approximation

$$(0.5)(f(0.5) + f(1.0) + f(1.5) + f(2.0) + f(2.5) + f(3.0)) \approx 1.334.$$

The "left rectangles" whose areas are represented by this Riemann sum are illustrated in Figure 6.37. The right endpoint rule (use $r = 1$ in the RSUM program) leads to the approximation

$$(0.5)(f(1.0) + f(1.5) + f(2.0) + f(2.5) + f(3.0) + f(3.5)) \approx 1.257.$$

The "right rectangles" whose areas are represented by this Riemann sum are illustrated in Figure 6.38.

The midpoint rule requires us to calculate the output values of the function at the midpoint of each subinterval:

$f(0.75) \approx 0.3167$ $f(1.25) \approx 0.8546$
$f(1.75) \approx 0.9527$ $f(2.25) \approx 0.4710$
$f(2.75) \approx 0.0556$ $f(3.25) \approx -0.0013$

This leads to the approximation (use $r = 0.5$ in the RSUM program)

$$(0.5)(f(0.75) + f(1.25) + f(1.75) + f(2.25) + f(2.75) + f(3.25)) \approx 1.325.$$

The "midpoint rectangles" whose areas are represented by this Riemann sum are illustrated in Figure 6.39. For comparison, a machine computation of higher precision yields $\int_{.5}^{3.5} \sin^3(x)\,dx \approx 1.315$, so in this case the midpoint rule gave the best approximation. ■

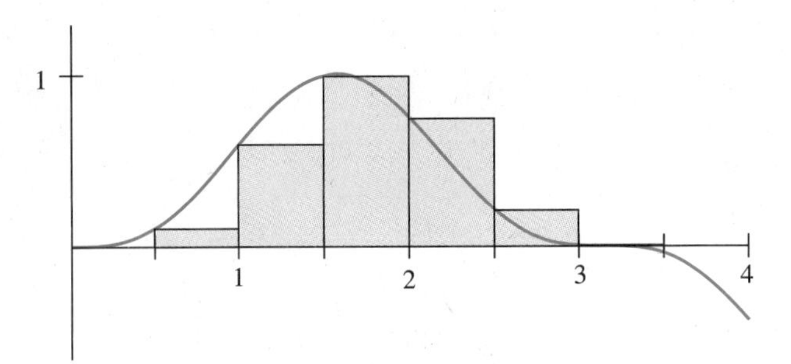

Figure 6.37 Left rectangle approximation of $\int_{.5}^{3.5} \sin^3(x)\,dx$ for a regular partition ($n = 6$).

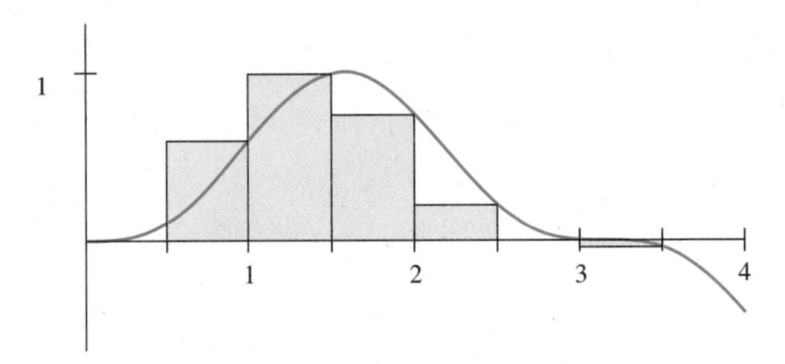

Figure 6.38 Right rectangle approximation of $\int_{.5}^{3.5} \sin^3(x)\,dx$ for a regular partition ($n = 6$).

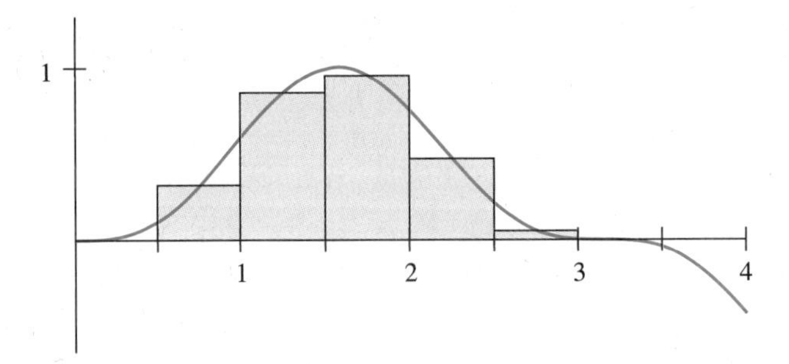

Figure 6.39 Midpoint approximation of $\int_{.5}^{3.5} \sin^3(x)\,dx$ for a regular partition ($n = 6$).

The right and left endpoint rules are sometimes called **right rectangle rule** and **left rectangle rule**.

Note that if a function f is *positive and increasing* over a given subinterval, then the area of the left rectangle is an underestimate of the area under the graph, while the area of the right rectangle is an overestimate. In this case, the area of the midpoint rectangle will be between this underestimate and overestimate (but not necessarily closer to the true area than each of the endpoint approximations). The situation is reversed when the function f is *positive and decreasing* over the subinterval. If the function f is not monotonic over a subinterval, then the relationship between the true area and the areas of the left, right, and midpoint rectangles cannot be determined without closer examination.

As the partition becomes finer (in other words, n is chosen larger and larger), one expects that these Riemann sum approximations should get closer to the actual value of the definite integral. In general, this must be true as long as the definite integral exists. However, for certain choices of n, it is possible that the particular sampling of inputs obtained by using the left, right, or midpoint rules may give a terrible approximation. Since all three of these methods sample at regular spaced intervals, a function that is periodic or has some graphical symmetry will be approximated badly for certain partition sizes n. Indeed, it is possible to produce a better result for a smaller value of n than for a larger value in some cases.

The next two techniques approximate the value of a definite integral by using *averages* of Riemann sums.

Trapezoidal rule

The **trapezoidal rule** for a regular partition of size n is the average of the results obtained by using the right and left endpoint rules for the same partition.

Trapezoidal rule estimate

$$= \frac{1}{2}(\text{Left Rectangle estimate}) + \frac{1}{2}(\text{Right Rectangle estimate}).$$

Once you have a program like RSUM, it is easy to calulate the trapezoidal approximation. First, calculate RSUM with $r = 0$. Call this LEFT. Next, calculate RSUM with $r = 1$. Call this RIGHT. Finally, average the results and call it

$$\text{TRAP} = (0.5)(\text{LEFT} + \text{RIGHT}).$$

EXAMPLE 33 Approximate $\int_{0.5}^{3.5} \sin^3(x)\, dx$ using the trapezoidal rule for a regular partition of size $n = 6$.

Solution We have already determined the results of the right and left endpoint rules for this definite integral for a regular partition of size $n = 6$. Therefore the trapezoidal rule approximation is $(1.334 + 1.257)/2 = 1.296$. ■

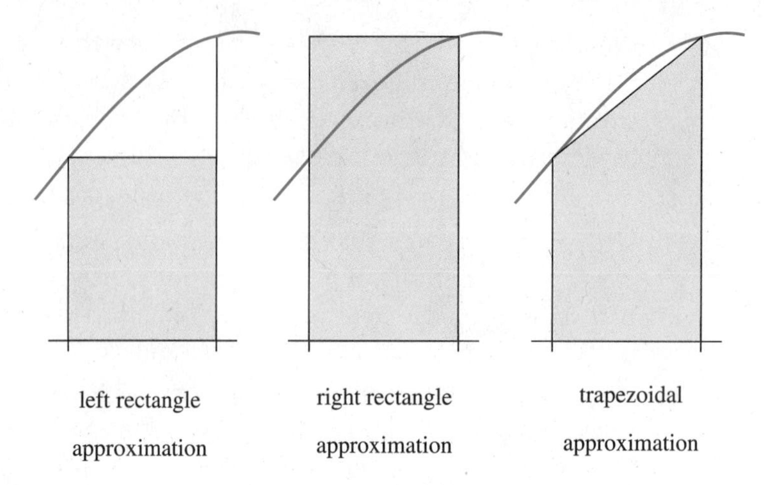

Figure 6.40 Trapezoidal rule is the average of the left and right endpoint rules.

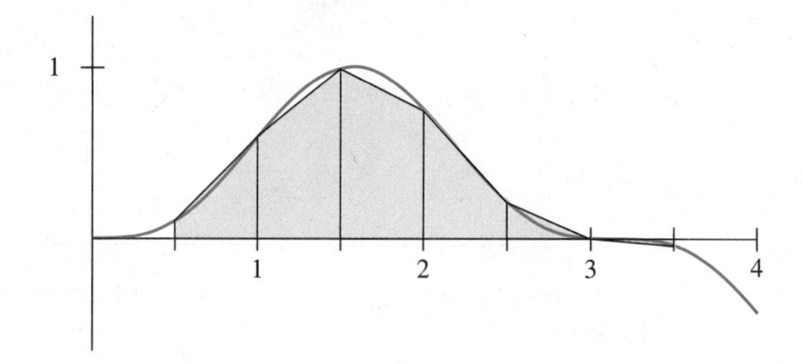

Figure 6.41 Trapezoidal approximation of $\int_{.5}^{3.5} \sin^3(x)\, dx$ for a regular partition ($n = 6$).

The idea behind the trapezoidal rule is that over intervals for which f is monotonic (either increasing or decreasing), one endpoint rule will give an underestimate and the other endpoint rule will give an overestimate. Hence, averaging the results from these two endpoint rules should give a better approximation to the value of the definite integral. The trapezoidal rule derives its name from the fact that the average of the areas of the right and left rectangles can be thought of as the area of a trapezoid with the same base (see Figure 6.40). The easiest way to remember the trapezoidal rule is as the average of the left and right rectangle rules.

Figure 6.41 illustrates the trapezoidal approximation for the definite integral of the previous example.

Simpson's Rule

An even better approximation to the value of a definite integral can be obtained by taking a *weighted* average of the midpoint and trapezoidal rules. The motivation behind this strategy is to take into account the concavity of the function's graph over each subinterval.

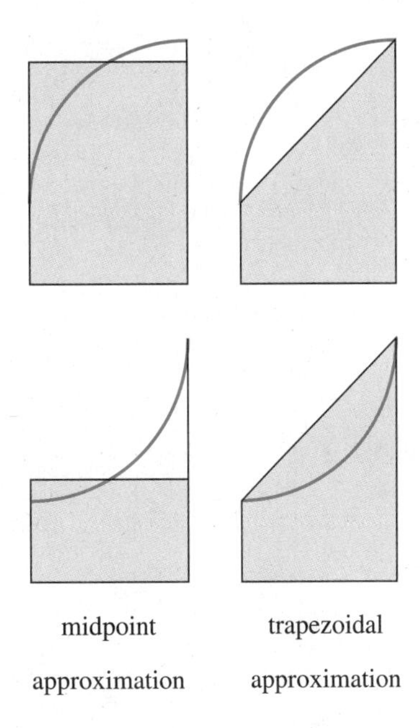

Figure 6.42 Comparing midpoint and trapezoidal approximations.

Figure 6.42 illustrates the midpoint and trapezoidal approximations over subintervals where the function graph is concave down and concave up. Look closely at this illustration. Note that for the concave down graph (the two pictures on the left), the midpoint rule overestimates the area, while the trapezoidal rule underestimates the area. Of the two estimates, the trapezoidal estimate appears to be approximately twice as far off as the midpoint estimate. For the concave up graph (the two pictures on the right), the midpoint rule now underestimates the area, while the trapezoidal rule overestimates the area. Again, the error of the trapezoidal estimate appears to be approximately twice as far off as the midpoint estimate.

This result suggests that the value whose distance to the midpoint estimate is half as far as the distance to the trapezoidal estimate is a much better approximation of the actual area under the graph. This is precisely the motivation behind the approximation technique known as **Simpson's rule**, named after the English mathematician Thomas Simpson (1710-61).

The Simpson's rule approximation value can be computed by using a weighted average of the trapezoidal and midpoint estimates, namely

Simpson's rule estimate

$$= \frac{1}{3}(\text{Trapezoidal estimate}) + \frac{2}{3}(\text{Midpoint estimate}).$$

Again, if you have a program like RSUM available, it is easy to program or calculate the Simpson's rule approximation. First, calculate TRAP as before. Next, calculate RSUM with $r = 0.5$. Call this result MID. Finally calculate the weighted average and call it

$$\text{SIMP} = \frac{2 \cdot \text{MID} + \text{TRAP}}{3}.$$

EXAMPLE 34 Approximate $\int_{0.5}^{3.5} \sin^3(x)\,dx$ using Simpson's rule for a regular partition of size $n = 6$.

Solution We have already determined the results of the midpoint rule and trapezoidal rules for this definite integral for a partition of size $n = 6$. The Simpson's rule approximation is

$$\frac{1.296}{3} + \frac{2(1.325)}{3} \approx 1.315.$$

Note that this approximation is accurate to three decimal places of the actual value of the definite integral. ■

Summary of the numerical integration techniques

Let's summarize by introducing some convenient notation. Suppose that we partition a closed interval $[a, b]$ into n equal-sized subintervals of length $\Delta x = \frac{b-a}{n}$. Let's label the function outputs at the n midpoints with odd subscripts:

$$y_1 = f(a + \frac{\Delta x}{2}), \quad y_3 = f(a + \frac{3\Delta x}{2}), \quad y_5 = f(a + \frac{5\Delta x}{2}), \quad \ldots$$

up to

$$y_{2n-1} = f(a + \frac{(2n-1)\Delta x}{2}) = f(b - \frac{\Delta x}{2}).$$

Now let's label the function outputs at the endpoints of the subintervals with even subscripts, starting with 0:

$$y_0 = f(a), \quad y_2 = f(a + \Delta x), \quad y_4 = f(a + 2\Delta x), \quad \ldots$$

up to

$$y_{2n} = f(a + n\Delta x) = f(b).$$

With this labeling scheme, we can write down an explicit formula for each of the rules discussed in this section.

Numerical approximations of $\int_a^b f(x)\,dx$ for a regular partition of size n

For a regular partition of n subintervals, we'll use the following abbreviations:

$L_n =$ left rectangle estimate. $R_n =$ right rectangle estimate.
$M_n =$ midpoint rule estimate. $T_n =$ trapezoidal rule estimate.
$S_{2n} =$ Simpson's rule estimate.

The subscript $2n$ in the notation S_{2n} for Simpson's rule is to indicate that we have effectively subdivided our interval $[a, b]$ into $2n$ subintervals, since we make use of both the endpoints and midpoints of each of our original n subintervals.

Left rectangle rule: $\int_a^b f(x)\,dx \approx L_n = \Delta x(y_0 + y_2 + \cdots + y_{2n-2}).$

Right rectangle rule: $\int_a^b f(x)\,dx \approx R_n = \Delta x(y_2 + y_4 + \cdots + y_{2n}).$

Midpoint rule: $\int_a^b f(x)\,dx \approx M_n = \Delta x(y_1 + y_3 + \cdots + y_{2n-1}).$

Trapezoidal rule: $\int_a^b f(x)\,dx \approx T_n = \dfrac{L_n + R_n}{2}.$

An explicit formula for the trapezoidal rule is

$$T_n = \frac{\Delta x}{2}(y_0 + 2y_2 + 2y_4 + \cdots + 2y_{2n-2} + y_{2n}).$$

Simpson's rule: $\int_a^b f(x)\,dx \approx S_{2n} = \dfrac{2M_n + T_n}{3}.$

An explicit formula for Simpson's rule is

$$S_{2n} = \frac{\Delta x}{6}(y_0 + 4y_1 + 2y_2 + 4y_3 + 2y_4 + \cdots + 2y_{2n-2} + 4y_{2n-1} + y_{2n}).$$

Uses of numerical integration

Calculators and computers may use numerical integration techniques to calculate the values of definite integrals. When an antiderivative cannot be found so that the second fundamental theorem can be used, there is no recourse but to use numerical techniques. Often, Simpson's rule or a closely related method is used, but there are other methods (which you might encounter in a more advanced course in numerical analysis).

As we mentioned earlier, when equally spaced inputs are sampled for a function having symmetry in its graph, the definite integral may not be approximated well by the techniques described here. One way to alleviate this problem is to sample irregularly spaced inputs. Another idea is to transform the function in some way that is likely to remove the symmetry, yet preserve the area under the graph.

We used the integral $\int_{0.5}^{3.5} \sin^3(x)\,dx$ as an example to illustrate the various techniques of numerical integration. However, one of the primary uses of numerical integration techniques is when the function has no known formula. Perhaps only a partial table of inputs and outputs is available (as is often the case when data are gathered from some experimental process), or perhaps we only have a graph of the function. Since the techniques described in this section depend only on a sampling of outputs from the function, we can just as easily use them when a function has only a numerical or graphical representation.

If we desire a certain level of accuracy in the value of a definite integral, how fine a partition should we use? In other words, how can we (or a machine) decide how large n should be ahead of time without knowing the actual value of the definite integral? (If we know the actual value of the definite integral, there is little point in approximating it.) In practice, a machine may follow these steps:

1. Compute the approximation of $\int_a^b f(x)\,dx$ for a starting value n.
2. Double the size of n, and compute the new approximation.
3. Repeat until three consecutive approximations are within the desired accuracy *of each other.*

Note that the criterion is how close together the approximations are, not their proximity to an unknown target value. (Of course, even if the approximations are close together, it is still possible that they all may be far away from the true value.)

EXERCISES for Section 6.6

For exercises 1–6: Using regular partitions of size $n = 2, 4, 8, 16$, and 32, find the left, right, and midpoint estimates for the definite integrals in exercises 1–6 by using a RSUM program for your calculator or computer.

1. $\displaystyle\int_0^1 \sqrt{1+x^2}\,dx$

2. $\displaystyle\int_{-1}^0 3^x\,dx$

3. $\displaystyle\int_{-1}^1 \arctan(x)\,dx$

4. $\displaystyle\int_1^4 \log_2(x)\,dx$

5. $\displaystyle\int_0^1 e^{-x^2}\,dx$

6. $\displaystyle\int_{0.5}^{3.5} \sin(x^3)\,dx$

For exercises 7–12: Using regular partitions of size $n = 2, 4, 8, 16, 32$ and the results from exercises 1–6, calculate TRAP and SIMP for exercises 7–12. Calculate each integral with a machine to five-decimal-place accuracy and compare these values with the five estimates you have obtained.

7. $\int_0^1 \sqrt{1+x^2}\,dx$

8. $\int_{-1}^0 3^x\,dx$

9. $\int_{-1}^1 \arctan(x)\,dx$

10. $\int_1^4 \log_2(x)\,dx$

11. $\int_0^1 e^{-x^2}\,dx$

12. $\int_{0.5}^{3.5} \sin(x^3)\,dx$

Table 6.7 shows the minute-by-minute speedometer readings of a car over the second 15 minutes of its trip.

time t in minutes	speed V in mph
15	28
16	24
17	20
18	16
19	12
20	9
21	6
22	3
23	0
24	1
25	1
26	2
27	3
28	4
29	6
30	8

Table 6.7

13. Estimate the distance covered over the interval $[15, 30]$ using $\Delta t = 1$ minutes and the trapezoidal rule.

14. Estimate the distance covered over the interval $[20, 30]$ using $\Delta t = 2$ minutes and Simpson's rule.

---

15. Using Table 6.8 for the continuous function f, estimate the definite integral of f over the entire interval using the trapezoidal rule.

x	$f(x)$
1.27319	3.81456
1.27320	3.86714
1.27321	3.90551
1.27322	3.92017
1.27323	4.34405
1.27324	4.66292
1.27325	4.69141
1.27326	4.65674
1.27327	4.61993
1.27328	4.59550
1.27329	4.58799
1.27330	4.52556

Table 6.8

16. Use Simpson's rule to find 5 terms of a sequence approximating

$$\int_0^1 \frac{4}{1+x^2}\,dx.$$

Let the number of subdivisions of $[0,1]$ be $2, 4, 6, 8, 10$. What does the limit of this sequence appear to be? How many decimal places of accuracy does the last approximation give? Using the trapezoidal approximation and 50 subdivisions of $[0,1]$, approximate the same integral. How many decimal places of accuracy do you get?

For exercises 17–20: Consider the definite integral

$$\int_0^4 x^2(x-1)(x-2)(x-3)(x-4)\,dx.$$

17. Find the trapezoidal estimates for regular partitions of size $n = 16$ and $n = 32$.

18. Find the Simpson's rule estimates for regular partitions of size $n = 4$ and $n = 8$ (that is, S_8 and for S_{16}).

19. Expand the polynomial $x^2(x-1)(x-2)(x-3)(x-4)$ and integrate over $[0,4]$ using the fundamental theorems of calculus.

20. Which estimate is better, the trapezoidal estimate for $n = 32$ or Simpson's rule for $n = 8$?

For exercises 21–28: You are given the graph of a function f on a grid. Assuming that the grid lines are spaced 1 unit apart both horizontally and vertically, estimate the value of

$$\int_1^5 f(x)\,dx$$

by using $\Delta x = 1$ unit and the trapezoidal rule.

21.

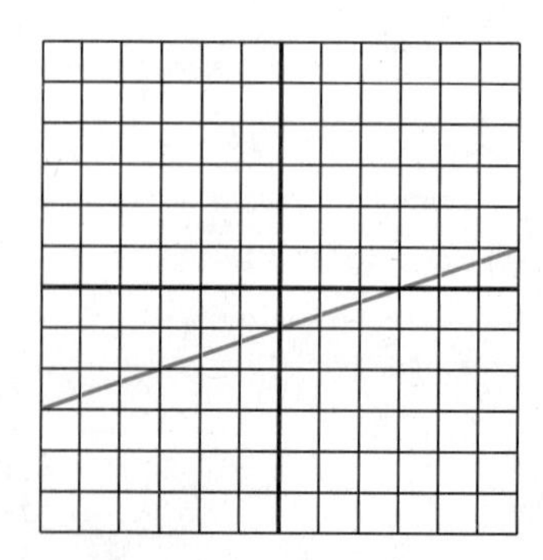

22.

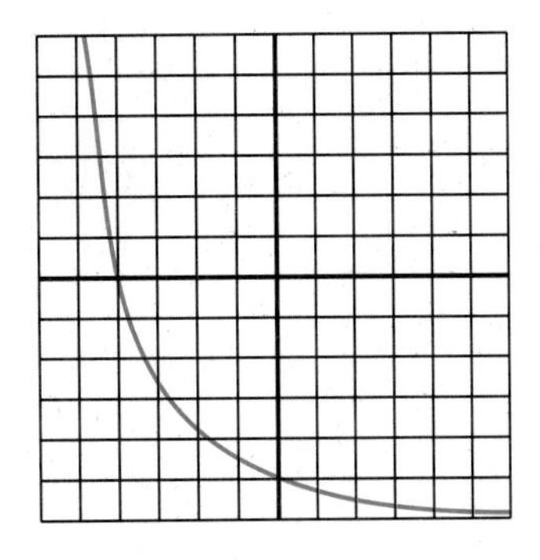

23.

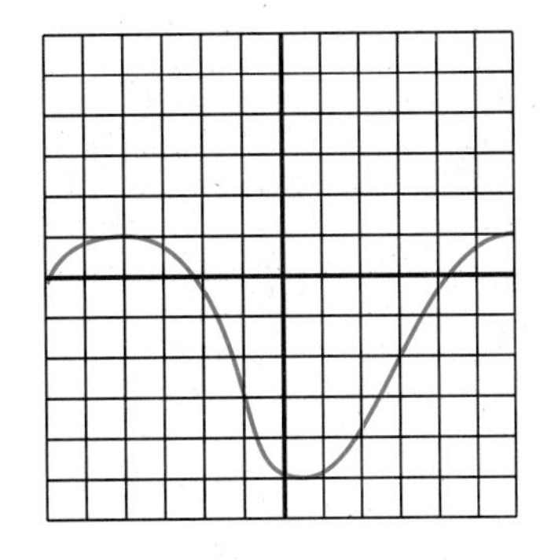

24.

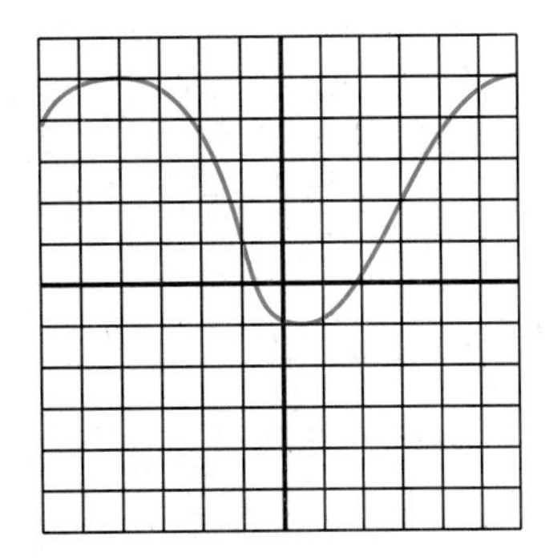

25.

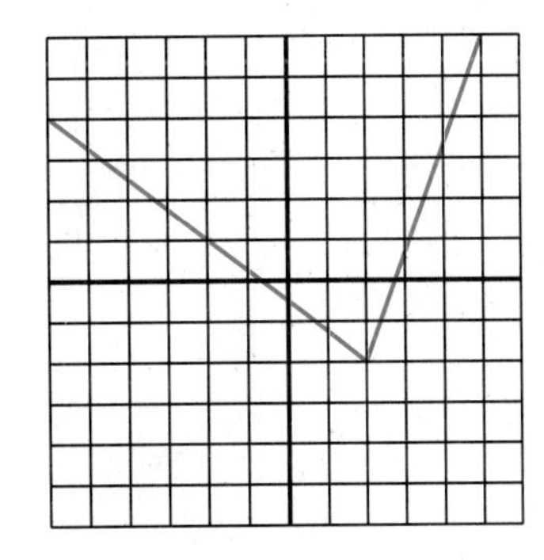

26.

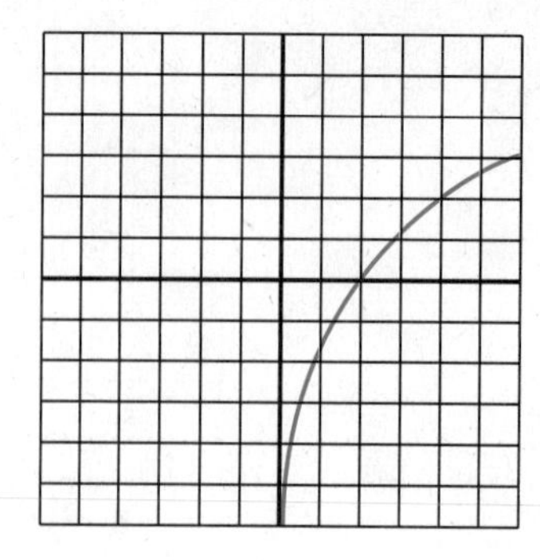

27.

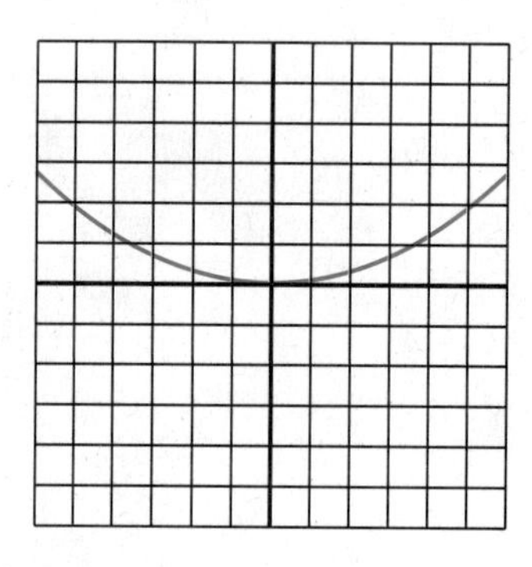

28.

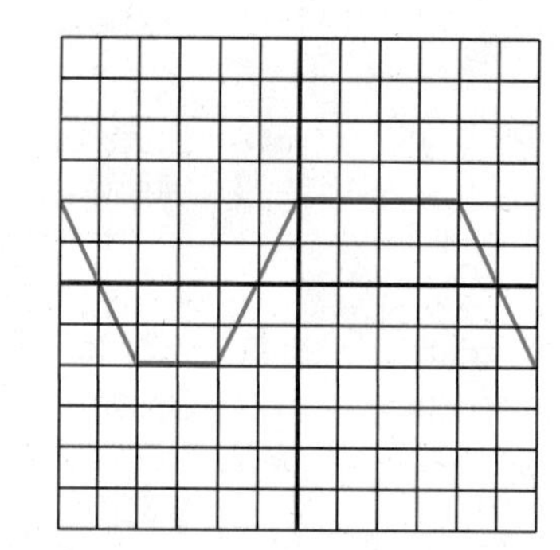

29. For which of the graphs in exercises 21-28 is the left and right rectangle estimates exactly correct? Why?

30. For which of the graphs in exercises 21-28 is the trapezoidal estimate exactly correct? Why?

---

31. The midpoint rule is sometimes called the **tangent rule**. To see why, consider the illustration.

Explain why the area of the rectangle formed by this midpoint rule is the same as the area of a trapezoid whose top is a tangent line segment through the midpoint.

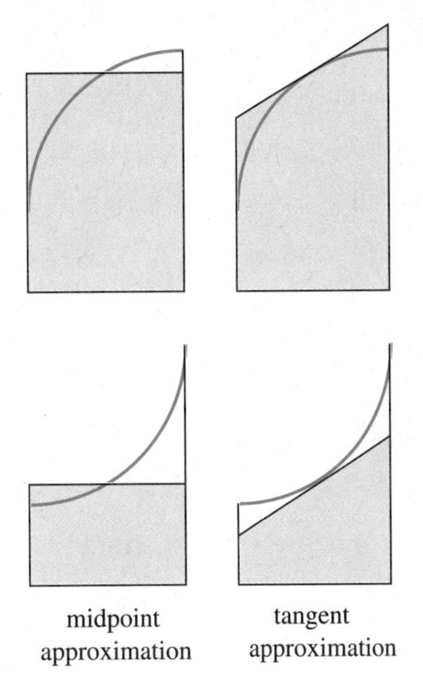

For Exercise 31

For exercises 32–45: The behavior of a function f over the interval $[a, b]$ is described in terms of its derivatives. For each function, answer the following questions:

(a) Which numerical approximation technique(s) will always produce an underestimate for $\int_a^b f(x)\,dx$?

(b) Which numerical approximation technique(s) will always produce an overestimate for $\int_a^b f(x)\,dx$?

(c) Which numerical approximation technique(s) will always produce an exactly correct result for $\int_a^b f(x)\,dx$?

(d) For which numerical approximation technique(s) is there not enough information to determine the relationship of the estimate to $\int_a^b f(x)\,dx$?

32. For all $a \le x \le b,\ f(x) > 0,\ f'(x) > 0,\ f''(x) > 0.$

33. For all $a \le x \le b,\ f(x) > 0,\ f'(x) > 0,\ f''(x) = 0.$

34. For all $a \le x \le b,\ f(x) > 0,\ f'(x) > 0,\ f''(x) < 0.$

35. For all $a \le x \le b,\ f(x) > 0,\ f'(x) < 0,\ f''(x) > 0.$

36. For all $a \le x \le b,\ f(x) > 0,\ f'(x) < 0,\ f''(x) = 0.$

37. For all $a \le x \le b,\ f(x) > 0,\ f'(x) < 0,\ f''(x) < 0.$

38. For all $a \le x \le b,\ f(x) > 0,\ f'(x) = 0,\ f''(x) = 0.$

39. For all $a \le x \le b,\ f(x) < 0,\ f'(x) > 0,\ f''(x) > 0.$

40. For all $a \le x \le b,\ f(x) < 0,\ f'(x) > 0,\ f''(x) = 0.$

41. For all $a \le x \le b$, $f(x) < 0$, $f'(x) > 0$, $f''(x) < 0$.
42. For all $a \le x \le b$, $f(x) < 0$, $f'(x) < 0$, $f''(x) > 0$.
43. For all $a \le x \le b$, $f(x) < 0$, $f'(x) < 0$, $f''(x) = 0$.
44. For all $a \le x \le b$, $f(x) < 0$, $f'(x) < 0$, $f''(x) < 0$.
45. For all $a \le x \le b$, $f(x) < 0$, $f'(x) = 0$, $f''(x) = 0$.

6.7 METHODS OF INTEGRATION—SUBSTITUTION

The general problem of indefinite integration, or antidifferentiation, is to find a function F satisfying

$$\int f(x)dx = F(x) + C.$$

This can be thought of as a problem of "derivative recognition." If we can recognize f as the derivative of another function F, that is

$$f(x) = F'(x),$$

then F is the function we're looking for.

Certainly, if f is continuous over an interval $[a, b]$, then the first fundamental theorem of calculus gives us a guaranteed solution, namely,

$$F(x) = \int_a^x f(t)\,dt,$$

which will satisfy $F'(x) = f(x)$ for $a < x < b$. However, evaluation of these area functions can require a great deal of computing power just to achieve approximate outputs. Finding an explicit formula for F has its advantages. This section is devoted to some techniques and methods for finding such formulas.

Integral formulas

We can develop several integral formulas by simply reversing basic derivative formulas. These formulas are reviewed below, where we have written them in terms of a variable of integration u:

$$\int u^r\,du = \frac{u^{r+1}}{r+1} + C \text{ for } r \neq -1 \qquad \int \frac{1}{u}\,du = \ln|u| + C$$

$$\int \sin u\,du = -\cos u + C \qquad \int \cos u\,du = \sin u + C$$

$$\int \sec^2 u\,du = \tan u + C \qquad \int \sec u \tan u\,du = \sec u + C$$

$$\int \csc^2 u\,du = -\cot u + C \qquad \int \csc u \cot u\,du = -\csc u + C$$

$$\int e^u\,du = e^u + C \qquad \int a^u\,du = \frac{a^u}{\ln(a)} + C$$

$$\int \frac{1}{\sqrt{1-u^2}}\,du = \arcsin(u) + C \qquad \int \frac{-1}{\sqrt{1-u^2}}\,du = \arccos(u) + C$$

$$\int \frac{1}{1+u^2}\,du = \arctan(u) + C \qquad \int \frac{-1}{1+u^2}\,du = \operatorname{arccot}(u) + C$$

$$\int \frac{1}{u\sqrt{u^2-1}}\,du = \operatorname{arcsec}|u| + C \qquad \int \frac{-1}{u\sqrt{u^2-1}}\,du = \operatorname{arccsc}|u| + C$$

▶▶▶ **CAUTION! These and any other integral formulas are valid only for those intervals over which the integrand is continuous.**

For example, $\int \frac{1}{x^3}\,dx = \int x^{-3}\,dx = \frac{x^{-2}}{-2} + C = -\frac{1}{2x^2} + C$ only for intervals that do not include $x = 0$, since $y = \frac{1}{x^3}$ is not continuous at $x = 0$. Similarly,

$$\int \sec^2 x\,dx = \tan x + C$$

is valid only for intervals that do not include any value $x = \frac{\pi}{2} + n\pi$ (n any integer) since $y = \sec^2 x$ is undefined at each of these values.

Note that the integral formula

$$\int \frac{1}{x} = \ln|x| + C$$

involves the absolute value. Since $1/x$ is undefined at $x = 0$, there are really two integral formulas involved: one for $x < 0$ and one for $x > 0$. We know that for $x > 0$,

$$\frac{d}{dx}(\ln(x)) = \frac{1}{x}.$$

If we examine the slope field generated by $1/x$ (see Figure 6.43), we can see that the antiderivative graphs for $x < 0$ are mirror images of those for $x > 0$ (reflected through the y-axis). Hence, for $x < 0$, we also have

$$\frac{d}{dx}(\ln(-x)) = \frac{1}{x}.$$

Since $|x| = x$ when $x > 0$ and $|x| = -x$ when $x < 0$, our integral formula is valid for both cases. Similarly, the integral formulas

$$\int \frac{1}{x\sqrt{x^2-1}}\,dx = \operatorname{arcsec}|x| + C \quad \text{and} \quad \int \frac{-1}{x\sqrt{x^2-1}}\,dx = \operatorname{arccsc}|x| + C$$

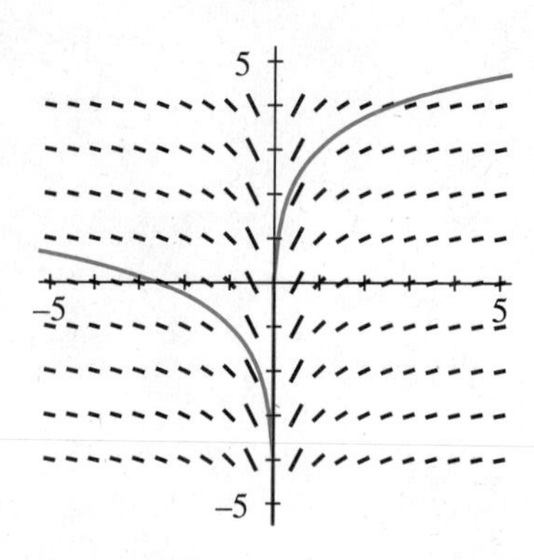

Figure 6.43 Antiderivatives of $\frac{1}{x}$ depend on the sign of x.

are valid for the separate cases where $x > 1$ and $x < -1$.

If an interval includes points of discontinuity for a function f, then an antiderivative may or may not be defined at those points. A different arbitrary constant must be designated for each subinterval lying between two points of discontinuity of the original function f.

EXAMPLE 35 Find the most general antiderivative of $y = \frac{1}{x}$ over the set of inputs

$$\{x : -1 < x < 3,\ x \neq 0\}.$$

Solution We write

$$\int \frac{1}{x}\,dx = \ln(-x) + C_1 \text{ for } -1 < x < 0 \quad \text{and} \quad \int \frac{1}{x}\,dx = \ln(x) + C_2 \text{ for } 0 < x < 3$$

to express the fact that two different arbitrary constants are involved for the two subintervals $-1 < x < 0$ and $0 < x < 3$. ■

For differentiation of many functions, one need only know the derivatives of a few basic functions and how to apply basic differentiation rules such as the product and chain rules. Unfortunately, there are no product and chain rules for integration, but there are some techniques we can use to find many more antiderivatives.

The method of substitution

The **method of substitution** is essentially a technique used to help us recognize a derivative produced by the *chain rule*. If we take the derivative of the composition of two functions $f \circ g$, then the chain rule gives us

$$\frac{d}{dx} f(g(x)) = f'(g(x))g'(x).$$

This means that if we encounter $f'(g(x))g'(x)$ as an integrand, we can reverse the process:

$$\int f'(g(x))g'(x)\,dx = f(g(x)) + C.$$

EXAMPLE 36 Use the fact that $\frac{d}{dx}\sin(x^2) = \cos(x^2)\cdot 2x$ to integrate $\int x\cos(x^2)\,dx$.

Solution Since $x\cos(x^2) = \frac{1}{2}(\cos(x^2)\cdot 2x)$, and we know that $\frac{d}{dx}(\sin(x^2)) = \cos(x^2)\cdot 2x$, we must have

$$\int x\cos(x^2)\,dx = \frac{1}{2}\int \cos(x^2)\cdot 2x\,dx = \frac{1}{2}\sin(x^2) + C.$$ ■

EXAMPLE 37 Use the fact that $\frac{d}{dx}[\tan^3(x)] = 3\tan^2(x)\sec^2(x)$ to integrate $\int \tan^2(x)\sec^2(x)\,dx$.

Solution Since $\tan^2(x)\sec^2(x) = \frac{1}{3}(3\tan^2(x)\sec^2(x))$, we must have

$$\int \tan^2(x)\sec^2(x)dx = \frac{1}{3}\int (3\tan^2(x)\sec^2(x))dx = \frac{1}{3}\tan^3(x) + C.$$ ■

In both of these examples, finding an antiderivative involved recognizing the integrand as a constant multiple of some derivative we had seen before.

▶▶▶ **Remember, only *constants* can be factored outside the $\int$ sign.**

Sometimes, a change in the variable of integration can put the integrand in a more recognizable form. This is the main idea behind the *method of substitution*. If we write $u = g(x)$, then the chain rule can be written as

$$\frac{d}{dx}f(u) = f'(u)\frac{du}{dx},$$

and the corresponding integral formula becomes

$$\int f'(u)\frac{du}{dx}\,dx = f(u) + C.$$

If we agree to use the shorthand

$$du = \frac{du}{dx}dx$$

(we refer to du as the **differential** of u with respect to x), then we can write this as

$$\int f'(u)du = f(u) + C,$$

which is a valid integral formula entirely in terms of the new variable u. If f' happens to be a derivative we more easily recognize, then this change of variables has been useful.

Let's carefully outline the method of substitution, and then apply it to several examples.

Method of Substitution

Step 1. Let $u = g(x)$.

Good choices of substitutions to try are suggested when $g(x)$ appears raised to a power, appears in the denominator or, in general, appears as an "inside" function of a composition.

Step 2. Compute $du = g'(x)\,dx$.

Step 3. Substitute u for $g(x)$ and du for $g'(x)\,dx$ in the integrand.

You may find it necessary to express x in terms of u in order to express the new integrand entirely in terms of u and du.

Step 4. Integrate and substitute $g(x)$ back for u. (Don't forget the arbitrary constant C.)

Step 5. Check your solution by differentiating and comparing to the original integrand.

You should note that the method of substitution carries with it no guarantee of success. Ultimately you (or a machine) must be able to recognize the integrand as the derivative of some function.

EXAMPLE 38 Find $\int \sin^2(x)\cos(x)\,dx$.

Solution Let $u = \sin(x)$. Then $du = \cos(x)\,dx$. Substituting u for $\sin(x)$ and du for $\cos(x)\,dx$ yields

$$\int \sin^2(x)\cos(x)\,dx = \int u^2\,du.$$

Antidifferentiating, we have

$$\int u^2\,du = \frac{u^3}{3} + C = \frac{\sin^3(x)}{3} + C.$$

We can check our answer by differentiating:

$$\frac{d}{dx}\left(\frac{\sin^3(x)}{3} + C\right) = \sin^2(x)\cos(x).$$

■

EXAMPLE 39 Find $\int x^4 e^{x^5}\, dx$.

Solution Let $u = x^5$. Then $du = 5x^4\, dx$. Substituting u for x^5 and $\frac{1}{5}du$ for $x^4\, dx$ yields

$$\int x^4 e^{x^5}\, dx = \frac{1}{5}\int e^u\, du = \frac{e^u}{5} + C = \frac{e^{x^5}}{5} + C.$$

We can check our answer by differentiating:

$$\frac{d}{dx}(\frac{e^{x^5}}{5} + C) = x^4 e^{x^5}.$$

■

EXAMPLE 40 Find $\int \frac{x^2}{5 + x^3}\, dx$.

Solution Let $u = 5 + x^3$. Then $du = 3x^2\, dx$. Substituting u for $5 + x^3$ and $\frac{1}{3}du$ for $3x^2\, dx$ yields

$$\int \frac{x^2}{5 + x^3}\, dx = \int \frac{\frac{1}{3}\, du}{u}.$$

Simplifying and antidifferentiating, we have

$$\frac{1}{3}\int \frac{1}{u}\, du = \frac{\ln|u|}{3} + C = \frac{\ln|5 + x^3|}{3} + C.$$

We can check our answer by differentiating:

$$\frac{d}{dx}(\frac{\ln|5 + x^3|}{3} + C) = \frac{x^2}{5 + x^3}.$$

■

EXAMPLE 41 Find $\int \csc^3(x)\cot(x)\, dx$.

Solution Let $u = \csc(x)$. Then $du = -\csc(x)\cot(x)\, dx$. If we substitute u^3 for $\csc^3(x)$, there does not appear to be a way to substitute du. However, if we think of the integrand as

$$\int \csc^3(x)\cot(x)\, dx = \int \csc^2(x)\csc(x)\cot(x)\, dx,$$

then we can substitute u^2 for $\csc^2(x)$ and $-du$ for $\csc(x)\cot(x)\, dx$. This yields

$$-\int u^2\, du = -\frac{u^3}{3} + C = -\frac{\csc^3(x)}{3} + C.$$

(Check the answer by differentiating.) ■

EXAMPLE 42 Find $\int \frac{\cos\sqrt{x}}{\sqrt{x}}\,dx$.

Solution Let $u = \sqrt{x} = x^{1/2}$. Then $du = \frac{1}{2}x^{-1/2}\,dx = \frac{dx}{2\sqrt{x}}$. Substituting u for $\sqrt{x}$ and $2\,du$ for $\frac{dx}{\sqrt{x}}$ yields

$$\int \frac{\cos\sqrt{x}}{\sqrt{x}}\,dx = 2\int \cos(u)\,du = 2\sin(u) + C = 2\sin(\sqrt{x}) + C.$$

(Check the answer by differentiating.) ■

EXAMPLE 43 Find $\int \frac{x}{x+1}\,dx$.

Solution Let $u = x + 1$. Then $du = dx$. In this case we can also write $x = u - 1$, and the substitutions yield

$$\int \frac{x}{x+1}\,dx = \int \frac{u-1}{u}\,du = \int (1 - \frac{1}{u})\,du$$

$$= u - \ln|u| + C = (x+1) - \ln|x+1| + C = x - \ln|x+1| + (C+1).$$

Since C is an arbitrary constant, there is no real need to include the additional constant term 1 ($C+1$ is as arbitrary as C), so we can write the final form as

$$\int \frac{x}{x+1}\,dx = x - \ln|x+1| + C.$$

We can check our answer by differentiating:

$$\frac{d}{dx}(x - \ln|x+1| + C) = 1 - \frac{1}{x+1} = \frac{x+1}{x+1} - \frac{1}{x+1} = \frac{x}{x+1}.$$ ■

Substitution and definite integrals

To apply the method of substitution to a *definite integral*

$$\int_a^b f(x)\,dx,$$

we have two options.

Option 1: Carry out the method of substitution all the way on the corresponding indefinite integral (antiderivative), then compute the difference of the values at $x = b$ and $x = a$ as usual.

Option 2: After making the substitutions for $u = g(x)$ and $du = g'(x)\,dx$, also substitute for the limits of integration: $u = g(a)$ when $x = a$ and $u = g(b)$ when $x = b$.

EXAMPLE 44 Compute $\int_1^2 \frac{x}{(x^2+3)^3}\,dx$ using option 1.

Solution With option 1, we first find the antiderivative $\int \frac{x}{(x^2+3)^3}\,dx$. Let $u = x^2+3$ and $du = 2x\,dx$. Substitute u for (x^2+3) and $\frac{du}{2}$ for $x\,dx$:

$$\int \frac{x}{(x^2+3)^3}\,dx = \int \frac{du}{2u^3} = \frac{1}{2}\int u^{-3}\,du = \frac{1}{2}\cdot\frac{u^{-2}}{-2} = \frac{-1}{4u^2} = \frac{-1}{4(x^2+3)^2}.$$

We've suppressed the arbitrary constant C in the antiderivative because it will cancel anyway when we evaluate the definite integral:

$$\int_1^2 \frac{x}{(x^2+3)^3}\,dx = \frac{-1}{4(x^2+3)^2}\Bigg]_{x=1}^{x=2} = \frac{-1}{196} - \frac{-1}{64} = \frac{33}{3136} \approx .010523. \quad \blacksquare$$

EXAMPLE 45 Now compute $\int_1^2 \frac{x}{(x^2+3)^3}\,dx$ using option 2.

Solution Let $u = x^2+3$ and $du = 2x\,dx$. When $x = 1$, $u = 1^2+3 = 4$. When $x = 2$, $u = 2^2+3 = 7$. Making substitutions in both the integrand and for the limits of integration, we have

$$\int_1^2 \frac{x}{(x^2+3)^3}\,dx = \int_4^7 \frac{du}{2u^3} = \frac{-1}{4u^2}\Bigg]_{u=4}^{u=7} = \frac{-1}{196} + \frac{1}{64} = \frac{33}{3136} \approx 0.10523. \quad \blacksquare$$

Other methods of integration—using tables of integrals

There are a number of other techniques of integration. *Integration by parts* is discussed in Chapter 8. (Just as the method of substitution helps us recognize derivatives produced by the chain rule, integration by parts helps us recognize derivatives produced by the product rule.) Other techniques of integration are discussed in the Appendices. Many of these other techniques turn out to be special cases of the method of substitution combined with some clever algebraic and/or trigonometric manipulations. At one time, these "tricks of the trade" were covered at length in beginning calculus courses, for they were the only tools available to compute integrals. Even then, the tricks cover relatively small special classes of functions. Now, technology provides us with additional tools to study both indefinite integrals (antiderivatives can be investigated graphically with slope fields) and definite integrals (using a machine's numerical integration routines).

Nevertheless, simple expressions for antiderivatives can be quite useful when we can find them. Many books (and software) contain long tables of integral forms that have been compiled to catalog many of the types of integrands encountered in applications. Quite often, these tables of integrals are written in terms of u and du with the expectation that the user of the table will first make a substitution to rewrite it in a form matching one of the entries in the table. Even when a computer algebra system is available, a change of variables may aid the system. For example, here is a formula from an integral table:

$$\int e^{au}\sin(bu)\,du = \frac{e^{au}}{a^2+b^2}(a\sin(bu) - b\cos(bu)) + C.$$

In this formula, it is understood that a and b are constants and that u represents some differentiable function. The next example shows how we can take advantage of this formula using the method of substitution.

EXAMPLE 46 Find $\int 3xe^{7x^2}\sin(5x^2)\,dx$.

Solution First, we'll make the substitution $u = x^2$ (so that $du = 2xdx$ and $dx = du/2x$):

$$\int 3xe^{7x^2}\sin(5x^2)\,dx = \int 3xe^{7u}\sin(5u)\,\frac{du}{2x} = \frac{3}{2}\int e^{7u}\sin(5u)\,du.$$

Now we can use the integral formula with $a = 7$ and $b = 5$:

$$\frac{3}{2}\int e^{7u}\sin(5u)\,du = \frac{3}{2}\left(\frac{e^{7u}}{7^2+5^2}\right)(7\sin(5u) - 5\cos(5u)) + C.$$

Substitute $u = x^2$ and simplify:

$$\int 3xe^{7x^2}\sin(5x^2)\,dx = \frac{3e^{7x^2}}{148}(7\sin(5x^2) - 5\cos(5x^2)) + C.$$

■

Some integral formulas involving powers of a function are called *reduction formulas*. They generally allow an integral to be expressed in terms of integrals involving smaller powers of the same function. Repeated application of the formula can therefore reduce the problem to one whose solution is known.

Here is an example of a reduction formula from an integral table:

$$\int \sin^n(u)\,du = -\frac{1}{n}\sin^{n-1}(u)\cos(u) + \frac{n-1}{n}\int \sin^{n-2}(u)\,du.$$

We illustrate how this formula is applied with the following example.

EXAMPLE 47 Find $\int \sin^5(x)\,dx$.

Solution Here $n = 5$, so a direct application of the formula gives us

$$\int \sin^5(x)\,dx = -\frac{1}{5}\sin^4(x)\cos(x) + \frac{4}{5}\int \sin^3(x)\,dx.$$

Note that we can apply the formula again to the last integral with $n = 3$:

$$\int \sin^3(x)\,dx = -\frac{1}{3}\sin^2(x)\cos(x) + \frac{2}{3}\int \sin(x)\,dx.$$

If we substitute this right-hand expression for $\int \sin^3(x)\,dx$ above, we have

$$\int \sin^5(x)\,dx = -\frac{1}{5}\sin^4(x)\cos(x) - \frac{4}{15}\sin^2(x)\cos(x) + \frac{8}{15}\int \sin(x)\,dx.$$

Finally, we have reduced the problem to one involving an integral we recognize immediately, so the final answer is

$$\int \sin^5(x)\,dx = -\frac{1}{5}\sin^4(x)\cos(x) - \frac{4}{15}\sin^2(x)\cos(x) - \frac{8}{15}\cos(x) + C. \quad ■$$

EXERCISES for Section 6.7

For exercises 1–40: Find the antiderivatives using the method of substitution.

1. $\int x\cos(x^2)\,dx$

2. $\int \sin(x)\cos^2(x)\,dx$

3. $\int \frac{x^4}{x^5 - 17}\,dx$

4. $\int (.05x - \pi)^{132}\,dx$

5. $\int \frac{x^5}{\sqrt[3]{2x^3 + 7}}\,dx$

6. $\int \sin(x)\sqrt{2\cos(x) + 3}\,dx$

7. $\int xe^{-x^2}\,dx$

8. $\int \frac{e^x}{1 + e^{2x}}\,dx$

9. $\int \frac{\ln(x)}{x}\,dx$

10. $\int \tan^3(x)\sec^2(x)\,dx$

11. $\int x^2\sin(4x^3 + 8)\,dx$

12. $\int \frac{1}{x^3}(1 + \frac{1}{x^2})^5\,dx$

13. $\int 3x^2(x^3 + 1)^4\,dx$

14. $\int \frac{x}{\sqrt{16 - x^2}}\,dx$

15. $\int (1 + \sin(x))^{5/2}\cos(x)\,dx$

16. $\int x\sin(x^2)\,dx$

17. $\int 4\cos(6x)\,dx$

18. $\int \frac{x}{9 - x^2}\,dx$

19. $\int x^2e^{4x^3}\,dx$

20. $\int \sin^2(x)\cos(x)\,dx$

21. $\int \frac{(1 + \sqrt{x})^4}{\sqrt{x}}\,dx$

22. $\int \frac{\cos(\sqrt{x})}{\sqrt{x}}\,dx$

23. $\int \frac{\sec^2(\ln(x))}{x}\,dx$

24. $\int \frac{3e^{4x}}{e^{4x} + 1}\,dx$

25. $\int \frac{e^x}{1 + e^{2x}}\,dx$

26. $\int \frac{x}{1 + x^4}\,dx$

27. $\displaystyle\int \frac{1}{x^2+4}\,dx$

28. $\displaystyle\int \frac{e^{\tan(x)}}{\cos^2(x)}\,dx$

29. $\displaystyle\int \frac{e^x \sec^2(e^x)}{\tan(e^x)}\,dx$

30. $\displaystyle\int \frac{\sec(x)\tan(x)}{1+\sec(x)}\,dx$

31. $\displaystyle\int \sin(x)\cos(x)e^{\cos^2(x)}\,dx$

32. $\displaystyle\int (x-1)e^{-x^2+2x}\,dx$

33. $\displaystyle\int \frac{(\ln(x)+1)^2}{x}\,dx$

34. $\displaystyle\int \frac{\cos(\ln(x))}{x}\,dx$

35. $\displaystyle\int \frac{(\ln(x))^4}{x}\,dx$

36. $\displaystyle\int \frac{\sec^2(x)}{5+\tan(x)}\,dx$

37. $\displaystyle\int \frac{\sec(\ln(x))\tan(\ln(x))}{x}\,dx$

38. $\displaystyle\int \frac{\sin(x)\cos(x)}{\sqrt{\sin^2(x)+5}}\,dx$

39. $\displaystyle\int \frac{2}{x(8+\ln(x))^{1/2}}\,dx$

40. $\displaystyle\int (3x^3-x)^5(18x^2-2)\,dx$

For exercises 41–50: You are given definite integrals whose integrands correspond to the indefinite integrals in exercises 1–10. For each one, graph the integrand over the interval of values indicated by the limits of integration and estimate visually the value of the definite integral. Compute the new limits of integration under the substitution used in the corresponding exercise (1–10). Calculate each definite integral using both options discussed in the text, and use a computer or calculator to compute the definite integral and compare results.

41. $\displaystyle\int_0^{\pi} x\cos(x^2)\,dx$

42. $\displaystyle\int_0^{2\pi} \sin(x)\cos^2(x)\,dx$

43. $\displaystyle\int_{-1}^{1} \frac{x^4}{x^5-17}\,dx$

44. $\displaystyle\int_0^{\pi} (.05x-\pi)^{132}\,dx$

45. $\displaystyle\int_{-1}^{2} \frac{x^5}{\sqrt[3]{2x^3+7}}\,dx$

46. $\displaystyle\int_0^{\pi/2} \sin(x)\sqrt{2\cos(x)+3}\,dx$

47. $\displaystyle\int_1^{\ln(2)} xe^{-x^2}\,dx$

48. $\displaystyle\int_0^{\ln(\pi/4)} \frac{e^x}{1+e^{2x}}\,dx$

49. $\displaystyle\int_1^{e} \frac{\ln(x)}{x}\,dx$

50. $\displaystyle\int_{\pi/3}^{2\pi/3} \tan^3(x)\sec^2(x)\,dx$

For exercises 51–54: Verify the trigonometric integration formulas using the indicated substitution.

51. $\displaystyle\int \tan(x)\,dx = -\ln|\cos(x)| + C.$

(Hint: write $\tan(x) = \dfrac{\sin(x)}{\cos(x)}$ and use the substitution $u = \cos(x)$.)

52. $\int \cot(x)\,dx = \ln|\sin(x)| + C.$

(Hint: write $\cot(x) = \dfrac{\cos(x)}{\sin(x)}$ and use the substitution $u = \sin(x)$.)

53. $\int \sec(x)\,dx = \ln|\sec(x) + \tan(x)| + C.$

(Hint: first multiply the integrand by $\dfrac{\sec(x)+\tan(x)}{\sec(x)+\tan(x)}$, then use the substitution $u = \sec(x) + \tan(x)$.)

54. $\int \csc(x)\,dx = \ln|\csc(x) - \cot(x)| + C.$

(Hint: first multiply the integrand by $\dfrac{\csc(x)-\cot(x)}{\csc(x)-\cot(x)}$, then use the substitution $u = \csc(x) - \cot(x)$.)

---

55. Use the integral formula

$$\int e^{au}\cos(bu)\,du = \frac{e^{au}}{a^2+b^2}(a\cos(bu) + b\sin(bu)) + C$$

to find

$$\int \frac{e^{-\arctan(x)}\cos(4\arctan(x))}{1+x^2}\,dx.$$

56. Use the reduction formula

$$\int \sec^n(x)\,dx = \frac{\sec^{n-2}(x)\tan(x)}{n-1} + \frac{n-2}{n-1}\int \sec^{n-2}(x)\,dx$$

to find $\int \sec^3(x)\,dx$.

The hyperbolic sine and cosine functions are defined as follows:

$$\sinh(x) = \frac{e^x - e^{-x}}{2} \qquad \text{and} \qquad \cosh(x) = \frac{e^x + e^{-x}}{2}.$$

The rest of the hyperbolic functions are defined in a way analogous to the corresponding trigonometric functions:

$$\tanh(x) = \frac{\sinh(x)}{\cosh(x)} \qquad \coth(x) = \frac{\cosh(x)}{\sinh(x)}$$

$$\operatorname{sech}(x) = \frac{1}{\cosh(x)} \qquad \operatorname{csch}(x) = \frac{1}{\sinh(x)}$$

For exercises 57–62: Graph the indicated hyperbolic function over the interval $[-10, 10]$. Then calculate both its derivative and antiderivative and express (if possible) in terms of other hyperbolic functions.

57. $\sinh(x)$

58. $\cosh(x)$

59. $\text{sech}(x)$

60. $\text{csch}(x)$

61. $\tanh(x)$

62. $\coth(x)$

For exercises 63–66: Find the following antiderivatives using the method of substitution.

63. $\displaystyle\int \frac{\text{sech}^2(\ln(x))}{x}\,dx$

64. $\displaystyle\int e^x \,\text{sech}(e^x)\tanh(e^x)\,dx$

65. $\displaystyle\int \frac{\sinh(x)}{1+\cosh(x)}\,dx$

66. $\displaystyle\int \tanh^3(2x)\,\text{sech}^2(2x)\,dx$

7

Applications and Extensions of the Integral

Integrals are powerful tools for measurement in a wide variety of applications. By its very definition, a definite integral can be used to measure certain areas. However, the utility of definite integration goes far beyond this particular geometric problem. In general, you can think of a definite integral

$$\int_a^b f(x)\,dx$$

as measuring the accumulated change or net effect of the function values $f(x)$ over the interval $[a, b]$ (see Figure 7.1).

Depending on the quantity the function values $f(x)$ represent, the definite integral represents some related quantity. For example, if we interpret $f(x)$ geometrically as the height of the graph of $y = f(x)$, then we can interpret the definite integral $\int_a^b f(x)\,dx$ as the net area *above* the x-axis. (As usual, we count area lying below the x-axis as negative.) However, if we interpret $f(x)$ as representing something other than height (such as velocity or force or area), we can, in turn, interpret the definite integral as something other than net area (like distance or work or volume). In this chapter, we use definite integration to measure area, volume, and curve length. We discuss the use of definite integrals to compute various "averages," and we examine physical applications of integration to particle motion, force, and work.

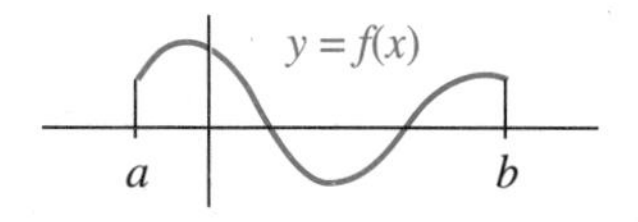

Figure 7.1 Definite integral $\int_a^b f(x)\,dx$ measures the "net effect" of f over $[a, b]$.

The hypotheses of both fundamental theorems of calculus require that the function integrand f be continuous over a closed bounded interval $[a, b]$. However, it is sometimes possible to integrate functions whose graphs have vertical asymptotes or integrate over infinitely long intervals. These activities are commonly referred to as *improper integration*, not because there is anything wrong, but rather to emphasize that they represent an extension beyond the usual setting of the fundamental theorems of calculus.

7.1 USING DEFINITE INTEGRALS TO MEASURE AREA

Cavalieri's principle (named after the Italian mathematician Bonaventur Cavalieri) states that the area of a region in a plane is completely determined by the heights of its cross sections (slices made perpendicular to the axis along its length). We illustrate the idea of Cavalieri's principle in Figure 7.2. Roughly speaking, if we know the height of a region at every point along its length, then we should be able to determine the area of the region. If we set up a coordinate axis along the length of the region as shown so that the region lies over the interval $[a, b]$, then we can mathematically describe the height of the cross section $h(x)$ as a function of the points x in $[a, b]$.

In terms of Riemann sums, we could imagine cutting a thin slice of the region between two points x and $x + \Delta x$ as shown. If the height h is a continuous function of x, then the area of the slice is approximately $h(x)\Delta x$. Now suppose that we add up the areas of n thin slices from a to b at points $x_1, x_2, \ldots, x_n$. If we take the limit as the slice width Δx approaches 0 (and n gets larger), we have

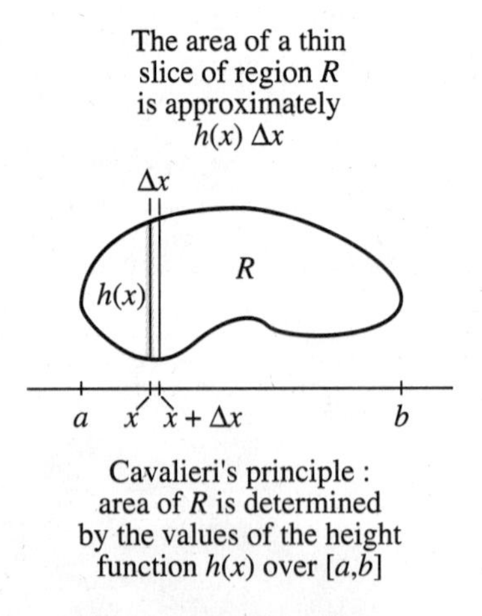

Figure 7.2 Cavalieri's principle: area of $R = \int_a^b h(x)\,dx$.

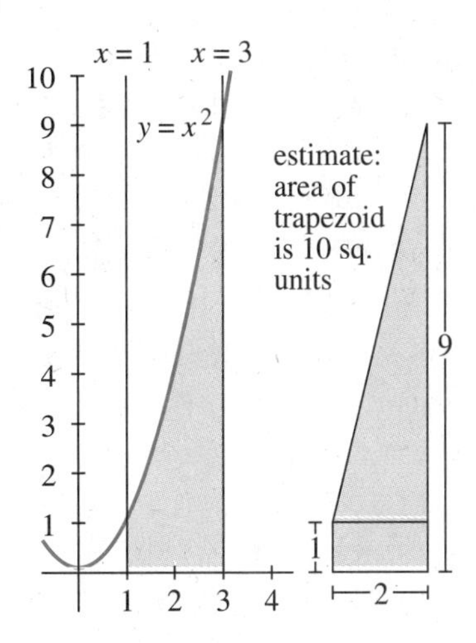

Figure 7.3 $\int_1^3 x^2\,dx$ gives the area of the shaded region.

$$\lim_{\Delta x \to 0} \sum_{i=1}^{n} h(x_i)\Delta x = \int_a^b h(x)\,dx.$$

This description allows us to write down the area of the region R as a definite integral:

$$\text{area of } R = \int_a^b h(x)\,dx.$$

Strictly speaking, there are regions with such strange shapes that either the cross-sectional height function h does not exist or it cannot be integrated. However, for any region whose height varies continuously over its length (or can be broken down into a finite number of subregions satisfying this property), we could *define* the area of the region as $\int_a^b h(x)\,dx$. In the rest of this section we apply this principle to several examples. In the simplest case, a single definite integral may give us the desired area.

EXAMPLE 1 Find the area of the region bounded by the x-axis, the vertical lines $x = 1$ and $x = 3$, and the graph of $y = x^2$.

Solution If we graph $y = x^2$ between the vertical lines $x = 1$ and $x = 3$ (see Figure 7.3), we can recognize the area of the region as being given by the definite integral

$$\int_1^3 x^2\,dx = \frac{26}{3} \text{ square units.}$$ ■

It is important to judge the reasonableness of your calculation by estimating the area visually. In this example, we can roughly estimate the area to be somewhat less than 10 square units by simply approximating the region with a trapezoid (or, if you prefer, the sum of the areas of a rectangle and triangle). Our exact calculation of $8\frac{2}{3}$ square units looks very reasonable in light of this estimate.

Powerful numerical integration routines exist in many computer software packages and on some hand-held calculators. These machines allow us to quickly calculate many definite integrals to high precision without the need for finding an antiderivative. However, a machine cannot tell us whether the definite integral we ask it to compute is the *right* one. Visually estimating the area is not foolproof, but it can often help you catch errors such as pushing a wrong button or an incorrect set-up. For example, if we had accidentally integrated $\int_1^3 x\,dx$ instead of $\int_1^3 x^2\,dx$, we would have obtained an area of 4. This is much smaller than our estimate of 10, and should prompt us to check our work very carefully. With luck, we might spot the missing exponent in our integrand.

It's important to keep in mind that when a function's graph lies below the x-axis for an interval $[a, b]$ (in other words, $f(x) < 0$), then the definite integral $\int_a^b f(x)$ is *negative*.

EXAMPLE 2 Find the total area enclosed between the graph of $y = \sin(x)$ and the x-axis for $0 \leq x \leq 2\pi$.

Solution If we simply integrate over $[0, 2\pi]$, we find

$$\int_0^{2\pi} \sin(x)\,dx = -\cos(x)\Big]_0^{2\pi} = -\cos(2\pi) - (-\cos(0)) = -1 - (-1) = 0.$$

What's going on here? If we look at the graph of $y = \sin(x)$ over this interval, we see the problem (Figure 7.4).

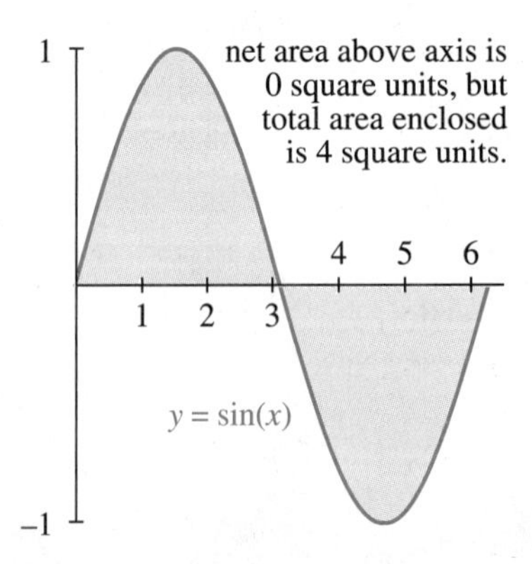

Figure 7.4 Net area versus total area.

The definite integral of $\sin(x)$ over $[0, \pi]$ is cancelled out by its definite integral over $[\pi, 2\pi]$. If we want the actual area enclosed by the graph and the x-axis over $[0, 2\pi]$, we'll need to take the absolute value of the definite integral over $[\pi, 2\pi]$ in our calculation:

$$\int_0^{\pi} \sin(x)\,dx = -\cos(x)\Big]_0^{\pi} = -\cos(\pi) - (-\cos(0)) = -(-1) - (-1) = 2,$$

while $\int_{\pi}^{2\pi} \sin(x)\,dx = -2$. Thus, the total area is $2 + |-2| = 4$. ■

In general, calculating the area of a region bounded by two function graphs $y = f(x)$ and $y = g(x)$ may first require finding the intersection points of the two graphs (solve $f(x) = g(x)$ for x) to determine the appropriate limits of integration. The value of the height function $h(x)$ will be either $f(x) - g(x)$ (in the case that $f(x) \geq g(x)$) or $g(x) - f(x)$ (in the case that $f(x) < g(x)$). In either case, we could write down the area of the region as

$$\int_a^b |f(x) - g(x)|\,dx,$$

where a and b are the first and last intersection points and the absolute value signs in the integrand take care of both possibilities at once.

Our next area example exploits the graphing, root-finding, and integration capabilities of a calculator or computer.

EXAMPLE 3 Find the area bounded by the graphs of $y = e^{-x^2}$ and $y = x^3 - x + 1$.

Solution First, we graph both functions simultaneously to obtain a plot like that pictured in Figure 7.5. By using a machine's root-finder on the difference of the two functions $(x^3 - x - 1) - e^{-x^2}$, we find three intersection points, at $a \approx -1.276638$, at 0, and at $b \approx 0.676228$. The intersection at $x = 0$ is easy to check, and the other two look quite reasonable from the graphs. (Can you tell why these are the only three intersection points?)

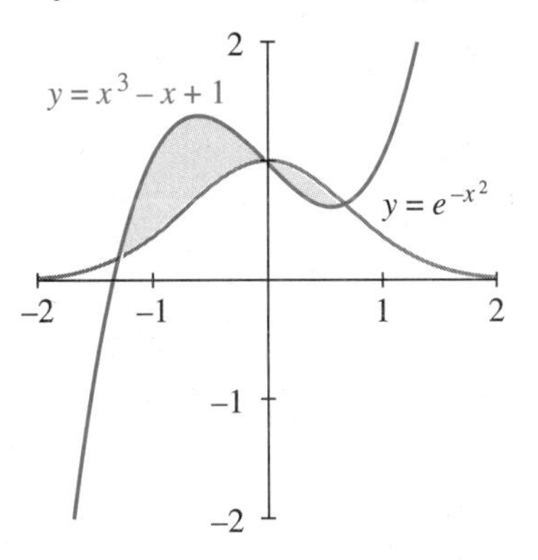

Figure 7.5 Graphs of $y = x^3 - x + 1$ and $y = e^{-x^2}$.

To calculate the area bounded by these two curves, we used a machine's numerical integrator to calculate

$$\int_{-1.276638}^{0.676228} |(x^3 - x + 1) - e^{-x^2}|\, dx \approx 0.6902.$$

Without using absolute values, we need to express the area as the sum of two definite integrals:

$$\int_{-1.276638}^{0} ((x^3 - x + 1) - e^{-x^2})\, dx + \int_{0}^{0.676228} (e^{-x^2} - (x^3 - x + 1))\, dx. \quad ■$$

Sometimes curves are more easily or naturally described as graphs of the form $x = f(y)$. To calculate the area enclosed by two curves of this type, we can integrate the width function of the region over an interval of y-values.

EXAMPLE 4 Find the area of the region bounded by the graphs of $x = y^2$ and $x = 4 - y^2$.

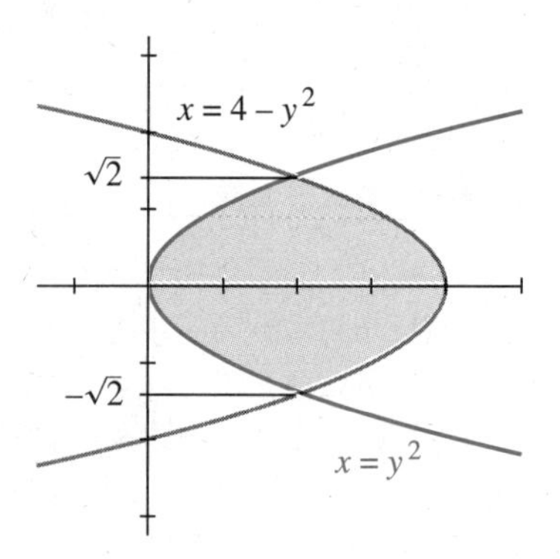

Figure 7.6 Region bounded by the graphs of $x = y^2$ and $x = 4 - y^2$.

Solution The graphs of $x = y^2$ and $x = 4 - y^2$ are shown in Figure 7.6. The two curves intersect when $y = \pm\sqrt{2}$. For any value y such that $-\sqrt{2} \le y \le \sqrt{2}$, the horizontal width of the region is $(4 - y^2) - y^2 = 4 - 2y^2$. We can calculate the area of the region using the definite integral

$$\int_{-\sqrt{2}}^{\sqrt{2}} (4 - 2y^2)\, dy = (4y - \frac{2y^3}{3})\Big]_{-\sqrt{2}}^{\sqrt{2}} = \frac{16\sqrt{2}}{3} \approx 7.5425. \quad ■$$

EXERCISES for Section 7.1

For exercises 1–15: Find the area of the indicated region using definite integration. Graph each region and judge the reasonableness of your answer. Some of the exercises may require the help of a machine.

1. Region enclosed between the graph of $y = x$ and the x-axis between $x = 0$ and $x = 5$.

2. Region enclosed between the graph of $y = x^2 - 9$ and the x-axis.

3. Region enclosed between the graph of $y = \frac{1}{2}\sin x$ and the x-axis between $x = 0$ and $x = \pi$.

4. Region enclosed between the graph of $y = e^{x-1}$ and the x-axis between $x = 0$ and $x = 3$.

5. Region enclosed between the graph of $y = \frac{|x|}{4} - 6$ and the x-axis.

6. Region enclosed between the graph of $y = e^{3x} - 3x - 3$ and the x-axis.

7. Region enclosed between the graph of $y = |2 - x|$ and the line $y = 1$.

8. Region enclosed between $y = \ln(x)$, the vertical line $x = 2$, and the horizontal line $y = -2$.

9. Region bounded by $x = 8 - y^2$ and $x = -y + 2$.

10. Region bounded by $x = y^3 - 3$, the x-axis, and $x = 1$.

11. Region bounded by $y = \arcsin(x)$ and $y = \arccos(x)$ between $y = \pi/6$ and $y = \pi/3$. (Hint: integrate in terms of y.)

12. Region bounded by $y = \sin\frac{1}{2}x$ and $y = \frac{1}{2}\sin x$ between 0 and π.

13. Region bounded by $y = \arctan(x)$, $y = \operatorname{arccot}(x)$ and the y-axis.

14. Region bounded by $y = \dfrac{3}{1+x^2}$ and $y = e^{x^2}$.

15. Region bounded by $y = \cos(x)$ and $y = \dfrac{x+1}{3}$.

---

16. Find the constant a so that the area bounded by $y = x^2 - a^2$ and $y = a^2 - x^2$ is exactly 72.

17. The area bounded by the curve $y = x^2$ and the line $y = 4$ is divided into two equal portions by the line $y = c$. Find c.

18. Calculate $\int_{-1}^{1} \sqrt{1 - x^2}\, dx$. The number π is sometimes *defined* as a certain integer multiple of this integral. What integer multiple should be used? Graph $y = \sqrt{1 - x^2}$ and describe the region whose area the definite integral represents.

19. Find the area enclosed by the ellipse $\dfrac{x^2}{25} + \dfrac{y^2}{49} = 1$.

20. Find the area enclosed by the ellipse $\dfrac{x^2}{a^2} + \dfrac{y^2}{b^2} = 1$ where a and b are positive constants.

For exercises 21–28: You are given the graph of a function f against a grid. Assuming that the grid lines are spaced 1 unit apart both horizontally and vertically, estimate the value of $\int_{-6}^{6} |f(x)|\, dx$ for each function. (If the graph does not appear over certain parts of the interval, assume that $f(x) = 0$ for these inputs.)

21.

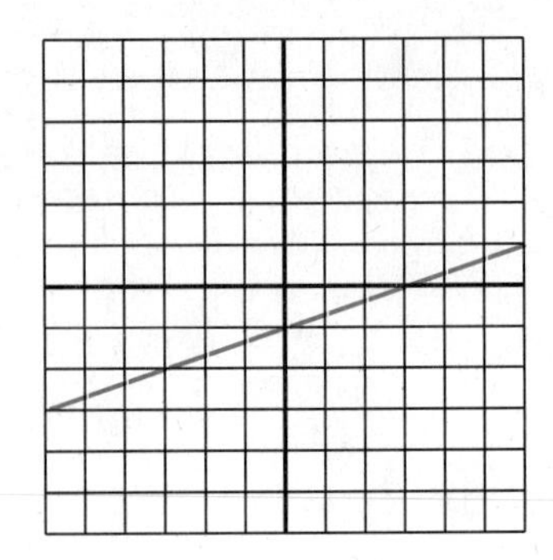

22.

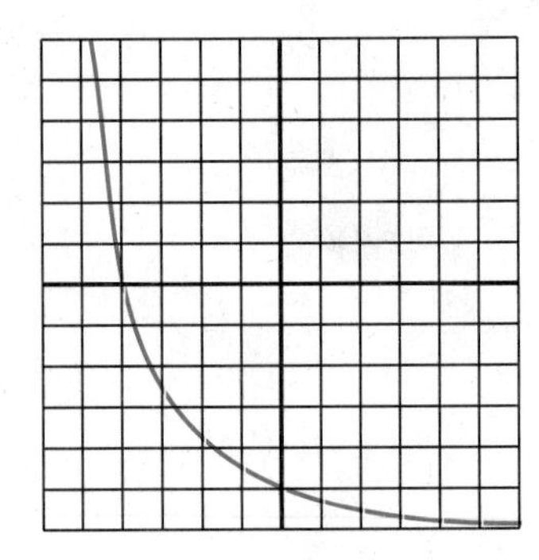

23.

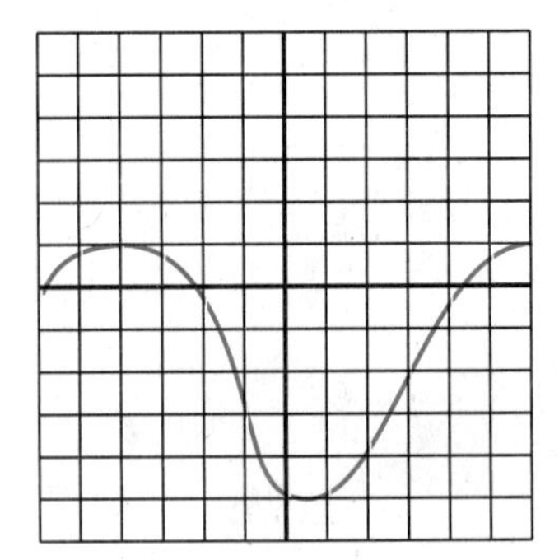

24.

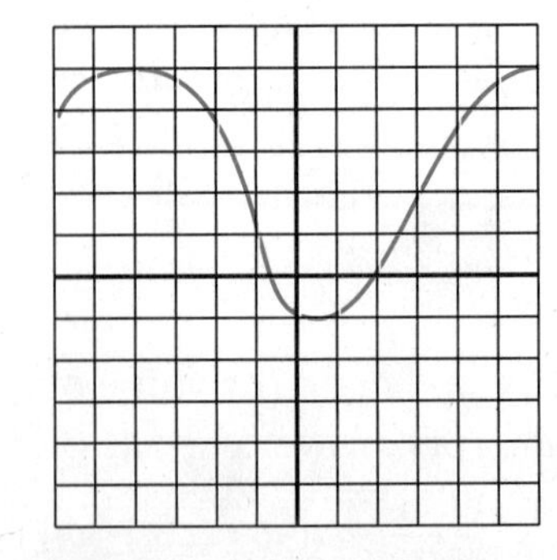

25.

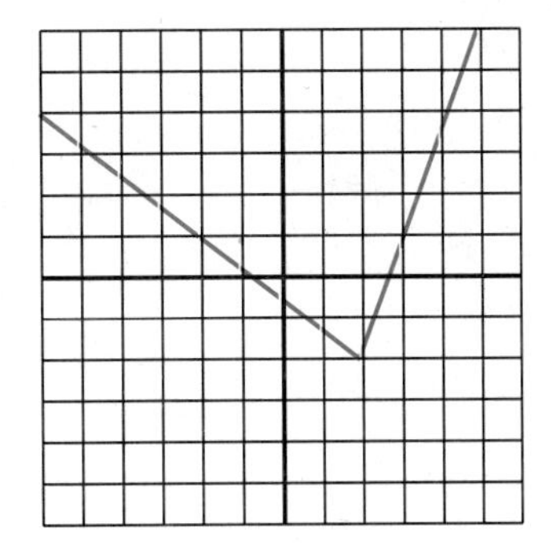

26.

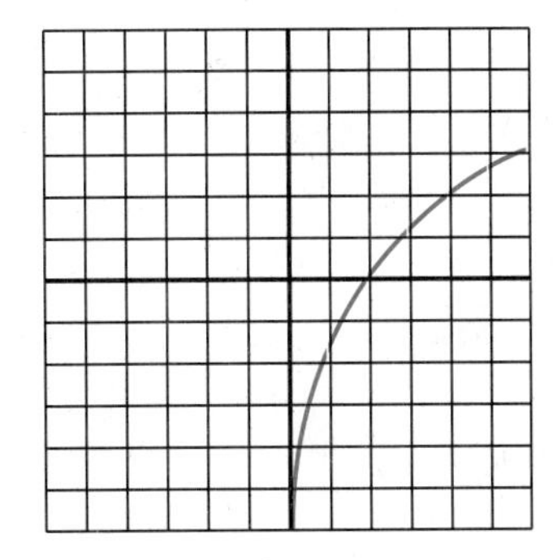

27.

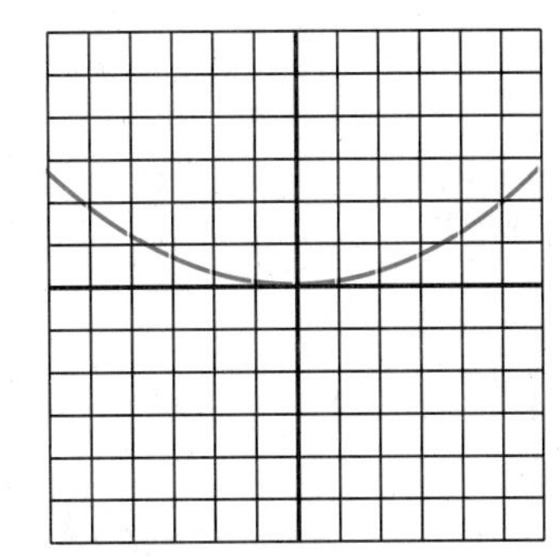

28.

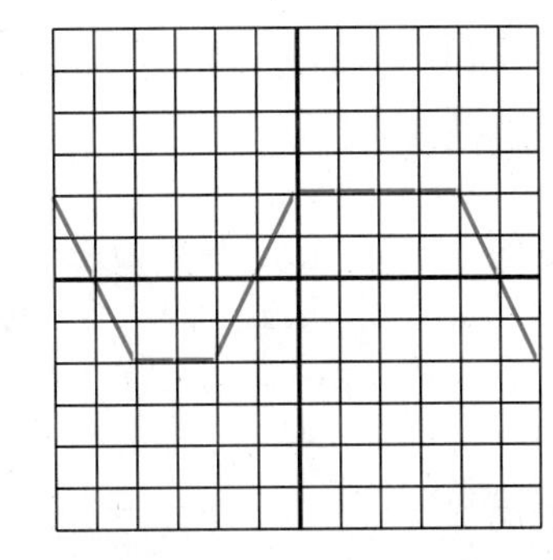

29. One can of paint will cover 50 ft^2. How many cans of paint should you buy to cover the region bounded by $y = -x^2 + 49$, the x-axis, and y-axis, assuming that units along the axes represent feet?

30. Suppose that $m \neq 0$ and $b \neq 0$. Show that the area of the region bounded by the line $y = mx + b$, the x-axis, and the y-axis is always given by $\dfrac{b^2}{2\,|m|}$.

7.2 USING DEFINITE INTEGRALS TO MEASURE VOLUME

Cavalieri's principle can also be stated for objects or regions in space: the volume of a region in space is completely determined by the areas of its cross sections (sliced perpendicular to an axis along its length).

Figure 7.7 illustrates a solid object over the interval $[a, b]$. The cross-sectional area $A(x)$ is the area of the plane region determined by slicing the object with a plane perpendicular to the axis at the point x. In terms of a definite integral, the volume of the region is given by

$$\text{volume} = \int_a^b A(x)\,dx.$$

The reasoning is similar to that given for finding areas. We slice the object into n very thin "slabs." The volume of a typical "slab " is its base area $A(x)$ times its thickness Δx (see Figure 7.8).

Summing up the volumes of all these slabs produces a Riemann sum, and taking the limit over finer partitions (thinner and thinner slices) gives us an integral

$$\lim_{n\to\infty} \sum_{i=1}^{n} A(x_i)\Delta x = \int_a^b A(x)\,dx.$$

EXAMPLE 5 An object lies over the interval $[2, 5]$, and its cross section at each point is a square of length x. Find its volume.

Solution Although there is not enough information to really tell exactly what the object looks like (there are infinitely many objects fitting the description), there is enough information to determine the volume of the object (all such objects have exactly the same volume). You might think of a deck of square cards as an illustration: the volume of the deck doesn't depend on how neatly the deck is stacked up.

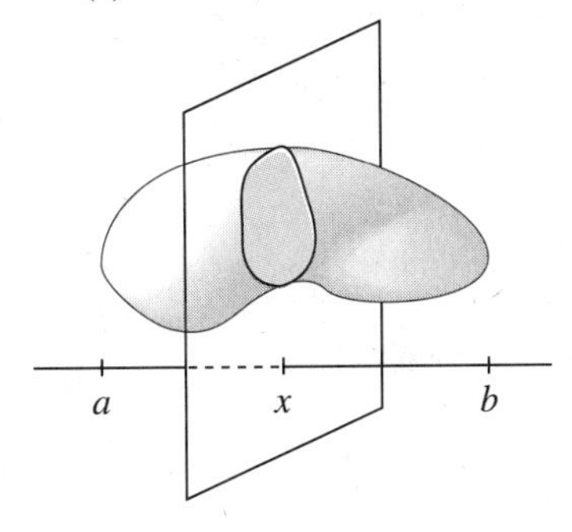

Figure 7.7 The volume of the region is $\int_a^b A(x)\,dx$.

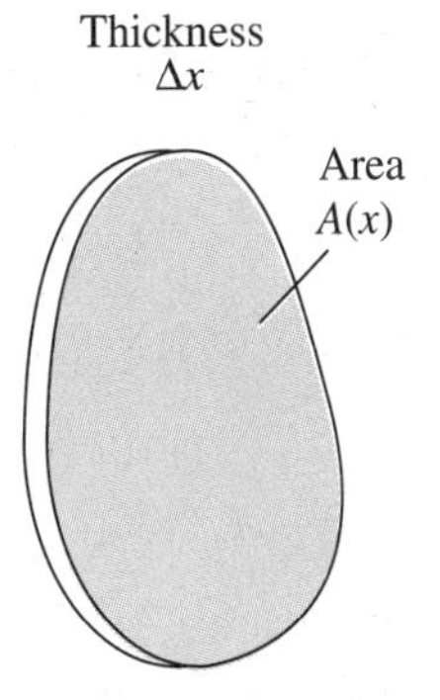

If the cross-sectional area is approximately $A(x)$ over an interval of length Δx, then the volume of the slab is approximately $A(x)\,\Delta x$.

Figure 7.8 Approximating the volume of a thin slice of the region.

The cross-sectional area function is given as $A(x) = x^2$ over the interval $[2, 5]$, so we can calculate the volume as

$$\int_2^5 x^2\,dx = \frac{x^3}{3}\Big]_2^5 = \frac{125}{3} - \frac{8}{3} = \frac{117}{3} = 39 \text{ cubic units.}$$ ■

EXAMPLE 6 Find the volume of a sphere of radius 5.

Solution Let's imagine an axis running along a diameter of the sphere with its origin at the center, so that the sphere lies along the interval $[-5, 5]$. The cross sections of the sphere perpendicular to this axis are circular. For each $x \in [-5, 5]$, the radius of the corresponding cross section is seen to be $r(x) = \sqrt{25 - x^2}$ using the Pythagorean Theorem (see Figure 7.9). Note that the radical symbol indicates the positive square root, so this formula is valid for both positive and negative values $x \in [-5, 5]$.

Hence, the area of each cross section is $A(x) = \pi(r(x))^2 = \pi(25 - x^2)$. A good check of the formula is to try some extreme or special values x: $A(-5) = A(5) = 0$, indicating that the cross-sectional area is 0 at the two ends of the sphere; $A(0) = 25\pi$, indicating that the cross-sectional area at the center of the interval is that of a circle of radius 5.

We find the volume (in cubic units) of the sphere by integrating $A(x)$ over the interval $[-5, 5]$:

$$V = \int_{-5}^{5} \pi(25 - x^2)\,dx = \pi(25x - \frac{x^3}{3})\Big]_{-5}^{5} = \frac{250\pi}{3} - (-\frac{250\pi}{3}) = \frac{500\pi}{3}.$$

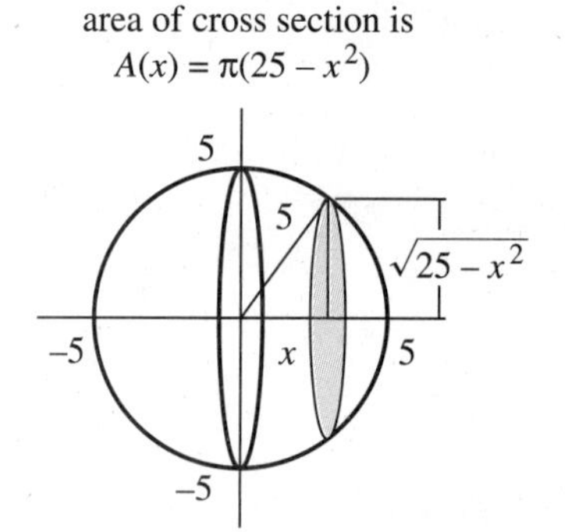

Figure 7.9 Cross sections of a sphere are circles.

This result matches exactly the value we obtain using the volume formula for a sphere $V = 4\pi R^3/3$ with $R = 5$. ■

In fact, we could use definite integration to *establish* this volume formula by replacing the specific radius 5 with an unspecified spherical radius R. Now, the sphere lies along the interval $[-R, R]$, and for each x, the radius of the circular cross section is $\sqrt{R^2 - x^2}$. The area function is given by

$$A(x) = \pi(R^2 - x^2).$$

If we integrate A over the interval $[-R, R]$, we obtain

$$V = \int_{-R}^{R} \pi(R^2 - x^2)\,dx = \pi(R^2 x - \frac{x^3}{3})\Big]_{-R}^{R} = \frac{2\pi R^3}{3} - (-\frac{2\pi R^3}{3}) = \frac{4\pi R^3}{3}.$$

Many volume formulas can be established similarly with definite integration.

EXAMPLE 7 Find the volume of a spike six inches long (Figure 7.10) whose cross sections are equilateral triangles with sides of length $1/6$ the distance from the point of the spike (so the side length at the blunt end is exactly 1 inch).

Solution If we set up a coordinate axis with the point of the spike at $a = 0$ and the other end at $b = 6$, then the cross section at any point $0 \leq x \leq 6$ is an equilateral triangle with side length $x/6$ inches. We can calculate the height of this triangle using the Pythagorean theorem to be $h(x) = \sqrt{3}x/12$. Figure 7.11 shows a typical cross section of the spike (at distance x inches from the point).

The area of this equilateral triangle is

$$A(x) = (\frac{1}{2})(\frac{x}{6})(\frac{\sqrt{3}x}{12}) = \frac{\sqrt{3}x^2}{144}.$$

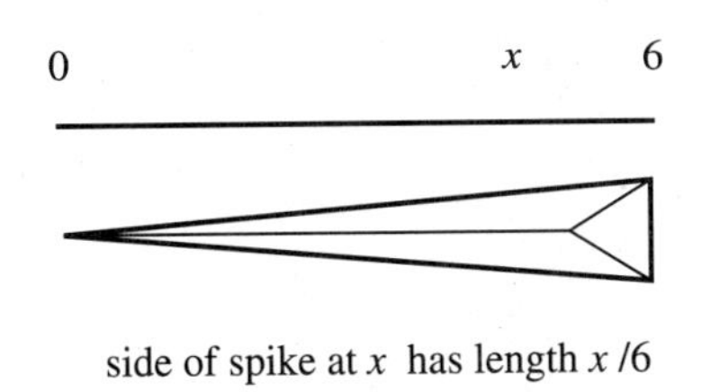

Figure 7.10 Find the volume of the spike.

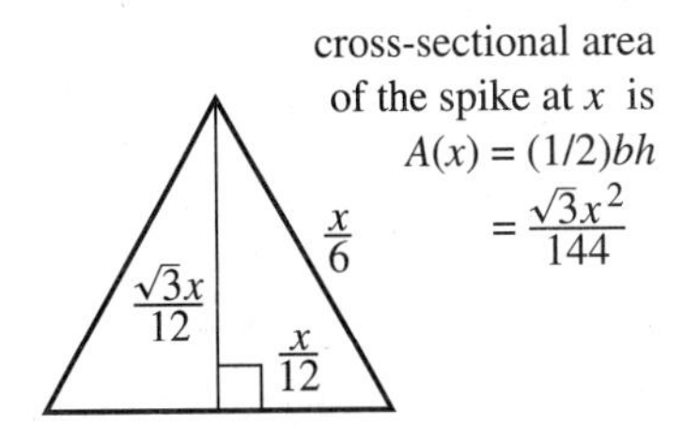

Figure 7.11 The cross-sectional area function for the spike.

We integrate $A(x)$ over the interval $[0, 6]$ to obtain the volume V of the spike:

$$V = \int_0^6 \frac{\sqrt{3}x^2}{144}\, dx = \frac{\sqrt{3}x^3}{432}\bigg]_0^6 = \frac{\sqrt{3}}{2} \text{ cubic inches.}$$ ■

Solids of revolution

The sphere is an example of a solid of revolution. A solid of revolution is any object obtained by rotating a plane region through space about some axis. For example, if we rotate the region enclosed by a circle about the axis of its diameter, we obtain a sphere. If we rotate a rectangle about an axis along one of its sides, we get a cylinder (see Figure 7.12).

Objects produced on machines such as wood lathes or pottery wheels are examples of more general solids of revolution. If we slice a solid of revolution perpendicular to the axis, we always get one of two shapes:

1. If the axis of rotation is in contact with the region, then the cross section will be a "disk." The radius r of the disk is determined by the furthest distance from the axis to the outer edge of the region, and the area of the disk is πr^2.

2. If there is any space between the region and the axis of rotation, then the cross section will be an annulus or "washer." In the case of

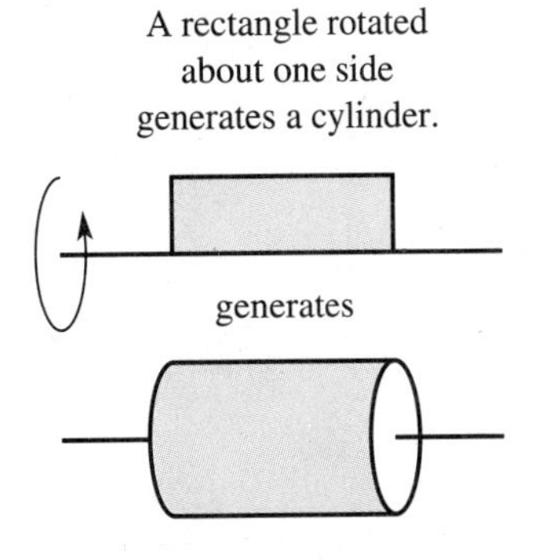

Figure 7.12 A cylinder is a solid of revolution generated by a rectangle.

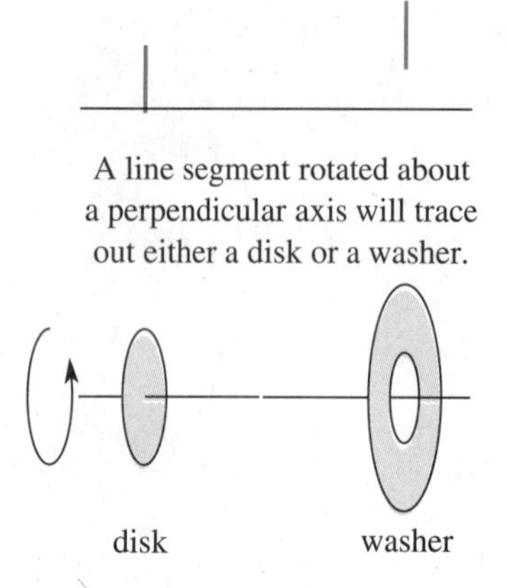

Figure 7.13 Possible cross sections for a solid of revolution.

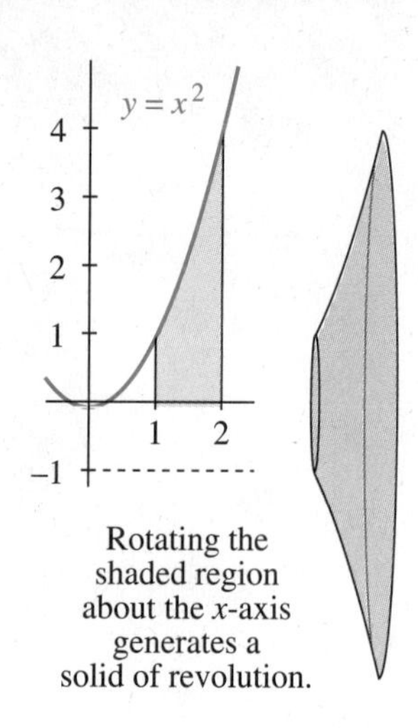

Figure 7.14 A solid of revolution having disks as cross sections.

an annulus, the area is the difference $\pi R^2 - \pi r^2$, where r is the inner radius (of the hole) and R is the outer radius.

In Figure 7.13 we see the possible resulting cross sections that can be obtained by rotating a line segment about a perpendicular axis. To calculate the value of the cross-sectional area function $A(x)$ at each point x along the axis of a solid of revolution, we need to determine first whether the cross section is a disk or washer; then we must express the radius ($r(x)$ in the case of a disk) or radii ($R(x)$ and $r(x)$ in the case of a washer) in terms of x in the appropriate area formula. Once we have determined the area function A, we can integrate it from one end of the solid to the other to find its volume.

No single simple formula handles all possible regions that might be rotated about an axis. Given a region and an axis of rotation, you may find it difficult to visualize what the resulting solid of revolution looks like. However, if you keep in mind that only two kinds of cross sections are possible, you should be able to visualize what a single cross section looks like at any specific point. For the purposes of determining the volume of the solid, this is exactly what we need to determine the cross-sectional area value $A(x)$ at the point x.

EXAMPLE 8 Find the volume of the solid of revolution obtained by rotating the region bounded by $y = x^2$, the x-axis, and the vertical lines $x = 1$ and $x = 2$ about the x-axis.

Solution The region and resulting solid are pictured in Figure 7.14. Since the region touches the axis of revolution, each cross section is a disk having radius

$r(x) = x^2$ for $1 \le x \le 2$. The area of each disk is

$$A(x) = \pi(r(x))^2 = \pi(x^2)^2 = \pi x^4.$$

The volume of the solid of revolution can be computed by integrating:

$$\int_1^2 \pi x^4\,dx = \pi\frac{x^5}{5}\Big]_1^2 = \frac{32\pi}{5} - \frac{\pi}{5} = \frac{31\pi}{5} \text{ cubic units.}$$

■

EXAMPLE 9 Find the volume of the solid of revolution obtained by rotating the region bounded by $y = x^2$, the x-axis and the vertical lines $x = 1$ and $x = 2$ about the line $y = -1$.

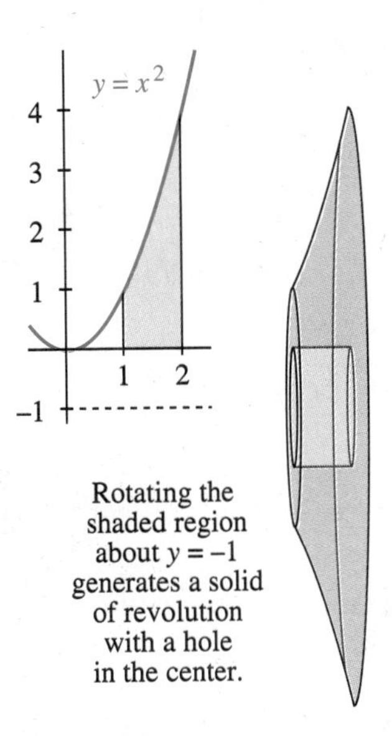

Figure 7.15 A solid of revolution having washers as cross sections.

Solution The region and resulting solid are pictured in Figure 7.16. Each cross section is a washer having outer radius $R(x) = x^2 + 1$ and inner radius $r(x) = 1$ for $1 \le x \le 2$. The area of each washer is

$$A(x) = \pi[R(x)^2 - r(x)^2] = \pi[(x^4 + 2x^2 + 1) - 1^2] = \pi(x^4 + 2x^2).$$

The volume of the solid of revolution can be computed by integrating:

$$\int_1^2 \pi(x^4 + 2x^2)\,dx = \pi\left(\frac{x^5}{5} + \frac{2x^3}{3}\right)\Big]_1^2 = \pi\left[\left(\frac{32}{5} + \frac{16}{3}\right) - \left(\frac{1}{5} + \frac{2}{3}\right)\right] \approx 34.14 \text{ cubic units.}$$

■

EXAMPLE 10 Express the volume of the solid of revolution obtained by rotating the region bounded by the graphs of $y = \sin(x)$ and $y = \cos(x)$ over the interval $[\pi/6, \pi/2]$ about the x-axis.

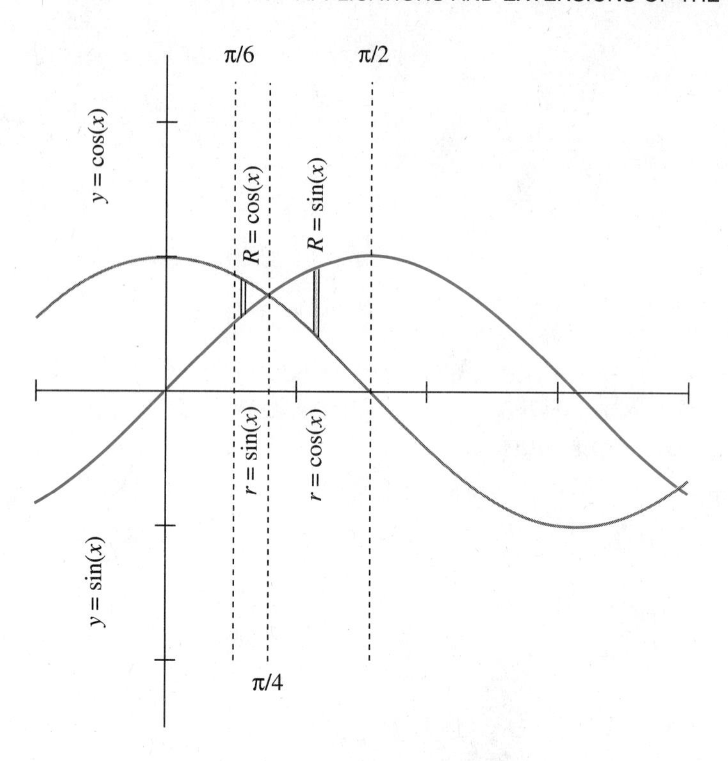

Figure 7.16 Analyzing cross sections for a solid of revolution.

Solution The region in question is illustrated in Figure 7.16. The illustration shows how the cross sections vary in form as we move through the interval $[\pi/6, \pi/2]$. For $\pi/6 \leq x \leq \pi/4$, the slices generate washers with an outer radius $R(x) = \cos(x)$ and an inner radius $r(x) = \sin(x)$. Hence, $A(x) = \pi[\cos^2(x) - \sin^2(x)]$ over this interval

and
$$\int_{\pi/4}^{\pi/2} A(x)\, dx = \pi/2.$$

For $\pi/4 \leq x \leq \pi/2$, the slices generate washers with an outer radius $R(x) = \sin(x)$ and an inner radius $r(x) = \cos(x)$. Hence, $A(x) = \pi[\sin^2(x) - \cos^2(x)]$ over this interval.

Summing the two integrals yields the total volume.

$$\begin{aligned}
\text{Volume} &= \int_{\pi/6}^{\pi/2} A(x)\, dx \\
&= \int_{\pi/6}^{\pi/4} \pi[\cos^2(x) - \sin^2(x)]\, dx + \int_{\pi/4}^{\pi/2} \pi[\sin^2(x) - \cos^2(x)]\, dx \\
&\approx 0.2104 + 1.5708 = 1.7812 \text{ cubic units.}
\end{aligned}$$

Here we used a machine numerical integrator to calculate the result. ■

Calculating volume using cylindrical shells

For the special case of a solid of revolution, there is an alternative method of calculating the volume that is quite different from the general cross-sectional area method (which is valid for *any* solid whose cross sections vary continuously along the axis). This method is sometimes preferred because the resulting definite integral may be easier to calculate using the fundamental theorems of calculus. (In other words, the antiderivative of the integrand may be easier to recognize.) Of course, given computing machines capable of approximating definite integrals to great precision, our primary concern is correctly modeling the volume of the object as the value of a definite integral.

The idea behind the method is to take slices of the rotated region that are *parallel* to the axis of rotation. When rotated about the axis, such a slice traces out a *cylindrical shell* centered about the axis of rotation. If the slice is thin enough, then a good approximation for the volume of this shell is the inner surface area of the shell times the thickness of the slice (see Figure 7.17). Hence, the volume of a thin cylindrical shell is $2\pi r(x)h(x)\Delta x$, where $r(x)$ is the distance from the parallel axis of rotation, $h(x)$ is the height of the shell, and Δx is the thickness of the shell.

If we start at the axis of rotation and sum up the volumes of these nested shells as we move out to the extreme edge of the solid, then we have an approximation for the total volume of the solid. Taking the limit of these approximations as the thickness of the slices approaches zero, we obtain a definite integral representing the exact volume of the solid:

$$\text{Volume} = \int_a^b 2\pi r(x)h(x)\,dx,$$

where $x = a$ is the location of the innermost shell and $x = b$ is the location of the outermost shell.

EXAMPLE 11 Find the volume of the solid of revolution obtained by rotating the region bounded by $y = x^2$, the x-axis, and the vertical lines $x = 1$ and $x = 2$ about the y-axis.

Solution The region and resulting solid are shown in Figure 7.18. Each vertical slice of the region corresponding to a particular value $x \in [1, 2]$ will trace out a cylinder whose height is $h(x) = x^2$ and whose radius from the y-axis is $r(x) = x$. Hence, the volume of the solid is given by the definite integral

$$\int_1^2 2\pi(x^2)x\,dx = 2\pi\int_1^2 x^3\,dx = \left.\frac{\pi x^4}{2}\right]_1^2 = \frac{15\pi}{2} \text{ cubic units.}$$

■

A line segment rotated about
a parallel axis will trace out
a cylinder of area $2\pi rh$.

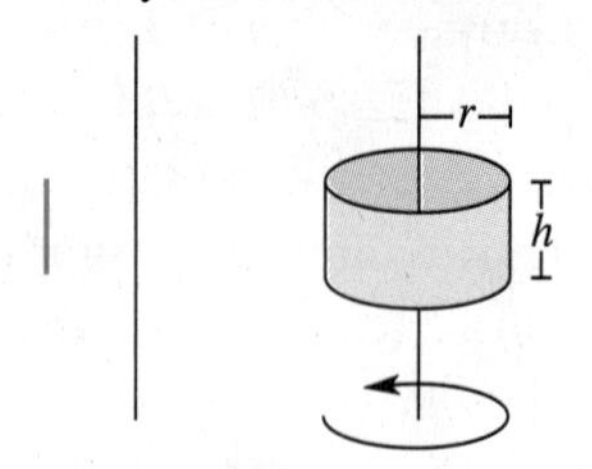

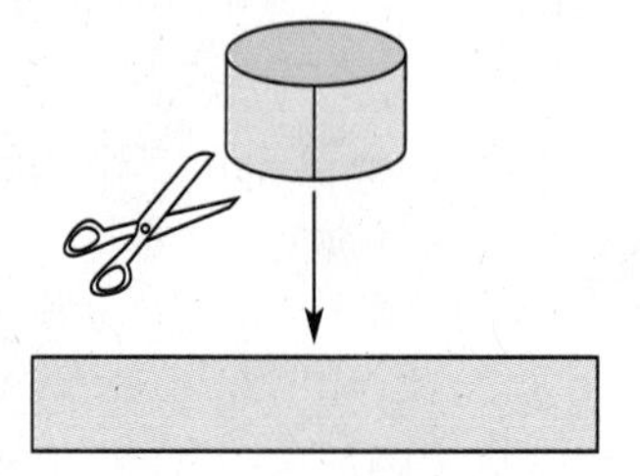

A solid revolution can
be built from a set of
nested cylindrical shells.

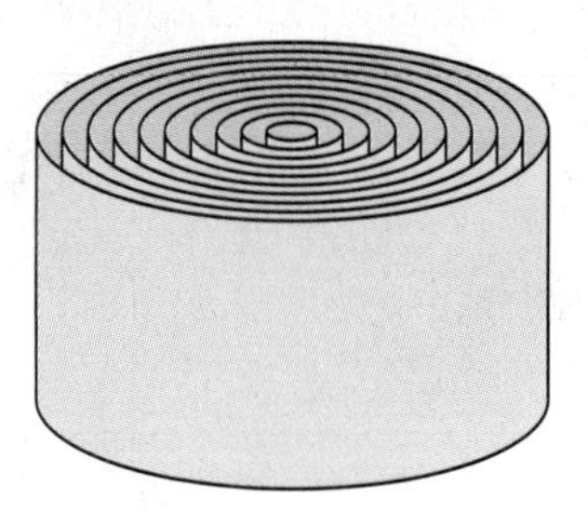

If each shell has
thickness Δx, then
the volume of each shell
is $2\pi r(x)\, h(x)\, \Delta x$

Figure 7.17 Rotation about a parallel axis.

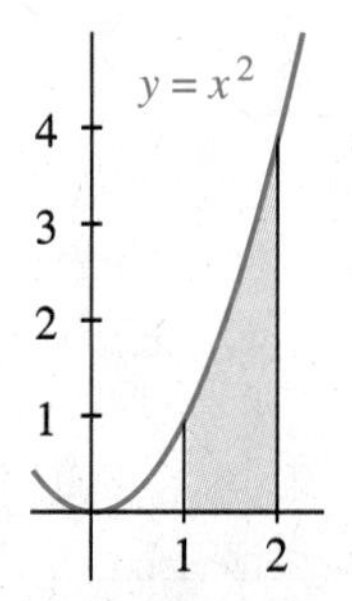

Rotating the shaded region
about the y-axis generates
the solid of revolution here.

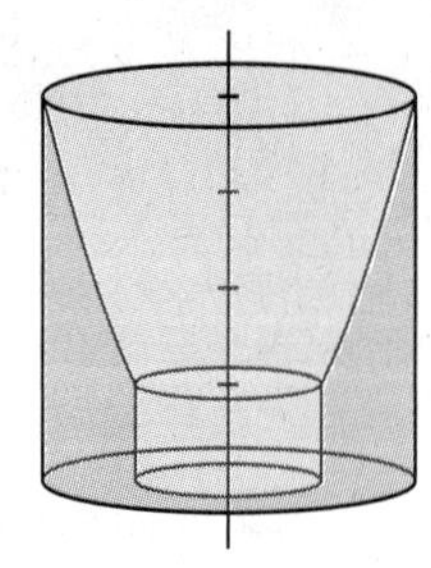

Figure 7.18 Another solid of revolution.

EXERCISES for Section 7.2

For exercises 1–6: Find the volume of the object whose cross section at x is described and which lies between the given points. (Some of the exercises may require the help of machine numerical integration.)

1. Cross section is a square with side length x. The object lies between $x = 0$ and $x = 5$.

2. Cross section is a square with side length $9 - x^2$. The object lies between $x = -3$ and $x = 3$.

3. Cross section is a square with side length $\frac{1}{2}\sin x$. The object lies between $x = 0$ and $x = \pi$.

4. Cross section is a circle with radius e^{x-1}. The object lies between $x = 0$ and $x = 3$.

5. Cross section is a square with side length $\frac{|x|}{4}$. The object lies between $x = -4$ and $x = 2$.

6. Cross section is an isosceles right triangle with legs of length $e^{3x} - 1$. The object lies between $x = 0$ and $x = 1$.

For exercises 7–15: Find the volume of the solid of revolution generated by rotating the described region about the (a) x-axis and (b) y-axis. For each problem, you should graph the region and determine carefully the cross-sectional area function. Then set up the required definite integral or integrals to calculate the volume. A machine root-finder and numerical integrator may be necessary to compute some of the resulting integrals.

7. Region enclosed between the graph of $y = |2 - x|$ and the line $y = 1$.

8. Region bounded by $y = \arctan(x)$, $y = \text{arccot}(x)$, and the y-axis.

9. Region bounded by $y = \dfrac{3}{1+x^2}$ and $y = e^{x^2}$.

10. Region bounded by $y = \cos(x)$ and $y = \dfrac{x+1}{3}$.

11. Region enclosed between $y = \ln(x)$, the vertical line $x = 2$, and the horizontal line $y = -2$.

12. Region bounded by $x = 8 - y^2$ and $x = -y + 2$.

13. Region bounded by $x = y^3 - 3$, $x = 1$, and the coordinate axes.

14. Region bounded by $y = \arcsin(x)$ and $y = \arccos(x)$ and the horizontal lines $y = \pi/6$ and $y = \pi/3$.

15. Region bounded by $y = \sin \frac{1}{2}x$ and $y = \frac{1}{2}\sin x$ between $x = 0$ and $x = \pi$.

---

16. The handle of a screwdriver is 4 inches long, and the tip of the blade is 4 inches from the handle. The handle has cross sections in the shape of regular hexagons. At the fat end furthest from the blade tip, the handle is 1 inch across. At the narrow end closest to the blade tip, the handle is 1/2 inch across. At any point in between, the width of the handle is 1/8 the distance from the blade tip. Find the volume of material in the handle.

17. Find a linear function f and an interval $[a, b]$, so that the region between the graph of f and the x-axis between $x = a$ and $x = b$ generates a cone (pointing left) of length 10 and radius 4 when rotated about the x-axis. Find the volume of this cone.

18. A cone of base radius R and height H can be thought of as the solid of revolution obtained by rotating the region bounded by $y = (R/H)x$, the

x-axis, and the line $x = H$ about the x-axis. Use this to derive the volume formula for a cone by definite integration.

19. A *torus* is a doughnut-shaped region obtained by rotating a circle about an axis not intersecting the circle. If R is the distance from the center of the circle to the axis and r is the radius of the circle, then the volume of the torus is known to be

$$V = 2\pi^2 Rr^2.$$

Establish this formula by calculating the volume of the solid of revolution obtained by rotating the region between the graphs of $y = R + \sqrt{r^2 - x^2}$ and $y = R - \sqrt{r^2 - x^2}$ about the x-axis.

20. Suppose that a container in the shape of the solid of revolution is obtained when the region bounded by $y = -x^2 + 49$, the x-axis, and y-axis is rotated about the y-axis. Assuming that the units along the axes represent cm, how many liters of water would it take to *fill* the solid?

For exercises 21–24: Using formulas for the volumes of cones and cylinders, determine the volumes of the solids of revolution described, given that f and g have the graphs shown.

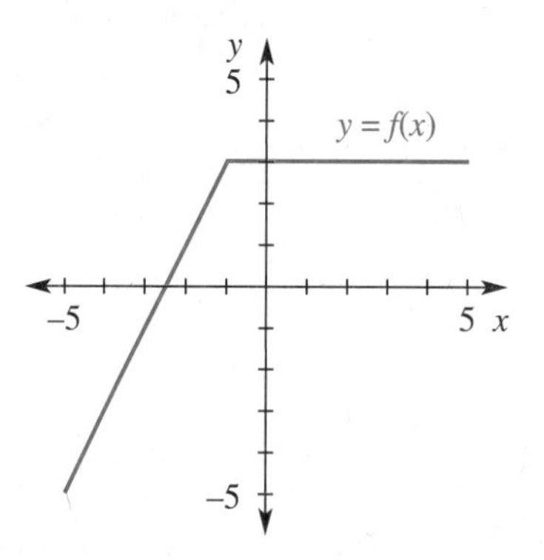

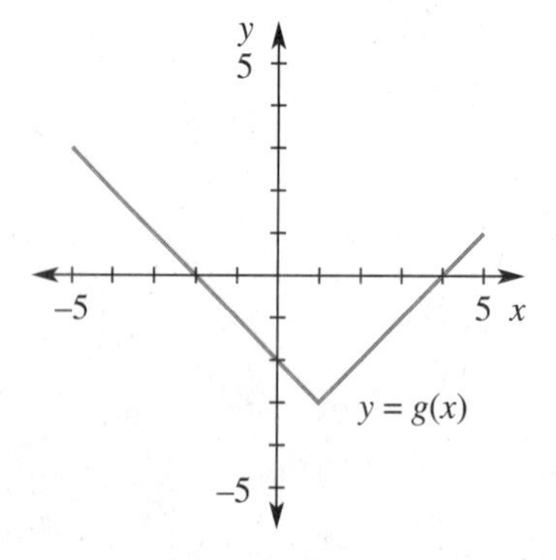

For Exercises 21–24

21. Region between the graph of f and the x-axis between $x = 0$ and $x = 5$ rotated about the x-axis.

22. Region between the graph of g and the x-axis between $x = 1$ and $x = 4$ rotated about the x-axis.

23. Region between the graph of f and the x-axis between $x = -5$ and $x = 0$ rotated about the y-axis.

24. Region between the graph of g and the x-axis between $x = -5$ and $x = -2$ rotated about the y-axis.

7.3 USING DEFINITE INTEGRALS TO MEASURE AVERAGES

Another use of definite integrals is in determining *average* or *mean* values of continuously varying quantities. The computation of an average is quite familiar in the case of a set of finitely many values. We simply sum the values and divide by the number of values. For example, if six students have test scores of 75, 98, 82, 75, 69, and 84, the average score is

$$\frac{75 + 98 + 82 + 75 + 69 + 84}{6} = \frac{483}{6} = 80.5.$$

Note that if all six students had the same score of 80.5, the total of their scores would be the same, since $6(80.5) = 483$. We might think of this as the "leveling" interpretation of average. That is, if all our values were at the same common level, the average is the common value yielding the same sum.

Now, suppose that we have a function f defined over an interval $[a, b]$, so that we have an output value $f(x)$ for each input $x \in [a, b]$. Is there a way of computing the average output value $f(x)$? It makes no sense to try to sum up all the values $f(x)$ for each x, because there are infinitely many of them. However, if we think of the leveling interpretation of average, we could ask a meaningful question: What common level value over the interval $[a, b]$ would produce the same net effect as f? In other words, what *constant* function gives us the same definite integral as $f(x)$ over the interval $[a, b]$?

We can determine h by stating this requirement as an equation to solve:

$$\int_a^b h\, dx = \int_a^b f(x)\, dx.$$

Since $\int_a^b h\, dx$ is simply $h(b - a)$, we can define the average value of an integrable function by solving for h.

Definition 1

The **average value** of $f(x)$ over the interval $[a, b]$ is

$$h = \frac{\int_a^b f(x)\,dx}{b-a},$$

provided the integral exists.

EXAMPLE 12 Find the average value of $f(x) = x^2$ over the interval $[1, 3]$.

Solution Here $a = 1$, $b = 3$, and $f(x) = x^2$, so

$$\text{average value of } f(x) = \frac{\int_a^b f(x)\,dx}{b-a} = \frac{\int_1^3 x^2\,dx}{3-1} = \frac{26/3}{2} = \frac{13}{3}.$$

■

Graphically, if $f(x)$ is positive over the interval $[a, b]$, then its average value is the height h of a rectangle of length $b - a$ having the same area as $\int_a^b f(x)\,dx$. In fact, if f is continuous over $[a, b]$, then this height must be achieved at least once by the function over the interval. In other words, there exists $a \le x_0 \le b$ such that $f(x_0) = h$. The *mean value theorem for integrals* states that any continuous function must achieve its average value at least once over a closed interval.

Theorem 7.1

Mean value theorem for integrals
Hypothesis: Suppose that f is a continuous function on $[a, b]$.
Conclusion: $f(x_0)(b - a) = \int_a^b f(x)\,dx$ for at least one value $a \le x_0 \le b$.

Reasoning Assume that f is a continuous function on $[a, b]$. Figure 7.19 illustrates the situation for a function f that is positive over the interval $[a, b]$, but all our observations will hold for continuous functions in general.

Suppose that M = maximum value $f(x)$ attains on $[a, b]$ and m = minimum value $f(x)$ attains on $[a, b]$. (Since f is continuous, we know that f must attain these values by the extreme value theorem.) This means that the graph $y = f(x)$ must lie between the horizontal lines $y = M$ and $y = m$ as shown in the illustration, and we must have

$$m(b-a) \le \int_a^b f(x)\,dx \le M(b-a).$$

For a positive function like the one pictured, geometrically this means that the area under the graph of $y = f(x)$ must be between the areas of the two rectangles of common length $b - a$ and heights m and M, respectively.

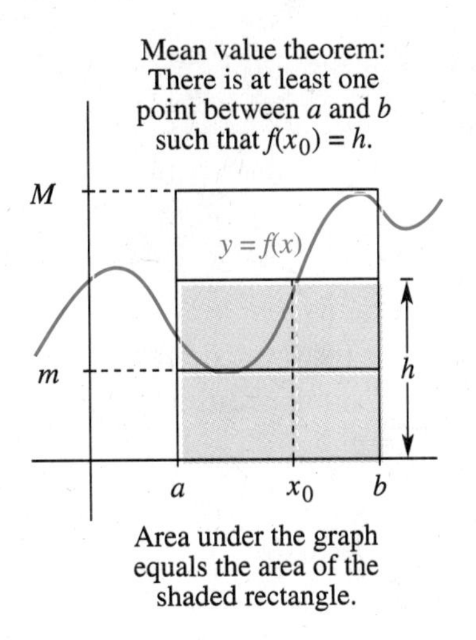

Figure 7.19 Illustration of the mean value theorem for integrals.

Hence, we can find a height $m \leq h \leq M$ for a rectangle of length $b-a$ whose area is exactly the same as the area under the graph of $y = f(x)$. (h is the average value of f over $[a, b]$.) If we divide the inequality through by the positive number $b - a$, we have

$$m \leq h = \frac{\int_a^b f(x)\, dx}{b-a} \leq M.$$

Since the value in the middle of this inequality lies between the extreme values m and M of the function, the intermediate value theorem for continuous functions guarantees that there exists at least one value x_0 such that

$$f(x_0) = h = \frac{\int_a^b f(x)\, dx}{b-a}.$$

Multiplying both sides by $(b - a)$ gives us the conclusion

$$f(x_0)(b-a) = \int_a^b f(x)\, dx.$$

□

Think of the graph as representing the elevation of the terrain faced by a road-building crew. If the crew wants to make a road at a certain level of elevation, then they must fill in the places below that level and excavate places above that level. They can use some of the material from the high places to fill in the low places. The mean value of the function represents an optimal level to choose, in the sense that no extra material would need to be trucked in or out.

Using a random number generator to estimate π

Many calculators and computers have a random number generator that can provide (almost) random numbers, usually between 0 and 1. If we use such a random number generator to choose an ordered pair (x, y) by first using it to choose x, then to choose y, we can think of this as a point (x, y) randomly chosen from the unit square $[0, 1] \times [0, 1]$. If we generate sufficiently many random points in this way, we can actually use them to make area measurements.

EXAMPLE 13 What is the probability that a randomly chosen point (x, y) from the unit square $[0, 1] \times [0, 1]$ is within 1 unit of the origin?

Solution In terms of area measurement, we can see that this probability is the ratio of the area of a quarter circle to the area of the unit square (see Figure 7.20). The area of the quarter circle of radius 1 is

$$\frac{\pi 1^2}{4} = \frac{\pi}{4}.$$

The unit square $[0, 1] \times [0, 1]$ has area 1, so the probability that the randomly chosen point (x, y) falls in the quarter circle is $\dfrac{\pi/4}{1} = \pi/4$. ■

This suggests that we can estimate $\pi/4$ by repeatedly choosing points at random in the square and finding the proportion of those actually falling within the quarter circle. Equivalently, we need to compute the proportion of points (x, y) in $[0, 1] \times [0, 1]$ satisfying the inequality

$$x^2 + y^2 \leq 1.$$

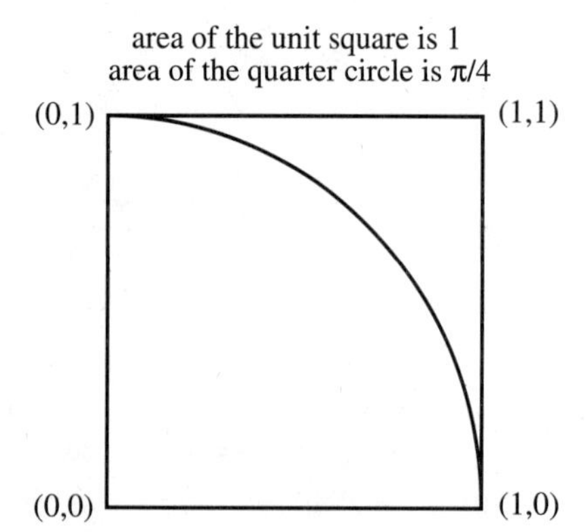

Figure 7.20 Points within the quarter circle are within 1 unit of the origin.

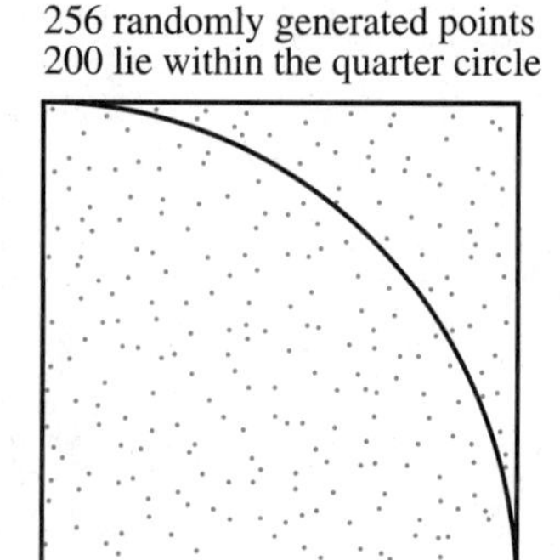

Figure 7.21 Estimating $\pi/4$ using randomly selected points.

Figure 7.21 shows the results of 256 points generated at random.

In 200 trials out of 256, the inequality was satisfied. This leads to the estimate $\pi/4 \approx 200/256 = 0.78125$. If we multiply the estimate by 4, we have

$$\pi \approx 3.125.$$

While we know that this is not a particularly accurate estimate of π, it illustrates the idea. With many more randomly generated points, we could expect a better approximation.

A Monte Carlo technique for approximating definite integrals

When a simulation involving random numbers is used to estimate a measurement, we call the strategy a **Monte Carlo** technique. (As you may know, Monte Carlo is the locale of several large gambling casinos.) If you have a random number generator on a calculator or computer, you can use it to approximate a definite integral

$$\int_a^b f(x)\,dx.$$

The idea behind the strategy uses the average value of the function. Recall that the average value h of $f(x)$ over $[a, b]$ is given by

$$h = \frac{\int_a^b f(x)\,dx}{b-a}.$$

If we had a way of estimating h directly, we could use it to approximate the value of the integral as

$$\int_a^b f(x)\,dx = h(b-a).$$

Here's a simple Monte Carlo technique for estimating $\int_a^b f(x)\,dx$.

Step 1. Randomly generate several numbers $x_1, x_2, x_3, \ldots, x_n$ lying between a and b.

If you have a machine that generates a random number r between 0 and 1, then the number $x = a + r(b-a)$ is a random number between a and b. For example, to generate a random number in the interval $[-2, 3]$, first generate a random number r in the interval $[0, 1]$, then calculate $x = -2+5r$.

Step 2. Evaluate $f(x_1), f(x_2), f(x_3), \ldots, f(x_n)$.

Step 3. Find the average c of these n function values. This is our estimate of the average value h of $f(x)$ over $[a, b]$:

$$h \approx c = \frac{f(x_1) + f(x_2) + f(x_3) + \cdots + f(x_n)}{n}.$$

Step 4. Use this value to approximate the definite integral:

$$\int_a^b f(x)\,dx \approx c(b-a).$$

Moving averages

Another kind of weighted average is useful in situations where the data is "noisy," that is, has lots of short-term ups and downs that can hide what is happening over a longer term. Stock anaylsts use a *moving average* to study stock market trends. This technique consists of computing each day the average stock price over some fixed previous period. For example, instead of charting the daily price of a particular stock, we might daily chart its average price over the previous 5 days, or previous 30 days, or whatever. This tends to smooth out the day-to-day fluctuations, making it easier to spot longer-term trends.

Definition 2 If f is a continuous function and A is a positive real number, then the **moving average of f over period A** is

$$\frac{\int_{x-A}^{x} f(u)\,du}{A}.$$

Note that the value of the moving average of f over period A at a point x is the average of f over the "previous" interval of the form $[x-A, x]$.

EXAMPLE 14 Compute the moving average over a period 1 of the function f, where

$$f(x) = \sin(4x).$$

Compare the graphs of the original function and the moving average function over the interval $[-3, 3]$.

Solution The moving average is given by

$$\frac{\int_{x-1}^{x} \sin(4u)\,du}{1} = -\frac{1}{4}\cos(4u)\Big]_{x-1}^{x} = -\frac{1}{4}(\cos(4x) - \cos(4x-4)).$$

Graphs of both the original and moving average functions are shown in Figure 7.22. The original function cycles between the values 1 and -1,

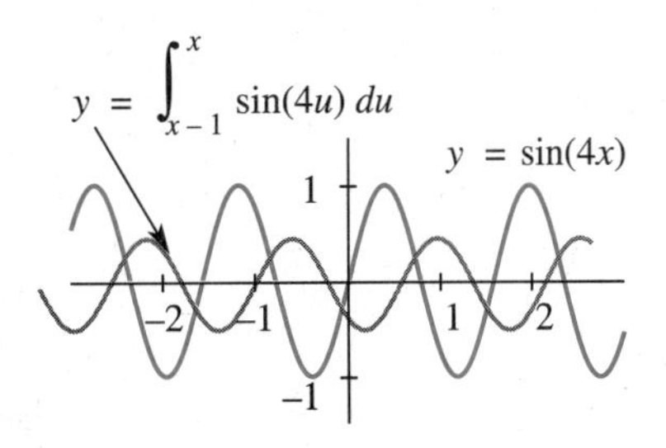

Figure 7.22 **Graphs of $y = \sin(4x)$ and its moving average over period 1.**

while the moving average has an amplitude less than half of the original function. ■

Note also how the moving average "lags" the original function. We see this effect in the difference between air and sea water temperature. The water acts as a thermal "averager," and is warmest in the fall and coldest in the spring (in the northern hemisphere). The temperature of sea water fluctuates much less than the air temperature.

EXERCISES for Section 7.3

For exercises 1–10: Find the average value of $f(x)$ over the given interval.

1. $f(x) = x$ over $[2, 4]$
2. $f(x) = x^2$ over $[0, 3]$
3. $f(x) = \sin 2x + \frac{1}{2}\cos x$ over $[0, \frac{\pi}{4}]$
4. $f(x) = e^x$ over $[1, 4]$
5. $f(x) = x^3 - \sqrt{x}$ over $[0, 1]$
6. $f(x) = 3x^2 - 6x + 4$ over $[0, 2]$
7. $f(x) = \sin(x) - \frac{1}{2}$ over $[\frac{\pi}{6}, \frac{5\pi}{6}]$
8. $f(x) = \sqrt{1 - x^2}$ over $[0, 1]$
9. $f(x) = \tan(x) - \sec(x)$ over $[-\frac{\pi}{2}, \frac{\pi}{3}]$.
10. $f(x) = e^x - \ln(x)$ over $[1/2, 10]$.

---

11. What is the average area of all possible circles with radii between 3 and 6?

12. The president of Platypus would like to know the average profit the company makes per worker-hour You know that there are fixed costs of being an employer of \$16000 per month (administration costs), no matter what the number of employees, and that the cost for x hours of employee work is \$ $28x$. The company brings in \$$(132 + .01x)$ for the xth person-hour worked in a month. Last month the company employees worked 10000 person-hours. What is the average value of the profit per person-hour?

For exercises 13–18: Suppose that the dartboard shown consists of concentric circles of radii 9 inches, 7 inches, 5 inches, 3 inches, and a bullseye of radius 1 inch. Suppose that a dart hits the dartboard at random.

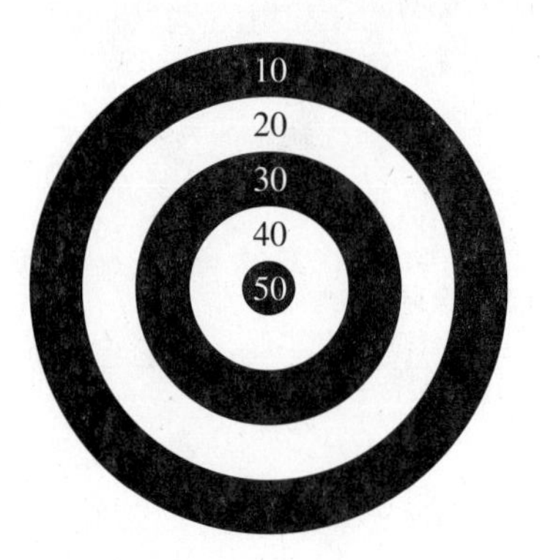

For Exercises 13–18

13. What is the probability of getting a score of 10?

14. What is the probability of getting a score of 20?

15. What is the probability of getting a score of 30?

16. What is the probability of getting a score of 40?

17. What is the probability of getting a score of 50?

18. What is the probability of the dart hitting the border between two regions?

---

19. Approximate $\int_0^1 x^3\,dx$ by randomly generating 20 numbers between 0 and 1 and averaging their cubes. How close is the approximation to the actual integral value?

20. Approximate $\int_{-1}^3 e^{-x^2}\,dx$ by the Monte Carlo approach described in the text with 10 points and 20 points. Then use Simpson's rule to calculate S_{10} and S_{20} for the same integral.

21. Thirty students throw a globe of the earth around so that everyone catches it. Of the thirty students, 21 note that their left index finger touched water when they caught the globe, while the remaining 9 touched land. Use this information to estimate how many square miles of the earth's surface is covered by water.

22. For each of the functions and intervals in exercises 1–10, find at least one point x_0 in the interval satisfying the mean value theorem for integrals.

For exercises 23–27: Find the moving average function over the indicated period. Compare the graphs of the original function and the moving average function over the interval $[-3, 3]$.

23. $y = \cos(x)$ over a period 1

24. $y = x$ over a period 2

25. $y = x$ over a period 3

26. $y = x^2 \sin(x^3)$ over a period 0.5

27. $y = x \cos(x^2)$ over a period 1

---

28. Find data on the daily high temperature in your area over the last thirty days. Starting with day 5, plot a line graph of these temperatures over the interval $[5, 30]$. (In other words, connect the dots with line segments.) Now compute the average high temperature for days 1–5, 2–6, 3–7, and so on up to 26–30. Plot these moving averages over the same interval $[5, 30]$ and note the effect on the fluctuation in the graph.

29. Suppose that a coaster of diameter 4 inches is thrown onto a floor of 8-inch by 8-inch square tiles. Assuming that the floor is large enough that there is no chance of the coaster leaning up against a wall, what is the probability that the coaster will land entirely within one of the square tiles (with no part touching a tile border)? Hint: the center of the coaster must land somewhere within one of the square tiles. Where must the center of the coaster be within the square so that the entire coaster is within the square?

For exercises 30–33: One of the more famous problems in probability is *Buffon's Needle Problem.* We can state it in the following way. Suppose that a needle of length $\ell = 1$ unit is thrown randomly onto a wooden floor with parallel boards of width $d = 2$ units (see the figure). What is the probability that the needle will land lying across one of the board lines? In analyzing this problem, a couple of simplifying assumptions are normally made. First, the horizontal position of the needle can be ignored. Second, throwing the needle randomly can be accurately modelled by randomly choosing a pair of numbers (x, y), where x is the distance between the center of the needle and the lower board edge and y is the angle in radians that the needle makes with a line parallel to the board edges. In other words, (x, y) is an ordered pair randomly chosen from $[0, 2] \times [0, \pi]$.

30. Show that the vertical distance from a tip of the needle to the horizontal line through its center is $\frac{1}{2}\sin(y)$.

31. Write down an inequality describing what pairs (x, y) represent needles that touch the board edges. (When does the vertical distance of the needle tip to its center exceed the distance to either the lower or upper board edge?)

32. Find the probability that the needle touches a board edge. (What "points" in the rectangle $[0, 2] \times [0, \pi]$ satisfy the inequality you obtained in the previous exercise?)

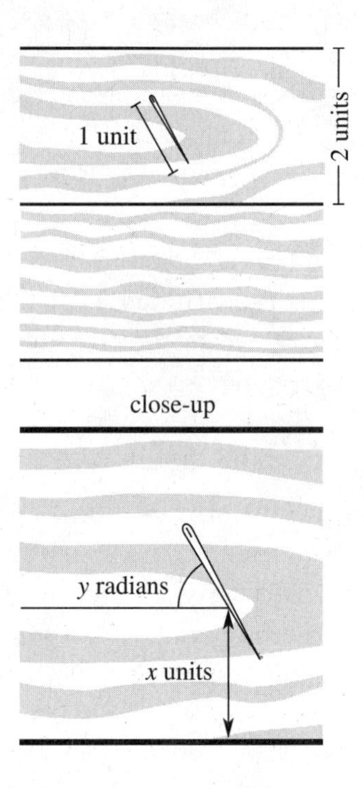

For Exercises 30–33

33. Suppose, in general, that the needle has a length ℓ and the distance between boards is d (and $d > \ell$). Find the probability (in terms of ℓ and d) that the needle lands across a board border.

7.4 APPLICATIONS TO PARTICLE MOTION

Net and total distance traveled

Let's review our example of the distance traveled by a car. If $s(t)$ represents the position of the car (or any other object) at time t, we know that the velocity v and acceleration a represent the first and second derivatives:

$$v(t) = s'(t) \qquad \text{and} \qquad a(t) = s''(t).$$

We can recover the position function from a knowledge of the velocity function and an initial position, or we can even recover it from a knowledge of the acceleration function and an initial velocity and position.

EXAMPLE 15 Suppose that an object moves with an acceleration $a(t) = -16t$ ft/sec^2, with an initial velocity $v(0) = 32$ ft/sec and an initial position $s(0) = 8$ ft. Find the velocity and position functions.

Solution We obtain the velocity by antidifferentiating the acceleration:

$$v(t) = \int a(t)\,dt = \int -16t\,dt = -8t^2 + C_1,$$

where the constant C_1 is determined by the initial velocity

$$32 = v(0) = -8(0)^2 + C_1 = C_1.$$

Therefore, $v(t) = -8t^2 + 32$ ft/sec. Now we can antidifferentiate the velocity function to find the position function:

$$s(t) = \int (-8t^2 + 32)\,dt = -\frac{8}{3}t^3 + 32t + C_2,$$

and the second constant is determined by the initial position

$$8 = s(0) = -\frac{8}{3}0^3 + 32(0) + C_2 = C_2.$$

Thus, $s(t) = -\frac{8}{3}t^3 + 32t + 8$ feet. ■

Since position s is the antiderivative of velocity v, we have

$$\int_a^b v(t)\,dt = s(b) - s(a).$$

In other words, integrating the velocity $v(t)$ over a time interval $[a, b]$ yields the *change in position of the object* over that time interval. We should think of this as the *net distance* traveled, and distinguish it carefully from the notion of *total distance* traveled. For example, if you walk 3 steps forward and then 2 steps backward, the net change in your position is 1 step forward, even though you have traveled a total of 5 steps.

The direction of movement is indicated by the sign of the velocity. A negative velocity indicates movement in the opposite direction of a positive velocity. The magnitude (absolute value) of the velocity indicates the *speed*, regardless of the direction. In terms of using integration to determine distance traveled, we have

$$\text{net distance traveled} = \int_a^b v(t)\,dt,$$

and

$$\text{total distance traveled} = \int_a^b |v(t)|\,dt.$$

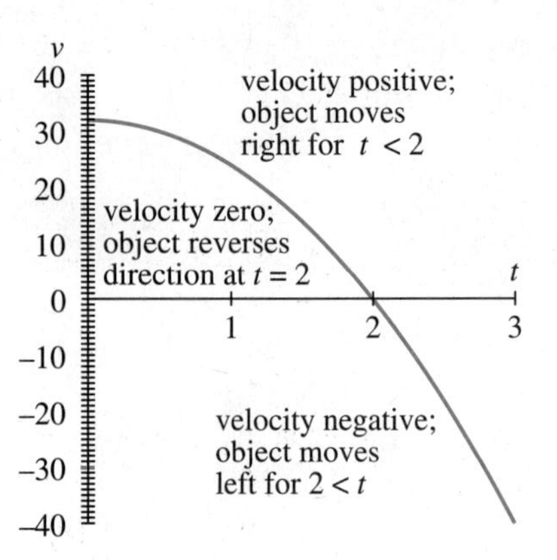

Figure 7.23 Graph of the velocity function.

EXAMPLE 16 An object moves horizontally, with distance to the right considered positive. Find the net and total distance traveled by the object over the time interval $1 \le t \le 3$ if it has velocity $v(t) = -8t^2 + 32$.

Solution Figure 7.23 shows the graph of this velocity v as a function of time t. We can tell what direction the object is moving at any particular time t by noting the sign of the velocity $v(t)$. In this case, the velocity is positive for $1 \le t < 2$, and the object moves to the right during this time. The velocity is negative for $2 < t \le 3$, and the object moves to the left during this time. The object reverses direction at the instant $t = 2$ when the velocity is zero. The net distance traveled by the object is measured by the net area above the t-axis over $[1, 3]$:

$$\int_1^3 (-8t^2 + 32)\, dt = -\frac{8}{3}t^3 + 32t\Big]_1^3 = 24 - \frac{88}{3} = -\frac{16}{3} \text{ ft.}$$

This means that the object moves a net distance of $16/3$ units to the *left*.

The speed $|v(t)|$ of the object is plotted in Figure 7.24. The total distance traveled is

$$\int_1^3 |-8t^2 + 32|\, dt = \int_1^2 (-8t^2 + 32)\, dt + \int_2^3 -(-8t^2 + 32)\, dt$$

$$= -\frac{8}{3}t^3 + 32t\Big]_1^2 + \frac{8}{3}t^3 - 32t\Big]_2^3 = \frac{40}{3} + \frac{56}{3} = \frac{96}{3} = 32 \text{ ft.}$$

From this computation, we can see that the object moved $40/3$ units to the right, reversed direction, and then moved $56/3$ units to the left, for the total distance of 32 units and the net distance of $16/3$ units to the left. ■

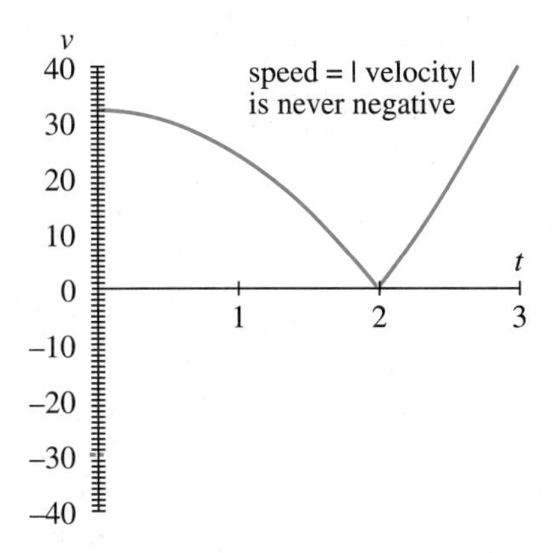

Figure 7.24 Graph of the speed function.

In this example, the integral of the absolute value of the velocity

$$\int_1^3 |v(t)|\, dt = 32$$

gives us the correct total distance traveled. Note that we get an entirely different result if we simply take the absolute value of the integral of velocity:

$$\left| \int_1^3 v(t)\, dt \right| = |-16/3| = 16/3.$$

▶▶▶ **Be careful with integrals involving absolute value. In general,**

$$\int_a^b |f(x)|\, dx \neq \left| \int_a^b f(x)\, dx \right|$$

unless f never changes sign over $[a, b]$.

EXERCISES for Section 7.4

For exercises 1–5: You are given an acceleration function for a moving object and an initial velocity and position. Use this information to find the velocity and position functions.

1. $a(t) = t - t^2 \quad v(0) = -2 \quad s(0) = 3$

2. $a(t) = e^{-t} \quad v(0) = 0 \quad s(0) = 4$

3. $a(t) = \sin(t) \quad v(0) = -1 \quad s(0) = 1$

4. $a(t) = \dfrac{3}{1+t^2} \quad v(0) = 3.5 \quad s(0) = 1.25$

5. $a(t) = \sqrt{t} \quad v(0) = -4 \quad s(0) = 2$

For exercises 6–10: You are given a velocity function. Use it to calculate the net and total distance traveled during the indicated time interval.

6. $v(t) = \ln(2 - t) \qquad 0.5 \le t \le 1.5$

7. $v(t) = e^{-t} \qquad -1 \le t \le 1$

8. $v(t) = \dfrac{2}{t^3} \qquad 0.5 \le t \le 2.35$

9. $v(t) = \sin(2\pi t) \qquad 0 \le t \le 1$

10. $v(t) = \sqrt{4 - t^2} \qquad 0 \le t \le 2$

---

11. A ball is thrown straight upwards at a velocity of 64 ft/sec at time $t = 0$. If it is being attracted by the gravity of the earth so that it falls with an acceleration of 32 ft/sec^2, how far does it travel in 3 seconds?

12. Assume that the brakes of an automobile produce a constant deceleration of k ft/sec^2. What is k if a car that is initially traveling 60 mph (88 ft/sec) is brought to a full stop 150 ft after braking begins? How far will the same automobile travel during the time it takes to slow from 60 mph to 30 mph by braking?

7.5 USING DEFINITE INTEGRALS TO MEASURE ARC LENGTH

When a curve or path is polygonal (that is, consisting of straight line segments laid end-to-end), we can compute its total length by summing the lengths of the individual segments. In this section, we turn to the measurement problem of calculating the length of a more general curve, which is called its **arc length.**

The main idea is simple enough: if we subdivide a smooth curve into several small pieces, each piece may be approximated by a straight line segment. Summing the lengths of these segments may provide a good approximation to the total length of the curve (see Figure 7.25).

The closer together we choose the subdivision points, the better we expect our approximation to be. Since the shortest distance between two points is along a straight line, our polygonal approximations will always be underestimates of the total length of the curve. Indeed, we *define* the **arc length** of a curve to be the single limiting value (if it exists) of these approximations as we increase the number of subdivision points to be arbitrarily large. (It is possible for a curve to have an infinite or undefined arc length if it "zigs" and "zags" infinitely often between its endpoints.) In this section we discuss how arc length can be determined by means of definite integration.

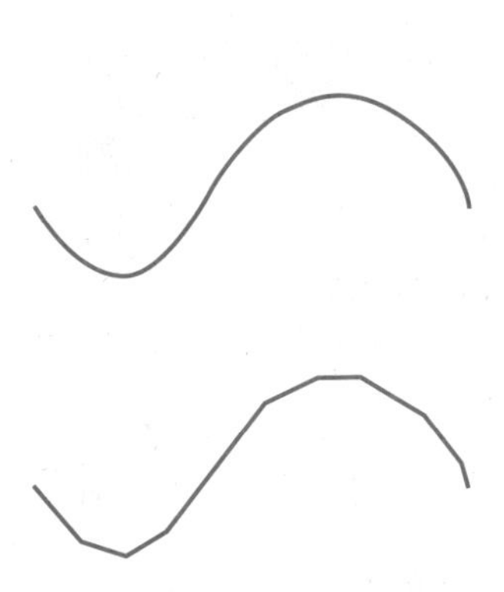

Figure 7.25 Approximating a curve with a polygonal path.

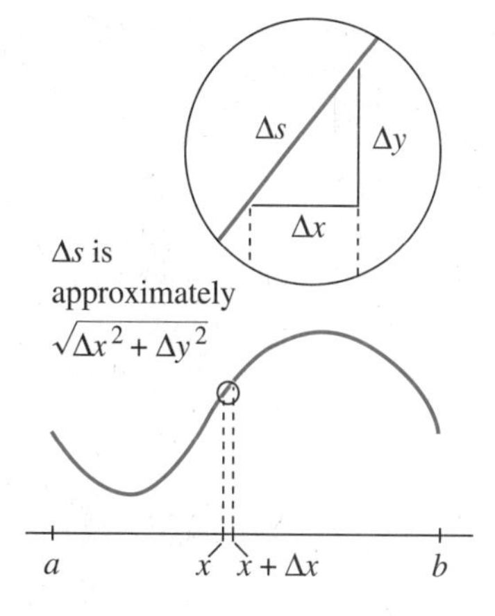

Figure 7.26 Approximating arc length.

Arc length of a function graph

Suppose that the curve or path of interest can be described as the graph of a differentiable function $y = f(x)$ over an interval $[a, b]$. If we partition the interval $[a, b]$ into small subintervals of equal length Δx and connect the points on the graph corresponding to the partition points, we have a polygonal approximation to the graph. If we zoom in on the graph over one of these subintervals, the graph will appear approximately straight (since a differentiable function is approximately locally linear). Figure 7.26 shows a magnified view of the graph of such a function over one of these tiny intervals.

We can see that the line segment approximation to the curve can be thought of as the hypotenuse of a right triangle with a horizontal leg of length Δx and a vertical leg of length Δy. If we denote the length of this hypotenuse Δs, then the length of the line segment is given by the Pythagorean theorem:

$$\Delta s \approx \sqrt{(\Delta x)^2 + (\Delta y)^2}.$$

If we factor out $\Delta x = \sqrt{(\Delta x)^2}$, we can rewrite this as

$$\Delta s \approx \Delta x \sqrt{1 + \left(\frac{\Delta y}{\Delta x}\right)^2}.$$

Since f is a differentiable function, the slope of the line segment is

$$\frac{\Delta y}{\Delta x} \approx f'(x)$$

for a point x in the subinterval.

Using this approximation, we have

$$\Delta s \approx \sqrt{1 + (f'(x))^2}\Delta x.$$

Now we sum these lengths Δs for each subinterval from a to b and take the limit as the number of subintervals increase and the subinterval length Δx approaches 0. If the limit exists, we have

$$\text{total arc length} = \lim_{n\to\infty} \sum_{i=1}^{n} \Delta s = \int_a^b \sqrt{1 + [f'(x)]^2}\, dx.$$

EXAMPLE 17 Find the arc length of the graph of $y = \sin(x)$ over one period.

Solution The function $f(x) = \sin(x)$ has a period of length 2π, so any interval of length 2π will serve our purposes. If we choose $[0, 2\pi]$ as the interval, then

$$\text{arc length} = \int_0^{2\pi} \sqrt{1 + (f'(x))^2}\, dx = \int_0^{2\pi} \sqrt{1 + \cos^2 x}\, dx \approx 7.640.$$ ■

EXAMPLE 18 Find the arc length of the graph of $y = x^3$ between $x = -1$ and $x = 1$.

Solution Since $\frac{d}{dx}(x^3) = 3x^2$, we can calculate the arc length of the graph as

$$\int_{-1}^{1} \sqrt{1 + (3x^2)^2}\, dx = \int_{-1}^{1} \sqrt{1 + 9x^4}\, dx \approx 3.096.$$ ■

In both of these examples, we used a calculator to approximate the value of the definite integral. Definite integrals for the arc length of even very common function graphs are often difficult or impossible to calculate using the second fundamental theorem of calculus.

Calculating the arc length of a parametrized curve

Recall that the coordinates (x, y) of the points on a curve in the plane are sometimes described as two separate functions of a parameter t. If we think of t as representing time, then the curve may be thought of as the path traced out by the points

$$(x(t), y(t)) \qquad \text{for } a \le t \le b.$$

In this situation, the derivatives dx/dt and dy/dt are the instantaneous rates of change in the $x-$ and $y-$ coordinates of the curve with respect to t. That is, over a very tiny time interval of length Δt, the change in position on the curve will be approximately $\Delta x = \frac{dx}{dt}\Delta t$ in the horizontal direction and $\Delta y = \frac{dy}{dt}\Delta t$ in the vertical direction. Thus, the actual distance Δs traveled along the curve is approximately

$$\Delta s \approx \sqrt{(\frac{dx}{dt}\Delta t)^2 + (\frac{dy}{dt}\Delta t)^2} = \sqrt{(\frac{dx}{dt})^2 + (\frac{dy}{dt})^2}\Delta t.$$

+++

If we sum the lengths Δs for each subinterval of time, we have

$$\text{arc length} = \lim_{n\to\infty}\sum_{i=1}^{n}\Delta s = \int_a^b \sqrt{(\frac{dx}{dt})^2 + (\frac{dy}{dt})^2}\, dt.$$

EXAMPLE 19 Find the arc length of the curve parametrized by

$$x(t) = t^3 \qquad y(t) = t^2 \qquad \text{for } 0 \le t \le 2.$$

Solution $\frac{dx}{dt} = 3t^2$ and $\frac{dy}{dt} = 2t$, so the arc length is

$$\int_0^2 \sqrt{(3t^2)^2 + (2t)^2}\, dt = \int_0^2 \sqrt{9t^4 + 4t^2}\, dt \approx 9.073.$$

■

A comment on notation for arc length

A notation sometimes used for the arc length of a curve C is

$$\int_C ds,$$

where ds is a shorthand for the appropriate integrand and depends on how the curve is described. For example, if the curve C is the graph $y = f(x)$ for $a \le x \le b$, then $ds = \sqrt{1 + [f'(x)]^2}\, dx$ and

$$\int_C ds = \int_a^b \sqrt{1 + [f'(x)]^2}\, dx.$$

If the curve C is described parametrically by $x(t)$ and $y(t)$ for $a \le t \le b$, then $ds = \sqrt{(\frac{dx}{dt})^2 + (\frac{dy}{dt})^2}\, dt$ and

$$\int_C ds = \int_a^b \sqrt{(\frac{dx}{dt})^2 + (\frac{dy}{dt})^2}\, dt.$$

Another possibility can be mentioned here. If we find it convenient to describe a curve C as the locus of points satisfying $x = g(y)$ for $a \le y \le b$ and

g is differentiable with respect to y, then we can write $ds = \sqrt{1 + [g'(y)]^2}\, dy$ and

$$\int_C ds = \int_a^b \sqrt{1 + [g'(y)]^2}\, dy.$$

EXAMPLE 20 Find the arc length of the graph of $x = \ln(y)$ for $1 \le y \le e$.

Solution Here $g(y) = \ln(y)$, so $g'(y) = 1/y$ and

$$\int_1^e \sqrt{1 + (\frac{1}{y})^2}\, dy \approx 2.003.$$

■

In this example, we could also describe the curve as the graph of $y = e^x$ for $0 \le x \le 1$. Here $f(x) = e^x$, so $f'(x) = e^x$ and

$$\int_0^1 \sqrt{1 + (e^x)^2}\, dx \approx 2.003.$$

Surface area of a surface of revolution

If a line segment is rotated about an axis, it traces out a band whose area is the length Δs of the segment times the average distance the two endpoints travel around the axis. If the average distance from the axis is r, then the average distance traveled around the axis is $2\pi r$. (The path is circular, and r is the radius.) Hence, the area of the band is

$$2\pi r \Delta s.$$

Now, suppose that we rotate a curve around an axis over an interval $[a, b]$. This curve traces out a surface known as a **surface of revolution**. If we first approximate the curve with a polygonal path, we can approximate the area of this surface by rotating the polygonal path about the same axis. Since the polygonal path is made up of line segments, the surface area of the surface of revolution will be the sum of the areas of several thin bands of the type just described (see Figure 7.27).

Of course, the radius of each band may vary, so we write the sum of the areas of the bands as

$$\sum_{i=1}^{n} 2\pi r(x) \Delta s$$

to denote that $r(x)$ depends on the location of the band over the interval. (The length of the band Δs also depends on the location of the band.) As we

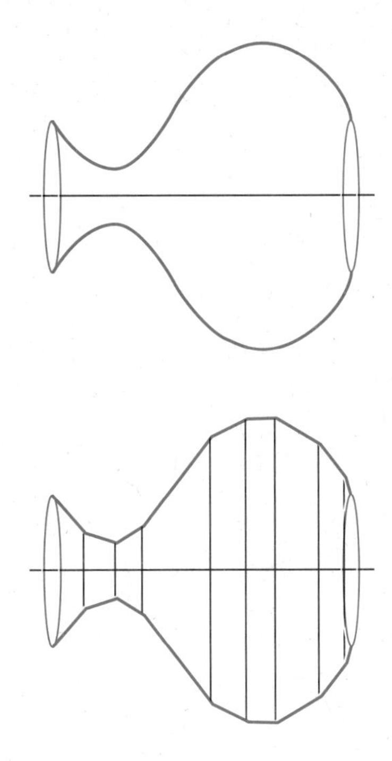

Figure 7.27 Surfaces of revolution.

take finer and finer partitions of the interval $[a, b]$ corresponding to better and better polygonal paths, this sum may converge on a single limiting value. Indeed, if the curve is the graph of a differentiable function or can be parametrized by differentiable functions, we can define the surface area of the surface of revolution to be the definite integral

$$\int_a^b 2\pi r(x)\, ds.$$

EXAMPLE 21 Find the surface area of the surface of revolution generated by the graph of $y = \sin x$ as it is rotated about the x-axis over the interval $[0, 2\pi]$.

Solution The radius of the surface is $r(x) = |\sin(x)|$ at any point $x \in [0, 2\pi]$. (The absolute value is necessary since $r(x)$ is the positive distance between the x-axis and the graph of the function.) We can take $ds = \sqrt{1 + \cos^2(x)}\, dx$ and set up the definite integral for surface area as

$$2\pi \int_0^{2\pi} |\sin(x)| \sqrt{1 + \cos^2(x)}\, dx \approx 28.85 \text{ sq. units.}$$

Here we used a machine to carry out the computation of the definite integral. ■

EXERCISES for Section 7.5

For exercises 1–6: Find the arc length of the graph of the given function over the interval $[\pi/4, \pi/3]$.

1. $y = \sin(x)$

2. $y = \cos(x)$

3. $y = \tan(x)$

4. $y = \sec(x)$

5. $y = \csc(x)$

6. $y = \cot(x)$

For exercises 7–10: Find the arc length of the graph of the given function over the interval $[1/4, 1/3]$.

7. $y = \arcsin(x)$

8. $y = \arccos(x)$

9. $y = \arctan(x)$

10. $y = \text{arccot}(x)$

For exercises 11–16: The hyperbolic sine and cosine functions are defined as follows:

$$\sinh(x) = \frac{e^x - e^{-x}}{2} \quad \text{and} \quad \cosh(x) = \frac{e^x + e^{-x}}{2}.$$

The rest of the hyperbolic functions are defined in a way analogous to the corresponding trigonometric functions:

$$\tanh(x) = \frac{\sinh(x)}{\cosh(x)} \qquad \coth(x) = \frac{\cosh(x)}{\sinh(x)}$$

$$\text{sech}(x) = \frac{1}{\cosh(x)} \qquad \text{csch}(x) = \frac{1}{\sinh(x)}$$

Find the arc length of the graph of the indicated hyperbolic function over the interval $[1, 4]$.

11. $\sinh(x)$

12. $\cosh(x)$

13. $\tanh(x)$

14. $\coth(x)$

15. $\text{sech}(x)$

16. $\text{csch}(x)$

For exercises 17–24: For each pair of parametric equations, find the arc length of the curve over the time interval $0 \le t \le 4$.

17. $x = 2\cos(t)$, $y = 3\sin(t)$

18. $x = -3\cos(t)$, $y = 2\sin(t)$

19. $x = 5 - t$, $y = 25 - 10t + t^2$

20. $x = 2t + 3$, $y = 3t + 2$

21. $x = t\cos(t)$, $y = t\sin(t)$

22. $x = \arctan(t)$, $y = t$

23. $x = |5 - t|$, $y = t$

24. $x = \sqrt{25 - t^2}$, $y = t$

For exercises 25–40: Take the functions and intervals indicated in exercises 1–16 and compute the surface area of the surface of revolution generated by rotating the curve about the x-axis.

7.6 USING DEFINITE INTEGRALS TO MAKE PHYSICAL MEASUREMENTS

In this section, we discuss some of the different physical applications that require the use of definite integration as a measurement tool.

When is a definite integral the right measurement tool?

There are many situations where a quantity can be expressed as a *constant* times the length of an interval. As we just mentioned, a rectangle's area is its *constant height* times its length. In physics, the notion of *work* can be thought of as a *constant force* times a distance traversed. The distance traveled by a moving object with *constant velocity* during a given time interval is simply that velocity times the length of the time interval. In general, the total change in any quantity changing at a *constant rate* over a time interval is the product of that rate times the length of the time interval.

In any of these cases, if we replace the constant with a *function* whose outputs vary continuously over the interval in question, then a definite integral is the appropriate measurement tool. If we partition an interval $[a, b]$ into sufficiently small subintervals of length Δx, then for many purposes we can treat a continuous function's outputs $f(x)$ as being relatively constant over each subinterval. This means that we can choose a *single* input x_i from each subinterval and use the corresponding function output $f(x_i)$ as the (approximately) constant value of the function over that subinterval. If the quantity we want to measure is approximated by

$$f(x_i)\Delta x$$

for each subinterval, we can add up all the products to approximate the total quantity.

What we have formed is a *Riemann sum approximation* for the definite integral of the continuous function f over the interval $[a, b]$. We might denote this Riemann sum approximation as

$$\sum_{i=1}^{n} f(x_i)\,\Delta x,$$

as long as we understand that the value $f(x)$ can change for each of the tiny subintervals and that we are summing the products $f(x)\Delta x$ for all the subintervals of $[a, b]$.

This Riemann sum approximation becomes more accurate as the partition becomes finer (as Δx is chosen smaller), and we define

$$\int_a^b f(x)\,dx = \lim_{n\to\infty} \sum_{i=1}^{n} f(x_i)\,\Delta x.$$

We can see the motivation behind the Leibniz notation of the definite integral. The $\int$ symbol denotes the limit of a *sum*, just as the Leibniz notation

$$\frac{dy}{dx} = \lim_{\Delta x\to 0} \frac{\Delta y}{\Delta x}$$

denotes the limit of a ratio.

To apply definite integration as a measurement tool, we need to identify both an interval of values $[a, b]$ and a functional quantity $f(x)$ defined over that interval. This may require us to set up a coordinate system for reference in a physical situation. When trying to identify the appropriate function over an interval, a good strategy to follow is outlined below.

Step 1. Pick some arbitrary value x in the interval $[a, b]$ and focus your attention on a tiny subinterval $[x, x + \Delta x]$.

Step 2. Calculate the desired quantity just for this subinterval. Any values depending on x should be written in terms of x. The goal is to express the result for this subinterval in the form

$$f(x)\,\Delta x$$

for some functional expression f.

Step 3. Calculate $\int_a^b f(x)\,dx$. If the function f has no simple antiderivative (so that you can use the fundamental theorems of calculus), you will need to use a computer or calculator that numerically approximates the value of the definite integral.

Step 4. Check the reasonableness of the result. If physical quantities are involved, check the units of the result. This can be found from Step 2: the units of the result are the product of the units of $f(x)$ and the units of x (which are the same as the units of Δx). Do these units make sense? For example, if the value of the integral represents distance traveled, then units of length should be expected. Check the magnitude of the result against some rough upper and lower estimates. A graph of f over the interval $[a, b]$ can be helpful in this regard.

▶▶▶ **Of course, there is nothing sacred about the use of the letter x for the independent variable in a physical application. You may find it more convenient to use a different letter for the independent variable in many cases.**

Work

One application we will describe in detail concerns the notion of **work** as it is defined in physics. Work can be thought of roughly as "force times distance." In the simplest case, we might imagine lifting a weight F (force due to gravity) a distance Δx (see Figure 7.28). The work performed in this instance is equal to the weight F times the distance Δx:

$$W = F\Delta x.$$

From this definition we can deduce appropriate units of measurement for work. In the English system, force is measured in pounds (lbs) and distance in feet (ft), so an appropriate unit for work would be the foot-pound (ft lb). In the metric system, force is measured in *newtons* (1 newton = 1 kg m/sec^2) whereas mass is measured in kilograms (kg), distance in meters (m), and time in seconds (sec). In this case, an appropriate unit for work would be the newton-meter, or equivalently, the *joule*. (If force is measured in dynes (g cm/sec^2 with mass measured in grams and distance in centimeters), then work is measured in dyne-centimeters or, equivalently, *ergs*.)

Now, suppose that the force varies as we move the object. For example, suppose that we push an object along an axis from $x = a$ to $x = b$, but the applied force $F(x)$ depends on the specific point x along the path. If the force $F(x)$ varies continuously over the interval $[a, b]$ and we restrict our attention to a very small subinterval $[x, x + \Delta x]$, then over this subinterval

Lifting an object requires
work = *force* × *distance.*

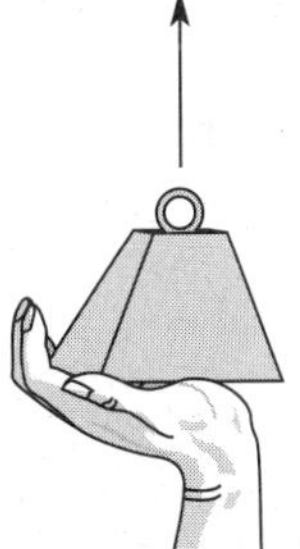

Figure 7.28 Work = force × distance.

the work performed is approximately

$$F(x)\Delta x.$$

If we compute the work over subintervals of length Δx from a to b (adjusting $F(x_i)$ for the computation over each subinterval) and add the results, we get an approximation to the total work performed:

$$\text{total work } W \approx \sum_{i=1}^{n} F(x_i)\Delta x.$$

Again we see the Riemann sum model, this time for work. Taking the limiting value of this sum as Δx approaches 0, we have

$$\text{total work } W = \int_a^b F(x)\,dx.$$

EXAMPLE 22 Find the work done by moving a particle along the x-axis from $x = 3$ to $x = 6$, if the force exerted on the particle at x is $x^2 + 3$ newtons and x is measured in meters.

Solution Here $F(x) = x^2 + 3$, so the work performed is

$$W = \int_3^6 (x^2 + 3)\,dx = \frac{x^3}{3} + 3x\Big]_3^6 = 90 - 18 = 72 \text{ joules.}$$ ■

Examples abound of forces that vary depending on distances or location, such as gravitational and magnetic forces. In the remainder of this section, we examine examples of various types of work.

Work performed in stretching or compressing a spring

One common example has to do with compressing and stretching springs. If we compress a spring, its tendency is to return to its natural length. The more we compress the spring, the harder the spring pushes back on our hand. Indeed, Hooke's law states that the force F required to compress (or stretch) a spring is proportional to the displacement x from its natural length. Figure 7.29 shows a spring before and after a weight F has been attached.

For example, if a weight of 10 pounds stretches the spring 4 inches from its natural length, then a weight of 30 pounds will stretch the spring 12 inches from its natural length. If x is the displacement from the natural length, then

$$F(x) = kx$$

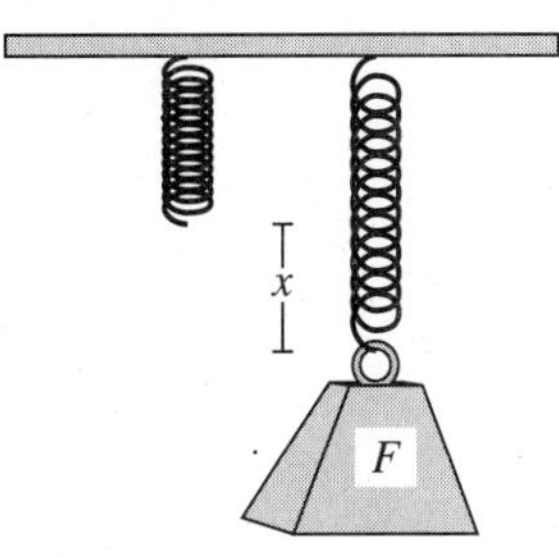

Figure 7.29 Hooke's law for springs.

for some positive constant k. The magnitude of this *spring constant* k depends on the size, content, and construction of the spring. The spring on a car's shock absorber has a large k value; the spring in a ballpoint pen has a small k value.

The spring constant for a given spring can be determined empirically by observing the force required to compress or stretch the spring a certain distance. For this spring, the spring constant is

$$k = \frac{10 \text{ pounds}}{4 \text{ inches}} = 2.5 \text{ pounds per inch.}$$

If we know the spring constant k, then we can calculate the work performed in stretching or compressing the spring from displacement $x = a$ to $x = b$:

$$W = \int_a^b kx\,dx.$$

EXAMPLE 23 If a spring has a natural length of 18 inches and a force of 10 pounds is sufficient to compress it to a length of 16 inches, what is the spring constant k and how much work would be done in compressing it from a length of 16 inches to a length of 12 inches?

Solution Since a force of 10 pounds compresses the spring 2 inches from its natural length, we have

$$k = \frac{10 \text{ pounds}}{2 \text{ inches}} = 5 \text{ pounds per inch.}$$

Compressing the spring from a length of 16 inches to a length of 12 inches represents a displacement from $x = 2$ to $x = 6$ inches from its natural length. Hence,

$$W = \int_2^6 5x\,dx = \frac{5x^2}{2}\bigg]_2^6 = 90 - 10 = 80 \text{ inch-pounds.}$$

■

Work lifting and pumping

Anytime we move an object up vertically, we have performed work against the force of gravity. For example, if we lift a 15-pound weight 8 inches, the work performed is

$$W = 15 \text{ pounds } \times \frac{2}{3} \text{ feet } = 10 \text{ foot-pounds.}$$

Integration becomes necessary if different parts of the object must be lifted different distances, as is illustrated in the next two examples.

EXAMPLE 24 A uniform cable 40 feet long and weighing 60 pounds hangs vertically from the top of a building. If a 500-pound weight is attached to the end of the cable, what work is required to pull it to the top?

Solution A picture of the situation is shown in Figure 7.30. It is easy to calculate the work required just to lift the weight itself to the top of the building:

$$W_{weight} = 500 \text{ lbs } \times 40 \text{ feet } = 20000 \text{ ft-lbs .}$$

The difficulty lies with the cable, for different parts of the cable must be lifted different distances. (The bottom of the cable must be lifted the entire 40 feet, but the middle of the cable must be lifted only 20 feet.)

Imagine a very small segment of cable of length Δx feet. Since the entire cable weighs 60 pounds and is 40 feet long, this small piece of cable weighs

$$\frac{60 \text{ lbs}}{40 \text{ feet}} \cdot \Delta x \text{ feet} = 1.5\Delta x \text{ lbs.}$$

If this piece of cable is at a distance x_i feet below the top of the building,

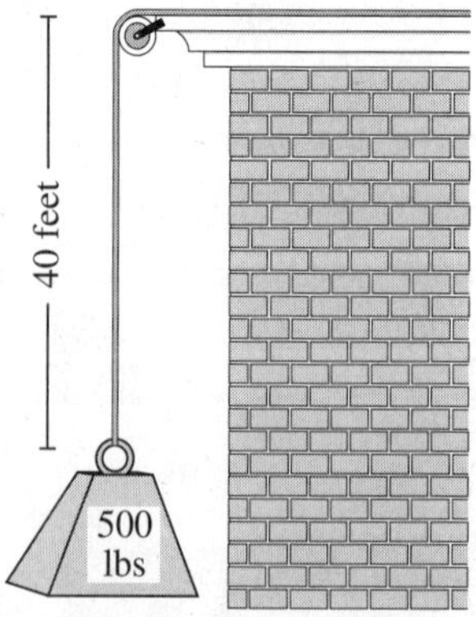

Figure 7.30 A weight hanging from a uniform cable.

the work required to lift it is approximately $1.5x_i\Delta x$ ft-lbs, and the total work to lift all the tiny segments is

$$W_{cable} \approx \sum_{i=1}^{n} 1.5x_i\Delta x.$$

Taking the limiting value as Δx approaches 0, we find that the exact total work required to pull the cable to the top of the building is

$$W_{cable} = \int_0^{40} 1.5x\,dx = 0.75x^2\Big]_0^{40} = 1200 \text{ ft-lbs.}$$

Adding the results for the weight and the cable gives us

$$W_{total} = W_{weight} + W_{cable} = 21200 \text{ ft-lbs.}$$ ■

Pumping fluid to a higher elevation is essentially a lifting problem. The next example illustrates how integration can be useful in measuring the work performed in this way.

EXAMPLE 25 Suppose that a tank has a rectangular base of 2 by 4 feet and a vertical height of 3 feet. If the tank is filled with water (62.5 pounds per cubic foot), find the work required to pump the water 2 feet above the top of the tank.

Solution Figure 7.31 illustrates the tank. If we think of the water as consisting of a stack of very thin layers of water, each of depth Δy feet, then we can approximate the work required to lift a single layer to the desired height:

$$\text{weight of layer} \times \text{distance lifted.}$$

The volume of water in a layer of thickness Δy is

$$2 \text{ feet} \times 4 \text{ feet} \times \Delta y \text{ feet} = 8\Delta y \text{ ft}^3$$

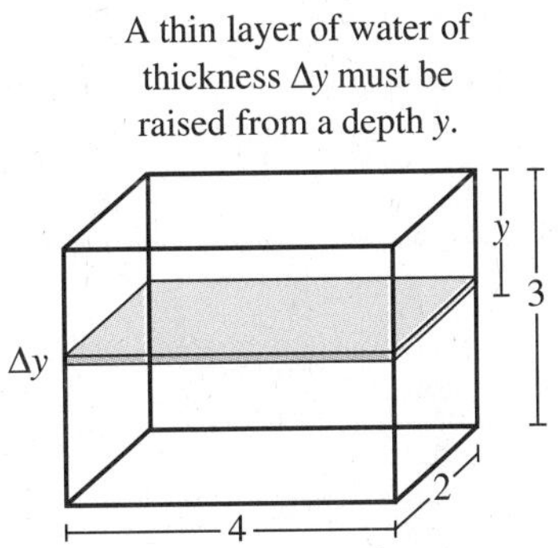

Figure 7.31 Pumping water from a rectangular tank.

and thus, the weight of the layer is

$$(62.5 \text{ lbs per cu ft })(8\Delta y \text{ cu ft}) = 500\Delta y \text{ lbs .}$$

If the layer is located y feet from the top, it must be lifted $y + 2$ feet. The work required to lift the layer is

$$500(y + 2)\Delta y \text{ ft-lbs.}$$

The total work in lifting all the layers is approximately

$$\sum_{0}^{3} 500(y + 2)\Delta y.$$

Taking the limit value as the thickness Δy approaches 0, we have the exact work as given by

$$\int_0^3 500(y + 2)\, dy = 250y^2 + 1000y\Big]_0^3 = 5250 \text{ ft-lbs.}$$ ■

In this example, the layers of water were of uniform dimensions because the tank was a rectangular box. In other cases, the size of the layer may depend on the depth it was taken from.

EXAMPLE 26 Suppose oil with a density of 50 pounds per cubic foot fills a hemispherical reservoir of radius 4 feet to a depth of 2 feet. How much work does it take to pump the oil out the top of the reservoir?

Solution Figure 7.32 illustrates the reservoir. If we use y to denote the depth of a thin layer of oil in the tank, then the radius r of the circular layer satisfies the Pythagorean theorem:

$$y^2 + r^2 = 4^2.$$

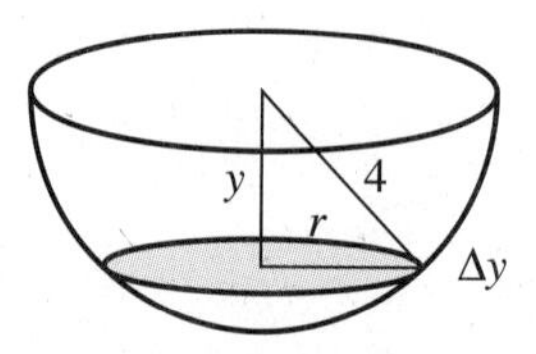

Figure 7.32 Pumping oil out of a hemispherical reservoir.

The volume of this layer is approximately $\pi r^2 \Delta y = \pi(16 - y^2)\Delta y$ cubic feet, and the weight of the layer is $50\pi(16 - x^2)\Delta y$ pounds. The work required to lift it the x feet to the top of the tank is approximately

$$50\pi y(16 - y^2)\Delta y.$$

Since the tank is filled only to a depth of 2 feet, the layers range from a depth of $y = 2$ feet to $y = 4$ feet. The total work performed in pumping out this tank is thus

$$\int_2^4 50\pi y(16 - y^2)\, dy = 50\pi(8y^2 - \frac{y^4}{4})\Big]_2^4 = 1800\pi \text{ ft-lbs.}$$ ■

EXERCISES for Section 7.6

1. Find the work done by a force of $3\sqrt{x}$ moving a particle along the x-axis from $x = 0$ to $x = 4$.

2. Find the work done by a force $F(x) = \sin \pi x$ from $x = -1$ to $x = 1$. Does this answer make sense? Explain.

3. A spring of natural length 13 inches stretches to a length of 18 inches under a weight of 8 pounds. Find the work done in stretching the spring from a length of 16 inches to a length of 20 inches.

4. A spring of natural length 15 inches stretches to a length of 16 inches under a weight of 4 pounds. Find the work done in stretching the spring from a length of 18 inches to a length of 23 inches.

5. A spring of natural length 13 inches compresses to a length of 6 inches under a weight of 6 pounds. Find the work done in compressing the spring from a length of 9 inches to a length of 5 inches.

6. A spring of natural length 12 inches compresses to a length of 5 inches under a weight of 8 pounds. Find the work done in compressing the spring from a length of 10 inches to a length of 6 inches.

7. A spring has a natural length of 1 foot, and a force of 15 pounds is required to hold it stretched to a total length of 2 feet. How much work is done in compressing this spring to a length of 6 inches?

8. A spring has a natural length of 6 inches. A 12000-pound force compresses it to $5\frac{1}{2}$ inches. Find the work done in compressing it from 6 inches to 5 inches.

9. A spring, which has a natural length of 4 feet and is stretched one foot by a force of 10 pounds, is attached to a wall. Another spring, which has a natural length of 3 feet and is stretched 1/2 feet by a force of 2 pounds, is attached to another wall 10 feet away. Find the force on the second spring if the two loose ends are connected. What is the length of each of the two springs when connected?

10. One observes that a force of 10 pounds stretches a spring .87 inches. How much work is required to stretch the spring one foot?

11. If one hangs a spring (of constant 10 lbs/ft) vertically and attaches a 10 lb. weight to the spring, how much work is done in raising the weight 6 inches from where it hangs naturally? (Note that we have two forces here: the spring and gravity.)

Suppose that a tank has a rectangular base of 2 by 4 feet and a height of 3 feet.

12. If the tank is filled with water (62.5 pounds per cubic foot), find the work required to pump the water out the top of the tank.

13. If the tank is half-filled with water (62.5 pounds per cubic foot), find the work required to pump the water 2 feet above the top of the tank.

14. If the tank is half-filled with oil (50 pounds per cubic foot), find the work required to pump the water out the top of the tank.

Suppose that a vertical cylindrical can has a diameter of 30 cm and a height of 60 cm.

15. If the can is filled with water, find the work done to pump the water out the top of the tank.

16. If the can is filled with water, find the work done to pump the water 20 cm above the top of the tank.

17. If the can is half-filled with water, find the work done to pump the water out the top of the tank.

18. If the can is half-filled with water, find the work done to pump the water 20 cm above the top of the tank.

Suppose that a vertical cone (point down) has a radius of 30 inches and a height of 40 inches.

19. If the cone is filled with water, find the work done to pump the water out the top of the cone.

20. If the cone is filled with water, find the work done to pump the water 20 inches above the top of the cone.

21. If the cone is filled to a depth of 20 inches with water, find the work done to pump the water out the top of the cone.

22. If the cone is half-filled with water, find the work done to pump the water to the top of the cone. (Note: "half-filled" means in terms of volume. This problem is different than the preceding one.)

---

23. A uniform cable 50 feet long and weighing 75 pounds hangs vertically from the top of a building. If a 400-pound weight is attached to the end of the cable, what work is required to pull it to the top?

24. A bucket weighing 20 lbs and containing 60 lbs of sand is attached to a rope 100 ft long and weighing 10 lbs is hanging in a well that is 150 ft deep. Find the work done in lifting the bucket to the top of the well.

25. A rectangular swimming pool full of water is 5 ft deep, 15 ft wide, and 25 ft long. Find the work required to pump the water out of the pool to a level 1 ft above the surface of the pool.

26. Another swimming pool full of water has a width of 5 meters and the dimensions shown. Find the work required to pump the water out of this pool.

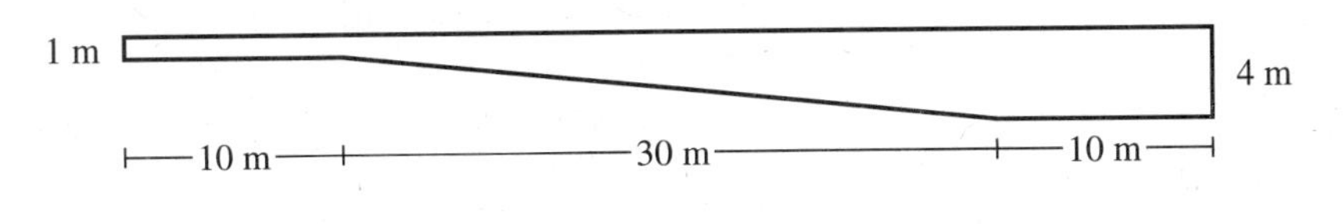

For Exercise 26

27. The magnitude of the repulsion of two electric charges Q_1 and Q_2 is $F = \dfrac{kQ_1Q_2}{R^2}$, where k is a constant and R is the distance between Q_1 and Q_2. How much work is required to move the charges from 10 centimeters apart to 10^{-6} cm. apart?

28. Newton's law of gravitation says that the force of attraction of two masses is $F = \dfrac{GM_1M_2}{R^2}$, where G is a constant and R is the distance between the centers of the two masses. In terms of the gravitational attraction between the earth and another object, this force is approximately $F = \dfrac{4000^2 M}{R^2}$, where M is the mass of the object and R is the distance in miles from the object to the center of the earth. How much work is required to lift a 1000-pound rocket from the surface of the earth to a 500-mile-high orbit? How much more work to lift it to a 1000-mile-high orbit?

7.7 IMPROPER INTEGRALS

Normally, a definite integral $\int_a^b f(x)\,dx$ is defined over a *closed* and *bounded* interval $[a, b]$. In this section, we want to extend the idea of integration beyond these restrictions in two different ways. First, we investigate when it is possible to assign a reasonable value to definite integrals over *unbounded* intervals such as $[a, \infty)$, $(-\infty, b]$, or even to the whole real line $(-\infty, \infty)$. Then we examine definite integrals that are not continuous over the given interval. In both cases, we refer to such integrals as **improper integrals**, since they do not satisfy the usual hypotheses of the fundamental theorems of calculus. However, we still may be able to assign a sensible value to the integral in some of these situations.

Improper integrals—horizontal type

First, let's consider functions defined over unbounded intervals. Figure 7.33 illustrates two possibilities. If the function values $f(x)$ are positive over the entire unbounded interval, then we can imagine the integration problem as one of measuring the area of an infinitely long region. At first thought, it might appear that an integral like

$$\int_a^\infty f(x)\,dx \qquad \text{or} \qquad \int_{-\infty}^b f(x)\,dx$$

could not help but represent an infinite quantity.

Nevertheless, there are cases where it makes sense to assign a finite value to such integrals. A physical example to keep in mind is the case of radioactive decay. Suppose that f represents the *rate of decay* of some piece of radioactive material. Such material never decays completely in any finite amount of time. On the other hand, the rate of decay becomes slower and slower as time passes. If we have 100 grams of the material present at time $t = 0$, then $\int_0^b f(t)\,dt$ yields the amount of decay at time $t = b$. Theoretically,

$$\int_0^\infty f(t)\,dt = 100 \text{ grams.}$$

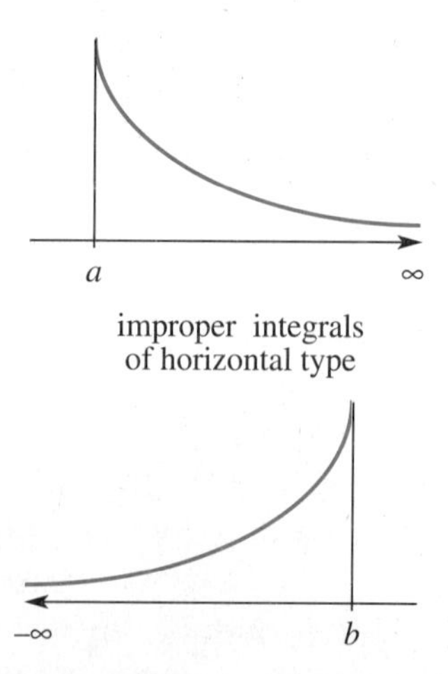

Figure 7.33 Improper integrals over unbounded intervals.

In other words, given an infinitely long period of time, the finite amount of material would decay completely.

Using the language of limits, what we are really saying is that the value of

$$\int_0^b f(t)\,dt$$

approaches 100 grams as b grows arbitrarily large.

Terminology of improper integrals

We will call integrals over unbounded intervals **horizontal type improper integrals**. A horizontal type improper integral can be thought of as the limiting value of a proper definite integral as one endpoint approaches ∞ or $-\infty$.

Definition 3

Horizontal type improper integrals

$$\int_a^\infty f(x)\,dx \quad \text{is shorthand for} \quad \lim_{b\to\infty}\int_a^b f(x)\,dx,$$

and

$$\int_{-\infty}^b f(x)\,dx \quad \text{is shorthand for} \quad \lim_{a\to-\infty}\int_a^b f(x)\,dx.$$

If the limiting value exists, then we say the improper integral **converges**. Otherwise, we say the improper integral **diverges**.

EXAMPLE 27 Determine whether $\int_1^\infty \frac{1}{x^2}\,dx$ converges or diverges. If it converges, find its value.

Solution First, we calculate $\int_1^b \frac{1}{x^2}\,dx$, using the parameter b as the upper limit of integration:

$$\int_1^b \frac{1}{x^2}\,dx = \int_1^b x^{-2}\,dx = -\frac{1}{x}\Big]_1^b = -\frac{1}{b} - (-\frac{1}{1}) = 1 - \frac{1}{b}.$$

Now, we take the limit.

$$\int_1^\infty \frac{1}{x^2}\,dx = \lim_{b\to\infty}\int_1^b \frac{1}{x^2}\,dx = \lim_{b\to\infty}(1-\frac{1}{b}) = 1,$$

since $\lim_{b\to\infty} 1/b = 0$. We say that this improper integral *converges* and has the value 1. ■

EXAMPLE 28 Determine whether $\int_4^\infty \frac{1}{\sqrt{x}}\,dx$ converges or diverges. If it converges, find its value.

Solution Using b as the upper limit of integration, we have

$$\int_4^b \frac{1}{\sqrt{x}}\,dx = \int_4^b x^{-1/2}\,dx = 2x^{1/2}\Big]_4^b = 2\sqrt{b} - 4.$$

Now,

$$\int_4^\infty \frac{1}{\sqrt{x}}\,dx = \lim_{b\to\infty} \int_4^b \frac{1}{\sqrt{x}}\,dx = \lim_{b\to\infty} (2\sqrt{b} - 4) = \infty,$$

since $2\sqrt{b}$ grows without bound as b grows without bound. We say that this improper integral *diverges*. ■

Note that both $\lim_{x\to\infty} \frac{1}{x^2} = 0$ and $\lim_{x\to\infty} \frac{1}{\sqrt{x}} = 0$. This shows that even if

$$\lim_{x\to\infty} f(x) = 0,$$

this is not a sufficient condition for the improper integral

$$\int_a^\infty f(x)\,dx$$

to converge. Evidently, $\frac{1}{x^2}$ approaches 0 much faster than $\frac{1}{\sqrt{x}}$ as x grows large (substituting large positive values x into both expressions supports this).

EXAMPLE 29 Determine whether $\int_{-\infty}^{-2} e^x\,dx$ converges or diverges. If it converges, find its value.

Solution First, we replace the lower limit of integration by a parameter a:

$$\int_a^{-2} e^x\,dx = e^x\Big]_a^{-2} = e^{-2} - e^a.$$

Now we take the limit as a approaches $-\infty$:

$$\int_{-\infty}^{-2} e^x\,dx = \lim_{a\to-\infty} \int_a^{-2} e^x\,dx = \lim_{a\to-\infty} (e^{-2} - e^a) = e^{-2},$$

since $\lim_{a\to-\infty} e^a = 0$. We say that the improper integral converges to the value $1/e^2$. ■

EXAMPLE 30 Determine whether $\int_{-\infty}^{0} \cos(x)\,dx$ converges or diverges. If it converges, find its value.

Solution $\int_{-\infty}^{0} \cos(x)\,dx = \lim_{a\to-\infty} \int_{a}^{0} \cos(x)\,dx = \lim_{a\to-\infty} \sin(x)\Big]_{a}^{0} = \lim_{a\to-\infty} -\sin(a).$

This limit does not exist, since $\sin(a)$ oscillates between -1 and 1 periodically. We say that the improper integral *diverges*. ■

If both limits of integration are infinite, we consider the integral to be a sum of two improper integrals of the type we've been discussing:

$$\int_{-\infty}^{\infty} f(x)\,dx = \int_{-\infty}^{c} f(x)\,dx + \int_{c}^{\infty} f(x)\,dx,$$

where c can be any real number we choose. If the graph $y = f(x)$ has symmetry about the vertical line $x = c$, then that would be a good choice. If there is no particular symmetry to the graph, then $c = 0$ is as good a choice as any. If *either* or both of the two integrals

$$\int_{-\infty}^{c} f(x)\,dx \qquad \text{and} \qquad \int_{c}^{\infty} f(x)\,dx$$

diverge, then we say that $\int_{-\infty}^{\infty} f(x)\,dx$ diverges.

EXAMPLE 31 Determine whether $\int_{-\infty}^{\infty} \frac{1}{1+x^2}\,dx$ converges or diverges. If it converges, find its value.

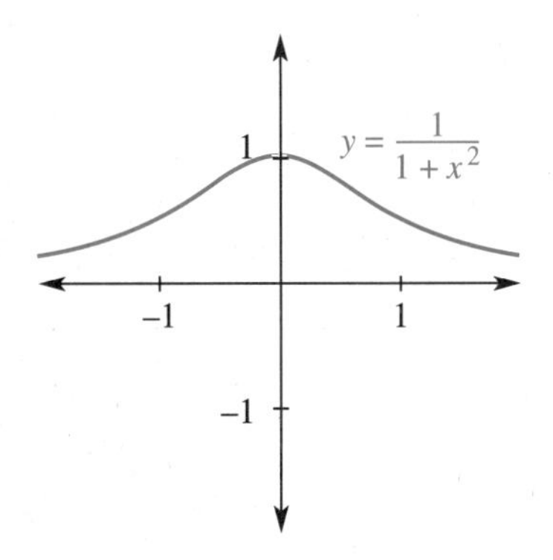

Figure 7.34 Graph of $y = 1/(1+x^2)$.

Solution The graph $y = \frac{1}{1+x^2}$ is a bell-shaped curve having symmetry about the vertical line $x = 0$ (see Figure 7.34). In other words, $y = 1 + x^2$ is an even function and we can write

$$\int_{-\infty}^{\infty} \frac{1}{1+x^2}\,dx = \int_{-\infty}^{0} \frac{1}{1+x^2}\,dx + \int_{0}^{\infty} \frac{1}{1+x^2}\,dx = 2\int_{0}^{\infty} \frac{1}{1+x^2}\,dx.$$

The improper integral $\int_0^\infty \frac{1}{1+x^2}\,dx$ can be evaluated as

$$\lim_{b\to\infty}\int_0^b \frac{1}{1+x^2}\,dx = \lim_{b\to\infty} \arctan(x)\Big]_0^b = \lim_{b\to\infty}\arctan(b) = \frac{\pi}{2}.$$

Hence, the improper integral converges, and

$$\int_{-\infty}^{\infty} \frac{1}{1+x^2}\,dx = 2(\frac{\pi}{2}) = \pi.$$

■

In Example 31, we were able to exploit the symmetry of the function to evaluate only one of the two "halves" of the integral.

▶▶▶ **Beware:**

$$\int_{-\infty}^{\infty} f(x)\,dx \quad \textbf{may or may not equal} \quad \lim_{a\to\infty}\int_{-a}^{a} f(x)\,dx.$$

Use of this shortcut may be injurious to the correctness of your result.

Improper integrals—vertical type

The second fundamental theorem of calculus guarantees that the definite integral

$$\int_a^b f(x)\,dx$$

exists, provided that the function f is continuous over the closed bounded interval $[a, b]$. We have just seen how it is sometimes possible to assign a finite value to improper integrals such as

$$\int_a^{\infty} f(x)\,dx \qquad \text{or} \qquad \int_{-\infty}^{b} f(x)\,dx$$

where the interval is not bounded. We call these *horizontal type* improper integrals.

Another way to relax the hypotheses of the second fundamental theorem of calculus is to not insist on the function being continuous over the interval. In an earlier discussion of integration, we pointed out that removable discontinuities ("holes," and even jump discontinuities) really present no problem, provided that there are only finitely many of them in the interval. For these types of discontinuities, one can simply split the interval up at these points, then redefine the function at all the newly created endpoints so that the second fundamental theorem applies over each.

In this section we take a look at a more serious type of discontinuity. **Vertical type** improper integrals are integrals of the form

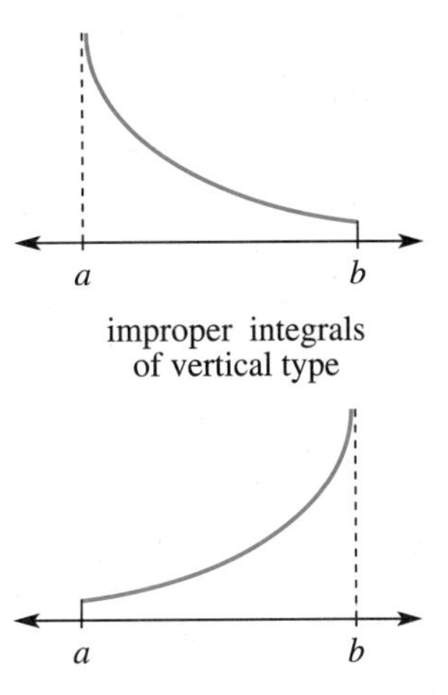

Figure 7.35 Improper integrals over intervals with a vertical asymptote.

$$\int_a^b f(x)\,dx,$$

where there is a *vertical asymptote* somewhere in the interval. Figure 7.35 illustrates two possibilities.

If the function values $f(x)$ are all positive except at the asymptote, then we can think of the improper integral as the measure of the area of an infinitely tall region. Whether or not this area is finite will depend on how fast the graph $y = f(x)$ approaches the vertical asymptote as x approaches the asymptote. The strategy for treating such an integral is very similar to the strategy for evaluating horizontal type improper integrals. If the vertical asymptote occurs at one end of the interval, we first replace that endpoint with a parameter (placeholder) and then study the limiting behavior of the definite integral as the parameter's value approaches the asymptote at the other end.

Definition 4

Vertical type improper integrals. If f is continuous over $(c, b]$, with a vertical asymptote at $x = c$, then

$$\int_c^b f(x)\,dx \quad \text{is shorthand for} \quad \lim_{a\to c^+} \int_a^b f(x)\,dx.$$

If f is continuous over $[a, c)$, with a vertical asymptote at $x = c$, then

$$\int_a^c f(x)\,dx \quad \text{is shorthand for} \quad \lim_{b\to c^-} \int_a^b f(x)\,dx.$$

In either case, if the limiting value exists, then we say that the improper integral **converges**. Otherwise, we say that the improper integral **diverges**.

We'll illustrate with several examples.

EXAMPLE 32 Determine whether $\int_0^1 \frac{1}{\sqrt{x}}\,dx$ converges or diverges. If the improper integral converges, find its value.

Solution Note that $1/\sqrt{x}$ is not defined at $x = 0$. However, $\int_a^1 \frac{1}{\sqrt{x}}\,dx$ is defined if $a > 0$, and we can compute

$$\int_a^1 \frac{1}{\sqrt{x}}\,dx = \int_a^1 x^{-1/2}\,dx = \left.\frac{x^{1/2}}{1/2}\right]_a^1 = 2 - 2\sqrt{a}.$$

Hence,

$$\int_0^1 \frac{1}{\sqrt{x}}\,dx = \lim_{a\to 0+} \int_a^1 \frac{1}{\sqrt{x}}\,dx = \lim_{a\to 0+} (2 - 2\sqrt{a}) = 2.$$

We say that the integral *converges* to 2. ■

EXAMPLE 33 Determine whether $\int_0^e \frac{1}{x}\,dx$ converges or diverges. If the improper integral converges, find its value.

Solution

$$\lim_{a\to 0+} \int_0^e \frac{1}{x}\,dx = \lim_{a\to 0+} \left(\ln|x|\Big]_a^e\right) = \lim_{a\to 0+} (\ln e - \ln a) = \lim_{a\to 0+} (1 - \ln a) = +\infty.$$

We say that the integral *diverges*. ■

EXAMPLE 34 Determine whether $\int_1^2 (x-2)^{-2/3}\,dx$ converges or diverges. If the improper integral converges, find its value.

Solution This time the vertical asymptote occurs at the right endpoint. So,

$$\int_1^2 (x-2)^{-2/3}\,dx = \lim_{b\to 2-} \int_1^b (x-2)^{-2/3}\,dx = \lim_{b\to 2-} 3(x-2)^{1/3}\Big]_1^b$$

$$= \lim_{b\to 2-} 3(b-2)^{1/3} - 3(1-2)^{1/3} = \lim_{b\to 2-} (3(b-2)^{1/3} + 3) = 3.$$

The improper integral converges to 3. ■

If a vertical asymptote appears between the endpoints, then we agree to split the interval into two pieces at the vertical asymptote. Again, if *either* or both of these improper integrals diverges, we say that the entire improper integral diverges.

EXAMPLE 35 Determine whether $\int_{-1}^{1} \frac{1}{x}\,dx$ converges or diverges. If the improper integral converges, find its value.

Solution A glance at the graph of $y = \frac{1}{x}$ might suggest that this integral should be 0, since the region below the x-axis is symmetrical to the region above. However, we cannot say that $\int_{-1}^{1} \frac{1}{x}\,dx$ converges unless each of

$$\int_{-1}^{0} \frac{1}{x}\,dx \quad \text{and} \quad \int_{0}^{1} \frac{1}{x}\,dx$$

converges.

$$\int_{a}^{1} \frac{1}{x}\,dx = \lim_{a \to 0+} \ln|x| \Big]_{a}^{1} = \lim_{a \to 0+} (\ln|1| - \ln|a|) = \lim_{a \to 0+} (0 - \ln|a|) = \infty.$$

So, this improper integral diverges. ■

EXAMPLE 36 Determine whether $\int_{1}^{4} (x-2)^{-2/3}\,dx$ converges or diverges. If the improper integral converges, find its value.

Solution The vertical asymptote $x = 2$ occurs in the interior of the interval.

$$\int_{1}^{4} (x-2)^{-2/3}\,dx = \lim_{b \to 2-} \int_{1}^{b} (x-2)^{-2/3}\,dx + \lim_{a \to 2+} \int_{a}^{4} (x-2)^{-2/3}\,dx.$$

We have already computed the first of these improper integrals and found it to converge to 3. As for the second improper integral,

$$\lim_{a \to 2+} \int_{a}^{4} (x-2)^{-2/3} = \lim_{a \to 2+} 3(x-2)^{1/3} \Big]_{a}^{4} = 3\sqrt[3]{2}.$$

Since both integrals converge, we conclude that the entire improper integral converges to $3 + 3\sqrt[3]{2}$. ■

EXERCISES for Section 7.7

For exercises 1–10: Determine whether the improper integral converges or diverges. If it converges, find its value.

1. $\int_{1}^{\infty} \frac{1}{x^3}\,dx$

2. $\int_{3}^{\infty} \frac{1}{x^{2/3}}\,dx$

3. $\int_{0.5}^{\infty} \frac{1}{x^2}\,dx$

4. $\int_{8}^{\infty} \frac{1}{x^{1/3}}\,dx$

5. $\int_{1}^{\infty} \frac{1}{x^{3/2}}\,dx$

6. $\int_{0.25}^{\infty} \frac{1}{x^{1/2}}\,dx$

7. $\int_1^\infty \frac{1}{x^{1.01}}\,dx$

8. $\int_1^\infty \frac{1}{x^{0.99}}\,dx$

9. $\int_1^\infty \frac{1}{x}\,dx$

10. $\int_1^\infty \frac{1}{x^{-1}}\,dx$

---

11. On the basis of your answers to exercises 1–10, formulate a conjecture regarding the convergence or divergence of

$$\int_1^\infty \frac{1}{x^p}\,dx.$$

Specifically, does the integral converge or diverge when $p < 1$, when $p = 1$, and when $p > 1$? Then test your conjecture by evaluating the integral in terms of p.

12. For what values p does the improper integral $\int_{-\infty}^{1} \frac{1}{x^p}\,dx$ converge?

For exercises 13–20: Determine whether the improper integral converges or diverges. If it converges, find its value.

13. $\int_0^\infty e^{2x}\,dx$

14. $\int_0^\infty e^{-2x}\,dx$

15. $\int_{-\infty}^0 e^{2x}\,dx$

16. $\int_{-\infty}^0 e^{-2x}\,dx$

17. $\int_0^\infty e^{x/2}\,dx$

18. $\int_0^\infty e^{-x/2}\,dx$

19. $\int_{-\infty}^0 e^{x/2}\,dx$

20. $\int_{-\infty}^0 e^{-x/2}\,dx$

---

21. On the basis of your answers to exercises 13–20, formulate a conjecture regarding the convergence or divergence of

$$\int_0^\infty e^{px}\,dx \quad \text{and} \quad \int_{-\infty}^0 e^{px}\,dx.$$

Specifically, what happens when $p < 0$ and when $p > 0$? In the cases when the integral converges, find its value in terms of p.

22. For the integrals in exercise 21, what happens when $p = 0$?

For exercises 23–26: Determine whether the improper integral converges or diverges. If it converges, find its value.

23. $\int_{-\infty}^\infty \frac{e^x}{1+e^{2x}}\,dx$

24. $\int_{-\infty}^\infty e^{-|x|}\,dx$

25. $\int_{-\infty}^\infty x\,dx$

26. $\int_2^\infty \frac{1}{x\sqrt{x^2-1}}\,dx$

For exercises 27–36: Determine whether the improper integral converges or diverges. If it converges, find its value.

27. $\int_{-1}^0 \frac{1}{x^3}\,dx$

28. $\int_{-3}^0 \frac{1}{x^{2/3}}\,dx$

29. $\int_{-0.5}^0 \frac{1}{x^2}\,dx$

30. $\int_{-8}^0 \frac{1}{x^{1/3}}\,dx$

31. $\int_0^2 \frac{1}{x^{3/2}}\,dx$

32. $\int_0^{0.25} \frac{1}{x^{1/2}}\,dx$

33. $\int_0^1 \frac{1}{x^{1.01}}\,dx$

34. $\int_0^1 \frac{1}{x^{0.99}}\,dx$

35. $\int_0^1 \frac{1}{x}\,dx$

36. $\int_0^1 \frac{1}{x^{-1}}\,dx$

---

37. On the basis of your answers to exercises 27–36, formulate a conjecture regarding the convergence or divergence of

$$\int_0^1 \frac{1}{x^p}\,dx.$$

Specifically, does the integral converge or diverge when $p < 1$, when $p = 1$, and when $p > 1$? Then test your conjecture by evaluating the integral in terms of p.

38. For what values p does the improper integral $\int_{-1}^0 \frac{1}{x^p}\,dx$ converge?

---

39. Determine whether $\int_0^4 \frac{1}{(x-1)^{1/3}}\,dx$ converges and, if it does, compute its value.

40. Determine whether $\int_0^1 \ln(x)\,dx$ converges and, if it does, compute its value.

41. Analyze the following problem:

$$\int_0^\pi \sec^2(x)\,dx = \tan x\Big]_0^\pi = \tan\pi - \tan 0 = 0.$$

If there is anything wrong with the solution, clearly state what is wrong and evaluate the integral correctly.

42. Determine whether $\int_1^2 \frac{x}{x^2-1}\,dx$ converges and, if it does, compute its value.

43. Determine whether $\int_1^3 \ln(x)\,dx$ converges and, if it does, determine its value.

44. A student looks at the graph of $y = 1/x$ over the interval $[-2, 2]$ and notes that the graph is symmetric with respect to the origin. The student concludes that

$$\int_{-2}^0 \frac{1}{x}\,dx = -\int_0^2 \frac{1}{x}\,dx,$$

and, therefore, that $\int_{-2}^2 \frac{1}{x}\,dx = 0$. Why is the student wrong?

45. Verify that integral $\int_{-a}^a x\,dx = 0$ for any positive number a. This, of course, means that

$$\lim_{a\to\infty} \int_{-a}^a x\,dx = 0.$$

Compare this with the answer you obtained in exercise 25. (This example shows why this method of evaluating an improper integral over $(-\infty, \infty)$ is unreliable.)

46. A nonnegative function $p(x)$ can be a probability density function, provided that the integral $\int_{-\infty}^{\infty} p(x)\, dx = 1$. Let

$$p(x) = \frac{1}{\sqrt{2\pi}} e^{-(x^2/2)}.$$

(This function p is known as the standard normal probability density function.) The graph of $y = p(x)$ is a bell-shaped curve symmetric about $x = 0$, so

$$\int_0^{\infty} p(x)\, dx = \int_{-\infty}^{0} p(x)\, dx.$$

Since $p(x)$ has no nice formula for its antiderivative, we cannot use the fundamental theorems of calculus to evaluate it. Using a numerical integrator, approximate

$$\int_0^b p(x)\, dx$$

for $b = 1$, 2, 3, 4, 5, and 10. Do you believe that $\int_{-\infty}^{\infty} p(x)\, dx = 1$?

47. In the theory of differential equations, if f is a function, then the **Laplace Transform** $L[s]$ of f is defined by

$$L[s] = \int_0^{\infty} e^{-sx} f(x)\, dx$$

for every real number s for which the improper integral converges. Find the Laplace Transform of $f(x) = \sin(x)$. In other words evaluate

$$\int_0^{\infty} e^{-sx} \sin x\, dx.$$

Your answer should be in terms of s. (Hint: treat s as a constant when integrating.)

48. The *Horn of Gabriel* is obtained by rotating the graph of $y = 1/x$ about the x-axis over the interval $[1, \infty)$. The surface area of Gabriel's Horn and the volume within Gabriel's Horn are both given by improper integrals, since the interval is infinite. Which of the two improper integrals converges? (It's been said that the only way to paint Gabriel's Horn is by filling it with paint.)

8

Differential Equations

Differential equations arise in a variety of contexts: physics, chemistry, biology, engineering, economics—even linguistics. The mathematical descriptions of so many phenomena are most often stated, and most easily understood, as relationships between rates of change (slopes) and other values. Examples include the laws of gravity (a freely falling body's velocity changes at a rate proportional to the gravitation acting on it), and chemical reactions (rate of production of a reaction product is proportional to the amounts of the reactants).

Differential equations often state a relationship between a function's input, its output, *and its rate of change.* Examples of differential equations include

$$\frac{dy}{dx} = x^2, \qquad \frac{dy}{dx} = y^2, \qquad \frac{dy}{dx} = y + x.$$

In each of these cases, the derivative dy/dx is expressed in terms of x, y, or *both.*

In Chapter 6, we studied antidifferentiation. The antiderivative of a function f can be thought of as the solution to a very simple kind of differential equation:

$$\frac{dy}{dx} = f(x).$$

The method of substitution is an integration technique that helps us antidifferentiate the results of differentiation using the chain rule. In this chapter, we start out by considering some additional techniques for solving antidifferentiation problems. In particular, we examine the technique of integration by parts, which helps us antidifferentiate results of the *product rule* for differentiation.

Then we turn to a very important class of differential equations that define the exponential model. These differential equations arise quite naturally. They govern such diverse phenomena as population growth and radioactive decay, and we consider several of these applications.

We also consider some of the symbolic, graphical, and numerical methods available for solving more general differential equations of the form

$$\frac{dy}{dx} = G(x, y),$$

where $G(x, y)$ is an expression involving both x and y.

The method of *separation of variables* provides a symbolic tool for solving certain differential equations. A *slope field* or *direction field* program is a graphical tool that is extremely useful in the study of differential equations. (You will need such a program for some of the exercises in this chapter. If you do not have one, but you have a programmable graphing calculator, you may be able to produce your own.) A slope field program takes an input expression such as $\frac{dy}{dx} = G(x, y)$, computes the value $G(x, y)$ at several predetermined points (x, y) in the Cartesian plane, and then plots a small line segment centered at each point (x, y) using the value $G(x, y)$ as slope. We end the chapter with a look at Euler's method, a technique for solving differential equations that is based on the numerical techniques of integration discussed in Chapter 6.

8.1 METHODS OF ANTIDIFFERENTIATION—INTEGRATION BY PARTS

The simplest types of differential equations are of the form

$$y' = \frac{dy}{dx} = f(x).$$

This is a problem of antidifferentiation: to solve the differential equation, we must find an antiderivative F for the function f. The general solution of the differential equation is

$$y = F(x) + C,$$

where C is an arbitrary constant. If we have an initial condition $y(a) = b$, we can solve for a specific value of this constant:

$$C = b - F(a).$$

EXAMPLE 1 Find a function y whose derivative y' satisfies the differential equation

$$y'(x) = x^2$$

and also satisfies the initial condition $y(0) = 2$.

Solution If we can recognize a solution to the differential equation, we are nearly done. In this simple case, the most general solution to the differential equation is

$$y(x) = \frac{x^3}{3} + C,$$

where C is an arbitrary constant. The initial condition will determine a specific value C:

$$y(0) = \frac{0^3}{3} + C = 2,$$

so $C = 2$ and the solution satisfying the initial condition is

$$y = \frac{x^3}{3} + 2.$$

■

Using the fundamental theorems of calculus

Even if we do not recognize a formula for the general antiderivative of a continuous function f, the fundamental theorems of calculus guarantee a solution. For any differential equation with initial condition

$$\frac{dy}{dx} = f(x), \qquad y(a) = b,$$

where f is continuous over a neighborhood of a, the fundamental theorems of calculus provide the solution

$$y = F(x) = b + \int_a^x f(t)\,dt.$$

We can check that

$$\frac{dy}{dx} = F'(x) = 0 + f(x) = f(x)$$

and

$$y(a) = F(a) = b + \int_a^a f(t)\,dt = b + 0 = b.$$

While all continuous functions have antiderivatives (by the fundamental theorems of calculus), many simple functions have antiderivatives that cannot be written in algebraic form.

EXAMPLE 2 Use the fundamental theorems of calculus to find the solution of the differential equation

$$\frac{dy}{dx} = \sqrt{\sqrt{x^2 + 1} + 1}$$

with initial condition $y(1) = 5$. Use the solution to estimate $y(2)$ to two decimal places of accuracy.

Solution In this case, we cannot recognize $\sqrt{\sqrt{x^2+1}+1}$ as the derivative of any function we know. (In fact, it is not the derivative of anything that can be written in algebraic form.) Even so, since $f(x) = \sqrt{\sqrt{x^2+1}+1}$ is continuous, the fundamental theorems of calculus provide the solution

$$y(x) = 5 + \int_1^x \sqrt{\sqrt{t^2+1}+1}\,dt.$$

We can use numerical integration techniques to approximate the value of the integral for any specific value x. For $x = 2$, we find that

$$y(2) = 5 + \int_1^2 \sqrt{\sqrt{t^2+1}+1}\,dt \approx 6.67.$$

■

Integration by parts

The method of substitution helps us recognize derivatives produced by the chain rule. The method known as *integration by parts* helps us recognize derivatives produced by the *product rule.*

The product rule for the derivative of fg gives us

$$\frac{d}{dx}(f(x)g(x)) = f'(x)g(x) + f(x)g'(x).$$

If we write u for $f(x)$ and v for $g(x)$, we have

$$\frac{d}{dx}(uv) = \frac{du}{dx}v + u\frac{dv}{dx}.$$

Following our convention of writing $du = \dfrac{du}{dx}\,dx$ and $dv = \dfrac{dv}{dx}\,dx$, we can reverse the product rule to be a statement about antiderivatives:

$$uv = \int v\,du + \int u\,dv.$$

When we subtract $\int vdu$ from both sides, the resulting statement is commonly known as the:

Integration by parts formula

$$\int u\,dv = uv - \int v\,du.$$

Given an integral of the form $\int u\,dv$, this formula is useful if the integral $\int v\,du$ that appears on the right-hand side is much easier to recognize than the original integral $\int u\,dv$.

Let's outline the method of integration by parts and then illustrate it with several examples.

Integration by Parts

Step 1. Let $u = f(x)$ and $dv = g(x)dx$, where $f(x)g(x)dx$ is the original integrand. Good choices to make are integrals $\int dv = \int g(x)dx$, which are easy to integrate.

Step 2. Compute $du = f'(x)dx$ and $v = \int g(x)dx$.

Step 3. Substitute u, v, du, and dv into the formula

$$\int u\,dv = uv - \int v\,du.$$

Step 4. Calculate $uv - \int vdu$.

If $\int v\,du$ is difficult or impossible to integrate, go back to Step 1 and consider other choices for u and dv.

Step 5. Check your solution by differentiating and comparing to the original integrand.

As with the method of substitution, integration by parts comes with no guarantee of success. However, it is a technique that works well on many integrals involving products of functions, particularly if certain transcendental functions appear as factors (such as logarithmic or inverse trigonometric functions). With experience, you can become skilled at choosing the appropriate factors u and dv to use in integration by parts.

EXAMPLE 3 Find $\int xe^x\,dx$.

Solution Let $u = x$ and $dv = e^x\,dx$. We find that $du = dx$ and

$$v = \int dv = \int e^x\,dx = e^x.$$

Substituting into the integration by parts formula, we have

$$\int xe^x\,dx = \int u\,dv = uv - \int v\,du = xe^x - \int e^x\,dx.$$

The last integral that appears is simple to integrate, and we have

$$\int xe^x\,dx = xe^x - e^x + C.$$

We can check our answer by differentiating:

$$\frac{d}{dx}(xe^x - e^x + C) = (1 \cdot e^x + x \cdot e^x) - e^x = xe^x.$$

■

EXAMPLE 4 Find $\int x^2 e^x \, dx$.

Solution Let $u = x^2$ and $dv = e^x \, dx$. We find that $du = 2x dx$ and

$$v = \int dv = \int e^x \, dx = e^x.$$

Substituting into the integration by parts formula, we have

$$\int x^2 e^x \, dx = \int u \, dv = uv - \int v \, du = x^2 e^x - \int 2xe^x \, dx.$$

The last integral can be written as $2 \int xe^x \, dx$, and we successfully integrated this by parts in Example 3. Substituting that result, we obtain

$$\int x^2 e^x \, dx = x^2 e^x - 2xe^x + 2e^x + C.$$

(Check the answer by differentiating.) ■

EXAMPLE 5 Find $\int \ln(x) \, dx$.

Solution Let $u = \ln(x)$ and $dv = 1 \, dx$. We find that $du = \frac{1}{x} \, dx$ and

$$v = \int dv = \int 1 \, dx = x.$$

Substituting into the integration by parts formula, we have

$$\int \ln(x) \, dx = \int u \, dv = uv - \int v \, du = x \cdot \ln(x) - \int x \cdot \frac{1}{x} \, dx.$$

After simplifying the last integrand and integrating, we have

$$\int \ln(x) \, dx = x \ln(x) - x + C.$$

We can check our answer by differentiating:

$$\frac{d}{dx}(x \ln(x) - x + C) = (1 \cdot \ln(x) + x \cdot \frac{1}{x}) - 1 = \ln(x).$$ ■

EXAMPLE 6 Find $\int \arctan(x) \, dx$.

Solution Let $u = \arctan(x)$ and $dv = 1 \, dx$. We find that $du = \frac{1}{1 + x^2} \, dx$ and

$$v = \int dv = \int 1 \, dx = x.$$

Substituting into the integration by parts formula, we have

$$\int \arctan(x) \, dx = \int u \, dv = uv - \int v \, du = x \cdot \arctan(x) - \int x \cdot \frac{1}{1 + x^2} \, dx.$$

Now, this last integral can be integrated using the method of substitution. Let $w = 1 + x^2$, so that $dw = 2x\,dx$. Then

$$\int \frac{x}{1+x^2}\,dx = \int \frac{1}{w}\frac{dw}{2} = \frac{1}{2}\int \frac{1}{w}\,dw = \frac{1}{2}\ln|w| + C = \frac{1}{2}\ln|1+x^2| + C.$$

Using this result, we can now write

$$\int \arctan(x)\,dx = x\arctan(x) - \frac{1}{2}\ln|1+x^2| - C.$$

Because $1 + x^2$ is positive for all real values x, we can drop the absolute value signs from this expression. Also, subtracting an arbitrary constant C is the same as adding an arbitrary constant (C can be any real number), so we might as well write this as

$$\int \arctan(x)\,dx = x\arctan(x) - \frac{\ln(1+x^2)}{2} + C.$$

(Check the answer by differentiating.) ■

EXAMPLE 7 Compute $\int_0^1 \arctan(x)\,dx$.

Solution We found the antiderivative of $\arctan(x)$ in Example 6. Hence,

$$\begin{aligned}\int_0^1 \arctan(x)\,dx &= \left(x\arctan(x) - \frac{\ln(1+x^2)}{2}\right)\Bigg]_{x=0}^{x=1} \\ &= \left(1\cdot\arctan(1) - \frac{\ln(1+1^2)}{2}\right) - \left(0\cdot\arctan(0) - \frac{\ln(1+0^2)}{2}\right) \\ &= \left(\frac{\pi}{4} - \frac{\ln 2}{2}\right) - (0-0) \\ &= \frac{\pi - 2\ln 2}{4} \approx 0.4388.\end{aligned}$$

■

EXERCISES for Section 8.1

For exercises 1–8: Use the fundamental theorems of calculus to solve the differential equations with the given initial conditions. Then use a numerical integration technique to approximate $y(3)$.

1. $y' = e^{-x^2/2}$; $y(0) = 0.5$

2. $y' = \ln(x^2+1)$; $y(0) = 1$

3. $y' = 0.2\sqrt{x+5}$; $y(2) = 2.5$

4. $y' = 1 + x$; $y(0) = 1$

5. $y' = 0.1((x+1)^2+1)^2$; $y(-1) = 1$

6. $y' = \sin(\sin(x)); \quad y(0) = 0$

7. $y' = \frac{1}{x^2+1}; \quad y(1) = 1$

8. $y' = \frac{1}{x^3+1}; \quad y(-0.5) = -2$

For exercises 9–50: Find the antiderivatives using integration by parts.

9. $\int \arcsin(x)\,dx$

10. $\int \operatorname{arccot}(x)\,dx$

11. $\int x^3 e^x\,dx$

12. $\int xe^{-x}\,dx$

13. $\int \arccos(x)\,dx$

14. $\int x^3 e^{-x}\,dx$

15. $\int x\ln(x)\,dx$

16. $\int x\cos(5x)\,dx$

17. $\int x^2\sin(x)\,dx$

18. $\int x(\ln(x^2))\,dx$

19. $\int x\cos(x)\,dx$

20. $\int x^{1/2}\ln(x)\,dx$

21. $\int x^{3/2}\ln(x)\,dx$

22. $\int x\ln(\frac{1}{x})\,dx$

23. $\int \frac{\ln(x)}{\sqrt{x}}\,dx$

24. $\int \ln(x^2+1)\,dx$

25. $\int (\ln(x))^3\,dx$

26. $\int x^2(\ln(x))^2\,dx$

27. $\int x^{-2}\ln(x)\,dx$

28. $\int x(\ln(x))^2\,dx$

29. $\int x^2\cos(x)\,dx$

30. $\int \cos^3(x)\,dx$ (Let $u = \cos^2(x)$.)

31. $\int x\sec(x)\tan(x)\,dx$

32. $\int x\csc^2(x)\,dx$

33. $\int x\sec^2(x)\,dx$

34. $\int \cos(x)\ln(\sin(x))\,dx$

35. $\int xe^{1-3x}\,dx$

36. $\int x\cos^2(x)\,dx$

37. $\int x\arctan(x)\,dx$

38. $\int \sin(2x)\cos(3x)\,dx$

39. $\int x^2\arctan(x)\,dx$

40. $\int x(x+1)^{10}\,dx$

41. $\int x^3(1-x^2)^{1/2}\,dx$ (Let $u = x^2$.)

42. $\int x^5(4-x^3)^{1/2}\,dx$ (Let $u = x^3$.)

43. $\int \sin(\ln(x))\,dx$

44. $\int \cos(\ln(x))\,dx$

45. $\int x\cosh(x)\,dx$

46. $\int e^x\sinh(x)\,dx$

47. Sometimes integration by parts leads us back to an expression involving the original integral. Use integration by parts twice on $\int e^x\cos(x)\,dx$ and then *solve* the resulting equation for the original integral.

48. Use integration by parts twice on $\int e^x\sin(x)\,dx$ and then *solve* the resulting equation for the original integral.

49. $\int e^{3x}\cos(3x)\,dx$

50. $\int e^{-2x}\sin(5x)\,dx$

8.2 THE EXPONENTIAL MODEL

When we gather data from a real-world process, we can attempt to mathematically model the process as a function

$$y = f(x).$$

The function f may arise as the solution to a differential equation when we have some knowledge of the rate of change of y with respect to x.

The linear model

One very important type of mathematical model is the *linear model.* If the outputs from a process appear to increase or decrease at a *constant rate*, a linear model is indicated. Numerically, we have evidence of a linear model if the *difference* in outputs is observed to be proportional to the difference in the inputs. We can think of this constant rate of change in terms of the very simple differential equation

$$y'(x) = m.$$

The solution of this differential equation has the familiar form

$$y(x) = mx + b.$$

Graphically, an easy way to recognize a linear process is to plot the graph of data outputs versus time and see if the points line up. Numerically, equally spaced inputs should produce equally spaced outputs.

Once we have determined that a process behaves linearly, we want to fit the model to the data by determining its *parameters*. A linear model has parameters slope m and the y-intercept b. The slope tells us about the growth rate, while the y-intercept communicates an initial condition $y(0) = b$. These can be completely determined from two data pairs (two points on the line). After we determine the parameters, we can check the linear model against other observed data or use it to make predictions.

The differential equations $y' = ky$

Another very important type of mathematical model is indicated when the outputs from a process appear to increase or decrease at a rate proportional to the outputs themselves. Numerically, we have evidence of this if the *ratio* of outputs is proportional to the difference in inputs.

We can think of this proportional rate of change in terms of the differential equation

$$y' = ky, \qquad y(0) = b,$$

where k and b are given constants. If we interpret the independent variable to represent time, then this differential equation describes some quantity whose rate of growth y' at any time is directly proportional to its value y at that same time. The initial condition $y(0) = b$ under this interpretation simply tells us the initial amount of the quantity. Remarkably, such differential equations arise very naturally in applications as diverse as population growth, heat transfer, and radioactive decay.

To solve this differential equation, we seek a function $y = f(x)$ whose derivative is a constant multiple k of the original function. Let's use a slope field to visualize the solution of a special case of this equation. Suppose we start out with the initial condition $y(0) = b = 1$, and the constant of proportionality is $k = 1$, so that we have

$$y' = y, \qquad y(0) = 1.$$

(Perhaps you can guess a solution to the problem. Do you know of a function y that is equal to its own derivative and also satisfies the equation $y(0) = 1$?)

The slope field generated by this differential equation consists of tangent line segments arranged in *horizontal* rows, since the slopes at each point should be the same as the y-value of that point ($y' = y$). A sketch of the slope field is shown in Figure 8.1.

For example, the row of parallel tangent line segments along $y = 1$ all have slope 1, and the row of parallel tangent line segments along $y = -2$ all have slope -2. The initial condition $y(0) = 1$ specifies that the point $(0, 1)$

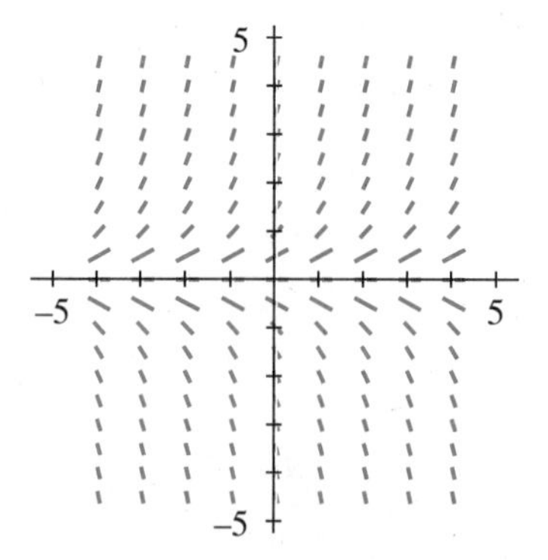

Figure 8.1 The slope field generated by $y' = y$.

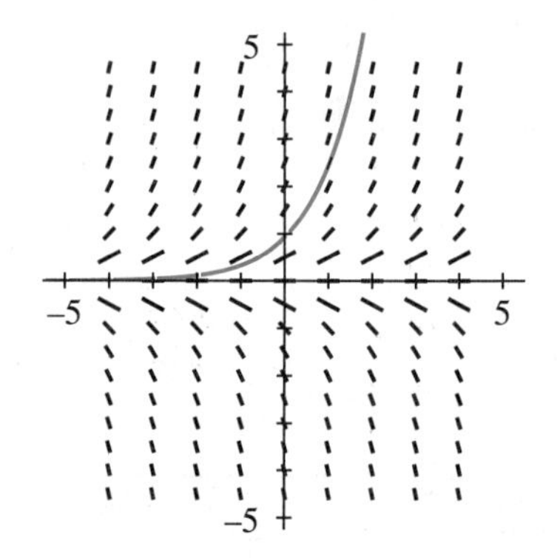

Figure 8.2 The solution graph for $y' = y$ with initial condition $y(0) = 1$.

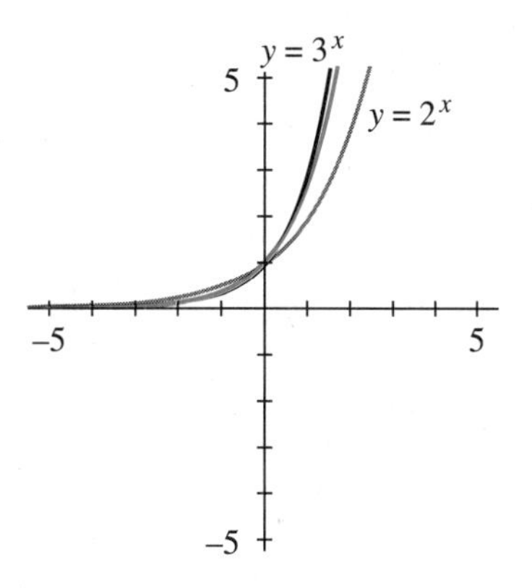

Figure 8.3 Comparing the solution curve to $y = 2^x$ and $y = 3^x$.

is on the graph of the solution. Using this and following the directions indicated by the slope field, we obtain a graph like that in Figure 8.2. This looks remarkably like the graph of an exponential function. In fact, if we superimpose the graphs of $y = 2^x$ and $y = 3^x$ on the graph obtained from this slope field and initial condition, the result suggests that we might find some real number $2 < a < 3$ that gives a very good fit of $y = a^x$ to the slope field (see Figure 8.3).

Perhaps you have guessed by now that the exponential expression we are looking for has the irrational number $e \approx 2.718281828459045$ as its base. The function $y(x) = e^x$ satisfies our differential equation and initial condition, since

$$y'(x) = \frac{d}{dx}(e^x) = e^x = y(x) \qquad \text{and} \qquad y(0) = e^0 = 1.$$

If we change the constant k, we have $\frac{d}{dx}(e^{kx}) = ke^{kx}$ for any k, so that $y = e^{kx}$ is a solution to the differential equation $y' = ky$.

If we change the initial condition, so that

$$y' = ky, \qquad y(0) = b,$$

you can check that the function

$$y(x) = be^{kx}$$

satisfies both the differential equation and the initial condition

$$y' = \frac{d}{dx}(be^{kx}) = k(be^{kx}) = ky \qquad \text{and} \qquad y(0) = be^{(k \cdot 0)} = be^0 = b.$$

The function $y = be^{kx}$ is a solution to the differential equation $y' = ky$ with initial condition $y(0) = b$.

EXAMPLE 8 Find the solution to the differential equation with initial condition

$$y' = 3y, \qquad y(0) = 5.7.$$

Solution We have $k = 3$ and $b = 5.7$ in the exponential model, so

$$y(x) = 5.7e^{3x}$$

is a solution to the differential equation satisfying the given initial condition. ■

EXAMPLE 9 Find the solution to the differential equation with initial condition:

$$y' = -2y, \qquad y(0) = 8.1.$$

Solution We have $k = -2$ and $b = 8.1$ in the exponential model, so

$$y(x) = 8.1e^{-2x}$$

is a solution to the differential equation satisfying the given initial condition. ■

Fitting the exponential model

Once we have determined that a process behaves exponentially, we want to fit the exponential model to the data by determining its *parameters*.

> In the case of an exponential model $y = be^{kx}$, the parameters are the proportionality constant k and the y-intercept b.

The constant k tells us about the growth rate, while the y-intercept represents an initial condition $y(0) = b$. These can be completely determined from two data pairs (two points on the exponential curve). After we determine the parameters, we can check the exponential model against other observed data or use it to make predictions. The next section is devoted to several applications of the exponential model.

EXERCISES for Section 8.2

For exercises 1–6: Samples of a population of bacteria taken 1 hour apart are presented. In some cases, the population was growing exponentially. In other cases, where an antibiotic was added to the culture, the population was *decreasing* exponentially. In other cases, where the bacteria were simply migrating, the populations were linear functions of time. Decide which are which, and for each predict the populations 3 hours after the last sample.

1. 4129, 4501, 4906, and 5347

2. 4129, 4831, 5652, and 6613

3. 4129, 4501, 4872, and 5244

4. 4129, 4061, 3992, and 3924

5. 4129, 4061, 3994, and 3928

6. 4129, 2890, 2023, and 1416

For exercises 7–14: Solve the indicated differential equations with initial conditions. Include the domain of definition of the solution. Which of the differential equations have an exponential function as a solution?

7. $y' = 4y; \quad y(1) = 42$

8. $\frac{3y'}{y} = -1; \quad y(0) = 1$

9. $\frac{y'}{y} = \frac{1}{x}; \quad y(0.1) = 0.1$

10. $y' = \frac{y}{x}; \quad y(-1) = 0.75$

11. $yy' = \frac{1}{x}; \quad y(2) = 1$

12. $y' = y + 2; \quad y(0) = 0$

13. $y' = \frac{x}{x^2+1}; \quad y(0) = 0$

14. $y' = \frac{-2x}{x^2+1}; \quad y(0) = 0$

For exercises 15–20: A pair of functions is given. Both of the functions are solutions to a single differential equation with different initial conditions. For each exercise, find the (not necessarily unique) differential equation and initial conditions. (Recall that $\exp(x) = e^x$.)

15. $y = 3\exp(2x); \quad y = -2\exp(2x)$

16. $y = 3\exp(2x); \quad y = 3\exp(2x) + 5$

17. $y = 5^{(3x+2)}; \quad y = 125^x$

18. $y = 5^{(x-1)}; \quad y = 0.2\exp(x\ln(5)) - 0.7$

19. $y = \log_2(x); \quad y = \log_2(x) + 5$

20. $y = \log_3(x); \quad y = \frac{1}{\ln(3)}(\ln(-x))$

8.3 APPLICATIONS OF THE EXPONENTIAL MODEL

The exponential model describes the growth or decay of many quantities over time. If we use t to represent the independent variable time and y for some quantity that changes over time, then the differential equation

$$y'(t) = \frac{dy}{dt} = ky, \qquad y(0) = b$$

describes an exponential model. Using the results of the previous section, we know that this differential equation has solution

$$y(t) = be^{kt}.$$

Occasionally, it is desirable to represent such a function as an exponential of another base. Note that $e^{kt} = (e^k)^t$, so if we choose to use $c = e^k$ as the base,

$$y(t) = bc^t.$$

Once we have determined that an exponential model describes the behavior of a process, we want to determine its parameters. In the case of the exponential model, the parameter k tells us about the growth rate ($k > 0$) or decay rate ($k < 0$) of the outputs over time, and the parameter b reflects the initial condition $y(0) = b$. (If we choose to write $c = e^k$, then $c > 1$ indicates growth and $c < 1$ indicates decay.)

These parameters can also be determined from two data pairs (two points on the exponential curve). Again, after we determine the parameters, we can check the exponential model against other observed data or use it to make predictions. In this section, we'll discuss several phenomena that the exponential model seems to describe quite well.

Population growth

In a colony of microorganisms supplied with abundant food, each *individual* reproduces at a predictable and constant rate. The number of new individuals produced in a time period will be proportional to the total number of individuals. Thus, an exponential model works well for this type of population growth.

EXAMPLE 10 Using the data of population versus time given in Table 8.1, predict the time at which the population will reach 1000000 and the time at which the population was 30.

time	individuals
9:00	372
10:00	4295
11:00	49531

Table 8.1 Bacteria population at certain times.

Solution Let t be the time in hours past $9:00$ and $y(t)$ be the number of individuals. First, note that the exponential model does fit the data, since

$$\frac{y(1)}{y(0)} \approx 11.55 \qquad \text{and} \qquad \frac{y(2)}{y(1)} \approx 11.53.$$

The solution is of the form

$$y(t) = Ae^{kt} = Ac^t \qquad \text{where } c = e^k$$

for some A and k. Since $A = y(0) = 372$, we know that

$$y(t) = 372c^t.$$

To find c, we need to use another reading, say at $t = 1$ hour.

$$y(1) = 372c^1 = 372c = 4295, \qquad \text{so} \qquad c \approx 11.55.$$

Note that c is the factor by which the number of individuals multiply over each hour. The solution is

$$y(t) \approx 372(11.55)^t.$$

As a check, we note that the model predicts that

$$y(2) \approx 372(11.55)^2 \approx 49626,$$

which is very close to the observed number of individuals at time $t = 2$ $(11:00)$. To solve $y(t) = 1000000$ for t, we set up the equation

$$372(11.55)^t = 1000000.$$

Dividing by 372 and taking the natural logarithm of both sides:

$$t\ln(11.55) = \ln(1000000) - \ln(372)$$

and dividing by $\ln(11.55)$, we obtain

$$t = \frac{\ln(1,000,000) - \ln(372)}{\ln(11.55)} \approx 3.23.$$

The time when the population reaches 1000000 therefore is about $12:14$.

To find the time when the population was 30, we only need replace 1000000 by 30 in our calculation:

$$t = \frac{\ln(30) - \ln(372)}{\ln(11.55)} \approx -1.03.$$

So the time was about $7:57$. ■

Continuously compounded interest

Suppose a savings account in a bank pays 5.25% yearly compounded quarterly. That is, starting with $\$100$, three months later your accrued interest is credited to your account and you have

$$\$100 + (\frac{0.0525}{4})\$100 = \$101.3125.$$

Three more months later and you have

$$\$101.3125 + (\frac{0.0525}{4})\$101.3125 \approx \$102.6422,$$

and so on. In general, the bank account balance A can be expressed in terms of the original balance P, the interest rate r, the number of times n it is compounded yearly, and the time t in years. In the case just discussed, $P = \$100$, $r = .0525$, and $n = 4$. If P, r, and n are known, we can consider A as a function of t:

$$A(t) = P(1 + \frac{r}{n})^{nt}.$$

Many savings accounts offer *daily* compounding of interest. However, rather than using $n = 365$ in the formula above, most banks use an *effective* interest rate that approximates *continuous* compounding. That is, they use a flat annual rate that gives approximately the same interest payment as obtained with the stated rate r and by letting the number of compounding periods n approaches ∞. Equivalently, you can think of this as letting r be the *instantaneous* interest rate, so that the instantaneous rate of change of our account balance is simply

$$A'(t) = rA(t).$$

This means that the account balance under continuous compounding follows an exponential model, with solution

$$A(t) = Pe^{rt}.$$

The effective annual interest rate for continuous compounding is $e^r - 1$.

EXAMPLE 11 Suppose that \$100 is invested for two years at 5.25% compounded quarterly and another \$100 is invested at 5.25% compounded continuously. Compare the ending account balances. What is the effective annual interest rate for continuous compounding at 5.25%?

Solution For quarterly compounding, the ending account balance in dollars is

$$(100)(1 + (\frac{0.0525}{4}))^{4 \cdot 2} \approx 111.00,$$

while for continuous compounding, the ending account balance is

$$100e^{0.0525 \cdot 2} \approx 111.07.$$

The effective annual interest rate for continuous compounding at 5.25% is $e^{0.0525} - 1 \approx .0539$ or 5.39%. ■

Radioactive decay

An atom of radioactive material has a fixed probability of undergoing radioactive decay in any given time period. It is as if in each second, all of the atoms rolled their own multi-sided die, and all those whose number came up transmuted to a different element or isotope. In every second a fixed fraction of the remaining material decays, so that the rate of radioactive decay is proportional to the amount present. It has become customary to express the decay rate in terms of the amount of time it takes half of the material to decay—that is, the **half-life** of the material. If some radioactive material has a half-life of N years, the amount $y(t)$ present as a function of time t, also in years, is given by

$$y(t) = A(\frac{1}{2})^{t/N}.$$

Every N years, the amount is decreased by half. This is why the storage of radioactive waste is such a difficult problem: its rate of decay gets slower as it decays, hence storage facilities must be able to protect it from the environment for extended periods.

EXAMPLE 12 The isotope carbon-14 (^{14}C), whose nucleus consists of 6 protons and 8 neutrons, has a half-life of approximately 5580 years. If a sample of material is found to have 0.027 g of ^{14}C now, how many years ago did it have 1.26 g?

Solution If we let $y(t)$ be the amount (in grams) of ^{14}C t years ago, then

$$y(t) = A \cdot (\frac{1}{2})^{(t/5580)}.$$

Since $0.027 = y(0) = A \cdot (\frac{1}{2})^{(0/5580)} = A$, we know that

$$y(t) = 0.027 \cdot (\frac{1}{2})^{(t/5580)}.$$

To find the time that 1.26 g were present, we need to solve

$$1.26 = 0.027 \cdot (\frac{1}{2})^{(t/5580)}$$

for t. Dividing both sides by 0.027, we obtain

$$\frac{1.26}{0.027} = (\frac{1}{2})^{(t/5580)},$$

and taking the natural logarithm (base e) of both sides yields

$$\ln(\frac{1.26}{0.027}) = \ln(\frac{1}{2})^{(t/5580)} = \left(\frac{t}{5580}\right)\ln(\frac{1}{2}).$$

Hence, $t = 5580 \cdot \dfrac{\ln(1.26/0.027)}{\ln(1/2)} \approx -30937$, and we conclude that the sample had 1.26 g of ^{14}C about 30937 years ago. ■

Drug concentrations

Drug levels in the body follow the same kind of pattern as radioactive decay. On each pass through the liver, kidneys, and other organs, a certain fraction of any particular foreign substance in the blood is removed. This is another area where the usual unit of measurement is the half-life.

EXAMPLE 13 Blood samples taken 1 hour apart show concentrations $7.57\,\mu\text{g cm}^3$ and $5.80\,\mu\text{g cm}^3$ of a particular non-steroidal anti-inflammatory drug (such as aspirin). What is the half-life of this drug in the blood?

Solution The concentration C as a function of time t in hours past the first sample is of the form

$$C(t) = A(1/2)^{t/k},$$

where k is the half-life in hours.

Since $7.57 = C(0) = A(\frac{1}{2})^{0/k} = A$, we see that we must solve

$$5.80 = C(1) = 7.57(\frac{1}{2})^{1/k}$$

for k. Dividing by 7.57 and then taking natural logarithms (base e) gives us

$$\ln(\frac{5.80}{7.57}) = \ln(\frac{1}{2})^{1/k} = \frac{1}{k}\ln(\frac{1}{2}),$$

so

$$\frac{1}{k} = \frac{\ln(\frac{5.80}{7.57})}{\ln(\frac{1}{2})} \approx 0.3842,$$

and $k \approx 2.60$. The half-life is about 2.6 hours. ■

Heat transfer

The rate of heat (thermal energy) exchange between two objects in contact is proportional to the temperature *difference* between the two. (Heat flows from the hotter to the colder object.) The constant of proportionality depends on the thermal contact (or insulation) between the two. Newton's law of cooling is stated as follows:

> *The rate of change of the temperature difference between an object and its surroundings is proportional to the temperature difference itself.*

EXAMPLE 14 The temperatures $68.00\ ^\circ F$, $66.50\ ^\circ F$, and $65.07\ ^\circ F$ are recorded indoors 5 minutes apart. During this time, all sources of heat (furnace, etc.) are shut off and the outdoor temperature is constant. What is the outdoor temperature?

Solution Let $i(t)$ be the indoor temperature, t the time in minutes past the first temperature reading, T the outdoor temperature, and $y(t) = i(t) - T$ the difference between the indoor and outdoor temperature. Newton's law of cooling states that $y(t) = Ae^{kt}$ for some A and k. If we write $c = e^k$, then

$$y(t) = Ac^t$$

and

$$i(t) = Ac^t + T.$$

Our temperature readings tell us

$$i(0) = Ac^0 + T = A + T = 68, \quad i(5) = Ac^5 + T = 66.50, \quad i(10) = Ac^{10} + T = 65.07.$$

Note that

$$i(5) - i(0) = Ac^5 - A = -1.5 \quad \text{and} \quad i(10) - i(5) = Ac^{10} - Ac^5 = -1.43,$$

so that

$$\frac{Ac^{10} - Ac^5}{Ac^5 - A} = \frac{c^5(Ac^5 - A)}{Ac^5 - A} = c^5 = \frac{-1.43}{-1.5},$$

from which we can solve for c. Now, $Ac^5 - A = -1.5$, so

$$A = \frac{-1.5}{c^5 - 1} = \frac{-1.5}{\frac{-1.43}{-1.5} - 1} \approx 32.14.$$

Since $A + T = 68$, we have $T = 68 - A \approx 68 - 32.14 = 35.86$ degrees. ■

EXERCISES for Section 8.3

For exercises 1–4: A hot object is plunged into a beaker of ice water maintained at $32\ ^\circ F$. One and two minutes later, the temperature of the object is measured to be $87\ ^\circ F$ and $76.2\ ^\circ F$, respectively.

1. What will the temperature be one minute after the last measurement?

2. What was the temperature when the object was plunged in the ice water?

3. If the water had been maintained at $40\ ^\circ F$ instead, what would the measurements have been after one and two minutes?

4. If the initial temperature of the object had been $120\ ^\circ F$, and the water had been maintained at $32\ ^\circ F$, what would the measurements have been after one and two minutes?

---

5. After 10 years, it is found that only 30% of the initial amount of a radioactive substance remains. What is the half-life of this substance?

6. An artifact is found containing only 4% of the amount of ^{14}C it had when it was created. Using a half-life of 5580 years for ^{14}C, determine the age of the artifact.

For exercises 7–9: A certain therapeutic drug has a half-life of 3.3 hours in the bloodstream. The minimal therapeutic dose requires 1.5 mg in the bloodstream.

7. How often should a dose of 3 mg be injected to guarantee that the minimum dose is maintained?

8. If a dose is to be injected every hour, how big should it be?

9. If, starting with no drug in the bloodstream, 3 mg is injected every 3 hours, how much is in the bloodstream just before the fifth injection? How much just before the 100th?

For exercises 10–14: Assume that $100 is invested at 5.25% compounded quarterly.

10. What interest rate r would yield the same account balance at the end of one year if the interest is compounded continuously?

11. How many years (rounded to the next quarter) will it take to double your initial balance?

12. What yearly interest rate would double your money in 10 years?

13. Another competing bank pays 5.28% but compounds only twice a year. Which account offers a better deal? What interest rate would make the two banks comparable?

14. A third bank offers a 7% yearly interest rate compounded quarterly but also has a $.10 per quarter service charge, which is deducted from your account at the same time the interest is credited.

If your starting balance is $100, which bank offers the best deal? If your starting balance is $1000, which bank offers the best deal?

---

15. Atmospheric pressure p (pounds per square inch) varies with altitude h (feet) according to the law

$$\frac{dp}{dh} = -kp,$$

where k is a constant. Given that p is 15 pounds per square inch at sea level and 10 pounds per square inch at 10000 feet, find p at 15000 feet.

16. Linguists have applied calculus to the dating of unfamiliar languages, using a method called *glottochronology*. Let $N(t)$ be the number of words in the language still in use at time t (with their original meanings). The assumption is that the rate at which words fall out of usage is directly proportional to the number still in use. In other words,

$$\frac{dN}{dt} = -kN(t),$$

where t is measured in *millenia* (thousands of years).

In 1950, Feng and Swadesh observed that of 210 words of ancient Chinese in use at 950 A.D., 167 words were still in use. Find k. How many of the words will still be in use in the year 2525?

8.4 GRAPHICAL AND SYMBOLIC METHODS FOR SOLVING $dy/dx = G(x, y)$

We obtained the function

$$y = 5 + \int_1^x \sqrt{\sqrt{t^2+1}+1}\,dt$$

as a solution to the differential equation with initial condition

$$y' = \sqrt{\sqrt{x^2+1}+1} \qquad y(1) = 5$$

in Section 8.1, using the fundamental theorems of calculus.

We can check the reasonableness of a solution to a differential equation visually by graphing the slope field of the differential equation as shown in Figure 8.4 and sketching the graph of the solution starting at the given initial condition. This equation defines $y(x)$, and we can use machine numerical integration techniques to graph it. All of these steps reinforce the reasonableness of our computed answer.

This solution is an example of a *transcendental function*. As can be seen from its graph, there is nothing very special about this function, and it looks quite ordinary. We know its derivative explicitly, and we can use it

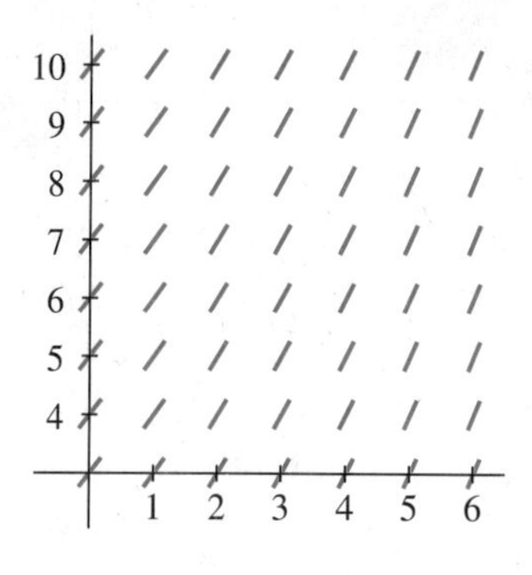

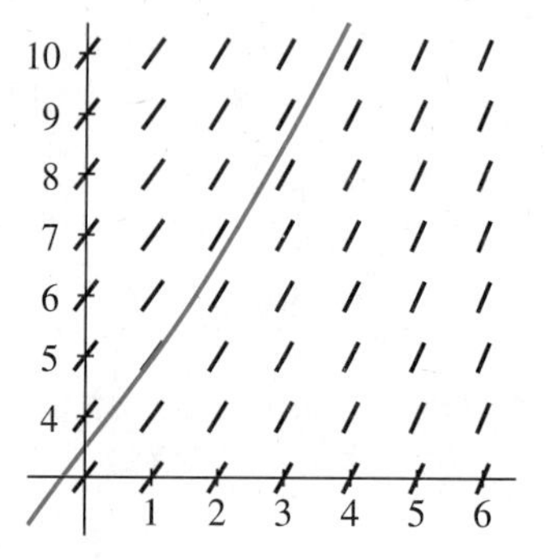

Figure 8.4 Slope field for $y' = \sqrt{\sqrt{x^2+1}+1}$ and solution graph.

as a building block in constructing other functions even though we don't have its definition in simple algebraic form.

In this section, we will look at some techniques for investigating and solving differential equations of the form

$$\frac{dy}{dx} = G(x, y),$$

where $G(x, y)$ is an expression (function) involving x and/or y.

In fact, you have already seen an example of this kind of differential equation arise from implicit differentiation. If we start with the equation of a circle of radius 3 centered at the origin,

$$x^2 + y^2 = 9,$$

implicit differentiation leads to the differential equation

$$2x + 2y\frac{dy}{dx} = 0$$

or, solving algebraically for $\frac{dy}{dx}$, assuming $y \neq 0$,

$$\frac{dy}{dx} = -\frac{x}{y}.$$

Suppose now that we started with this differential equation and a single point on the circle (our initial condition). How could we work backward to recover the circle?

EXAMPLE 15 Sketch the slope field corresponding to the differential equation

$$\frac{dy}{dx} = -\frac{x}{y}$$

in the region $[-3, 3] \times [-3, 3]$. Sketch both the solution with initial condition $y(0) = 3$ and the solution with initial condition $y(0) = -3$ in this same region.

Solution In this case the slope depends not only on x but also on y. We need to compute the slope y' at a grid of points in the x-y plane. Choosing points with integer coordinates and computing the slope at each (for example, point $y' = -(-2/3) = 2/3$) at the point $(-2, 3)$ gives the slope field pictured in Figure 8.5.

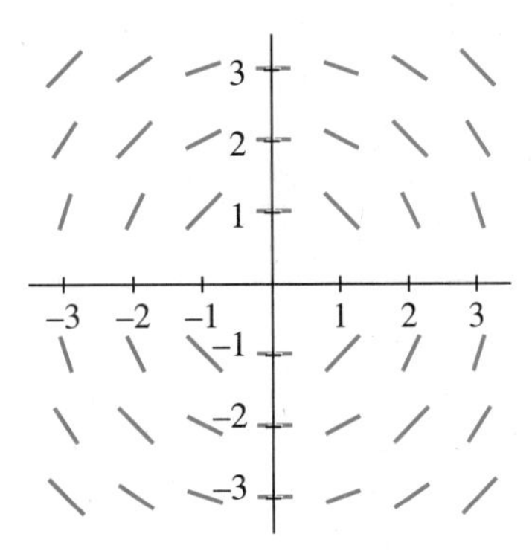

Figure 8.5 Slope field corresponding to $y' = -x/y$.

Sketching the solution of the differential equation with initial condition $y(0) = 3$ and then with initial condition $y(0) = -3$ results in the curves shown in Figure 8.6. These are two halves of the circle. The reason we did not obtain the whole circle with either initial condition is that, in forming the differential equation, we divided by y, assuming $y \neq 0$. The slope field is therefore undefined along the x-axis. If we joined the two solutions together, we have a graph that does not pass the vertical line test for function graphs. ■

Using the slope field to approximate solutions

A typical example of the slope of a function that depends on the *output* of the function is *friction*. In a system subject to friction, the acceleration

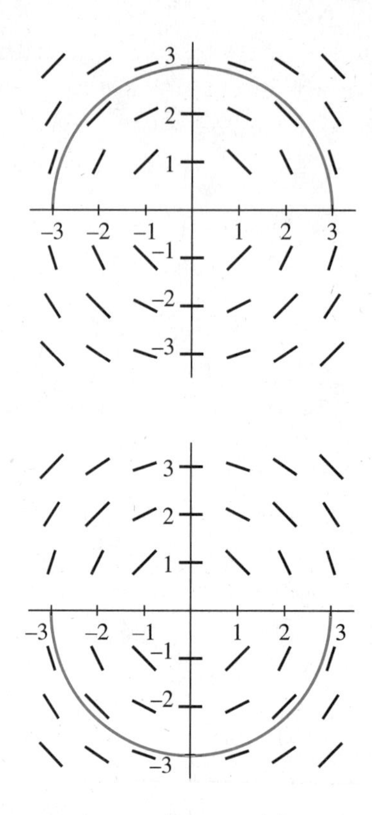

Figure 8.6 Solutions of $y' = -x/y$ with $y(0) = 3$ and with $y(0) = -3$.

of the object due to friction, dv/dt, is proportional to the velocity (in many cases). That is to say, the faster you go, the more friction you encounter.

EXAMPLE 16 Suppose that the velocity $v(t)$ meters per second (m/s) of a satellite at time t seconds is unknown. On approach to a certain planet, the component of acceleration (dv/dt) of the satellite due to the gravitational force of the planet is approximately 15 meters per second (m/s^2), and the component due to atmospheric friction is $-0.2v$ m/s^2. Hence, the total acceleration is

$$\frac{dv}{dt} = (15 - 0.2v)\ \mathrm{m/s^2}.$$

Graph the slope field corresponding to this differential equation in the region $0 \le t \le 100$, $50 \le v \le 100$, with grid points spread apart 10 s horizontally and 5 m/s vertically. Sketch solutions with initial condition $v(0) = 100$ m/s and also $v(0) = 50$ m/s, and interpret the curves.

Solution Note that in this case, the slope dv/dt depends on v but not on t (time has no effect on the interplay of forces), so once we have plotted a single column of line segments, every other column looks identical (see Figure 8.7).

In the case of the initial condition $v(0) = 50$ m/s, the satellite speeds up under gravity until the increasing force of friction just balances the force

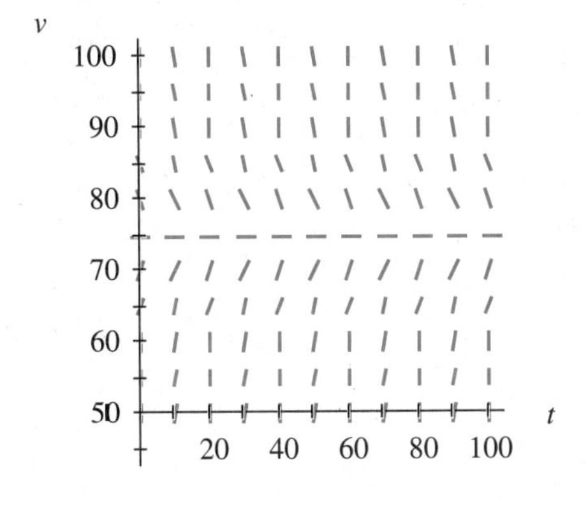

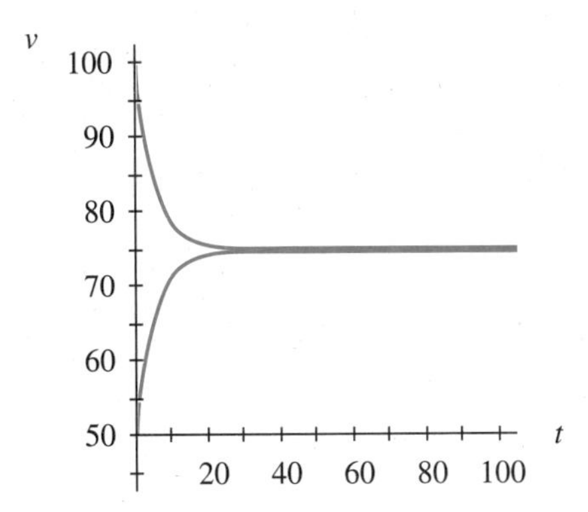

Figure 8.7 Slope field solution to the satellite acceleration problem.

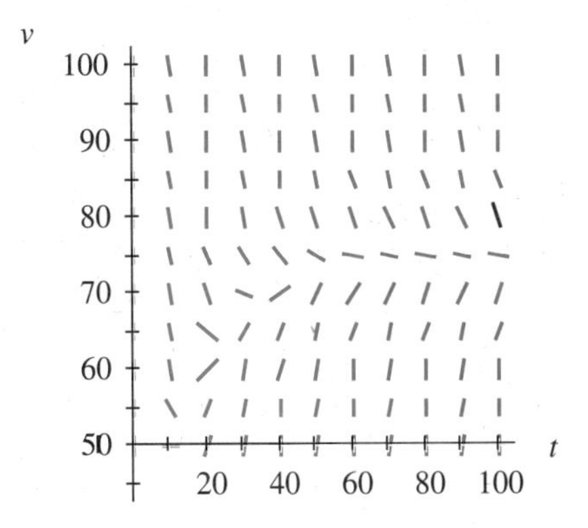

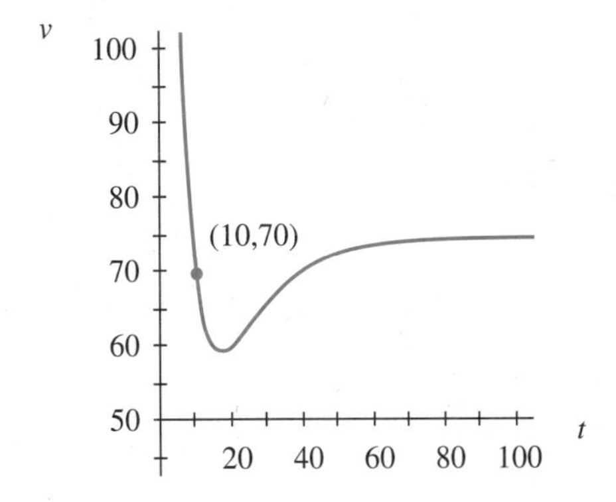

Figure 8.8 Slope field solution to the satellite problem with time-dependent acceleration.

of gravity, and the satellite then moves at a constant speed (the "terminal velocity"). Similarly, if the satellite starts off with an initial velocity of $v(0) = 100$ m/s that is *faster* than the terminal velocity, friction will slow it down, again until gravity and friction just balance. ■

EXAMPLE 17 Suppose that, in addition to the accelerations described in Example 16, the satellite experiences a time-dependent acceleration component equal to $-10/2^{0.1t}$ m/s^2. Sketch the corresponding slope field using the same grid, and sketch the solution with initial condition $v(10) = 70$ m/s.

Solution In this case, the total acceleration is given by

$$\frac{dv}{dt} = (15 - 0.2v - \frac{10}{2^{0.1t}}).$$

This produces slopes that are constant neither horizontally nor vertically, so the slopes of the line segments need to be recomputed for each grid element. For instance, at the grid point $t = 10$, $v = 70$, $\frac{dv}{dt} = 15 - 12 - 10/2^1 = 3 - 5 = -2$, so the slope is -2 and the satellite is slowing down. Plotting all the segments produces Figure 8.8, and the solution satisfying the initial condition $v(10) = 70$ m/s is shown. ■

Separation of variables

Sometimes it is possible to "separate the variables" in a differential equation of the form

$$\frac{dy}{dx} = G(x, y),$$

transforming it to a "equation of differentials,"

$$f(y)\, dy = g(x)\, dx.$$

We can then antidifferentiate both sides of the equation (the left-hand side with respect to y, and the right-hand side with respect to x):

$$\int f(y)\, dy = \int g(x)\, dx.$$

Let's illustrate with the differential equation we obtained from Example 15.

EXAMPLE 18 Use separation of variables to solve the differential equation

$$\frac{dy}{dx} = \frac{-x}{y}$$

with initial condition $y(0) = 3$.

Solution Multiplying both sides by y (we need to assume $y \neq 0$) and both sides by dx yields

$$y\, dy = -x\, dx.$$

Antidifferentiating both sides yields

$$\frac{y^2}{2} + C_1 = -\frac{x^2}{2} + C_2.$$

An *arbitrary* constant arises on both sides of the equation. If we combine the arbitrary constants (subtract C_1 from both sides) and multiply both sides by 2, we can rewrite the equation with a single arbitrary constant:

$$y^2 = -x^2 + C.$$

Using the initial condition $y(0) = 3$, we can solve for C:

$$3^2 = -0^2 + C = C.$$

Hence $C = 9$ and we have recovered the equation of the circle (after adding x^2 to both sides):

$$x^2 + y^2 = 9.$$

Note that we must add the provision $y \neq 0$ in our solution, since the original differential equation does not make sense for this value. Graphically, the circle has vertical tangents at the points $(-3, 0)$ and $(3, 0)$, where the slope $\frac{dy}{dx} = \frac{-x}{y}$ is undefined. ■

The justification for the method of separation of variables involves the chain rule and implicit differentiation. Starting with the equation

$$\frac{dy}{dx} = G(x, y),$$

suppose that we are able to rewrite the equation as

$$f(y)\frac{dy}{dx} = g(x).$$

If $F(y)$ is an antiderivative of $f(y)$ and we treat y implicitly as a function of x, and the chain rule gives us

$$\frac{d}{dx}(F(y(x)) = F'(y)\frac{dy}{dx} = f(y)\frac{dy}{dx} = g(x).$$

This means that $F(y(x))$ is an antiderivative of $g(x)$ also. Treating the differentials dy and dx separately in rewriting the equation as

$$f(y)\,dy = g(x)\,dx$$

is simply a handy symbolic way of leading us quickly to this antidifferentiation step.

EXAMPLE 19 Solve the differential equation

$$y' = \frac{x}{y^2}$$

with initial condition $y(0) = 2$.

Solution First, we write $y' = \frac{dy}{dx}$

$$\frac{dy}{dx} = \frac{x}{y^2}$$

and separate the variables (we will need to assume that $y \neq 0$) to obtain

$$y^2\,dy = x\,dx.$$

Integrating both sides of the equation yields

$$\frac{1}{3}(y^3) + C_1 = \frac{x^2}{2} + C_2.$$

Multiplying both sides by 3 and combining the arbitrary constants, we have

$$y^3 = \frac{3}{2}x^2 + C$$

for some arbitrary constant C, and we use the initial condition to find C. Since $y(0) = 2$, and

$$(y(0))^3 = \frac{3}{2}0^2 + C,$$

we have $C = 2^3 = 8$. Thus, $y(x)^3 = (\frac{3}{2}x^2 + 8)$, and

$$y(x) = \sqrt[3]{\frac{3}{2}x^2 + 8}.$$

Note that y is never zero, which agrees with our assumption. ■

EXERCISES for Section 8.4

For exercises 1–8: Sketch the slope field of each differential equation in the region $[-3, 3] \times [0, 3]$ using integer grid points. Sketch the graph of the differential equation with the given initial condition in the same region.

1. $y' = \dfrac{1}{x^3 + 1}$; $y(-0.5) = 2$

2. $y' = 0.2\sqrt{x + 5}$; $y(2) = 2.5$

3. $y' = 1 + x$; $y(0) = 1$

4. $y' = 0.1((x + 1)^2 + 1)^2$; $y(-1) = 1$

5. $y' = \sin(\sin(x))$; $y(0) = 0$

6. $y' = \dfrac{1}{x^2 + 1}$; $y(1) = 1$

7. $y' = e^{-x^2/2}$; $y(0) = 0.5$

8. $y' = \ln(x^2 + 1)$; $y(0) = 1$

For exercises 9–13: Sketch the solution of the indicated differential equation that satisfies the given initial condition.

9. $\dfrac{dy}{dx} = \exp(-y/x)$; $y(2) = 2$

10. $\dfrac{dp}{dt} = \dfrac{p^2 + t^2}{2}$; $p(0) = 0$

11. $\dfrac{dx}{du} = -1$ for $0 \leq u$ and $\dfrac{dx}{du} = -1 - u$ for $u < 0$; $x(1) = 1$

12. $\dfrac{dy}{dt} = y \cdot \sin(t)$; $y(0) = 0$

13. $\dfrac{dy}{dx} = \tan(x)$; $y(0) = 0$

---

14. An injection of a particular medication is absorbed into the blood at a rate of 5 mg/hr. The same medication is removed by the liver at a rate proportional to the amount in the blood (0.5 mg/hr per mg in the blood). If an injection of 10 mg is given, sketch the graph of the amount in the blood over the next 5 hours. When does the amount peak? How much is left after 5 hours?

15. A particular bacterium reproduces at a rate of $(2.8 - (T - 70)^2 \times 0.1)$ new bacteria per hour per bacterium, where T is the temperature in degrees Fahrenheit. In other words, at $70°F$, each bacterium splits into 2.2 each hour (on average) and somewhat fewer if the temperature is warmer or colder. In one lab, the temperature is cycled between 65° and 70° each hour: $T = 2.5\sin(t \cdot 2\pi) + 67.5$, t in hours. If there are 1000 bacteria at the start of the day, sketch the number vs. time over the course of a day.

16. Galileo initially conjectured that the velocity of a freely falling body was proportional to the distance it had fallen. If we denote the distance traveled at time t by $s(t)$ for a freely falling body, then Galileo's conjecture is

$$\frac{ds}{dt} = cs.$$

Use this model to predict the velocity of a ball dropped from the top of a skyscraper at a height of 1000 feet. Discuss the plausibility of Galileo's initial model.

17. The question of whether a body subject to no other forces than air resistance can in time come to a standstill only on account of air resistance amounts mathematically to considering velocity functions satisfying

$$\frac{dv}{dt} = -k^2v^2.$$

What are these functions?

18. The motion of a freely falling body, taking into consideration air resistance, is mathematically given by the differential equation

$$\frac{dv}{dt} = g - d^2v^2.$$

Determine its solutions.

For exercises 19–25: The solution of each of the following differential equations is a well-known transcendental function. Sketch the slope field on an integer grid of the indicated differential equation. Use a viewing window of $[-4, 4] \times [-2, 2]$. Then sketch the solution of the differential equation with the indicated initial condition. Can you identify the function by name from its graph?

19. $\dfrac{dy}{dx} = \dfrac{1}{1 + x^2}$; $y(0) = 0$.

20. $\dfrac{dy}{dx} = \dfrac{1}{\sqrt{1 - x^2}}$; $y(0) = 0$.

21. $\dfrac{dy}{dx} = \dfrac{-1}{1+x^2}$; $y(0) = 1.5708.$

22. $\dfrac{dy}{dx} = \dfrac{-1}{x\sqrt{x^2-1}}$; $y(2) = 1.52360.$

23. $\dfrac{dy}{dx} = \dfrac{1}{x\sqrt{x^2-1}}$; $y(-2) = 2.09440.$

24. $\dfrac{dy}{dx} = \dfrac{-1}{\sqrt{1-x^2}}$; $y(1) = 0.$

25. $\dfrac{dy}{dx} = \dfrac{1}{x}$; $y(1) = 0.$

---

26. Look up $\int \operatorname{arcsec}(x)\,dx$ and $\int \operatorname{arccsc}(x)\,dx$ in an integral table or using a computer algebra system. Graph the slope fields generated by $\dfrac{dy}{dx} = \operatorname{arcsec} x$ and $\dfrac{dy}{dx} = \operatorname{arccsc} x$ and graph the antiderivatives you find. Do the results make sense?

For exercises 27–32: Use separation of variables to solve the given differential equation with the given initial condition.

27. $\dfrac{dy}{dx} = \dfrac{1}{y^2}$; $y(0) = 4$

28. $\dfrac{dy}{dx} = -x^2y^2$; $y(4) = 4$

29. $\dfrac{dy}{dx} = \dfrac{1+x}{\sqrt{y}}$; $y(2) = 9$

30. $\dfrac{dy}{dx} = \dfrac{y^3}{x^2}$; $y(3) = 2$

31. $\dfrac{dy}{dx} + y\dfrac{dy}{dx} = x$; $y(0) = 1$

32. $\dfrac{dy}{dx} = \dfrac{1}{y^3+y}$; $y(1) = 1$

8.5 EULER'S METHOD

Finding the antiderivative of a function is a typical example of solving a differential equation. Finding $\int f(x)\,dx$ is equivalent to finding a solution F to $\dfrac{dF}{dx} = f(x)$.

Numerical antidifferentiation—graphing Riemann sums

Suppose that we use the slope field to approximate the solution as follows. Starting at our initial point (x_0, y_0), we calculate the slope $f(x_0)$ and move along the corresponding line segment until we have covered a short horizontal x-distance Δx, landing at a new point (x_1, y_1). Now we compute the slope at this new point $f(x_1)$, and move along the new corresponding line segment Δx horizontally, landing at (x_2, y_2). We continue to repeat this process n times to get to (x_n, y_n), where $x_n = x_0 + n\Delta x$. What we have just described is simply an automatization of our process of sketching the graph from the slope field.

Let's calculate the final output value y_n and compare it with other expressions we know. First, note that the line segment connecting (x_0, y_0)

with (x_1, y_1) has slope $f(x_0)$, so

$$y_1 = y_0 + f(x_0)\Delta x.$$

In general, the line segment connecting (x_i, y_i) with (x_{i+1}, y_{i+1}) has slope $f(x_i)$, so

$$y_{i+1} = y_i + f(x_i)\Delta x.$$

This means that our final point has y-coordinate

$$y_n = y_0 + f(x_0)\Delta x + f(x_1)\Delta x + f(x_2)\Delta x + \cdots + f(x_{n-1})\Delta x,$$

which is essentially the value y_0 plus the left-endpoint approximation for

$$\int_{x_0}^{x_n} f(x)\,dx$$

for a regular partition of size n (See Figure 8.9).

Alternatively, and with equal justification, we could use $f(x_{i+1})$ to determine the slope of the line segment from (x_i, y_i) to (x_{i+1}, y_{i+1}). In this case, the resulting expression for y_n becomes

$$y_n = y_0 + f(x_1)\Delta x + f(x_2)\Delta x + \cdots + f(x_n)\Delta x,$$

which is essentially the value y_0 plus the right-endpoint approximation for

$$\int_{x_0}^{x_n} f(x)\,dx$$

for a partition of size n (see Figure 8.10).

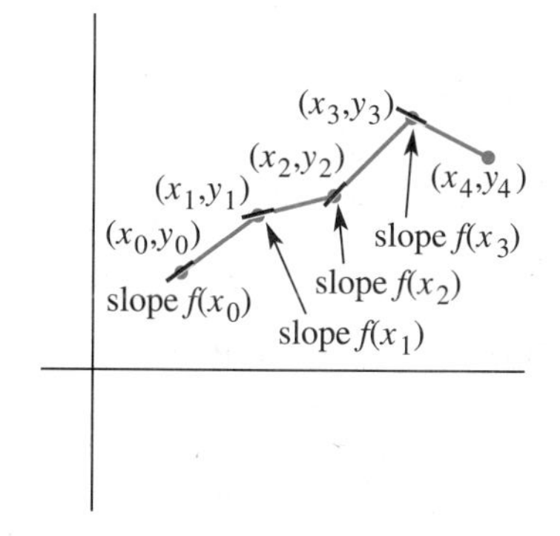

Figure 8.9 Finding y_n using left endpoint slope information.

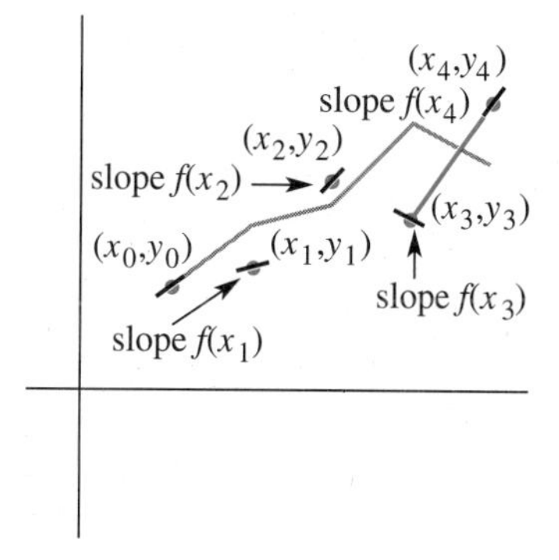

Figure 8.10 Finding y_n using right endpoint slope information.

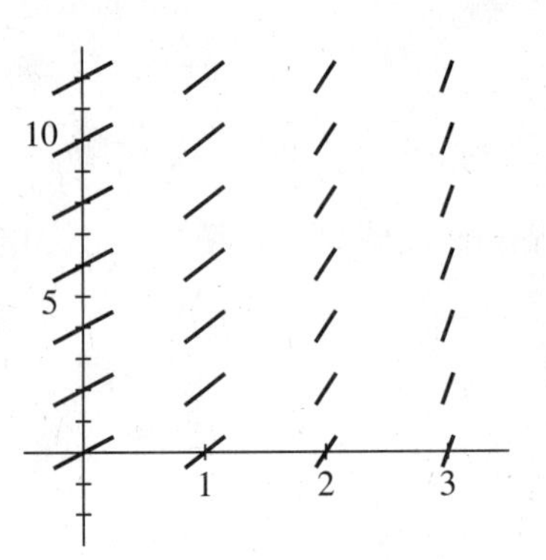

Figure 8.11 Slope field for the differential equation $\frac{dF}{dx} = x^2 + 2$.

EXAMPLE 20 Interpret graphically the left-endpoint Riemann sum approximation with a regular partition of $n = 5$ to

$$\int_0^3 (x^2 + 2)\, dx.$$

Solution This corresponds to finding the solution of the differential equation $\frac{dF}{dx} = x^2 + 2$ with initial condition $F(0) = 0$, and then computing $F(3)$. The slope field is plotted in Figure 8.11 for reference.

To use the left-endpoint Riemann sum approximation with $n = 5$, we divide the interval $[0, 3]$ into five subintervals ($\Delta x = 3/5 = 0.6$) and use the slope at the left endpoint of each subinterval—that is, at the points $x = 0$, 0.6, 1.2, 1.8, and 2.4. These slopes are listed in Table 8.2.

x_i	$x_i^2 + 2$
0	2
0.6	2.36
1.2	3.44
1.8	5.24
2.4	7.76

Table 8.2 Table of slopes at the left endpoints for $\frac{dF}{dx} = x^2 + 2$.

Starting with $x_0 = 0$, we have:

$$y_1 = y_0 + (x_0^2 + 2)\Delta x = 0 + 2(0.6) = 1.2$$

$$y_2 = y_1 + (x_1^2 + 2)\Delta x = 1.2 + (2.36)(0.6) = 2.616$$

$$y_3 = y_2 + (x_2^2 + 2)\Delta x = 2.616 + (3.44)(0.6) = 4.68$$

$$y_4 = y_3 + (x_3^2 + 2)\Delta x = 4.68 + (5.24)(0.6) = 7.824$$

$$y_5 = y_4 + (x_4^2 + 2)\Delta x = 7.824 + (7.76)(0.6) = 12.48.$$

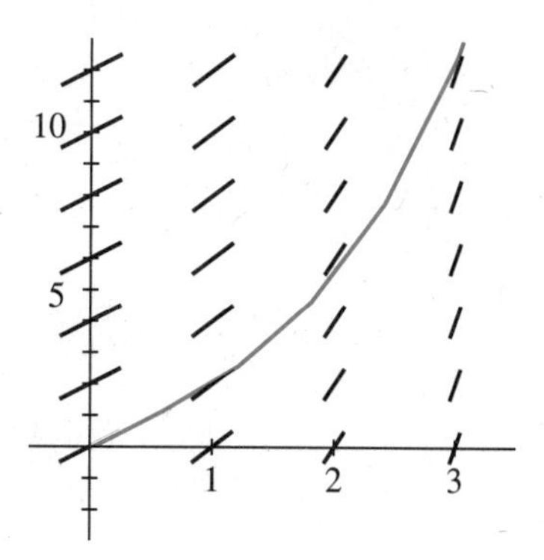

Figure 8.12 Graphical interpretation of left-endpoint Riemann sum.

The predicted value $F(3) = y_5 = 12.48$ is just the left-endpoint Riemann sum. The graphical steps taken in reaching this value are illustrated in Figure 8.12.

■

Euler's method

The method of interpreting the Riemann sum gives not only the value of the sum but an approximate solution to the differential equation at *all* points between the endpoints (which themselves can be very far apart). We just use the piece-wise linear graph to linearly interpolate the output $y = F(x)$ for any input x between two consecutive partition points x_{i-1} and x_i. This method of approximating the solution of the differential equation, called **Euler's method**, can be applied even in cases not related to approximations of integrals.

In general, we can apply Euler's method whenever we have the slope field information at the partition points. Suppose we know that

$$\frac{dy}{dx} = G(x, y) \text{ with initial condition } y(x_0) = y_0,$$

where $G(x, y)$ is an expression involving both x and y. We can write Euler's method for approximating the solution to this differential equation using the equally spaced points $x_0, x_1, \ldots, x_{n-1}$, by letting

$$y_i \approx y(x_i) = y_0 + G(x_0, y_0)\Delta x + G(x_1, y_1)\Delta x + G(x_2, y_2)\Delta x + \cdots + G(x_{i-1}, y_{i-1})\Delta x.$$

Note that you may need to compute each of the intermediate values, $y_1, \ldots, y_{i-1}$, before you can compute y_i. This is because the slope $G(x, y)$ may depend on both the x-coordinate and y-coordinate at each step.

EXAMPLE 21 Use Euler's method to approximate the solution to $\frac{dy}{dx} = xy - 1$ with initial condition $y(0) = 0$ using a regular partition of five points over the interval $[0, 5]$. Find an approximation to $y(1.5)$, and $y(4.2)$.

Solution The five inputs we'll use are 0, 1, 2, 3, and 4, with $\Delta x = 1$. The differential equation tells us the slope at each point (x, y) is $m = xy - 1$.

At $x_0 = 0$, $y_0 = 0$ (by the initial condition), so the slope is $m = 0 \cdot 0 - 1 = -1$. Therefore, at $x_1 = 1$, our approximation is

$$y_1 \approx y(1) = 0 - 1 \cdot 1 = -1,$$

and the slope at the new point $(x_1, y_1) = (1, -1)$ is $m = 1(-1) - 1 = -2$. At $x_2 = 2$, our approximation is

$$y_2 \approx y(2) = -1 - 2 \cdot 1 = -3,$$

and the slope at $(x_2, y_2) = (2, -3)$ is $m = 2(-3) - 1 = -7$. Hence, at $x_3 = 3$, our approximation is

$$y_3 \approx y(3) = -3 - 7 \cdot 1 = -10,$$

and the slope at $(3, -10)$ is $m = 3(-10) - 1 = -31$. At $x_4 = 4$, the approximation is

$$y_4 \approx y(4) = -10 - 31 \cdot 1 = -41,$$

and the slope at $(4, -41)$ is $m = 4(-41) - 1 = -165$. Finally, at $x_5 = 5$, the approximation is

$$y_5 \approx y(5) = -41 - 165 \cdot 1 = -206.$$

The resulting graph is shown in Figure 8.13.

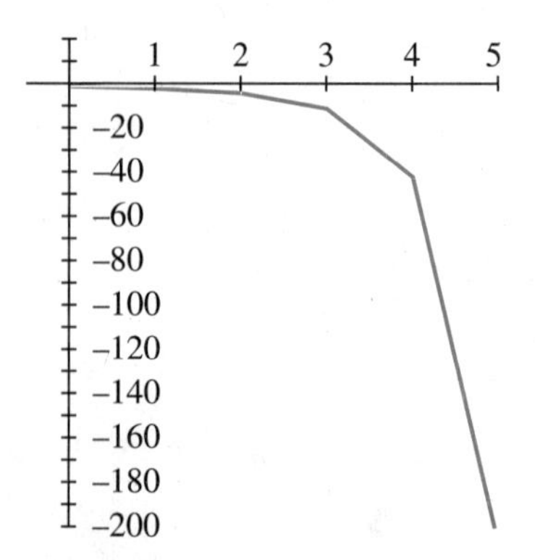

Figure 8.13 Solution by Euler's method to $\frac{dy}{dx} = xy - 1$, with $y(0) = 0$.

Now, to approximate $y(1.5)$, we use the midpoint of the line segment connecting $(1, -1)$ and $(2, -3)$. This point is $(1.5, -2)$, so

$$y(1.5) \approx -2.$$

To approximate $y(4.2)$, we use the line segment connecting $(4, -41)$ and $(5, -196)$. The y-coordinate of the point above $x = 4.2$ is our approximation

$$y(4.2) \approx -41 + 0.2(-165) = -74. \qquad ■$$

EXERCISES for Section 8.5

For exercises 1–5:

(a) Graph the left-endpoint Riemann sum approximation to the given integral using a regular partition of size $n = 10$.

(b) Graph the right-endpoint Riemann sum approximation to the given integral using a regular partition of size $n = 10$.

(c) Graph the midpoint Riemann sum approximation to the given integral using a regular partition of size $n = 10$.

1. $\displaystyle\int_2^{12} \frac{x^2+1}{x^3-1}\,dx$

2. $\displaystyle\int_0^{\pi} \sin(x)\,dx$

3. $\displaystyle\int_1^{8} \ln(x)\,dx$

4. $\displaystyle\int_{-1}^{1} \frac{1}{x^2+1}\,dx$

5. $\displaystyle\int_0^{\pi/4} \frac{1}{\cos(x)}\,dx$

---

6. Explain how you could use your graphs to plot a trapezoidal approximation to the definite integrals in exercises 1–5.

7. One of the **Runge-Kutta** methods of numerically approximating the solution to a differential equation essentially plots a Simpson's Rule approximation for a definite integral. Explain how you could use your graphs to plot a Runge-Kutta approximation to the definite integrals in exercises 1–5.

8. The illustration is supposed to show a pair of solutions to a differential equation $\dfrac{dy}{dx} = F(x, y)$, with initial conditions $y(x_0) = y_0$ and $y(x_1) = y_1$. It is found that the two solution curves intersect at the point (x_2, y_2). Is this possible? If so, describe an example. If not, explain why not.

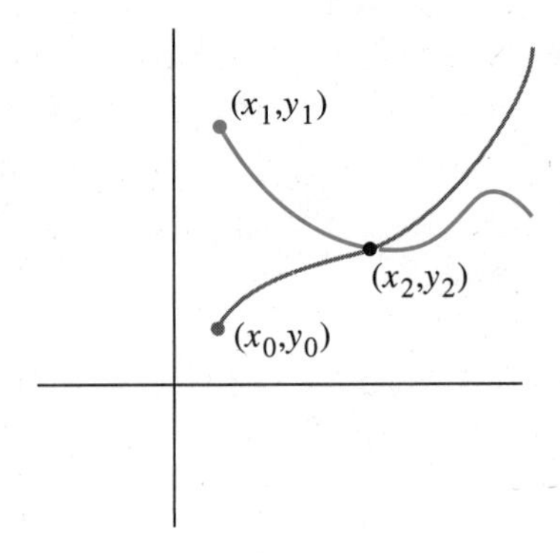

For Exercise 8

For exercises 9–13: Use Euler's method to approximate the solution to the differential equations with given initial conditions. In each case, use the six points 0, 0.5, 1, 1.5, 2.0, and 2.5 over the interval $[0,3]$ and approximate the value of $y(1.2)$ and $y(3)$.

9. $\dfrac{dy}{dx} = \dfrac{y^2+1}{x^3-1}$; $\quad y(0) = 0$

10. $\dfrac{dy}{dx} = \sin(x+y)$; $\quad y(0) = 1.6$

11. $\dfrac{dy}{dx} = \ln(1+x+y)$; $\quad y(0) = 1$

12. $\dfrac{dy}{dx} = \dfrac{1}{x^2+y^2}$; $\quad y(0) = -1$

13. $\dfrac{dy}{dx} = \dfrac{1}{\cos(xy)}$; $\quad y(0) = 0$

For exercises 14–17: Consider the differential equation $\dfrac{du}{dt} = 0.6u(4-u^2)$. (Note: Each of these exercises builds on the previous exercise.)

14. Sketch the slope field of the differential equation and the solution with initial condition $u(0) = 1$, the solution with initial condition $u(0) = 3$, and the solution with initial condition $u(0) = 2$.

15. Sketch the entire family of solutions of the differential equation with initial value $u(0) > 0$. What can you say about $u(t)$ for t very large?

16. Graph the approximate solutions with initial conditions $u(0) = 1$ and with $u(0) = 3$ using Euler's method and a regular partition with a step size $\Delta t = 0.5$ for $0 \le t \le 5$. How do these graphs compare with those shown in the illustration above?

17. Explain how you could determine whether a sufficiently small step-size would eliminate this kind of behavior.

For exercises 18–24: Some people claim that in cold weather you should turn down your thermostat at night to save energy. Others say that, since it takes energy to warm up the house from its cold state, it doesn't matter. The exercises below explore this issue using Newton's law of cooling: the rate of change of temperature of two bodies in contact is proportional to the difference in their temperatures.

18. Suppose that the outside temperature is 35° and the constant of proportionality (with the furnace off) is 5° per hour per degree difference in temperature. The house temperature T satisfies $\dfrac{dT}{dt} = 0.75(35 - T)$ when the furnace is off (t is in hours). Sketch the slope field of this differential equation and the solution with initial condition $T(0) = 70$.

19. Use the slope field to determine about how long it will take the house to go from 70° to 40°, and the approximate house temperature after 6 hours.

20. In this house under these conditions, the furnace has a temperature of 90°, so the differential equation for the temperature with the furnace on is $\dfrac{dT}{dt} = 0.75(90 - T)$. Sketch the slope field of this differential equation and the solution with initial condition $T(0) = 35$.

21. Use the slope field to determine about how long will it take the house to go from 35° to 70°, and the approximate house temperature after 2 hours.

22. If we shut the furnace off at night when the house temperature is 70° and turn it on again so that the temperature returns to 70° eight hours later, about how long will the furnace have been on?

23. Suppose that the thermostat shuts the furnace off at 70° and turns it back on at 65°. Sketch a graph of the house temperature over an eight-hour period.

24. In this case, about how much time (in total) will the furnace have been on? Which uses less energy: leaving the furnace on, or turning it off? About what fraction of the energy used by the less efficient method does the more efficient method use?

Application to Heat Exchange

Platypus Company has decided to enter the environmental products market. Having experience in sheet-metal products, they decide that their first product should be a heat-exchanging vent. Since the advent of super-insulated houses, in which air exchange with the outside is minimized to prevent heat loss, indoor air pollution has become a problem. One solution is a heat-exchanging vent, which is basically an insulated air duct with an outgoing and incoming chamber. The outgoing air and incoming air are sealed from each other but held in close contact so that the outgoing warm air can warm the incoming air before it reaches the living space. This allows fresh air to come in and stale air to go out while keeping the heat from escaping.

The Platypus marketing department decides that the minimum requirements for the unit are:

(a) it should be able to carry 0.5 cfs (cubic feet per second) of air in each direction, and

(b) the air entering the living space should be not more than 3°C different than the interior temperature when the outside air is 20°C colder than the interior.

The manufacturing and engineering departments settle on an initial design: a two-chambered duct with a rectangular cross section, each chamber 8 in. by 1 in. and sharing an 8-in. wall. They then turn it over to the R&D department to test and finalize the design.

Amanda, the head design engineer, finalizes the design and performs some initial experiments to determine the rate of heat exchange between the chambers. By filling the two sides of the chamber with air of different temperatures and observing the temperature change over time, she determines that the heat exchange rate is approximately 4°C per second per °C difference in temperature between the sides.

Not having much experience in heat exchange, Amanda decides to run a simulation of the vent to gain some insight into its behavior. She partitions the chambers into ten "compartments." In this model, the air in each compartment stays there for a fixed period of time, exchanging heat with the adjacent compartment across the incoming-outgoing wall.

After this heat exchange, the air in the compartment is moved to the next incoming or outgoing compartment, as appropriate, with the air leaving either end of the sequence of ten chambers being discarded from further consideration. At the start of each exchange, the first compartment of each chamber is initialized to the interior temperature (20°C) or exterior temperature (0°C), respectively.

The graphs show the temperature in the outgoing chamber from one end to the other over time.

25. Recalling the target flow rate of 0.5 cfs, and taking as a working assumption that the vent is 15 ft long, if the vent is partitioned into ten chambers, how long will an air "particle" spend in a given chamber?

26. Using Newton's law of cooling, if T_{in} is the temperature in an incoming compartment and T_{out} is the temperature of an outgoing compartment, then, in Amanda's model, the temperatures after these are kept in contact for t seconds are given by:

Time evolution of the outgoing side of the heat exchanger model. Outside air is to the left, inside air to the right. Time increases downward from frame to frame.

Outside Inside

High temp

Low temp

For Exercises 25–26

$$T'_{in} = \frac{1}{2}(T_{in} + T_{out}) + \frac{1}{2}\exp(-4t) \cdot (T_{in} - T_{out})$$

$$T'_{out} = \frac{1}{2}(T_{in} + T_{out}) - \frac{1}{2}\exp(-4t) \cdot (T_{in} - T_{out}).$$

How much will the temperature change in a compartment in the time you found in exercise 25 if the temperature is 20°C warmer than the temperature in the compartment on the other side of the wall? What if the temperature is only 3°C warmer?

9

Function Approximations

Suppose that you were asked to evaluate the functions

$$y = x^3 - 2x + 5, \quad y = \sin(x), \quad y = 2^x, \quad y = \log_3 x, \quad y = \arctan(x)$$

at the input $x = 1.35$. Evaluating a polynomial function, such as $y = x^3 - 2x + 5$, requires nothing more than addition, subtraction, multiplication, and (possibly) division—the operations provided by a four-function calculator. All of the other evaluations require either a more sophisticated machine or tables of values.

Machines that can evaluate transcendental functions (such as trigonometric, exponential, logarithmic, and inverse trigonometric functions) are readily available. However, polynomial functions are particularly nice for a variety of reasons: they are easy to compute, compare, differentiate, integrate, and so on. Moreover, polynomials are, in a sense, the *only* functions you can calculate directly with only basic arithmetic. Approximating functions by polynomials is useful in many settings.

The tangent line approximation to a function at a specific point is the first-degree Taylor polynomial approximation, and it represents the *best linear approximation* to a function at that point. We'll examine more closely what we mean by "best" and look at the behavior of quadratic (second-degree) and higher-degree Taylor polynomials.

Goals of function approximation

When we approximate a number (as we do with root-finding techniques, for example), we generally have a choice of goals. We can either try to guarantee that our approximation is "close" to the desired number, or we can try to guarantee that it "behaves like" the desired number. For example, if we are approximating a root x_r of an equation $f(x) = 0$, we can either look for a number x_0 that is close to x_r or look for a number x_0 that behaves like x_r. To behave like the root of the equation simply means that $f(x_0)$ is very close to 0, not necessarily that x_0 is very close to x_r. For many purposes, approximating behavior is perfectly adequate.

Similarly, when we want to approximate a target function f with another function like a polynomial p, we have a choice of goals. We can try to guarantee that all of the approximation function's outputs $p(x)$ are close to the target function's outputs $f(x)$, or we can try to guarantee that the approximation function behaves like the target function. Behaviors of a function include whether it is increasing or decreasing, concave up, concave down, flat, and so on. These behaviors are all determined by the values of the function and *its derivatives* at a particular input.

The function approximations we study in this chapter were designed to accomplish one or both of these goals. *Interpolation* strives to fit a function to a given set of inputs and outputs. *Taylor polynomials* approximate the behavior of a function at a particular point $x = a$. We'll see how zooming in on the graphs of functions can be used as an analytic tool for comparing their behavior. We end the chapter by discussing cubic splines, approximations that fit both points and slopes.

9.1 INTERPOLATION—ERROR BOUNDS FOR NUMERICAL INTEGRATION

When we have data in the form of ordered pairs (x, y) of inputs and outputs, one way to model the data is to graph the ordered pairs and fit a curve through the points. For example, if we have only two data points, (x_0, y_0) and (x_1, y_1), and $x_0 \neq x_1$, we can always find a line

$$y = mx + b$$

that fits the data. (The graph contains the two points.)

Now, if we have 3 points (no two of which have the same x-coordinate), it may not be possible to find a line passing through all three points. We have several options:

1. we could fit a line segment through the first and second points, then another through the second and third (called *piece-wise linear interpolation*);

2. we could still use a single line and fit it as closely to the points as we can (called the *regression line*); or

3. we could fit a parabola through all three points (called *quadratic interpolation*).

We have seen piece-wise linear interpolation before. Regression lines are extremely important in the statistical study of linear models. Our interest here is in quadratic interpolation.

EXAMPLE 1 Find a quadratic function

$$y = ax^2 + bx + c$$

whose graph passes through the three points $(0, -3)$, $(1, 4)$ and $(2, 15)$.

Solution We have three parameters a, b, and c to solve for. Substituting each of the three points (x, y) into the function equation will provide us with 3 equations in three unknowns.

For $(x, y) = (0, -3)$: $-3 = a(0)^2 + b(0) + c$, so $c = -3$.

For $(x, y) = (1, 4)$: $4 = a(1)^2 + b(1) + (-3)$, so $a + b = 7$.

For $(x, y) = (2, 15)$: $15 = a(2)^2 + b(2) + (-3)$, so $4a + 2b = 18$.

If we solve the second equation for $b = 7 - a$ and substitute into the third equation, we have

$$4a + 2(7 - a) = 14 + 2a = 18.$$

From this, we can solve for $a = 2$ and substitute back for $b = 7 - 2 = 5$. Thus,

$$y = 2x^2 + 5x - 3$$

is our quadratic interpolating function. ■

Similarly, if we have 4 points, all with different x-coordinates, we can find a polynomial of degree 3 (or less) whose graph contains all 4 points. In general, if we have $n + 1$ points, all with different x-coordinates, we can fit an interpolating polynomial of degree n or less whose graph contains all the points.

Piece-wise quadratic interpolation—numerical integration revisited

Given an odd number of data points, we can consider piece-wise quadratic interpolation. For example, suppose that we have 7 data points (in ascending order of x-coordinates):

$$(x_0, y_0), \quad (x_1, y_1), \quad (x_2, y_2), \quad (x_3, y_3), \quad (x_4, y_4), \quad (x_5, y_5), \quad (x_6, y_6).$$

We could consider fitting one parabolic segment passing through

$$(x_0, y_0), \quad (x_1, y_1), \quad (x_2, y_2),$$

a second parabolic segment passing through

$$(x_2, y_2), \quad (x_3, y_3), \quad (x_4, y_4),$$

and a third parabolic segment through

$$(x_4, y_4), \quad (x_5, y_5), \quad (x_6, y_6).$$

(Note: If any of these threesomes happens to be collinear, we'll use a line segment instead for that piece.)

Piece-wise interpolation gives us another way of thinking about our numerical integration approximations for a definite integral

$$\int_a^b f(x)\,dx.$$

When we subdivide the interval $[a, b]$ into n subintervals, we can obtain the graph of a piece-wise linear function by connecting the points $(x_i, f(x_i))$ corresponding to the endpoints of these subintervals. The trapezoidal rule is simply the approximation we obtain when we integrate this piece-wise linear function instead of our original function f!

Now, instead of connecting the points at the ends of each subinterval with a straight line segment, suppose we find a *parabola* that passes through both of these points *and* the middle graph point. (Three non-collinear points determine a parabola just as two points determine a line; if the two endpoints and the midpoint line up, we can just connect them with a straight line instead of a parabola.) Figure 9.1 illustrates this idea for a given subinterval.

Note how closely the parabola approximates the graph. If we connect these parabolic pieces end-to-end for each subinterval, we obtain the graph of a *piece-wise quadratic function*. It turns out that Simpson's rule is simply the approximation we obtain when we integrate this piece-wise quadratic function instead of our original function f. (We'll establish this in the exercises.) Figure 9.2 shows the piece-wise quadratic fit for the example we computed earlier. The graph appears virtually identical to the original graph and, consequently, the values of the definite integrals agree to three decimal places. Simpson's rule did require us, however, to sample almost twice as many inputs as the trapezoidal rule for the same partition.

Error estimates for trapezoidal and Simpson's rules

Calculators and computers may use numerical integration techniques to calculate the values of definite integrals. When an antiderivative cannot be found so that the fundamental theorems can be used, there is no recourse but to use numerical techniques. Often, Simpson's rule or a closely related method is used, but there are other methods. (You might encounter these in a more advanced course in numerical analysis.)

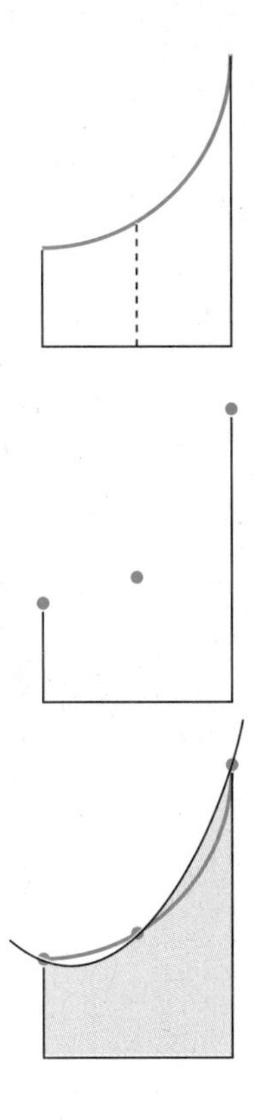

Figure 9.1 Approximating the graph with a parabola through three points.

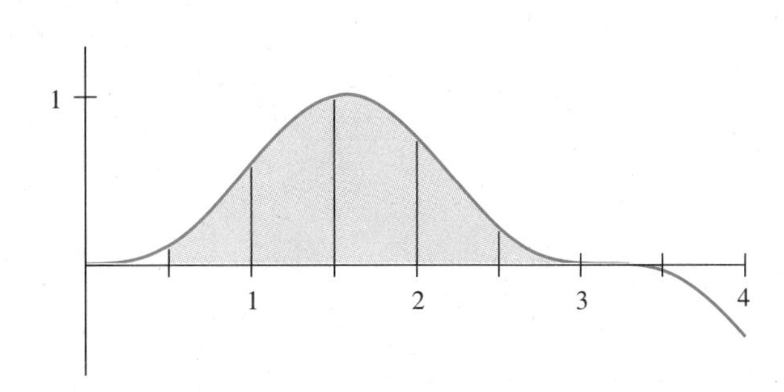

Figure 9.2 Simpson's approximation of $\int_{.5}^{3.5} \sin^3(x)\,dx$ for a partition of size $n = 6$.

We used the integral $\int_{0.5}^{3.5} \sin^3(x)\,dx$ as an example to illustrate the various techniques of numerical integration. However, one of the primary uses of numerical integration techniques is to integrate functions that have no known formulas. Perhaps only a partial table of inputs and outputs is available (as is often the case when data are gathered from some experimental process), or perhaps we have a graphical representation of the function. Since the trapezoidal rule and Simpson's rule depend only on a sampling of outputs from the function, we can just as easily use them when a function has only a numerical or graphical representation.

If we desire a certain level of accuracy in the value of a definite integral, how fine a partition should we use? In other words, how can we (or a machine) decide how large n should be without knowing the actual value of the definite integral? (If we know the actual value of the definite integral, there is little point in approximating it.)

Provided that f is well-behaved (in other words, has sufficiently many continuous derivatives), there are some bounds that can be placed on the worst (largest) possible error in the case of the trapezoidal and Simpson's rule estimates. The two theorems below provide the criteria and bounds on the worst errors when we attempt to approximate

$$\int_a^b f(x)\,dx$$

with the trapezoidal and Simpson's rules, respectively.

Theorem 9.1

Trapezoidal rule error bound for $\int_a^b f(x)\,dx$
Hypothesis 1: The second derivative f'' is continuous over $[a, b]$.
Hypothesis 2: The second derivative's value over $[a, b]$ is bounded by M. That is, for any $x \in [a, b]$, we have

$$|f''(x)| \leq M.$$

Conclusion: The error of the trapezoidal rule estimate T_n is bounded by $\dfrac{M(b-a)^3}{12n^2}$. That is,

$$\text{error} = \left| \int_a^b f(x)\,dx - T_n \right| \leq \frac{M(b-a)^3}{12n^2}.$$

□

We won't provide a proof of this theorem, but we can discuss why it is reasonable that the error bound has this form. Note that the error depends on:

1. the length $(b-a)$ of the interval $[a, b]$ (the larger our original interval is, the larger we can expect the error to be);

2. the number of subintervals n of the partition (as we make the partition finer, that is, n larger, the smaller we expect the error to be); and

3. the largest magnitude M of the second derivative $f''(x)$.

The second derivative gives a measure of how fast the slope of the graph of $y = f(x)$ changes. Since the trapezoidal rule corresponds to using a piece-wise linear approximation of the function f, we would expect the error of the trapezoidal estimate to be greater for functions whose slopes change quickly.

EXAMPLE 2 What is the error bound for approximating $\int_{0.5}^{3.5} \sin^3(x)\,dx$ using the trapezoidal rule for a regular partition of size $n = 6$?

Solution The second derivative of $f(x) = \sin^3(x)$ is

$$f''(x) = 6\cos^2(x)\sin(x) - 3\sin^3(x).$$

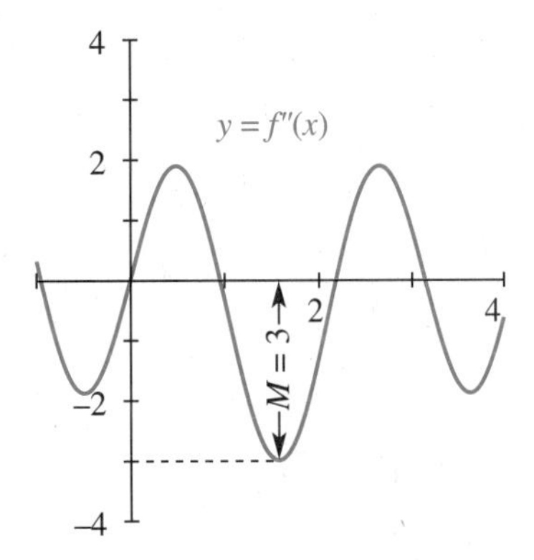

Figure 9.3 $|f''(x)| \leq 3$ over the interval $[0.5, 3.5]$.

For this particular function, it is fairly easy to find a bound M for the second derivative. We know that

$$-1 \leq \sin(x) \leq 1 \qquad \text{and} \qquad -1 \leq \cos(x) \leq 1$$

for *any* value x, so $M = 6 - (-3) = 9$ is certainly as large as the second derivative could possibly be. Using this as our bound M, we have

$$\text{error} = \left| \int_{0.5}^{3.5} \sin^3(x)\, dx - T_6 \right| \leq \frac{9(3^3)}{12(6^2)} = 0.5625.$$

Actually, we can find a much better bound M than the value $M = 9$ used here (we were very conservative). If we graph the second derivative $y = f''(x) = 6\cos^2(x)\sin(x) - 3\sin^3(x)$ over the interval $[0.5, 3.5]$, then M is simply the farthest distance between the graph and the x-axis. Figure 9.3 shows that the value $M = 3$ can safely be taken as a bound for our purposes. Using this better bound for the second derivative, we conclude that

$$\text{error} = \left| \int_{0.5}^{3.5} \sin^3(x)\, dx - T_6 \right| \leq \frac{3(3^3)}{12(6^2)} = 0.1875.$$

Since the trapezoidal estimate $T_6 = 1.296$, we can conclude that the true value of the integral satisfies

$$1.1085 = (1.296 - 0.1875) \leq \int_{0.5}^{3.5} \sin^3(x)\, dx \leq (1.296 + 0.1875) = 1.4835. \qquad \blacksquare$$

▶▶▶ **The error bound should be interpreted as a "worst case" scenario. The trapezoidal estimate may actually be much better than the error bound computed by this theorem.**

For instance, the actual error of our trapezoidal estimate for this example is

$$\text{error} = \left| \int_{0.5}^{3.5} \sin^3(x)\, dx - T_6 \right| \approx |1.315 - 1.296| = .019,$$

which is much better than the worst case bound we obtained from the theorem. The real importance of Theorem 9.1 is that it allows us to calculate the bound on our error even when we have no way of calculating the true value of the definite integral.

The error bound for Simpson's rule is given in the following theorem.

Theorem 9.2

Simpson's rule error bound for $\int_a^b f(x)\,dx$
Hypothesis 1: The fourth derivative $f^{(4)}$ is continuous over $[a, b]$.
Hypothesis 2: The fourth derivative's value over $[a, b]$ is bounded by M. That is, for any $x \in [a, b]$, we have

$$|f^{(4)}(x)| \leq M.$$

Conclusion: The error of Simpson's rule estimate S_{2n} is bounded by $\dfrac{M(b-a)^5}{180(2n)^4}$. That is,

$$\text{error} = \left| \int_a^b f(x)\,dx - S_{2n} \right| \leq \frac{M(b-a)^5}{180(2n)^4}.$$

□

As with the trapezoidal rule estimate, the error depends on

1. the length $(b-a)$ of the interval $[a, b]$, and
2. the number of subintervals n of the partition.

Simpson's rule corresponds to using a piece-wise quadratic approximation of the function f. Hence, the error also depends on

3. a measure of how far the function strays from this quadratic approximation. The magnitude of the fourth derivative provides such a measure.

EXAMPLE 3 What is the error bound for approximating $\int_{0.5}^{3.5} \sin^3(x)\,dx$ using Simpson's rule?

Solution The fourth derivative of $f(x) = \sin^3(x)$ is

$$f^{(4)}(x) = -60\cos^2(x)\sin(x) + 21\sin^3(x).$$

(A symbolic algebra system is handy here!) For this particular function, we could take a conservative bound $M = 60 + 21 = 81$ for the fourth derivative. (Here we are assuming that we know $-1 \leq \sin(x) \leq 1$ and $-1 \leq \cos(x) \leq 1$

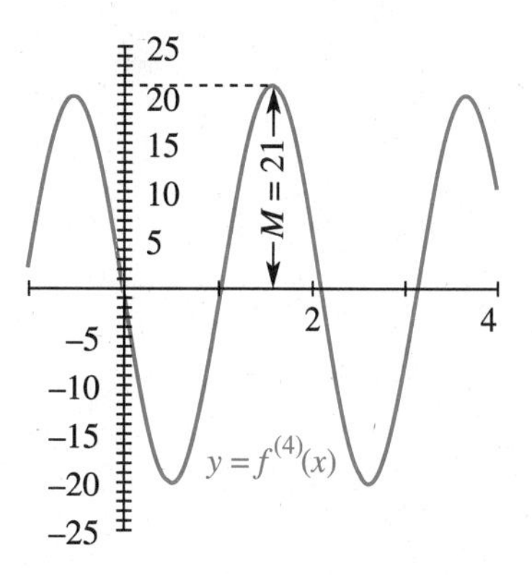

Figure 9.4 $|f^{(4)}(x)| \leq 21$ over the interval $[0.5, 3.5]$.

for all x.) Using this as our bound M, we have

$$\text{error} = \left| \int_{0.5}^{3.5} \sin^3(x)\,dx - S_{12} \right| \leq \frac{81(3^5)}{180(12^4)} = 0.00527.$$

If we actually graph the fourth derivative $y = f^{(4)}(x) = -60\cos^2(x)\sin(x) + 21\sin^3(x)$ over the interval $[0.5, 3.5]$, then Figure 9.4 shows that we can use a much smaller bound $M = 21$ for our purposes. Using this better bound for the second derivative, we can conclude that

$$\text{error} = \left| \int_{0.5}^{3.5} \sin^3(x)\,dx - S_{12} \right| \leq \frac{21(3^5)}{180(12^4)} \approx 0.00137.$$

This tells us the worst possible error in our Simpson's rule estimate. Indeed, $S_{12} \approx 1.315$ is accurate to the nearest thousandth. ■

EXERCISES for Section 9.1

For exercises 1–6: Using regular partitions of size $n = 2$, 4, 8, 16, and 32, find the error bound for the trapezoidal estimate of the definite integrals. Use a graphing calculator or software to find a suitable bound for the second derivative in each exercise.

1. $\int_0^1 \sqrt{1+x^2}\,dx$

2. $\int_{-1}^0 3^x\,dx$

3. $\int_{-1}^1 \arctan(x)\,dx$

4. $\int_1^4 \log_2(x)\,dx$

5. $\int_0^1 e^{-x^2}\,dx$

6. $\int_{0.5}^{3.5} \sin(x^3)\,dx$

For exercises 7–12: Using regular partitions of size $n = 1$, 2, 4, 8, and 16, find the error bound for the Simpson's rule estimate S_{2n} of the definite integrals. Use a graphing calculator or software to find a suitable bound for the fourth derivative in each exercise.

7. $\int_0^1 \sqrt{1+x^2}\,dx$

8. $\int_{-1}^0 3^x\,dx$

9. $\int_{-1}^{1} \arctan(x)\, dx$ **10.** $\int_{1}^{4} \log_2(x)\, dx$
11. $\int_{0}^{1} e^{-x^2}\, dx$ **12.** $\int_{0.5}^{3.5} \sin(x^3)\, dx$

For exercises 13–18: Using regular partitions of size $n = 2, 4, 8, 16, 32,$ and so on, for what value n would a machine stop trying trapezoidal approximations T_n if it used the criteria of three successive approximations within .0001 for each integral?

13. $\int_{0}^{1} \sqrt{1+x^2}\, dx$ **14.** $\int_{-1}^{0} 3^x\, dx$
15. $\int_{-1}^{1} \arctan(x)\, dx$ **16.** $\int_{1}^{4} \log_2(x)\, dx$
17. $\int_{0}^{1} e^{-x^2}\, dx$ **18.** $\int_{0.5}^{3.5} \sin(x^3)\, dx$

For exercises 19–24: Using regular partitions of size $n = 1, 2, 4, 8, 16,$ and so on, for what value n would a machine stop trying Simpson's rule approximations if it used the criteria of three successive approximations within .0001?

19. $\int_{0}^{1} \sqrt{1+x^2}\, dx$ **20.** $\int_{-1}^{0} 3^x\, dx$
21. $\int_{-1}^{1} \arctan(x)\, dx$ **22.** $\int_{1}^{4} \log_2(x)\, dx$
23. $\int_{0}^{1} e^{-x^2}\, dx$ **24.** $\int_{0.5}^{3.5} \sin(x^3)\, dx$

---

25. What is the error bound for the trapezoidal rule estimate when f is any linear function (over any closed interval $[a, b]$ and with any regular partition of size n)? Explain graphically why this makes sense.

26. What is the error bound for the Simpson's rule estimate when f is any polynomial function of degree 3 or lower? (In other words, f can be any linear, quadratic, or cubic function over any closed interval $[a, b]$ and with any regular partition of size $2n$.)

27. If we write Δx for the subinterval length, show that the trapezoidal rule error bound in T_n can be written

$$\text{error} \leq \frac{M''(b-a)}{12}(\Delta x)^2,$$

where M'' represents the bound on the second derivative of f.

28. If we write Δx for the subinterval length, show that the Simpson's rule error bound in S_{2n} can be written

$$\text{error} \leq \frac{M^{(4)}(b-a)}{180}(\Delta x)^4,$$

where $M^{(4)}$ represents the bound on the fourth derivative of f.

29. Use the results of exercises 27 and 28 to find the ratio of Simpson's error bound to the trapezoidal error bound when Δx is taken the same size for both approximation methods, then

$$\frac{\text{Simpson's error bound}}{\text{trapezoidal error bound}} = \frac{M^{(4)}}{15M''}(\Delta x)^2.$$

30. Use exercise 29 to explain why it is possible for the trapezoidal estimate to be better than Simpson's estimate for small regular partitions, but why, in general, as the partition size gets larger, Simpson's estimate is better.

Let $f(x) = x^3 + mx^2 + dx - 7$, where m is the month of your birth and d is the date of your birth. (For example, if you were born on May 12, your function is $f(x) = x^3 + 5x^2 + 12x - 7$.)

31. Find

$$\int_{-1}^{1} f(x)\,dx$$

for your birthday function.

32. Find a quadratic function $g(x) = ax^2 + bx + c$ whose graph goes through $(-1, f(-1))$, $(0, f(0))$ and $(1, f(1))$ for your birthday function.

33. Find

$$\int_{-1}^{1} g(x)\,dx$$

using the quadratic function you found.

Suppose that three points (x_0, y_0), (x_1, y_1), and (x_2, y_2) are given with

$$x_0 + \frac{\Delta x}{2} = x_1 = x_2 - \frac{\Delta x}{2}.$$

34. Find a quadratic function $g(x) = ax^2 + bx + c$ whose graph contains all three points. Express a, b, and c in terms of the x_i's, the y_i's, and Δx.

35. Find $\int_{x_0}^{x_2} g(x)\,dx$, expressing it in terms of the y_i's and Δx.

36. Now suppose that (x_0, y_0), (x_1, y_1), ..., (x_{2n}, y_{2n}) are points with the x-coordinates spaced equally a distance $\Delta x/2$. Using the results of exercises 34 and 35, show that

$$\int_{x_0}^{x_{2n}} g(x)\,dx = \frac{\Delta x}{6}(y_0 + 4y_1 + 2y_2 + 4y_3 + 2y_4 + \cdots + 2y_{2n-2} + 4y_{2n-1} + y_{2n})$$

where $g(x)$ is the piece-wise quadratic through the set of points. This shows that Simpson's rule is equivalent to integrating the piece-wise quadratic.

9.2 QUADRATIC APPROXIMATIONS AND CURVATURE

Just as the first derivative enables us to find the best linear approximation to a function at a point, the second derivative enables us to find the best quadratic (second degree) approximation.

The best linear approximation to a function f at a point x_0 has a graph that passes through the point $(x_0, f(x_0))$ and has a slope equal to the derivative value $f'(x_0)$ (the slope of the tangent line). If we call this linear approximation function g, we can state these requirements as

$$g(x_0) = f(x_0) \qquad \text{and} \qquad g'(x_0) = f'(x_0).$$

These two requirements completely determine the linear function g.

The **best quadratic approximation** p to f at x_0 is the second-degree polynomial $p(x) = ax^2 + bx + c$ that satisfies the *three* requirements:

$$p(x_0) = f(x_0), \qquad p'(x_0) = f'(x_0), \qquad \text{and} \quad p''(x_0) = f''(x_0).$$

These three requirements completely determine the three coefficients a, b, and c, just as the two requirements for the best linear approximation completely determine its slope and y-intercept. Let's illustrate with an example.

EXAMPLE 4 Find the best quadratic approximation p to the function $f(x) = \cos x$ at $x = 0$.

Solution First, we calculate

$$f'(x) = -\sin x \qquad \text{and} \qquad f''(x) = -\cos x.$$

The first two derivatives of a general quadratic $p(x) = ax^2 + bx + c$ are

$$p'(x) = 2ax + b \qquad \text{and} \qquad p''(x) = 2a.$$

The requirements for the *best* quadratic approximation for f at x_0 are $p(x_0) = f(x_0)$, $p'(x_0) = f'(x_0)$, and $p''(x_0) = f''(x_0)$, so now we must match up the values of f and p and their first two derivatives at $x = 0$:

$$p(0) = a \cdot 0^2 + b \cdot 0 + c = c \qquad f(0) = \cos 0 = 1$$

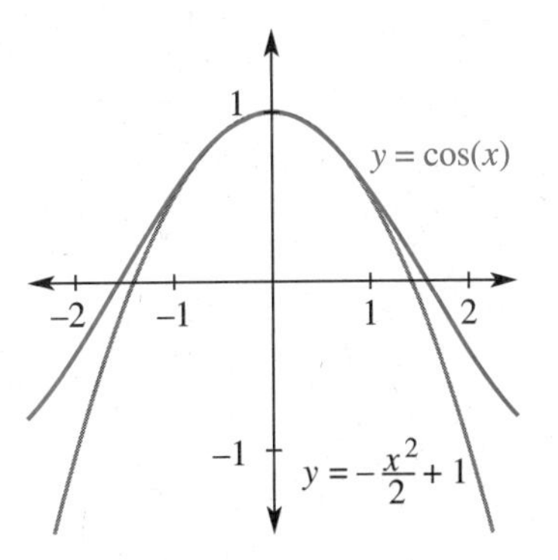

Figure 9.5 The graphs of $y = \cos(x)$ and its best quadratic approximation at $x = 0$.

$$p'(0) = 2a \cdot 0 + b = b \qquad f'(0) = -\sin 0 = 0$$
$$p''(0) = 2a \qquad f''(0) = -\cos 0 = -1.$$

From these we can see that

$$c = 1, \qquad b = 0, \qquad a = -\frac{1}{2},$$

so that $p(x) = -\dfrac{x^2}{2} + 1$. ■

In Figure 9.5 we have graphed both $y = \cos(x)$ and $y = -\dfrac{x^2}{2} + 1$, and we can see how "snug" the fit is between the two graphs near $x = 0$. At any value x_0 where the first and second derivatives exist, we can calculate a best quadratic approximation to a function. In general, it is convenient to write a best quadratic approximation in *Taylor form.*

Definition 1

If f is twice differentiable at x_0 (the first and second derivatives both exist), then the **second-order Taylor polynomial approximation** to f at $x = x_0$ is given by

$$p(x) = f(x_0) + f'(x_0)(x - x_0) + \frac{f''(x_0)}{2}(x - x_0)^2.$$

Note that x_0, $f(x_0)$, $f'(x_0)$, and $f''(x_0)$ are all specific values (constants), so

$$p'(x) = f'(x_0) + f''(x_0)(x - x_0) \qquad \text{and} \qquad p''(x) = f''(x_0).$$

Let's verify that the second-order Taylor polynomial approximation $p(x)$ fits the requirements of a best quadratic approximation at x_0:

$$p(x_0) = f(x_0) + f'(x_0)(x_0 - x_0) + \frac{f''(x_0)}{2}(x_0 - x_0)^2 = f(x_0) + 0 + 0 = f(x_0),$$

$$p'(x_0) = f'(x_0) + f''(x_0)(x_0 - x_0) = f'(x_0) + 0 = f'(x_0),$$

$$p''(x_0) = f''(x_0).$$

Thus, all three requirements are satisfied.

EXAMPLE 5 Find the second-degree Taylor polynomial approximation to $f(x) = \dfrac{1}{x}$ at $x = 2$.

Solution We have $f'(x) = -\dfrac{1}{x^2}$ and $f''(x) = \dfrac{2}{x^3}$. Hence,

$$f(2) = \frac{1}{2}, \qquad f'(2) = \frac{-1}{2^2} = -\frac{1}{4}, \qquad f''(2) = \frac{2}{2^3} = \frac{1}{4}.$$

The second-degree Taylor polynomial approximation to f at $x = 2$ is

$$p(x) = f(x_0) + f'(x_0)(x - x_0) + \frac{f''(x_0)}{2}(x - x_0)^2 = \frac{1}{2} - \frac{1}{4}(x - 2) + \frac{1}{8}(x - 2)^2. \quad \blacksquare$$

Curvature

At each point $(x_0, f(x_0))$ of the graph of $y = f(x)$, we can use the first derivative to find the slope $f'(x_0)$. We can use this information to derive the equation of the tangent line (the graph of the best linear approximation)

$$y = y_0 + m(x - x_0),$$

where $y_0 = f(x_0)$ and $m = f'(x_0)$.

The second derivative can be used to give us a measure of the *concavity* of a function graph. In turn, we can use this additional information to derive the best quadratic approximation to f:

$$y = f(x_0) + f'(x_0)(x - x_0) + \frac{f''(x_0)}{2}(x - x_0)^2.$$

We can think of the tangent line as the "line of best fit" to the curve at a point. Similarly, the graph of the best quadratic approximation is the "parabola of best fit." How about a "circle of best fit?" By this, we mean what circle would approximate the shape of the curve best locally?

Perhaps it is not surprising to find that the notion of curvature depends on both the slope and concavity of the curve.

Definition 2

The **curvature** κ of the graph of $y = f(x)$ at the point $(x_0, f(x_0))$ is

$$\kappa = \frac{|f''(x_0)|}{(1 + [f'(x_0)]^2)^{3/2}}.$$

The **radius of curvature** r at the same point is the reciprocal of the curvature

$$r = 1/\kappa,$$

provided that $\kappa \neq 0$.

EXAMPLE 6 Calculate the curvature κ and the radius of curvature r at the point $(-1, 1)$ on the graph of $y = f(x) = x^3 - 2x$.

Solution The first derivative is $f'(x) = 3x^2 - 2$ and the second derivative is $f''(x) = 6x$. Using the formula for κ with $x_0 = -1$, we have

$$\kappa = \frac{6}{(1 + [1]^2)^{3/2}} = \frac{6}{2^{3/2}} \approx 2.12,$$

and the radius of curvature is $r = 1/\kappa \approx 0.4714$. ■

Note that the formula for curvature κ depends both on the concavity, as measured by the second derivative f'', and the slope as measured by f'.

By definition, curvature and radius of curvature are inversely related. This reflects the idea that a small circle has great curvature (a point traveling on the circle must turn quickly in a tight space), while a large circle has little curvature (a person can walk in a large circle while believing the path is straight). If the definition of radius of curvature is to be reasonable, then it should match our usual notion of radius when the formula is actually applied to a circle.

EXAMPLE 7 Find the curvature and radius of curvature at the point $(3, 4)$ on a circle of radius 5 centered at the origin.

Solution The top half of the circle can be represented as the graph of the function

$$f(x) = \sqrt{25 - x^2}$$

over the interval $[-5, 5]$. The first derivative is

$$f'(x)\frac{-x}{\sqrt{25 - x^2}}$$

and the second derivative is

$$f''(x) = \frac{-25}{(25 - x^2)^{3/2}}.$$

From these derivatives, we have $f'(3) = -3/4$ and $f''(3) = -25/64$. The curvature is

$$\kappa = \frac{|-25/64|}{(1 + [-3/4]^2)^{3/2}} = \frac{25/64}{(25/16)^{3/2}} = \frac{25/64}{125/64} = \frac{1}{5},$$

hence the radius of curvature is $r = 1/\kappa = 1/(1/5) = 5$, the same as the radius of the original circle. ■

The osculating circle

We can use the radius of curvature to define the **osculating circle** (or **circle of curvature**) for a graph $y = f(x)$. The osculating circle for f at the point $(x_0, f(x_0))$ is a circle whose tangent at that point is the same as the tangent line to the graph of $y = f(x)$ and whose radius is the same as the radius of curvature $r = 1/\kappa$ at that point. There are two such circles satisfying these requirements (they "kiss" at the point of tangency). The osculating circle is the one on the same side of the tangent line as the function graph, and we can think of it as the "circle of best fit." Figure 9.6 illustrates the osculating circle at the point $(-1, 1)$ for the graph of $y = f(x) = x^3 - 2x$.

Linear, parabolic and circular segments are widely used in design, because they can be described by simple equations that involve no operations more mathematically complicated than addition, subtraction, multiplication, and squaring. If a curve can be described as the graph of a differentiable function, calculus provides us with the tools to determine the line, parabola, or circle that best fits the curve at any point.

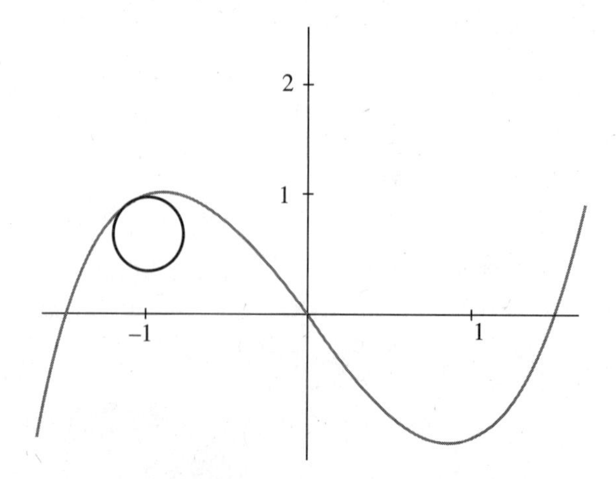

Figure 9.6 Osculating circle.

EXERCISES for Section 9.2

For exercises 1–10: Find the best quadratic approximation p of the given function f at the specified point x_0. Then compare $p(x)$ and $f(x)$ at

$$x = x_0 + 1, \qquad x = x_0 - 1, \qquad x = x_0 + .001, \quad \text{and} \quad x = x_0 - .001$$

by calculating $|p(x) - f(x)|$ for each point. Finally, graph both the original function and its best quadratic approximation over the interval $[x_0 - 1, x_0 + 1]$.

1. $f(x) = x^2; \quad x_0 = -3$
2. $f(x) = \sqrt{x}; \quad x_0 = 9$
3. $f(x) = x^{2/3}; \quad x_0 = -8$
4. $f(x) = x^3 - 4x; \quad x_0 = -1.5$
5. $f(x) = \sin x; \quad x_0 = 0$
6. $f(x) = \cos x; \quad x_0 = \pi/3$
7. $f(x) = \tan x; \quad x_0 = \pi/4$
8. $f(x) = 1/x; \quad x_0 = -2$
9. $f(x) = x; \quad x_0 = 0$
10. $f(x) = 5.42; \quad x_0 = 132.78$

For exercises 11–20: Find

(a) the curvature κ,

(b) the radius of curvature r, and

(c) the equation of the osculating circle at the $((x_0, f(x_0))$,

and then graph both the circle and the original function in a viewing window centered at $(x_0, f(x_0))$.

11. $f(x) = x^2 + x + 1; \quad x_0 = 1.6$
12. $f(x) = 2x^2 - 7x + 3; \quad x_0 = 3/2$
13. $f(x) = x^3 - 12x; \quad x_0 = -2$
14. $f(x) = \dfrac{3x - 17}{5}; \quad x_0 = 4$
15. $f(x) = x^5; \quad x_0 = 1$
16. $f(x) = 3; \quad x_0 = 2$
17. $f(x) = \sin^2 x; \quad x_0 = \pi/3$
18. $f(x) = \tan x; \quad x_0 = 3\pi/4$
19. $f(x) = \sin x^2; \quad x_0 = 0$
20. $f(x) = \sqrt{25 - x^2}; \quad x_0 = 4$

---

21. Show that the curvature of a linear function $f(x) = mx + b$ is zero at every input x_0.

22. Show that the vertex of a parabola $y = ax^2 + bx + c$ is at $x = \dfrac{-b}{2a}$ and that the curvature of the parabola is greatest at the vertex.

23. Suppose that f is a twice differentiable function and $(x_0, f(x_0))$ is an inflection point of the graph of $y = f(x)$. Show that the best quadratic approximation to f at x_0 is actually linear and the curvature at x_0 is $\kappa = 0$.

24. Suppose that $f(2) = 3$, $f'(2) = 0$, and $f''(2) = 1$. Find the center of the osculating circle to $y = f(x)$ at $x = 2$.

25. The graph of $y = f(x)$ passes through the point $(3, 2)$ with slope -1 and curvature $\kappa = 1/4$. If the graph is concave down at $(3, 2)$, find the best quadratic approximation to f at $x = 3$.

26. You need to build a parabolic mirror having a curvature of $\kappa = 1/2$ at its vertex. Let $y = ax^2$ describe a radial cross section of the mirror, so that its vertex is at the origin. Find a.

A general cubic polynomial has the form

$$y = q(x) = ax^3 + bx^2 + cx + d.$$

27. Show that q can have zero, one, or two critical values, but that its graph always has exactly one inflection point. Where is the inflection point?

28. What is the slope at this inflection point?

29. If the cubic q has no critical values, show that the minimum slope occurs at the inflection point. If the cubic has one critical value, show that it is at the same location as the inflection point. If the cubic has two critical values, show that the inflection point occurs exactly halfway between them.

30. Find the curvature and the best quadratic approximation p to the general cubic at $x = 0$. What is $q(x) - p(x)$?

9.3 TAYLOR POLYNOMIALS

To see how Taylor polynomials are determined, let's review the cases of the best linear and quadratic approximations. Suppose that we are given a function f that is differentiable at the point $x = a$. The best linear approximation p_1 can be written

$$p_1(x) = f(a) + f'(a)(x - a).$$

This linear polynomial is designed to satisfy *two* criteria:

$$p_1(a) = f(a) + f'(a)(a - a) = f(a) \qquad \text{and} \qquad p_1'(a) = f'(a).$$

In other words, p_1 has the same output and same derivative value at $x = a$ as the function f does. Indeed, this completely determines p_1.

If f is twice differentiable at $x = a$, then the best quadratic approximation p_2 at that point can be written

$$p_2(x) = f(a) + f'(a)(x - a) + \frac{f''(a)}{2}(x - a)^2.$$

This quadratic polynomial is designed to satisfy *three* criteria:

$$p_2(a) = f(a), \qquad p_2'(a) = f'(a), \qquad p_2''(a) = f''(a).$$

We can extend this analysis to higher-degree polynomials p_n. If f is n times differentiable at $x = a$, then an nth degree polynomial p_n can be designed to satisfy $n+1$ criteria:

$$\begin{aligned} p_n(a) &= f(a) \\ p_n'(a) &= f'(a) \\ p_n''(a) &= f''(a) \\ &\vdots \\ p_n^{(n)}(a) &= f^{(n)}(a). \end{aligned}$$

The nth degree polynomial p_n has $n+1$ coefficients that are determined by these requirements. If we write

$$p_n(x) = c_0 + c_1(x-a) + c_2(x-a)^2 + c_3(x-a)^3 + \cdots + c_n(x-a)^n$$

and compute the output of p_n and its first n derivatives at $x = a$, our requirements are

$$\begin{aligned} p_n(a) &= c_0 = f(a) \\ p_n'(a) &= c_1 = f'(a) \\ p_n''(a) &= 2c_2 = f''(a) \\ p_n'''(a) &= 3 \cdot 2c_3 = f'''(a) \\ p_n^{(4)}(a) &= 4 \cdot 3 \cdot 2c_4 = f^{(4)}(a) \\ &\vdots \\ p_n^{(n)}(a) &= n \cdot (n-1) \cdots 3 \cdot 2c_n = f^{(n)}(a). \end{aligned}$$

Now we can solve for the coefficients and find that

$$p_n(x) = f(a) + f'(a)(x-a) + \frac{f''(a)}{2}(x-a)^2 + \frac{f'''(a)}{6}(x-a)^3 + \cdots + \frac{f^{(n)}(a)}{n!}(x-a)^n.$$

In fact, if we agree to write $f^{(0)}$ to mean the original function f, and since $0! = 1$, $1! = 1$ and $2! = 2$, we have a nice formula for any coefficient c_k, for $0 \le k \le n$:

$$c_k = \frac{f^{(k)}(a)}{k!}.$$

If f is continuous and n-times differentiable at $x = a$, then the Taylor polynomial approximation of f at $x = a$ of degree n is given by

$$p_n(x) = f(a) + f'(a)(x-a) + \frac{f''(a)}{2}(x-a)^2 + \cdots + \frac{f^{(n)}(a)}{n!}(x-a)^n$$
$$= \sum_{k=0}^{n} \frac{f^{(k)}(a)}{k!}(x-a)^k.$$

EXAMPLE 8 Find the fourth-degree Taylor polynomial of $y = \sqrt{x}$ at $x = 9$ and graph both over the interval $[2, 16]$.

Solution The polynomial is

$$p_4(x) = c_0 + c_1(x-9) + c_2(x-9)^2 + c_3(x-9)^3 + c_4(x-9)^4$$

where

$$c_0 = \sqrt{9} = 3,$$
$$c_1 = \left[\frac{d}{dx}\sqrt{x}\right]\Bigg|_{x=9} = \frac{1}{2} \cdot \frac{1}{\sqrt{9}} = \frac{1}{6}$$
$$c_2 = \frac{1}{2}\left[\frac{d^2}{dx^2}\sqrt{x}\right]\Bigg|_{x=9} = -\frac{1}{2} \cdot \frac{1}{4} \cdot \frac{1}{9\sqrt{9}} = -\frac{1}{216}$$
$$c_3 = \frac{1}{3 \cdot 2}\left[\frac{d^3}{dx^3}\sqrt{x}\right]\Bigg|_{x=9} = \frac{1}{3 \cdot 2} \cdot \frac{3}{8} \cdot \frac{1}{81\sqrt{9}} = \frac{1}{3888}$$
$$c_4 = \frac{1}{4 \cdot 3 \cdot 2}\left[\frac{d^4}{dx^4}\sqrt{x}\right]\Bigg|_{x=9} = \frac{1}{4 \cdot 3 \cdot 2} \cdot \frac{15}{16} \cdot \frac{1}{729\sqrt{9}} = -\frac{5}{279936}.$$

The graphs of $y = \sqrt{x}$ and $y = p_4(x)$ are both shown in Figure 9.7.

Note that near the input $x = 9$, the two graphs are virtually indistinguishable. ■

The examples below show graphically how higher-order Taylor polynomials can incorporate more of the behavior of the approximated function.

EXAMPLE 9 Find the first- through sixth-degree Taylor polynomials at $x = 1$ of the function $y = \ln(x)$ Graph each of the approximations, along with $y = \ln(x)$.

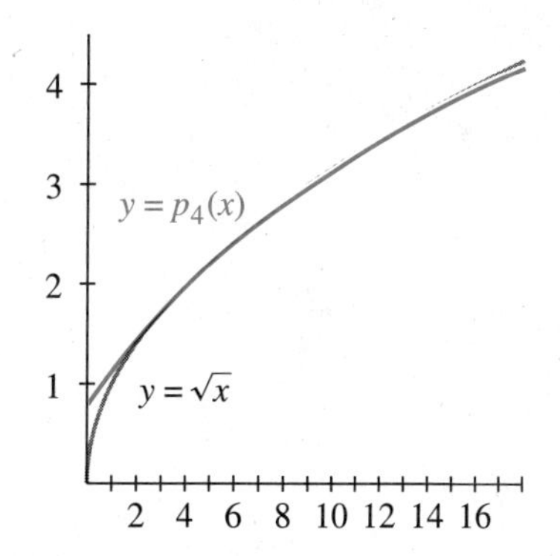

Figure 9.7 Graph of $y = \sqrt{x}$ and its fourth-degree Taylor polynomial at $x = 9$.

Solution First, we compute the first six derivatives of $y = \ln(x)$ and evaluate each at $x = 1$:

$$\begin{aligned}
y &= \ln(x) & y(1) &= 0 \\
y' &= x^{-1} & y'(1) &= 1 \\
y'' &= -1 \cdot x^{-2} & y''(1) &= -1 \\
y''' &= 2x^{-3} & y'''(1) &= 2 \\
y^{(4)} &= -6x^{-4} & y^{(4)}(1) &= -6 \\
y^{(5)} &= 24x^{-5} & y^{(5)}(1) &= 24 \\
y^{(6)} &= -120x^{-6} & y^{(6)}(1) &= -120
\end{aligned}$$

Note that $c_0 = 0$. For $k \geq 1$, we have $y^{(k)}(1) = (-1)^{k-1}(k-1)!$. Thus,

$$c_k = \frac{y^{(k)}(1)}{k!} = \frac{(-1)^{k-1} \cdot (k-1)!}{k!} = \frac{(-1)^{k-1}}{k} \qquad (k \geq 1).$$

Now we have a general formula for p_n, the nth degree Taylor polynomial approximation:

$$\sum_{k=1}^{n} \frac{(-1)^{k-1}}{k}(x-1)^k.$$

We can use this formula to find p_1 through p_6:

$$p_1(x) = x - 1$$

$$p_2(x) = (x-1) - \frac{1}{2}(x-1)^2$$

$$p_3(x) = (x-1) - \frac{1}{2}(x-1)^2 + \frac{1}{3}(x-1)^3$$

$$p_4(x) = (x-1) - \frac{1}{2}(x-1)^2 + \frac{1}{3}(x-1)^3 - \frac{1}{4}(x-1)^4$$

$$p_5(x) = (x-1) - \frac{1}{2}(x-1)^2 + \frac{1}{3}(x-1)^3 - \frac{1}{4}(x-1)^4 + \frac{1}{5}(x-1)^5$$

$$p_6(x) = (x-1) - \frac{1}{2}(x-1)^2 + \frac{1}{3}(x-1)^3 - \frac{1}{4}(x-1)^4 + \frac{1}{5}(x-1)^5 - \frac{1}{6}(x-1)^6$$

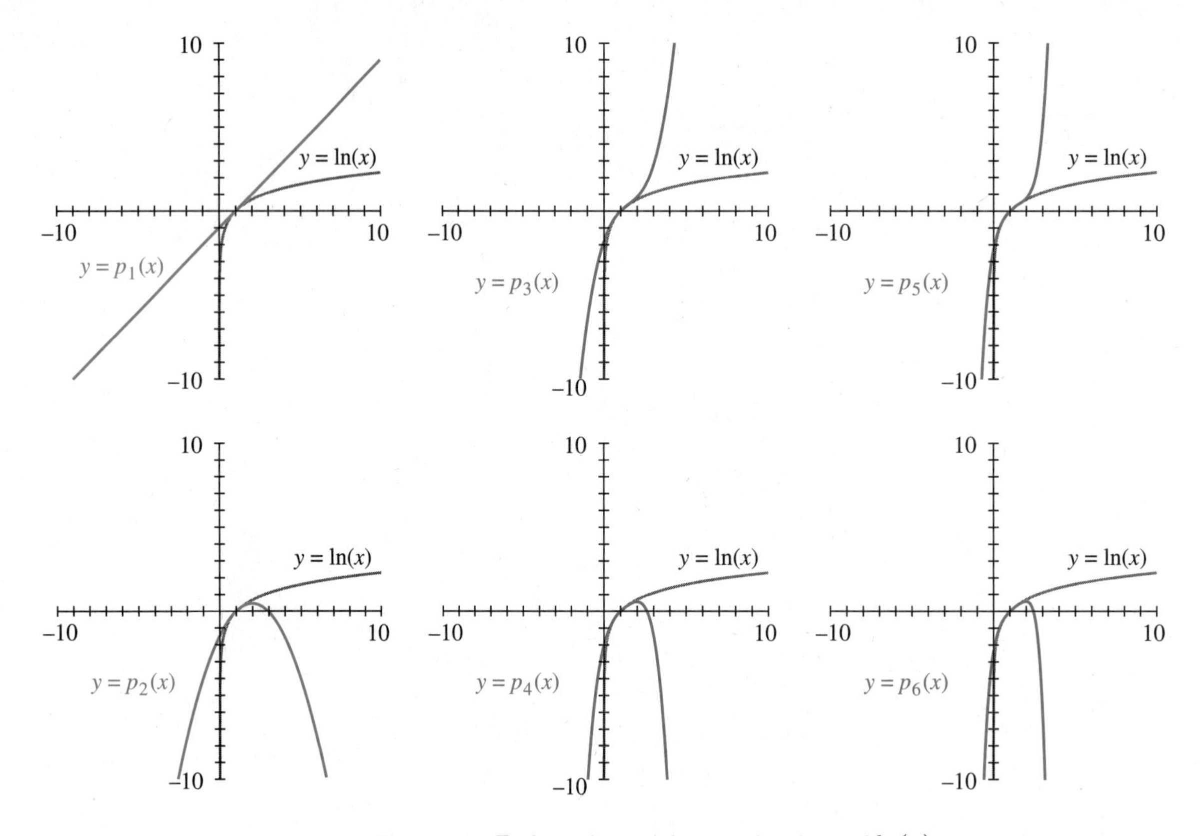

Figure 9.8 Taylor polynomial approximations of $\ln(x)$ at $x = 1$.

The graphs of p_1 through p_6 are shown in Figure 9.8. ■

Maclaurin polynomials

A Taylor polynomial approximation at $x = 0$ is sometimes called a **Maclaurin polynomial**, named after the Scottish mathematician Colin Maclaurin (1698-1746).

EXAMPLE 10 Find the degree 1, 3, 5, 7, 9, and 11 Maclaurin polynomials (Taylor polynomials at $x = 0$) of the function $y = \sin(x)$. Graph each approximation, along with $y = \sin(x)$.

Solution The derivatives of $y = \sin(x)$ cycle as follows:

$$y' = \cos(x), \qquad y'' = -\sin(x), \qquad y''' = -\cos(x), \qquad y^{(4)} = \sin(x),$$

and we're back to our original function. If we evaluate the original function and its derivatives at $x = 0$, we have

$$y(0) = 0, \qquad y'(0) = 1 \qquad y''(0) = 0 \qquad y'''(0) = -1,$$

and this pattern continues indefinitely.

This means that all the even coefficients $c_0, c_2, c_4, \ldots$ are 0, and the odd coefficients are

$$c_1 = 1,\ c_3 = -\frac{1}{6},\ c_5 = \frac{1}{120},\ c_7 = -\frac{1}{5040},\ c_9 = \frac{1}{9!},\ \text{and } c_{11} = -\frac{1}{11!}.$$

In general, the degree $2n+1$ Maclaurin polynomial for $\sin(x)$ can be written

$$\sum_{k=0}^{n} \frac{(-1)^k}{(2k+1)!} x^{2k+1}.$$

Hence:

$$p_1(x) = x$$

$$p_3(x) = x - \frac{1}{6}x^3$$

$$p_5(x) = x - \frac{1}{6}x^3 + \frac{1}{120}x^5$$

$$p_7(x) = x - \frac{1}{6}x^3 + \frac{1}{120}x^5 - \frac{1}{5040}x^7$$

$$p_9(x) = x - \frac{1}{6}x^3 + \frac{1}{120}x^5 - \frac{1}{5040}x^7 + \frac{1}{9!}x^9$$

$$p_{11}(x) = x - \frac{1}{6}x^3 + \frac{1}{120}x^5 - \frac{1}{5040}x^7 + \frac{1}{9!}x^9 - \frac{1}{11!}x^{11}$$

The graphs are shown in Figure 9.9. ■

EXAMPLE 11 Find the first- through sixth-degree Maclaurin polynomials of the function $y = e^x + 1$. Graph each of the approximations, along with $y = e^x + 1$.

Solution All of the derivatives are the same:

$$y^{(k)} = e^x \qquad \text{for } k = 1,\ 2,\ 3\ \ldots$$

Since $(e^0 + 1) = 1 + 1 = 2$, the constant term is 2 and we can write the degree n Maclaurin polynomial as

$$2 + \sum_{k=1}^{n} \frac{1}{k!} x^k.$$

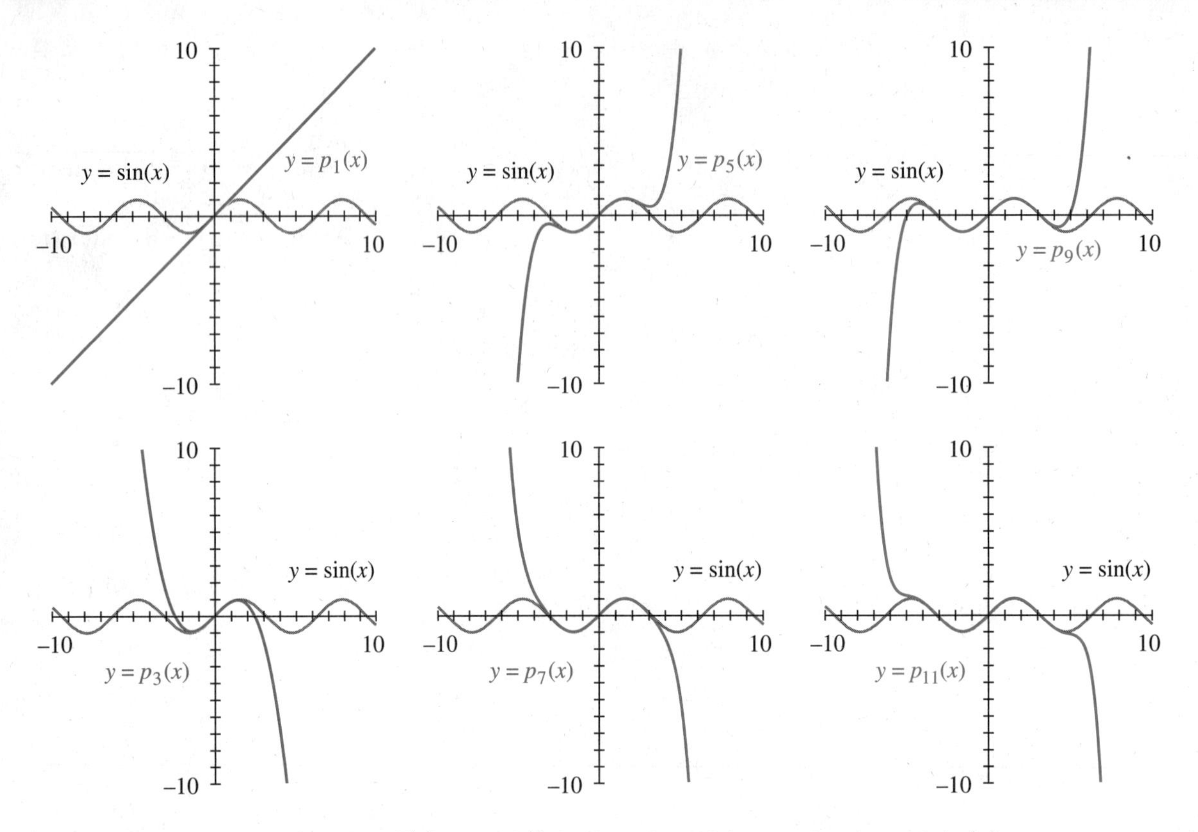

Figure 9.9 Maclaurin polynomial approximations of $\sin(x)$.

Thus,

$$p_1(x) = 2 + x$$

$$p_2(x) = 2 + x + \frac{1}{2}x^2$$

$$p_3(x) = 2 + x + \frac{1}{2}x^2 + \frac{1}{6}x^3$$

$$p_4(x) = 2 + x + \frac{1}{2}x^2 + \frac{1}{6}x^3 + \frac{1}{24}x^4$$

$$p_5(x) = 2 + x + \frac{1}{2}x^2 + \frac{1}{6}x^3 + \frac{1}{24}x^4 + \frac{1}{120}x^5$$

$$p_6(x) = 2 + x + \frac{1}{2}x^2 + \frac{1}{6}x^3 + \frac{1}{24}x^4 + \frac{1}{120}x^5 + \frac{1}{720}x^6.$$

The graphs of these approximations are shown in Figure 9.10. ■

Note how the polynomial approximations diverge from the graph of $y = e^x + 1$ as we move away from the input $x = 0$. For any given p_n of higher degree, we would still see this graphical behavior. The graph of our

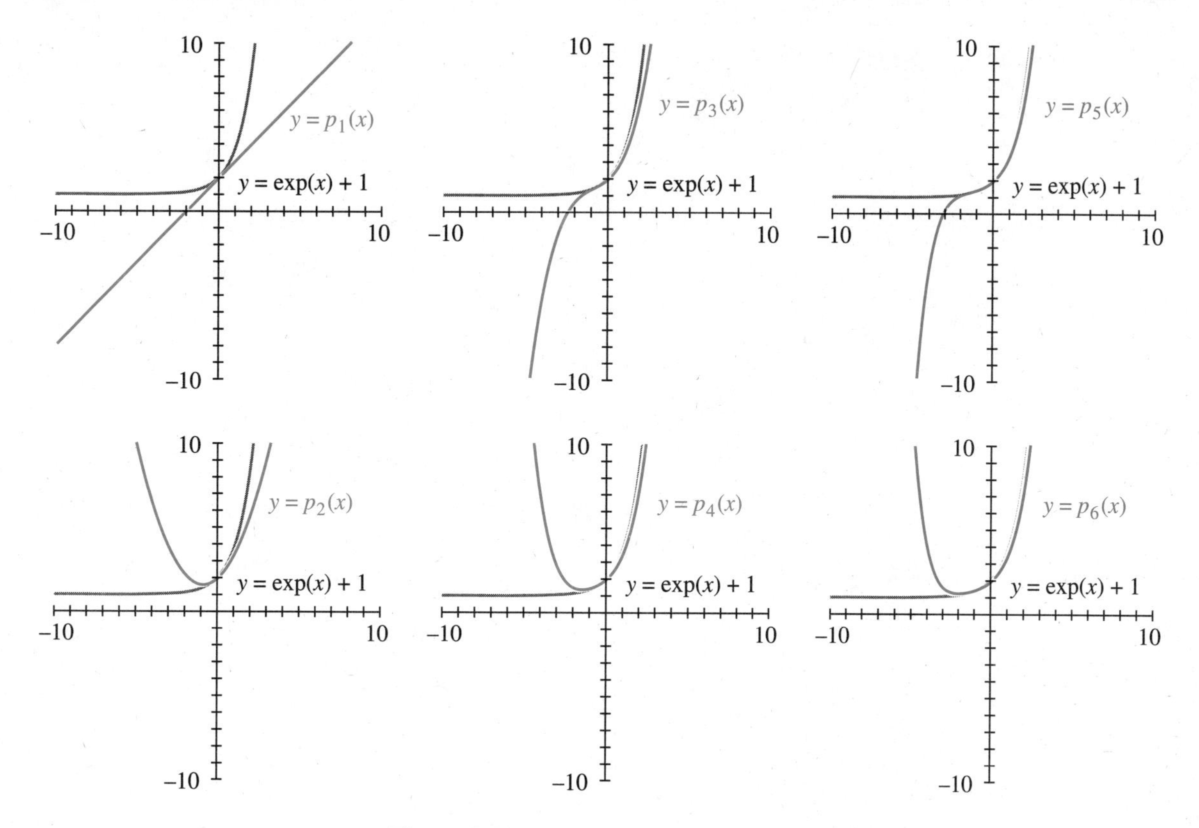

Figure 9.10 Maclaurin polynomial approximations of $e^x + 1$.

function $y = e^x + 1$ has a horizontal asymptote $y = 1$, since

$$\lim_{x \to -\infty} (e^x + 1) = 1.$$

However, no polynomial p_n of degree $n \geq 1$ will have a horizontal asymptote.

▶▶▶ **Taylor polynomial approximations are *local* approximations. They approximate a function's behavior near a particular point $x = a$. For values x far from a, the Taylor polynomial approximation may be very poor.**

In some sense, the best approximation of $y = e^x + 1$ for large-magnitude negative values x is the *constant* Taylor polynomial

$$p_0(x) = 1.$$

EXAMPLE 12 Find the first- through sixth-degree Taylor polynomials at $x = 3$ of the function $y = x^{-1}$. Graph each of the approximations, along with $y = x^{-1}$.

Solution Since

$$y' = -1 \cdot x^{-2},$$

$$y'' = \frac{d}{dx}(-1 \cdot x^{-2}) = (-2) \cdot (-1) \cdot (x^{-3}) = 2x^{-3},$$

$$y''' = \frac{d}{dx}(-2) \cdot (-1) \cdot (x^{-3}) = (-3) \cdot (-2) \cdot (-1) \cdot (x^{-4}) = -6x^{-4},$$

and so on, we have

$$y^{(k)} = (-1)^k \cdot k! \cdot x^{-(k+1)} \qquad \text{and} \qquad y^{(k)}(3) = (-1)^k \cdot k! \cdot 3^{-(k+1)}.$$

We can write the degree n Taylor polynomial at $x = 3$ as

$$\sum_{k=0}^{n} \frac{(-1)^k \cdot k! \cdot 3^{-(k+1)}}{k!}(x-3)^k = \sum_{k=0}^{n}(-1)^k \cdot 3^{-(k+1)} \cdot (x-3)^k.$$

So,

$$\begin{aligned}
p_1(x) =& \frac{1}{3} - \frac{1}{9}(x-3)\\
p_2(x) =& \frac{1}{3} - \frac{1}{9}(x-3) + \frac{1}{27}(x-3)^2\\
p_3(x) =& \frac{1}{3} - \frac{1}{9}(x-3) + \frac{1}{27}(x-3)^2 - \frac{1}{81}(x-3)^3\\
p_4(x) =& \frac{1}{3} - \frac{1}{9}(x-3) + \frac{1}{27}(x-3)^2 - \frac{1}{81}(x-3)^3 + \frac{1}{243}(x-3)^4\\
p_5(x) =& \frac{1}{3} - \frac{1}{9}(x-3) + \frac{1}{27}(x-3)^2 - \frac{1}{81}(x-3)^3\\
&+ \frac{1}{243}(x-3)^4 - \frac{1}{729}(x-3)^5\\
p_6(x) =& \frac{1}{3} - \frac{1}{9}(x-3) + \frac{1}{27}(x-3)^2 - \frac{1}{81}(x-3)^3\\
&+ \frac{1}{243}(x-3)^4 - \frac{1}{729}(x-3)^5 + \frac{1}{2187}(x-3)^6.
\end{aligned}$$

The graphs are shown in Figure 9.11. ■

Note in the graphs presented in these examples how more of the behavior—the "shape" of the function graph near the point of interest—is reflected in the higher-order Taylor and Maclaurin polynomials. Also note that, for some functions, the higher-order Taylor polynomials seem to

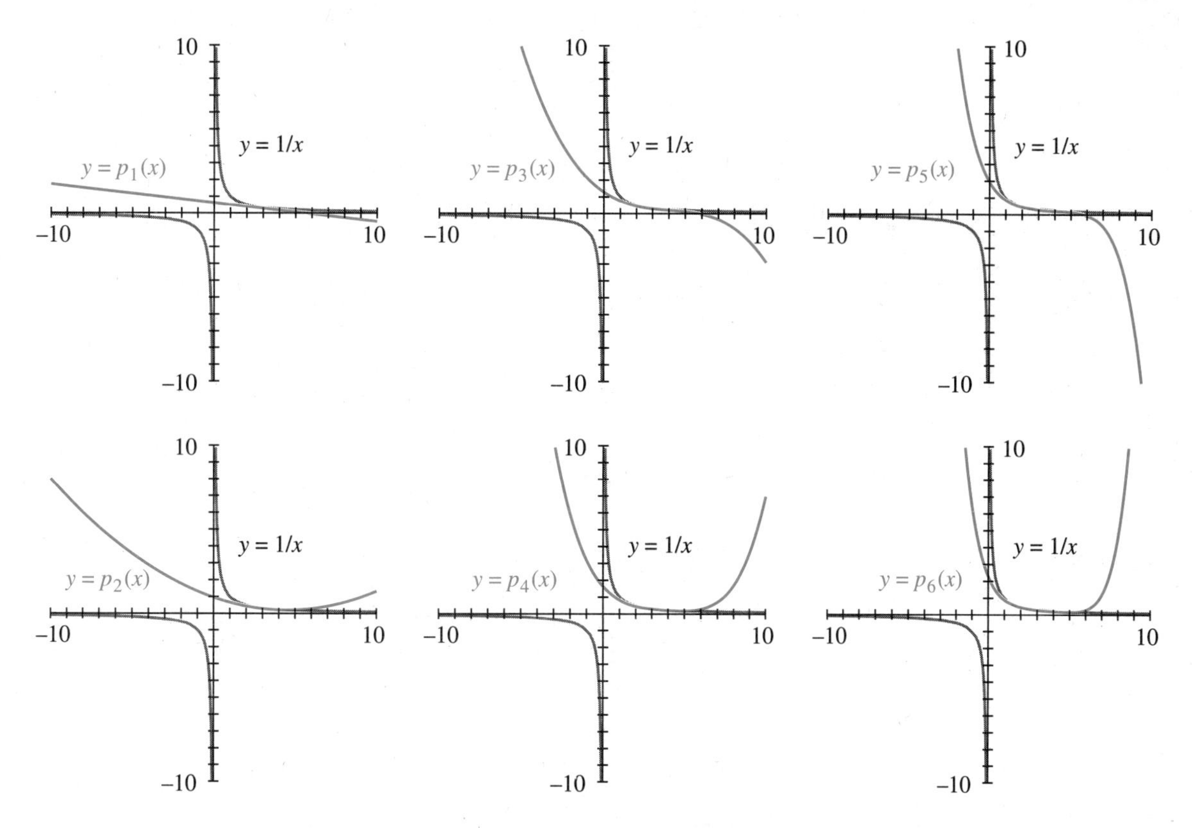

Figure 9.11 Taylor polynomial approximations at $x = 3$ of $1/x$.

get generally closer to the approximated function, while in other cases the higher-order Taylor polynomials get closer near the point of interest but seem to move further away in other regions.

Suppose now that we are trying to use the Taylor polynomials at $x = a$ to estimate the function value of f at some other point, say $x = b$. Will it be true that higher-order Taylor polynomials yield closer approximations to the function value? Absolutely not. The only sense in which the Taylor polynomials at $x = a$ are *guaranteed* to be on their best behavior is near $x = a$.

Using Taylor polynomials to solve equations

While the Taylor polynomial approximation is sometimes useful for a function you know a lot about, it is more often used to approximate otherwise unknown functions. For example, we can use Taylor polynomials to approximate solutions to rather difficult equations. In this context, note that to find a Taylor polynomial approximation, we need only find the values of the derivatives of a function at a single point. Any method allowing us to produce these values provides an approximation to the function.

Let us examine two such situations. In the first, we use implicit differentiation to inductively determine derivatives of a function satisfying an equation that cannot be solved algebraically.

EXAMPLE 13 Find a cubic Taylor polynomial for a function $y = f(x)$ approximating a solution to the equation

$$f(x) + \sin(f(x)) = x.$$

Solution The first step in the solution is to find an input $x = a$ and corresponding output value $f(a)$ such that

$$f(a) + \sin(f(a)) = a.$$

This will give us a point a around which to construct a Taylor polynomial, the first term being $f(a)$. Nothing beyond guesswork and trial-and-error will help at this stage. However, trying the obvious guess, $a = 0$, and noting that $\sin(0) = 0$, we find that a possibility is $0 = a = f(a)$. With this as a starting point, we can systematically build a Taylor polynomial of as high an order as we wish.

To get the next term in the Taylor polynomial, $\frac{f'(0)}{1!}x$, we need to find $f'(0)$. To do this, we implicitly differentiate our original equation with respect to x:

$$f'(x) + \cos(f(x)) \cdot f'(x) = 1.$$

We only need to know $f'(0)$, and we already know that $f(0) = 0$. Therefore, $f'(0)$ satisfies

$$f'(0) \cdot (1 + \cos(f(0))) = f'(0) \cdot (1 + \cos(0)) = 2f'(0) = 1,$$

so $f'(0) = 0.5$, and we now know the first two terms of the Taylor polynomial:

$$0 + 0.5x + \cdots.$$

To find the next term, we implicitly differentiate once more to obtain

$$f''(x) \cdot (1 + \cos(f(x))) - (f'(x))^2 \sin(f(x)) = 0.$$

Again, we only need to know $f''(0)$, and we already know $f(0) = 0$ and $f'(0) = 0.5$. Therefore, $f''(0)$ satisfies

$$f''(0) \cdot (1 + \cos(0)) - (0.5)^2 \sin(0) = f''(0) \cdot (2) - 0 = 0,$$

so $f''(0) = 0$, and we now know the first three terms of the Taylor polynomial:

$$0 + 0.5x + \frac{0}{2!}x^2 + \cdots.$$

To find the fourth term, we implicitly differentiate again:

$$f'''(x) \cdot (1 + \cos(f(x))) - 3f''(x)f'(x)\sin(f(x)) - (f'(x))^3 \cos(f(x)) = 0.$$

Again, we only need to know $f'''(0)$, and we already know $f(0) = 0$, $f'(0) = 0.5$, and $f''(0) = 0$. The value $f'''(0)$ must satisfy

$$f'''(0) \cdot (1 + \cos(f(0))) - 3f''(0)f'(0)\sin(f(0)) - (f'(0))^3 \cos(f(0)) = 0$$

or

$$f'''(0) \cdot (2) - (0.5)^3 = 0.$$

Hence, $f'''(0) = 0.625$, and we have the four terms of the cubic Taylor polynomial:

$$0 + 0.5x + \frac{0}{2!}x^2 + \frac{0.625}{3!}x^3.$$

Figure 9.12 shows the graph of the third-degree Taylor polynomial represented by these known terms, together with the graph of the actual solution obtained by numerically solving, for each x plotted, $y + \sin(y) = x$ for y. ■

The method we have used to construct this Taylor polynomial was based on matching derivative values. This method can be used in general to find polynomial approximations to solutions of differential equations.

EXAMPLE 14 Find a third-degree polynomial about $x = 0$ that approximates the solution of the differential equation

$$y' = x + \frac{y}{2} \qquad \text{with initial condition} \qquad y(0) = 1.$$

Solution A third-degree polynomial about $x = 0$ has the general form

$$y = c_0 + c_1 x + c_2 x^2 + c_3 x^3,$$

whose derivative is $y' = c_1 + 2c_2 x + 3c_3 x^2$. Substituting y and y' into the given differential equation, we have

$$c_1 + 2c_2 x + 3c_3 x^2 = x + \frac{c_0 + c_1 x + c_2 x^2 + c_3 x^3}{2}.$$

The initial condition $y(0) = 1$ tells us that $c_0 = 1$, and we have

$$c_1 + 2c_2 x + 3c_3 x^2 = \frac{1}{2} + (1 + \frac{c_1}{2})x + \frac{c_2}{2}x^2 + \frac{c_3}{2}x^3.$$

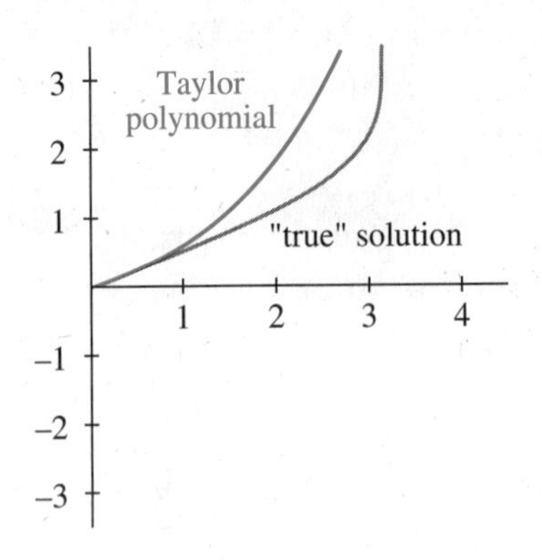

Figure 9.12 A Taylor approximation to the solution of $f(x) + \sin(f(x)) = x$.

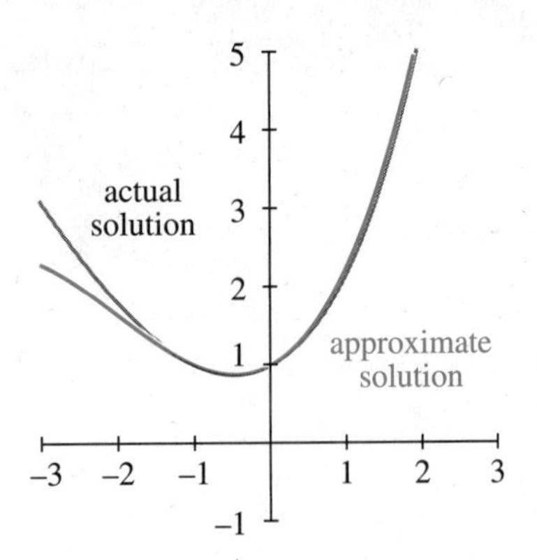

Figure 9.13 Actual and approximate solutions to $y' = x + \frac{y}{2}$ with $y'(0) = 1$.

We can equate coefficients of the two sides of the equation to see that

$$c_1 = \frac{1}{2} \qquad 2c_2 = 1 + \frac{c_1}{2} \qquad 3c_3 = \frac{c_2}{2}$$

or

$$c_1 = \frac{1}{2} \qquad c_2 = \frac{5}{8} \qquad c_3 = \frac{5}{48}.$$

We are unable to match up the coefficient of x^3 on the right-hand side of the equation. That will be the source of the error in our approximation. (If we match up all the coefficients, then our polynomial is an exact solution to the differential equation.) Note that we could extend this analysis to any degree n in a similar way. We have the coefficients we need for a third-degree polynomial approximation

$$y(x) = 1 + \frac{x}{2} + \frac{5x^2}{8} + \frac{5x^3}{48}.$$

Figure 9.13 shows a graph of the actual solution to the differential equation and the graph of our third-degree polynomial approximation. ■

EXERCISES for Section 9.3 Some symbolic algebra systems can compute Taylor polynomials. However, these systems may automatically expand and collect terms in powers of x. This is less than desirable if you wish to have your Taylor polynomial expansion in terms of powers of $(x - a)$ instead.

Here's a way to "fool" your system if it behaves this way. If you desire a Taylor polynomial expansion of the function f about $x = a$, let your system find the Taylor polynomial expansion of $f(t+a)$ about $t=0$. After the system has finished simplifying, just replace every appearance of t with $(x-a)$.

For exercises 1–10: Find the first five Taylor polynomial approximations to each function ($n = 1, 2, 3, 4$, and 5) at the specified point $x = a$. Then plot each polynomial as well as the graph of the original function at the given point.

1. $y = \sin(2x+1)$ $\quad a = -1$
2. $y = \cos(\frac{2\pi}{x^2+1})$ $\quad a = 0$
3. $y = \tan(x)$ $\quad a = \pi/4$
4. $y = \sec(x)$ $\quad a = 0$
5. $y = \csc(-x)$ $\quad a = \pi/2$
6. $y = -\cot(x)$ $\quad a = 3\pi/4$
7. $y = e^{2x+1}$ $\quad a = -1$
8. $y = 2/(x^2+1)$ $\quad a = 0$
9. $y = \sqrt{x^2+1}$ $\quad a = 0$
10. $y = 1/x$ $\quad a = 4$

In Exercises 1–10 above, you saw graphically the convergence of the Taylor polynomial approximations. In general, the higher the degree n for a Taylor polynomial, the better the approximation. Certainly that is true at the point $x = a$. However, at other points, the story may be different.

For exercises 11–20: For each of the functions below, you are given the degrees of two Taylor polynomials at a point $x = a$. Find and graph the two Taylor polynomials. Then find a point $x = b \neq a$ where the Taylor polynomial of *lower* degree gives a better approximation than the Taylor polynomial of higher degree, and another point $x = c \neq a$ where the Taylor polynomial of *higher degree* gives a better approximation than the Taylor polynomial of lower degree.

11. $f(x) = \sin(x-3)\exp(x-3)$, degrees 1 and 2, at $x = 3$
12. $f(x) = \ln(x)$, degrees 3 and 4, at $x = 1$
13. $f(x) = \dfrac{x+1}{x+9}$, degrees 3 and 4, at $x = 0$
14. $f(x) = \sqrt{x}$, degrees 2 and 3, at $x = 1$
15. $f(x) = \dfrac{x^3+x^2+x+1}{x+5}$, degrees 2 and 3, at $x = 1$
16. $f(x) = \arctan(x)$, degrees 1 and 3, at $x = 0$
17. $f(x) = x^2 + \sin(x)$, degrees 2 and 3 at $x = 0$
18. $f(x) = \sqrt{x^2+1}$, degrees 1 and 2, at $x = 1$
19. $f(x) = \dfrac{1}{x}$, degrees 2 and 3, at $x = 5$
20. $f(x) = (x^2+1)e^x$, degrees 2 and 3, at $x = 0$

For exercises 21–26: Find a third-degree (cubic) Taylor polynomial of a function f satisfying the given equation about the given point, $x = a$.

21. $x^2 - f(x) = \ln(f(x)) \qquad a = 1$

22. $f(x)\exp(x + f(x) - 1) = 1 \qquad a = 0$

23. $\sqrt{f(x) + x} + \sqrt{f(x) + x^2} - 2 = 0 \qquad a = 0$

24. $x\cos(f(x)) - f(x) = 0 \qquad a = 0$

25. $\exp(\ln(x)f(x)) = f(x) \qquad a = 1$

26. $f(x)^5 - 3f(x)^3 + 3f(x) - x = 0 \qquad a = 1$

For exercises 27–30: Find a fifth-degree polynomial approximation about $x = 0$ to approximate the solution to the given differential equation with initial condition $y(0) = 0$.

27. $y' = x^2 - (0.1) \cdot (x + y)$

28. $y' = \cos(y)$

29. $y' = 1 - y^2$

30. $y' = x\cos(y/2)$

---

31. Suppose that 2 is a critical value for the function f and that the graph of $y = f(x)$ has a single inflection point at $(2, -7)$. If $f'''(2) = 5$, what is the third-degree Taylor polynomial approximation of $f(x)$ at $a = 2$?

32. Find a function whose degree 2 Taylor polynomial at 0 is everywhere (but at $x = 0$) a better approximation to the function than the degree 1 Taylor polynomial.

33. Find a function whose degree 1 Taylor polynomial at 0 is a better approximation for all *large* x than the degree 2 Taylor polynomial.

34. Suppose that the second-degree Taylor polynomial at $x = a$ of $f(x)$ is

$$c_0 + c_1(x - a) + \frac{c_2}{2}(x - a)^2,$$

and that the second-degree Taylor polynomial at $y = c_0$ of $g(y)$ is

$$q_0 + q_1(y - c_0) + \frac{q_2}{2}(y - c_0)^2.$$

What is the second-degree Taylor polynomial at $x = a$ of $h(x) = g(f(x))$?

35. Explain why the symbolic algebra system strategy discussed at the beginning of the exercises works.

9.4 COMPARING FUNCTIONS GRAPHICALLY

When two continuous functions have a common value

$$f(a) = g(a),$$

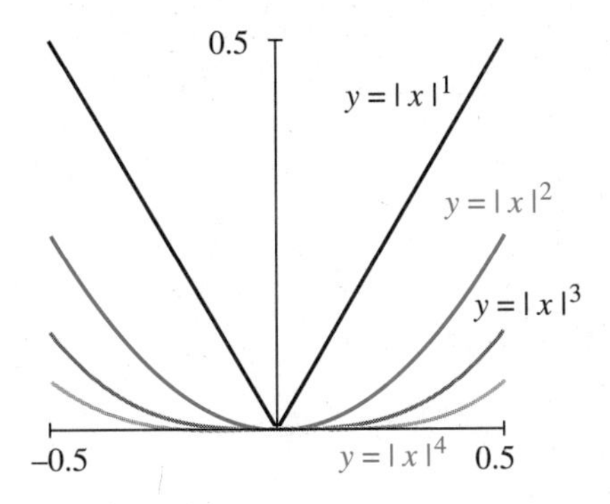

Figure 9.14 Ordering of $|x|^n$ for x near 0.

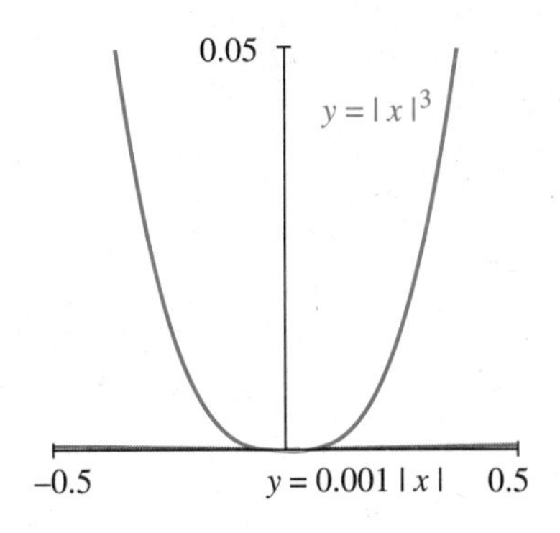

Figure 9.15 Graphs of f and g with a viewing window $[-0.5, 0.5] \times [0, .05]$.

we say that f and g *agree* at $x = a$. Using the language of limits, this means

$$\lim_{x \to a} (f(x) - g(x)) = 0.$$

How *closely* the two functions agree near $x = a$ depends on *how fast* the difference $f(x) - g(x)$ approaches 0 as x approaches a. We can develop a useful graphical "yardstick" for measuring how closely two functions agree near a given point.

The functions

$$|x|^n \quad \text{for } n = 1,\ 2,\ 3,\ \ldots$$

all have limiting value 0 at 0. However, for small, nonzero x,

$$|x| > |x|^2 > |x|^3 > \ldots.$$

This is shown as an ordering of the graphs for x near 0 (see Figure 9.14). This ordering persists near zero even if we multiply various powers of $|x|$ by very different constant factors.

EXAMPLE 15 If $f(x) = 0.001\,|x|$ and $g(x) = |x|^3$, which approaches 0 most quickly as x approaches 0?

Solution Using a graphing calculator or computer, we can graph both functions in a viewing window of $[-0.5, 0.5] \times [0, 0.05]$. It appears that the graph of $f(x) = 0.001\,|x|$ lies below that of $g(x) = |x|^3$ (see Figure 9.15).

If we zoom in to the viewing window $[-0.06, 0.06] \times [0, 0.0006]$, we can see in Figure 9.16 that the order has switched so that the graph of $g(x) = |x|^3$ now lies below that of $f(x) = 0.001\,|x|$. If we continue to zoom in, this ordering persists. We say that $|x|^3$ *goes to zero faster than* $0.001\,|x|$. ■

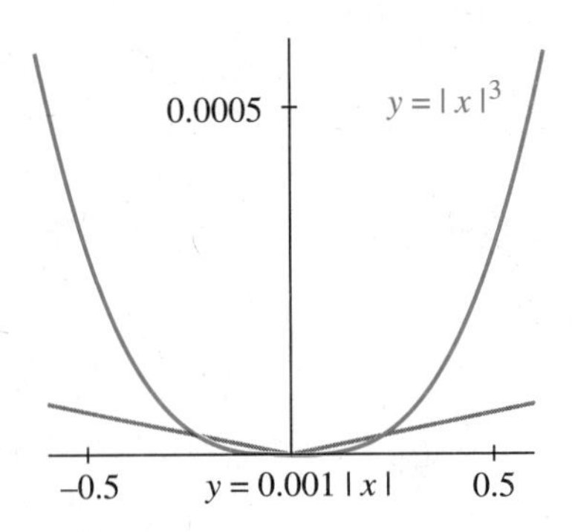

Figure 9.16 Graphs of f and g with a viewing window $[-0.06, 0.06] \times [0, 0.0006]$.

In fact, $|x|^3$ goes to zero faster than $A \cdot |x|^1$ for any $A > 0$.

As x approaches 0, $|x|^n$ approaches 0 faster than $A|x|^m$ for $A > 0$, $m < n$.

Orders of agreement

We can use zooming to measure the closeness of agreement of two functions at a point by examining the "shapes" of the functions' graphs. Suppose that we zoom in by a factor of, say, 10 horizontally and 10^n vertically. For convenience, let's call this a **power zoom** of order n. If we repeatedly power zoom of order n, then the shape of the graph of $y = |x|^n$ will appear *unchanged*, while the graphs of $y = |x|^m$ for $m > n$ will become increasingly "flatter" and those of $y = |x|^m$ for $m < n$ will become increasingly more "pointy."

For example, suppose that we graph $f(x) = |x|^2$, $g(x) = |x|^3$, and $h(x) = |x|^4$ all in the same viewing window $[-0.5, 0.5] \times [-0.25, 0.25]$ and then zoom in by a factor of 10 horizontally and $10^3 = 1000$ vertically. The graph of f becomes more pointy, the graph of h becomes flatter, but the graph of g stays the same (see Figure 9.17.) ■

We can use this behavior to use power zooms to measure how well two functions agree near a particular input $x = a$. We say that two functions f and g **agree to order** 1 **at** 0 if $|f(x) - g(x)|$ goes to zero at 0 at least as fast as $|x|^1$. Similarly, we say that f and g **agree to order** 2 **at** 0 if $|f(x) - g(x)|$ goes to zero at 0 at least as fast as $|x|^2$, and so on. We can determine how well f and g agree at 0 by zooming in on the graph of $|f(x) - g(x)|$ using a factor of 10 horizontally and 10^n vertically. If the graph stays the same, or gets flatter, f and g agree at least to order n.

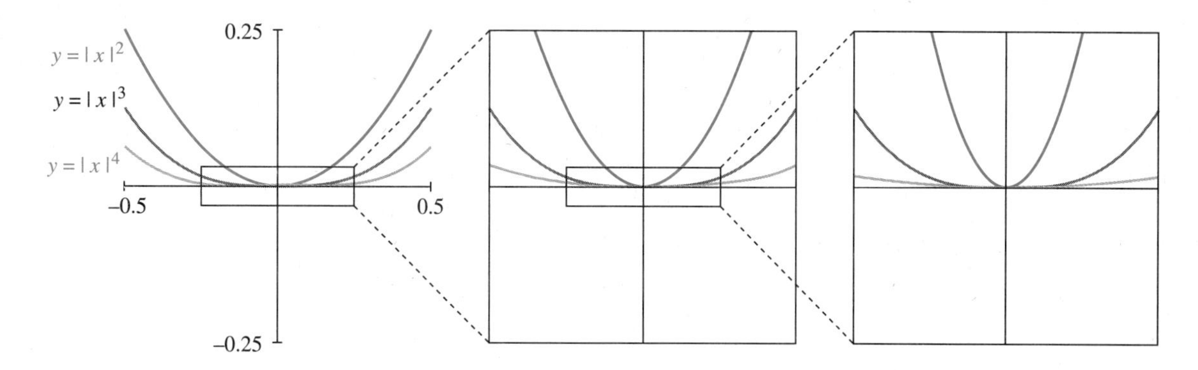

Figure 9.17 Power zooms of order 3.

EXAMPLE 16 Determine graphically how well the functions

$$f(x) = \cos(2x) \quad \text{and} \quad g(x) = 1$$

agree near $x = 0$.

Solution Graphing $|f(x) - g(x)| = |\cos(2x) - 1|$ with a viewing window $[-1, 1] \times [-1, 1]$ suggests a parabola (that is, order 2). To test this, we repeatedly zoom in with a factor of 10 horizontally and $10^2 = 100$ vertically. We see that the graph doesn't change shape at all which suggests that f and g agree to order 2 at $x = 0$ (see Figure 9.18). It is not necessary to compare functions only at $x = 0$. We can zoom in around any point. ■

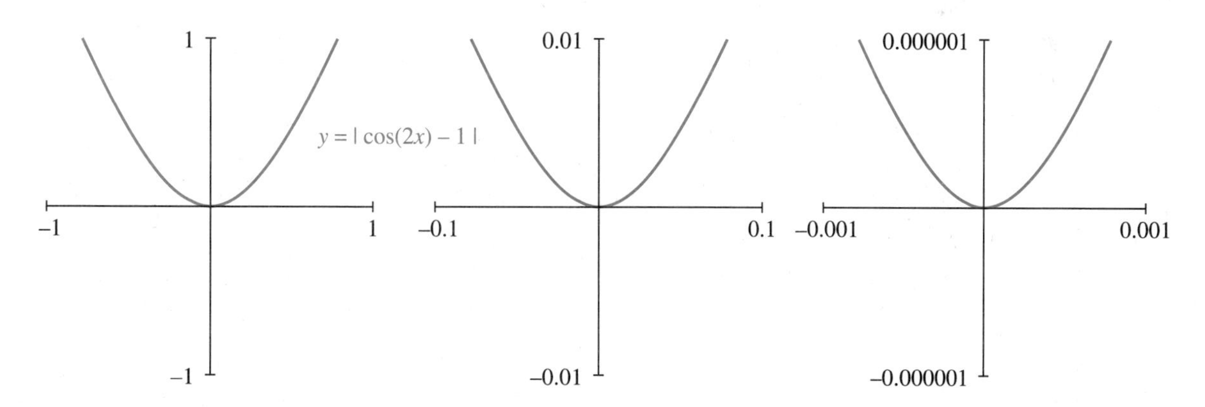

Figure 9.18 Power zoom of order 2 on the graph of $|\cos(2x) - 1|$.

EXAMPLE 17 Determine graphically how well the functions

$$f(x) = \sqrt{(x+1)} \qquad \text{and} \qquad g(x) = \sqrt{2} + \frac{1}{16\sqrt{2}}(10x - x^2 - 9)$$

agree near $x = 1$.

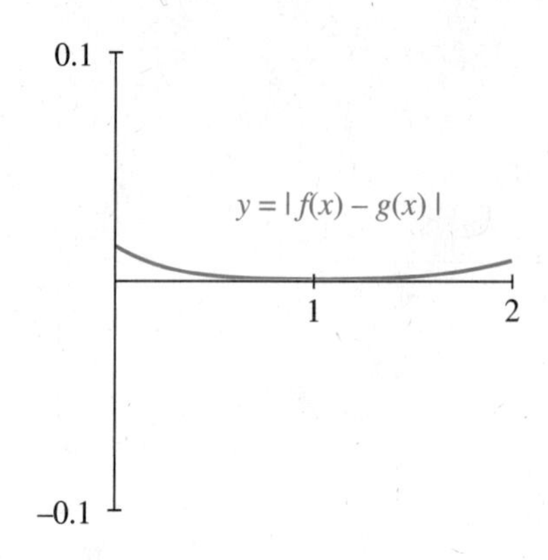

Figure 9.19 Graph of $|f(x) - g(x)|$ in a viewing window $[0, 2] \times [-0.1, 0.1]$

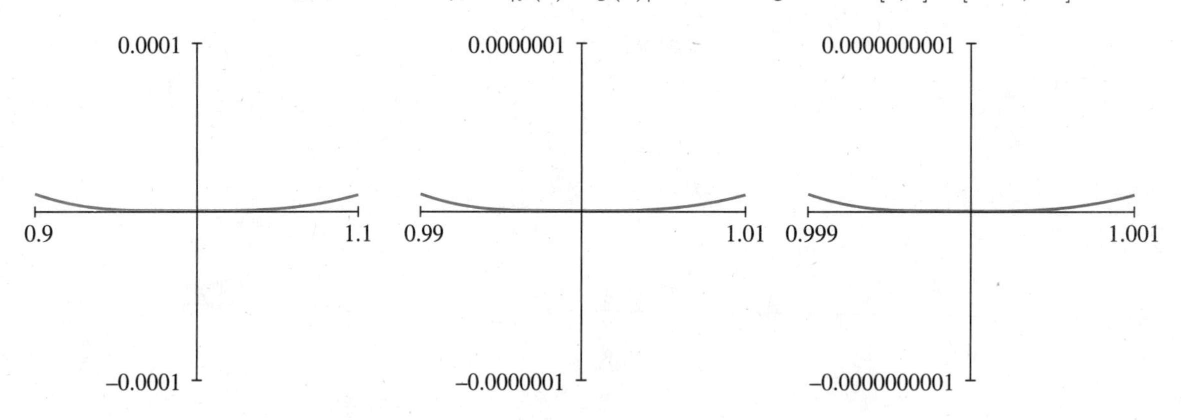

Figure 9.20 Power zoom of order 3 on the graph of $|f(x) - g(x)|$.

Solution Graphing $|f(x) - g(x)|$ in a viewing window $[0, 2] \times [-0.1, 0.1]$ gives the graph shown in Figure 9.19. If we zoom in repeatedly with a factor of 10 horizontally and a factor of $10^2 = 100$ vertically, we find that the graph gets flatter and flatter, suggesting that they agree to more than order 2. Trying a factor of 10 horizontally and a factor of 1000 vertically yields the sequence of graphs shown in Figure 9.20. The fact that the shape doesn't change suggests that f and g agree to order 3 at input $x = 1$. ■

EXERCISES for Section 9.4

For exercises 1–4: Graph the indicated functions with viewing window as given. Then zoom in until it is clear that the higher power lies at or below the lower power. Find the horizontal range at which this is true.

1. $f(x) = |x|^3$ and $g(x) = (0.01)\,|x|^1$; $[-1, 1] \times [-0.2, 0.2]$

2. $f(x) = |x|^3$ and $g(x) = (0.01)\,|x|^2$; $[-1, 1] \times [-1, 1]$

3. $f(x) = |x|^3$ and $g(x) = (100)\,|x|^4$; $[-0.2, 0.2] \times [-1, 1]$

4. $f(x) = |x|^2$ and $g(x) = (300)\,|x|^4$; $[-0.2, 0.2] \times [-1, 1]$

For exercises 5–13: For each pair of functions given, determine which approaches 0 fastest at $x = 0$.

5. $f(x) = |\sin x|$ and $g(x) = |x|^2$

6. $f(x) = |\sin x^2|$ and $g(x) = |x|$

7. $f(x) = |1 - \cos x|$ and $g(x) = |x|$

8. $f(x) = |x - \sin x|$ and $g(x) = |x|^2$

9. $f(x) = \left|\sqrt{x^2 + 4} - 2 - 0.25x^2\right|$ and $g(x) = |x|^2$

10. $f(x) = \left|\sqrt{x^2 + 4} - 2 - 0.25x^2\right|$ and $g(x) = |x|^3$

11. $f(x) = \left|x^2 \sin \dfrac{1}{x}\right|$ and $g(x) = |x|$

12. $f(x) = \left|x^2 \sin \dfrac{1}{x}\right|$ and $g(x) = |x|^2$

13. $f(x) = \left|e^{-1/|x|}\right|$ and $g(x) = |x|^8$

For exercises 14–24: Graphically determine the order of agreement for each pair of functions near the specified input $x = a$.

14. $f(x) = 27\left(\dfrac{x-2}{x+3}\right)$ and $g(x) = -5x^2 + 15x - 18$, $x = 0$

15. $f(x) = \sin(x)$ and $g(x) = x^2$, $x = 0$

16. $f(x) = x^4 - 3x^3 + 2x$ and $g(x) = x^4 - 3.5x^3 + 2x$, $x = 0$

17. $f(x) = (\sqrt{x+1})^3$ and $g(x) = 1 + 3\dfrac{x}{2} + x^4$, $x = 0$

18. $f(x) = |x|^{3/2}$ and $g(x) = 0$, $x = 0$

19. $f(x) = (\sqrt{x+2})^3$ and $g(x) = (\sqrt{x+1} + \sqrt{2} - 1)^3$, $x = 0$

20. $f(x) = (x-1)^2$ and $g(x) = (x-1)^3$, $x = 1$

21. $f(x) = \cos((x-1)^2)$ and $g(x) = 1$, $x = 1$

22. $f(x) = \sin(x^2 + 2x + 1)$ and $g(x) = \sin^2(x+1)$, $x = -1$

23. $f(x) = x^3 - 1$ and $g(x) = (x-1)^3$, $x = 0$

24. $f(x) = \dfrac{\sin(x)}{x}$ (for $x \neq 0$), $f(0) = 1$ and $g(x) = 1$, $\quad x = 0$

For exercises 25–34: For each function, find the Taylor polynomial of the indicated degree at the point $x = a$ specified. Then find the order of agreement between the function and its Taylor polynomial approximation at that point.

25. $f(x) = \sin(x-3)e^{x-3}$, degrees 1 and 2, at $x = 3$

26. $f(x) = \ln(x)$, degrees 3 and 4, at $x = 1$

27. $f(x) = \dfrac{x+1}{x+9}$, degrees 3 and 4, at $x = 0$

28. $f(x) = \sqrt{x}$, degrees 2 and 3, at $x = 1$

29. $f(x) = \dfrac{x^3 + x^2 + x + 1}{x+5}$, degrees 2 and 3, at $x = 1$

30. $f(x) = \arctan(x)$, degrees 1 and 3, at $x = 0$

31. $f(x) = x^2 + \sin(x)$, degrees 2 and 3, at $x = 0$

32. $f(x) = \sqrt{x^2+1}$, degrees 1 and 2, at $x = 1$

33. $f(x) = \dfrac{1}{x}$, degrees 2 and 3, at $x = 5$

34. $f(x) = (x^2+1)e^x$, degrees 2 and 3, at $x = 0$

35. On the basis of these results, what would you conjecture about the order of agreement between a function and its Taylor polynomial approximation at $x = a$?

9.5 L'HÔPITAL'S RULE

In the last section, we discussed using graphical methods to compare two functions. In particular, we saw how zooming in on the graph of

$$|f(x) - g(x)|$$

allows us to measure the order of agreement of f and g at a common value. In this section, we examine how calculus can be used to investigate the limiting behavior of the *ratio* of two functions.

Indeterminate quotients—0/0

One way to compare the behaviors of two functions f and g at a point $x = a$ is to examine the behavior of their quotient $\dfrac{f(x)}{g(x)}$ at that point. Now, if

$$\lim_{x \to a} f(x) = L \qquad \text{and} \qquad \lim_{x \to a} g(x) = M,$$

then we can say

$$\lim_{x \to a} \frac{f(x)}{g(x)} = \frac{L}{M} \qquad \text{(provided } M \neq 0\text{)}.$$

If $\lim_{x \to a} g(x) = 0$ and $\lim_{x \to a} f(x) = L \neq 0$, then we can say that

$$\lim_{x \to a} \frac{f(x)}{g(x)} \qquad \text{does not exist.}$$

We may be able to say a bit more about the behavior of the quotient near $x = a$ depending on the behavior of g and whether the limit of $f(x)$ is positive or negative. We'll use the notations 0^+ and 0^- to indicate quantities approaching 0 through strictly positive or negative values, respectively. With those meanings understood, we can make the following observations:

Determining the Limit Behavior of $\frac{f(x)}{g(x)}$

$\lim_{x \to a} f(x)$	$\lim_{x \to a} g(x)$	$\lim_{x \to a} \frac{f(x)}{g(x)}$
$L > 0$	0^+	$+\infty$
$L < 0$	0^+	$-\infty$
$L > 0$	0^-	$-\infty$
$L < 0$	0^-	$+\infty$
0	$M \neq 0$	0
$L \neq 0$	$M \neq 0$	L/M
0	0	**?**

We need to emphasize that $\lim_{x \to a} \frac{f(x)}{g(x)}$ is undefined in the first four lines of the third column of the table. The symbols $+\infty$ and $-\infty$ simply describe the behavior of the quotient $f(x)/g(x)$ as x approaches a. Each result should make sense to you. For example, in the third line, we say that if the numerator approaches a *positive* value and the *negative* denominator becomes *smaller and smaller in magnitude*, then the quotient will be a *negative* number of *larger and larger magnitude*.

We've left a question mark for the result of the last line of the table, when both $f(x)$ and $g(x)$ approach 0 as x approaches a. Depending on "how fast" the numerator and denominator approach 0, respectively, we could obtain almost any result.

EXAMPLE 18 Find the following limits, if they exist:

$$\lim_{x \to 0} \frac{3x}{2x}, \qquad \lim_{x \to 0} \frac{3x^2}{2x}, \qquad \lim_{x \to 0} \frac{3x}{2x^2}.$$

Solution In all three of these quotients, the values of the expressions in the numerator and denominator both approach 0 as x approaches 0.

In the first quotient, $\dfrac{3x}{2x} = \dfrac{3}{2}$ for every $x \neq 0$, so

$$\lim_{x \to 0} \frac{3x}{2x} = \frac{3}{2}.$$

In the second quotient, $\dfrac{3x^2}{2x} = \dfrac{3x}{2}$ for every $x \neq 0$. Hence,

$$\lim_{x \to 0} \frac{3x^2}{2x} = \lim_{x \to 0} \frac{3x}{2} = 0.$$

In the third quotient, $\dfrac{3x}{2x^2} = \dfrac{3}{2x}$ for every $x \neq 0$. Since

$$\lim_{x \to 0+} \frac{3}{2x} = \infty \quad \text{and} \quad \lim_{x \to 0-} \frac{3}{2x} = -\infty,$$

there is no limiting value and $\lim_{x \to 0} \dfrac{3x}{2x^2}$ *does not exist.* ■

Limits of quotients such as these are said to be of the indeterminate form $0/0$. The expression $0/0$ is not a real number; it is simply shorthand for

$$\lim_{x \to a} \frac{f(x)}{g(x)},$$

when both $f(x)$ and $g(x)$ approach 0 as x approaches a. As you can see, an indeterminate form may have a zero limit, a nonzero limit, or no limit at all. In the example above, we were able to determine the limiting behavior of each quotient by examining an equivalent expression for values $x \neq a$. This is not always possible to do. Recall that we found

$$\lim_{x \to 0} \frac{\sin x}{x} = 1$$

in Chapter 2 by use of the squeezing principle. There is no algebraic or trigonometric simplification allowing us to determine this limit. In fact, whenever we attempt to calculate the derivative of a function at a point

$$f'(a) = \lim_{x \to a} \frac{f(x) - f(a)}{x - a},$$

we are working with the indeterminate form $0/0$. Interestingly, we can turn the tables and use derivatives to help us calculate the limit of an indeterminate form $0/0$.

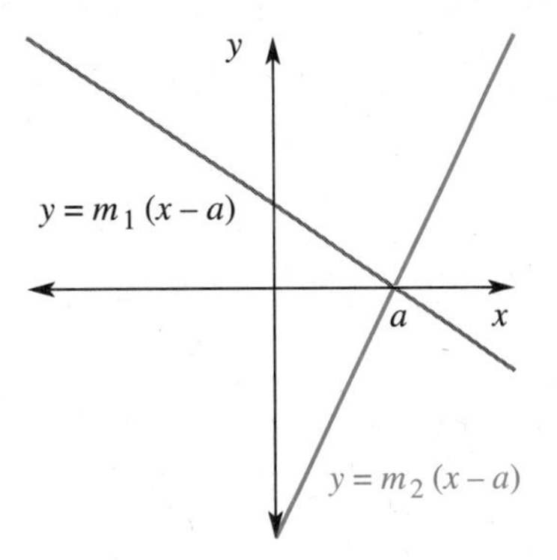

Figure 9.21 Two linear functions with a common x-intercept a.

L'Hôpital's rule

To see how derivatives might help find limits of indeterminate forms, let's first look at a problem involving linear functions. Suppose that we have

$$f(x) = m_1(x - a) \qquad \text{and} \qquad g(x) = m_2(x - a).$$

This means that the graphs of $y = f(x)$ and $y = g(x)$ are straight lines with slopes m_1 and m_2, respectively, and a common x-intercept at $x = a$. Figure 9.21 shows a typical illustration of such a situation.

Now $\lim\limits_{x \to a} \dfrac{f(x)}{g(x)}$ has the indeterminate form $0/0$, but for $x \neq a$,

$$\frac{f(x)}{g(x)} = \frac{m_1(x-a)}{m_2(x-a)} = \frac{m_1}{m_2}.$$

We can conclude that

$$\lim_{x \to a} \frac{f(x)}{g(x)} = \frac{m_1}{m_2}.$$

In other words, the limit of the quotient of the two linear functions at $x = a$ is the *quotient of their slopes.*

Now, imagine that we have two functions f and g that are differentiable, except possibly at $x = a$, and both functions have a common limit 0 at $x = a$:

$$\lim_{x \to a} f(x) = \lim_{x \to a} g(x) = 0.$$

A typical situation is illustrated in Figure 9.22.

Since f and g are differentiable (approximately locally linear), zooming in on the graph could result in a picture very similar to that of the two linear functions. This suggests that when x is sufficiently close to a, the value of $\dfrac{f(x)}{g(x)}$ will be close to $\dfrac{f'(x)}{g'(x)}$, the ratio of the slopes of f and g. This is,

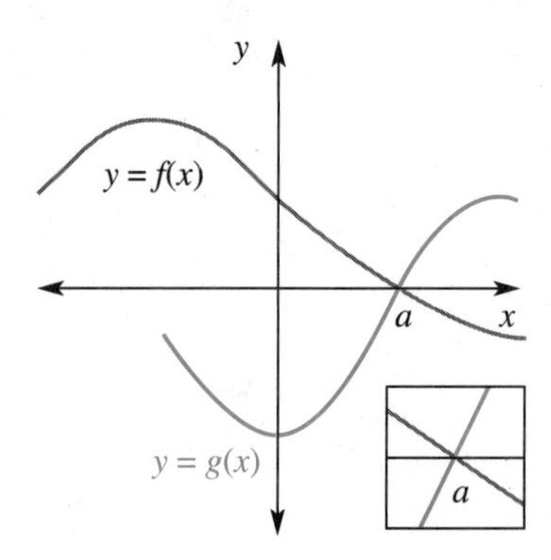

Figure 9.22 Two functions with a common limit $L = 0$ at $x = a$.

indeed, the case, and the result is known as L'Hôpital's rule, named after Guillaume Francois Antoine de L'Hôpital (1661-1704), the author of the first calculus textbook!

Theorem 9.3

L'Hôpital's rule (for the indeterminate form $0/0$)

Hypothesis 1: $\lim_{x \to a} f(x) = 0 = \lim_{x \to a} g(x)$.

Hypothesis 2: $\lim_{x \to a} \dfrac{f'(x)}{g'(x)} = L$.

Conclusion: $\lim_{x \to a} \dfrac{f(x)}{g(x)} = L$.

□

EXAMPLE 19 Find $\lim_{x \to 0} \dfrac{\sin x}{x}$ using L'Hôpital's rule.

Solution

$$\lim_{x \to 0} \frac{\sin x}{x} = \lim_{x \to 0} \frac{\cos x}{1} = 1.$$

(Graphically, when we zoom in on the graph of $y = \sin x$, it becomes indistinguishable from the line $y = x$; both have slope 1 at $x = 0$.) ■

EXAMPLE 20 Find $\lim_{x \to \pi/4} \dfrac{\tan x - 1}{4x - \pi}$.

Solution $\lim_{x \to \pi/4} \dfrac{\tan x - 1}{4x - \pi} = \lim_{x \to \pi/4} \dfrac{\sec^2 x}{4} = \dfrac{2}{4} = \dfrac{1}{2}$. ■

It is possible that $\lim_{x \to a} \dfrac{f'(x)}{g'(x)}$ is also of the indeterminate form $0/0$. (This might be evident graphically because both graphs appear to have a horizontal tangent line $y = 0$ at $x = a$.) In this situation, L'Hôpital's rule can simply be applied a second time, a third time, and so on until the form is no longer indeterminate.

EXAMPLE 21 Find $\lim_{x \to 0} \frac{\sin(x) - x}{\cos(x) - 1}$.

Solution Applying L'Hôpital's rule once, we have

$$\lim_{x \to 0} \frac{\sin(x) - x}{\cos(x) - 1} = \lim_{x \to 0} \frac{\cos(x) - 1}{-\sin(x)}.$$

This last limit is still of the indeterminate form $0/0$, so we apply L'Hôpital's rule once again:

$$\lim_{x \to 0} \frac{\cos(x) - 1}{-\sin(x)} = \lim_{x \to 0} \frac{-\sin(x)}{-\cos(x)} = \frac{0}{-1} = 0.$$

■

▶▶▶ **WARNING! Using L'Hôpital's rule on a limit that is *not* of the indeterminate form $0/0$ can produce an *incorrect result.***

Here's a simple example to illustrate what happens if the limit is not of the indeterminate form $0/0$. With no need to use L'Hôpital's rule, we can compute

$$\lim_{x \to 2} \frac{7x - 5}{5 - x} = \frac{14 - 5}{5 - 2} = \frac{9}{3} = 3,$$

but if we do apply L'Hôpital's rule erroneously, we obtain

$$\lim_{x \to 2} \frac{7}{-1} = -7. \qquad \text{WRONG!}$$

Extensions of L'Hôpital's rule

L'Hôpital's rule also holds for one-sided limits. That is, we can replace $x \to a$ with either $x \to a^+$ or $x \to a^-$ throughout the theorem with the same result. We can also extend L'Hôpital's rule to limits at infinity.

If $\lim_{x \to \infty} f(x) = 0 = \lim_{x \to \infty} g(x)$ and $\lim_{x \to \infty} \frac{f'(x)}{g'(x)} = L$, then

$$\lim_{x \to \infty} \frac{f(x)}{g(x)} = L.$$

Note that we can rewrite these limits in terms of a different variable. If we let $h = 1/x$, then $x = 1/h$ and

$$\lim_{x \to \infty} \frac{f(x)}{g(x)} = \lim_{h \to 0^+} \frac{f(1/h)}{g(1/h)}.$$

We can apply L'Hôpital's rule (with respect to h) to obtain

$$\lim_{h\to 0+}\frac{f(1/h)}{g(1/h)}=\lim_{h\to 0+}\frac{f'(1/h)\cdot(-1/h^2)}{g'(1/h)\cdot(-1/h^2)}=\lim_{h\to 0+}\frac{f'(1/h)}{g'(1/h)}.$$

The last limit is the same as $\lim_{x\to\infty}\frac{f'(x)}{g'(x)}$.

A similar argument can be applied to

$$\lim_{x\to -\infty}\frac{f(x)}{g(x)}=\lim_{h\to 0-}\frac{f(1/h)}{g(1/h)}.$$

If $\lim_{x\to-\infty} f(x)=0=\lim_{x\to-\infty} g(x)$ and $\lim_{x\to-\infty}\frac{f'(x)}{g'(x)}=L$, then

$$\lim_{x\to-\infty}\frac{f(x)}{g(x)}=L.$$

Throughout the rest of this section, any statement we make regarding L'Hôpital's rule for $\lim_{x\to a}$ will also hold for one-sided limits $\lim_{x\to a^+}$ and $\lim_{x\to a^-}$ and the limits at infinity $\lim_{x\to\infty}$ and $\lim_{x\to-\infty}$.

Another indeterminate form that L'Hôpital's rule can be applied to is ∞/∞. The statement of the theorem governing this application follows.

Theorem 9.4

L'Hôpital's rule (for the indeterminate form ∞/∞)

Hypothesis 1: $\lim_{x\to a} f(x)=\infty$ or $-\infty$ and $\lim_{x\to a} g(x)=\infty$ or $-\infty$.

Hypothesis 2: $\lim_{x\to a}\frac{f'(x)}{g'(x)}=L$.

Conclusion: $\lim_{x\to a}\frac{f(x)}{g(x)}=L$.

□

Following is an example to illustrate this version of L'Hôpital's rule in action.

EXAMPLE 22 Find $\lim_{x\to 0+}\frac{\ln(x^2)}{1/x}$.

Solution Note that $\lim_{x\to 0+}\ln(x^2)=\infty$ and $\lim_{x\to 0+}(1/x)=\infty$. Hence, the limit has the indeterminate form ∞/∞. We apply L'Hôpital's rule to find $\lim_{x\to 0+}\frac{\ln(x^2)}{1/x}=\lim_{x\to 0+}\frac{\frac{1}{x^2}\cdot(2x)}{-1/x^2}=\lim_{x\to 0+}-2x=0.$ ■

EXAMPLE 23 Find $\lim_{x\to\infty} \dfrac{e^{-x}}{\ln(1+\frac{1}{x})}$.

Solution This is of the indeterminate form $0/0$, since $e^{-x} = \dfrac{1}{e^x}$ approaches 0 and $\ln(1+\frac{1}{x})$ approaches $\ln 1 = 0$ as x grows larger and larger. Using L'Hôpital's rule repeatedly, we have

$$\lim_{x\to\infty} \frac{e^{-x}}{\ln(1+\frac{1}{x})} = \lim_{x\to\infty} \frac{-e^{-x}}{\frac{1}{1+\frac{1}{x}} \cdot \frac{-1}{x^2}} = \lim_{x\to\infty} \frac{e^{-x}}{\frac{1}{x^2+x}}$$

$$= \lim_{x\to\infty} \frac{x^2+x}{e^x} = \lim_{x\to\infty} \frac{2x+1}{e^x} = \lim_{x\to\infty} \frac{2}{e^x} = 0.$$

■

Note that in the second line of this limit computation, the quotient was rewritten in the indeterminate form ∞/∞.

There are many other indeterminate forms that can pose problems when we attempt to find limits. Fortunately, L'Hôpital's rule can be applied to many of these forms just by rewriting the expression in either of the indeterminate quotient forms $0/0$ or ∞/∞.

Indeterminate difference $\infty - \infty$

Two functions are sometimes compared by examining their difference. In the case of a limit

$$\lim_{x\to a} (f(x) - g(x)),$$

where both $f(x)$ and $g(x)$ approach ∞ or $-\infty$, we can rewrite the expression so that it takes the form $0/0$ or ∞/∞ and then apply L'Hôpital's rule.

EXAMPLE 24 Find $\lim_{x\to\infty} (x - \sqrt{x})$.

Solution We can rewrite this as

$$\lim_{x\to\infty} (x-\sqrt{x}) = \lim_{x\to\infty} \left((x-\sqrt{x}) \cdot \frac{x+\sqrt{x}}{x+\sqrt{x}}\right) = \lim_{x\to\infty} \frac{x^2-x}{x+\sqrt{x}}.$$

Now the limit has the form ∞/∞ and we can apply L'Hôpital's rule:

$$\lim_{x\to\infty} \frac{x^2-x}{x+\sqrt{x}} = \lim_{x\to\infty} \frac{2x-1}{1+\frac{1}{2\sqrt{x}}} = \infty,$$

because the numerator grows without bound and the denominator approaches 1.

■

Indeterminate exponentials 1^∞, 0^0, ∞^0

These exponentials refer to limits of the form

$$\lim_{x\to a} f(x)^{g(x)}.$$

They are indeterminate when any of the following situations is present:

1. $\lim_{x\to a} f(x) = 1$ and $\lim_{x\to a} g(x) = \pm\infty$,
2. $\lim_{x\to a} f(x) = 0 = \lim_{x\to a} g(x)$, or
3. $\lim_{x\to a} f(x) = \pm\infty$ and $\lim_{x\to a} g(x) = 0$.

Here's a technique for handling these exponential forms:

Step 1. Take the natural logarithm ln of the limit expression.

Step 2. Compute this new limit.

Step 3. Take the natural exponential exp of the result.

The natural logarithm and exponential functions are continuous, so

$$\exp(\lim_{x\to a} \ln(f(x))) = \lim_{x\to a} f(x).$$

EXAMPLE 25 Find $\lim_{x\to\infty}\left(1+\frac{1}{x}\right)^x$.

Solution This is of the indeterminate form 1^∞.

Step 1. We first take the natural logarithm of the expression:

$$\lim_{x\to\infty} \ln\left(1+\frac{1}{x}\right)^x = \lim_{x\to\infty} x\ln\left(1+\frac{1}{x}\right).$$

Step 2. We compute this new limit:

$$\lim_{x\to\infty}\frac{\ln(1+1/x)}{1/x} = \lim_{x\to\infty}\frac{\frac{1}{1+1/x}\cdot\frac{-1}{x^2}}{-1/x^2} = \lim_{x\to\infty}\frac{1}{1+1/x} = 1.$$

Step 3. We take the natural exponential to find the original limit value:

$$\lim_{x\to\infty}\left(1+\frac{1}{x}\right)^x = e^1 = e.$$

■

EXAMPLE 26 Find $\lim_{x \to \infty} x^{1/x}$.

Solution This has the indeterminate form ∞^0.

We compute the limit of the natural logarithm of the expression:

$$\lim_{x \to \infty} \ln(x^{\frac{1}{x}}) = \lim_{x \to \infty} \frac{1}{x} \ln(x) = \lim_{x \to \infty} \frac{\ln(x)}{x}.$$

This has the indeterminate form ∞/∞, so we may use L'Hôpital's rule to find

$$\lim_{x \to \infty} \frac{\ln(x)}{x} = \lim_{x \to \infty} \frac{1/x}{1} = \lim_{x \to \infty} \frac{1}{x} = 0.$$

Taking the natural exponential, we have $\lim_{x \to \infty} x^{1/x} = e^0 = 1$. ■

EXAMPLE 27 Find $\lim_{x \to 0+} x^x$.

Solution This has the indeterminate form 0^0. We compute the limit of the natural logarithm of the expression:

$$\lim_{x \to 0+} \ln(x^x) = \lim_{x \to 0+} x \ln x = \lim_{x \to 0+} \frac{\ln x}{1/x} = \lim_{x \to 0+} \frac{1/x}{-1/x^2} = \lim_{x \to 0+} -x = 0.$$

So $\lim_{x \to 0+} x^x = e^0 = 1$. ■

EXERCISES for Section 9.5

For exercises 1–14: You are given a limit having an indeterminate form. For each, identify the form and investigate the limiting behavior by graphing. Then use L'Hôpital's rule to evaluate the limit. (Note: Remember to make sure that you have an appropriate indeterminate form whenever you use L'Hôpital's rule.)

1. $\lim_{x \to \frac{1}{2}} \frac{2x - \sin \pi x}{4x^2 - 1}$

2. $\lim_{x \to \infty} \frac{2e^{3x} + \ln x}{e^{3x} + x^2}$

3. $\lim_{x \to 10} \frac{\ln(x-9)}{x - 10}$

4. $\lim_{x \to \infty} \left(1 + \frac{1}{x}\right)^x$

5. $\lim_{x \to 1^+} (x-1)^{\ln x}$

6. $\lim_{x \to 0} \left(\frac{1}{x} - \frac{1}{\ln(x+1)}\right)$

7. $\lim_{x\to\infty} x^{-\frac{1}{x}}$

8. $\lim_{x\to 0} \frac{2e^x - x^2 - 2x - 2}{x^3}$

9. $\lim_{x\to\infty} \left(\sqrt[5]{x^5 - 3x^4 + 17} - x\right)$

10. $\lim_{x\to\infty} \frac{x + \cos(x)}{x}$

11. $\lim_{x\to 0} \frac{\sin(x) - x}{x - \tan(x)}$

12. $\lim_{x\to 0^+} \frac{e^{-1/x}}{x}$

13. $\lim_{x\to\infty} \left(\sqrt{x + \sqrt{x}} - \sqrt{x}\right)$

14. $\lim_{x\to\infty} \frac{x^{1/x}}{x}$

---

15. Show that for any real number a,

$$e^a = \lim_{x\to\infty} \left(1 + \frac{a}{x}\right)^x.$$

16. Show that for any real number a,

$$e^a = \lim_{x\to 0} (1 + x)^{a/x}.$$

How fast do exponential functions grow?

17. Find $\lim_{x\to\infty} \frac{e^x}{x^{10}}$.

18. Find $\lim_{x\to\infty} \frac{e^x}{x^{100}}$.

19. What is $\lim_{x\to\infty} \frac{e^x}{x^n}$, for any positive integer n?

How slow does a logarithmic function grow?

20. Find $\lim_{x\to\infty} \frac{\ln x}{x^{1/10}}$.

21. Find $\lim_{x\to\infty} \frac{\ln x}{x^{1/100}}$.

22. What is $\lim_{x\to\infty} \frac{\ln x}{x^{1/n}}$, for any positive integer n?

23. What could grow slower that $\ln x$? Find $\lim_{x\to\infty} \frac{\ln(\ln x)}{\ln x}$.

---

24. (The indeterminate product $0 \cdot \infty$). In the case of a limit of the form

$$\lim_{x\to a} f(x) \cdot g(x),$$

where $f(x) \to 0$ and $g(x) \to \infty$ or $-\infty$, the limiting value is unclear. (One factor grows large while the other grows small.) However, we can rewrite this as

$$\lim_{x\to a} \frac{f(x)}{1/g(x)} \qquad \left(\frac{0}{0}\right)$$

or $$\lim_{x \to a} \frac{g(x)}{1/f(x)} \qquad \left(\frac{\infty}{\infty}\right)$$

so that it takes on one of the indeterminate forms for L'Hôpital's rule.

Find $\lim_{x \to \infty} x \tan \frac{1}{x}$.

9.6 CUBIC SPLINES

When data are gathered in the form of ordered pairs of inputs and outputs, a first step in "fitting a curve" to the data is to plot the ordered pairs and connect them with straight line segments (linear interpolation). The result is the graph of a piece-wise linear function. The properties of this approximation are:

1. its graph passes through all the data points, and
2. it is a continuous function.

Now, suppose that we also know the slope at each of the points we plot. Can we fit a *smooth* curve to the data so that it passes through all the points *and* has the right slope at each point?

Piece-wise linear approximations will not meet these criteria. In general, we'll need either to sacrifice having the right slopes for the sake of continuity or to sacrifice continuity to have the right slopes (see Figure 9.23). Our goal, then, is to create a continuous function such that:

1. its graph passes through all the data points,
2. the slopes are correct at each data point, and
3. its first derivative is continuous.

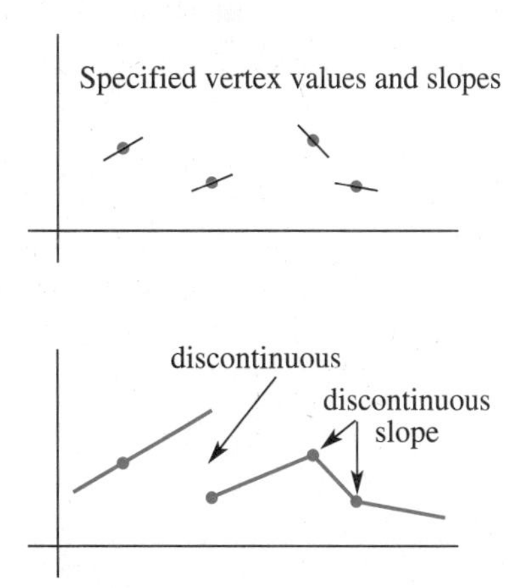

Figure 9.23 Fitting piece-wise linear functions to both slopes and outputs.

The third requirement guarantees that the graph is smooth by disallowing sudden changes in slope (sharp corners).

Given a finite set of data points, we can accomplish this goal by using piece-wise *cubic* rather than linear functions. Such a function is called a **cubic spline**. Cubic splines are used in some computer graphics programs to produce smooth curves through a set of given points. Since polynomials are easy to work with computationally, cubic splines are sometimes used in place of transcendental functions such as trigonometric or exponential functions.

Let's examine how one determines a cubic spline approximation function. If we have a given set of data points (vertices), then between each pair of consecutive inputs x_0 and x_1 our cubic spline function p will have some evaluation formula

$$p(x) = ax^3 + bx^2 + cx + d$$

for the right choices of the parameters a, b, c, and d. Between another pair of vertices, the choices of a, b, c, and d may change.

Now, we assume that we know the outputs y_0 and y_1 as well as the slopes y_0' and y_1' corresponding to the two inputs x_0 and x_1. Our task is to find a cubic function p that matches the outputs

$$y_0 = f(x_0) \qquad \text{and} \qquad y_1 = f(x_1),$$

as well as the first derivative values

$$y_0' = f'(x_0) \qquad \text{and} \qquad y_1' = f'(x_1).$$

How can we determine the parameters a, b, c, and d? Note that we have four separate pieces of information (the two outputs and two slopes) that we can use to solve for these four unknown parameters. Let's look at an example to illustrate.

EXAMPLE 28 Find a cubic function $p(x) = ax^3 + bx^2 + cx + d$ whose values and slopes agree with $f(x) = \sin(x)$ at $x = 0$ and $x = 1$. Compare its graph with that of $f(x) = \sin(x)$ on the interval $[0, 2]$.

Solution First, let's gather our pieces of information:

$$\frac{d\,(\sin(x))}{d\,x} = \cos(x),$$

so for $x_0 = 0$, we have

$$y_0 = \sin(0) = 0 \qquad \text{and} \qquad y_0' = \cos(0) = 1,$$

and for $x_1 = 1$, we have

$$y_1 = \sin(1) \approx 0.84147 \qquad \text{and} \qquad y_1' = \cos(1) \approx 0.54030.$$

Our cubic function f has derivative $f'(x) = 3ax^2 + 2bx + c$, so

$$f(0) = d = y_0 = 0 \qquad \text{and} \qquad f'(0) = c = y_0' = 1,$$

from which we can see that $d = 0$ and $c = 1$.

Now, at $x_1 = 1$, f must satisfy

$$f(1) = a + b + 1 = y_1 \approx 0.84147 \qquad \text{and} \qquad f'(1) = 3a + 2b + 1 \approx 0.54030.$$

We can solve for a and b to obtain $a \approx -0.14264$ and $b \approx -0.0.015889$. With all the parameters determined, we have our cubic spline function

$$p(x) \approx (-0.14264)x^3 - (0.015889)x^2 + x.$$

The graphs of p and $f(x) = \sin(x)$ over the interval $[0, 2]$ are shown in Figure 9.24. Note that the two curves fit quite closely over the whole interval $[0, 1]$, but begin diverging outside this interval. ■

With this example as a guide, we can generalize the method to find a cubic spline approximation over any interval $[x_0, x_1]$ where the outputs y_0 and y_1 and the slopes y_0' and y_1' are known at the endpoints. The two pairs of requirements that must be met are:

Slope requirements:

$$p'(x_0) = 3ax_0^2 + 2bx_0 + c = y_0' \qquad p'(x_1) = 3ax_1^2 + 2bx_1 + c = y_1'$$

Output requirements:

$$p(x_0) = ax_0^3 + bx_0^2 + cx_0 + d = y_0 \qquad p(x_1) = ax_1^3 + bx_1^2 + cx_1 + d = y_1$$

These four equations allow us to solve for the four unknown parameters. When $x_0 \neq 0$, it is convenient to write our cubic polynomial in terms of powers of $x - x_0$ instead of x.

Recipe for a cubic spline
The cubic polynomial that passes through the point (x_0, y_0) with slope y_0' and through the point (x_1, y_1) with slope y_1' is

$$p(x) = a(x - x_0)^3 + b(x - x_0)^2 + c(x - x_0) + d,$$

where $d = y_0$, $c = y_0'$,

$$b = \frac{3(y_1 - y_0)}{(x_1 - x_0)^2} - \frac{2y_0' + y_1'}{x_1 - x_0}, \qquad a = \frac{y_1' + y_0'}{(x_1 - x_0)^2} - \frac{2(y_1 - y_0)}{(x_1 - x_0)^3}.$$

EXAMPLE 29 Find and graph a cubic polynomial function that passes through the point $(x_0, y_0) = (1, 1)$ with slope $y_0' = 1$ and through the point $(x_1, y_1) = (2.5, 1.5)$ with slope $y_1' = 0$.

Solution The cubic polynomial function will have the form

$$p(x) = a(x - 1)^3 + b(x - 1)^2 + c(x - 1) + d,$$

where $d = 1$, $c = 1$,

$$b = \frac{3(1.5 - 1)}{(2.5 - 1)^2} - \frac{2(1) + 0}{2.5 - 1} = -\frac{2}{3}$$

and

$$a = \frac{0 + 1}{(2.5 - 1)^2} - \frac{2(1.5 - 1)}{(2.5 - 1)^3} = \frac{4}{27}.$$

Hence, the cubic polynomial function is

$$p(x) = \frac{4}{27}(x - 1)^3 - \frac{2}{3}(x - 1)^2 + (x - 1) + 1$$

and its graph (between 1 and 2.5) is shown in Figure 9.25. ■

If we have more than two data points (with the corresponding slope at each point), then we can compute a cubic polynomial for each pair of consecutive points and then "glue" or *spline* them together. Since the slope at the right endpoint of one cubic piece matches the slope at the left endpoint of the next cubic piece, the resulting cubic spline function is differentiable and will have a smooth graph.

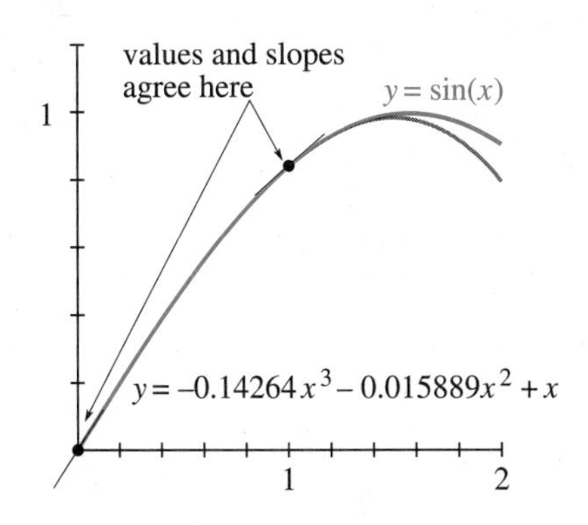

Figure 9.24 Graphs of $y = \sin(x)$ and a cubic spline approximation p.

Figure 9.25 Cubic with slope 1 at $(1, 1)$ and slope 0 at $(2.5, 1.5)$.

EXAMPLE 30 Find and graph the cubic spline that passes through the following points with the indicated slopes:

point $(0, 0)$ with slope 2 | point $(1, 1)$ with slope 1
point $(2.5, 1.5)$ with slope 0 | point $(3, 2)$ with slope -1.

Solution The first cubic polynomial piece must have slope 2 at the point $(0, 0)$ and slope 1 at the point $(1, 1)$. Using $(x_0, y_0) = (0, 0)$, $(x_1, y_1) = (1, 1)$, $y_0' = 2$, and $y_1' = 1$, the formula gives us

$$p(x) = x^3 - 2x^2 + 2x \qquad \text{for } 0 \le x \le 1.$$

In the last example, we computed the cubic polynomial piece having slope 1 at $(1, 1)$ and slope 0 at $(2.5, 1.5)$ to be

$$p(x) = \frac{4}{27}(x-1)^3 - \frac{2}{3}(x-1)^2 + (x-1) + 1 \qquad \text{for } 1 \le x \le 2.5.$$

Finally, we need the cubic polynomial piece having slope 0 at $(2.5, 1.5)$ and slope -1 at $(3, 2)$. Using the formula once more, we find

$$p(x) = -12(x-2.5)^3 + 8(x-2.5)^2 + 1.5 \qquad \text{for } 2.5 \le x \le 3.$$

By graphing all three pieces together, we obtain the graph of the entire cubic spline p over the interval $[0, 3]$ as shown in Figure 9.26.

EXAMPLE 31 Find the cubic spline approximation p to $f(x) = e^{x/2}$ on the interval $[0, 3]$ using the points corresponding to $x = 0$, 1, 2, and 3.

Solution Our approximation will have a split definition with three subintervals: $[0, 1]$, $[1, 2]$, and $[2, 3]$. On each of these subintervals we can use the formula we described above.

On the first subinterval, with $x_0 = 0$ and $x_1 = 1$, we have

$$y_0 = \exp(0), \qquad y_1 = e^{1/2}, \qquad y_0' = \frac{1}{2}e^0 = \frac{1}{2}, \qquad y_1' = \frac{1}{2}e^{1/2},$$

so that over $[0, 1]$

$$p(x) \approx 0.026918x^3 + 0.12180x^2 + 0.5x + 1.$$

On the second subinterval, with $x_0 = 1$ and $x_1 = 2$, we have

$$y_0 = e^{1/2}, \qquad y_1 = e^1 = e, \qquad y_0' = \frac{1}{2}e^{1/2}, \qquad y_1' = \frac{1}{2}e^1 = \frac{e}{2},$$

so that over $[1, 2]$

$$p(x) \approx 0.044380(x-1)^3 + 0.20082(x-1)^2 + 0.82436(x-1) + 1.648721.$$

On the last subinterval, with $x_0 = 2$ and $x_1 = 3$, we have

$$y_0 = e^1 = e, \qquad y_1 = e^{1/2}, \qquad y_0' = \frac{1}{2}e^1 = \frac{e}{2}, \qquad y_1' = \frac{1}{2}e^{3/2},$$

so that over $[2, 3]$

$$p(x) \approx 0.073171(x-2)^3 + 0.33110(x-2)^2 + 1.3591(x-2) + 2.71828.$$

Altogether we can describe the cubic spline function p as

$$p(x) \approx \begin{cases} 0.026918x^3 + 0.12180x^2 + 0.5x + 1 & \text{for } 0 \le x \le 1 \\ 0.044380(x-1)^3 + 0.20082(x-1)^2 + 0.82436(x-1) + 1.648721 & \\ & \text{for } 1 \le x \le 2 \\ 0.073171(x-2)^3 + 0.33110(x-2)^2 + 1.3591(x-2) + 2.71828 & \\ & \text{for } 2 \le x \le 3 \\ \text{undefined otherwise.} & \end{cases}$$

■

Bézier curves

Cubic splines (and geometric extensions of them) play an extremely important role in computer-aided design (CAD systems). In this context, they are called Bézier curves, after Pierre Bézier, whose work for a French automobile manufacturer greatly expanded their use in CAD systems. To understand their use in this context, we'll use a purely geometric construction. Recall that the data which determine a section of a cubic spline include two points and the corresponding slopes. We'll illustrate the Bézier curve technique with a specific example.

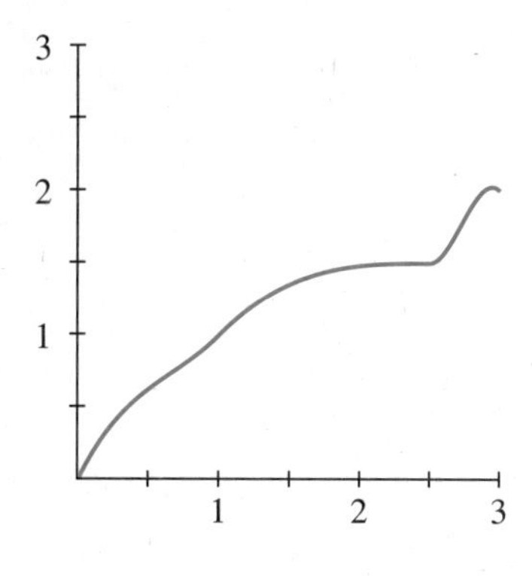

Figure 9.26 A cubic spline.

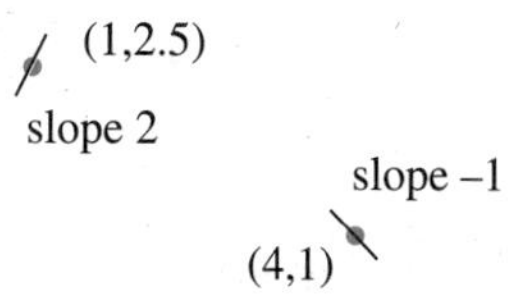

(1,2.5)
slope 2
slope –1
(4,1)

Figure 9.27 Endpoints and slopes to determine a cubic spline.

EXAMPLE 32 Find the cubic spline Bézier curve through the two points $(1, 2.5)$ and $(4, 1)$ with slopes 2 and -1, respectively.

Solution Figure 9.27 illustrates the requirements for our curve. To construct a cubic spline Bézier curve, we need four *control points* with equally spaced x-coordinates. Two of these control points are the given endpoints at $x = 1$ and $x = 4$. The other two must be located at $x = 2$ and $x = 3$.

The y-coordinate of the control point at $x = 2$ is chosen so that the line segment connecting it to the endpoint $(1, 2.5)$ has the desired slope 2. When we solve

$$\frac{y - 2.5}{2 - 1} = 2$$

for y, we find that this point must be $(2, 4.5)$.

Similarly, we choose the y-coordinate of the control point at $x = 3$ so that the line segment between it and the second point $(4, 1)$ has the desired slope -1. When we solve

$$\frac{1 - y}{4 - 3} = -1$$

for y, we find that this point must be $(3, 2)$.

Now that we have our four control points, we can explain the Bézier process:

Procedure for Constructing a Bézier Curve

Step 1. Connect the four consecutive control points with three line segments (see Figure 9.28).

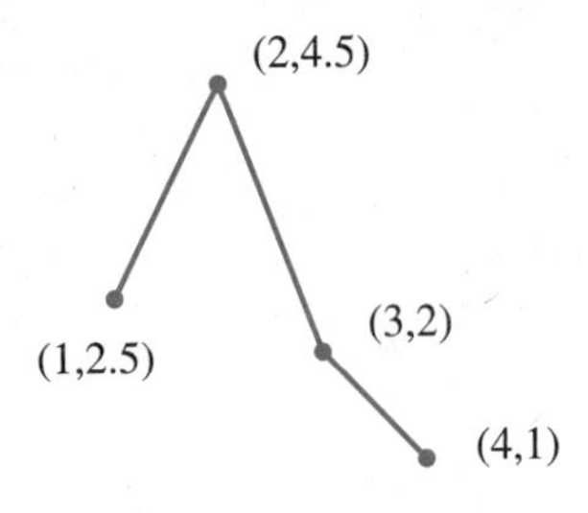

Figure 9.28 Connecting the control points.

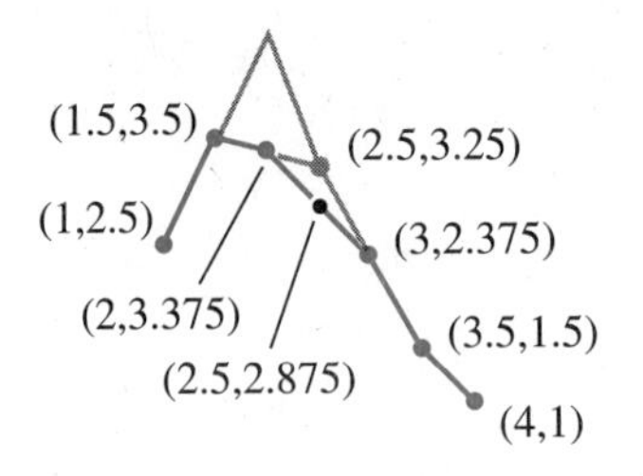

Figure 9.29 The first pass completed.

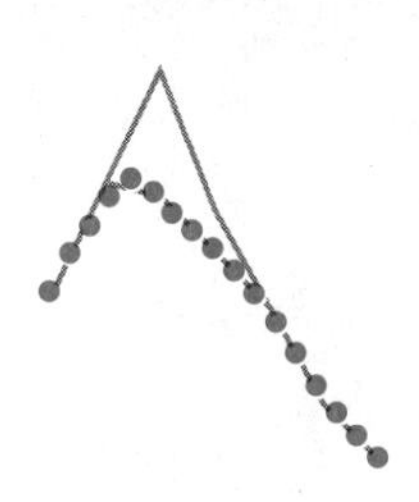

Figure 9.30 Fifteen new points on the cubic spline determined geometrically.

Step 2. Find the midpoints of these three line segments:

$$(1.5, 3.5), \qquad (2.5, 3.25), \qquad \text{and} \qquad (3.5, 1.5).$$

Step 3. Connect *these* points with line segments and find *their* midpoints:

$$(2, 3.375) \qquad \text{and} \qquad (3, 2.375)$$

Step 4. Connect these two points and find the midpoint of this final line segment:

$$(2.5, 2.875).$$

This is a new point on the Bézier curve. (Figure 9.29 illustrates steps 2 through 4.) Now, we have three consecutive line segments connecting $(1, 2.5)$ and $(2.5, 2.875)$ and also three consecutive line segments connecting $(2.5, 2.875)$ and $(4, 1)$. Note that the endpoints of each set of three line segments have equally spaced x-coordinates.

Repeating this procedure (Steps 2 through 4) with these two new sets of control points gives us two new points on the Bézier curve and *four* new sets of control points. Repeating again gives us four new points on the curve and eight new sets of control points. Repeating once more gives us eight new points on the curve and sixteen new sets of control points. We now have a total of 15 new points on the curve as shown in Figure 9.30. ■

Given any four control points to start with, you can still follow the same midpoint procedure and produce a generalized Bézier curve. However, if the points do not have equally spaced x-coordinates, then the curve won't be the graph of a cubic polynomial. In fact, it may not even satisfy the vertical line test for the graph of a function! An example is shown in Figure 9.31.

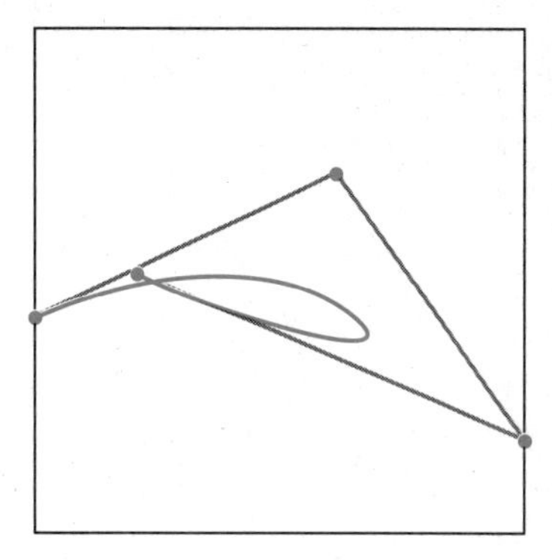

Figure 9.31 A generalized Bézier curve may not satisfy the vertical line test.

EXERCISES for Section 9.6

For exercises 1–14: A typical use for cubic splines and Bézier curves is in industrial design. In fact, they were first used extensively in the design of the body shape of automobiles. The illustration shows a typical automobile profile likely to have been produced with Bézier curves. The x and y coordinates of points, labeled a-r, and slopes at those points have been measured along the hood and roof and are given below.

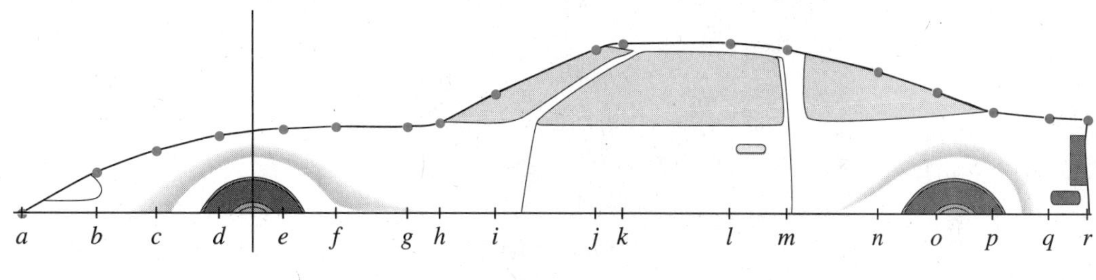

For Exercises 1–14

a	(−16.4, 0.0)	0.6670
b	(−11.04, 2.84)	0.4370
c	(−6.84, 4.32)	0.3370
d	(−2.4, 5.36)	0.1820
e	(2.16, 5.84)	0.0472
f	(5.92, 6.0)	−0.0244
g	(11.0, 6.0)	0.4790
h	(13.32, 6.28)	0.4680
i	(17.28, 8.28)	−0.3250
j	(24.36, 11.36)	0.3020
k	(26.24, 11.76)	0.0122
l	(33.96, 11.8)	−0.0805
m	(38.12, 11.4)	−0.1580
n	(44.68, 9.88)	−0.2810
o	(48.92, 8.48)	−0.3420

p	(52.92, 7.08)	−0.2790
q	(56.92, 6.68)	−0.0734
r	(59.68, 6.56)	−0.0524

1. Graph the cubic splines determined by the points a,b; b,c; c,d; and d,e.

2. Graph the cubic splines determined by the points e,f; f,g; g,h; and h,i.

3. Graph the cubic splines determined by the points i,j; j,k; k,l; and l,m.

4. Graph the cubic splines determined by the points m,n; n,o; o,p; p,q; and q,r.

5. Can any of the points b, c, or d be omitted without altering the Bézier curve?

6. Can any of the points f, g, or h be omitted without altering the Bézier curve?

7. Can any of the points j, k, or l be omitted without altering the Bézier curve?

8. Can any of the points n, o, p, or q be omitted without altering the Bézier curve?

9. Is there any evidence that control points other than those determined by equally spaced x-coordinates were used in the part of the curve from point a to point e?

10. Is there any evidence that control points other than those determined by equally spaced x-coordinates rule were used in the part of the curve from point e to point i?

11. Is there any evidence that control points other than those determined by equally spaced x-coordinates were used in the part of the curve from point i to point m?

12. Is there any evidence that control points other than those determined by equally spaced x-coordinates were used in the part of the curve from point m to point r?

13. Could you add an "air scoop" (bump on the hood) by changing only the slopes of two points? If so, give an example. If not, explain why not.

14. Could you change the curve between two points (still using splines) without altering the Bézier curve outside this region? If so, give an example. If not, explain why not.

---

15. What does it mean algebraically if I can omit a determining point on a cubic spline? That is, if I draw a cubic spline from point (x_0, y_0) to point (x_1, y_1) and then from point (x_1, y_1) to point (x_2, y_2), and I end up with the same curve as if I had drawn it directly from point (x_0, y_0) to point (x_2, y_2), what does that result say about the second and higher derivatives of the curve at point (x_1, y_1)?

16. Find an algebraic method for determining whether a determining point can be omitted from a cubic spline.

For exercises 17–22: Use the geometric method to construct 15 new points on the cubic spline Bézier curve determined by the given coordinate pairs and slopes.

17. $(-2, 2)$ slope -5.5; $(1, 0)$ slope 3.

18. $(1, 8.2)$ slope 5; $(5, 0)$ slope -2.

19. $(-4, -1)$ slope 1; $(3, -1)$ slope 1.

20. $(2.75, 2.75)$ slope 0; $(7, 11)$ slope 0.

21. $(2, 2)$ slope 2; $(5, 0)$ slope 2.

22. $(-1, 1)$ slope 3; $(1, 1)$ slope 3.

---

23. Given two points (x_0, y_0) and (x_1, y_1) and the corresponding slopes m_0 and m_1, find a formula for (x, y), the first new point on the corresponding cubic spline Bézier curve as determined by the geometric method.

24. The graph of the upper half of the unit circle can be obtained by graphing $y = \sqrt{1 - x^2}$ on the interval $[-1, 1]$. Using this and the illustration shown, find the cubic spline approximation to the unit circle on the intervals $[-\frac{\sqrt{2}}{2}, 0]$ and $[0, \frac{\sqrt{2}}{2}]$. Graph your cubic spline over the interval $[-1, 1]$.

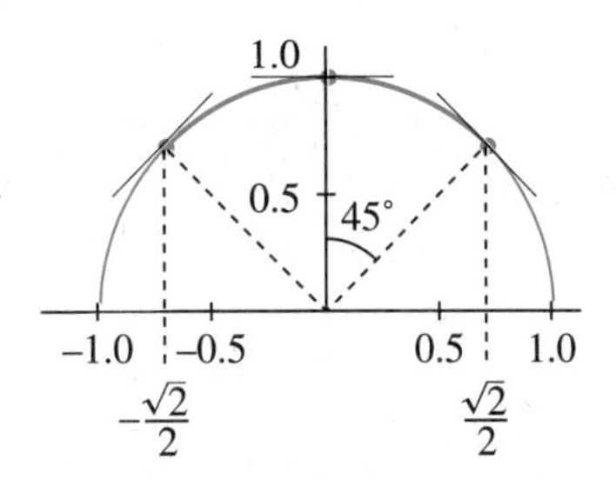

For Exercise 24

25. Graph both $y = e^{x/2}$ and $y = p(x)$ over the interval $[0, 3]$, where

$$p(x) \approx \begin{cases} 0.026918x^3 + 0.12180x^2 + 0.5x + 1 & \text{for } 0 \le x \le 1 \\ 0.044380(x-1)^3 + 0.20082(x-1)^2 + 0.82436(x-1) + 1.648721 & \text{for } 1 \le x \le 2 \\ 0.073171(x-2)^3 + 0.33110(x-2)^2 + 1.3591(x-2) + 2.71828 & \text{for } 2 \le x \le 3 \\ \text{undefined otherwise.} \end{cases}$$

(Note: This is the cubic spline approximation we developed for $e^{x/2}$ over this interval.)

For exercises 26–32: You are given a function, f, and points x_0 and x_1. In each exercise, compute and graph both the cubic spline approximation to f with vertices x_0 and x_1, and the second-order Taylor polynomial approximation to f at x_0. Compare these with f (i.e., graph the error) and find a point, $x_0 < c < x_1$, where the cubic spline is a better approximation and a point, $x_0 < c < x_1$, where the Taylor polynomial is a better approximation. If one or the other of these points doesn't exist, state that fact.

26. $f(x) = \sin(x) \qquad x_0 = 0,\ x_1 = \pi/2$

27. $f(x) = \sqrt{x+1} - \sqrt{x} - 1 \qquad x_0 = 2,\ x_1 = 5.5$

28. $f(x) = \dfrac{1}{x^2+1} \qquad x_0 = 0,\ x_1 = 2$

29. $f(x) = x^4 \qquad x_0 = 0,\ x_1 = 1$

30. $f(x) = 1 - \cos(x) \qquad x_0 = 0,\ x_1 = 2\pi$

31. $f(x) = \tan(x) \qquad x_0 = 0,\ x_1 = \pi/4$

32.

$$f(x) = \begin{cases} x & \text{for } x \le 1 \\ 2 - x & \text{otherwise} \end{cases} \qquad x_0 = 0,\ x_1 = 2$$

---

33. You are given the task of building a ramp for a special motorcycle stunt. The driver gives you these specifications. The initial incline of the ramp is to be $5°$. The ramp should gradually increase slope over a horizontal distance of 100 feet, until the other end of the ramp is at an incline of $45°$ and a height of 30 feet. Of course, the ramp should be *smooth*. You decide to model the ramp as a cubic spline, with one end at the origin and the other end at $(100, 30)$. What is the equation of the ramp?

10

Infinite Processes— Sequences and Series

Approximations and infinite processes are two of the distinguishing features of calculus, and in many ways the ideas of approximation and infinite processes go hand in hand.

The idea of an infinite process is a recurring central theme in calculus. The derivative can be thought of as the limiting value of an infinite sequence of secant line slopes. The definite integral is the limiting value of an infinite sequence of Riemann sums. In this chapter, we study infinite processes and sequences in more detail.

With any sequence of real numbers is associated a *series*, which can be thought of as the "sum" of all the terms in the sequence. Note that a decimal number can be thought of as a series. For example,

$$\frac{1}{3} = 0.3 + 0.03 + 0.003 + 0.0003 + \cdots$$

Sequences can often be described iteratively. You have seen two examples of iterative processes already: the bisection method (Chapter 2) and Newton's method (Chapter 4) for approximating roots of functions.

A polynomial is a sum of terms that are multiples of powers of x. Just as a series can be thought of as the "sum" of infinitely many real numbers, a *power series* can be thought of as a "polynomial" with infinitely many terms. You will see that power series can be used to define functions. The limit of the infinite sequence of Taylor polynomial approximations is called a *Taylor series*.

10.1 SEQUENCES

To get some feel for the ideas involved in sequences and series, let's look at a familiar example. Suppose that you want to express the fraction $22/7$ as a

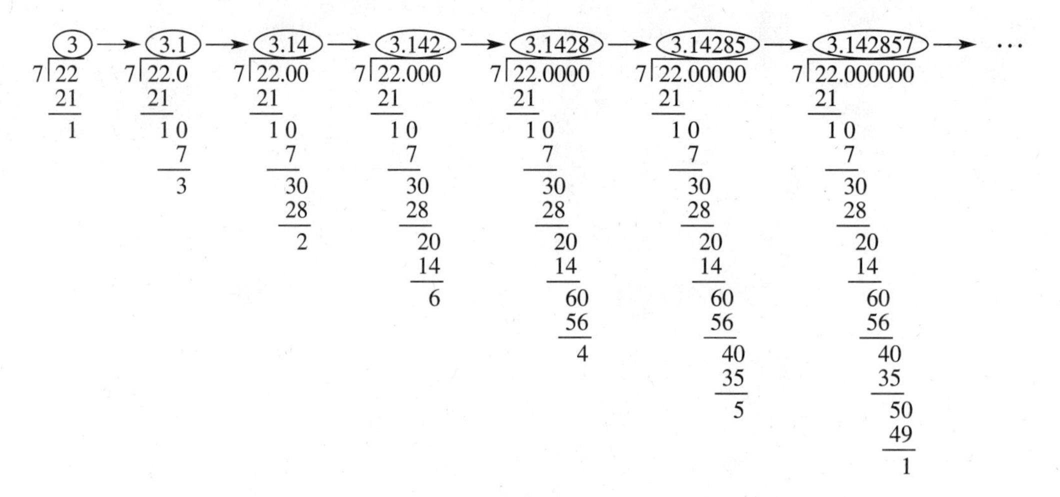

Figure 10.1 Long division as an infinite process.

decimal. As we perform the long division of 22 by 7 as shown in Figure 10.1, we get a sequence of partial results

$$a_1 = 3,\ a_2 = 3.1,\ a_3 = 3.14,\ a_4 = 3.142,\ a_5 = 3.1428, \ldots.$$

Since $22/7$ is reduced to lowest terms and its denominator 7 is not a factor of any power of 10, we know that this long division process will never end. We say that the decimal representation of $22/7$ does not terminate. We can think of the partial results as forming an infinite sequence of decimal approximations, each one closer to the exact value $22/7$.

When you first encountered such a long division problem years ago, the realization that the process would never end may have troubled you, since it means that it is impossible to write down the "complete" decimal expansion of $22/7$. Nevertheless, this infinite sequence of results somehow does have a definite "end," in the sense that it represents $22/7$. We could say that the real number $22/7$ is the *limit* of the sequence. Similarly, the real number $\sqrt{2}$ is the limit of the sequence

$$b_1 = 1,\ b_2 = 1.4,\ b_3 = 1.41,\ b_4 = 1.414,\ b_5 = 1.4142, \ldots.$$

You can generally think of a *sequence* as an *infinitely long list* of numbers (or any other objects, for that matter). We call the individual numbers in a sequence the **terms**, and we identify them by their position in the list. For example, in the sequence

$$a_1 = 3,\ a_2 = 3.1,\ a_3 = 3.14,\ a_4 = 3.142,\ a_5 = 3.1428,\ \ldots,$$

we call a_1 the first term, a_2 the second term, a_3 the third term, and so on. In general, a_n is called the nth term of the sequence. The subscript n used to label the terms of the sequence is sometimes called the **index**.

Technically speaking, a sequence of real numbers can be considered a function from the set of positive integers $\mathbb{N} = \{1, 2, 3, \ldots\}$ to the set of real numbers $\mathbb{R}$. In other words, the numbers in the list

$$a_1, a_2, a_3, \ldots, a_n, \ldots$$

can be viewed as the outputs

$$f(1), f(2), f(3), \ldots, f(n), \ldots$$

of a function $$f : \mathbb{N} \to \mathbb{R}.$$

The notation for a sequence is $\{a_n\}_{n=1}^{\infty}$.

Examples of sequences

The **harmonic sequence** consists of the reciprocals of the positive integers in order:

$$1, \frac{1}{2}, \frac{1}{3}, \frac{1}{4}, \ldots, \frac{1}{n}, \ldots.$$

The positive integers themselves form a sequence: $1, 2, 3, 4, \ldots$.

The values appearing as terms in a sequence need not all be distinct. The sequence

$$0, 1, 2, 0, 1, 2, 0, 1, 2, \ldots$$

has infinitely many terms (as does any sequence), but only three distinct values. It's quite possible to have a **constant sequence** such as

$$-\frac{5}{7}, -\frac{5}{7}, -\frac{5}{7}, -\frac{5}{7}, \ldots,$$

with only one value appearing.

If the signs of the terms in a sequence alternate between positive and negative, we call it an **alternating sequence**. The **alternating harmonic sequence** is

$$1, -\frac{1}{2}, \frac{1}{3}, -\frac{1}{4}, \frac{1}{5}, -\frac{1}{6}, \ldots$$

Describing sequences

As we mentioned above, a sequence of real numbers can be thought of as a function assigning a real number a_n to each positive integer index n. Certainly, it's impossible to write down all the terms in a sequence. However, we could say that we "know " a sequence if we have some means by which we can generate the value of any term in the sequence.

The most convenient way this could be accomplished is if we have a *formula*

$$a_n = f(n)$$

providing the value a_n in terms of n. In this case, we can write

$$\{f(n)\}_{n=1}^{\infty}.$$

EXAMPLE 1 Find a formula describing the harmonic sequence

$$1, \frac{1}{2}, \frac{1}{3}, \frac{1}{4}, \ldots.$$

Solution If we use a_1 to represent the first term, we can note that

$$a_1 = 1, \; a_2 = \frac{1}{2}, \; a_3 = \frac{1}{3}, \; a_4 = \frac{1}{4}, \; \ldots.$$

In general, $a_n = f(n) = \frac{1}{n}$, so we can write the harmonic sequence

$$\{\frac{1}{n}\}_{n=1}^{\infty}.$$

■

EXAMPLE 2 Find a formula describing the alternating harmonic sequence

$$1, -\frac{1}{2}, \frac{1}{3}, -\frac{1}{4}, \frac{1}{5}, -\frac{1}{6}, \ldots.$$

Solution Note that $a_1, a_3, a_5, \ldots$ are all positive and $a_2, a_4, a_6, \ldots$ are all negative. We need some means of describing these alternating signs. The factor $(-1)^{n+1}$ works well for this purpose. When n is odd ($n = 1, 3, 5, 7, \ldots$), then $n+1$ is even and $(-1)^{n+1} = 1$. When n is even ($n = 2, 4, 6, 8, \ldots$), then $n+1$ is odd and $(-1)^{n+1} = -1$. In general, $a_n = f(n) = \frac{(-1)^{n+1}}{n}$, and we can write the alternating harmonic sequence as

$$\{\frac{(-1)^{n+1}}{n}\}_{n=1}^{\infty}.$$

■

EXAMPLE 3 Find a formula describing the constant sequence

$$-\frac{5}{7},\ -\frac{5}{7},\ -\frac{5}{7},\ \ldots.$$

Solution Every term $a_n = -5/7$, so we can simply write

$$\left\{-\frac{5}{7}\right\}_{n=1}^{\infty}.$$

■

Occasionally, it is convenient to have the index n start out with a value other than $n = 1$. In particular, $n = 0$ is often a starting index value for a sequence. For example, the sequence of powers of two

$$1,\ 2,\ 4,\ 8,\ 16,\ 32,\ \ldots,$$

can be written as

$$\{2^n\}_{n=0}^{\infty},$$

since $2^0 = 1$, $2^1 = 2$, $2^2 = 4$, and so on.

If you are trying to find a closed-form formula for a sequence, you certainly should check that the formula generates the correct values for some specific index values n.

▶▶▶ **We should be careful to distinguish between a sequence and an infinite set. A sequence has a definite ordering of its terms, while a set is simply a collection of objects with no particular ordering.**

Arithmetic sequences

One important type of sequence is an **arithmetic sequence**. An arithmetic sequence is distinguished by the fact that the *difference of any two consecutive terms is constant.* In other words, given any term, we obtain the next term by adding a specific constant. The following are examples of arithmetic sequences:

$$1,\ 2,\ 3,\ 4,\ 5,\ \ldots \qquad \text{(constant difference } = 1)$$

$$1,\ 3,\ 5,\ 7,\ 9,\ \ldots \qquad \text{(constant difference } = 2)$$

$$-17,\ -22,\ -27,\ -32,\ \ldots \qquad \text{(constant difference } = -5).$$

An arithmetic sequence can be spotted by examining the difference between consecutive terms to see if it is constant. We can find a formula describing any arithmetic sequence, provided that we know the value of the initial term and the constant difference. It is convenient to start with the index $n = 0$ so that a_0 is the initial term. If d is the constant difference, then a formula for the arithmetic sequence is

$$\{a_0 + dn\}_{n=0}^{\infty}.$$

The formula $a_0 + dn$ generates

$$a_0, \; a_0 + d, \; a_0 + 2d, \; a_0 + 3d, \; \ldots$$

for $n = 0, 1, 2, 3, \ldots$.

EXAMPLE 4 Find formulas for each of the arithmetic sequences described above.

Solution For the first sequence $1, 2, 3, \ldots$, we have $a_0 = 1$ and $d = 1$, so we can write

$$\{1 + n\}_{n=0}^{\infty}.$$

For the second sequence $1, 3, 5, 7, 9, \ldots$, we have $a_0 = 1$ and $d = 2$, so we can write

$$\{1 + 2n\}_{n=0}^{\infty}.$$

For the third sequence $-17, -22, -27, -32, \ldots$, we have $a_0 = -17$ and $d = -5$, so we can write

$$\{-17 - 5n\}_{n=0}^{\infty}.$$

■

Geometric sequences

A **geometric sequence** is distinguished by the fact that the *ratio of any two consecutive terms is constant.* In other words, given any term, we obtain the next term by multiplying by a specific constant. The following are examples of geometric sequences:

$$1, 2, 4, 8, 16, \ldots \qquad \text{(constant ratio} = 2)$$

$$3, \frac{3}{2}, \frac{3}{4}, \frac{3}{8}, \frac{3}{16}, \ldots \qquad \text{(constant ratio} = \frac{1}{2})$$

$$-7, \frac{7}{3}, -\frac{7}{9}, \frac{7}{27}, -\frac{7}{81}, \ldots \qquad \text{(constant ratio} = -\frac{1}{3}).$$

A geometric sequence can be spotted by examining the ratio of consecutive terms to see if it is constant. We can find a formula for any geometric sequence provided that we know the value of the initial term and the constant ratio. Again, it is convenient to start with the index $n = 0$ so that a_0 is the initial term. If r is the constant ratio, we can write the geometric sequence as

$$\{a_0 r^n\}_{n=0}^{\infty}.$$

The formula $a_0 r^n$ generates

$$a_0,\ a_0 r,\ a_0 r^2,\ a_0 r^3,\ \ldots$$

for $n = 0,\ 1,\ 2,\ 3,\ \ldots$.

EXAMPLE 5 Find formulas for each of the geometric sequences described above.

Solution For the first sequence $1,\ 2,\ 4,\ 8,\ 16,\ \ldots$, we have $a_0 = 1$ and $r = 2$, so we can write

$$\{2^n\}_{n=0}^{\infty}.$$

For the second sequence $3,\ \frac{3}{2},\ \frac{3}{4},\ \frac{3}{8},\ \frac{3}{16},\ \ldots$ we have $a_0 = 3$ and $r = \frac{1}{2}$, so we can write

$$\left\{\frac{3}{2^n}\right\}_{n=0}^{\infty}.$$

For the third sequence $-7,\ \frac{7}{3},\ -\frac{7}{9},\ \frac{7}{27},\ -\frac{7}{81},\ \ldots$ we have $a_0 = -7$ and $r = -\frac{1}{3}$, so we can write

$$\left\{\frac{-7}{(-3)^n}\right\}_{n=0}^{\infty}.$$

■

EXAMPLE 6 Is the harmonic sequence arithmetic, geometric, or neither?

Solution The harmonic sequence is

$$1,\ \frac{1}{2},\ \frac{1}{3},\ \frac{1}{4},\ \frac{1}{5},\ \ldots.$$

To check whether this is an arithmetic sequence, we note that $1/2 - 1 = -1/2$, but $1/3 - 1/2 = -1/6$, so the difference between consecutive terms is not constant, and the sequence cannot be arithmetic.

To check whether this is a geometric sequence, we note that $\frac{1/2}{1} = 1/2$, but $\frac{1/3}{1/2} = 2/3$, so the ratio of consecutive terms is not constant, and the sequence cannot be geometric.

We conclude that the harmonic sequence is neither arithmetic nor geometric. ■

Convergence and divergence of sequences

A sequence of real numbers $\{a_n\}_{n=1}^{\infty}$ is said to *converge* if the terms in the sequence eventually "stabilize" toward some single limiting value. Otherwise, we say the sequence *diverges*. Two questions we'll explore are:

1. How can you tell whether a sequence converges or diverges?
2. If a sequence converges, how can you determine the limiting value?

The following formal definition states more precisely what we mean by convergence and divergence of a sequence.

Definition 1

A sequence $\{a_n\}_{n=1}^{\infty}$ **converges to a limit** L, provided that for any given tolerance $\epsilon > 0$, there is a specific index N for which

$$L - \epsilon < a_n < L + \epsilon$$

whenever $n \geq N$. In this case, we write

$$\lim_{n \to \infty} a_n = L.$$

If a sequence does not converge, we say it **diverges**.

You can think of N as the position at which the "tail" of the sequence has only terms that are within ϵ of L (see Figure 10.2). No matter how small a positive tolerance ϵ we are given, we must be able to find a tail of the sequence with all the terms within that tolerance of L. Since we use decimal numbers so often to represent real numbers, you may find it convenient to think of the tolerance ϵ in terms of *decimal places of agreement*: given any number of decimal places, there must be a term in the sequence after

$$a_1, a_2, a_3, \ldots, \underbrace{a_N, a_{N+1}, a_{N+2}, \ldots}$$

All of these terms are within ε of the limit L.

Figure 10.2 The tail of a sequence.

which all the terms are indistinguishable from the limit when rounded to that number of decimal places.

For example, consider the sequence

$$\{a_n\}_{n=1}^{\infty} = \{(1+\frac{1}{n})^n\}_{n=1}^{\infty}.$$

Let's examine the first few terms of this sequence:

$$a_1 = (1+1)^1 = 2$$

$$a_2 = (1+\frac{1}{2})^2 = 2.25$$

$$a_3 = (1+\frac{1}{3})^3 \approx 2.37037037037$$

$$a_4 = (1+\frac{1}{4})^4 = 2.44140625000$$

$$a_5 = (1+\frac{1}{5})^5 = 2.48832000000.$$

Now, let's move further down the sequence and examine a few more terms:

$$a_{10} = (1.1)^{10} \approx 2.59374246010$$

$$a_{100} = (1.01)^{100} \approx 2.70481382942$$

$$a_{1000} = (1.001)^{1000} \approx 2.71692393224$$

$$a_{10000} = (1.0001)^{10000} \approx 2.71814592683$$

$$a_{100000} = (1.00001)^{100000} \approx 2.71826823717$$

$$a_{1000000} = (1.000001)^{1000000} \approx 2.71828046932$$

$$a_{10000000} = (1.0000001)^{10000000} \approx 2.71828169254$$

$$\vdots$$

Note how the terms in the sequence appear to be stabilizing. Indeed, as n increases by a power of 10, all the subsequent terms agree to another decimal place. That is, all the terms following a_{100} agree to the first decimal place, all the terms following a_{1000} agree to two decimal places, and so on. This behavior suggests that the sequence converges to a single limiting value. In fact, it is known that

$$\lim_{n\to\infty}(1+\frac{1}{n})^n = e \approx 2.71828182846.$$

The index $n = N$ required to guarantee that all subsequent terms agree to a given number of decimal places gives us a measure of the *speed of convergence*. If we need only a relatively small increase in the index value N to guarantee more decimal places of agreement among the subsequent terms $a_N, a_{N+1}, \ldots,$ then our sequence converges quickly. If a relatively large increase in index value N is required to guarantee another decimal place of agreement, then our sequence converges slowly.

Here's another sequence that converges to e:

$$b_1 = 1$$

$$b_2 = 1 + \frac{1}{1} = 2$$

$$b_3 = 1 + \frac{1}{1} + \frac{1}{1 \cdot 2} = 2.5$$

$$b_4 = 1 + \frac{1}{1} + \frac{1}{1 \cdot 2} + \frac{1}{1 \cdot 2 \cdot 3} \approx 2.66666666667$$

$$b_5 = 1 + \frac{1}{1} + \frac{1}{1 \cdot 2} + \frac{1}{1 \cdot 2 \cdot 3} + \frac{1}{1 \cdot 2 \cdot 3 \cdot 4} \approx 2.70833333334$$

$$b_5 = 1 + \frac{1}{1} + \frac{1}{1 \cdot 2} + \frac{1}{1 \cdot 2 \cdot 3} + \frac{1}{1 \cdot 2 \cdot 3 \cdot 4} + \frac{1}{1 \cdot 2 \cdot 3 \cdot 4 \cdot 5} \approx 2.71666666667$$

$$b_6 = 1 + \frac{1}{1} + \frac{1}{1 \cdot 2} + \frac{1}{1 \cdot 2 \cdot 3} + \frac{1}{1 \cdot 2 \cdot 3 \cdot 4} + \frac{1}{1 \cdot 2 \cdot 3 \cdot 4 \cdot 5} + \frac{1}{1 \cdot 2 \cdot 3 \cdot 4 \cdot 5 \cdot 6}$$
$$\approx 2.71805555556$$

$$b_7 = 1 + \frac{1}{1} + \frac{1}{1 \cdot 2} + \frac{1}{1 \cdot 2 \cdot 3} + \frac{1}{1 \cdot 2 \cdot 3 \cdot 4} + \frac{1}{1 \cdot 2 \cdot 3 \cdot 4 \cdot 5} + \frac{1}{1 \cdot 2 \cdot 3 \cdot 4 \cdot 5 \cdot 6}$$
$$+ \frac{1}{1 \cdot 2 \cdot 3 \cdot 4 \cdot 5 \cdot 6 \cdot 7} \approx 2.71825396826$$

$$b_8 = 1 + \frac{1}{1} + \frac{1}{1 \cdot 2} + \frac{1}{1 \cdot 2 \cdot 3} + \frac{1}{1 \cdot 2 \cdot 3 \cdot 4} + \frac{1}{1 \cdot 2 \cdot 3 \cdot 4 \cdot 5} + \frac{1}{1 \cdot 2 \cdot 3 \cdot 4 \cdot 5 \cdot 6}$$
$$+ \frac{1}{1 \cdot 2 \cdot 3 \cdot 4 \cdot 5 \cdot 6 \cdot 7} + \frac{1}{1 \cdot 2 \cdot 3 \cdot 4 \cdot 5 \cdot 6 \cdot 7 \cdot 8} \approx 2.71827876985$$
$$\vdots$$

The sequence $\{b_n\}_{n=1}^{\infty}$ converges much more quickly to e than the sequence $\{a_n\}_{n=1}^{\infty}$.

▶▶▶ **Speed of convergence can be misleading. If a sequence converges very slowly, the numerical evidence we obtain by ex-**

amining the first few terms may suggest that the sequence diverges. On the other hand, the first few terms of a divergent sequence might suggest that the sequence is converging.

To prove that a sequence $\{a_n\}_{n=1}^{\infty}$ has a limit L, we must demonstrate that for any given $\epsilon > 0$, we can find N such that

$$|a_n - L| < \epsilon \qquad \text{whenever} \qquad n \geq N.$$

EXAMPLE 7 Prove that the alternating harmonic sequence $\left\{\frac{(-1)^n}{n}\right\}_{n=1}^{\infty}$

$$-1, \ \frac{1}{2}, \ -\frac{1}{3}, \ \frac{1}{4}, \ -\frac{1}{5}, \ \ldots$$

converges to the limit $L = 0$.

Solution Given any positive tolerance ϵ, we can choose N so large that

$$\left|\frac{(-1)^n}{n} - 0\right| = \frac{1}{n} < \epsilon \quad \text{for all} \quad n \geq N.$$

(Just pick $N > \frac{1}{\epsilon}$ so that $\frac{1}{N} < \epsilon$.) ■

Types of divergent behavior–unbounded, oscillatory, chaotic

Convergent behavior of a sequence is marked by the eventual stabilization of its terms to a single limiting value. If the terms in decimal form are flashed before our eyes in quick succession, we should see a "fixing" of more and more of the decimal places. Or, if enough terms are listed vertically in a long column with the decimal points aligned, we can often spot this stabilization (warning: *enough* could be a lot). Divergent behavior, on the other hand, can take on many different forms.

A **bounded** sequence is one whose terms fall within some bounded interval of real numbers, while an **unbounded** sequence contains *arbitrarily* large positive and/or negative terms. An unbounded sequence can never converge to a single finite limiting value.

The sequence of positive integers $\{n\}_{n=1}^{\infty}$

$$1, \ 2, \ 3, \ 4, \ 5, \ \ldots$$

is divergent, for the terms simply increase without bound. Another example of an unbounded sequence is

$$-2,\ 4,\ 6,\ -8,\ 10,\ 12,\ -14,\ \ldots.$$

(All the terms are even, and every third term is negative.) The geometric sequence $\{(1.01)^n\}_{n=1}^{\infty}$,

$$1.01,\ 1.0201,\ 1.030301,\ \ldots$$

is also an unbounded sequence, though its terms grow very slowly. (What's the thousandth term $a_{1000} = 1.01^{1000}$?)

However, even if a sequence is bounded, it need not converge. The terms of the sequence

$$0,\ 1,\ 0,\ 1,\ 0,\ 1,\ \ldots$$

oscillate forever between 0 and 1. The sequence is *bounded* (certainly all the terms lie within the interval $[0, 1]$), but it *diverges* because the terms do not tend toward a single limiting value.

This example shows that divergent behavior need not be wild, unbounded, or unpredictable. Sequences whose terms oscillate between two values or cycle periodically through some set of values are certainly "well-behaved," but they not convergent.

EXAMPLE 8 Find the 1000th term of the sequence $\{a_n\}_{n=1}^{\infty}$, where the terms a_n follow the pattern

$$1,\ 2,\ 3,\ 1,\ 2,\ 3,\ 1,\ 2,\ 3,\ \ldots.$$

Solution This sequence cycles through the values 1, 2, 3 over and over again. We can see that 3 appears every third term (in other words, $3 = a_3,\ a_6,\ a_9,\ \ldots$). So $a_{999} = 3$, and the 1000th term $a_{1000} = 1$. This sequence definitely does not converge. ■

Of course, a sequence whose terms wildly fluctuate in a chaotic manner without ever stabilizing is divergent. We should point out that mathematicians and scientists alike are finding many examples of seemingly chaotic behavior that nevertheless can be described by fairly simple mathematical patterns and relations.

Monotonic sequences

Convergence and divergence are words used to describe whether or not a sequence has a limit. We can also describe how the terms of a sequence behave relative to one other.

Definition 2

A **monotonically increasing** sequence $\{a_n\}_{n=1}^{\infty}$ has the property

$$a_1 \leq a_2 \leq a_3 \leq \cdots \leq a_n \leq \ldots,$$

and a **strictly monotonically increasing** sequence $\{a_n\}_{n=1}^{\infty}$ has the stronger property

$$a_1 < a_2 < a_3 < \cdots < a_n < \ldots.$$

Similarly, a **monotonically decreasing** sequence $\{a_n\}_{n=1}^{\infty}$ has the property

$$a_1 \geq a_2 \geq a_3 \geq \cdots \geq a_n \geq \ldots,$$

and a **strictly monotonically decreasing** sequence $\{a_n\}_{n=1}^{\infty}$ has the stronger property

$$a_1 > a_2 > a_3 > \cdots > a_n > \ldots.$$

Any sequence that is either monotonically increasing or decreasing may be referred to as **monotonic**.

EXAMPLE 9 Which of the following sequences are monotonic?

a) $\left\{\frac{1}{n}\right\}_{n=1}^{\infty}$ (b) $\{2^n\}_{n=0}^{\infty}$ (c) $0, 1, 0, 1, 0, 1, \ldots$

Solution (a) The first few terms of the harmonic sequence $\left\{\frac{1}{n}\right\}_{n=1}^{\infty}$ are

$$1, \frac{1}{2}, \frac{1}{3}, \frac{1}{4}, \ldots, \frac{1}{n}, \ldots.$$

This sequence is monotonically decreasing. In fact, it is strictly monotonically decreasing, since $\frac{1}{n} > \frac{1}{n+1}$ for any $n = 1, 2, 3, \ldots$.

(b) The first few terms of the geometric sequence $\{2^n\}_{n=0}^{\infty}$ are

$$1, 2, 4, 8, 16, \ldots.$$

This sequence is monotonically increasing. In fact, it is strictly monotonically increasing, since $2^n < 2^{n+1}$ for any $n = 0, 1, 2, 3, \ldots$.

(c) The sequence

$$0, 1, 0, 1, 0, 1, \ldots$$

is neither monotonically increasing nor decreasing, since its terms oscillate between 0 and 1. ■

We can conclude that a convergent sequence must be bounded. The reasoning here is that all the terms in a tail of the sequence must be close to a single value L. That accounts for all but the finitely many terms preceding the tail. This means we can find a bounded interval big enough to include the tail of the sequence, as well as all terms preceding the tail.

Even though a convergent sequence must be bounded, the converse is not true: there are certainly bounded sequences that don't converge (remember $0, 1, 0, 1, 0, 1, \ldots$). However, if a sequence is both bounded *and* monotonic, then it must converge. The reasoning makes use of a fundamental property of real numbers: given any bounded set of real numbers, there is a *smallest* closed interval containing all the numbers in the set. For example, the *smallest* closed interval containing all the numbers in the harmonic sequence $\left\{\frac{1}{n}\right\}_{n=1}^{\infty}$ is $[0, 1]$. Now, if the sequence is monotonic (as is the harmonic sequence), then the terms in the sequence will have to cluster at one end or the other of this closed interval. The endpoint is the limit of the sequence. (The harmonic sequence is monotonically decreasing, so its terms approach 0, the left endpoint of the interval.)

We summarize all these observations below.

Theorem 10.1

Hypothesis: $\{a_n\}_{n=1}^{\infty}$ is a sequence of real numbers.
Conclusion 1: If $\{a_n\}_{n=1}^{\infty}$ is convergent, then $\{a_n\}_{n=1}^{\infty}$ is bounded (but the converse need not hold).
Conclusion 2: If $\{a_n\}_{n=1}^{\infty}$ is bounded *and* monotonic, then $\{a_n\}_{n=1}^{\infty}$ is convergent.

□

Limit properties of sequences

If the nth term of a sequence is given by an explicit formula in terms of n,

$$a_n = f(n),$$

then we can investigate the behavior of the sequence both numerically and graphically.

Numerically, we can substitute the values $n = 1, 2, 3, \ldots$ into the formula to get a feel for the sequence. You can see convergent behavior numerically in the stabilization of the digits in the decimal form of each term. That is, if $a_1, a_2, a_3, \ldots,$ are flashed before our eyes quickly in sequence (with the position of the decimal point fixed in place), then the result is like a movie where the digits become fixed from left to right. How long the movie must run for a convergent sequence to show stabilization of each digit is an indication of the speed of convergence of the sequence.

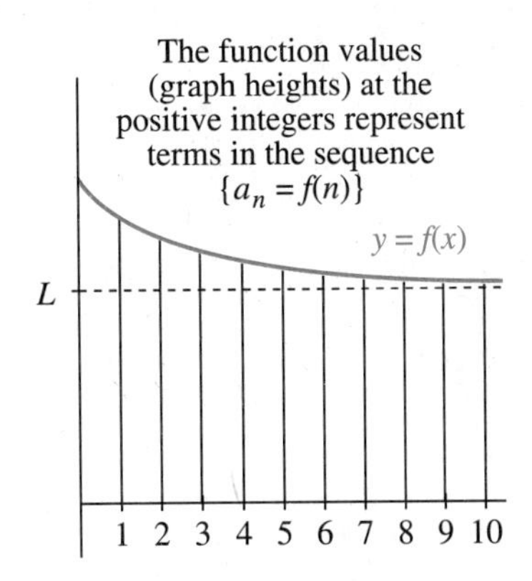

Figure 10.3 Investigating a sequence graphically.

Substituting large values of n may (or may not) give us a good approximation to the limit of a convergent sequence. Also, if you use a machine to compute the values a_n for large n, be particularly sensitive to round-off and cancellation errors that might occur.

Graphically, we can plot

$$y = f(x)$$

and examine the graph for large values of x. The y-coordinates of the points

$$(n, f(n))$$

that lie on this graph correspond to terms of the sequence. A limiting value L to the sequence will correspond to a horizontal asymptote $y = L$ to the graph of $y = f(x)$ (see Figure 10.3).

If you use a machine grapher to explore the behavior of a sequence, beware that it is subject to the same limitations as the machine's numerical computations. These numerical and graphical explorations can help give you a better feel for the behavior of the sequence, but ultimately neither can provide a definitive answer to the question: What is $\lim_{n\to\infty} a_n$?

If the formula describing a_n is composed or built up algebraically from familiar functions, then the same limit properties enjoyed by functions described in Chapter 2 are shared by sequences. More precisely, if $\lim_{n\to\infty} a_n = L_1$ and $\lim_{n\to\infty} b_n = L_2$, then all of the following are true:

$\lim_{n\to\infty}(a_n + b_n) = L_1 + L_2$	$\lim_{n\to\infty}(a_n - b_n) = L_1 - L_2$
$\lim_{n\to\infty} a_n b_n = L_1 L_2$	$\lim_{n\to\infty} c a_n = c L_1$ (c a constant)
$\lim_{n\to\infty} a_n/b_n = L_1/L_2$	(provided b_n's and $L_2 \neq 0$)
$\lim_{n\to\infty} f(a_n) = f(L_1)$	(f a continuous function)

EXAMPLE 10 Consider the two sequences

$$\{a_n\}_{n=1}^{\infty} = \{(1+\frac{1}{n})^n\}_{n=1}^{\infty} \quad \text{and} \quad \{b_n\}_{n=1}^{\infty} = \{(2-\frac{1}{n})\}_{n=1}^{\infty}.$$

Find the limits of the following sequences:

(a) $\{a_n + b_n\}_{n=1}^{\infty}$ (b) $\{a_n - b_n\}_{n=1}^{\infty}$

(c) $\{a_n b_n\}_{n=1}^{\infty}$ (d) $\{a_n/b_n\}_{n=1}^{\infty}$

(e) $\{3b_n\}_{n=1}^{\infty}$ (f) $\{\ln(a_n)\}_{n=1}^{\infty}$.

Solution We noted earlier in this section that

$$\lim_{n\to\infty} a_n = \lim_{n\to\infty} (1+\frac{1}{n})^n = e.$$

Since $\frac{1}{n}$ approaches 0 as n grows larger,

$$\lim_{n\to\infty} b_n = \lim_{n\to\infty} (2-\frac{1}{n}) = 2.$$

Using the limit properties of sequences, we can compute the limits of each of the given sequences as follows:

(a) $\lim_{n\to\infty}(a_n + b_n) = e + 2$ (b) $\lim_{n\to\infty}(a_n - b_n) = e - 2$

(c) $\lim_{n\to\infty} a_n b_n = 2e$ (d) $\lim_{n\to\infty} a_n/b_n = e/2$

(e) $\lim_{n\to\infty} 3b_n = 3 \cdot 2 = 6$ (f) $\lim_{n\to\infty} \ln(a_n) = \ln(e) = 1$.

■

EXERCISES for Section 10.1

For exercises 1–4: Give a formula for the nth term of the arithmetic sequence with given initial term and constant difference.

1. $a_0 = 3,\ d = -5$
2. $a_0 = -4,\ d = 0.5$
3. $a_0 = \pi,\ d = 0$
4. $a_0 = 0,\ d = \pi$

For exercises 5–8: Give a formula for the nth term of the geometric sequence with given initial term and constant ratio.

5. $a_0 = 3,\ r = -5$
6. $a_0 = -4,\ r = 0.5$
7. $a_0 = \pi,\ r = 2$
8. $a_0 = 2,\ r = \pi$

For exercises 9–12: Indicate whether each of the statements is true or false. If true, state why it is true. If false, give an example.

9. All bounded, monotonic sequences converge.
10. All non-monotonic sequences diverge.

11. All bounded sequences converge.

12. All unbounded sequences diverge.

For exercises 13–16: List the first 5 terms of each sequence $\{a_n\}_{n=1}^{\infty}$. For each, classify as bounded or not, monotonic or not, convergent or not.

13. $a_n = 2^{\cos n\pi}$

14. $a_n = (\frac{n-1}{n+1})^n$

15. $-2, -3.1, -4.01, -5.001, \ldots$ (continues with same pattern)

16. the illustrated sequence continuing with the same pattern

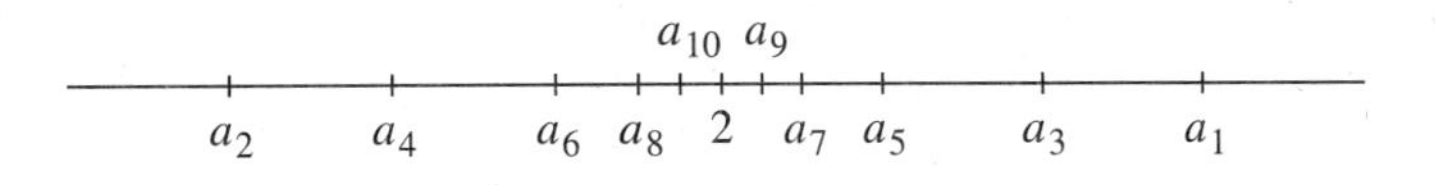

For Exercise 16

For exercises 17–20: Consider the sequence whose nth term is $a_n = 1 + (-1)^n(\frac{1}{n})$. Note that $\lim_{n\to\infty} a_n = 1$.

17. Plot and label the first 7 terms of the sequence $\{a_n\}_{n=1}^{\infty}$.

18. Find the first term in the sequence that is within .1 less than the limit.

19. Find the first term in the sequence that is within .1 more than the limit.

20. Find the first 2 terms in the sequence that are within .1 of each other.

For exercises 21–25: Give three examples of sequences satisfying the given descriptions.

21. bounded, monotonic

22. bounded, non-monotonic, convergent

23. unbounded, monotonic

24. unbounded, non-monotonic

25. bounded, non-monotonic, divergent

---

26. Let $a_n = (1 + \frac{1}{n})^n$. Find a_1, a_2, a_3, a_{1000}, a_{2000}, a_{3000}. Is the sequence $\{a_n\}$ bounded and/or monotonic? If so, what does the limit appear to be? Approximately, how close is a_{3000} to the limit?

27. The nth term of a sequence $\{a_n\}_{n=1}^{\infty}$ is given by $a_n = \frac{1}{n!}$. (Note: $n! = 1 \cdot 2 \cdot 3 \cdot \cdots \cdot n$.) Find the limit of the sequence, and then find the smallest value N such that all the terms after a_N in the sequence $\{a_n\}_{n=1}^{\infty}$ are within .001 of this limit.

28. The nth term of a sequence $\{a_n\}_{n=1}^{\infty}$ is given by $a_n = \frac{1}{2^n}$. Find the limit of the sequence, and then find the smallest value N such that all the terms after a_N in the sequence $\{a_n\}_{n=1}^{\infty}$ are within .001 of this limit.

29. Compare the rates of convergence of the sequences in the last two exercises.

30. The nth term of a sequence $\{a_n\}_{n=1}^{\infty}$ is given by $a_n = n\sin(\frac{\pi}{n})$. Find the limit of the sequence, and then find the smallest value N such that all the terms after a_N in the sequence $\{a_n\}_{n=1}^{\infty}$ are within .001 of this limit.

10.2 SERIES

We can roughly think of a series as the sum of the infinitely many terms in a sequence. Before embarking on our study of series, let's first take a look at an important property of real numbers.

The Archimedean property of real numbers

Suppose that we take a positive real number r and start adding it to itself over and over again. No matter how small r is ($r > 0$), this process will produce arbitrarily larger and larger sums. This fact is known as the **Archimedean property of real numbers**, and we can state it more precisely as follows: If r, M are any two positive real numbers, then there exists a positive integer N such that $Nr > M$. Note that there is absolutely no restriction on how small r can be (as long as it is positive) nor on how large M can be.

The quantity Nr represents a sum:

$$Nr = \sum_{n=1}^{N} r = r + r + r + \cdots r \qquad (N \text{ addends of } r).$$

The ancient Greek mathematicians did not have a language or notation that included anything like our symbol ∞ in their mathematics, but we can write the Archimedean property as follows:

$$\text{For any } r > 0, \qquad \lim_{N\to\infty} Nr = \infty.$$

Zeno's paradox

We might think of the Archimedean property as saying that a "sum" of *infinitely many* terms $r > 0$ is infinite. Is there any way that the "sum" of

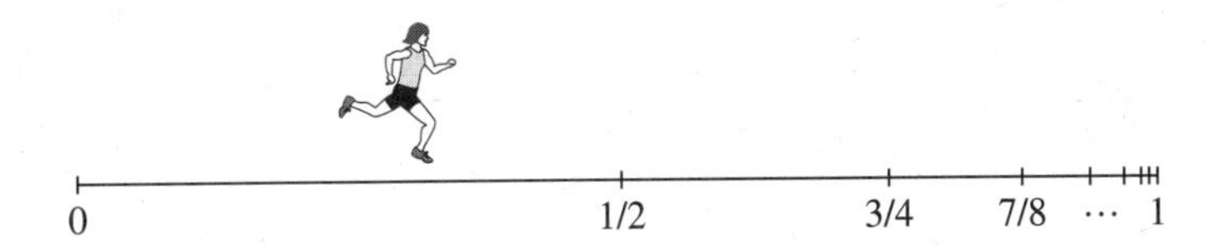

Figure 10.4 Zeno's racecourse.

infinitely many positive numbers could not be infinite? Many of the ancient Greek mathematicians did not think so, because of the Archimedean property. However, this belief was shaken by what is known as **Zeno's paradox**.

Zeno's paradox goes like this: Suppose that a person runs along a racecourse of length 1 mile. Before the race is completed, the person must first cover half the distance. Now, of the half-mile remaining, the person must cover half of it (or $1/4$ of a mile) to reach the $3/4$ mile mark. Of the final quarter-mile, the person must first cover half of it ($1/8$ mile) to reach the $7/8$ mile mark. This process occurs over and over: given any distance remaining, the person must first cover half of the distance before the race is completed (see Figure 10.4).

Each of these distances is positive, and the person must cover infinitely many of them. The Archimedean property might suggest that the total distance is infinite and that the person cannot possibly complete the race. It is clear, however, that people complete such races regularly. This paradox forces us to admit that it is reasonable to write something like

$$\frac{1}{2} + \frac{1}{4} + \frac{1}{8} + \cdots = 1.$$

The word *paradox* usually refers to a statement or situation contradicting itself or some firmly established truth. Zeno's paradox is not really a paradox, for it does *not* contradict the Archimedean property. Unlike the situation of adding the *same* positive number r to itself infinitely often, the racecourse example has us adding infinitely many *different* positive numbers, each one smaller (by the factor one-half) than the number preceding it. Evidently, in this different situation, it may be reasonable to assign a finite total to a sum of infinitely many positive terms.

What is a series?

The notion of a series is convenient for describing situations like Zeno's paradox or any other infinite process producing a sequence of running totals. In fact, using the terms in any sequence of real numbers $\{a_n\}_{n=1}^{\infty}$, we can build a new sequence of running totals. A **series** is the limit of this new sequence. The notation for a series uses summation notation for sums, and we write

$$\sum_{n=1}^{\infty} a_n$$

as shorthand for

$$a_1 + a_2 + a_3 + a_4 + \cdots + a_n + \cdots .$$

It is impossible to add infinitely many numbers together by actually summing them, so mathematically the series is the limit of a sequence of **partial sums** S_N:

$$\begin{aligned}
S_1 &= a_1 \\
S_2 &= a_1 + a_2 \\
S_3 &= a_1 + a_2 + a_3 \\
S_4 &= a_1 + a_2 + a_3 + a_4 \\
&\vdots \\
S_N &= a_1 + a_2 + \cdots + a_N \\
&\vdots
\end{aligned}$$

Using summation notation,

$$\sum_{n=1}^{\infty} a_n = \lim_{N \to \infty} \sum_{n=1}^{N} a_n = \lim_{N \to \infty} S_N.$$

EXAMPLE 11 Find the first four partial sums of the series $\sum_{n=1}^{\infty} \frac{1}{2^n}$.

Solution

$$\begin{aligned}
S_1 &= \frac{1}{2^1} = \frac{1}{2} \\
S_2 &= \frac{1}{2^1} + \frac{1}{2^2} = \frac{3}{4} \\
S_3 &= \frac{1}{2^1} + \frac{1}{2^2} + \frac{1}{2^3} = \frac{7}{8} \\
S_4 &= \frac{1}{2^1} + \frac{1}{2^2} + \frac{1}{2^3} + \frac{1}{2^4} = \frac{15}{16}.
\end{aligned}$$

Can you come up with a formula that gives the Nth partial sum S_N? ■

Definition 3

A series is said to **converge** if the sequence of partial sums converges. Finding the **sum of a series** means finding the limit of the sequence of its partial sums. If a series does not converge, then we say the series **diverges** and it has no sum.

We can numerically investigate the convergence or divergence of a series in much the same way we investigate the limiting behavior of any sequence: by actually evaluating the partial sums S_N and examining their behavior as N grows larger without bound. Note that even if we have a formula for the *nth term* a_n of a series, it may be difficult to find a formula for the *Nth partial sum* S_N of the series $\sum_{n=1}^{\infty} a_n$.

Examples of series

A **telescoping series** gets its name from the behavior of its partial sums. The terms of a telescoping series can be written as a sum of differences of quantities, all of which cancel except for the first and last, collapsing (like an old spyglass telescope) to a single difference. Thus, we can find a formula for the Nth partial sum and more easily investigate its limiting behavior.

EXAMPLE 12 Does $\sum_{n=1}^{\infty}(\frac{1}{n} - \frac{1}{n+1})$ converge, and if so, what is its sum?

Solution The first few partial sums of the series are

$$S_1 = a_1 = \frac{1}{1} - \frac{1}{2} = \frac{1}{2}$$

$$S_2 = a_1 + a_2 = \left(1 - \frac{1}{2}\right) + \left(\frac{1}{2} - \frac{1}{3}\right) = 1 - \frac{1}{3} = \frac{2}{3}$$

$$S_3 = a_1 + a_2 + a_3 = \left(1 - \frac{1}{2}\right) + \left(\frac{1}{2} - \frac{1}{3}\right) + \left(\frac{1}{3} - \frac{1}{4}\right) = 1 - \frac{1}{4} = \frac{3}{4}$$

$$S_4 = a_1 + a_2 + a_3 + a_4 = \left(1 - \frac{1}{2}\right) + \left(\frac{1}{2} - \frac{1}{3}\right) + \left(\frac{1}{3} - \frac{1}{4}\right) + \left(\frac{1}{4} - \frac{1}{5}\right) = \frac{4}{5}.$$

Notice the cancellation involving the "internal terms." We can write

$$S_N = a_1 + a_2 + \cdots + a_N = 1 - \frac{1}{N+1}$$

and we can see that $\sum_{n=1}^{\infty} a_n = \lim_{N\to\infty}(1 - \frac{1}{N+1}) = 1.$ ■

Geometric series

The terms of a **geometric series** form a geometric sequence; each term is a constant ratio times the preceding term. For example, the series $\sum_{n=1}^{\infty} \frac{1}{2^n}$ of Zeno's paradox is a geometric series.

In general, a geometric series has the form

$$a + ar + ar^2 + ar^3 + ar^4 + \cdots ar^n + \cdots,$$

where a is the initial term and r is the constant ratio. If we use the power of r as the index, then we can start with $n = 0$ and write the series as

$$\sum_{n=0}^{\infty} ar^n.$$

Let's see how the sum of a geometric series depends on the ratio r. If $r = 1$, then

$$\sum_{n=0}^{\infty} ar^n = a + a + a + a + \cdots$$

will *diverge* for any *nonzero* a.

If $r = -1$, then

$$\sum_{n=0}^{\infty} ar^n = a - a + a - a + \cdots$$

also diverges because the partial sums oscillate between a and 0:

$$S_0 = a, \quad S_1 = 0, \quad S_2 = a, \quad S_3 = 0,$$

and so on.

Now let's look at the cases where $r \neq \pm 1$. The Nth partial sum is

$$S_N = a + ar + ar^2 + \cdots + ar^N.$$

Multiplying both sides by r, we obtain

$$rS_N = ar + ar^2 + ar^3 + \cdots + ar^N + ar^{N+1}.$$

Then, subtracting the two sides from the original equation for S_N, we have

$$\begin{aligned} S_N - rS_N &= a + ar + ar^2 + \cdots + ar^N \\ &\qquad - ar - ar^2 - \cdots - ar^N - ar^{N+1} \\ &= a - ar^{N+1}. \end{aligned}$$

Since $S_N - rS_N = (1-r)S_N$, we can solve for S_N, provided that $r \neq 1$:

$$S_N = \frac{a - ar^{N+1}}{(1-r)} = \frac{a(1-r^{N+1})}{(1-r)}.$$

Using this formula for S_N, we can determine the sum of the geometric series

$$\sum_{n=0}^{\infty} ar^n = \lim_{n\to\infty} \frac{a(1-r^{N+1})}{1-r} \qquad (r \neq 1).$$

If $|r| > 1$ ($r > 1$ or $r < -1$), then r^{N+1} will become larger in magnitude and the limit will not exist.

If $|r| < 1$ ($-1 < r < 1$), then $\lim_{N\to\infty} r^{N+1} = 0$ and

$$\sum_{n=0}^{\infty} ar^n = \frac{a(1-0)}{1-r} = \frac{a}{1-r}.$$

Summarizing all the cases, we have the following theorem.

Theorem 10.2

If $a \neq 0$, then the geometric series $\sum_{n=0}^{\infty} ar^n$ *diverges* if $r \geq 1$ or $r \leq -1$ and *converges* if $-1 < r < 1$. If the geometric series $\sum_{n=0}^{\infty} ar^n$ converges, its sum is $\dfrac{a}{1-r}$.

□

EXAMPLE 13 Does the geometric series

$$7 + \frac{7}{5} + \frac{7}{25} + \frac{7}{125} + \cdots$$

converge or diverge? If the series converges, what is the sum?

Solution This series can also be written in summation notation as

$$\sum_{n=0}^{\infty} 7\left(\frac{1}{5}\right)^n.$$

The first term is $a = 7$, and the ratio is $r = 1/5$. Since $-1 < 1/5 < 1$, we know that the series must *converge*, and

$$\sum_{n=0}^{\infty} 7\left(\frac{1}{5}\right)^n = \frac{7}{1-1/5} = \frac{7}{4/5} = \frac{35}{4}.$$

■

EXAMPLE 14 Does the series

$$\sum_{n=0}^{\infty}(-3)^{1-n}$$

converge or diverge? If the series converges, what is the sum?

Solution If we write the first few terms of the series, we may more easily recognize that it is a geometric series:

$$-3+1-\frac{1}{3}+\frac{1}{9}-\frac{1}{27}+\frac{1}{81}+\cdots,$$

where the first term is $a=-3$, and the ratio is $r=-1/3$.

Since $-1<-1/3<1$, we know that the series must *converge*, and

$$\sum_{n=0}^{\infty}(-3)^{1-n}=\frac{-3}{1-(-1/3)}=\frac{-3}{4/3}=\frac{-9}{4}.$$ ■

EXAMPLE 15 Does the series $.01+.02+.04+.08+\cdots$ converge or diverge? If the series converges, what is the sum?

Solution This is a geometric series with first term $a=.01$ and ratio $r=2$ (the terms double at each step). Since $r\geq 1$, the series *diverges*. ■

EXAMPLE 16 Does the series $\sum_{n=2}^{\infty}\frac{5}{4^n}$ converge or diverge? If the series converges, what is the sum?

Solution Note that the starting index is $n=2$. If we write the first few terms of the series, we have

$$\frac{5}{4^2}+\frac{5}{4^3}+\frac{5}{4^4}+\cdots,$$

so the first term is $a=5/16$ and the ratio is $r=1/4$.

Since $-1<1/4<1$, the series *converges*, and

$$\sum_{n=2}^{\infty}\frac{5}{4^n}=\frac{5/16}{1-1/4}=\frac{5}{12}.$$ ■

▶▶▶ **Be careful to distinguish between the limit of a** *sequence* $\{a_n\}_{n=1}^{\infty}$ **and the the associated** *series* $\sum_{n=1}^{\infty}a_n$**. It is quite possible that the sequence of individual** *terms* **converges, while the sequence of** *partial sums* **diverges.**

A simple example of this is the constant sequence

$$1,\ 1,\ 1,\ 1,\ \ldots,$$

which certainly converges to 1, while the associated series

$$1+1+1+1+1+1+\cdots$$

diverges (by the Archimedean property of real numbers).

Harmonic series

The **harmonic series** is the sum of the terms of the harmonic sequence:

$$\sum_{n=1}^{\infty}\frac{1}{n}=1+\frac{1}{2}+\frac{1}{3}+\frac{1}{4}+\cdots.$$

The *harmonic sequence converges to* 0, but the *harmonic series diverges.* One way to see this is to look at the partial sums S_1, S_2, S_4, S_8, S_{16}, $\cdots$. The first few of these partial sums are

$$\begin{aligned}
S_1 &= 1\\
S_2 &= 1+\frac{1}{2}=1.5\\
S_4 &= 1+\frac{1}{2}+\frac{1}{3}+\frac{1}{4}>2\\
S_8 &= 1+\frac{1}{2}+\frac{1}{3}+\frac{1}{4}+\frac{1}{5}+\frac{1}{6}+\frac{1}{7}+\frac{1}{8}>2.5\\
S_{16} &= 1+\cdots+\frac{1}{16}>3.
\end{aligned}$$

Each time we double the number of terms in the partial sum, we have added at least $1/2$ to the running total. This means that

$$S_{2^n}=1+\frac{1}{2}+\frac{1}{3}+\cdots+\frac{1}{2^n}\geq 1+\frac{n}{2}.$$

The partial sums will grow larger without bound, since we can keep doubling the number of terms indefinitely. Hence, the harmonic series *diverges.*

The **alternating harmonic series** is the sum of the terms of the alternating harmonic sequence

$$\sum_{n=1}^{\infty}\frac{(-1)^{n+1}}{n}=1-\frac{1}{2}+\frac{1}{3}-\frac{1}{4}+\frac{1}{5}-\cdots.$$

It is unclear whether or not the alternating harmonic series converges or diverges from looking at the first few partial sums. Interestingly, it is known that the alternating harmonic series *converges* and has a sum $L=\ln(2)$.

Properties of series

Because a series is the limit of a sequence of partial sums, some of the limit properties of sequences also apply to properties of series.

If $\sum_{n=1}^{\infty} a_n = L_1$ and $\sum_{n=1}^{\infty} b_n = L_2$, then all of the following are true.

$$\sum_{n=1}^{\infty}(a_n + b_n) = L_1 + L_2$$

$$\sum_{n=1}^{\infty}(a_n - b_n) = L_1 - L_2$$

$$c\sum_{n=1}^{\infty} a_n = cL_1 \quad (c \text{ a constant}).$$

If $\sum_{n=1}^{\infty} a_n$ diverges and $\sum_{n=1}^{\infty} b_n$ converges, then

$$\sum_{n=1}^{\infty}(a_n + b_n) \quad \text{diverges}$$

$$\sum_{n=1}^{\infty}(a_n - b_n) \quad \text{diverges}$$

$$c\sum_{n=1}^{\infty} a_n \quad \text{diverges if } c \neq 0.$$

EXAMPLE 17 Assuming that the alternating harmonic series $\sum_{n=1}^{\infty} \frac{(-1)^{n+1}}{n}$ converges to the sum $\ln(2)$, find the sums of the following series:

(a) $\sum_{n=1}^{\infty}(\frac{(-1)^{n+1}}{n} + \frac{1}{2^n})$

(b) $\sum_{n=1}^{\infty}(\frac{(-1)^{n+1}}{n} - \frac{1}{2^n})$

(c) $\sum_{n=1}^{\infty}(\frac{1}{n} + \frac{1}{2^n})$

(d) $\sum_{n=1}^{\infty}(\frac{1}{n} - \frac{1}{2^n})$

(e) $\sum_{n=1}^{\infty} \frac{(-1)^{n+1}5}{n}$

(f) $\sum_{n=1}^{\infty} \frac{5}{n}$.

Solution We know that the geometric series $\sum_{n=1}^{\infty} \frac{1}{2^n}$ converges to the sum 1, while the harmonic series $\sum_{n=1}^{\infty} \frac{1}{n}$ diverges. Using this fact, we can determine that:

(a) $\sum_{n=1}^{\infty}(\frac{(-1)^{n+1}}{n} + \frac{1}{2^n}) = \ln(2) + 1.$

(b) $\sum_{n=1}^{\infty}(\frac{(-1)^{n+1}}{n} - \frac{1}{2^n}) = \ln(2) - 1.$

(c) $\sum_{n=1}^{\infty}(\frac{1}{n} + \frac{1}{2^n})$ diverges.

(d) $\sum_{n=1}^{\infty}(\frac{1}{n} - \frac{1}{2^n})$ diverges.

(e)$\sum_{n=1}^{\infty}(\frac{(-1)^{n+1}5}{n}) = 5\ln(2).$

(f) $\sum_{n=1}^{\infty} \frac{5}{n}$ diverges.

■

EXERCISES for Section 10.2

For exercises 1–16: Determine whether the given series converges or diverges. If the series converges, find the sum.

1. $\sum_{n=1}^{\infty}(-1/3)^n$
2. $\sum_{n=0}^{\infty}(1/3)^n$
3. $\sum_{n=1}^{\infty} e^{-n}$
4. $\sum_{n=0}^{\infty} \dfrac{3^n+2^n}{4^n}$
5. $\sum_{n=1}^{\infty}(-1)^n$
6. $\sum_{n=0}^{\infty}(1/2)$
7. $\frac{1}{11} - \frac{10}{11^2} + \frac{100}{11^3} - \frac{1000}{11^4} \cdots$
8. $\sum_{n=1}^{\infty} n$
9. $.001 - .003 + .009 - .027 \ldots$
10. $\sum_{n=1}^{\infty} \dfrac{2}{n}$
11. $\sum_{n=2}^{\infty} \dfrac{e^n}{3^{n-2}}$
12. $\sum_{n=1}^{\infty} \dfrac{(-1)^n}{2n}$
13. $\sum_{n=3}^{\infty} \left(\dfrac{1}{n-1} - \dfrac{1}{n+1}\right)$
14. $\sum_{n=1}^{\infty} \left(\dfrac{3}{2n-1} - \dfrac{3}{2n+1}\right)$
15. $\sum_{n=1}^{\infty} \left(\dfrac{1}{3^{n+1}} - \dfrac{1}{3^n}\right)$
16. $\sum_{n=0}^{\infty} \sin(\pi n)$

---

17. Find two different geometric series, both of which converge to $17/3$.

18. If a geometric series converges to 1, then the sum of its first term a and the ratio r is 1. Why? Does the converse hold?

19. Find the first ten partial sums of $\sum_{n=0}^{\infty} 1/n!$, where $n! = 1 \cdot 2 \cdot 3 \cdots n$ for $n \geq 1$ and $0! = 1$. Does the apparent limiting value look familiar?

20. Find S_{10}, S_{100}, and S_{1000} for the alternating harmonic series and compare these values to $\ln(2)$.

21. A ball is dropped from a height of six feet and begins bouncing up and down. The height of each bounce is $3/4$ the height of the previous bounce. Find the total vertical distance traveled by the ball.

22. Let

$$c_n = 1 + \frac{1}{2} + \frac{1}{3} + \frac{1}{4} + \cdots + \frac{1}{n} - \ln(n).$$

Find c_{40}, c_{50}, and c_{60}. The sequence $\{c_n\}$ converges to a number known as **Euler's constant** $\gamma \approx 0.5772$.

Cantor's middle-third set, named for the mathematician Georg Cantor (1835-1918) is constructed as follows:

First, the open interval $(\frac{1}{3}, \frac{2}{3})$ is "erased" from the closed interval $[0, 1]$. This leaves two closed intervals, $[0, \frac{1}{3}]$ and $[\frac{2}{3}, 1]$.

Next, the middle third of each of these two remaining closed intervals is erased. That is, the open intervals $(\frac{1}{9}, \frac{2}{9})$ and $(\frac{7}{9}, \frac{8}{9})$ are erased, leaving four closed intervals, $[0, \frac{1}{9}]$, $[\frac{2}{9}, \frac{1}{3}]$, $[\frac{2}{3}, \frac{7}{9}]$, and $[\frac{8}{9}, 1]$.

We continue in the same way, erasing the open middle third of each remaining closed subinterval to obtain eight new closed subintervals. The illustration shows the original interval $[0, 1]$ and what remains after each of the first three stages. We continue this process indefinitely, at each stage erasing the open middle third of each remaining closed subinterval.

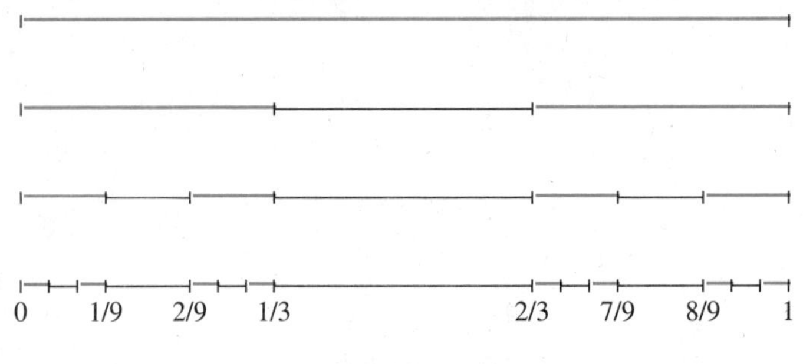

For Exercises 23–25

23. Find the total length of all the subintervals erased (using a geometric series).

24. Give an example of a point that is *never* erased.

25. How many points are left in the Cantor set?

10.3 CONVERGENCE AND DIVERGENCE OF SERIES

It may be difficult to find a formula that describes the Nth partial sum $S_N = \sum_{n=1}^{N} a_n$ of a series $\sum_{n=1}^{\infty} a_n$. With the use of computers or calculators, we can certainly calculate many of these partial sums quickly, and for large index values N we can get a feel for the limiting behavior of the series and approximate its sum if it converges.

However, note that any partial sum will have a finite value (perhaps large), so the convergence or divergence of a series is impossible to determine just by examining the values of some of these partial sums. For example, the harmonic series

$$\sum_{n=1}^{\infty} \frac{1}{n}$$

diverges, but very slowly. Indeed, the harmonic series will appear to converge if we calculate the partial sums using a machine with fixed precision.

If we could determine in advance that a given series $\sum_{n=1}^{\infty} a_n$ converges, then we might be able to approximate its sum closely with a partial sum $S_N = \sum_{n=1}^{N} a_n$ of suitably large index N. There are a variety of **convergence tests** for series. Sometimes a convergence test can also give us information regarding the number N of terms so that a partial sum achieves a given level of accuracy. In this section, we will discuss several of these convergence tests. For each of the tests we describe, it is important to pay special attention to:

1. the requirements that must be fulfilled so that the test can be applied,
2. the criteria for making a decision regarding convergence or divergence, and
3. any accuracy estimates for approximating the sum of a convergent series.

For each of the tests described in this section, we'll provide some discussion of how the test works and illustrate it with some examples.

Nth term test

Requirements:

The Nth **term test** can be applied to any series.

Criteria:

If $\lim_{n\to\infty} a_n \neq 0$, then $\sum_{n=1}^{\infty} a_n$ diverges.

If $\lim_{n\to\infty} a_n = 0$, then $\sum_{n=1}^{\infty} a_n$ *may* or *may not* converge.

Discussion:

For the partial sums to converge to a single limiting value, the individual terms a_n must approach 0. The Nth term test simply relies on this observation.

EXAMPLE 18 Use the Nth term test on each of the following series:
(a) $\sum_{n=1}^{\infty} n$ (b) $\sum_{n=1}^{\infty}(-1)^n$ (c) $\sum_{n=1}^{\infty}(1-\frac{1}{n})$ (d) $\sum_{n=1}^{\infty}\frac{1}{n}$ (e) $\sum_{n=1}^{\infty}\frac{1}{2^n}$

Solution (a) $\sum_{n=1}^{\infty} n$ *diverges*, since $\lim_{n\to\infty} n = \infty \neq 0$.

(b) $\sum_{n=1}^{\infty}(-1)^n$ *diverges*, since $\lim_{n\to\infty}(-1)^n$ does not exist. (Note that $(-1)^n$ oscillates between 1 and -1, depending on whether n is even or odd.)

(c) $\sum_{n=1}^{\infty}(1-\frac{1}{n})$ *diverges*, since $\lim_{n\to\infty}(1-\frac{1}{n}) = 1 \neq 0$.

(d) The Nth term test provides no information regarding the convergence or divergence of the harmonic series

$$\sum_{n=1}^{\infty}\frac{1}{n},$$

since $\lim_{n\to\infty} \frac{1}{n} = 0$. (However, we do know that this series *diverges* from the previous section.)

(e) The Nth term test provides no information regarding the geometric series

$$\sum_{n=1}^{\infty} \frac{1}{2^n},$$

since $\lim_{n\to\infty} \dfrac{1}{2^n} = 0$. (However, we do know this series *converges* and has a sum equal to 1.) ■

As parts (d) and (e) of this example show, $\lim_{n\to\infty} a_n = 0$ is a *necessary* but not *sufficient* condition for the series $\sum_{n=1}^{\infty} a_n$ to converge. The Nth term test can determine that a series diverges, but it does not give us conclusive information that a series converges.

Integral test

Requirements:

The **integral test** can be applied to any series whose terms $a_n = f(n)$, where f can be considered a *continuous, positive, decreasing* function of a real variable x.

Criteria:

If $\int_1^{\infty} f(x)\,dx$ converges, then $\sum_{n=1}^{\infty} a_n$ converges.

If $\int_1^{\infty} f(x)\,dx$ diverges, then $\sum_{n=1}^{\infty} a_n$ diverges.

Discussion:

The integral test allows us to decide the convergence or divergence of a series by comparing it to an improper integral. If all the terms a_n in

$$\sum_{n=1}^{\infty} a_n$$

are positive, we can represent them as the *areas* of rectangles under the curve $y = f(x)$ (see Figure 10.5). The base of each rectangle is 1, so the height of the nth rectangle must be a_n.

If $a_n = f(n)$, then the graph $y = f(x)$ passes through the upper right corner of each rectangle. If the function f is decreasing, then all of the rectangles starting with the second one fit *under* the graph. Hence, if the improper integral

$$\int_1^{\infty} f(x)\,dx = L,$$

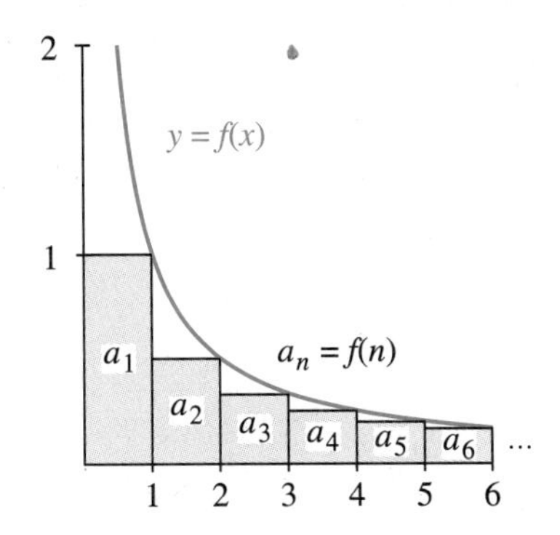

Figure 10.5 If $\int_1^\infty f(x)\,dx$ is finite, so is the total area $\sum_1^\infty a_n$.

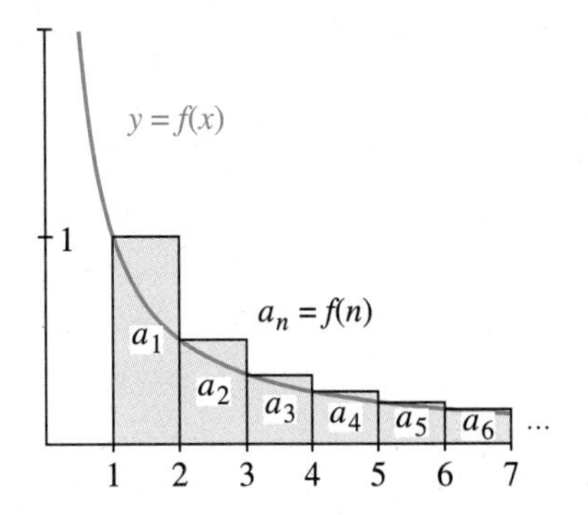

Figure 10.6 If $\int_1^\infty f(x)\,dx$ is infinite, so is the total area $\sum_1^\infty a_n$.

then

$$\sum_{n=1}^{\infty} a_n \leq L + a_1.$$

Each term a_n makes a positive contribution to the total, so the partial sums S_N are increasing as N increases. Since the partial sums form a *monotonically increasing bounded sequence*, they must converge to a single limiting value.

Suppose that we considered the rectangles shifted one unit to the right, as in Figure 10.6. Now the graph $y = f(x)$ passes through all the upper left corners of the rectangles and

$$\int_1^{\infty} f(x)\,dx \leq \sum_{n=1}^{\infty} a_n.$$

Hence, if $\int_1^\infty f(x)\,dx$ *diverges*, then so must $\sum_{n=1}^\infty a_n$.

EXAMPLE 19 Use the integral test to test the convergence of the harmonic series $\sum_{n=1}^\infty \frac{1}{n}$.

Solution The integral test can be applied because $1/x$ is positive, continuous, and decreasing over the interval $[1, \infty)$:

$$\int_1^{\infty} \frac{1}{x}\,dx = \lim_{b\to\infty} \int_1^{b} \frac{1}{x}\,dx = \lim_{b\to\infty} \ln|b| = \infty.$$

This improper integral diverges, so the harmonic series $\sum_{n=1}^\infty \frac{1}{n}$ diverges. ■

EXAMPLE 20 Use the integral test to test the convergence of the series $\sum_{n=1}^\infty \frac{1}{n^2}$.

Solution The integral test can be applied because $1/x^2$ is positive, continuous, and decreasing over the interval $[1, \infty)$:

$$\int_1^\infty \frac{1}{x^2}\,dx = \lim_{b\to\infty} \int_1^b \frac{1}{x^2}\,dx = \lim_{b\to\infty} \frac{-1}{b} + 1 = 1.$$

This improper integral converges, so the series $\sum_{n=1}^\infty \frac{1}{n^2}$ converges. (Note: The sum of the *series* is not 1, however.) ■

EXAMPLE 21 Why can't the integral test be applied to the alternating harmonic series?

Solution The integral test cannot be applied to the alternating harmonic series

$$\sum_{n=1}^\infty \frac{(-1)^{n+1}}{n}$$

because the terms are not all positive. (Check the requirements for the integral test.) ■

EXAMPLE 22 Why can't the integral test be applied to the series $\sum_{n=1}^\infty \sin^2(\pi n)$?

Solution The integral test cannot be applied to the series

$$\sum_{n=1}^\infty \sin^2(\pi n)$$

because $\sin^2(\pi x)$ is not decreasing over $[1, \infty)$. (Check the requirements for the integral test.) ■

Integral test estimate:

When the integral test indicates that a series $\sum_{n=1}^\infty a_n$ converges, we can get an estimate of how good an approximation the partial sum

$$S_N = \sum_{n=1}^N a_n = a_1 + a_2 + \cdots + a_N$$

is to the actual sum of the series. Let's use the notation R_N to indicate the remaining "tail" of the series,

$$R_N = \sum_{n=N+1}^\infty a_n = a_{N+1} + a_{N+2} + \cdots,$$

so that

$$S_N + R_N = \sum_{n=1}^\infty a_n.$$

From our previous analysis, we can see that this remainder tail is "trapped" between two improper integrals

$$\int_{N+1}^{\infty} f(x)\,dx \leq R_N \leq \int_{N}^{\infty} f(x)\,dx.$$

If we use the lower bound $\int_{N+1}^{\infty} f(x)$ as an approximation for R_N, then the worst error possible is the difference between the lower bound and upper bound:

$$\int_{N}^{\infty} f(x)\,dx - \int_{N+1}^{\infty} f(x)\,dx = \int_{N}^{N+1} f(x)\,dx.$$

This all means that:

> If $\sum_{n=1}^{\infty} a_n$ converges by the integral test, then
>
> $$\sum_{n=1}^{\infty} a_n = \sum_{n=1}^{N} a_n + \int_{N+1}^{\infty} f(x)\,dx \quad + \quad \text{error},$$
>
> where $0 < \text{error} \leq \int_{N}^{N+1} f(x)\,dx$.

EXAMPLE 23 Estimate $\sum_{n=1}^{\infty} \frac{1}{n^2}$ to within .0001 of its sum.

Solution The approximation we need is

$$\sum_{n=1}^{\infty} \frac{1}{n^2} \approx \sum_{n=1}^{N} \frac{1}{n^2} + \int_{N+1}^{\infty} \frac{1}{x^2}\,dx.$$

We need to choose N large enough so that the

$$\text{error} \leq \int_{N}^{N+1} f(x)\,dx \leq .0001.$$

Now,

$$\int_{N}^{N+1} \frac{1}{x^2}\,dx = \left.\frac{-1}{x}\right]_{N}^{N+1} = \frac{-1}{N+1} + \frac{1}{N} = \frac{1}{N(N+1)},$$

and when $N = 100$, we have

$$\frac{1}{N(N+1)} = \frac{1}{(100)(101)} < .0001.$$

Thus, we can use $N = 100$ to make our estimate:

$$\sum_{n=1}^{\infty} \frac{1}{n^2} \approx \sum_{n=1}^{100} \frac{1}{n^2} + \int_{101}^{\infty} \frac{1}{x^2}\,dx.$$

We use a calculator or computer to compute

$$\sum_{n=1}^{100} \frac{1}{N^2} \approx 1.63498$$

to five decimal places, and

$$\int_{101}^{\infty} \frac{1}{x^2}\, dx = \lim_{b\to\infty} \frac{-1}{b} + \frac{1}{101} = \frac{1}{101} \approx .0099.$$

Thus,

$$\sum_{n=1}^{\infty} \frac{1}{n^2} \approx 1.64488,$$

accurate to within .0001. ■

p-series

Let's use the tests we have developed on an important family of series of the form

$$\sum_{n=1}^{\infty} \frac{1}{n^p},$$

where p is a fixed power. In Section 7.7 on improper integrals, we noted that

$$\int_{1}^{\infty} \frac{1}{x^p}\, dx$$

converges for $p > 1$ and diverges for $p \le 1$.

For $p > 0$, $1/x^p$ is positive and decreasing on $[1, \infty)$, and we can apply the integral test to "p-series" of the form

$$\sum_{n=1}^{\infty} \frac{1}{n^p}$$

and conclude that $\sum_{n=1}^{\infty} \frac{1}{n^p}$ converges for $p > 1$ and diverges for $0 < p \le 1$.

For $p = 0$, $\lim_{n\to\infty} \frac{1}{n^p} = 1$, and for $p < 0$, $\lim_{n\to\infty} \frac{1}{n^p} = \infty$. In either case, $\sum_{n=1}^{\infty} \frac{1}{n^p}$ diverges by the Nth term test. Summarizing, we have:

$$\sum_{n=1}^{\infty} \frac{1}{n^p} \text{ converges if } p > 1 \text{ and diverges if } p \leq 1.$$

EXAMPLE 24 Determine the convergence or divergence of the following p-series:

(a) $\sum_{n=1}^{\infty} \frac{1}{n^3}$ (b) $\sum_{n=1}^{\infty} \frac{1}{n^{3/2}}$ (c) $\sum_{n=1}^{\infty} \frac{1}{n^{1.01}}$

(d) $\sum_{n=1}^{\infty} \frac{1}{\sqrt{n}}$ (e) $\sum_{n=1}^{\infty} \frac{1}{\sqrt[3]{n}}$ (f) $\sum_{n=1}^{\infty} \frac{1}{n^{0.99}}$

Solution The first three series,

$$\text{(a)} \sum_{n=1}^{\infty} \frac{1}{n^3} \qquad \text{(b)} \sum_{n=1}^{\infty} \frac{1}{n^{3/2}} \qquad \text{(c)} \sum_{n=1}^{\infty} \frac{1}{n^{1.01}},$$

all *converge* ($p = 3$, $p = 3/2$, $p = 1.01$, respectively). The last three series,

$$\text{(d)} \sum_{n=1}^{\infty} \frac{1}{\sqrt{n}} \qquad \text{(e)} \sum_{n=1}^{\infty} \frac{1}{\sqrt[3]{n}} \qquad \text{(f)} \sum_{n=1}^{\infty} \frac{1}{n^{0.99}},$$

however, all *diverge* ($p = \frac{1}{2}$, $p = \frac{1}{3}$, $p = 0.99$, respectively). ■

Alternating series test

Requirements:

The terms in the series are alternately positive and negative. Such a series can be written

$$\sum_{n=1}^{\infty} (-1)^{n+1} c_n \qquad (c_n > 0)$$

if the first term is positive, or

$$\sum_{n=1}^{\infty} (-1)^{n} c_n \qquad (c_n > 0)$$

if the first term is negative.

Criteria:

If the magnitudes of the terms are strictly decreasing, so that

$$c_n > c_{n+1} > 0$$

for every n, and if

$$\lim_{n \to \infty} c_n = 0,$$

then the alternating series *converges.* If $\lim_{n\to\infty} c_n \neq 0$, then the series *diverges* by the Nth term test.

EXAMPLE 25 Does the alternating harmonic series $\sum_{n=1}^{\infty} \frac{(-1)^{n+1}}{n}$ converge or diverge?

Solution Here $c_n = \frac{1}{n}$. The alternating series test applies since the terms alternate signs and

$$\frac{1}{n} > \frac{1}{n+1} > 0$$

for every n.

Since $\lim_{n\to\infty} \frac{1}{n} = 0$, the alternating series test tells us that the alternating harmonic series *converges.* ■

Discussion:

Let's compute the first few partial sums of the alternating harmonic series:

$$S_1 = 1$$

$$S_2 = 1 - \frac{1}{2} = \frac{1}{2}$$

$$S_3 = 1 - \frac{1}{2} + \frac{1}{3} = \frac{5}{6}$$

$$S_4 = 1 - \frac{1}{2} + \frac{1}{3} - \frac{1}{4} = \frac{7}{12}$$

$$S_5 = 1 - \frac{1}{2} + \frac{1}{3} - \frac{1}{4} + \frac{1}{5} = \frac{47}{60}$$

$$S_6 = 1 - \frac{1}{2} + \frac{1}{3} - \frac{1}{4} + \frac{1}{5} - \frac{1}{6} = \frac{37}{60}.$$

If we plot these on a number line, we see that the even partial sums $S_2, S_4, S_6, \ldots$ strictly increase, while the odd partial sums strictly decrease (see Figure 10.7). A similar configuration of partial sums will be the case for any alternating series satisfying the criteria of the alternating series test. From the starting point S_1 we take a sequence of smaller and smaller steps, reversing direction each time. At any point in our "trip," all future points will be between our last two consecutive points. Since the distance between our last two points, S_{n-1} and S_n, is simply the size of our last step, c_n, and c_n approaches 0, the partial sums must converge to a single point.

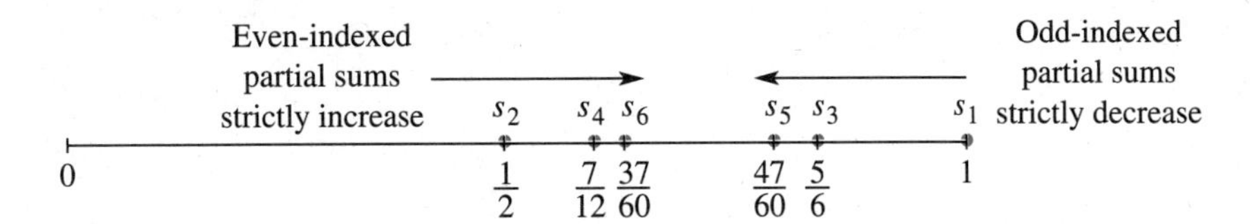

Figure 10.7 Partial sums of $\sum_{n=1}^{\infty} \frac{(-1)^{n+1}}{n}$.

Alternating series estimate:

This also means that we have a definite idea of how close we are to the limit L after any step, since L is between S_n and S_{n+1} for every n. If we use S_n as an approximation for L, then the remainder has magnitude

$$|R_n| < c_{n+1}.$$

We can tell whether S_n is on the right or left of the limit by the sign of the $(n+1)$st term.

EXAMPLE 26 Find the limit of the alternating harmonic series within .001.

Solution We choose $N = 1000$ so that

$$c_{N+1} = \frac{1}{N+1} = \frac{1}{1001} < .001.$$

Now we compute

$$\sum_{n=1}^{1000} \frac{(-1)^{n+1}}{n} \approx 0.69265$$

(to five decimal places). We mentioned that it is known that

$$\sum_{n=1}^{\infty} \frac{(-1)^{n+1}}{n} = \ln(2).$$

We note that $\ln(2) \approx 0.69315$ to five decimal places. ■

EXERCISES for Section 10.3

For exercises 1–4: Apply the alternating series test to each of these series.

1. $\sum_{n=1}^{\infty}(-1)^n \ln(1+\frac{1}{n})$

2. $\sum_{n=1}^{\infty}(-1)^n \frac{\ln(n)}{n}$

3. $\sum_{n=1}^{\infty}(-1)^n \frac{\arctan(n)}{n^3}$

4. $\sum_{n=1}^{\infty} \frac{(-1)^n n}{2n^2-1}$

5. For each series in exercises 1-4 that converges, find its sum accurate to four decimal places.

For exercises 6–9: Apply the integral test to each of these series.

6. $\sum_{n=1}^{\infty} 3e^{-n}$
7. $\sum_{n=1}^{\infty} ne^{-n}$
8. $\sum_{n=1}^{\infty} \frac{\ln(n)}{n}$
9. $\sum_{n=1}^{\infty} \frac{1}{4n^2+9}$

10. For each series in exercises 6-9 that converges, find its sum accurate to four decimal places.

For exercises 11–12: Explain why the integral test does not apply to each of these series.

11. $\sum_{n=1}^{\infty} e^{-n} \sin n$
12. $\sum_{n=1}^{\infty} \frac{(-1)^n}{n}$

---

13. Given the series $\sum_{n=1}^{\infty} \frac{1}{n^6}$, find the least positive integer N such that the remainder tail $R_N = \sum_{n=N+1}^{\infty} \frac{1}{n^6}$ is less than 2×10^{-11}. Find S_N, and give an upper and lower bound for the sum of the series.

14. Given the series $\sum_{n=0}^{\infty} \frac{(-1)^n}{n!}$, find the least positive integer N such that $|R_N| < .000005$. The value S_N will approximate the series sum accurate to 5 decimal places. (Note: It is known that $\sum_{n=0}^{\infty} \frac{(-1)^n}{n!} = \frac{1}{e}$. Use this to check your result.)

15. Show that the series $\sum_{n=1}^{\infty} \ln(1 + \frac{1}{n})$ *diverges* using the integral test. Use integration by parts, letting $u = \ln(1 + \frac{1}{x})$ and $dv = dx$. (Note: When evaluating the integral, you will need to use L'Hôpital's rule, since the indeterminate form $0 \cdot \infty$ appears.)

For exercises 16–20: Explain why each of the given statements is *false* by providing an example that contradicts the statement.

16. If $\lim_{n\to\infty} a_n = 0$, then the series $\sum_{n=1}^{\infty} a_n$, $a_n > 0$ for all n, converges.

17. If the sequence $\{a_n\}_{n=1}^{\infty}$ converges, then the series $\sum_{n=1}^{\infty} a_n$ converges.

18. If $\sum_{n=1}^{\infty} a_n$ diverges (where $a_n > 0$ for all n), then the alternating series $\sum_{n=1}^{\infty} (-1)^n a_n$ also diverges.

19. If $\sum_{n=1}^{\infty} a_n$ and $\sum_{n=1}^{\infty} b_n$ both diverge, then $\sum_{n=1}^{\infty} (a_n + b_n)$ must also diverge.

20. If $\sum_{n=1}^{\infty} a_n$ converges, then $\sum_{n=1}^{\infty} (-1)^n a_n$ must also converge.

10.4 MORE TESTS OF CONVERGENCE—ABSOLUTE AND CONDITIONAL CONVERGENCE

Sometimes we can judge the convergence or divergence of one series by comparing it to another series whose behavior is known. The next two tests are of this type.

Comparison test

Requirements:

The two series $\sum_{n=1}^{\infty} a_n$ and $\sum_{n=1}^{\infty} b_n$ must each have nonnegative terms. That is,

$$a_n \geq 0, \qquad b_n \geq 0 \qquad \text{for all } n.$$

Criteria:

If $a_n \leq b_n$ for each n, and $\sum_{n=1}^{\infty} b_n$ converges, then $\sum_{n=1}^{\infty} a_n$ converges.

If $b_n \leq a_n$ for each n, and $\sum_{n=1}^{\infty} b_n$ diverges, then $\sum_{n=1}^{\infty} a_n$ diverges.

Discussion:

The requirement that the terms a_n and b_n all be nonnegative guarantees that the partial sums of both series are *monotonically increasing*; hence, either series will converge *if and only if* its partial sums are *bounded*.

The way this test is used in practice is as follows: If the behavior of a given series

$$\sum_{n=1}^{\infty} a_n$$

is unknown and each term $a_n \geq 0$, then we search for (or devise) a comparison series $\sum_{n=1}^{\infty} b_n$ with $b_n \geq 0$.

If we suspect that $\sum_{n=1}^{\infty} a_n$ converges, then we search for a "larger" series $\sum_{n=1}^{\infty} b_n$ (in other words, $b_n \geq a_n$ for each n) that we know converges.

If we suspect that $\sum_{n=1}^{\infty} a_n$ diverges, then we search for a "smaller" series $\sum_{n=1}^{\infty} b_n$ (in other words, $b_n \leq a_n$ for each n) that we know diverges.

In either case, success in finding the series $\sum_{n=1}^{\infty} b_n$ with the property we desire means that we can use the comparison test to deduce the convergence or divergence of the original series $\sum_{n=1}^{\infty} a_n$.

What are good series $\sum_{n=1}^{\infty} b_n$ to look for? In general, any series whose behavior you know is a candidate. Geometric series and p-series are good candidates, because they provide us with a large storehouse of both convergent and divergent series.

How do you choose a particular series $\sum_{n=1}^{\infty} b_n$? If you're looking for a "larger" series, try making some simplifying changes to the terms a_n that will result in larger terms (for example, decreasing denominators, increasing numerators, adding a positive amount, etc.). If you're looking for a "smaller" series, try making simplifying changes that will result in smaller terms (increasing denominators, decreasing numerators, subtracting a positive amount, etc.).

EXAMPLE 27 Does the series $\sum_{n=1}^{\infty} \dfrac{2^n}{3^n + n^4}$ converge or diverge?

Solution To get a feel for the series, let's write the first few terms in the sum:

$$\frac{2}{4} + \frac{4}{25} + \frac{8}{108} + \frac{16}{337} + \cdots.$$

These terms appear to be decreasing in size quite quickly, and the form of the series suggests that we try comparing it to a geometric series. Since we suspect that the series converges, we look for a "larger" series that we know converges.

If we remove n^4 from the denominator, we have

$$a_n = \frac{2^n}{3^n + n^4} \le \frac{2^n}{3^n} = b_n$$

for each n. The geometric series $\sum_{n=1}^{\infty} (\frac{2}{3})^n$ converges $(-1 < r = 2/3 < 1)$, so

$$\sum_{n=1}^{\infty} \frac{2^n}{3^n + n^4}$$

converges by the comparison test. ■

EXAMPLE 28 Does the series $\sum_{n=1}^{\infty} \dfrac{1}{n + \sqrt{n}}$ converge or diverge?

Solution If we remove $\sqrt{n}$ from the denominator, we get a "larger" series,

$$\sum_{n=1}^{\infty} \frac{1}{n},$$

that diverges. Note, though, that this result is of no help to us. (Similarly, finding a "smaller" series that converges will tell us no information about the original series). If, however, we replace $\sqrt{n}$ by n, we obtain a "*smaller*" series,

$$\sum_{n=1}^{\infty} \frac{1}{n+n} = \sum_{n=1}^{\infty} \frac{1}{2n} = \frac{1}{2} \sum_{n=1}^{\infty} \frac{1}{n},$$

that we know diverges. We can conclude that $\sum_{n=1}^{\infty} \dfrac{1}{n + \sqrt{n}}$ *diverges* by the comparison test. ■

EXAMPLE 29 Why can't the comparison test be used on the alternating harmonic series?

Solution The comparison test cannot be used on the alternating harmonic series

$$\sum_{n=1}^{\infty} \frac{(-1)^{n+1}}{n}$$

because some of its terms are negative. (Check the requirements of the comparison test.) ■

Since any partial sum S_N is necessarily finite (adding finitely many real numbers always yields a finite result), it is always the remainder tail R_N that decides whether or not a series converges. This means that the requirements and criteria of the comparison test need only be satisfied by all the terms in a common remainder tail of two series being compared.

Consider the two series

$$\sum_{n=1}^{\infty} \frac{1}{2^n+1} = \frac{1}{3} + \frac{1}{5} + \frac{1}{9} + \frac{1}{17} + \cdots$$

and

$$\sum_{n=1}^{\infty} \frac{1}{n^2-2} = -1 + \frac{1}{2} + \frac{1}{7} + \frac{1}{14} + \cdots .$$

Note that the first term of the second series is negative and smaller than the first term of the first series. However, starting with the second terms, the second series has consistently larger terms. This means that the comparison test can be used with these two series. That is, if the first diverges, so does the second. If the second converges, so does the first. (By the way, which is it?)

Limit comparison test

Requirements:

Both series $\sum_{n=1}^{\infty} a_n$ and $\sum_{n=1}^{\infty} b_n$ must have positive terms

$$a_n > 0, \qquad b_n > 0 \qquad \text{for all } n.$$

Criteria:

If $\lim_{n\to\infty} \dfrac{a_n}{b_n} = \infty$ and $\sum_{n=1}^{\infty} b_n$ diverges, then $\sum_{n=1}^{\infty} a_n$ diverges.

If $\lim_{n\to\infty} \dfrac{a_n}{b_n} = 0$ and $\sum_{n=1}^{\infty} b_n$ converges, then $\sum_{n=1}^{\infty} a_n$ converges.

If $\lim_{n\to\infty} \dfrac{a_n}{b_n} = L \neq 0$ (L a real number), then $\sum_{n=1}^{\infty} a_n$ and $\sum_{n=1}^{\infty} b_n$ behave the same. That is, either both series converge or both diverge.

Discussion:

Recall that a necessary (but not sufficient) condition for a series $\sum_{n=1}^{\infty} a_n$ to converge is that $\lim_{n\to\infty} a_n = 0$ (the Nth term test). Even if the terms do approach 0, they might not approach 0 "fast enough" for the series to converge. (The harmonic series is the best known example of this phenomenon.)

The limit comparison test looks at the ratio of the terms a_n/b_n from two series. If both $\lim_{n\to\infty} a_n = 0$ and $\lim_{n\to\infty} b_n = 0$, then

$$\lim_{n\to\infty} \frac{a_n}{b_n}$$

gives us a measure of the relative speeds that a_n and b_n approach 0.

If $\lim_{n\to\infty} \dfrac{a_n}{b_n} = \infty$, then a_n approaches 0 much "slower" than b_n.

If $\lim_{n\to\infty} \dfrac{a_n}{b_n} = 0$, then a_n approaches 0 much "faster" than b_n.

If $\lim_{n\to\infty} \dfrac{a_n}{b_n} = L \neq 0$, then a_n and b_n approach 0 at "comparable" speeds.

Like the comparison test, the limit comparison test is used to decide the divergence or convergence of a series $\sum_{n=1}^{\infty} a_n$ by choosing or devising a comparison sequence $\sum_{n=1}^{\infty} b_n$ whose behavior is known. If a_n can be described by a formula, then a good choice for b_n is to use only the dominant (fastest growing) terms of the formula. Constant coefficients can usually be changed to $+1$ or -1, depending on the sign.

EXAMPLE 30 Does $\sum_{n=1}^{\infty} \dfrac{6}{\sqrt{17n^3+5}}$ converge or diverge?

Solution The fastest growing term in the denominator under the radical sign is $17n^3$. We'll choose $b_n = \dfrac{1}{\sqrt{n^3}}$, for the purposes of comparison. Now,

$$\lim_{n\to\infty} \frac{a_n}{b_n} = \lim_{n\to\infty} \frac{\dfrac{6}{\sqrt{17n^3+5}}}{\dfrac{1}{\sqrt{n^3}}} = \lim_{n\to\infty} \frac{6\sqrt{n^3}}{\sqrt{17n^3+5}} = \lim_{n\to\infty} 6\sqrt{\frac{n^3}{17n^3+5}}.$$

Since $\lim_{n\to\infty} \dfrac{n^3}{17n^3+5} = \dfrac{1}{17}$, we have

$$\lim_{n\to\infty} \frac{a_n}{b_n} = \frac{6}{\sqrt{17}} \neq 0.$$

The limit comparison test tells us that both $\sum_{n=1}^{\infty} a_n$ and $\sum_{n=1}^{\infty} b_n$ have the same behavior. Since

$$\sum_{n=1}^{\infty} b_n = \sum_{n=1}^{\infty} \frac{1}{\sqrt{n^3}} = \sum_{n=1}^{\infty} \frac{1}{n^{3/2}}$$

converges, we conclude that $\sum_{n=1}^{\infty} \dfrac{6}{\sqrt{17n^3+5}}$ also *converges*. ■

EXAMPLE 31 Why can't the limit comparison test be applied to the alternating harmonic series?

Solution Again, the limit comparison test cannot be used on the alternating harmonic series

$$\sum_{n=1}^{\infty} \frac{(-1)^{n+1}}{n}$$

because some of the terms are negative (check the requirements of the limit comparison test). ■

Absolute and conditional convergence

When a series has both positive and negative terms, such as an alternating series, the notions of *absolute convergence* and *conditional convergence* become relevant.

Definition 4

Suppose that a series $\sum_{n=1}^{\infty} a_n$ converges.
If the series $\sum |a_n|$ converges, we say that $\sum_{n=1}^{\infty} a_n$ is **absolutely convergent**.
If the series $\sum |a_n|$ diverges, we say that $\sum_{n=1}^{\infty} a_n$ is **conditionally convergent**.

EXAMPLE 32 Are the following series absolutely convergent, conditionally convergent, or divergent?

(a) $\sum_{n=1}^{\infty} \frac{(-1)^{n+1}}{n}$ (b) $\sum_{n=1}^{\infty} (-\frac{1}{2})^n$

Solution (a) The alternating harmonic series is conditionally convergent because

$$\sum_{n=1}^{\infty} \frac{(-1)^{n+1}}{n}$$

converges, but

$$\sum_{n=1}^{\infty} \left| \frac{(-1)^{n+1}}{n} \right| = \sum_{n=1}^{\infty} \frac{1}{n}$$

diverges.

(b) The geometric series

$$\sum_{n=1}^{\infty}(-\frac{1}{2})^n$$

is absolutely convergent because

$$\sum_{n=1}^{\infty}\left|(-\frac{1}{2})^n\right| = \sum_{n=1}^{\infty}(\frac{1}{2})^n$$

converges. ■

A useful result is the following theorem.

Theorem 10.3

Hypothesis: $\sum_{n=1}^{\infty}|a_n|$ converges.
Conclusion: $\sum_{n=1}^{\infty}a_n$ converges.

In other words, if we replace each term in a series by its absolute value and the resulting series converges, then the original series must converge. In fewer words, *an absolutely convergent series converges.*

Reasoning Suppose that we have a series $\sum_{n=1}^{\infty}a_n$ and we know that

$$\sum_{n=1}^{\infty}|a_n|$$

converges. If we let $b_n = a_n + |a_n|$, we'll either get $b_n = 0$ (when a_n is negative) or $b_n = 2|a_n|$ (when a_n is positive). Either way, we can say that

$$0 \le b_n = a_n + |a_n| \le 2|a_n|.$$

Using the comparison test, we can see that $\sum_{n=1}^{\infty}b_n$ converges because $\sum_{n=1}^{\infty}2|a_n|$ converges. Finally, that means $\sum_{n=1}^{\infty}a_n = \sum_{n=1}^{\infty}(b_n - |a_n|)$ must converge also. □

This theorem is useful because we have several tests requiring all our terms to be nonnegative (the integral test, the comparison test, and the limit comparison test). If we have a series $\sum_{n=1}^{\infty}a_n$ not satisfying this requirement, we can try replacing a_n by $|a_n|$. All the terms of $\sum_{n=1}^{\infty}|a_n|$ are nonnegative, so there are more tests that are available to use. If we find $\sum_{n=1}^{\infty}|a_n|$ converges, then this theorem tells us that $\sum_{n=1}^{\infty}a_n$ must also converge. However, if we find $\sum_{n=1}^{\infty}|a_n|$ diverges, we really don't have any more information about $\sum_{n=1}^{\infty}a_n$, because it could be conditionally convergent.

There are two convergence tests for series that can be used to test for absolute convergence.

Ratio test

Requirements:

$\sum_{n=1}^{\infty} a_n$ can be any series.

Criteria:

If $\lim_{n\to\infty} |\frac{a_{n+1}}{a_n}| = L$, then

$\sum_{n=1}^{\infty} a_n$ is absolutely convergent when $L < 1$,

$\sum_{n=1}^{\infty} a_n$ is divergent when $L > 1$,

and the ratio test *fails to provide any information when* $L = 1$.

Discussion:

When $\lim_{n\to\infty} |\frac{a_{n+1}}{a_n}| = L < 1$, this tells us that the terms $|a_n|$ are decreasing fast enough for the series $\sum |a_n|$ to converge. (Essentially, for some remainder tail of the series $\sum |a_n|$, we can find a larger convergent geometric series by choosing a factor $L < r < 1$ and use the comparison test.) If $\lim_{n\to\infty} |\frac{a_{n+1}}{a_n}| = L > 1$, then the terms a_n are not approaching 0 and the series $\sum_{n=1}^{\infty} a_n$ must diverge.

The ratio test is often useful when the index n appears as an exponent in the formula for a_n (as it does for geometric series), or when the formula for a_n involves $n!$ (n factorial).

EXAMPLE 33 Use the ratio test to test for the absolute convergence of the series

$$\sum_{n=0}^{\infty} \frac{(-1)^n}{n!}.$$

Solution The first few terms in the sum are

$$1 + (-1) + \frac{1}{2} - \frac{1}{6} + \frac{1}{24} - \frac{1}{120} + \cdots.$$

This is an alternating series whose terms strictly decrease in magnitude. Since

$$\lim_{n\to\infty} \frac{1}{n!} = 0,$$

the series converges. To check for absolute convergence, we first form the ratio

$$\left|\frac{a_{n+1}}{a_n}\right| = \left|\frac{\frac{(-1)^{n+1}}{(n+1)!}}{\frac{(-1)^n}{n!}}\right| = \frac{n!}{(n+1)!} = \frac{1}{n+1}.$$

(If the last step in the above equality seems confusing to you, try evaluating $\frac{n!}{(n+1)!}$ for $n = 1, 2, 3, 4$ to see the pattern.)

Now, $\lim_{n\to\infty}\left|\frac{a_{n+1}}{a_n}\right| = \lim_{n\to\infty}\frac{1}{n+1} = 0 < 1$. So the ratio test tells us that the series $\sum_{n=0}^{\infty}\frac{(-1)^n}{n!}$ is absolutely convergent. ■

EXAMPLE 34 Use the ratio test to test for the absolute convergence of the series $\sum_{n=1}^{\infty}\frac{2^n}{n^5}$.

Solution The first few terms in the sum are

$$2 + \frac{1}{8} + \frac{8}{243} + \frac{16}{1024} + \cdots$$

and at first glance, these terms appear to be approaching 0 rapidly. However, if we apply the ratio test, we find

$$\lim_{n\to\infty}\left|\frac{a_{n+1}}{a_n}\right| = \lim_{n\to\infty}\frac{\frac{2^{n+1}}{(n+1)^5}}{\frac{2^n}{n^5}} = \lim_{n\to\infty} 2\cdot(\frac{n}{n+1})^5 = 2 > 1.$$

The ratio test tells us that this series diverges. ■

EXAMPLE 35 Use the ratio test to test for the absolute convergence of the alternating harmonic series $\sum_{n=1}^{\infty}\frac{(-1)^{n+1}}{n}$.

Solution $\lim_{n\to\infty}\left|\frac{a_{n+1}}{a_n}\right| = \lim_{n\to\infty}\left|\frac{\frac{(-1)^{n+2}}{(n+1)}}{\frac{(-1)^{n+1}}{n}}\right| = \lim_{n\to\infty}\frac{n}{n+1} = 1$. The ratio test fails to provide us any information in this case (though we know that the alternating harmonic series conditionally converges). ■

Root test

Requirements:

$\sum_{n=1}^{\infty} a_n$ can be any series.

Criteria:

If $\lim_{n\to\infty} \sqrt[n]{|a_n|} = L$, then

$\sum_{n=1}^{\infty} a_n$ is absolutely convergent when $L < 1$,

$\sum_{n=1}^{\infty} a_n$ is divergent when $L > 1$,

and the root test *fails to provide any information when* $L = 1$.

Discussion:

The root test is more powerful than the ratio test in the following sense: whenever the ratio test provides information, so will the root test; however, there are instances where the ratio test fails but the root test does not. In practice, you will probably find the ratio test much easier to apply. (Essentially, if $L \neq 1$, then the root test follows from applying the limit comparison test to the series $\sum |a_n|$ and the geometric series $\sum r^n$, where r is chosen to be some number between 1 and L.)

EXAMPLE 36 Use the root test to test for the absolute convergence of the series

$$\sum_{n=1}^{\infty} \frac{(-1)^n}{n^n}.$$

Solution

$$\lim_{n\to\infty} \sqrt[n]{|a_n|} = \lim_{n\to\infty} \sqrt[n]{\frac{1}{n^n}} = \lim_{n\to\infty} \frac{1}{n} = 0 < 1.$$

The root test tells us that this series is absolutely convergent. ■

Summary of Convergence Tests

Test	*Form*	*Converges*	*Diverges*
N*th* **term**	$\sum_{n=1}^{\infty} a_n$	no information	$\lim_{n\to\infty} a_n \neq 0$
Integral test	$\sum_{n=1}^{\infty} a_n$ where $a_n = f(n)$	$\int_1^{\infty} f(x)\,dx$ converges	$\int_1^{\infty} f(x)\,dx$ diverges

(NOTE: f must be continuous, positive, and decreasing.)

Integral test estimate:

$$\sum_{n=1}^{\infty} a_n = \sum_{n=1}^{N} a_n + \int_{N+1}^{\infty} f(x)\,dx + \text{error}, \qquad \text{where error} \leq \int_{N}^{N+1} f(x)\,dx.$$

Alternating	$\sum_{n=1}^{\infty}(-1)^{n+1}c_n$ $0 < c_{n+1} < c_n$	$\lim_{n\to\infty} c_n = 0$	$\lim_{n\to\infty} c_n \neq 0$

Alternating series estimate:

$$\sum_{n=1}^{\infty}(-1)^{n-1}c_n = \sum_{n=1}^{N}(-1)^{n-1}c_n \pm \text{error}, \qquad \text{where the error} \leq c_{N+1}.$$

Summary of Convergence Tests

Test	*Form*	*Converges*	*Diverges*
Comparison	$\sum_{n=1}^{\infty} a_n$	$0 \leq a_n \leq b_n$, and $\sum_{n=1}^{\infty} b_n$ converges	$0 \leq b_n \leq a_n$, and $\sum_{n=1}^{\infty} b_n$ diverges
Limit comparison	$\sum_{n=1}^{\infty} a_n$ $(a_n, b_n > 0)$	$\lim_{n\to\infty} \frac{a_n}{b_n} = L \geq 0$ and $\sum_{n=1}^{\infty} b_n$ converges	$\lim_{n\to\infty} \frac{a_n}{b_n} = L > 0$ or ∞ and $\sum_{n=1}^{\infty} b_n$ diverges
Ratio	$\sum_{n=1}^{\infty} a_n$	$\lim_{n\to\infty} \left\lvert \frac{a_{n+1}}{a_n} \right\rvert < 1$	$\lim_{n\to\infty} \left\lvert \frac{a_{n+1}}{a_n} \right\rvert > 1$
Root	$\sum_{n=1}^{\infty} a_n$	$\lim_{n\to\infty} \sqrt[n]{\lvert a_n \rvert} < 1$	$\lim_{n\to\infty} \sqrt[n]{\lvert a_n \rvert} > 1$

Some Special Series

Series	*Form*	*Converges*	*Diverges*
Telescoping	$\sum_{n=1}^{\infty}(b_n - b_{n+1})$	$\lim_{n\to\infty} b_n = 0$	$\lim_{n\to\infty} b_n \neq 0$
Geometric	$\sum_{n=0}^{\infty} ar^n$	$\lvert r \rvert < 1$	$\lvert r \rvert \geq 1$
p-series	$\sum_{n=1}^{\infty} \frac{1}{n^p}$	$p > 1$	$p \leq 1$

EXERCISES for Section 10.4

For exercises 1–5: Determine whether the given series converges or diverges, using the indicated test.

1. $\sum_{n=0}^{\infty}(-1)^n \frac{e^n}{e^{2n}+1}$ (Use ratio test.)
2. $\sum_{n=1}^{\infty} \frac{(1-\pi)^n}{2^{n+1}}$ (Use root test.)
3. $\sum_{n=1}^{\infty} \frac{2^{3n}}{7^n}$ (Use root test.)
4. $\sum_{n=1}^{\infty} \frac{n!n^2}{(2n)!}$ (Use ratio test.)

5. $\sum_{n=1}^{\infty} \frac{(-1)^{n+1}2^{3n+2}}{n^n}$ (Use root test.)

---

6. Consider the series

$$\sum_{n=1}^{\infty} \frac{n}{2n^2-1}.$$

Does the ratio test indicate convergence, divergence, or no information?

7. Consider the series

$$\sum_{n=1}^{\infty} \frac{n}{2n^2-1}.$$

Does the root test indicate convergence, divergence, or no information?

8. Use the ratio test to show that the series $\sum_{n=0}^{\infty} \frac{(-1)^n}{(2n)!}$ absolutely converges. Find the smallest N such that S_N is accurate to 6 decimal places. Give the estimate for the sum of the series accurate to 6 decimal places.

9. Determine whether $\sum_{n=1}^{\infty}(-1)^{n+1}\frac{n^{2n}}{(3n^2+1)^n}$ absolutely converges, converges conditionally, or diverges.

10. Show that the ratio test is inconclusive when applied to the series

$$\sum_{n=1}^{\infty}(-1)^{n+1}\frac{\pi^{1/n}}{n}.$$

Then use any tests necessary to determine whether the series absolutely converges, conditionally converges, or diverges.

11. Suppose that I have a p-series $\sum_{n=1}^{\infty} \frac{1}{n^p}$ where p is a specific positive number. Show that the ratio test *always* fails to give any information about the convergence or divergence of this series.

12. Suppose that I have an alternating p-series $\sum_{n=1}^{\infty} \frac{(-1)^n}{n^p}$ where p is a specific positive number. For what values of p will this series converge?

13. Determine whether $\sum_{n=1}^{\infty}(-1)^{n+1}3e^{-n}$ converges absolutely, converges conditionally, or diverges.

14. Find the sum of the series $\sum_{n=1}^{\infty} \frac{2^n}{3^{n-1}}$.

15. Decide whether $\sum_{n=1}^{\infty} \frac{1}{3+5^n}$ converges or diverges by using the comparison test with the geometric series $\sum_{n=1}^{\infty} \frac{1}{5^n}$.

16. Decide whether $\sum_{n=1}^{\infty} \frac{e^{1/n}}{n}$ converges or diverges by using the limit comparison test with $\sum_{n=1}^{\infty} \frac{1}{n}$.

For exercises 17–38: For each series, indicate whether it converges absolutely, converges conditionally, or diverges. Indicate what test or tests you use in each case.

17. $\sum_{n=1}^{\infty} \frac{n^2}{\sqrt{n^5}}$

18. $\sum_{n=1}^{\infty} \frac{1}{(-5)^n}$

19. $\sum_{n=1}^{\infty} \frac{1}{n+1000000}$

20. $\sum_{n=1}^{\infty} (-e)^{-n}$

21. $\sum_{n=1}^{\infty} \frac{\sin^2 \frac{1}{n}}{2^n}$

22. $\sum_{n=1}^{\infty} \frac{1}{2^{1/n}}$

23. $\sum_{n=1}^{\infty} \frac{n^n}{n!}$

24. $\sum_{n=1}^{\infty} (2-e)^n$

25. $\sum_{n=1}^{\infty} \frac{3^n}{n!}$

26. $\sum_{n=1}^{\infty} \frac{n \ln n}{n^2+1}$

27. $\sum_{n=1}^{\infty} \frac{1}{\sqrt{n}}$

28. $\sum_{n=1}^{\infty} \frac{(-1)^n}{\sqrt{n}}$

29. $\sum_{n=1}^{\infty} \frac{(-1)^n}{\sqrt[n]{10}}$

30. $\sum_{n=1}^{\infty} \frac{e^n}{2^n}$

31. $\sum_{n=1}^{\infty} \sin(n\pi/2)$

32. $\sum_{n=1}^{\infty} \frac{n^2}{n^3+n}$

33. $\sum_{n=2}^{\infty} \frac{(-1)^n}{\ln n}$

34. $\sum_{n=1}^{\infty} \left(\frac{n-1}{n}\right)^n$

35. $\sum_{n=1}^{\infty} \frac{3^n}{2^n+4^n}$

36. $\sum_{n=1}^{\infty} n \sin(1/n)$

37. $\sum_{n=1}^{\infty} \frac{(-5)^n}{n!}$

38. $\sum_{n=1}^{\infty} n e^{-n^2}$

10.5 POWER SERIES

A **power series** with real number coefficients has the form

$$\sum_{n=0}^{\infty} c_n x^n = c_0 + c_1 x + c_2 x^2 + c_3 x^3 + \cdots + c_n x^n + \cdots,$$

where each c_n is a real number and x is a variable. Roughly speaking, a power series is a polynomial with infinitely many terms. More precisely, it is the limit of a sequence of polynomials:

$$\begin{aligned}
p_0(x) &= c_0 \\
p_1(x) &= c_0 + c_1 x \\
p_2(x) &= c_0 + c_1 x + c_2 x^2 \\
p_3(x) &= c_0 + c_1 x + c_2 x^2 + c_3 x^3 \\
&\vdots
\end{aligned}$$

where $p_n(x) = c_0 + c_1 x + c_2 x^2 + c_3 x^3 + \cdots + c_n x^n$ is a polynomial of degree n. These polynomials play the role of partial sums, and

$$\sum_{n=0}^{\infty} c_n x^n = \lim_{n \to \infty} p_n(x).$$

We'll see that power series may be manipulated much like polynomials. Polynomial functions are particularly easy to work with in calculus, and it is remarkable that so many non-polynomial functions (such as the trigonometric functions) can be represented as power series.

Sometimes it is convenient to have a particular real number a as a point of reference. In this case, we may wish to write a power series in terms of $(x - a)$ instead of x:

$$\sum_{n=0}^{\infty} c_n (x-a)^n = c_0 + c_1(x-a) + c_2(x-a)^2 + c_3(x-a)^3 + \cdots + c_n(x-a)^n + \cdots$$

A power series written this way is said to be represented *about* $x = a$. A power series written in terms of powers of x is said to be represented about $x = 0$. For example,

$$\sum_{n=0}^{\infty} x^n = 1 + x + x^2 + x^3 + \cdots$$

is a power series represented about $x = 0$, and

$$\sum_{n=0}^{\infty} \frac{(x-1)^n}{n} = 1 + (x-1) + \frac{(x-1)^2}{2} + \frac{(x-1)^3}{3} + \cdots$$

is a power series represented about $x = 1$.

To evaluate a power series $\sum_{n=0}^{\infty} c_n x^n$ at a specific input value $x = x_0$, we substitute the value x_0 and obtain a "regular" series:

$$\sum_{n=0}^{\infty} c_n x_0^n$$

that may or may not converge to finite value. This raises the question: for exactly which input values x does the power series $\sum_{n=0}^{\infty} c_n x^n$ converge?

Radius and interval of convergence

If $\sum_{n=0}^{\infty} c_n x^n$ is a power series represented about $x = 0$, then there is always one value x that guarantees convergence—namely, $x = 0$. Note that substituting $x = 0$ makes all the terms 0 except, perhaps, the constant term c_0.

Similarly, if $\sum_{n=0}^{\infty} c_n (x-a)^n$ is a power series represented about $x = a$, then substituting $x = a$ guarantees convergence. To find the entire set of input values for which a power series converges, the ratio or root test may be used.

EXAMPLE 37 Find the set of input values x for which the power series $\sum_{n=0}^{\infty} \frac{x^n}{3^{2n}}$ converges.

Solution Using the ratio test, we find that

$$\lim_{n\to\infty} \left| \frac{x^{n+1}/3^{2(n+1)}}{x^n/3^{2n}} \right| = \lim_{n\to\infty} |x| \frac{3^{2n}}{3^{2n+2}} = \lim_{n\to\infty} \frac{|x|}{9} = \frac{|x|}{9}.$$

This limit value depends on x, and the ratio test tells us that the power series

$\sum_{n=0}^{\infty} \frac{x^n}{3^{2n}}$ *converges* if $\frac{|x|}{9} < 1$, and $\sum_{n=0}^{\infty} \frac{x^n}{3^{2n}}$ *diverges* if $\frac{|x|}{9} > 1$.

We still need to determine the behavior for $\frac{|x|}{9} = 1$ or, equivalently, for $x = \pm 9$. We can substitute these two values directly back into the power series. For $x = 9$, we have

$$\sum_{n=0}^{\infty} \frac{9^n}{3^{2n}} = \sum_{n=0}^{\infty} 1,$$

which *diverges*. For $x = -9$, we have

$$\sum_{n=0}^{\infty} \frac{(-9)^n}{3^{2n}} = \sum_{n=0}^{\infty} (-1)^n,$$

which also *diverges*. We can conclude that the power series converges precisely when $\frac{|x|}{9} < 1$ or, equivalently, on the interval

$$\{x \,:\, -9 < x < 9\}.$$

We note that the same conclusion can be reached by using the root test. In this case, we examine

$$\lim_{n\to\infty} \sqrt[n]{\left|\frac{x^n}{3^{2n}}\right|} = \lim_{n\to\infty} \frac{|x|}{3^2} = \frac{|x|}{9}.$$

The criteria for the root test are the same as for the ratio test, so the analysis is exactly the same. ■

The power series $\sum_{n=0}^{\infty} \frac{x^n}{3^{2n}}$ is represented about $x = 0$. Note that the set of values for which this power series converges is an *interval* $(-9, 9)$ *centered* at 0. This is no coincidence.

Theorem 10.4

Hypothesis: $\sum_{n=0}^{\infty} c_n(x-a)^n$ is a power series represented about $x = a$.
Conclusion: The set of values for which the power series converges is an *interval* centered at a.

This interval is called the **interval of convergence** for the power series. The radius R of this interval (in other words, the distance from the center a to either endpoint) is called the **radius of convergence**.

The interval of convergence may take any of the forms

$$[a-R, a+R], \qquad [a-R, a+R), \qquad (a-R, a+R], \qquad (a-R, a+R),$$

depending on which endpoints, if any, are included.

Reasoning If we use the root test on any power series $\sum_{n=0}^{\infty} c_n(x-a)^n$, our criteria for convergence requires us to find the values x such that

$$\lim_{n\to\infty} \sqrt[n]{|c_n(x-a)^n|} = \lim_{n\to\infty} \sqrt[n]{|c_n|}\,|x-a| < 1.$$

If $\lim_{n\to\infty} \sqrt[n]{|c_n|} = \infty$, then the power series converges only for $x = a$. In this situation, $R = 0$ is the radius of convergence, and the interval of convergence is the single point $\{a\}$.

If $\lim_{n\to\infty} \sqrt[n]{|c_n|} = 0$, then the power series converges for *any* real number x. In this situation, we say $R = \infty$ is the radius of convergence, and the interval of convergence is the whole real line $(-\infty, \infty)$.

If $\lim_{n\to\infty} \sqrt[n]{|c_n|} = L \neq 0$, then the power series converges for those values x satisfying

$$L\,|x-a| < 1 \qquad \text{or} \qquad |x-a| < R,$$

where we have written $R = 1/L$. In addition, the power series may or may not converge at the two values $x = a - R$ or $x = a + R$. In any case, the set of values in this situation is a bounded interval centered at $x = a$. □

In general, we can use the root or ratio test to find an open interval of convergence $(a - R, a + R)$ and then check the endpoints by direct substitution into the power series.

EXAMPLE 38 Find the interval and radius of convergence for the power series

$$\sum_{n=0}^{\infty} \frac{3^n (x+2)^n}{n!}.$$

Solution Using the ratio test, we have

$$\lim_{n\to\infty} \frac{\left|3^{n+1}(x+2)^{n+1}/(n+1)!\right|}{\left|3^n (x+2)^n/n!\right|} = \lim_{n\to\infty} \frac{3\,|x+2|}{n+1} = 0$$

for any value x. Therefore, the interval of convergence is $(-\infty, \infty)$ and the radius of convergence is $R = \infty$. ■

EXAMPLE 39 Find the interval and radius of convergence for the power series

$$\sum_{n=0}^{\infty} \frac{3^n (x+2)^n}{n+1}.$$

Solution Using the ratio test, we have

$$\lim_{n\to\infty} \frac{\left|3^{n+1}(x+2)^{n+1}/(n+2)\right|}{\left|3^n (x+2)^n/(n+1)\right|} = \lim_{n\to\infty} \frac{3(n+1)\,|x+2|}{n+2} = 3\,|x+2|,$$

since $\lim_{n\to\infty} \dfrac{n+1}{n+2} = 1$. By the ratio test, the power series converges for any value x satisfying

$$3\,|x+2| < 1 \qquad \text{or} \qquad \frac{-7}{3} < x < \frac{-5}{3}.$$

We must check the behavior at the endpoints $x = -7/3$ and $x = -5/3$ by direct substitution into the power series $\sum_{n=0}^{\infty} \dfrac{3^n (x+2)^n}{n+1}$.

For $x = -7/3$, we have $\sum_{n=0}^{\infty} \dfrac{3^n (-1/3)^n}{n+1} = \sum_{n=0}^{\infty} \dfrac{(-1)^n}{n+1}$. This series satisfies the requirements of the alternating series test and *converges*. Therefore, we include $x = -7/3$ in the interval of convergence.

For $x = -5/3$, we have $\sum_{n=0}^{\infty} \dfrac{3^n (1/3)^n}{n+1} = \sum_{n=0}^{\infty} \dfrac{1}{n+1}$. This is just the harmonic series, which we know diverges. Therefore, we do *not* include $x = -5/3$ in the interval of convergence.

Hence, the interval of convergence is

$$[-7/3, -5/3),$$

with center at $a = -2$ and radius of convergence $R = 1/3$. ■

EXAMPLE 40 Find the interval and radius of convergence of $\sum_{n=0}^{\infty}(-1)^n n! x^n$.

Solution By the ratio test, we have

$$\lim_{n\to\infty} \frac{\left|(-1)^{n+1}(n+1)! x^{n+1}\right|}{(-1)^n n! x^n} = \lim_{n\to\infty} |x|\,(n+1),$$

which is infinite for any $x \neq 0$. Hence, the interval of convergence $\{0\}$ contains only one point $x = 0$, and the radius of convergence is $R = 0$. ■

Calculus and power series

If we use a power series to define a function f, so that

$$f(x) = \sum_{n=0}^{\infty} c_n (x-a)^n,$$

then the domain of f is the interval of convergence for the power series. A function defined by a power series in this way is continuous on the interval of convergence. In fact, it can be differentiated and antidifferentiated term-by-term just like a polynomial!

Theorem 10.5

Hypothesis: The function f is defined by a power series

$$f(x) = \sum_{n=0}^{\infty} c_n (x-a)^n.$$

Conclusion: The derivative

$$f'(x) = \sum_{n=0}^{\infty} n c_n (x-a)^{n-1}$$

and the antiderivative

$$\int f(x)\,dx = C + \sum_{n=0}^{\infty} \frac{c_n (x-a)^{n+1}}{n+1}$$

have the same radius of convergence as f.

□

EXAMPLE 41 Suppose that $f(x) = 1+x+x^2+x^3+\cdots = \sum_{n=0}^{\infty} x^n$. Express the derivative and antiderivative of f as power series, and find their radius of convergence.

Solution We have

$$f'(x) = 0 + 1 + 2x + 3x^2 + \cdots = \sum_{n=0}^{\infty} nx^{n-1},$$

and

$$\int f(x)\,dx = C + x + \frac{x^2}{2} + \frac{x^3}{3} + \frac{x^4}{4} + \cdots = C + \sum_{n=0}^{\infty} \frac{x^{n+1}}{n+1},$$

where C is an arbitrary constant.

The radius of convergence for $f(x) = \sum_{n=0}^{\infty} x^n$ is $R = 1$. (It's a geometric series with ratio x.) By the theorem, the derivative f' and antiderivative $\int f(x)\,dx$ must have the same radius of convergence. (However, the *interval* of convergence for f and f' is $(-1, 1)$, while the antiderivative also converges for $x = -1$.) ■

▶▶▶ **Be careful! Two power series can have different intervals of convergence, even if the center a and radius of convergence R are the same. This is because the behavior at the *endpoints* $x = a - R$ and $x = a + R$ may be different for the two power series.**

Functions defined by power series

We have seen that we can define a function using a power series. The domain of the function is the interval of convergence for the power series. Many familiar functions may be represented by a suitable power series.

EXAMPLE 42 (a) Find the domain and a formula for the function f defined by

$$f(x) = \sum_{n=0}^{\infty} x^n.$$

(b) Find a power series representation for the derivative $f'(x)$ over the same domain.

(c) Find a power series representation and a formula for the antiderivative $F(x)$ satisfying $F(0) = 0$ over the same domain.

Solution (a) The power series for $f(x)$ can be thought of as a geometric series with ratio $r = x$. As such, it converges to $\dfrac{1}{1-x}$ for $-1 < x < 1$, and we can write

$$f(x) = \frac{1}{1-x} \qquad \text{with domain } (-1, 1).$$

(b) To find a power series representation for

$$f'(x) = \frac{1}{(1-x)^2}$$

valid for $-1 < x < 1$, we can differentiate the power series representation for $f(x)$:

$$\frac{1}{(1-x)^2} = 1 + 2x + 3x^2 + \cdots = \sum_{n=0}^{\infty} nx^{n-1}.$$

(c) If we antidifferentiate f, we obtain the power series

$$\int f(x)\,dx = C + x + \frac{x^2}{2} + \frac{x^3}{3} + \frac{x^4}{4} + \cdots = C + \sum_{n=0}^{\infty} \frac{x^{n+1}}{n+1},$$

which must also converge for $-1 < x < 1$. Note that

$$F(x) = -\ln(1-x)$$

is an antiderivative for f satisfying the initial condition $F(0) = 0$ and whose formula is valid for $-1 < x < 1$. If we set $C = 0$, we have found a power series representation for $F(x)$:

$$-\ln(1-x) = x + \frac{x^2}{2} + \frac{x^3}{3} + \frac{x^4}{4} + \cdots = \sum_{n=0}^{\infty} \frac{x^{n+1}}{n+1}.$$ ■

Since a function f defined by power series has a derivative f' that is also represented as a power series, we can continue differentiating to find power series representations for the higher-order derivatives f'', f''', $f^{(4)}$, and so on indefinitely. In other words, f is infinitely differentiable, and all its derivatives have the same radius of convergence.

Taylor and Maclaurin series

Suppose now that f is an infinitely differentiable function (as are almost all the functions we have dealt with), we can extend the sequence of Taylor polynomials indefinitely to give the **Taylor series** at $x = a$ for f,

$$\sum_{k=0}^{\infty} \frac{f^{(k)}(a)}{k!}(x-a)^k,$$

and, taking $a = 0$, the **Maclaurin series** for f,

$$\sum_{k=0}^{\infty} \frac{f^{(k)}(0)}{k!} x^k.$$

EXAMPLE 43 Compute the Maclaurin series for $f(x) = e^x$.

Solution Since $f(x) = f'(x) = f''(x) = \cdots = e^x$ and $f(0) = 1$, we have

$$\sum_{k=0}^{\infty} \frac{f^{(k)}(0)}{k!} x^k = \sum_{k=0}^{\infty} \frac{1}{k!} x^k.$$ ■

We can ask two questions regarding this power series:

(1) For what values x does the Taylor (or Maclaurin) series converge?

(2) In particular, for what values x does the series converge to $f(x)$?

The partial sums of a Taylor series are Taylor polynomials, so we are really asking about the convergence of the sequence of Taylor polynomials.

If $p_n(x)$ is the nth-order Taylor polynomial for $f(x)$ about $x = a$, then the **remainder** is

$$R_n(x) = f(x) - p_n(x).$$

The convergence of the Taylor series to $f(x)$ is then equivalent to the convergence of the remainders $R_n(x)$ to 0. That is, the equality

$$f(x) = \sum_{k=0}^{\infty} \frac{f^{(k)}(a)}{k!} (x - a)^k$$

holds if and only if $\lim_{n \to \infty} R_n(x) = 0$. The appendix includes a discussion of this remainder term $R_n(x)$ and ways in which it can be expressed.

A Taylor series need not converge everywhere in the domain of the function. For example, Figure 10.8 shows the graphs of the $5th$- and $10th$-order Taylor polynomials at $x = 1$ of $f(x) = \sqrt{x}$. It appears from these graphs that the series is diverging from the function outside the region $(0, 2)$ and converging for some region inside this one. You can check that the interval of convergence for the Taylor series is $(0, 2)$ by using the ratio test.

A **point of validity** for a Taylor series is an input x for which the power series *converges to the function output* $f(x)$. For reference, following is a table of common Maclaurin series and their respective intervals of validity.

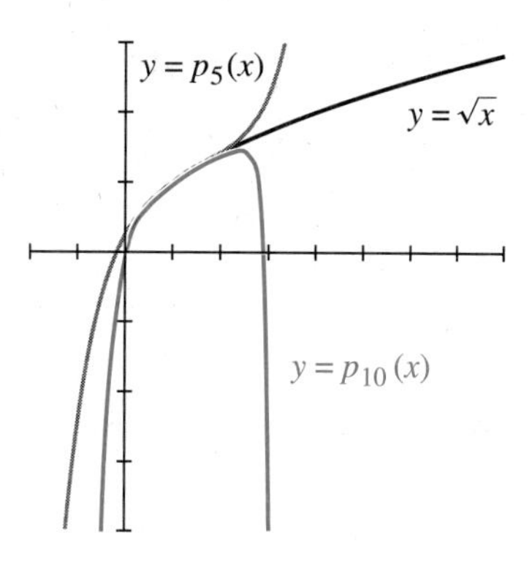

Figure 10.8 The $5th$- and $10th$-order Taylor polynomials at $x = 1$ of $\sqrt{x}$.

Maclaurin Series	**Interval of Validity**
$e^x = \sum_{k=0}^{\infty} \frac{x^k}{k!} = 1 + x + \frac{x^2}{2!} + \frac{x^3}{3!} + \frac{x^4}{4!} + \cdots$	$-\infty < x < +\infty$
$\sin x = \sum_{k=0}^{\infty} (-1)^k \frac{x^{2k+1}}{(2k+1)!} = x - \frac{x^3}{3!} + \frac{x^5}{5!} - \frac{x^7}{7!} + \cdots$	$-\infty < x < +\infty$
$\cos x = \sum_{k=0}^{\infty} (-1)^k \frac{x^{2k}}{(2k)!} = 1 - \frac{x^2}{2!} + \frac{x^4}{4!} - \frac{x^6}{6!} + \cdots$	$-\infty < x < +\infty$
$\ln(1+x) = \sum_{k=0}^{\infty} (-1)^k \frac{x^{k+1}}{k+1} = x - \frac{x^2}{2} + \frac{x^3}{3} - \frac{x^4}{4} + \cdots$	$-1 < x \leq 1$
$\arctan x = \sum_{k=0}^{\infty} (-1)^k \frac{x^{2k+1}}{2k+1} = x - \frac{x^3}{3} + \frac{x^5}{5} - \frac{x^7}{7} + \cdots$	$-1 \leq x \leq 1$
$\frac{1}{1-x} = \sum_{k=0}^{\infty} x^k = 1 + x + x^2 + x^3 + \cdots$	$-1 < x < 1$
$\sinh x = \sum_{k=0}^{\infty} \frac{x^{2k+1}}{(2k+1)!} = x + \frac{x^3}{3!} + \frac{x^5}{5!} + \frac{x^7}{7!} + \cdots$	$-\infty < x < +\infty$
$\cosh x = \sum_{k=0}^{\infty} \frac{x^{2k}}{(2k)!} = 1 + \frac{x^2}{2!} + \frac{x^4}{4!} + \frac{x^6}{6!} + \cdots$	$-\infty < x < +\infty$

EXERCISES for Section 10.5

1. Find the interval and radius of convergence for $\sum_{n=0}^{\infty} \frac{2^n x^n}{n!}$.
2. Find the interval and radius of convergence for $\sum_{n=0}^{\infty} \frac{(-1)^n x^n}{3^n n}$.
3. Find the interval and radius of convergence for $\sum_{n=0}^{\infty} \frac{(-1)^n (x-3)^n}{2^n}$.

Power series representations for new functions can be derived from known representations through substitution, differentiation, and antidifferentiation.

For exercises 4–7: Use the power series representation

$$f(x) = \frac{1}{1-x} = \sum_{n=0}^{\infty} x^n = 1 + x + x^2 + x^3 + \cdots \qquad \text{for } -1 < x < 1$$

to answer these questions.

4. Find a power series representation for

$$g(x) = \frac{1}{1+x}$$

by substituting $-x$ for x. What is the interval of convergence for g?

5. Find a power series representation of $h(x) = \ln(1+x)$ by antidifferentiating the power series in exercise 4. (What's the initial condition?)

6. Use the ratio test to determine the interval of convergence for $h(x)$. Be sure to check the endpoints.

7. Let $x = 1$. Estimate $\ln(2)$ by adding the first 101 terms of the power series representation for $h(x)$. Use the alternating series remainder to determine the accuracy of the result. To how many decimal places does this agree with the value of $\ln(2)$?

For exercises 8–13: We can represent $f(x) = e^x$ by the power series

$$e^x = \sum_{n=0}^{\infty} \frac{x^n}{n!} = 1 + x + \frac{x^2}{2} + \frac{x^3}{6} + \frac{x^4}{24} + \cdots.$$

8. Show that the interval of convergence for this power series is $(-\infty, \infty)$.
9. Find a power series representation for e^{-x}.
10. Find a power series representation for $1 - e^{-x}$.
11. Find a power series representation for $\dfrac{1-e^{-x}}{x}$.
12. Find a power series representation for the antiderivative of $\dfrac{1-e^{-x}}{x}$.
13. Use your answer to exercise 12 to approximate $\int_0^{1/2} \frac{1-e^{-x}}{x}\,dx$ to within 1×10^{-10}.

For exercises 14–16: Here are power series representation of two trigonometric functions:

$$\sin(x) = x - \frac{x^3}{6} + \frac{x^5}{120} - \frac{x^7}{7!} + \cdots = \sum_{n=0}^{\infty} \frac{(-1)^n x^{2n+1}}{(2n+1)!}$$

$$\cos(x) = 1 - \frac{x^2}{2} + \frac{x^4}{24} - \frac{x^6}{6!} + \cdots = \sum_{n=0}^{\infty} \frac{(-1)^n x^{2n}}{(2n)!}$$

14. Show that the interval of convergence for both of these power series is $(-\infty, \infty)$.

15. Find a power series representation for

$$f(x) = \frac{x - \sin x}{x^3 \cos x}.$$

Graph the function.

16. Evaluate $\lim_{x\to 0} \frac{x-\sin x}{x^3 \cos x}$ using the result in exercise 15. Does the graph support your answer? Note that L'Hôpital's rule is appropriate here (but rather undesirable).

10.6 ITERATION

Iterative and recursive sequences

When we say that a sequence $\{a_n\}_{n=1}^{\infty}$ is described in **closed form,** we mean that we have an explicit formula for a_n written in terms of n. For example, the geometric sequence

$$a_0 = 1,\ a_1 = \frac{1}{2}, a_2 = \frac{1}{4},\ a_3 = \frac{1}{8},\ a_4 = \frac{1}{16},\ \ldots$$

can be described by the formula

$$a_n = \frac{1}{2^n} \quad \text{for} \quad n = 0,\ 1,\ 2,\ \ldots.$$

In fact, we could write the sequence as

$$\{\frac{1}{2^n}\}_{n=0}^{\infty}.$$

Sometimes the terms in a sequence depend directly on one or more of the preceding terms in the sequence. When this is the case, it may be preferable or more convenient to describe the sequence using this relationship.

A sequence is said to be defined **recursively** or **inductively** if the first term is given (or the first few terms are given) and we have explicit instructions on how to obtain the subsequent terms using the values of preceding terms.

EXAMPLE 44 Describe the geometric sequence $1, \frac{1}{2}, \frac{1}{4}, \frac{1}{8}, \ldots$ recursively.

Solution

$$a_0 = 1$$

$$a_n = \frac{1}{2}a_{n-1} \quad \text{for} \quad n = 1, 2, 3, \ldots$$

■

A recursive description of a sequence allows us to "build" up the terms much like a stack of blocks. In this example, we are given

$$a_0 = 1.$$

The **recursion formula** $a_n = \frac{1}{2}a_{n-1}$ is used over and over again to obtain the subsequent terms:

$$a_1 = \frac{1}{2}a_{1-1} = \frac{1}{2}a_0 = \frac{1}{2} \cdot 1 = \frac{1}{2},$$

$$a_2 = \frac{1}{2}a_{2-1} = \frac{1}{2}a_1 = \frac{1}{2} \cdot \frac{1}{2} = \frac{1}{4},$$

$$a_3 = \frac{1}{2}a_{3-1} = \frac{1}{2}a_2 = \frac{1}{2} \cdot \frac{1}{4} = \frac{1}{8}.$$

$$\vdots$$

Any geometric sequence can be described recursively in a similar way. If a is the first term in the geometric sequence and r is the constant ratio, then the sequence

$$a, \ ar, \ ar^2, \ ar^3, \ \ldots$$

can be described recursively:

$$a_0 = a$$

$$a_n = ra_{n-1}.$$

Similarly, any arithmetic sequence can be described recursively.

EXAMPLE 45 Describe the arithmetic sequence 3, 7, 11, 15, 19, ... recursively.

Solution $a_0 = 3$ and $a_n = a_{n-1} + 4$ for $n = 1, 2, \ldots$. ■

In general, if a is the first term of an arithmetic sequence and d is the constant difference, then the sequence

$$a, \; a+d, \; a+2d, \; a+3d, \; \ldots$$

can be described recursively: $a_0 = a$ and $a_n = a_{n-1} + d$ for $n = 1, 2, \ldots$.

Perhaps the most famous of all sequences is the so-called **Fibonacci sequence**. Fibonacci, also known as Leonardo di Pisa, was a thirteenth century Italian mathematician. The sequence named after him is usually described recursively as follows:

$$a_0 = 1$$

$$a_1 = 1$$

$$a_n = a_{n-1} + a_{n-2} \quad \text{for } n = 2, 3, 4, \ldots.$$

In other words, the first two terms of the Fibonacci sequence are both 1, and each subsequent term is determined by adding the previous two terms. The Fibonacci sequence starts out

$$1, \; 1, \; 2, \; 3, \; 5, \; 8, \; 13, \; 21, \; 34, \; 55, \; 89, \; \ldots$$

The Fibonacci sequence appears quite often in number patterns arising in nature, including the population growth rates of rabbits, the genealogy of honey bees, and seed and leaf arrangements in vegetation, among others. The sequence has such a multitude of interesting properties, that an entire journal (*The Fibonacci Quarterly*) is devoted to it.

The recursive descriptions for arithmetic and geometric sequences are examples of *iteration*. An **iterative process** is one in which we start with an initial input x_0 and then successively apply a function f by using the output at each stage as the input to the next. For example, if

$$f(x) = x + 4$$

and our initial input (also called the initial *seed*) is $x_0 = 3$, then

$$x_1 = f(x_0) = f(3) = 7$$

$$x_2 = f(x_1) = f(7) = 11$$

$$x_3 = f(x_2) = f(11) = 15$$

$$x_4 = f(x_3) = f(15) = 19$$

$$\vdots$$

We can see that this function f, along with the initial input $x_0 = 3$, generates the arithmetic sequence $3, 7, 11, \ldots$.

▶▶▶ **Any function f and initial input x_0 can be used to define an iterative sequence, provided that the output at each step is in the domain of the function.**

EXAMPLE 46 Find the first 5 terms of the iterative sequence defined by

$$g(x) = \frac{x^2 + 2}{2x}$$

with initial input $x_0 = 1$.

Solution With $x_0 = 1$, we have

$$x_1 = g(x_0) = g(1) = \frac{1^2 + 2}{2} = \frac{3}{2} = 1.5$$

$$x_2 = g(x_1) = g(1.5) = \frac{(1.5)^2 + 2}{3} \approx 1.41666666667$$

$$x_3 = g(x_2) \approx f(1.41666666667) \approx 1.41421568627$$

$$x_4 = g(x_3) \approx f(1.41421568627) \approx 1.41421356237$$

$$x_5 = g(x_4) \approx f(1.41421356237) \approx 1.41421356237.$$

The values listed for x_2, x_3, x_4, and x_5 are rounded to eleven decimal places, and from the result of x_5 we would anticipate that the subsequent terms x_6, x_7, and so on will stay "locked on" to the value 1.41421356237. ■

Many approximation methods are essentially iterative processes—an initial guess for a solution is tested and then adjusted accordingly. This yields an infinite sequence of approximations, each better (one hopes) than the one preceding it. Both the bisection method and Newton's method are examples of iterative root-finding approximation procedures.

Fixed points

In the case of Newton's method, we developed an *iterating function* for a differentiable function f:

$$g(x) = x - \frac{f(x)}{f'(x)}.$$

Starting with an initial seed x_0, we compute a sequence of values

$$x_1 = g(x_0), \quad x_2 = g(x_1), \quad x_3 = g(x_2), \quad \ldots, \quad x_n = g(x_{n-1}), \quad \ldots.$$

In other words, we keep using the *output* at one stage as the *input* for the next. If this sequence converges to single limiting value x_r satisfying

$$x_r = g(x_r),$$

then x_r is a *root* of the function f.

In fact, the function g, where $g(x) = \dfrac{x^2+2}{2x}$, is the iterating function for

$$f(x) = x^2 - 2.$$

The value x_r is also called a **fixed point** of the function g, since feeding it in as an input to g results in the same fixed value as output.

The fixed points of a function f are simply the solutions to the equation

$$f(x) = x.$$

Graphically, the fixed points are the intersections of the graph of $y = f(x)$ and the diagonal line $y = x$. Figure 10.9 illustrates the fixed point of a linear function $f(x) = mx + b$ (with $m \neq 1$). If (x_r, x_r) is the point of intersection, then x_r is a fixed point of f. In this case, we can solve the equation

$$mx + b = x$$

to find that the fixed point

$$x = x_r = \frac{b}{1-m}.$$

For a more general function f, the equation

$$f(x) = x$$

may be more difficult, or impossible, to solve using algebra.

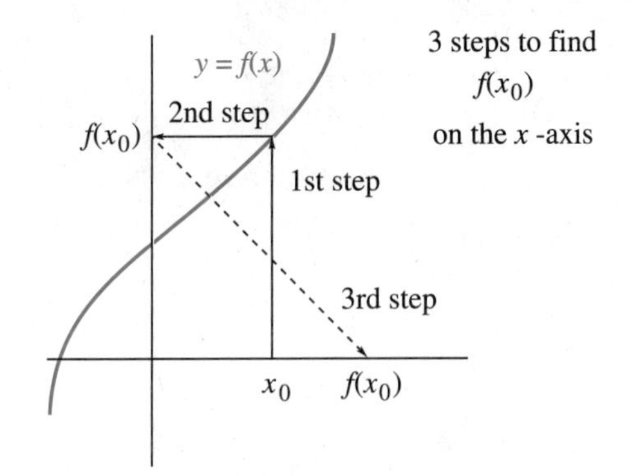

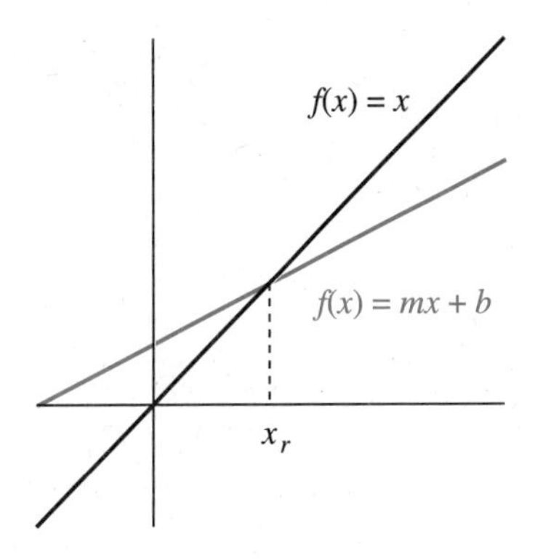

Figure 10.9 If $m \neq 1$, the graph of $y = mx + b$ must intersect the diagonal.

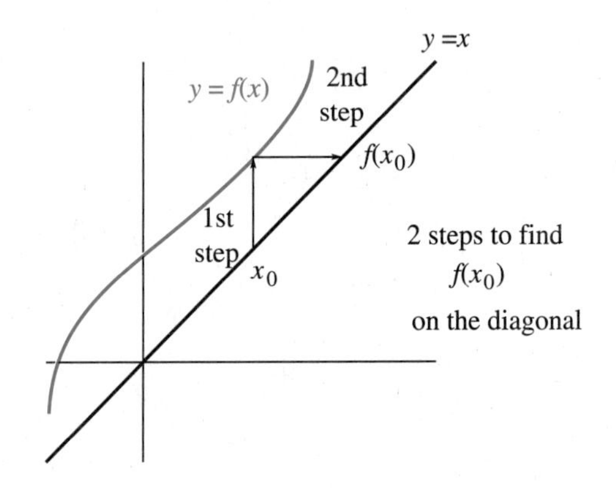

Figure 10.10 Graphing input-to-output relationship without and with use of the diagonal.

Iterating a function graphically

Normally, we think of an input to a function f as a point on the horizontal x-axis, and the output as a point on the vertical y-axis. We could graphically connect the input x_0 to the output $f(x_0)$ by drawing a vertical line from the x-axis to the graph of $y = f(x)$ and then a horizontal line from the graph to the y-axis. If we want to iterate the function, we then need to find the point representing the number $f(x_0)$ on the horizontal x-axis to use as input so that we can repeat the process again.

There is another simple but effective way of graphing the iteration process using the graph of the function $y = f(x)$ and the diagonal $y = x$. If we find the input x_0 on the diagonal $y = x$ (actually the point (x_0, x_0)), we can "bounce" vertically to the graph of $y = f(x)$ and then horizontally back to the diagonal to find $f(x_0)$ (actually the point $(f(x_0), f(x_0))$). This process is easy to iterate by just repeating it, using the new point. Figure 10.10 illustrates both techniques.

For example, using an initial seed $x_0 = .5$, we can graphically find 3 iterates of the linear function $f(x) = .8(x - 2) + 2$, as shown in the viewing

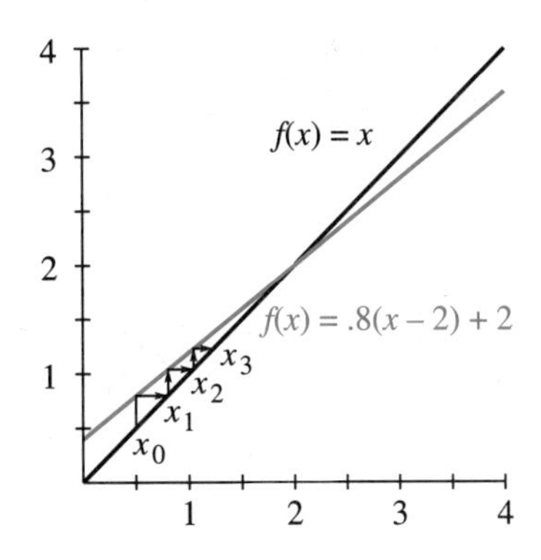

Figure 10.11 Graphing three iterates of $f(x) = .8(x-2)+2$.

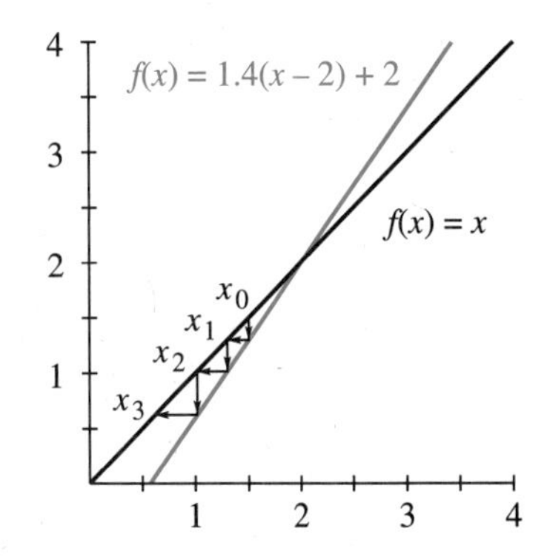

Figure 10.12 Graphing three iterates of $f(x) = 1.4(x-2)+2$.

window $[0,4] \times [0,4]$. of Figure 10.11. This function has a fixed point $x_r = 2$, since $f(2) = 2$. Note that the iterates are "moving" *toward* the fixed point.

On the other hand, Figure 10.12 shows 3 iterates of the linear function $f(x) = 1.4(x-2)+2$ in the viewing window $[0,4] \times [0,4]$, using an initial seed $x_0 = 1.5$. Note that this function also has a fixed point $x_r = 2$, but now the iterates are "moving" *away* from the fixed point.

Contractions and the fixed point theorem

A **contraction** is a function whose outputs are always closer together than the corresponding inputs. For example, a linear function

$$f(x) = mx + b$$

is a contraction, provided that $|m| < 1$. In the two previous examples, the first linear function had a slope of 0.8 and therefore is a contraction. The second linear function had a slope of 1.4 and therefore is *not* a contraction.

If we iterate a contraction by feeding its output back in as an input repeatedly, then the resulting sequence converges to a fixed point. Equipped with this graphing technique, we can look at four generic cases of iteration for linear functions: where the slope is between 0 and 1, where the slope is between -1 and 0, where the slope is greater than 1, and where the slope is less than -1. These cases are shown in Figure 10.13.

If the slope is positive, the iterates either "stairstep" toward or away from the fixed point, depending on whether the slope is less than or greater than 1, respectively. If the slope is negative, the iterates "spiral" toward or away from the fixed point, again as the slope is less than or greater than 1, respectively.

If we zoom in on the graph of a differentiable function, we expect to see a straight line. This suggests that we can use the information above

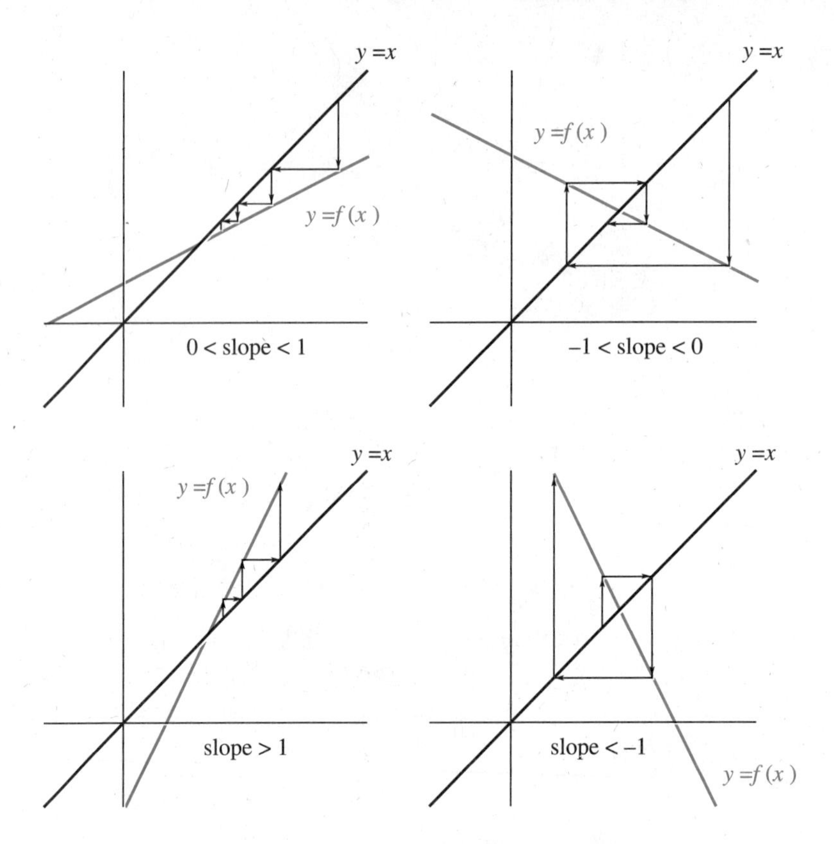

Figure 10.13 Four generic cases of iteration.

to find fixed points of non-linear functions, provided that we restrict our attention to a small enough neighborhood of a fixed point. Unfortunately, if we knew enough about the function to zoom in on the fixed point, we wouldn't need iteration to find the fixed point! Here's a theorem that gives us useful criteria for judging how close we need to be to a fixed point for this analysis to work.

Theorem 10.6

Fixed point theorem
Suppose that f is differentiable on $[a, b]$.
Hypothesis 1: $f(x) \in [a, b]$ for all $x \in [a, b]$.
Hypothesis 2: $|f'(x)| < 1$ for all $x \in [a, b]$.
Conclusion: There is exactly one point $a \leq x_r \leq b$ such that $f(x_r) = x_r$ and any iteration sequence starting with $x_0 \in [a, b]$ converges to x_r.

□

The next two examples discuss why each hypothesis is important.

EXAMPLE 47 If f is differentiable on $[a, b]$ but has *no* fixed points on $[a, b]$, which of the hypotheses must be violated?

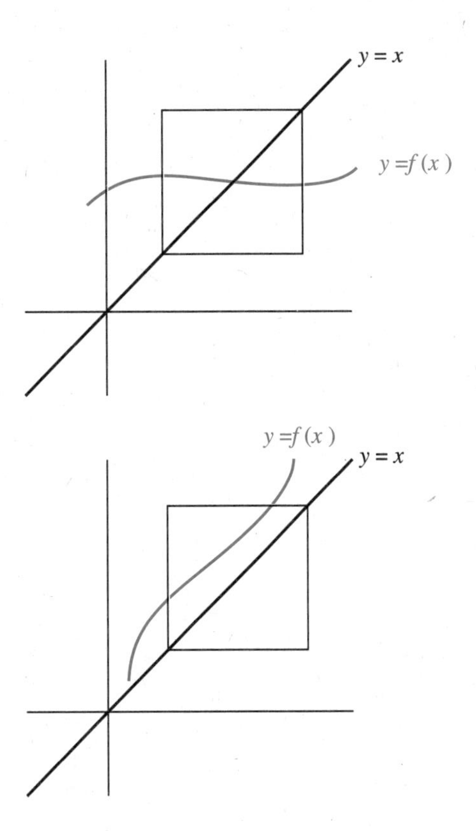

Figure 10.14 Geometric interpretation of hypothesis 1 and a violation of it.

Solution Geometrically, hypothesis 1 says that the graph of f over $[a, b]$ lies entirely within the square box, with corners (a, a), (b, b), (a, b), and (b, a) (see Figure 10.14). A differentiable function is continuous, and since the graph at the left endpoint must be on or above the diagonal, and the graph at the right endpoint must be on or below the diagonal, the intermediate value theorem tells us that somewhere in the interval the graph must cross the diagonal, yielding at least one fixed point. The only way the graph of $y = f(x)$ could connect the points $(a, f(a))$ and $(b, f(b))$ without crossing the diagonal would be for the graph to leave the box entirely, violating hypothesis 1. ■

EXAMPLE 48 If f is differentiable on $[a, b]$ but has *two* (or more) fixed points on $[a, b]$, which of the hypotheses must be violated?

Solution If $f(x_1) = x_1$ and $f(x_2) = x_2$, then the mean value theorem tells us that there is some point $x = c$ such that

$$f'(c) = \frac{f(x_2) - f(x_1)}{x_2 - x_1} = \frac{x_2 - x_1}{x_2 - x_1} = 1.$$

But this violates hypothesis 2. ■

Hypothesis 2 guarantees that our function is a contraction over the interval $[a, b]$. In fact, the value of the derivative over this interval gives us a measure of *how fast* we can expect the iteration to converge to the fixed point.

Criteria for the convergence of Newton's method

An especially important special case of the iteration method for finding roots is *Newton's method*, which we discussed in Chapter 4. To solve an equation $f(x) = 0$ by Newton's method, you use the iterating function

$$g(x) = x - \frac{f(x)}{f'(x)}.$$

To see why Newton's method is so effective, note that the derivative of g is

$$g'(x) = 1 - \frac{f'(x)f'(x) - f(x)f''(x)}{(f'(x))^2} = \frac{f(x)f''(x)}{(f'(x))^2}.$$

If x_r is a root of f, then $g'(x_r) = 0$, provided it is defined. This suggests that our iteration function will converge *very fast*, provided that we start with a seed x_0 sufficiently close to the root x_r. We can use the fixed-point theorem to derive criteria for convergence of Newton's method.

Suppose that $f'(x) \neq 0$ and $f''(x)$ is defined on $[a, b]$ (so that g is differentiable).
Criterion 1: $a < x - \dfrac{f(x)}{f'(x)} < b$ for all $x \in [a, b]$.
Criterion 2: $\left|\dfrac{f(x)f''(x)}{(f'(x))^2}\right| < 1$ for all $x \in [a, b]$.
Conclusion: For any $x_0 \in [a, b]$, Newton's method converges to a root of f.

The two criteria just correspond to the two hypotheses of the fixed-point theorem applied to the function $g(x) = x - \dfrac{f(x)}{f'(x)}$. Hypothesis 1 requires the graph of $g(x)$ to stay within the "box" $[a, b] \times [a, b]$. Hypothesis 2 requires that $|g'(x)|$ be less than 1 over the interval $[a, b]$.

EXAMPLE 49 Does the iteration function for Newton's method applied to the equation $x^3 - 19 = 0$ satisfy the criteria for convergence in the interval $[2, 3]$?

Solution We have

$$f(x) = x^3 - 19, \qquad f'(x) = 3x^2, \qquad f''(x) = 6x.$$

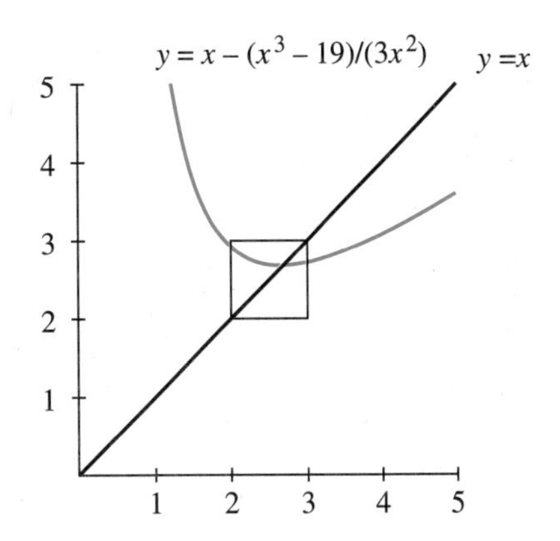

Figure 10.15 Graph of $y = g(x)$ satisfies the "box test" on $[2, 3]$.

We can see that $f'(x) \neq 0$ and $f''(x)$ is defined over the interval $[2, 3]$, so the iteration function

$$g(x) = x - \frac{f(x)}{f'(x)} = x - \frac{x^3 - 19}{3x^2}$$

is differentiable. If we graph $y = g(x)$ and apply the "box test" to the interval $[2, 3]$, we find that the first criterion holds (see Figure 10.15).

As for the second criterion, we have

$$\left|\frac{f(x)f''(x)}{(f'(x))^2}\right| = \left|\frac{6x^4 - 114x}{9x^4}\right| = \left|\frac{2}{3} - \frac{38}{3x^3}\right|,$$

which is less than 1 for $2 \leq x \leq 3$. Thus, both criteria are satisfied, and taking any initial seed $x_0 \in [2, 3]$ will guarantee convergence. Starting with $x_0 = 3$, for example,

$$\left|\sqrt[3]{19} - x_0\right| \approx 0.035302$$

$$\left|\sqrt[3]{19} - x_1\right| \approx 0.00045893$$

$$\left|\sqrt[3]{19} - x_2\right| \approx 0.00000007892$$

$$\left|\sqrt[3]{19} - x_3\right| = 0 \quad \text{to more than 12 digits.}$$

■

EXERCISES for Section 10.6

For exercises 1–4: Describe the arithmetic sequence with given initial term a_0 and constant difference d with a recursive formula.

1. $a_0 = 3$, $d = -5$

2. $a_0 = -4$, $d = 0.5$

3. $a_0 = \pi$, $d = 0$

4. $a_0 = 0$, $d = \pi$

For exercises 5–8: Describe the geometric sequence with given initial term a_0 and constant ratio r with a recursive formula.

5. $a_0 = 3$, $r = -5$

6. $a_0 = -4$, $r = 0.5$

7. $a_0 = \pi$, $r = 2$

8. $a_0 = 2$, $r = \pi$

---

9. If $a_1 = \sqrt{3}$ and $a_n = \sqrt{3a_{n-1}}$ for $n \geq 2$, find the first five terms of the sequence (starting with $n = 1$).

10. If $a_1 = 1$ and $a_{n+1} = \frac{1}{1+a_n}$ for $n \geq 1$, find the first five terms of the sequence (starting with $n = 1$).

For exercises 11–14: The initial term and a function are given. Find the first five terms of the iterative sequence based on this information.

11. $x_0 = 0$, $f(x) = x - \cos(x)$

12. $x_0 = 1$, $f(x) = \dfrac{x+1}{2}$

13. $x_0 = 0.5$, $f(x) = x^2$

14. $x_0 = 10$, $f(x) = 1/x$

For exercises 15–20: The following sequence of numbers approaches the golden ratio $\dfrac{1+\sqrt{5}}{2}$:

$$\frac{1}{1}, \frac{2}{1}, \frac{3}{2}, \frac{5}{3}, \frac{8}{5}, \frac{13}{8}, \ldots$$

15. Describe the pattern you see in the numerators. Describe the pattern you see in the denominators.

16. What is the first term in the sequence that is within .001 less than the golden ratio?

17. What is the first term in the sequence that is within .001 more than the golden ratio?

18. What are the first two consecutive terms in the sequence that are within .000001 of each other?

19. Find the first 10 terms of the sequence whose nth term is given by

$$a_n = \frac{1}{\sqrt{5}}\left[\left(\frac{1+\sqrt{5}}{2}\right)^n - \left(\frac{1-\sqrt{5}}{2}\right)^n\right].$$

This is the closed-form formula for what sequence?

20. Use exercise 19 to find a closed-form formula for the sequence

$$\frac{1}{1}, \frac{2}{1}, \frac{3}{2}, \frac{5}{3}, \frac{8}{5}, \frac{13}{8}, \ldots.$$

For exercises 21–30: Verify that the corresponding Newton iteration function for each equation satisfies the criteria for convergence over the given interval. If so, use the iteration function to find three successive approximations to the root, using the left endpoint as initial seed x_0.

21. $x^2 - 3.2 = 0; \quad [1, 2]$

22. $x^3 - 23 = 0; \quad [2, 3]$

23. $\sin(x) - 0.7 = 0; \quad [0.7, 0.8]$

24. $x^5 + 3.6x^4 - 2.51x^3 - 22.986x^2 - 28.24x - 10.4 = 0; \quad [2, 3]$

25. $x + \sqrt{x} + \sqrt{x^3} - 7 = 0; \quad [1.8, 2.6]$

26. $x \exp(x^2) - \sqrt{x^2 + 1} = 0; \quad [0.4, 1]$

27. $\ln(x^2 + \ln(x)) = 0; \quad [0.625, 1.35]$

28. $x^3 - \sqrt{x^2 + 1} + x - 3 = 0; \quad [1.1, 1.6]$

29. $3 \cos(\cos(x)) - 2x = 0; \quad [1.1, 2.2]$

30. $\sqrt[4]{x} + x^3 - x - 0.5 = 0; \quad [0.2, 1.2]$

Appendices

The appendices contain additional material for your review or reference.

Appendix 1 includes review material on right triangle trigonometry.

Appendix 2 explains techniques of integration using trigonometric identities and relationships.

Appendix 3 discusses the method of partial fractions, an algebraic technique useful for simplifying some integrals.

Appendix 4 consists of a brief introduction to polar coordinates and their use in differential and integral calculus.

Appendix 5 discusses complex numbers and their algebraic and geometric representations.

Appendix 6 extends the material on Taylor polynomials with a discussion of Taylor's formula.

Additional practice exercises on differentiation and integration are included.

The appendices conclude with a collection of useful facts and formulas from algebra, trigonometry, and analytic geometry. Tables of differentiation and integration formulas can be found in the end pages of the book, as well as formulas from plane and solid geometry.

A.1 TRIANGLE TRIGONOMETRY

In a right triangle with legs of lengths a and b and a hypotenuse of length c, we know from the Pythagorean theorem the familiar relationship

$$a^2 + b^2 = c^2.$$

Figure A.1 illustrates the definitions of the three principal trigonometric ratios associated with an angle θ (the Greek letter theta) in terms of the sides of the triangle.

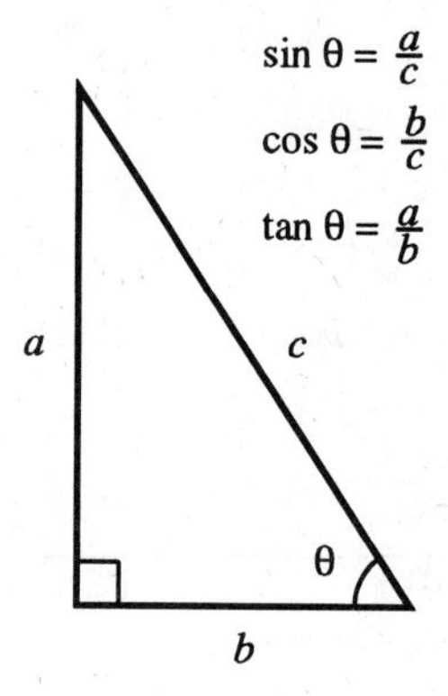

Figure A.1 Trigonometric ratios.

$$\text{sine } \theta = \frac{\textit{opposite}}{\textit{hypotenuse}} = \frac{a}{c}$$

$$\text{cosine } \theta = \frac{\textit{adjacent}}{\textit{hypotenuse}} = \frac{b}{c}$$

$$\text{tangent } \theta = \frac{\textit{opposite}}{\textit{adjacent}} = \frac{a}{b}$$

The nonsense word "SOHCAHTOA" may help you in memorizing these definitions. Note that every three letters of the word form the initials for one of the trigonometric ratio definitions.

The common abbreviations for sine θ, cosine θ, and tangent θ are

$$\sin\theta, \qquad \cos\theta, \qquad \tan\theta,$$

respectively. Three additional trigonometric ratios are obtained by taking the reciprocals of these ratios.

$$\text{cosecant } \theta = \frac{1}{\text{sine } \theta} = \frac{\textit{hypotenuse}}{\textit{opposite}} = \frac{c}{a}$$

$$\text{secant } \theta = \frac{1}{\text{cosine } \theta} = \frac{\textit{hypotenuse}}{\textit{adjacent}} = \frac{c}{b}$$

$$\text{cotangent } \theta = \frac{1}{\text{tangent } \theta} = \frac{\textit{adjacent}}{\textit{opposite}} = \frac{b}{a}.$$

The common abbreviations for cosecant θ, secant θ, and cotangent θ are

$$\csc\theta, \qquad \sec\theta, \qquad \cot\theta,$$

respectively.

EXAMPLE 1 A simple example of a right triangle is the "3–4–5" triangle, with $a = 3$, $b = 4$, and $c = 5$. If θ is the angle opposite side a, find the six trigonometric ratios associated with θ.

Solution Figure A.2 shows the right triangle and angle θ under consideration.

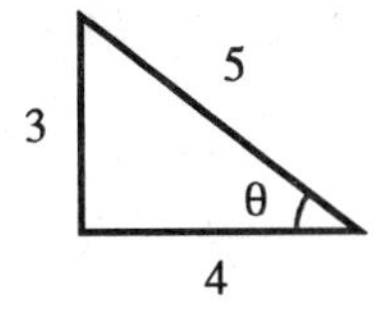

Figure A.2 A 3–4–5 right triangle.

Using the definitions of the trigonometric ratios, we have:

$$\text{sine } \theta = \frac{3}{5}, \qquad \text{cosine } \theta = \frac{4}{5}, \qquad \text{tangent } \theta = \frac{3}{4},$$

$$\text{cosecant } \theta = \frac{5}{3}, \qquad \text{secant } \theta = \frac{5}{4}, \qquad \text{cotangent } \theta = \frac{4}{3}.$$ ■

Two triangles of different sizes are called *similar* if they have the same shape. More precisely, two triangles are similar if the three side lengths of one are all the same multiple of the corresponding side lengths of the other. Here's a key fact from geometry:

> If two triangles are similar, then corresponding angles must be equal in measure. Conversely, if corresponding angles of two triangles are equal in measure, then the two triangles must be similar.

Another useful fact from geometry is:

> The measures of the angles in any triangle sum to 180°.

For instance, if we double the lengths of all three sides of the triangle in the previous example, then we obtain a 6–8–10 right triangle having the same angle θ. Note that all the trigonometric ratios remain exactly the same (see Figure A.3).

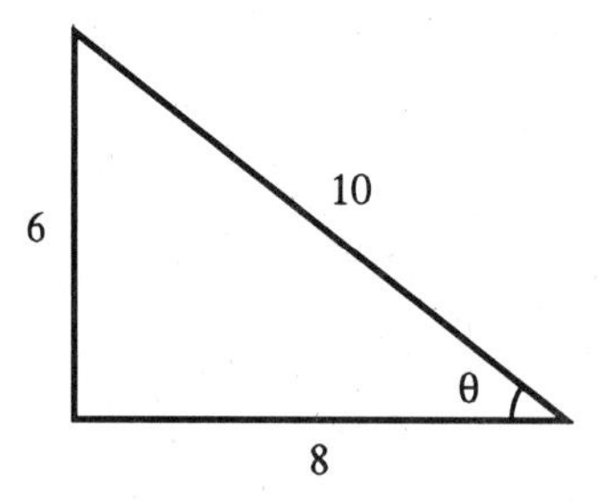

Figure A.3 A 6–8–10 right triangle.

The same observation holds for any triangle similar to our 3–4–5 triangle. On the other hand, any right triangle with this same angle θ must be similar to our 3–4–5 triangle. (Since the angle measures of a triangle sum up to 180°, the remaining angle in both triangles must measure $90° - \theta$.) This means that any trigonometric ratio like $\sin\theta$ really depends only on θ, and not on the size of any of the infinitely many similar right triangles that could be chosen to compute it.

This is why trigonometric ratios can be used to compute distances so effectively. Extensive trigonometry tables were indispensable aids before the relatively recent development of inexpensive calculators.

EXAMPLE 2 A rocket is launched straight up. From a ground tracking station exactly 50 miles away from the launch site, you record the angle of elevation of the rocket after five minutes to be $37.4°$. What is the altitude a of the rocket at that moment?

Solution Figure A.4 illustrates the problem situation.

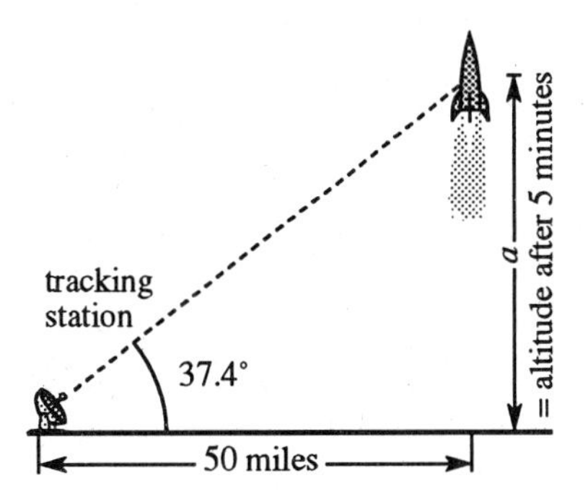

Figure A.4 Tracking the altitude of a rocket.

In the right triangle shown, we can see that the side adjacent to the angle of elevation is the distance between the tracking station and the launch site, and the side opposite is the altitude a. Hence,

$$\tan 37.4° = \frac{a}{50 \text{ miles}}.$$

Solving for a (and using a calculator to compute $\tan 37.4°$), we have

$$a = (\tan 37.4°)(50 \text{ miles}) \approx (.7646)(50 \text{ miles}) = 38.23 \text{ miles}.$$

■

Radian measure for angles

To extend the use of trigonometric functions beyond right-triangle computations, we will consider another system of angle measurement and broaden the range of values an angle measure can have.

While degree measure for angles is still commonly used in many applications, we will often find **radian** measure more convenient for calculus. If a circle is drawn having the vertex of an angle at its center, then an angle of one radian subtends an arc of length equal to the radius of the circle (see Figure A.5).

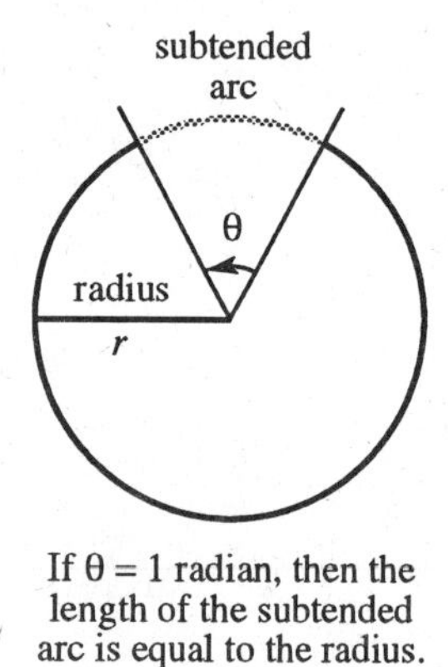

Figure A.5 Radian measure of angles.

A circle of radius r has circumference $2\pi r$, so the full $360°$ angle of a circle is equivalent to 2π radians. This gives us the conversion formulas between degrees and radians:

$$1° = \frac{\pi}{180} \text{ radians} \approx 0.0174533 \text{ radians}$$

and

$$1 \text{ radian} = \frac{180°}{\pi} \approx 57.3°.$$

Now we can talk about positive and negative angle measures by agreeing that positive angles are measured counterclockwise and negative angles are measured clockwise. Angles larger than $360°$ or 2π radians in magnitude can also be considered as "wrapping around" the circle more than one revolution. Figure A.6 illustrates several angles measured in either degrees or radians.

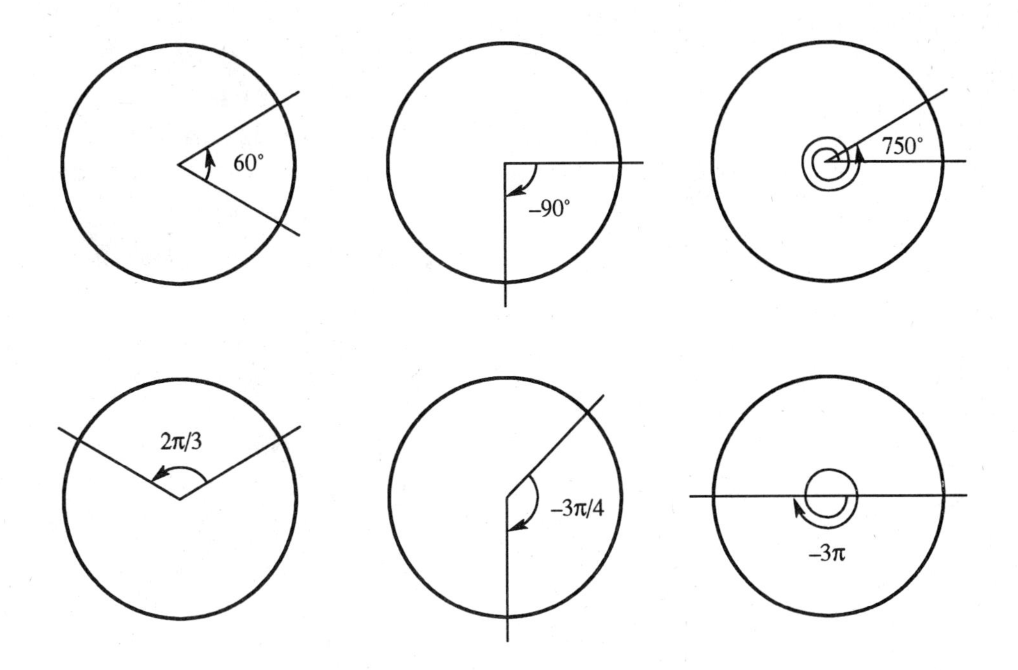

Figure A.6 Examples of angle measure.

EXAMPLE 3 Convert the following to radian measure:

$$45^\circ, \qquad 90^\circ, \qquad -120^\circ, \qquad 600^\circ.$$

Solution $45^\circ = 45\pi/180 = \pi/4$ radians.

$90^\circ = 90\pi/180 = \pi/2$ radians.

$-120^\circ = -120\pi/180 = -2\pi/3$ radians.

$600^\circ = 600\pi/180 = 10\pi/3$ radians. ■

EXAMPLE 4 Convert the following to degree measure:

$$\pi/3 \text{ radians}, \qquad -3\pi/2 \text{ radians}, \qquad 25 \text{ radians}.$$

Solution $\pi/3$ radians $= \dfrac{\pi}{3}\left(\dfrac{180^\circ}{\pi}\right) = 60^\circ.$

$-3\pi/2$ radians $= \dfrac{-3\pi}{2}\left(\dfrac{180^\circ}{\pi}\right) = -270^\circ.$

25 radians $= (25)\left(\dfrac{180^\circ}{\pi}\right) \approx 1432.4^\circ.$ ■

Law of sines and law of cosines

Relationships between the sides and angles of an arbitrary triangle (not just a right triangle) can be described using trigonometric functions. The two most important of these relationships are called the law of sines and the law of cosines.

Figure A.7 shows a triangle with sides a, b, c, and with angles α, β, γ opposite those sides, respectively.

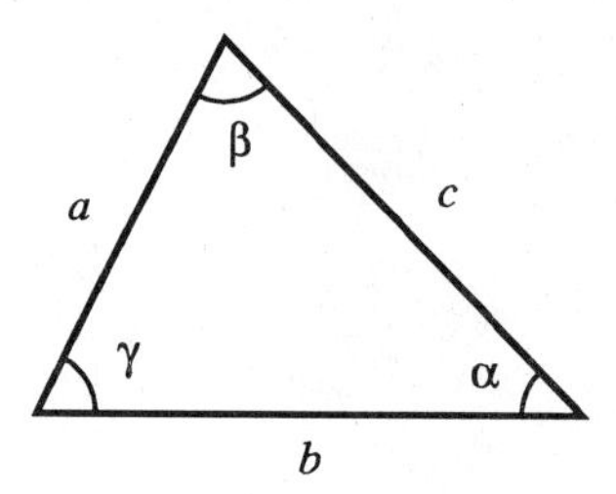

Figure A.7 Triangle with sides a, b, c, and opposite angles α, β, γ.

The law of sines states that the ratio of the sine of an angle to the length of the side opposite it is the same for each angle in the triangle.

Law of sines: $$\frac{\sin\alpha}{a} = \frac{\sin\beta}{b} = \frac{\sin\gamma}{c}.$$

The law of cosines provides a generalization of the Pythagorean theorem, and allows us to compute the length of the third side of any triangle, provided we know the lengths of the other two sides and the angle between them.

Law of cosines:

$$a^2 = b^2 + c^2 - 2bc\cos\alpha$$

$$b^2 = a^2 + c^2 - 2ac\cos\beta$$

$$c^2 = a^2 + b^2 - 2ab\cos\gamma.$$

Notice that if γ is a right angle (90°), then $\cos\gamma = 0$, and the last equation is the usual statement of the Pythagorean theorem.

EXERCISES for Section A.1

For exercises 1-6: Draw a triangle with sides of length $a = 5$, $b = 12$, and $c = 13$, with angle θ opposite side a.

1. Find $\sin\theta$.
2. Find $\cos\theta$.
3. Find $\sec\theta$.
4. Find $\csc\theta$.
5. Find $\tan\theta$.
6. Find $\cot\theta$.

For exercises 7-12: Convert each angle measure θ in radians to degrees, and evaluate each of the six trigonometric functions at θ.

7. $\theta = \pi/5$ radians.
8. $\theta = 7\pi/2$ radians.
9. $\theta = -5\pi/4$ radians.
10. $\theta = 371\pi$ radians.
11. $\theta = 8\pi/3$ radians.
12. $\theta = -21\pi/6$ radians.

For exercises 13-18: Convert each angle measure θ in degrees to radians, and evaluate each of the six trigonometric functions at θ.

13. $\theta = 100°$.
14. $\theta = -45°$.
15. $\theta = 270°$.
16. $\theta = 1000°$.
17. $\theta = -270°$.
18. $\theta = \pi°$.

For exercises 19-23: Of the three angles and three sides of triangle ABC, you are given some of the measurements. Determine the three missing measurements.

19. angle $A = 35°$, angle $B = 45°$, side $c = 7$ cm.
20. side $b = 20$ cm, side $c = 60$ cm, angle $A = 40°$.
21. side $b = 130$ miles, side $c = 150$ miles, angle $B = 110°$.
22. side $a = 7$ meters side $b = 8$ meters, side $c = 10$ meters.
23. side $a = 2$ inches, angle $C = 90°$, side $b = 3$ inches.

---

24. Suppose side $a = 7$ feet, and angle $B = 150°$. Find a value for the length of side b for which angle A has

a) no possible value, b) exactly one possible value, c) two possible values.

25. A rocket is launched straight up. From a ground tracking station exactly 40 miles away from the launch site, you record the angle of elevation of the rocket after ten minutes to be 62.5°. What is the altitude a of the rocket at that moment?

26. Radar station A is 120 miles due south of radar station B. Station A detects an unidentified flying object at a bearing of N 47° E (that is, at an angle 47° measured clockwise from due North) at exactly the same time that station B detects the UFO at a bearing of S 50° E (that is, at an angle 50° measured counterclockwise from due South). Find the distance from the UFO to both stations.

27. Two planes, one flying at 360 mph and the other at 540 mph, leave an airport at the same time. Three hours later they are exactly 1440 miles apart. What is the angle between their flight paths?

28. Two lighthouses are 74 miles apart on a beach and sight a ship in distress at angles of 59° and 40° with the beach. What is the nearest the ship could be to either lighthouse?

29. A surveyor at location C sights two points A and B on opposite sides of a reservoir. She knows that she is 1000 meters from A and 1500 meters from B, and measures angle $ACB = 30°$. How wide is the reservoir?

30. A television antenna tower is mounted at the top of a building. From a point 150 meters from the base of the building at ground level, the angle of elevation to the top of the building is 34°, while the angle of elevation to the top of the antenna is 50°. How tall is the antenna tower?

A.2 TECHNIQUES OF INTEGRATION

Numerical techniques of integration such as the trapezoidal or Simpson's rules provide powerful methods of approximating the value of a definite integral

$$\int_b^a f(x)\,dx.$$

The problem of finding an antiderivative (indefinite integral) of a function f requires finding another function F such that

$$F'(x) = f(x).$$

Once we have found one such antiderivative, any other antiderivative will differ from F only by a constant. Written in terms of integral notation

$$\int f(x)\,dx = F(x) + C,$$

where C represents an arbitrary constant.

There are two basic methods of antidifferentation–substitution and integration by parts. Essentially, the method of substitution requires one to recognize an antiderivative of the form

$$\int f(g(x))g'(x)\,dx.$$

By substituting $u = g(x)$ (so that $du = g'(x)\,dx$) we have

$$\int f(u)\,du$$

whose antiderivative may be easier for us to recognize.

Integration by parts requires two substitutions, and is based on the product rule of differentiation:

$$\int u\,dv = uv - \int v\,du.$$

Integration by parts is particularly useful when it is easier for us to identify the antiderivative $\int v\,du$ than the original $\int u\,dv$.

To facilitate the use of these basic methods of integration, there are several techniques involving algebraic and trigonometric manipulations. In this section, we discuss some of the most popular of these techniques, and provide examples of each. There are additional practice exercises at the end of the appendices.

Powers of trigonometric functions

To find antiderivatives of the form

$$\int \sin^m x \cos^n x\,dx \qquad \text{and} \qquad \int \tan^m x \sec^n x\,dx$$

you can take advantage of different trigonometric identities, depending on whether the powers m and n are even or odd. First, let's consider

$$\int \sin^m x \cos^n x\,dx.$$

Case 1. If n is odd, rewrite the integral as

$$\int (\sin^m x \cos^{n-1} x)(\cos x)\,dx$$

and make the substitution

$$u = \sin x \qquad du = (\cos x)\,dx$$

We can rewrite $\cos^{n-1} x$ (an even power of $\cos x$ because n is odd) in terms of $\sin x$ using the Pythagorean identity $\cos^2 x = 1 - \sin^2 x$.

EXAMPLE 5 Find $\int \cos^3 x \sin^2 x\, dx$.

Solution First, we rewrite the integral as

$$\int \cos^2 x \sin^2 x (\cos x\, dx).$$

Now using $\cos^2 x = 1 - \sin^2 x$, we have

$$\int (1 - \sin^2 x) \sin^2 x (\cos x\, dx) = \int (\sin^2 x - \sin^4 x)(\cos x\, dx).$$

Substituting $u = \sin x$ and $du = \cos x\, dx$ gives us

$$\int (u^2 - {}^4) du = \frac{u^3}{3} - \frac{u^5}{5} + C$$

Substituting $\sin x$ back for u yields the antiderivative in terms of x:

$$\int \cos^3 x \sin^2 x\, dx = \frac{\sin^3 x}{3} - \frac{\sin^5 x}{5} + C.$$ ■

Case 2. If m is odd, rewrite the integral as

$$-\int (\sin^{m-1} x \cos^n x)(-\sin x)\, dx$$

and make the substitution

$$u = \cos x \qquad du = (-\sin x)\, dx$$

We can rewrite $\sin^{m-1} x$ (an even power of $\sin x$ because m is odd) in terms of $\cos x$ using the Pythagorean identity $\sin^2 x = 1 - \cos^2 x$.

EXAMPLE 6 Find $\int \sin^5 x\, dx$.

Solution First, we rewrite the integral as

$$-\int \sin^4 x (-\sin x\, dx) = -\int (\sin^2 x)^2 (-\sin x\, dx).$$

Now, using $\sin^2 x = 1 - \cos^2 x$, we have

$$-\int (1 - \cos^2 x)^2 (-\sin x\, dx) = -\int (1 - 2\cos^2 x + \cos^4 x)(-\sin x\, dx).$$

Substituting $u = \cos x$ and $du = -\sin x\, dx$ gives us

$$-\int (1 - 2u^2 + u^4)du = -(u - \frac{2u^3}{3} + \frac{u^5}{5}) + C = -u + \frac{2u^3}{3} - \frac{u^5}{5} + C.$$

Substituting $\cos x$ back for u yields the antiderivative in terms of x:

$$\int \sin^5 x\, dx = -\cos x + \frac{2\cos^3 x}{3} - \frac{\cos^5 x}{5} + C.$$

■

Note that if both m and n are odd, you can choose to treat it as either Case 1 or Case 2.

Case 3. If both m and n are even use the half-angle formulas,

$$\sin^2 x = \frac{1 - \cos 2x}{2} \qquad \text{and} \qquad \cos^2 x = \frac{1 + \cos 2x}{2},$$

repeating if necessary.

EXAMPLE 7 Find $\int \sin^4 x\, dx$.

Solution In this case we write

$$\int \sin^4 x\, dx = \int (\sin^2 x)(\sin^2 x)dx$$

and use the half-angle formula $\sin^2 x = \dfrac{1 - \cos 2x}{2}$ to obtain

$$\int \left(\frac{1 - \cos 2x}{2}\right)\left(\frac{1 - \cos 2x}{2}\right) dx$$

$$= \frac{1}{4}\int (1 - 2\cos 2x + \cos^2 2x)\, dx$$

$$= \frac{1}{4}\int 1\, dx - \frac{1}{2}\int \cos 2x\, dx + \frac{1}{4}\int \cos^2 2x\, dx.$$

Now, $\frac{1}{4}\int 1\, dx = \frac{x}{4} + C_1$, and $-\frac{1}{2}\int \cos 2x\, dx = -\frac{1}{4}\sin 2x + C_2$ (using the substitution $u = 2x$, $du = 2\,dx$). For the last term we apply the other half-angle formula

$$\cos^2 2x = \frac{1 + \cos 4x}{2}$$

to obtain

$$\frac{1}{4}\int \frac{1+\cos 4x}{2}\,dx = \frac{1}{4}\left(\frac{1}{2}\int 1\,dx + \frac{1}{2}\int \cos 4x\,dx\right) = \frac{x}{8} + \frac{1}{32}\sin 4x + C_3.$$

We add up the results and sum the three constants to a single arbitrary constant:

$$\int \sin^4 x\,dx = \frac{3x}{8} - \frac{\sin 2x}{4} + \frac{\sin 4x}{32} + C.$$

■

A similar set of strategies can be used to find antiderivatives of

$$\int \tan^m x \sec^n x\,dx.$$

Case 1. If n is even, write the integral as

$$\int (\tan^m x)(\sec^{n-2} x)(\sec^2 x\,dx),$$

make the substitutions $u = \tan x$ and $du = \sec^2 x\,dx$, and write $\sec^{n-2} x$ in terms of $\tan x$ using the Pythagorean identity

$$\sec^2 x = 1 + \tan^2 x.$$

EXAMPLE 8 Find $\int \tan x \sec^4 x\,dx$.

Solution First, we rewrite the integral as

$$\int \tan x \sec^4 x\,dx = \int \tan x \sec^2 x(\sec^2 x\,dx)$$

and use the Pythagorean identity $\sec^2 x = 1 + \tan^2 x$ to obtain

$$\int \tan x(1+\tan^2 x)(\sec^2 x\,dx) = \int (\tan x + \tan^3 x)(\sec^2 x\,dx).$$

Substituting $u = \tan x$ and $du = \sec^2 x\,dx$ gives us

$$\int (u + u^3)\,du = \frac{u^2}{2} + \frac{u^4}{4} + C.$$

Substituting $\tan x$ back for u yields the antiderivative in terms of x:

$$\int \tan x \sec^4 x\,dx = \frac{\tan^2 x}{2} + \frac{\tan^4 x}{4} + C.$$

■

Case 2. If m is odd, write the integral as

$$\int (\tan^{m-1} x)(\sec^{n-1} x)(\sec x \tan x\, dx),$$

make the substitutions $u = \sec x$ and $du = \sec x \tan x\, dx$, and write $\tan^{m-1} x$ in terms of $\sec x$ using the Pythagorean identity

$$\tan^2 x = \sec^2 x - 1.$$

EXAMPLE 9 Find $\int \tan^3 x \sec x\, dx$.

Solution First, we rewrite the integral as

$$\int \tan^3 x \sec x\, dx = \int \tan^2 x(\sec x \tan x\, dx)$$

and use the Pythagorean identity $\tan^2 x = \sec^2 x - 1$ to obtain

$$\int (\sec^2 x - 1)(\sec x \tan x\, dx).$$

Substituting $u = \sec x$ and $du = \sec x \tan x\, dx$ gives us

$$\int (u^2 - 1)du = \frac{u^3}{3} - u + C.$$

Substituting $\sec x$ back for u yields the antiderivative in terms of x:

$$\int \tan^3 x \sec x\, dx = \frac{\sec^3 x}{3} - \sec x + C.$$

■

Note that if m is odd and n is even, you can choose to treat it as either Case 1 or Case 2.

Case 3. If m is even and n is odd, then one can use the Pythagorean identity $\tan^2 x = \sec^2 x - 1$ to rewrite $\tan^m x$ in terms of $\sec x$. This will produce a sum of integrals of odd powers of $\sec x$, and each such integral can be found using integration by parts, or by repeated use of the reduction formula

$$\int \sec^n x\, dx = \frac{1}{n-1} \tan x \sec^{n-2} x + \frac{n-2}{n-1} \int \sec^{n-2} x\, dx.$$

EXAMPLE 10 Find $\int \tan^2 x \sec^3 x \, dx$.

Solution Using the Pythagorean identity $\tan^2 x + 1 = \sec^2 x$, we can write

$$\int \tan^2 x \sec^3 x \, dx = \int (\sec^2 x - 1) \sec^3 x \, dx = \int \sec^5 x \, dx - \int \sec^3 x \, dx.$$

Applying the reduction formula to the first integral with $n = 5$, we have

$$\int \sec^5 x \, dx = \frac{1}{4} \tan x \sec^3 x + \frac{3}{4} \int \sec^3 x \, dx.$$

Hence,

$$\int \sec^5 x \, dx - \int \sec^3 x \, dx = \frac{1}{4} \tan x \sec^3 x - \frac{1}{4} \int \sec^3 x \, dx.$$

Now we apply the reduction formula again to find

$$\begin{aligned} \int \sec^3 x \, dx &= \frac{1}{2} \sec x \tan x + \frac{1}{2} \int \sec x \, dx \\ &= \frac{1}{2} \sec x \tan x + \frac{1}{2} \ln|\sec x + \tan x|. \end{aligned}$$

Combining the results, we finally have

$$\begin{aligned} \int \tan^2 x \sec^3 x \, dx &= \frac{1}{4} \tan x \sec^3 x - \frac{1}{4}\left(\frac{1}{2} \sec x \tan x + \frac{1}{2} \ln|\sec x + \tan x|\right) + C \\ &= \frac{1}{4} \tan x \sec^3 x - \frac{1}{8} \sec x \tan x + \frac{1}{8} \ln|\sec x + \tan x| + C. \end{aligned}$$

■

Trigonometric substitutions

A trigonometric substitution is useful in many cases where the integrand involves the sum or difference of squares of a constant a and a differentiable function u. Here is a guide for making trigonometric substitutions:

Form	Substitution to make	Pythagorean identity used	Substitute back for
$a^2 - u^2$	$u = a \sin\theta$ $du = a \cos\theta \, d\theta$	$a^2 - a^2 \sin^2\theta$ $= a^2 \cos^2\theta$	$\theta = \arcsin(\frac{u}{a})$
$a^2 + u^2$	$u = a \tan\theta$ $du = a \sec^2\theta \, d\theta$	$a^2 + a^2 \tan^2\theta$ $= a^2 \sec^2\theta$	$\theta = \arctan(\frac{u}{a})$
$u^2 - a^2$	$u = a \sec\theta$ $du = a \sec\theta \tan\theta \, d\theta$	$a^2 \sec^2\theta - a^2$ $= a^2 \tan^2\theta$	$\theta = \arctan(\frac{u}{a})$

EXAMPLE 11 Find $\int \frac{1}{\sqrt{9-x^2}}dx$.

Solution The expression $9-x^2$ is of the form a^2-u^2 where $a=3$ and $u=x$. We use the substitution

$$x = 3\sin\theta \quad \text{and} \quad dx = 3\cos\theta\, d\theta$$

and rewrite the integral as

$$\int \frac{1}{\sqrt{9-x^2}}dx = \int \frac{1}{\sqrt{9-(3\sin\theta)^2}}(3\cos\theta\, d\theta) = \int \frac{3\cos\theta d\theta}{\sqrt{9-9\sin^2\theta}}$$
$$= \int \frac{3\cos\theta d\theta}{3\sqrt{1-\sin^2\theta}} = \int \frac{\cos\theta\, d\theta}{\sqrt{\cos^2\theta}}.$$

Note that we can write $\sqrt{\cos^2\theta} = \cos\theta$ since $\theta = \arcsin\frac{x}{3}$ will always lie between $-\pi/2$ and $\pi/2$ and $\cos\theta$ must be positive. Thus, we have

$$\int \frac{\cos\theta\, d\theta}{\sqrt{\cos^2\theta}} = \int \frac{\cos\theta}{\cos\theta}\, d\theta = \int d\theta = \theta + C.$$

Substituting back for θ yields $\int \frac{1}{\sqrt{9-x^2}}dx = \arcsin\frac{x}{3} + C.$ ■

EXAMPLE 12 Find $\int \frac{x^2\, dx}{(25-x^2)^{3/2}}$.

Solution The integrand involves $25-x^2$ which is of the form

$$a^2-u^2,$$

where $a=5$ and $u=x$. We make the substitution

$$x = 5\sin\theta \quad \text{and} \quad dx = 5\cos\theta,$$

resulting in

$$\int \frac{x^2\, dx}{(25-x^2)^{3/2}} = \int \frac{(25\sin^2\theta)(5\cos\theta\, d\theta)}{(25-25\sin^2\theta)^{3/2}} = \int \frac{\sin^2\theta\cos\theta\, d\theta}{\cos^3\theta} = \int \tan^2\theta\, d\theta.$$

Now we carry out the integration:

$$\int \tan^2\theta\, d\theta = \int (\sec^2\theta - 1)\, d\theta = \tan\theta - \theta + C.$$

Finally, we substitute for θ in terms of x. Using $x = 5\sin\theta$, we have

$$\theta = \arcsin\left(\frac{x}{5}\right) \quad \text{and} \quad \tan\theta = \frac{x}{\sqrt{25-x^2}},$$

and we can write

$$\int \frac{x^2\,dx}{(25-x^2)^{3/2}} = \frac{x}{\sqrt{25-x^2}} - \arcsin\left(\frac{x}{5}\right) + C.$$

We can check by differentiating that

$$\frac{d}{dx}\left(\frac{x}{\sqrt{25-x^2}} - \arcsin\left(\frac{x}{5}\right) + C\right) = \frac{x^2}{(25-x^2)^{3/2}}.$$

■

EXAMPLE 13 Find $\int \frac{x^2 dx}{4+25x^2}$.

Solution This integral expression involves the form a^2+u^2, where $a=x$ and $u=5x$. We use the substitution $u = a\tan\theta$ or $5x = 2\tan\theta$. Thus,

$$x = \frac{2}{5}\tan\theta \qquad \text{and} \qquad dx = \frac{2}{5}\sec^2\theta d\theta,$$

and

$$\int \frac{x^2 dx}{4+25x^2} = \int \frac{(\frac{4}{25}\tan^2\theta)(\frac{2}{5}\sec^2\theta\, d\theta)}{4+25(\frac{4}{25}\tan^2\theta)} = \frac{2}{125}\int \frac{\tan^2\theta\sec^2\theta\, d\theta}{1+\tan^2\theta}.$$

Using the identity $1+\tan^2\theta = \sec^2\theta$ we can simplify the integral to

$$\frac{2}{125}\int \frac{\tan^2\theta\sec^2\theta d\theta}{\sec^2\theta} = \frac{2}{125}\int \tan^2\theta d\theta = \frac{2}{125}(\tan\theta - \theta) + C.$$

Substituting back into terms of x, we note that

$$\tan\theta = \frac{5}{2}x \qquad \text{and} \qquad \theta = \arctan(\frac{5}{2}x).$$

Hence,

$$\int \frac{x^2 dx}{4+25x^2} = \frac{2}{125}\left(\frac{5}{2}x - \arctan\left(\frac{5}{2}x\right)\right) + C = \frac{x}{25} - \frac{2}{125}\arctan\left(\frac{5}{2}x\right) + C.$$

■

EXAMPLE 14 Find $\int \frac{dx}{x^2\sqrt{2x^2-10}}$ for $x > \sqrt{5}$.

Solution This expression involves the form $u^2 - a^2$ where $u = \sqrt{2}x$ and $a = \sqrt{10}$. We use the substitution $u = a\sec\theta$ or $\sqrt{2}x = \sqrt{10}\sec\theta$.

With $x = \frac{\sqrt{10}}{\sqrt{2}}\sec\theta = \sqrt{5}\sec\theta$ and $dx = \sqrt{5}\sec\theta\tan\theta\, d\theta$, we have

$$\int \frac{dx}{x^2\sqrt{2x^2-10}} = \int \frac{\sqrt{5}\sec\theta\tan\theta d\theta}{5\sec^2\theta\sqrt{2(5\sec^2\theta)-10}}$$

$$= \frac{1}{\sqrt{50}}\int \frac{\tan\theta d\theta}{\sec\theta\sqrt{\sec^2\theta-1}}.$$

Using the identity $\tan^2\theta = \sec^2\theta - 1$ we have $\frac{1}{\sqrt{50}}\int \frac{\tan\theta d\theta}{\sec\theta\sqrt{\tan^2\theta}}$.

Now with $x > \sqrt{5}$, we must have $0 < \theta < \frac{\pi}{2}$ and $\tan\theta > 0$. Thus $\sqrt{\tan^2\theta} = \tan\theta$ and the integral simplifies to

$$\frac{1}{\sqrt{50}}\int \frac{d\theta}{\sec\theta} = \frac{1}{\sqrt{50}}\int \cos\theta d\theta = \frac{1}{\sqrt{50}}\sin\theta + C.$$

To rewrite this in terms of x, note that

$$\sin\theta = \sqrt{1-\cos^2\theta} = \sqrt{1-\frac{1}{\sec^2\theta}} = \sqrt{1-\frac{5}{x^2}}.$$

Thus,

$$\int \frac{dx}{x^2\sqrt{2x^2-10}} = \frac{1}{\sqrt{50}}\sqrt{1-\frac{5}{x^2}} + C = \frac{\sqrt{2x^2-10}}{10x} + C.$$ ■

EXAMPLE 15 Find $\int \frac{dx}{2x^2+6x+7}$.

Solution In this case, we need to write the denominator of the integrand as a sum of a squared term and a constant term. We do this by "completing the square," as illustrated here:

$$2x^2+6x+7 = 2(x^2+3x)+7 = 2(x^2+2\cdot\frac{3}{2}x+(\frac{3}{2})^2) - 2(\frac{3}{2})^2 + 7.$$

We can factor $(x^2+2(\frac{3}{2}x)+(\frac{3}{2})^2) = (x+\frac{3}{2})^2$ and write the quadratic as

$$2(x+\frac{3}{2})^2 - \frac{9}{2} + 7 = 2(x+\frac{3}{2})^2 + \frac{5}{2}.$$

The original integral can now be written as

$$\int \frac{dx}{2x^2+6x+7} = \int \frac{dx}{2(x+\frac{3}{2})^2+\frac{5}{2}} = \frac{1}{2}\int \frac{dx}{(x+\frac{3}{2})^2+\frac{5}{4}}.$$

Now we can proceed with a trigonometric substitution for the form a^2+u^2, where

$$a = \frac{\sqrt{5}}{2} \quad \text{and} \quad u = (x+\frac{3}{2}).$$

Substituting $x+\frac{3}{2} = \frac{\sqrt{5}}{2}\tan\theta$ and $du = dx = \frac{\sqrt{5}}{2}\sec^2\theta\, d\theta$, we have

$$\frac{1}{2}\int \frac{dx}{(x+\frac{3}{2})^2+\frac{5}{4}} = \frac{1}{2}\int \frac{\frac{\sqrt{5}}{2}\sec^2\theta\, d\theta}{\frac{5}{4}\tan^2\theta+\frac{5}{4}} = \frac{\sqrt{5}/2}{5/2}\int \frac{\sec^2\theta\, d\theta}{\tan^2\theta+1}$$

$$= \frac{\sqrt{5}}{5}\int \frac{\sec^2\theta\, d\theta}{\sec^2\theta} = \frac{\sqrt{5}}{5}\int d\theta = \frac{\sqrt{5}\theta}{5}+C = \frac{\sqrt{5}\arctan\left(\frac{2}{\sqrt{5}}(x+\frac{3}{2})\right)}{5}+C. \quad \blacksquare$$

EXERCISES for Section A.2

For exercises 1-16: Find each of the antiderivatives, making use of the Pythagorean identities of trigonometry.

1. $\int \cos^3 x\, dx$

2. $\int \sin^2 x \cos^2 x\, dx$

3. $\int \sin^3 x \cos^2 x\, dx$

4. $\int \sin^6 x\, dx$

5. $\int \tan^3 x \sec^4 x\, dx$

6. $\int \tan^3 x \sec^3 x\, dx$

7. $\int \tan^6 x\, dx$

8. $\int \sqrt{\sin x}\cos^3 x\, dx$

9. $\int (\tan x + \cot x)^2\, dx$

10. $\int \sin^3 x\, dx$

11. $\int \cos^4 x\, dx$

12. $\int \sec^4 x\, dx$

13. $\int \csc^4 x \cot^4 x\, dx$

14. $\int \frac{\cos x}{2-\sin x}\, dx$

15. $\int \frac{\sec^2 x}{(1+\tan x)^2}\, dx$

16. $\int \cos^5 x\, dx$

For exercises 17-26: Find each of the antiderivatives, using an appropriate trigonometric substitution.

17. $\int \frac{x^2}{\sqrt{4-x^2}}\, dx$

18. $\int \frac{1}{x\sqrt{9+x^2}}\, dx$

19. $\int \frac{1}{x^2\sqrt{x^2-25}}\, dx$

20. $\int \frac{x}{\sqrt{4-x^2}}\, dx$

21. $\displaystyle\int \frac{1}{(x^2-1)^{3/2}}\,dx$

22. $\displaystyle\int \frac{1}{(36+x^2)^2}\,dx$

23. $\displaystyle\int \sqrt{9-4x^2}\,dx$

24. $\displaystyle\int \frac{x}{(16-x^2)^2}\,dx$

25. $\displaystyle\int \frac{x^3}{\sqrt{9x^2+49}}\,dx$

26. $\displaystyle\int \frac{1}{x^4\sqrt{x^2-3}}\,dx$

For exercises 27-34: Find each of the antiderivatives, completing the square as necessary.

27. $\displaystyle\int \frac{1}{x^2-4x+8}\,dx$

28. $\displaystyle\int \frac{1}{\sqrt{4x-x^2}}\,dx$

29. $\displaystyle\int \frac{2x+3}{\sqrt{9-8x-x^2}}\,dx$

30. $\displaystyle\int \frac{1}{x^3-1}\,dx$

31. $\displaystyle\int \frac{1}{(x^2+4x+5)^2}\,dx$

32. $\displaystyle\int \frac{1}{(x^2+6x+13)^{3/2}}\,dx$

33. $\displaystyle\int \frac{1}{2x^2-3x+9}\,dx$

34. $\displaystyle\int \frac{(4+x^2)^2}{x^3}\,dx$

A.3 METHOD OF PARTIAL FRACTIONS

Simplification is in the eye of the beholder. You are no doubt familiar with the algebra involved in "simplifying" the sum of rational expressions. For example, given

$$\frac{2x-4}{x^2+1}+\frac{4}{5x-3},$$

we can rewrite this by finding a common denominator for the two rational expressions:

$$\begin{aligned}\frac{2x-4}{x^2+1}+\frac{4}{5x-3} &= \frac{(2x-4)(5x-3)}{(x^2+1)(5x-3)}+\frac{4(x^2+1)}{(5x-3)(x^2+1)}\\ &= \frac{(2x-4)(5x-3)+4(x^2+1)}{(5x-3)(x^2+1)}\\ &= \frac{(10x^2-26x+12)+(4x^2+4)}{5x^3-3x^2+5x-3}\\ &= \frac{14x^2-26x+16}{5x^3-3x^2+5x-3}.\end{aligned}$$

This final expression is simpler in the sense that it is a single rational expression instead of the sum of two. However, given the choice of finding an antiderivative of either form, we will have a much simpler time dealing with the original expression, for

$$\int \left(\frac{2x-4}{x^2+1} + \frac{4}{5x-3}\right) dx = \int \frac{2x}{x^2+1}\,dx - 4\int \frac{1}{x^2+1}\,dx + \int \frac{4}{5x-3}\,dx$$

$$= \ln(x^2+1) - 4\arctan x + \frac{4\ln|5x-3|}{5} + C.$$

(In the first integral, we made use of the substitution $u = x^2+1$, $du = 2x\,dx$; in the third integral, we made use of the substitution $u = 5x-3$, $du = 5\,dx$.)

Partial fractions provide a technique for breaking down a rational function into simpler parts (at least for integration purposes). In other words, starting with a rational expression such as

$$\frac{14x^2 - 26x + 16}{5x^3 - 3x^2 + 5x - 3}$$

we want to obtain its *partial fraction decomposition*

$$\frac{2x-4}{x^2+1} + \frac{4}{5x-3}.$$

Strictly speaking, the method of partial fractions is simply an algebraic procedure, and not a technique of integration. While it is used to simplify integrals, the method is also useful in other areas of mathematics. (If you go on in your study of differential equations, you will encounter the method of partial fractions in simplifying *Laplace transforms*.)

We will describe a step-by-step procedure for the method, and then apply it to several integration examples.

Procedure for the Method of Partial Fractions

Problem: Find $\int \frac{p(x)}{q(x)}\,dx$, where $p(x)$ and $q(x)$ are polynomials.

Step 1. Check that the degree of the numerator is less than the degree of the denominator. If not, do long division and work with the remainder.

Step 2. Factor the denominator completely into linear and quadratic terms. (This can always be done, even though the algebra might be complicated.)

Step 3. Examine the factors of the denominator.

If the factor $(x+a)$ appears n times, associate with it the sum of n terms

$$\frac{A_1}{(x+a)} + \frac{A_2}{(x+a)^2} + \cdots + \frac{A_n}{(x+a)^n}.$$

If (x^2+bx+c) appears m times, associate with it the sum of m terms

$$\frac{B_1x + C_1}{(x+a)} + \frac{B_2x + C_2}{(x^2+bx+c)^2} + \cdots + \frac{B_mx + c_m}{(x^2+bx+c)^m}.$$

Step 4. Add up these terms from Step 3 and set the sum equal to the original fraction.

Step 5. Clear the denominators, multiply out, and collect terms.

Step 6. Set the corresponding coefficients of the numerator of each side of the equation equal to each other. Use these equations to solve for the unknowns introduced in Step 3.

Step 7. Now each of these partial fractions can be antidifferentiated using either linear substitutions or trigonometric substitutions.

EXAMPLE 16 Find $\int \frac{2-x}{x^2+x}\,dx$.

Solution To find the antiderivative, we use the method of partial fractions. The factors of the denominator are x and $(x+1)$. Now we find must find two real numbers, A and B, such that

$$\frac{2-x}{x^2+x} = \frac{A}{x} + \frac{B}{x+1}.$$

Multiply both sides of this equation by the common denominator $x(x+1)$, to obtain

$$2 - x = A(x+1) + B(x).$$

When $x = 0$, then $2 - 0 = A(0+1) + B(0)$, and we see that $A = 2$. When $x = -1$, then $2 - (-1) = A(0) + B(-1)$ and we see that $B = -3$. We can now write the integral as follows:

$$\begin{aligned} \int \frac{2-x}{x^2+x}\,dx &= \int \left(\frac{2}{x} - \frac{3}{x+1}\right) dx \\ &= 2\int \frac{1}{x}\,dx - 3\int \frac{1}{x+1}\,dx \\ &= 2\ln x - 3\ln|x+1| + C. \end{aligned}$$

■

EXAMPLE 17 Find $\int \frac{3x+11}{(x+2)(x+3)}dx$

Solution To find the antiderivative, we use the method of partial fractions. First, we write

$$\frac{3x+11}{(x+2)(x+3)} = \frac{A}{x+2} + \frac{B}{x+3} = \frac{A(x+3)+B(x+2)}{(x+2)(x+3)}$$

The numerator of the right-hand side is

$$A(x+3)+B(x+2) = Ax+3A+Bx+2B = (A+B)x+(3A+2B).$$

Setting the numerators equal, we have

$$(A+B)x+(3A+2B) = 3x+11.$$

Equating the coefficients of like powers of x, we have

$$A+B=3 \qquad \text{and} \qquad 3A+2B=11.$$

Solving for A and B, we find that $A=5$ and $B=-2$. Thus,

$$\frac{3x+11}{(x+2)(x+3)} = \frac{5}{x+2} - \frac{2}{x+3},$$

and

$$\int \frac{3x+11}{(x+2)(x+3)}dx = \int \left(\frac{5}{x+2} - \frac{2}{x+3}\right)dx = 5\int \frac{dx}{x+2} - 2\int \frac{dx}{x+3}.$$

Using the formula $\int \frac{du}{u} = \ln|u| + C$, where $u=(x+2)$ in the first integral, $u=(x+3)$ in the second, and $du=dx$ in both. We obtain

$$5\ln|x+2| - 2\ln|x+3| + C.$$

■

EXAMPLE 18 Find $\int \frac{x^3+6x^2+3x+6}{x^3+2x^2}dx.$

Solution Since the denominator is of the same power as the numerator, we can divide the numerator by the denominator, and write the integral as :

$$\int \left(1+\frac{4x^2+3x+6}{x^3+2x^2}\right)dx = \int 1\,dx + \int \frac{4x^2+3x+6}{x^3+2x^2}dx$$

$$= x + \int \frac{4x^2+3x+6}{x^3+2x^2}dx.$$

We now use partial fractions on the "remainder" integral.

Since $x^3 + 2x^2$ can be factored as $x^2(x+2)$, we have three terms:

$$\frac{A}{x}, \quad \frac{B}{x^2}, \quad \text{and} \quad \frac{C}{(x+2)}.$$

We now find three numbers A, B, and C such that

$$\frac{4x^2+3x+6}{x^3+2x^2} = \frac{A}{x} + \frac{B}{x^2} + \frac{C}{x+2}.$$

Multiply both sides of the equation by $x^3 + 2x^2$ to obtain

$$\begin{aligned} 4x^2+3x+6 &= Ax(x+2) + B(x+2) + Cx^2 \\ &= Ax^2 + 2Ax + Bx + 2B + Cx^2 \\ &= (A+C)x^2 + (2A+B)x + 2B. \end{aligned}$$

Equate the coefficients of like powers of x to find

$$A + C = 4 \qquad 2A + B = 3 \qquad 2B = 6.$$

Therefore, $A = 0$, $B = 3$, and $C = 4$, and we substitute these values to finally obtain

$$\begin{aligned} \int \left(1 + \frac{4x^2+3x+6}{x^3+2x^2}\right) dx &= x + \int \frac{4x^2+3x+6}{x^3+2x^2}\, dx \\ &= x + \int \left(\frac{0}{x} + \frac{3}{x^2} + \frac{4}{x+2}\right) dx \\ &= x - \frac{3}{x} + 4\ln|x+2| + C. \end{aligned}$$

■

EXAMPLE 19 Find $\displaystyle\int \frac{x^3+5x^2+2x-4}{(x^4-1)}\, dx.$

Solution To antidifferentiate, we use the method of partial fractions. The denominator (x^4-1) can be factored as

$$x^4 - 1 = (x^2-1)(x^2+1) = (x-1)(x+1)(x^2+1).$$

Thus,

$$\frac{x^3+5x^2+2x-4}{(x^4-1)} = \frac{A}{x-1} + \frac{B}{x+1} + \frac{Cx+D}{x^2+1}$$

$$= \frac{A(x+1)(x^2+1) + B(x-1)(x^2+1) + (Cx+D)(x-1)(x+1)}{(x-1)(x+1)(x^2+1)}.$$

Multiplying out the terms in the numerator of the left-hand side and collecting like terms, we have

$$\begin{aligned}
&A(x+1)(x^2+1)+B(x-1)(x^2+1)+(Cx+D)(x-1)(x+1)\\
=&Ax^3+Ax^2+Ax+A+Bx^3-Bx^2+Bx-B+Cx^3+Dx^2-Cx-D\\
=&(A+B+C)x^3+(A-B+D)x^2+(A+B-C)x+(A-B-D).
\end{aligned}$$

Setting this numerator equal to x^3+5x^2+2x-4, and equating coefficients of like powers of x, we obtain

$$A+B+C=1 \qquad A-B+D=5$$

$$A+B-C=2 \qquad A-B-D=-4$$

The solutions to these equations are

$$A=1, \qquad B=\frac{1}{2}, \qquad C=-\frac{1}{2}, \qquad \text{and} \qquad D=\frac{9}{2}.$$

Thus,

$$\begin{aligned}
\frac{x^3+5x^2+2x-4}{(x^4-1)} &= \frac{1}{x-1}+\frac{\frac{1}{2}}{x+1}+\frac{-\frac{1}{2}x+\frac{9}{2}}{x^2+1}\\
&=\frac{1}{x-1}+\frac{1}{2(x+1)}+\frac{9-x}{2(x^2+1)}\\
&=\frac{1}{x-1}+\frac{1}{2(x+1)}+\frac{9}{2}\left(\frac{1}{x^2+1}\right)-\frac{1}{2}\left(\frac{x}{x^2+1}\right).
\end{aligned}$$

Then $\displaystyle\int \frac{x^3+5x^2+2x-4}{x^4-1}\,dx$

$$\begin{aligned}
&=\int\frac{dx}{x-1}+\frac{1}{2}\int\frac{dx}{x+1}+\frac{9}{2}\int\frac{dx}{x^2+1}-\frac{1}{2}\int\frac{x\,dx}{x^2+1}\\
&=\ln|x-1|+\frac{1}{2}\ln|x+1|+\frac{9}{2}\arctan x-\frac{1}{4}\ln(x^2+1)+C.
\end{aligned}$$

(Note, we used the substitution $\displaystyle\int\frac{du}{u}=\ln|u|+C$ three times: on the first integral with $u=x-1$ and $du=dx$, on the second integral with $u=x+1$ and $du=dx$, and on the fourth integral with $u=x^2+1$ and $du=2x\,dx$.) ■

EXAMPLE 20 Find $\displaystyle\int \frac{x^2+4x}{(x-2)^2(x^2+4)}\,dx.$

Solution To antidifferentiate, we use the method of partial fractions to write

$$\begin{aligned}\frac{x^2+4x}{(x-2)^2(x^2+4)} &= \frac{A}{(x-2} + \frac{B}{(x-2)^2} + \frac{Cx+D}{(x^2+4)}\\ &= \frac{A(x-2)(x^2+4)+B(x^2+4)+(Cx+D)(x-2)^2}{(x-2)^2(x^2+4)}.\end{aligned}$$

Expanding the numerator, we have

$$\begin{aligned}&A(x-2)(x^2+4)+B(x^2+4)+(Cx+D)(x-2)^2\\ =&(A+C)x^3+(-2A+B-4C+D)x^2+(4A+4C-4D)x+(-8A+4B+4D).\end{aligned}$$

Equate the coefficients of like powers of x to obtain the equations

$$A+C=0 \qquad -2A+B-4C+D=1$$

$$4A+4C-4D=4 \qquad -8A+4B+4D=0.$$

Solving these equations, we find

$$A=\frac{1}{4}, \quad B=\frac{3}{2}, \quad C=-\frac{1}{4} \quad \text{and} \quad D=-1.$$

Hence,

$$\begin{aligned}\int \frac{x^2+4x}{(x-2)^2(x^2+4)}\,dx &= \int \frac{\frac{1}{4}}{x-2}\,dx + \int \frac{\frac{3}{2}}{(x-2)^2}\,dx - \int \frac{\frac{1}{4}x-1}{x^2+4}\,dx\\ &= \frac{1}{4}\int \frac{dx}{x-2} + \frac{3}{2}\int \frac{dx}{(x-2)^2} - \frac{1}{4}\int \frac{x\,dx}{x^2+4} - \int \frac{dx}{x^2+4}.\end{aligned}$$

We can use the substitution $u=x-2$ and $du=dx$ on the first two integrals, and $u=x^2+4$ and $du=2x\,dx$ on the third to obtain

$$\int \frac{x^2+4x}{(x-2)^2(x^2+4)}\,dx$$

$$= \frac{1}{4}\ln|x-2| - \frac{3}{2(x-2)} - \frac{1}{8}\ln(x^2+4) - \frac{1}{2}\arctan\left(\frac{x}{2}\right) + C.$$

■

EXAMPLE 21 Find $\int \frac{x^4 - x^3 + 2x^2 - x + 2}{(x-1)(x^2+2)^2} dx$.

Solution To antidifferentiate, we use the method of partial fractions to write

$$\frac{x^4 - x^3 + 2x^2 - x + 2}{(x-1)(x^2+2)^2} = \frac{A}{x-1} + \frac{Bx+C}{x^2+2} + \frac{Dx+E}{(x^2+2)^2}$$

$$= \frac{A(x^2+2)^2 + (Bx+C)(x-1)(x^2+2) + (Dx+E)(x-1)}{(x-1)(x^2+2)^2}.$$

Expanding the numerator and collecting like terms, we have

$$\begin{aligned} &A(x^2+2)^2 + (Bx+C)(x-1)(x^2+2) + (Dx+E)(x-1) \\ =&(A+B)x^4 + (C-B)x^3 + (4A - C + 2B + D)x^2 \\ &+ (2C - 2B + E - D)x + (4A - 2C - E). \end{aligned}$$

Now equate the coefficients of like powers of x with $x^4 - x^3 + 2x^2 - x + 2$, the numerator of the left-hand side:

$$A + B = 1, \qquad C - B = -1,$$

$$4A - C + 2B + D = 2, \qquad 2C - 2B + E - D = -1, \qquad 4A - 2C - E = 2.$$

Solving for A, B, C, D, and E we find

$$A = \frac{1}{3}, \qquad B = \frac{2}{3}, \qquad C = -\frac{1}{3}, \qquad D = -1, \qquad E = 0.$$

Substituting these values, we have $\int \frac{x^4 - x^3 + 2x^2 - x + 2}{(x-1)(x^2+2)^2} dx$

$$= \frac{1}{3}\int \frac{dx}{x-1} + \int \frac{\frac{2}{3}x - \frac{1}{3}}{x^2+2} dx - \int \frac{x\,dx}{(x^2+2)^2}$$

$$= \frac{1}{3}\int \frac{dx}{x-1} + \frac{1}{3}\int \frac{2x\,dx}{x^2+2} - \frac{1}{3}\int \frac{dx}{x^2+2} - \int \frac{x\,dx}{(x^2+2)^2}.$$

For the first integral, use the substitution $u = x - 1$ and $du = dx$.

For the second and fourth integrals, use the substitution $u = x^2 + 2$ and $du = 2x\,dx$. For the third integral, use the formula

$$\int \frac{du}{u^2 + a^2} = \frac{1}{a} \arctan \frac{u}{a},$$

letting $u = x$, and $a = \sqrt{2}$. Finally, we obtain $\int \frac{x^4 - x^3 + 2x^2 - x + 2}{(x-1)(x^2+2)^2} dx$

$$= \frac{1}{3}\ln|x-1| + \frac{1}{3}\ln(x^2+2) - \frac{\sqrt{2}}{6}\arctan\frac{x}{\sqrt{2}} + \frac{1}{2(x^2+2)} + C.$$

■

EXERCISES for Section A.3

For exercises 1-16: Find each of the antiderivatives, using the method of partial fractions.

1. $\displaystyle\int \frac{5x-12}{x(x-4)}\,dx$

2. $\displaystyle\int \frac{37-11x}{(x+1)(x-2)(x-3)}\,dx$

3. $\displaystyle\int \frac{6x-11}{(x-1)^2}\,dx$

4. $\displaystyle\int \frac{x+16}{x^2+2x-8}\,dx$

5. $\displaystyle\int \frac{5x^2-10x-8}{x^3-4x}\,dx$

6. $\displaystyle\int \frac{2x^2-25x-33}{(x-1)^2(x-5)}\,dx$

7. $\displaystyle\int \frac{9x^4+17x^3+3x^2-8x+3}{x^5+3x^4}\,dx$

8. $\displaystyle\int \frac{x^3+3x^2+3x+63}{(x^2-9)^2}\,dx$

9. $\displaystyle\int \frac{5x^2+11x+17}{x^3+5x^2+4x+20}\,dx$

10. $\displaystyle\int \frac{x^2+3x+1}{x^4+5x^2+4}\,dx$

11. $\displaystyle\int \frac{2x^3+10x}{(x^2+1)^2}\,dx$

12. $\displaystyle\int \frac{x^3+3x-2}{x^2-x}\,dx$

13. $\displaystyle\int \frac{x^6-x^3+1}{x^4+9x^2}\,dx$

14. $\displaystyle\int \frac{2x^3-5x^2+46x+98}{(x^2+x-12)^2}\,dx$

15. $\displaystyle\int \frac{4x^3+2x^2-5x-18}{(x-4)(x+1)^3}\,dx$

16. $\displaystyle\int \frac{2x^4-2x^3+6x^2-5x+1}{x^3-x^2+x-1}\,dx$

A.4 POLAR COORDINATES

A very useful alternative coordinate system for the plane is the **polar coordinate system**. To locate a point in the (two-dimensional) plane requires specifying two real numbers or coordinates. In the rectangular or Cartesian coordinate system, the two coordinates make reference to two perpendicular real axes intersecting at the origin.

We can imagine a point's coordinates (x, y) as specifying directions to a person at the origin. The x-coordinate gives the person the precise distance and direction to walk in the horizontal direction, and the y-coordinate gives the precise distance and direction to walk in the vertical direction. For example, we can locate the point $(3, -2)$ by walking 3 units to the right and 2 units down.

An alternative method of communicating a point's location would be to specify the point's distance from the origin and the direction to walk straight out to the point. For example, if we were given the information that a point located exactly 6 units from the origin along a line making a $40°$ angle measured counterclockwise from the positive x-axis, we can find the point precisely (see Figure A.8).

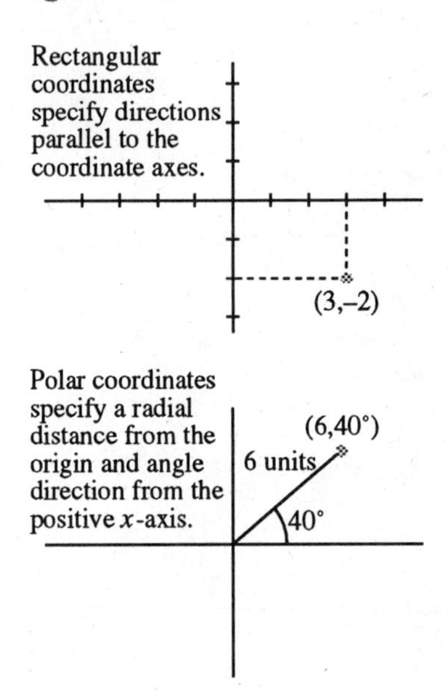

Figure A.8 Rectangular and polar coordinate systems.

The convention for specifying polar coordinates is to list the distance r and angle θ as an ordered pair (r, θ). The angle θ could be measured in either degrees or radians, but we will usually use radian measure.

EXAMPLE 22 Locate the following points given their polar coordinates:

$$P = (2, \frac{\pi}{4}), \qquad Q = (5, \frac{2\pi}{3}), \qquad R = (3, -\frac{5\pi}{6}) \qquad S = (2, \frac{9\pi}{4}).$$

Solution The points are illustrated in Figure A.9. Notice that the point $(2, \frac{9\pi}{4})$ represents the same point as $(2, \frac{\pi}{4})$. In other words, points P and S coincide.

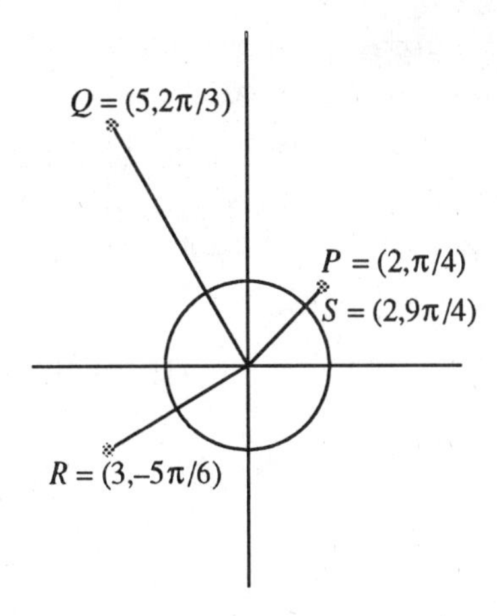

Figure A.9 Locating points with polar coordinates ■

Both the Cartesian and polar coordinate systems require an ordered pair of real numbers to specify a point's location on the plane. An important difference between the systems has to do with *uniqueness of representations*. In the Cartesian system, every point has exactly one ordered pair (x, y) associated with it. However, in the polar coordinate system, a point has infinitely many representations (r, θ) because

$$(r, \theta + 2\pi n)$$

gives the same location as (r, θ) for any integer n. For example, $(2, \frac{\pi}{4})$, $(2, \frac{9\pi}{4})$, $(2, \frac{17\pi}{4})$, and $(2, -\frac{15\pi}{4})$ all represent the same point.

A negative radius r can be specified as a polar coordinate by adopting the convention that $(-r, \theta)$ and $(r, \theta + \pi)$ represent the same point. Geometrically, the point $(-r, \theta)$ is the reflection of (r, θ) through the origin (see Figure A.10).

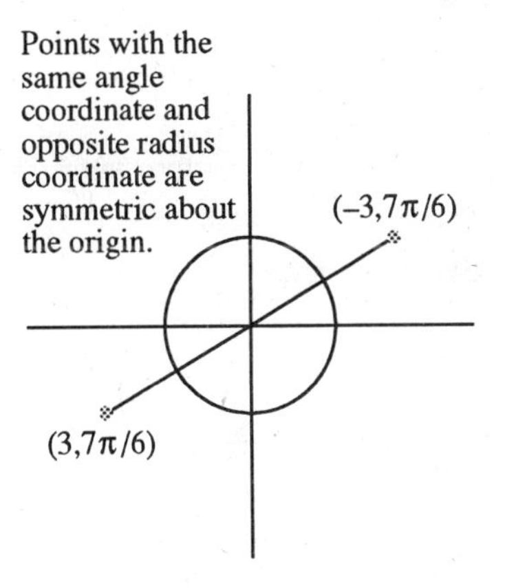

Figure A.10 Comparing (r, θ) and $(-r, \theta)$.

A special case occurs when $r = 0$. Notice that $(0, \theta)$ represents the origin, regardless of the value of θ.

For points other than the origin, we could gain a unique polar coordinate representation by arbitrarily restricting the radius r to be positive and the angle measure θ to lie in some predetermined interval of length 2π, say

$$0 \leq \theta < 2\pi$$

or

$$-\pi < \theta \leq \pi.$$

Such restrictions may be useful in certain applications, but we will generally allow both r and θ to take on any real number values.

Conversions between coordinate systems

Given a point whose location is specified by polar coordinates (r, θ), we can find the corresponding rectangular coordinates (x, y) through some simple trigonometry. Figure A.11 illustrates the situation for a point in the first quadrant.

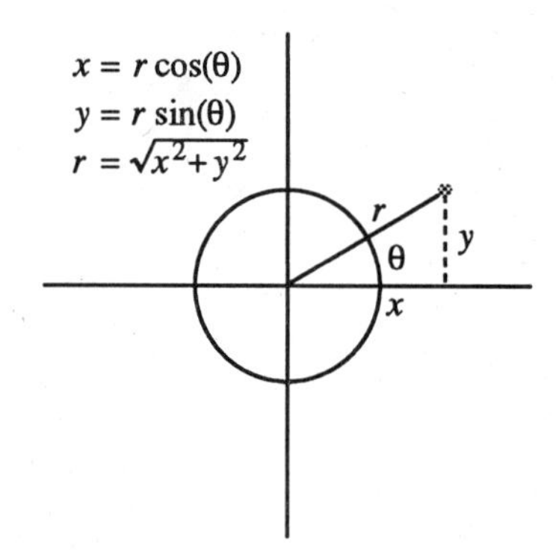

Figure A.11 Conversions between rectangular and polar coordinates.

Specifically,

$$x = r\cos(\theta) \qquad \text{and} \qquad y = r\sin(\theta).$$

EXAMPLE 23 Convert the following from polar coordinates to rectangular coordinates:

$$(4, 3\pi/4) \quad \text{and} \quad (-2.5, -638^\circ).$$

Solution For $(4, 3\pi/4)$, we have $r = 4$ and $\theta = 3\pi/4$, so

$$x = r\cos(\theta) = 4 \cdot \frac{-\sqrt{2}}{2} = -2\sqrt{2} \quad \text{and} \quad y = r\sin(\theta) = 4 \cdot \frac{\sqrt{2}}{2} = 2\sqrt{2}.$$

Hence, $(4, 3\pi/4)$ in polar coordinates corresponds to

$$(-2\sqrt{2}, 2\sqrt{2}) \approx (-2.8284, 2.8284)$$

in rectangular coordinates.

For $(-2.5, -638^\circ)$, we have

$$x = (-2.5)\cos(-638^\circ) \approx -0.3479 \quad \text{and} \quad y = (-2.5)\sin(-638^\circ) \approx -2.4757,$$

so $(-2.5, -638^\circ)$ in polar coordinates corresponds approximately to

$$(-0.3479, -2.4757)$$

in rectangular coordinates. ■

Given a point whose location is specified with rectangular coordinates (x, y), we can find corresponding polar coordinates (r, θ) for the same point. First, we note that

$$r = \sqrt{x^2 + y^2}$$

by using the Pythagorean theorem.

If $r = 0$, then any value θ may be used. If $r \neq 0$, we can find a suitable value $0 \leq \theta < 2\pi$ by noting that

$$\sin(\theta) = y/r \quad \text{and} \quad \cos(\theta) = x/r.$$

More directly, if we compute $\arctan(y/x)$, then either

$$\theta = \arctan(y/x) \quad \text{or} \quad \theta = \arctan(y/x) + \pi,$$

depending on the quadrant (x, y) is in (the first value applies to Quadrants I and IV; the second value applies to Quadrants II and III).

EXAMPLE 24 Convert the following from rectangular coordinates to polar coordinates:

$$(3,4) \qquad \text{and} \qquad (-7.51,-6.28).$$

Solution For $(3,4)$ we have $x=3$ and $y=4$, so

$$r=\sqrt{3^2+4^2}=\sqrt{25}=5.$$

Since $(3,4)$ is in the first quadrant, we can use

$$\theta=\arctan(y/x)=\arctan(4/3)\approx 0.9273 \text{ radians}$$

or, using degree measure, $\theta \approx 53.13°$. Thus, $(3,4)$ in rectangular coordinates corresponds approximately to

$$(5,0.9273) \qquad \text{or} \qquad (5,53.13°)$$

in polar coordinates.

For $(-7.51,-6.28)$, we have

$$r=\sqrt{(-7.51)^2+(-6.28)^2}\approx 9.79.$$

Since $(-7.51,-6.28)$ is in the third quadrant, we can use

$$\theta=\arctan(y/x)+\pi=\arctan(\frac{-6.28}{-7.51})+\pi\approx 3.838 \text{ radians}$$

or, using degree measure, $\theta \approx 219.9°$. Thus, $(-7.51,-6.28)$ in rectangular coordinates corresponds approximately to

$$(9.79,3.838) \qquad \text{or} \qquad (9.79,219.9°)$$

in polar coordinates. ■

Polar graphs

Sometimes it is more convenient to describe a curve using polar coordinates rather than Cartesian coordinates. This is particularly true when the curve is defined in terms of distance to a reference point. The simplest example of such a curve is a circle. For example, a circle of radius 3 centered at the origin has the equation

$$r=3$$

in polar coordinates.

The grid markings on graph paper correspond to constant values of the two coordinates. For Cartesian coordinates, the grid lines are horizontal and vertical, corresponding to equations of the form

$$x = a \quad \text{and} \quad y = b,$$

where a and b are constants.

For polar coordinates, the grid lines are concentric circles centered at the origin, corresponding to equations of the form

$$r = a,$$

and lines through the origin, corresponding to equations of the form

$$\theta = b,$$

where a and b are constants. Figure A.12 shows a polar grid that could be used as an aid in plotting polar graphs by hand.

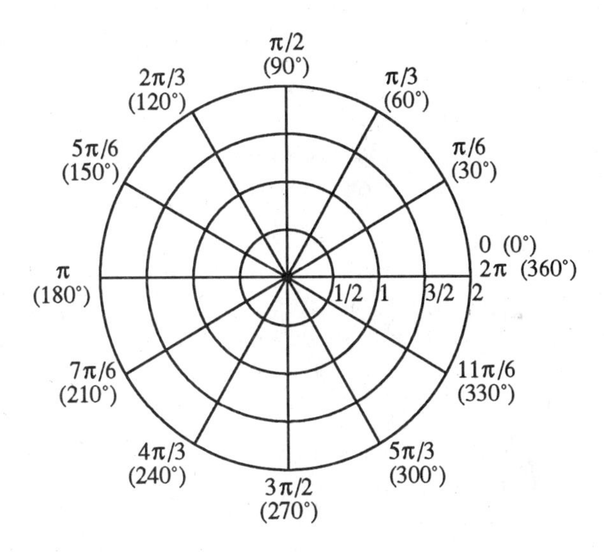

Figure A.12 Polar grid lines are concentric circles and lines through the origin.

A functional equation of the form

$$r = r(\theta)$$

describes the distance r from the origin as a function of the angle θ. You might think of a radar screen with a beam emanating from the origin sweeping around in a circle, recording the distance r out to a curve for each value θ.

EXAMPLE 25 Plot $r = 2\sin(\theta)$.

Solution Figure A.13 shows the plot of points for this polar equation. We can see that we have obtained what looks like a circle of radius 1 centered at the Cartesian point $(0, 1)$.

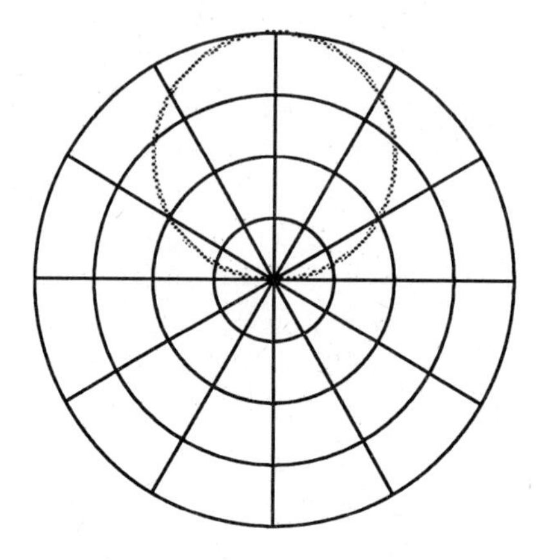

Figure A.13 Graph of $r = 2\sin(\theta)$.

Can we be sure this is a circle? If we multiply both sides of the equation by r, we obtain

$$r^2 = 2r\sin(\theta).$$

Converting to Cartesian coordinates, we find that this is equivalent to

$$x^2 + y^2 = 2y.$$

On the other hand, a circle of radius 1 centered at $(0, 1)$ will have the equation

$$x^2 + (y - 1)^2 = 1^2$$

or, after expanding,

$$x^2 + y^2 - 2y + 1 = 1.$$

We can see that this is equivalent to our polar equation. ■

Some curves are much more easily described with polar coordinates than rectangular coordinates. Figure A.14 shows the graph of a "hyperbolic spiral" $r = 2\pi/\theta$ for $0 < \theta \leq 4\pi$. The radius r is undefined for $\theta = 0$, and the spiral approaches the horizontal asymptote $y = 2\pi$ as θ approaches 0 through positive values. In comparison, the rectangular description of this curve is much more complicated (try it!).

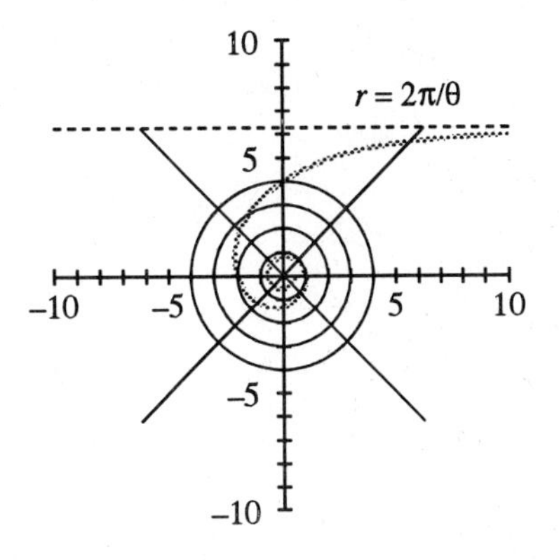

Figure A.14 The hyperbolic spiral $r = 2\pi/\theta$ for $0 < \theta \le 4\pi$.

When r is a periodic function of θ (like many functions built up from trigonometric functions), then the graph of $r = r(\theta)$ will come back to its starting point over one period. In this case, the graph may determine one or more closed curves. The appearance of the resulting "loops" of such a curve provide the motivation for many colorful (and descriptive) names for particular polar graphs. For example, Figure A.15 shows an example of a heart-shaped polar graph, aptly named a "cardioid."

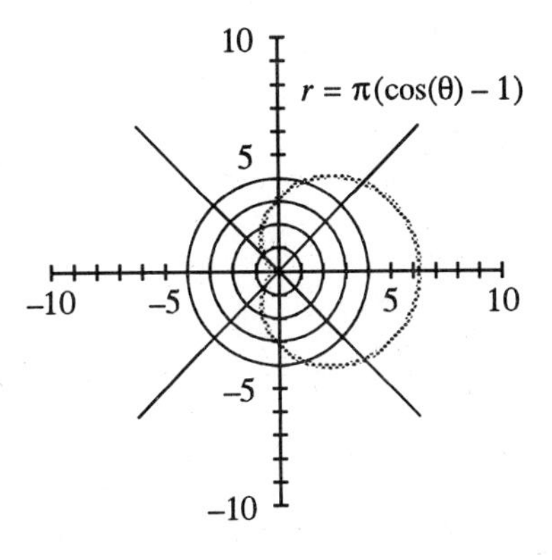

Figure A.15 The cardioid $r = \pi(\cos(\theta) - 1)$.

Polar graphs as parametric curves

We can think of polar plotting as a special case of parametric plotting. Recall that a curve can be described by expressing the coordinates as functions of a third variable (parameter) t:

$$(x(t), y(t)).$$

If we use t instead of θ as a parameter, then we can use the fact that $x = r\cos t$ and $y = r\sin t$ to express the curve

$$r = f(t)$$

parametrically as

$$x(t) = f(t)\cos(t)$$
$$y(t) = f(t)\sin(t).$$

EXAMPLE 26 Express the polar graph $r = 2\sin(t)$, $0 \le t \le 2\pi$ as a parametric curve $(x(t), y(t))$.

Solution Substituting into the usual conversion formulas for changing from polar to rectangular coordinates, we obtain

$$x(t) = 2\sin(t)\cos(t)$$
$$y(t) = 2\sin^2(t).$$

Try graphing this with a parametric plotter over the interval $0 \le t \le 2\pi$ to see that it does trace out the same circle of radius 1 with center at $(0, 1)$. ■

Hence, any machine grapher capable of plotting parametric equations is automatically capable of plotting polar equations. Of course, some graphers have a special polar graphing feature.

Differentiation using polar coordinates

The slope $\frac{dy}{dx}$ of a polar graph $r = r(\theta)$ can be determined by using the chain rule and the two conversion formulas

$$x = r(\theta)\cos(\theta) \qquad \text{and} \qquad y = r(\theta)\sin(\theta)$$

to obtain

$$\frac{dy}{dx} = \frac{\frac{dy}{d\theta}}{\frac{dx}{d\theta}}.$$

Taking the indicated derivatives with respect to θ in the numerator and denominator yields

$$\frac{dy}{dx} = \frac{\frac{dr}{d\theta}\sin\theta + r(\theta)\cos\theta}{\frac{dr}{d\theta}\cos\theta - r(\theta)\sin\theta}.$$

EXAMPLE 27 Find the slope of the polar graph of $r = 2\sin\theta$ at $\theta = \pi/3$.

Solution Using the derivative formula for $\dfrac{dy}{dx}$ we just developed, we have

$$\frac{dy}{dx} = \frac{2\cos\theta\sin\theta + 2\sin\theta\cos\theta}{2\cos\theta\cos\theta - 2\sin\theta\sin\theta} = \frac{2\cos\theta\sin\theta}{\cos^2\theta - \sin^2\theta} = \frac{\sin(2\theta)}{\cos(2\theta)} = \tan(2\theta).$$

For $\theta = \pi/3$, we have

$$\left.\frac{dy}{dx}\right|_{\theta=\pi/3} = \tan(2\pi/3) = -\sqrt{3}.$$

Examine the polar graph of $r = 2\sin\theta$ for $\theta = \pi/3$ to see that this slope value is reasonable. ■

Integration using polar coordinates

To see how we can extend definite integration to regions defined in terms of polar coordinates, let's first review the situation for rectangular coordinates. The area of a region bounded by the graph of $y = f(x)$ and the x-axis between $x = a$ and $x = b$ is given by the definite integral

$$\int_a^b |f(x)|\,dx.$$

The absolute value signs are necessary to guarantee that area both above and below the x-axis is counted as positive contributions to the total area of the region. The value $|f(x)|\,\Delta x$ is the area of a small rectangle of width Δx and height $|f(x)|$, and it represents the approximate area of the region swept out by the graph over a small change in the independent variable Δx. In the limiting process associated with definite integration, this value corresponds to the differential $|f(x)|\,dx$.

Now, let's use that same idea for polar graphs. Suppose $r = r(\theta)$ is given and we want to approximate the area swept out by the graph for a small change in the independent variable $\Delta\theta$. Figure A.16 illustrates the area swept out by such a graph.

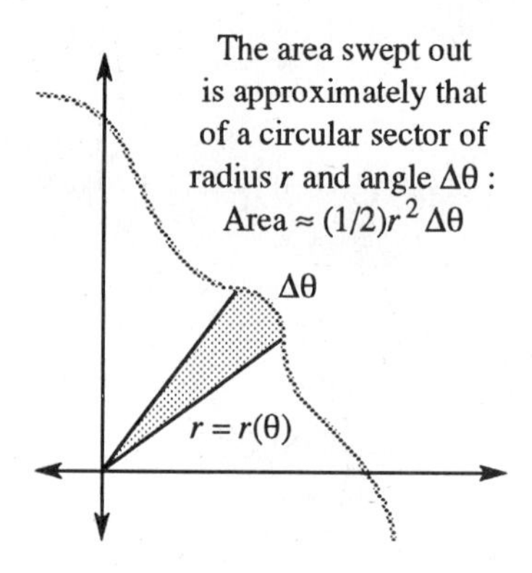

Figure A.16 Measuring area bounded by a polar graph.

The shaded region in the figure has approximately the area of a circular sector of angle $\Delta\theta$ and radius $r = f(\theta)$, for some θ in the tiny angle interval. Since a circle of radius r has area πr^2, the area of a circular sector of angle $\Delta\theta$ is given by

$$\frac{\Delta\theta}{2\pi}\pi r^2 = \frac{1}{2}r^2\Delta\theta.$$

To approximate the total area enclosed by the graph between $\theta = a$ and $\theta = b$, we can partition the angle interval into many such tiny subintervals and add the areas of the resulting circular sector area approximations:

$$\text{total area enclosed} \quad \approx \quad \sum_{i=1}^{n}\frac{1}{2}r^2(\theta_i)\Delta\theta,$$

where θ_i is the particular angle value chosen from each subinterval. The limiting value of these approximations as $\Delta\theta$ approaches 0 is given by a definite integral:

$$\text{total area enclosed} \quad = \quad \frac{1}{2}\int_a^b r^2(\theta)\,d\theta.$$

EXAMPLE 28 Using definite integration, find the total area bounded by the curve $r = 2\sin(\theta)$.

Solution The graph of this polar function is shown in Figure A.17.

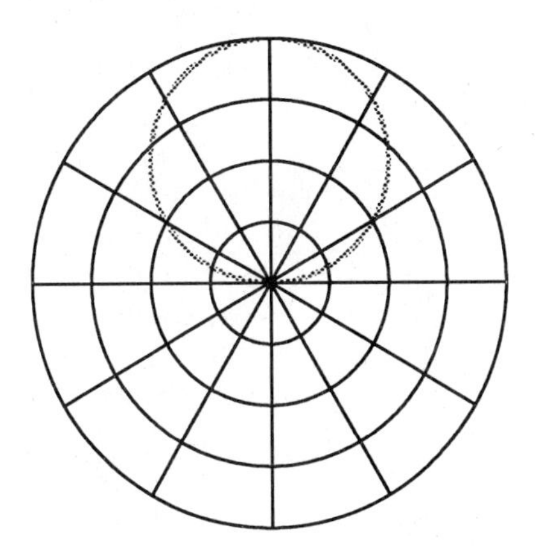

Figure A.17 Polar graph of $r = 2\sin(\theta)$.

In this case, we know that the graph is a circle of radius 1, so the area bounded by the graph certainly must be $\pi \cdot 1^2 = \pi$. To find this area by definite integration, we need to first determine the interval of integration. Although the period of $2\sin(\theta)$ is 2π, the entire graph is traced out over the interval $[0, \pi]$. Hence, the area is given by the integral

$$\frac{1}{2}\int_0^{\pi} r^2\, d\theta = \frac{1}{2}\int_0^{\pi} 4\sin^2(\theta)\, d\theta = 2\int_0^{\pi} \sin^2(\theta)\, d\theta \approx 2 \cdot (1.5708) = 3.1416.$$

(The integral was computed by machine.) ■

A polar graphing utility on a computer or calculator can be a great aid in checking that the interval of integration is the one you want. In the previous example, we would have obtained an erroneous area of 2π if we had used the interval $[0, 2\pi]$, because the circle is actually traced *twice* over this interval.

EXAMPLE 29 Find the total area of the cardioid $r = \pi(\cos(\theta) - 1)$.

Solution In this case, the entire cardioid is traced out over an interval $[0, 2\pi]$. Hence, the total area is given by

$$\frac{1}{2}\int_0^{2\pi} r^2\, d\theta = \frac{1}{2}\int_0^{2\pi} \pi^2(\cos(\theta) - 1)^2\, d\theta = \frac{\pi^2}{2}\int_0^{2\pi} (\cos^2(\theta) - 2\cos(\theta) + 1)\, d\theta = \frac{3\pi^3}{2}.$$

To judge the reasonableness of this answer, we can estimate the area from the graph (see Figure A.18).

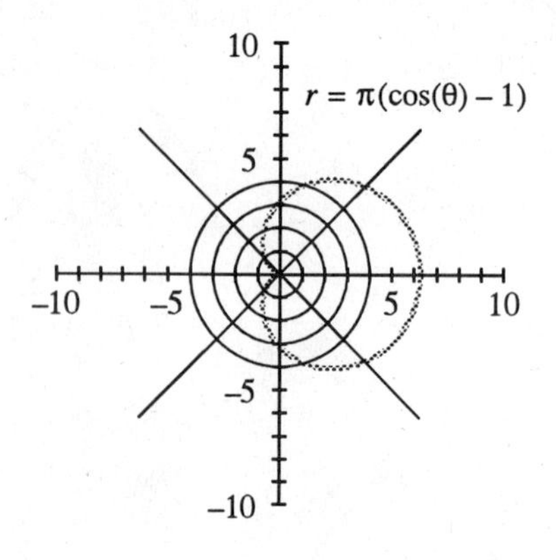

Figure A.18 Find the area of the cardioid.

The graph is roughly approximated by a circle of radius 4, whose area is $\pi \cdot 4^2 \approx 50$. On the other hand, the value we obtained for the area of the cardioid is

$$\frac{3\pi^3}{2} \approx 46.5.$$

■

More generally, the area bounded between the two graphs $y = f(x)$ and $y = g(x)$ between $x = a$ and $x = b$ is given by the definite integral

$$\int_a^b |f(x) - g(x)|\, dx.$$

For the region bounded between two polar graphs $r = r_1(\theta)$ and $r = r_2(\theta)$ between $\theta = a$ and $\theta = b$, we have the integral

$$\frac{1}{2}\int_a^b |r_1^2(\theta) - r_2^2(\theta)|\, d\theta.$$

The absolute value signs here simply indicate that we should always subtract the smaller squared radius from the larger in our integral.

EXERCISES for Section A.4

For exercises 1-8: Convert the indicated polar coordinates to rectangular coordinates.

1. $(3, 60°)$

2. $(1.414, -765°)$

3. $(3, -60°)$

4. $(-3.5, -600°)$

5. (π, π)

6. $(-5, -8\pi/3)$

7. $(0, 1000)$

8. $(1000, 0)$

For exercises 9-16: Convert the indicated rectangular coordinates to polar coordinates, both with θ measured in degrees and radians.

9. $(3, 4)$
10. $(-5, -5)$
11. $(2.789, -3.254)$
12. $(-2.789, -3.254)$
13. (π, π)
14. $(-5, -8\pi/3)$
15. $(0, 1000)$
16. $(1000, 0)$

For exercises 17-26: Graph the given polar function over an appropriate interval (experiment with intervals having lengths that are multiples of π) for values of the parameter $a = 1/4$, $1/2$, 1, 2 and 4. On the basis of these graphs, determine what characteristic of the graph a controls. Predict the appearance of the graph for $a = 1/3$ and for $a = 3$, and then check your predictions by graphing the polar function for these parameter values. (When the given graph has a special name, it appears in parentheses.)

17. $r = 2a\cos(\theta)$ (Circle)

18. $r = a\sin(\theta)\cos^2(\theta)$ (Bifolium)

19. $r = a(\cos(\theta) + 1)$ (Cardioid)

20. $r = a\sin(\theta)\tan(\theta)$ (Cissoid of Diocles)

21. $r = a\sec(\theta) + 1$ (Conchoid of Nicomedes)

22. $r = \sec(\theta) + a$ (Conchoid of Nicomedes)

23. $r = 1 + a\cos(\theta)$ (Limaçon of Pascal)

24. $r = a + \cos(\theta)$ (Limaçon of Pascal)

25. $r = a\cos(2\theta)\sec(\theta)$ (Strophoid)

26. $r = 2a\theta/\pi$ (Spiral of Archimedes)

Conic sections (parabolas, hyperbolas, and ellipses) can all be described using polar coordinates. In fact, a single polar equation can generate all three types of conic sections:

$$r = \frac{ae}{1 - e\cos(\theta)}$$

where a and e are parameters (e is *not* the special transcendental number used in exponential functions). The value of e is called the **eccentricity** of the conic section.

For exercises 27-30: Let $a = 3$ and graph the polar function

$$r = \frac{3e}{1 - e\cos(\theta)}$$

over the interval $0 \leq \theta \leq 4\pi$ for values of the parameter $e = 1/4$, $1/2$, 1, 2 and 4.

27. On the basis of these graphs, guess which type of conic is generated for $e = 1/3$ and for $e = 3$, and then check your predictions by graphing the polar function for these values e.

28. Graph the polar function for $e = .1$, $e = .01$, and $e = .001$. What kind of curve is the limiting case as e approaches 0?

29. How will the answers to exercise 27 change if the value of a is changed from 3 to some other real value?

30. If $e = 1$, how does changing the value a change the appearance of the graph?

For exercises 31-34: A "rose" is obtained by graphing either of the polar equations

$$r = a\cos(k\theta) \qquad \text{or} \qquad r = a\sin(k\theta).$$

Graph both of these polar functions over the interval $0 \leq \theta \leq 12\pi$ for values of the parameter $a = 1/2$, 1, and 2 and for $k = 1$, 2, 3, and 4 (twenty-four graphs in all).

31. What does the value a control? (Look at the size of the leaves.)

32. What does the value k control? (Count the number of the leaves.)

33. What does the choice of $\sin(\theta)$ or $\cos(\theta)$ control? (Look at the location of the leaves.)

34. On the basis of your answers to exercises 31-33, predict the appearance of the graphs of $r = 3\cos(5\theta)$ and $r = 1.5\sin(6\theta)$, including size, number, and location of the leaves of the rose. Then check your prediction by graphing the polar equations.

For exercises 35-41: Using as many examples from exercises 17-26 as you like, determine the graphical effect of each of the substitutions described. In other words, how is the new graph related to the old graph?

35. Replace θ with $-\theta$.

36. Replace θ with $(\pi + \theta)$.

37. Replace θ with $(\pi - \theta)$.

38. Replace r by $-r$.

39. Replace r by $-r$ and θ with $-\theta$.

40. Replace r by $-r$ and θ with $(\pi - \theta)$.

41. Replace θ by $(\theta + \pi/2)$.

For exercises 42-50: For each of the polar equations described, convert from the polar description of the curve to a rectangular description in terms of x and y. Then, using the original polar form, replace θ by t and express in terms of parametric equations $x(t)$ and $y(t)$. Graph both the polar and the parametric forms to check your answers. Find $\frac{dr}{d\theta}$ and the slope $\frac{dy}{dx}$ at $\theta = \pi/3$ and $\theta = 5\pi/4$. Judge the reasonableness of your slope values from the graph.

42. $r = 6\cos(\theta)$

43. $r = 3\sin(\theta)\cos^2(\theta)$

44. $r = -2(\cos(\theta) + 1)$

45. $r = 5\sin(\theta)\tan(\theta)$

46. $r = 4\sec(\theta) + 1$

47. $r = \sec(\theta) - 7$

48. $r = 1 + \frac{1}{3}\cos(\theta)$

49. $r = -3 + \cos(\theta)$

50. $r = \cos(2\theta)\sec(\theta)$

For exercises 51-60: Find the area of region swept out by the graph over the interval $\pi/6 \leq \theta \leq \pi/4$. You will need to use a machine numerical integrator.

51. $r = 6\cos(\theta)$

52. $r = 3\sin(\theta)\cos^2(\theta)$

53. $r = -2(\cos(\theta) + 1)$

54. $r = 5\sin(\theta)\tan(\theta)$

55. $r = 4\sec(\theta) + 1$

56. $r = \sec(\theta) - 7$

57. $r = 1 + \frac{1}{3}\cos(\theta)$

58. $r = -3 + \cos(\theta)$

59. $r = \cos(2\theta)\sec(\theta)$

60. $r = 4\theta/\pi$

For exercises 61-68: Find the total area enclosed by the indicated polar graph.

61. $r = 1 - \sin(\theta)$

62. $r = 1 + \cos(\theta)$

63. $r = \sin(\theta) - 1$

64. $r = \cos(\theta) - 1$

65. $r = 1 + \cos(2\theta)$

66. $r = 1 + \sin(2\theta)$

67. $r = 1 - \sin(2\theta)$

68. $r = 1 - \cos(2\theta)$

For exercises 69-72: Find the area enclosed by the inner loop of the indicated polar graph.

69. $r = 1 + 2\cos(\theta)$

70. $r = 1 + 2\sin(\theta)$

71. $r = 1 - 2\sin(\theta)$

72. $r = 1 - 2\cos(\theta)$

For exercises 73-78: Find the total area enclosed by one "leaf" of the indicated polar graph.

73. $r = \cos(2\theta)$

74. $r = \sin(2\theta)$

75. $r = \cos(3\theta)$

76. $r = \sin(3\theta)$

77. $r = -\cos(3\theta)$

78. $r = -\sin(3\theta)$

For exercises 79-80: A "rose" is obtained by graphing either of the polar equations

$$r = a\cos(k\theta) \qquad \text{or} \qquad r = a\sin(k\theta),$$

where a is a positive real number and k is a positive integer.

79. Find the area of one leaf of the rose $r = a\cos(k\theta)$ in terms of a and k.

80. Find the area of one leaf of the rose $r = a\sin(k\theta)$ in terms of a and k.

A.5 COMPLEX NUMBERS

Points on a line can represent real numbers. We'll see that points in a plane can represent **complex numbers**. Usually, a complex number z is thought of as having the form $z = x + iy$, where x, y are real numbers and i formally satisfies the identity

$$i^2 = -1.$$

Since no *real* number satisfies this property, i has traditionally been called an **imaginary number**. This is rather unfortunate terminology, since i is just as "genuine " as any real number—it simply satisfies different properties.

If $z = x + iy$ is a complex number, we call x the **real part** and y the **imaginary part** of z and write

$$x = Re(z) \text{ and } y = Im(z).$$

Note that the imaginary part of a complex number is itself a *real number* **, because it represents the** *coefficient* **of i in $z = x + yi$.**

EXAMPLE 30 Identify $Re(z)$ and $Im(z)$ for each of the following complex numbers:

$$2 + 3i, \qquad -7 + \frac{i}{2}, \qquad -\pi i - \sqrt{2}, \qquad \sqrt[3]{17}, \qquad 13i, \qquad 0$$

Solution

$$\begin{array}{ll} Re(2+3i) = 2 & Im(2+3i) = 3 \\ Re(-7+\frac{i}{2}) = -7 & Im(-7+\frac{i}{2}) = \frac{1}{2} \\ Re(-\pi i - \sqrt{2}) = -\sqrt{2} & Im(-\pi i - \sqrt{2}) = -\pi \\ Re(\sqrt[3]{17}) = \sqrt[3]{17} & Im(\sqrt[3]{17}) = 0 \\ Re(13i) = 0 & Im(13i) = 13 \\ Re(0) = 0 & Im(0) = 0. \end{array}$$

■

The real and/or the imaginary part of a complex number may be 0. If $z = x$ had no imaginary part ($Im(z) = 0$) then we call it a *pure real number*.

If $z = iy$ has no real part ($Re(z) = 0$) then we call it a *pure imaginary number*. For example, $\sqrt[3]{17}$ is a pure real number; $13i$ is a pure imaginary number; 0 is *both* a pure real and pure imaginary number!

Arithmetic of complex numbers

Addition, subtraction and multiplication of complex numbers is accomplished by simply following the usual rules of algebra, and then using the identity $i^2 = -1$ to reduce the results if necessary.

EXAMPLE 31 Suppose $z = 2 + 3i$ and $w = -1 + 2i$. Find $z + w$, $z - w$, and zw.

Solution

$$z + w = (2 + 3i) + (-1 + 2i) = 1 + 5i$$

$$z - w = (2 + 3i) - (-1 + 2i) = 3 + i$$

$$zw = (2 + 3i)(-1 + 2i) = -2 - 3i + 4i + 6i^2 = -2 + i - 6 = -8 + i.$$

■

The **conjugate** $\overline{z}$ of a complex number z has the same real part, but the opposite imaginary part of z:

$$\text{if} \quad z = x + iy \qquad \text{then} \quad \overline{z} = x - iy.$$

The product of any complex number and its conjugate is a pure real number, as we can verify in general. Writing $z = x + iy$ and $\overline{z} = x - iy$, note that

$$z\overline{z} = (x + iy)(x - iy) = x^2 - i^2y^2 = x^2 + y^2.$$

The **modulus** or **absolute value** of a complex number z is *defined* as the positive square root of $z\overline{z}$:

$$|z| = \sqrt{z\overline{z}} = \sqrt{x^2 + y^2}.$$

Conjugates are useful in reducing the result of a quotient of two complex numbers as shown in the following example.

EXAMPLE 32 Suppose $z = 2 + 3i$ and $w = -1 + 2i$. Find $\frac{z}{w}$.

Solution We can simplify $\frac{z}{w}$ by multiplying by $1 = \frac{\overline{w}}{\overline{w}}$.

$$\frac{z}{w} = \frac{2+3i}{-1+2i} = \frac{2+3i}{-1+2i} \cdot \frac{(-1-2i)}{(-1-2i)} = \frac{4-7i}{5} = \frac{4}{5} - \frac{7}{5}i.$$

■

Ordered pair representations of complex numbers

If we use a Cartesian coordinate system for the plane, then we can associate each point to a complex number by identifying the real part with the x-coordinate and the imaginary part with the y-coordinate:

$$x + iy \qquad \text{corresponds to the point} \qquad (x, y).$$

In fact, we can refer to the x-axis as the *real axis* and the y-axis as the *imaginary axis*.

EXAMPLE 33 Here are some correspondences between complex numbers and points in the Cartesian plane:

$$\begin{array}{cll} 2+3i & \text{corresponds to the point} & (2,3) \\ -1+2i & \text{corresponds to the point} & (-1,2) \\ 1 & \text{corresponds to the point} & (1,0) \\ i & \text{corresponds to the point} & (0,1) \\ 0 & \text{corresponds to the point} & (0,0). \end{array}$$

■

This identification allows us to drop any mention of the imaginary number i, if we wished. We could simply restrict ourselves to the ordered pair notation and define the arithmetic operations accordingly. If $z = (x_1, y_1)$ and $w = (x_2, y_2)$, then we have

$$z + w = (x_1, y_1) + (x_2, y_2) = (x_1 + x_2, y_1 + y_2)$$

$$z - w = (x_1, y_1) - (x_2, y_2) = (x_1 - x_2, y_1 - y_2)$$

$$zw = (x_1, y_1)(x_2, y_2) = (x_1x_2 - y_1y_2, x_1y_2 + y_1x_2)$$

$$\frac{z}{w} = \frac{(x_1, y_1)}{(x_2, y_2)} = \left(\frac{x_1x_2 + y_1y_2}{\sqrt{x_2^2 + y_2^2}}, \frac{-x_1y_2 + y_1x_2}{\sqrt{x_2^2 + y_2^2}}\right).$$

This is all well and good, but the fact of the matter is that it is sometimes much easier to maintain the "i" notation for computational purposes, because it only requires the usual algebraic rules and the single rule $i^2 = -1$, without the need for four more special definitions to handle the operations of $+$, $-$, $\cdot$ and $\div$ of ordered pairs.

Geometry of complex numbers

The advantage of using points to represent complex numbers becomes evident when we examine the geometrical interpretations they afford. In Figure A.19 we illustrate some of these interpretations.

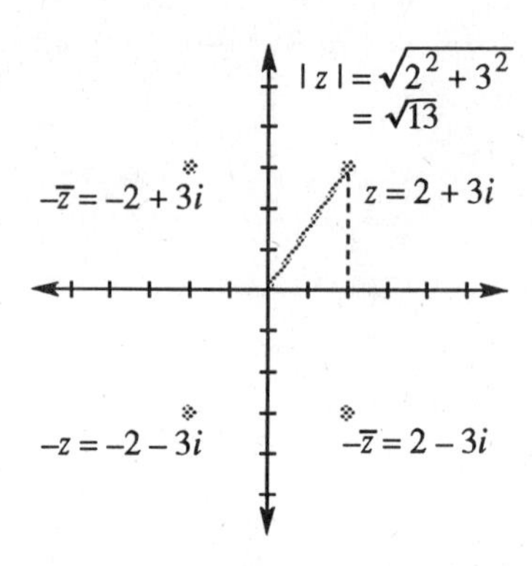

Figure A.19 Geometric interpretations of conjugates and absolute value.

The conjugate $\overline{z}$ is the reflection of z in the x-axis. The additive inverse $-z$ is the reflection of z in the origin. (The additive inverse of the conjugate $-\overline{z}$ is the reflection of z in the y-axis.) The absolute value $|z|$ is simply its distance from the origin (exactly the same geometrical meaning of absolute value for the real number line).

Addition of complex numbers also has a geometric interpretation, sometimes known as the parallelogram law: if we draw line segments from the origin to the points representing z and w, then the sum $z + w$ can be found by drawing the diagonal of the parallelogram determined by z and w (unless z and w are collinear with origin) as shown in Figure A.20.

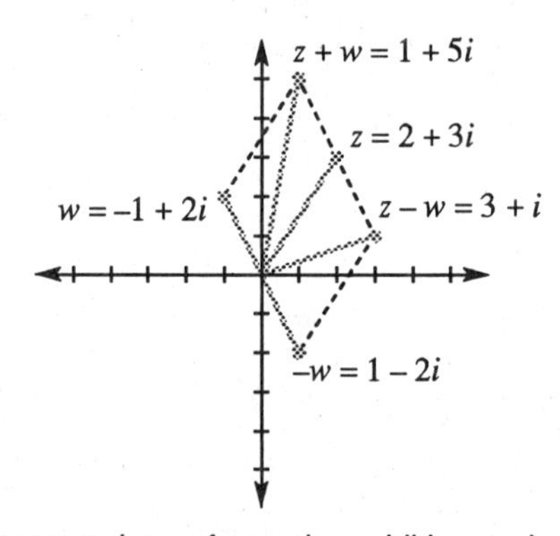

Figure A.20 Geometric interpretations of complex addition and subtraction: Parallelogram Law

If we write $z - w = z + (-w)$ then we can also find the difference of two complex numbers by the parallelogram law.

The geometric interpretation of complex number multiplication is best appreciated if we use polar coordinates.

For a complex number $z = x + iy$, we have

$$r = \sqrt{x^2 + y^2} = |z|,$$

so r is just the modulus (absolute value) of z.

The **principal argument** of z is the angle $-\pi < \theta \leq \pi$ such that $x = r\cos\theta$ and $y = r\sin\theta$. Hence,

$$z = r(\cos(\theta) + i\sin(\theta)).$$

This polar form is used so often, there is a special shorthand notation for complex numbers written in this way. By definition,

$$\operatorname{cis}(\theta) = \cos\theta + i\sin\theta.$$

So

$$z = r\operatorname{cis}\theta.$$

We'll call this the polar form of z, in contrast to the rectangular form $z = x + iy$.

EXAMPLE 34 Express $4\operatorname{cis}(\frac{2\pi}{3})$ in rectangular form.

Solution

$$4\operatorname{cis}(\frac{2\pi}{3}) = 4(\cos(\frac{2\pi}{3}) + i\sin(\frac{2\pi}{3})) = 4[(-\frac{1}{2}) + i(\frac{\sqrt{3}}{2})] = -2 + 2\sqrt{3}i.$$

■

EXAMPLE 35 Express $-3 - 4i$ in polar form.

Solution If we convert $(-3, -4)$ to polar form, we obtain $(r, \theta) \approx (5, -2.2143)$. The polar form of the complex number is $5\operatorname{cis}(-2.2143)$ ■

If we multiply two complex numbers written in polar form together, we notice a remarkable property. Suppose

$$z = r_1\operatorname{cis}\theta_1 \quad \text{and} \quad w = r_2\operatorname{cis}\theta_2$$

Then

$$zw = r_1\operatorname{cis}\theta_1 \cdot r_2\operatorname{cis}\theta_2 = r_1(\cos\theta_1 + i\sin\theta_1) \cdot r_2(\cos\theta_2 + i\sin\theta_2).$$

If we multiply the expression out using $i^2 = -1$, we find

$$zw = r_1 r_2[(\cos\theta_1\cos\theta_2 - \sin\theta_1\sin\theta_2) + i(\cos\theta_1\sin\theta_2 + \sin\theta_1\cos\theta_2)]$$

This looks rather messy, but if we examine the angle addition formulas for sine and cosine from trigonometry, we find

$$\cos(\theta_1 + \theta_2) = \cos\theta_1 \cos\theta_2 - \sin\theta_1 \sin\theta_2$$

$$\sin(\theta_1 + \theta_2) = \cos\theta_1 \sin\theta_2 + \sin\theta_1 \cos\theta_2$$

If we substitute these into our previous expression, we now have

$$zw = r_1 r_2(\cos(\theta_1 + \theta_2) + i\sin(\theta_1 + \theta_2)).$$

Summarizing, we can see that if z has modulus r_1 and argument θ_1 and w has modulus r_2 and argument θ_2, then

$$zw \text{ has modulus } r_1 r_2 \text{ and argument } \theta_1 + \theta_2.$$

In other words, the modulus of the product is the product of the moduli, while the argument of the product is the *sum* of the arguments. (Note that we can't say *principal* argument here, since the sum of two arguments between $-\pi$ and π could fall outside that interval.)

A similar property holds for division of complex numbers:

$$\frac{z}{w} \text{ has modulus } \frac{r_1}{r_2} \text{ and argument } \theta_1 - \theta_2.$$

In other words, the modulus of the quotient is the quotient of the moduli (provided $r_2 \neq 0$), while the argument of the quotient is the *difference* of the arguments.

EXAMPLE 36 Suppose $z = 10\,\text{cis}(\pi/2) = 10i$ and $w = \sqrt{2}\,\text{cis}(-\pi/4) = 1 - i$. Calculate the product zw and quotient $\frac{z}{w}$ using both polar and rectangular forms, and then check that the results are equivalent between forms.

Solution Using the polar forms, we have

$$zw = 10\,\text{cis}(\pi/2) \cdot \sqrt{2}\,\text{cis}(-\pi/4) = 10\sqrt{2}\,\text{cis}(\pi/2 + (-\pi/4)) = 10\sqrt{2}\,\text{cis}(\pi/4),$$

and

$$\frac{z}{w} = \frac{10\,\text{cis}(\pi/2)}{\sqrt{2}\,\text{cis}(-\pi/4)} = \frac{10}{\sqrt{2}}\,\text{cis}(\pi/2 - (-\pi/4)) = 5\sqrt{2}\,\text{cis}(3\pi/4).$$

Using the rectangular forms, we have

$$zw = (10i)(1 - i) = 10i - 10i^2 = 10 + 10i,$$

and

$$\frac{z}{w} = \frac{10i}{1 - 1i} = \frac{10i}{1 - 1i}\frac{1 + 1i}{1 + 1i} = \frac{10i + 10i^2}{2} = -5 + 5i.$$

We can check that these are equivalent by converting our polar results to rectangular form:

$$zw = 10\sqrt{2}\,\mathrm{cis}(\pi/4) = 10\sqrt{2}(\cos(\pi/4) + i\sin(\pi/4)) = 10\sqrt{2}\cdot\frac{1+i}{\sqrt{2}} = 10 + 10i,$$

and

$$\frac{z}{w} = 5\sqrt{2}\,\mathrm{cis}(3\pi/4) = 5\sqrt{2}(\cos(3\pi/4) + i\sin(3\pi/4)) = 5\sqrt{2}\cdot\frac{-1+i}{\sqrt{2}} = -5 + 5i.$$

We can see that the results match exactly. ■

Powers and roots of complex numbers

The observation just made regarding the product of two complex numbers leads inductively to a result known as **de Moivre's Theorem**:

If $z = \mathrm{cis}(\theta)$, then $z^n = \mathrm{cis}(n\theta)$ for any positive integer n.

This result follows simply by considering the power z^n as a product of n factors z. De Moivre's Theorem is a special case of a more general power rule for complex numbers:

If $z = r\,\mathrm{cis}(\theta)$, then $z^n = r^n\,\mathrm{cis}(n\theta)$.

If we work backwards, then we can use this to find the nth root of a complex number $z = r\,\mathrm{cis}(\theta)$. If $w_0 = r^{1/n}\,\mathrm{cis}(\frac{\theta}{n})$, then

$$(w_0)^n = (r^{1/n})^n\,\mathrm{cis}(n\cdot(\frac{\theta}{n})) = r\,\mathrm{cis}(\theta) = z.$$

This is not the only nth root of z. In fact, every nonzero complex number z has exactly n distinct nth roots. To see why, note that $z = r\,\mathrm{cis}(\theta)$ can also be written as

$$z = r\,\mathrm{cis}(\theta + 2\pi k)$$

for any integer k. If we let

$$w_k = r^{1/n}\,\mathrm{cis}(\frac{\theta}{n} + \frac{2\pi k}{n}),$$

then we also have

$$(w_k)^n = r\,\mathrm{cis}(\theta + 2\pi k) = z.$$

Each w_k is a distinct complex number for $k = 0, 1, 2, \ldots, n-1$. When $k = n$ we have come "full circle," since

$$w_n = r^{1/n} \operatorname{cis}(\frac{\theta}{n} + \frac{2\pi n}{n}) = r^{1/n} \operatorname{cis}(\frac{\theta}{n} + 2\pi) = r^{1/n} \operatorname{cis}(\frac{theta}{n}) = w_0.$$

For any other integers $k > n$ or $k < 0$ we also obtain duplicates of the $w_0, w_1, w_2, \ldots, w_{n-1}$ that we have already accounted for.

All n of these roots have the same modulus $r^{1/n}$, so geometrically they are spaced at equal angles around a circle of radius $r^{1/n}$.

EXAMPLE 37 Find all four fourth roots of $16i = 16 \operatorname{cis} \frac{\pi}{2}$.

Solution Here $n = 4$, $r = 16$ and $\theta = \frac{\pi}{2}$. So,

$$r^{1/4} = 2 \qquad \text{and} \qquad \theta/n = \pi/8.$$

The four roots w_0, w_1, w_3, and w_4 will be spaced at angle intervals $2\pi/4 = \pi/2$ apart on a circle of radius 2 centered at the origin:

$$w_0 = 2\operatorname{cis}(\pi/8), \quad w_1 = 2\operatorname{cis}(5\pi/8, \quad w_2 = 2\operatorname{cis}(9\pi/8), \quad w_3 = 2\operatorname{cis}(13\pi/8).$$

The four roots are pictured in Figure A.21.

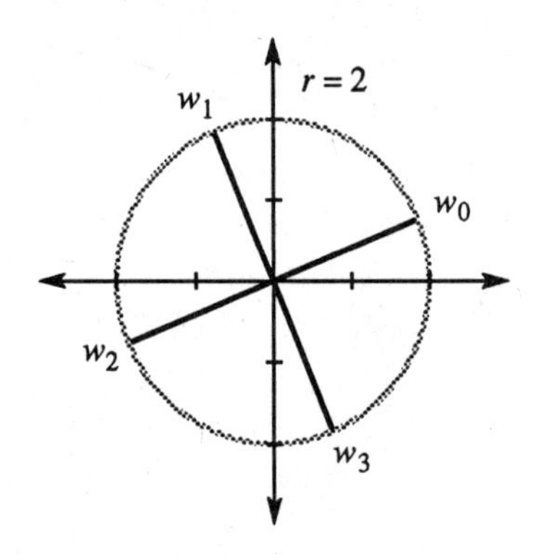

Figure A.21 The four fourth roots of $16i$.

EXERCISES for Section A.5

1. Convert $z = 4 - 7i$ to polar form $r\operatorname{cis}(\theta)$ and plot z.
2. Convert $z = 3.6\operatorname{cis}(3.69)$ to rectangular form $x + yi$ and plot z.

For exercises 3-6: Evaluate the expressions, writing your answers in rectangular $(a + bi)$ form.

3. $(6 - 5i) + (-4 - 2i)$
4. $(-6 - 3i) - (2 + 8i)$

5. $(6-5i)(-4-2i)$

6. $\dfrac{6-5i}{2-4i}$

7. Convert the complex numbers in exercises 5 and 6 to polar form and recompute their values in polar form. Then compute your results back to rectangular form and check with your original answers in rectangular form.

For exercises 8-10: Evaluate the expressions, writing your answers in polar ($r\,\text{cis}(\theta)$) form, where $-180° < \theta \leq 180°$.

8. $(25\,\text{cis}(-70°)(4\,\text{cis}(120°)$

9. $\dfrac{20\,\text{cis}(-40°)}{5\,\text{cis}(-10°)}$

10. $(3\,\text{cis}(20°))^{15}$

---

11. Shown in the illustration is one 9th root of a complex number. Graphically display the other 8 roots. Be as precise as possible. Are there any real roots? If so, what are they? Which pairs of roots are conjugates?

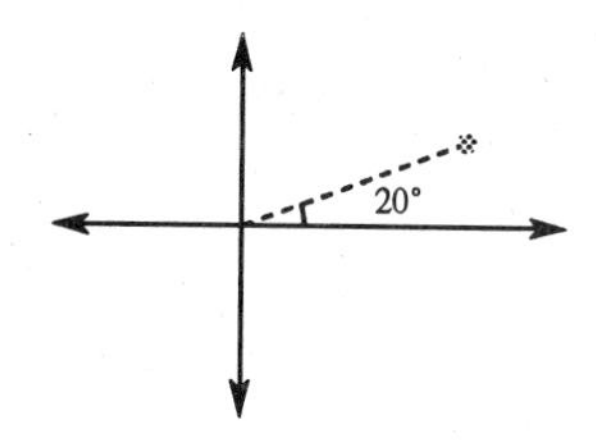

12. Suppose one of the six 6th roots of a complex number is the positive real number 3. What are the other five 6th roots?

13. For a given positive integer n, what is the maximum number of distinct real nth roots that a complex number z can have? Justify your answer.

14. Graph $f(x) = x^5 + 32$. What does the information from the sketch tell you about the type and number of roots (real vs. complex non-real) you can expect to find when solving $x^5 + 32 = 0$? Solve $x^5 + 32 = 0$ for all 5 roots.

15. Find all square roots of $z = -4 + 3i$. Plot these roots. Check your answers by squaring each.

16. Find all tenth roots of $z = 25$. Plot these roots. Check your answers by raising each to the tenth power.

17. Find all fourth roots of $z = 16$. Plot these roots. Check your answers by raising each to the fourth power.

18. Find all sixth roots of $z = 1$. Plot these roots. Check your answers by raising each to the sixth power. (These roots are called the sixth roots of unity.)

19. Solve $x^3 + 10 = 0$ for all 3 roots.

20. The transcendental number e can be raised to an imaginary power θi by using the definition

$$e^{\theta i} = \text{cis}(\theta).$$

Using this definition, verify that the following equation holds:

$$e^{\pi i} + 1 = 0.$$

This equation involves all five of the most important numbers in mathematics!

A.6 TAYLOR'S THEOREM

While it is true that a Taylor polynomial is not guaranteed to be a good approximation to a function other than very near the specified point $x = a$, we can get a handle on the error by means of a theorem which relates the error to the first "missing" derivative of the function.

Theorem A.1

Taylor's Theorem
Hypothesis 1: f is continuous and $(n+1)$-times differentiable on $[a, b]$.
Hypothesis 2: $p_n(x)$ is the nth degree Taylor polynomial approximation at $x = a$ to $f(x)$.
Conclusion: There is at least one point c, with $a < c < b$, such that

$$\frac{f^{(n+1)}(c)}{(n+1)!} = \frac{f(b) - p_n(b)}{(b-a)^{n+1}}.$$

Similarly, the theorem holds when the order of a and b are reversed $(b < c < a)$.

□

The conclusion of Taylor's Theorem is often written as follows (after multiplying both sides by $(b-a)^{n+1}$ and adding $p_n(b)$ to both sides:

$$f(b) = p_n(b) + \frac{f^{(n+1)}(c)(b-a)^{n+1}}{(n+1)!}.$$

The quantity $\frac{f^{(n+1)}(c)}{(n+1)!}(b-a)^{n+1}$ is often called the **Lagrange form** of the remainder (error term) $R_n(b)$ of the Taylor polynomial. Lagrange (1736-1813) was an Italian-French mathematician (who played a leading role in the introduction of the metric system in France). Using this notation, the conclusion of Taylor's theorem can be written

$$f(b) = p_n(b) + R_n(b) = \sum_{k=0}^{n} \frac{f^{(k)}(a)}{k!}(b-a)^k + R_n(b).$$

In the special case $n = 0$, we can consider the Taylor polynomial to be the constant function $p_0(x) = f(a)$. The conclusion of Taylor's Theorem in this case becomes

$$f'(c) = \frac{f(b) - f(a)}{b - a},$$

which is simply a restatement of the Mean Value Theorem, and we can think of Taylor's Theorem as a generalization of the Mean Value Theorem.

Taylor's theorem can be used to turn an estimate for the $(n+1)$st derivative of a function into an estimate of the error in the n degree Taylor polynomial approximation:

$$|f(b) - p_n(b)| = \left| \frac{f^{(n+1)}(c)}{(n+1)!}(b-a)^{n+1} \right|.$$

EXAMPLE 38 Suppose f is continuous and five times differentiable on $[1, 3]$, and that

$$\left| f^{(5)}(x) \right| < 0.1$$

for $x \in [1, 3]$. What is the biggest possible error if we use fourth Taylor polynomial approximation at $x = 1$ to approximate $f(3)$?

Solution $|f(3) - p_4(3)| = \left| \frac{f^{(5)}(c)}{(5)!}(3-1)^5 \right|$ for some $1 < c < 3$ so that

$$|f(3) - p_4(3)| < \left| \frac{0.1}{120} 2^5 \right| \approx 0.026667.$$

■

EXAMPLE 39 Use Taylor's Theorem to estimate the error at 0.5 for the fourth degree Maclaurin polynomial approximation to $y = \sin(x)$.

Solution Since $|\sin(x)| \leq 1$ and $|\cos(x)| \leq 1$ for all x. Together these mean that we have a simple estimate for the nth derivative of f, namely $\left|f^{(n)}(x)\right| \leq 1$ for all x. Using this estimate in the remainder, we have

$$|\sin(0.5) - p_4(0.5)| \leq \left|\frac{1}{120}(0.5)^5\right| \approx 0.00026.$$

■

EXAMPLE 40 For which values of x does the Maclaurin series for $f(x) = e^x$ converge to e^x?

Solution The remainder for the nth degree Maclaurin polynomial in this case is

$$R_n(x) = \frac{e^c}{(n+1)!}x^{n+1}$$

where c is between 0 and x (note that c depends on n). Since e^x is positive and increasing, we can estimate the remainder by noting that $e^c \leq e^{|x|}$ for any c between 0 and x. Using the ratio test, we find that the series converges for all x, so its terms must approach 0.

This means $\lim_{k \to \infty} \frac{x^k}{k!} = 0$, and since $|R_n(x)| \leq e^{|x|}\left|\frac{x^k}{k!}\right|$, we can conclude that $\lim_{k \to \infty} R_k(x) = 0$ *for any* x. ■

The remainder term $R_n(b)$ is sometimes expressed in its **integral form** as

$$R_n(b) = \frac{1}{n!}\int_a^b (b-x)^n f^{(n+1)}(x)\, dx.$$

EXERCISES for Section A.6

For exercises 1-10: Graphically determine the point c between the given a and b that determines the remainder $R_3(b)$ of the third degree Taylor polynomial. In other words, find where the graph of $y = f^{(4)}(x)/24$ crosses the graph of the horizontal line

$$y = \frac{f(b) - p_3(b)}{(b-a)^4}$$

over the interval $[a, b]$.

1. $y = \sin(2x + 1)$ $a = -1, \quad b = -0.5$

2. $y = \cos(\frac{2\pi}{x^2+1})$ $a = 0, \quad b = 1$

3. $y = \tan(x)$ $a = \pi/4, \quad b = \pi/6$

4. $y = \sec(x)$ $a = 0, \quad b = 0.5$

5. $y = \csc(-x)$ $a = \pi/2, \quad b = 5\pi/6$

6. $y = -\cot(x)$ $a = 3\pi/4, \quad b = 7\pi/8$

7. $y = \exp(2x + 1)$ $a = -1, \quad b = 0$

8. $y = \frac{2}{x^2+1}$ $a = 0, \quad b = 1$

9. $y = \sqrt{x^2 + 1}$ $a = 0, \quad b = 1$

10. $y = \frac{1}{x}$ $a = 4, \quad b = 4.5$

---

11. Calculate $\ln(1.2)$ with an error of at most 0.001 using a Taylor polynomial at 1 of $y = \ln(x)$.

12. Calculate $\sqrt{(1.2)}$ with an error of at most 0.001 using a Taylor polynomial at 1 of $y = \sqrt{(x)}$.

13. Calculate $e = \exp(1)$ with an error of at most 0.001 using a Taylor polynomial at 0 of $y = \exp(x)$.

14. Calculate $\sin(0.5)$ with an error of at most 0.0001 using a Taylor polynomial at 0 of $y = \sin(x)$.

DIFFERENTIATION PRACTICE

If you want lots of practice in finding derivatives "by the rules," here are 100 exercises to try. For each, find the derivative of the function indicated.

1. $\frac{ds}{dt}$, if $s = (2t+1)^2$
2. $\frac{dy}{dx}$, if $y = \frac{x^{-2} + 2x^{1/3}}{3x^3 - x + 1}$
3. $\frac{dM}{dw}$, if $M = \frac{w^2 - 4w + 3}{w^{3/2}}$
4. $\frac{dy}{dx}$, if $y = 10x^{3/2} + 3x^{-1/2}$
5. $\frac{dy}{dx}$, if $y = 6x^2 - 5x^{-1} + 2x^{-2/3}$
6. $\frac{dy}{dx}$, if $y = x^{-2} + 2x^{1/3}$
7. $\frac{dN}{dt}$, if $N = t^{2/3} - t^{-1/3}$
8. $\frac{dy}{dx}$, if $y = 6x^{4/3} + 4x^{-1/2}$
9. $\frac{dy}{dr}$, if $y = (5r-4)^2$
10. $\frac{dx}{dw}$, if $x = (2w+1)^3$
11. $\frac{dy}{dx}$, if $y = \sqrt{2x}$
12. $\frac{dy}{dx}$, if $y = \sqrt{4x^2 - 7x + 4}$
13. $\frac{dy}{dt}$, if $y = \sqrt{6t+5}$
14. $\frac{dy}{ds}$, if $y = \sqrt[3]{5s-8}$
15. $\frac{dy}{dz}$, if $y = \sqrt[3]{2z^2 + 4z + 8}$
16. $\frac{dy}{dv}$, if $y = \frac{1}{\sqrt{(v^4 + 7v^2)^3}}$
17. $\frac{dy}{dx}$, if $y = 6\sqrt[3]{x^4} + \frac{4}{\sqrt{x}}$
18. $\frac{dy}{dx}$, if $y = 10\sqrt{x^3} + \frac{3}{\sqrt[3]{x}}$
19. $\frac{dy}{dt}$, if $y = \sqrt[3]{t^2} - \frac{1}{\sqrt{t^3}}$
20. $\frac{dy}{dx}$, if $y = 6x^2 - \frac{5}{x} + \frac{2}{\sqrt[3]{x^2}}$
21. $\frac{dy}{dx}$, if $y = (x^5 - 4x + 8)^7$
22. $\frac{dy}{dx}$, if $y = (8x^3 - 2x^2 + x - 7)^5$
23. $\frac{dL}{dw}$, if $L = (w^4 - 8w^2 + 15)^4$
24. $\frac{dy}{dv}$, if $y = (17v - 5)^{1000}$
25. $\frac{dy}{dx}$, if $y = \frac{(3x^2-1)^4}{6}$
26. $\frac{dy}{ds}$, if $y = (3s)^{-4}$
27. $\frac{dT}{ds}$, if $T = (2s^{-4} + 3s^{-2} + 2)^{-6}$
28. $\frac{dP}{dv}$, if $P = (v^{-1} - 2v^{-2})^{-3}$
29. $\frac{dy}{dx}$, if $y = (3 + 2x^{-2} + 4x^{-3})^{1/3}$
30. $\frac{dy}{dt}$, if $y = \left[\left(1 + \frac{1}{t}\right)^{-1} + 1\right]^{-1}$
31. $\frac{dy}{dx}$, if $y = [7x + \sqrt{x^2+6}]^4$
32. $\frac{dy}{dx}$, if $y = [7x + \sqrt{x^3+3}]^6$
33. $\frac{dA}{dz}$, if $A = [1 + (1+2z)^{1/2}]^{1/2}$
34. $\frac{ds}{dt}$, if $s = \sqrt{t^2+t+1}\sqrt[3]{4t-9}$
35. $\frac{dA}{ds}$, if $A = \sqrt[4]{s^2+9}(4s+5)^4$
36. $\frac{dV}{dw}$, if $V = w^3(9w+1)^5$
37. $\frac{dy}{dx}$, if $y = 7x(x^2+1)^2$
38. $\frac{dy}{dz}$, if $y = (2z+5)^3(3z-1)^4$
39. $\frac{dy}{dx}$, if $y = \sqrt{2x-5}$
40. $\frac{dA}{ds}$, if $A = \sqrt[4]{s^2+9}$
41. $\frac{ds}{dt}$, if $s = \sqrt{t^2+t+1}$
42. $\frac{dy}{dx}$, if $y = \sqrt[4]{3x^3 - x + 1}$
43. $\frac{dy}{dx}$, if $y = 7x + \sqrt{x^2+6}$
44. $\frac{dy}{dz}$, if $y = [(z^2-1)^5 - 1]^5$
45. $\frac{dx}{dz}$, if $x = [z^2 + (z^2+9)^{1/2}]^{1/2}$
46. $\frac{dy}{dx}$, if $y = [(x-6)^{-1} + 1]^{-1}$
47. $\frac{dy}{dx}$, if $y = [(x^2-6)^3 + 1]^3$
48. $\frac{dy}{dx}$, if $y = \left[\sqrt[4]{3x^2 - x + 1} + 1\right]^4$
49. $\frac{dy}{dx}$, if $y = \left(\frac{x}{x+1}\right)^{5/2}$
50. $\frac{ds}{dt}$, if $s = \left(\frac{3t+4}{6t-7}\right)^3$

51. $\frac{dy}{dx}$, if $y = \left(\frac{3x^2-5}{2x^2+7}\right)^2$

52. $\frac{dy}{ds}$, if $y = \left(\frac{8s^2-4}{1-9s^3}\right)^4$

53. $\frac{dy}{dx}$, if $y = (6x-7)^3(8x^2+9)^2$

54. $\frac{dy}{dw}$, if $y = (2w^2-3w+1)(3w+2)^4$

55. $\frac{dx}{dy}$, if $x = (15y+2)(y^2-2)^{3/4}$

56. $\frac{dy}{dx}$, if $y = (x^2+4)^{5/3}(x^3+1)^{3/5}$

57. $\frac{dy}{dx}$, if $y = (x^6+1)^5(3x+2)^3$

58. $\frac{dy}{dx}$, if $y = (3x-8)^{-2}(7x^2+4)^{-3}$

59. $\frac{dx}{dy}$, if $x = (7y-2)^{-2}(2y+1)^{2/3}$

60. $\frac{dy}{dx}$, if $y = (3x+1)^6\sqrt{2x-5}$

61. $\frac{dA}{dr}$, if $A = \sqrt{r}\sqrt{r+1}\sqrt{r+2}$

62. $\frac{ds}{dt}$, if $s = 2t(2t+1)^2(2t+3)^3$

63. $\frac{dy}{dx}$, if $y = \sqrt[4]{3x^3-x+1}(x^2-6)^3$

64. $\frac{dy}{dx}$, if $y = \sqrt[4]{3x^3-x+1}\left(x^{-2}+2x^{1/3}\right)^3$

65. $\frac{dy}{dx}$, if $y = 8x^2\sqrt{x}+3x^3\sqrt{x}$

66. $\frac{dy}{dw}$, if $y = \sqrt{w^3(9w+1)^5}$

67. $\frac{dy}{dx}$, if $y = \sqrt[5]{(3x+2)^4}$

68. $\frac{dy}{dv}$, if $y = \sqrt{(v^4+7v^2)^3}$

69. $\frac{dy}{dx}$, if $y = \sqrt{\frac{x^{-2}+2x^{1/3}}{3x^3-x+1}}$

70. $\frac{dy}{dx}$, if $y = \sqrt{\frac{x^2-6}{3x^3-x+1}}$

71. $\frac{dy}{du}$, if $y = \sqrt{\frac{2u+5}{7u-9}}$

72. $\frac{dx}{dw}$, if $x = \frac{(w^2+1)^3}{(4w-5)^5}$

73. $\frac{dy}{dz}$, if $y = \frac{9z^3+5z}{(6z+1)^3}$

74. $\frac{dy}{dx}$, if $y = \frac{(x^2-6)^3}{\sqrt[4]{3x^2-x+1}}$

75. $\frac{dR}{dw}$, if $R = \frac{(w-1)(w-3)}{(w+1)(w+3)}$

76. $\frac{dA}{ds}$, if $A = \frac{1}{(8-5s+7s^2)^{10}}$

77. $\frac{ds}{dt}$, if $s = \frac{4}{(9t^2+16)^{2/3}}$

78. $\frac{dy}{dx}$, if $y = \frac{6}{(3x^2-1)^4}$

79. $\frac{dy}{dx}$, if $y = \frac{7x(x^2-1)^2}{(3x+10)^4}$

80. $\frac{dy}{dx}$, if $y = \frac{(x^{-2}+2x^{1/3})^3}{\sqrt[4]{(3x^3-x+1)}}$

81. $f'(x)$, if $f(x) = \frac{3x+1}{e^{x^2}}$

82. $f'(x)$, if $f(x) = \sin^{1/3}(4x)$

83. $f'(x)$, if $f(x) = \tan^{5/3}(x^2)$

84. $f'(x)$, if $f(x) = \cos^3(\sqrt{x})$

85. $f'(x)$, if $f(x) = \sec^3(4x^2-8)$

86. $f'(x)$, if $f(x) = \sin(x^3+1)^{1/3}$

87. $f'(x)$, if $f(x) = \tan^2(3x^2-5)^3$

88. $f'(x)$, if $f(x) = \sec(\sqrt[3]{x})$

89. $f'(x)$, if $f(x) = \sin^4(\csc(x))$

90. $f'(x)$, if $f(x) = e^{\cos(x)}$

91. $f'(x)$, if $f(x) = [\tan(e^x)]^3$

92. $f'(x)$, if $f(x) = e^{\sec(x^2)}$

93. $f'(x)$, if $f(x) = \tan(\sqrt{x})$

94. $f'(x)$, if $f(x) = \sin(e^{2x}+e^{-2x})$

95. $f'(x)$, if $f(x) = (e^x+e^{3x})^7$

96. $f'(x)$, if $f(x) = (x\cos(3x))^{1/2}$

97. $f'(x)$, if $f(x) = x\cos(\frac{1}{x})$

98. $f'(x)$, if $f(x) = e^{-1/x}\tan(x^2)$

99. $f'(x)$, if $f(x) = \sin^{3/2}(\frac{1}{x})e^{\cos(x)}$

100. $f'(x)$, if $f(x) = \tan\left(\frac{x^2-1}{x^3+1}\right)$

INTEGRATION PRACTICE

1. $\int x \arcsin x \, dx$

2. $\int \ln(1+x)\, dx$

3. $\int \cos^3 2x \sin^2 2x \, dx$

4. $\int \tan x \sec^5 x \, dx$

5. $\int \frac{1}{(x^2+25)^{3/2}}\, dx$

6. $\int \frac{\sqrt{4-x^2}}{x}\, dx$

7. $\int \frac{x^3+1}{x(x-1)^3}\, dx$

8. $\int \frac{x^3-20x^2-63x-198}{x^4-81}\, dx$

9. $\int \frac{x}{\sqrt{4+4x-x^2}}\, dx$

10. $\int \frac{\sqrt[3]{x+8}}{x}\, dx$

11. $\int e^{2x} \sin 3x \, dx$

12. $\int \sin^3 x \cos^3 x \, dx$

13. $\int \frac{x}{\sqrt{4-x^2}}\, dx$

14. $\int \frac{x^5-x^3+1}{x^3+2x^2}\, dx$

15. $\int \frac{1}{x^{3/2}+x^{1/2}}\, dx$

16. $\int e^x \sec e^x \, dx$

17. $\int x^2 \sin 5x \, dx$

18. $\int \sin^3 x \cos^{1/2} x \, dx$

19. $\int e^x \sqrt{1+e^x}\, dx$

20. $\int \frac{x^2}{\sqrt{4x^2+25}}\, dx$

21. $\int \sec^2 x \tan^2 x \, dx$

22. $\int x \cot x \csc x \, dx$

23. $\int x^2(8-x^3)^{1/3}\, dx$

24. $\int \cos \sqrt{x}\, dx$

25. $\int \frac{e^{3x}}{1+e^x}\, dx$

26. $\int \frac{x^2-4x+3}{\sqrt{x}}\, dx$

27. $\int \frac{x^3}{\sqrt{16-x^2}}\, dx$

28. $\int \frac{1-2x}{x^2+12x+35}\, dx$

29. $\int \arctan 5x \, dx$

30. $\int \frac{e^{\tan x}}{\cos^2 x}\, dx$

31. $\int \frac{1}{\sqrt{7+5x^2}}\, dx$

32. $\int \cot^6 x \, dx$

33. $\int x^3 \sqrt{x^2-25}\, dx$

34. $\int (x^2 - \operatorname{sech}^2 4x)\, dx$

35. $\int x^2 e^{-4x}\, dx$

36. $\int \frac{3}{\sqrt{11-10x-x^2}}\, dx$

37. $\int \tan 7x \cos 7x \, dx$

38. $\int \frac{4x^2-12x-10}{(x-2)(x^2-4x+3)}\, dx$

39. $\int (x^3+1)\cos x \, dx$

40. $\int \frac{\sqrt{9-4x^2}}{x^2}\, dx$

41. $\int (x-\cot 3x)^2\, dx$

42. $\int \frac{1}{x(\sqrt{x}+\sqrt[4]{x})}\, dx$

43. $\int \frac{\sin x}{\sqrt{1+\cos x}}\, dx$

44. $\int \frac{x^2}{(25+x^2)^2}\, dx$

45. $\int \tan^3 x \sec x \, dx$

46. $\int \frac{2x^3+4x^2+10x+13}{x^4+9x^2+20}\, dx$

47. $\int \frac{(x^2-2)^2}{x}\, dx$

48. $\int x^{3/2} \ln x \, dx$

49. $\int \frac{x^2}{\sqrt[3]{2x+3}}\, dx$

50. $\int x^3 e^{x^2}\, dx$

USEFUL FACTS AND FORMULAS

English Weights and Measures

LENGTH

12 inches = 1 foot
3 feet = 1 yard
$16\frac{1}{2}$ feet = 1 rod
63,360 inches = 1 mile
5,280 feet = 1 mile
1760 yards = 1 mile

AREA

144 square inches = 1 square foot
9 square feet = 1 square yard
160 square rods = 1 acre
$30\frac{1}{4}$ square yards = 1 square rod
4840 square yards = 1 acre
640 acres = 1 square mile

VOLUME

1728 cubic inches = 1 cubic foot
27 cubic feet = 1 cubic yard

DRY MEASURE

2 pints = 1 quart
8 quarts = 1 peck
4 pecks = 1 bushel
1 bushel = 2150.42 cubic inches

LIQUID MEASURE

8 ounces = 1 cup
2 cups = 1 pint
2 pints = 1 quart
4 quarts = 1 gallon
$31\frac{1}{2}$ gallons = 1 barrel
1 gallon = 231 cubic inches

WEIGHT

16 ounces = 1 pound
2000 pounds = 1 ton

TEMPERATURE

Freezing point of water occurs at 0° Celsius or 32° Fahrenheit.

Boiling point of water occurs at 100° Celsius or 212° Fahrenheit.

If C represents degrees Celsius and F represents degrees Fahrenheit, then

$$C = \frac{5}{9}(F - 32) \qquad \text{and} \qquad F = \frac{9}{5}C + 32.$$

Metric System

The metric weights and measures are derived by combining the following six numerical prefixes with the words *meter, gram,* and *liter:*

milli = one-thousandth	*deka* = ten
centi = one-hundredth	*hecto* = one hundred
deci = one-tenth	*kilo* = one thousand

For example,

10 millimeters = 1 centimeter	10 meters = 1 dekameter
10 centimeters = 1 decimeter	10 dekameters = 1 hectometer
10 decimeters = 1 meter	10 hectometers = 1 kilometer

APPROXIMATE METRIC EQUIVALENTS

1 inch	= 2.54001 centimeters
1 foot	= 30.48006 centimeters
1 yard	= 91.4402 centimeters
1 centimeter	= 0.032808 feet
1 mile	= 1.70935 kilometers
1 square mile	= 2, 589, 998 square meters
1 acre	= 4046.873 square meters
1 meter	= 39.37 inches

1 kilometer = 0.62137 mile = 1093.61 yards = 3, 280.83 feet
1 kilogram = 2.20462 pounds = 35.27396 ounces
1 liter = 1.05671 liquid quarts = 0.908102 dry quart

1 pound	= 0.453592 kilograms
1 gallon	= 3.78533 liters
1 liquid quart	= 0.946333 liter
1 liter	= 61.0250 cubic inches
1 cubic inch	= 16.3872 cubic centimeters
1 cubic meter	= 35.314 cubic feet
1 dry quart	= 1.10120 liters
1 kilogram per square meter	= 0.204817 pound per square foot
1 pound per square fool	= 4.88241 kilograms per square meter
1 fluid ounce	= 29.573 cubic centimeters

Miscellaneous physical constants

g (average value) = 32.16 ft/sec^2 = 980 cm/sec^2

g (sea level, lat. 45°) = 32.172 ft/sec^2 = 980.616 cm./sec^2

1 hp (horsepower) = 550 ft-lb/min = 76.0404 kg-m/sec = 745.70 watts

Weight of 1 cubic foot of water = 62.425 lb (mass density)

Velocity of sound in dry air at 0° C = 33,136 cm/sec = 1,087 ft/sec

1 mph (miles per hour) = 88 ft/min = 1.467 ft/sec = 0.8684 knot

1 knot = 101.3 ft/min = 1.689 ft/sec = 1.152 mph

1 micron = 10^{-4} cm   1 angstrom unit = 10^{-8} cm

Mean radius of earth = 3,959 miles = 6,371 km

Equatorial diameter of earth = 7,926.68 miles = 12,756.78 km

Polar diameter of earth = 7,926.68 miles = 12,756.78 km

Constant of gravitation = 6.670×10^{-8} dyne· cm^2/gram^2

Electronic charge = 4.803×10^{-10} e.s.u.

Mass of electron = 9.107×10^{-28} gram

Mass of hydrogen atom = 1.673×10^{-24} gram

Avogadro's number = 6.023×10^{23}mole^{-1}

Planck's constant = 6.624×10^{-27} erg sec

Variation

If y varies directly as x, then $y = kx$.   (k = constant)

If y varies inversely as x, then $y = \dfrac{k}{z}$.

If y varies jointly as x and z, then $y = kxz$.

If y varies directly as x and inversely as z, then $y = \dfrac{kx}{z}$.

FORMULAS FROM ALGEBRA

Exponents

If p is a positive integer, $a^p = a \cdot a \cdot a \cdots$ to p factors.

$a^0 = 1 \quad (a \neq 0)$ $\qquad$ $a^{-n} = \dfrac{1}{a^n}$

$a^m \cdot a^n = a^{m+n}$ $\qquad$ $(ab)^n = a^n b^n$

$a^m \div a^n = a^{m-n}$ $\qquad$ $\left(\dfrac{a}{b}\right)^n = \dfrac{a^n}{b^n}$

$(a^m)^n = a^{mn}$ $\qquad$ $a^{p/q} = \sqrt[q]{a^p} = (\sqrt[q]{a})^p$

Radicals

If $r^q = A$, then r is a qth root of A. The **principal** qth **root** is denoted $\sqrt[q]{A}$.

$$\sqrt[q]{A} \text{ is } \begin{cases} \text{positive if } A \text{ is positive} \\ \text{negative if } A \text{ is negative and } q \text{ odd} \\ \text{imaginary if } A \text{ is negative and } q \text{ even} \end{cases}$$

$$\sqrt[q]{a^q} = \begin{cases} a \text{ if } a \geq 0 \\ a \text{ if } a < 0 \text{ and } q \text{ odd} \\ -a \text{ if } a < 0 \text{ and } q \text{ even} \end{cases}$$

$\sqrt[q]{a} \cdot \sqrt[q]{b} = \sqrt[q]{ab}$ except for $a < 0$, $b < 0$, and q even. For this case, use the rules given below for complex numbers.

$$\sqrt[q]{\frac{a}{b}} = \frac{\sqrt[q]{a}}{\sqrt[q]{b}}$$

Logarithms

Let M, N, b be positive and $b \neq 1$. Then

$\log_b MN = \log_b M + \log_b N$ $\qquad$ $\log_b \dfrac{M}{N} = \log_b M - \log_b N$

$\log_b M^k = k \log_b M$ $\qquad$ $\log_b \sqrt[q]{M} = \dfrac{1}{q} \log_b M$

$\log_b b = 1 \qquad \log_b 1 = 0$ $\qquad$ $b^{\log_b M} = M \qquad \log_a M = \dfrac{\log_b M}{\log_b a}$

$\ln M = \log_e M \approx 2.3026 \log_{10} M$ $\qquad$ $\log_{10} M \approx (0.43429) \log_e M$

Complex numbers

$$i = \sqrt{-1}, \qquad i^2 = -1, \qquad i^3 = -i, \qquad i^4 = 1, \qquad i^5 = i, \qquad \text{etc.}$$

$$i^{4p} = 1, \qquad i^{4p+1} = i, \qquad i^{4p+2} = -1, \qquad i^{4p+3} = -i. \qquad (p \text{ an integer})$$

$a + bi = c + di$ if and only if $a = c$ and $b = d$, and $a + bi = 0$ if and only if $a = b = 0$.

$$(a + bi) + (c + di) = (a + c) + (b + d)i$$

$$(a + bi) - (c + di) = (a - c) + (b - d)i$$

$$(a + bi)(c + di) = (ac - bd) + (ad + bc)i$$

$$\frac{a + bi}{c + di} = \frac{(a + bi)(c - di)}{(c + di)(c - di)} = \frac{ac + bd}{c^2 + d^2} + \frac{bc - ad}{c^2 + d^2}i$$

Polar form of complex numbers:

$a + bi = r(\cos\theta + i\sin\theta)$, where $r = \sqrt{a^2 + b^2}$ and $\tan\theta = \frac{b}{a}$.

Suppose $z = r(\cos\alpha + i\sin\alpha)$ and $w = R(\cos\beta + i\sin\beta)$. Then

$$zw = rR[\cos(\alpha + \beta) + i\sin(\alpha + \beta)]$$

$$\frac{z}{w} = \frac{r}{R}[\cos(\alpha - \beta) + i\sin(\alpha - \beta)]$$

$$z^n = r^n[\cos n\alpha + i\sin n\alpha]$$

$$z^{1/n} = r^{1/n}\left[\cos\tfrac{\alpha + k360°}{n} + i\sin\tfrac{\alpha + k360°}{n}\right], \ k = 0, 1, 2, \ldots, n - 1.$$

Quadratic equations

Let r_1, r_2 be the roots of $ax^2 + bx + c = 0 \ (a \neq 0)$. Then

$$r_1, r_2 = \frac{-b \pm \sqrt{b^2 - 4ac}}{2a} \qquad r_1 + r_2 = -\frac{b}{a} \qquad r_1 r_2 = \frac{c}{a}.$$

If a, b, c are real and if

$b^2 - 4ac > 0$, then the roots are real and unequal;

$b^2 - 4ac = 0$, then the roots are real and equal;

$b^2 - 4ac < 0$, then the roots are imaginary and unequal.

If a, b, c are rational and if

$b^2 - 4ac$ is a perfect square, then the roots are rational;

$b^2 - 4ac$ is not a perfect square, then the roots are irrational.

TRIGONOMETRIC IDENTITIES

The following identities hold for all values of the angles *for which both sides of the equation are defined.* Where a double sign ($\pm$) occurs, the choice depends upon the quadrant in which the angle is located.

Basic identities

$$\csc\theta = \frac{1}{\sin\theta} \qquad \sec\theta = \frac{1}{\cos\theta} \qquad \tan\theta = \frac{\sin\theta}{\cos\theta} = \frac{1}{\cot\theta}$$

Pythagorean identities

$$\sin^2\theta + \cos^2\theta = 1 \qquad 1 + \tan^2\theta = \sec^2\theta \qquad 1 + \cot^2\theta = \csc^2\theta$$

Power identities

$$\sin^2\theta = \tfrac{1}{2}(1 - \cos 2\theta) \qquad \cos^2\theta = \tfrac{1}{2}(1 + \cos 2\theta)$$

$$\sin^3\theta = \tfrac{1}{4}(3\sin\theta - \sin 3\theta) \qquad \cos^3\theta = \tfrac{1}{4}(3\cos\theta + \cos 3\theta)$$

$$\sin^4\theta = \tfrac{1}{8}(3 - 4\cos 2\theta + \cos 4\theta) \qquad \cos^4\theta = \tfrac{1}{8}(3 + 4\cos 2\theta + \cos 4\theta)$$

Double and multiple angle identities

$$\sin 2\theta = 2\sin\theta\cos\theta = \frac{2\tan\theta}{1 + \tan^2\theta} \qquad \tan^2\theta = \frac{1 - \cos 2\theta}{1 + \cos 2\theta}$$

$$\cos 2\theta = \cos^2\theta - \sin^2\theta = 2\cos^2\theta - 1 = 1 - 2\sin^2\theta = \frac{1 - \tan^2\theta}{1 + \tan^2\theta}$$

$$\tan 2\theta = \frac{2\tan\theta}{1 - \tan^2\theta} \qquad \cot 2\theta = \frac{\cot^2\theta - 1}{2\cot\theta}$$

$$\sin 3\theta = 3\sin\theta - 4\sin^3\theta \qquad \cos 3\theta = 4\cos^3\theta - 3\cos\theta$$

$$\sin 4\theta = 4\sin\theta\cos\theta - 8\sin^3\theta\cos\theta \qquad \cos 4\theta = 8\cos^4\theta - 8\cos^2\theta + 1$$

Half-angle identities

$$\sin\tfrac{1}{2}\theta = \pm\sqrt{\frac{1 - \cos\theta}{2}} \qquad \cos\tfrac{1}{2}\theta = \pm\sqrt{\frac{1 + \cos\theta}{2}}$$

$$\tan\tfrac{1}{2}\theta = \pm\sqrt{\frac{1 - \cos\theta}{1 + \cos\theta}} = \frac{1 - \cos\theta}{\sin\theta} = \frac{\sin\theta}{1 + \cos\theta}$$

Angle sum and difference identities

$$\sin(\alpha+\beta) = \sin\alpha\cos\beta + \cos\alpha\sin\beta \qquad \cos(\alpha+\beta) = \cos\alpha\cos\beta - \sin\alpha\sin\beta$$

$$\tan(\alpha+\beta) = \frac{\tan\alpha + \tan\beta}{1-\tan\alpha\tan\beta} \qquad \cot(\alpha+\beta) = \frac{\cot\beta\cot\alpha - 1}{\cot\beta + \cot\alpha}$$

$$\sin(\alpha-\beta) = \sin\alpha\cos\beta - \cos\alpha\sin\beta \qquad \cos(\alpha-\beta) = \cos\alpha\cos\beta + \sin\alpha\sin\beta$$

$$\tan(\alpha-\beta) = \frac{\tan\alpha - \tan\beta}{1+\tan\alpha\tan\beta} \qquad \cot(\alpha-\beta) = \frac{\cot\beta\cot\alpha + 1}{\cot\beta - \cot\alpha}$$

$$\sin\alpha + \sin\beta = 2\sin\frac{\alpha+\beta}{2}\cos\frac{\alpha-\beta}{2} \qquad \sin\alpha - \sin\beta = 2\cos\frac{\alpha+\beta}{2}\sin\frac{\alpha-\beta}{2}$$

$$\cos\alpha + \cos\beta = 2\cos\frac{\alpha+\beta}{2}\cos\frac{\alpha-\beta}{2} \qquad \cos\alpha - \cos\beta = -2\sin\frac{\alpha+\beta}{2}\sin\frac{\alpha-\beta}{2}$$

$$\sin(\alpha+\beta) + \sin(\alpha-\beta) = 2\sin\alpha\cos\beta \qquad \sin(\alpha+\beta) - \sin(\alpha-\beta) = 2\cos\alpha\sin\beta$$

$$\cos(\alpha+\beta) + \cos(\alpha-\beta) = 2\cos\alpha\cos\beta \qquad \cos(\alpha+\beta) - \cos(\alpha-\beta) = -2\sin\alpha\sin\beta$$

$$\sin(\alpha+\beta)\sin(\alpha-\beta) = \sin^2\alpha - \sin^2\beta = \cos^2\beta - \cos^2\alpha$$

$$\cos(\alpha+\beta)\cos(\alpha-\beta) = \cos^2\alpha - \sin^2\beta = \cos^2\beta - \sin^2\alpha$$

$$\tan\alpha + \tan\beta = \frac{\sin(\alpha+\beta)}{\cos\alpha\cos\beta} \qquad \tan\alpha - \tan\beta = \frac{\sin(\alpha-\beta)}{\cos\alpha\cos\beta}$$

$$\cot\alpha + \cot\beta = \frac{\sin(\alpha+\beta)}{\sin\alpha\sin\beta} \qquad \cot\alpha - \cot\beta = \frac{\sin(\beta-\alpha)}{\sin\alpha\sin\beta}$$

$$\frac{\sin\alpha + \sin\beta}{\sin\alpha - \sin\beta} = \frac{\tan\frac{1}{2}(\alpha+\beta)}{\tan\frac{1}{2}(\alpha-\beta)} \qquad \frac{\sin\alpha + \sin\beta}{\cos\alpha - \cos\beta} = \cot\tfrac{1}{2}(\beta-\alpha)$$

$$\frac{\sin\alpha + \sin\beta}{\cos\alpha + \cos\beta} = \tan\tfrac{1}{2}(\alpha+\beta) \qquad \frac{\sin\alpha - \sin\beta}{\cos\alpha + \cos\beta} = \tan\tfrac{1}{2}(\alpha-\beta)$$

Equivalent expressions for $\sin\theta$ and $\cos\theta$

$$\sin\theta = \pm\sqrt{1-\cos^2\theta} = \frac{\tan\theta}{\pm\sqrt{1+\tan^2\theta}} = \frac{1}{\pm\sqrt{1+\cot^2\theta}} = \frac{\pm\sqrt{\sec^2\theta - 1}}{\sec\theta}$$

$$= \frac{1}{\csc\theta} = \cos\theta\tan\theta = \pm\sqrt{\frac{1-\cos 2\theta}{2}} = 2\sin\frac{1}{2}\theta\cos\frac{1}{2}\theta$$

$$\cos\theta = \pm\sqrt{1-\sin^2\theta} = \frac{1}{\pm\sqrt{1+\tan^2\theta}} = \frac{\cot\theta}{\pm\sqrt{1+\cot^2\theta}} = \frac{1}{\sec\theta}$$

$$= \frac{\pm\sqrt{\csc^2\theta - 1}}{\csc\theta} = \sin\theta\cot\theta = \pm\sqrt{\frac{1+\cos 2\theta}{2}} = \cos^2\frac{1}{2}\theta - \sin^2\frac{1}{2}\theta.$$

INVERSE TRIGONOMETRIC FUNCTIONS

Principal values

$-\frac{\pi}{2} \leq \arcsin x \leq \frac{\pi}{2},$	$-1 \leq x \leq 1$
$-\frac{\pi}{2} < \arctan x \leq \frac{\pi}{2},$	$-\infty < x < \infty$
$0 \leq \arccos x \leq \pi,$	$-1 \leq x \leq 1$
$0 < \operatorname{arccot} x < \pi,$	$-\infty < x < \infty$
$0 \leq \operatorname{arcsec} x < \frac{\pi}{2},$	$x \geq 1$
$-x \leq \operatorname{arcsec} x < -\frac{\pi}{2},$	$x \leq -1$
$0 < \operatorname{arccsc} x \leq \frac{\pi}{2},$	$x \geq 1$
$-\pi < \operatorname{arccsc} x \leq -\frac{\pi}{2},$	$x \leq -1$

Fundamental identities involving principal values

$$\arcsin x + \arccos x = \frac{\pi}{2} \qquad \arctan x + \operatorname{arccot} x = \frac{\pi}{2}$$

If $\theta = \arcsin x$, then

$\sin\theta = x$	$\tan\theta = \dfrac{x}{\sqrt{1-x^2}}$	$\sec\theta = \dfrac{1}{\sqrt{1-x^2}}$
$\cos\theta = \sqrt{1-x^2}$	$\cot\theta = \dfrac{\sqrt{1-x^2}}{x}$	$\csc\theta = \dfrac{1}{x}$

If $\theta = \arccos x$, then

$\sin\theta = \sqrt{1-x^2}$	$\tan\theta = \dfrac{\sqrt{1-x^2}}{x}$	$\sec\theta = \dfrac{1}{x}$
$\cos\theta = x$	$\cot\theta = \dfrac{x}{\sqrt{1-x^2}}$	$\csc\theta = \dfrac{1}{\sqrt{1-x^2}}$

If $\theta = \arctan x$, then

$\sin\theta = \dfrac{x}{\sqrt{1+x^2}}$	$\tan\theta = x$	$\sec\theta = \sqrt{1+x^2}$
$\cos\theta = \dfrac{1}{\sqrt{1+x^2}}$	$\cot\theta = \dfrac{1}{x}$	$\csc\theta = \dfrac{\sqrt{1+x^2}}{x}$

FORMULAS FROM ANALYTIC GEOMETRY

Lines

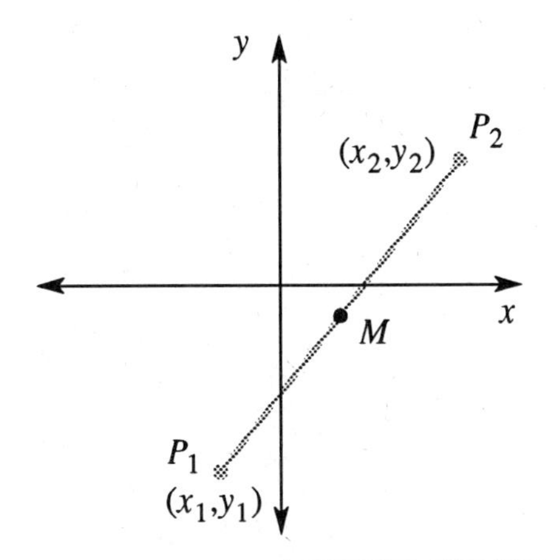

length of $\overline{P_1P_2}$: $d = \sqrt{(x_2 - x_1)^2 + (y_2 - y_1)^2}$

midpoint M : $\left(\frac{x_1 + x_2}{2}, \frac{y_1 + y_2}{2}\right)$

slope of $\overleftrightarrow{P_1P_2}$: $m = \frac{y_2 - y_1}{x_2 - x_1}$

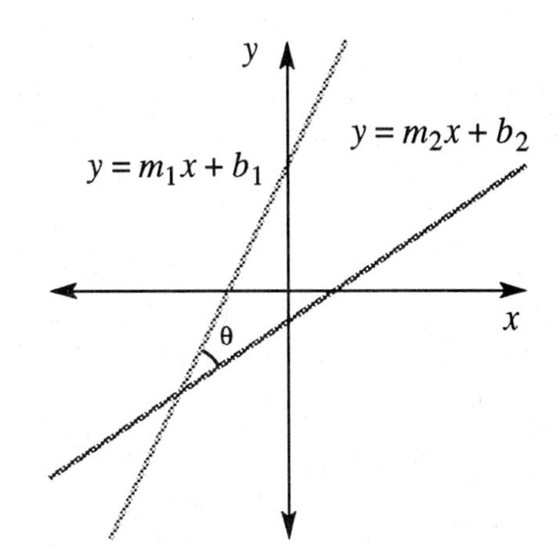

angle between two lines :

$$\tan\theta = \frac{m_2 - m_1}{1 + m_1m_2}$$

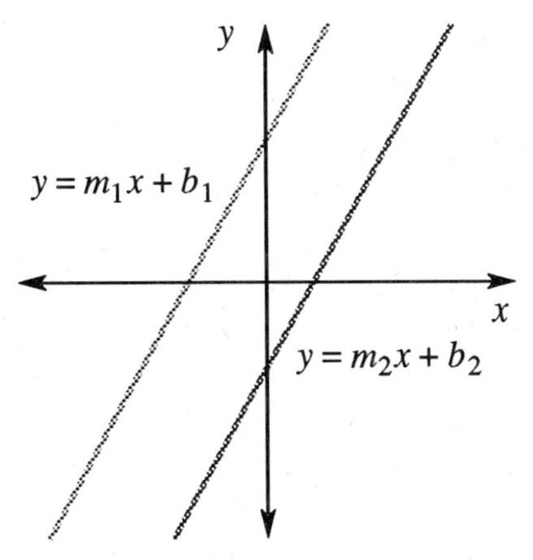

parallel lines : $m_1 = m_2$

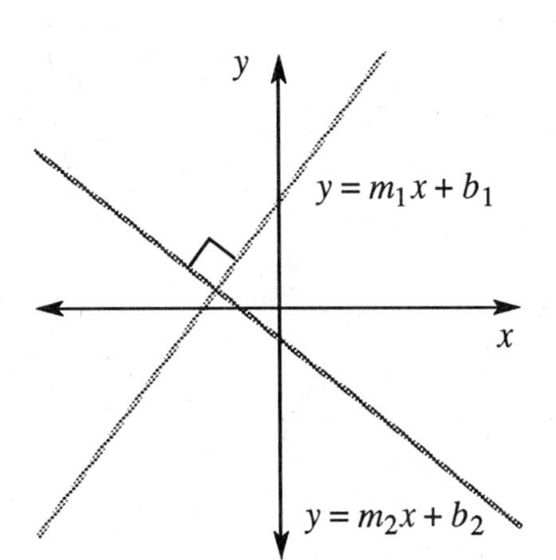

perpendicular lines : $m_1m_2 = -1$

Circles

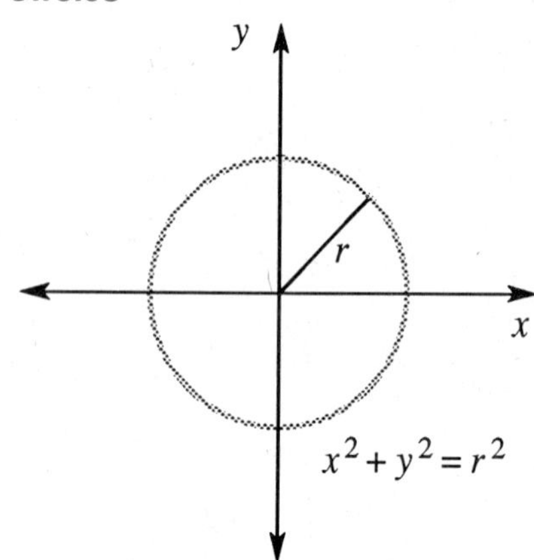

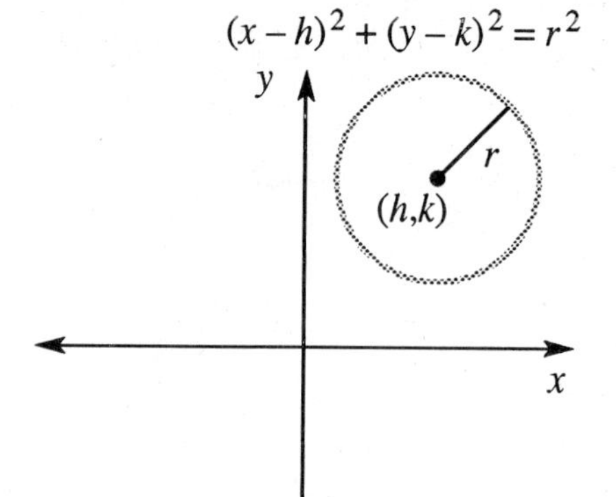

Ellipses

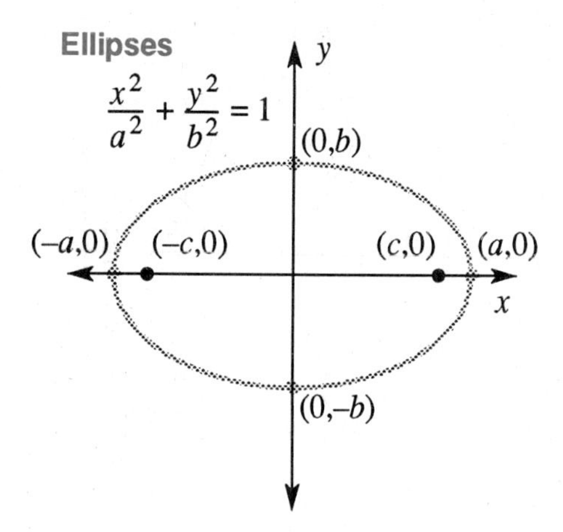

Center at (0,0) with horizontal major axis
Foci at $(\pm c,0)$
where $c = \sqrt{a^2 - b^2}$

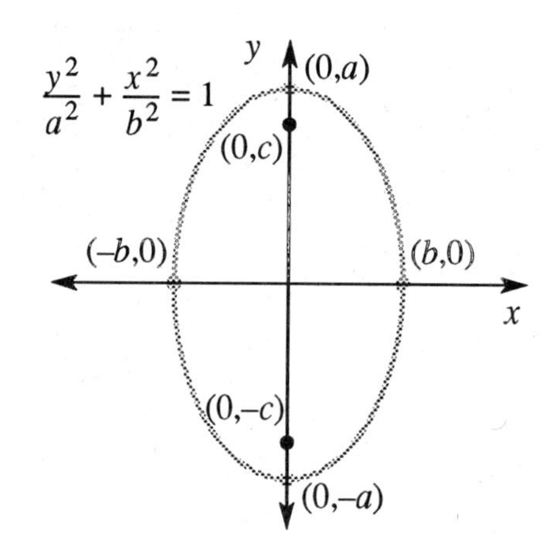

Center at (0,0) with vertical major axis
Foci at $(0,\pm c)$
where $c = \sqrt{a^2 - b^2}$

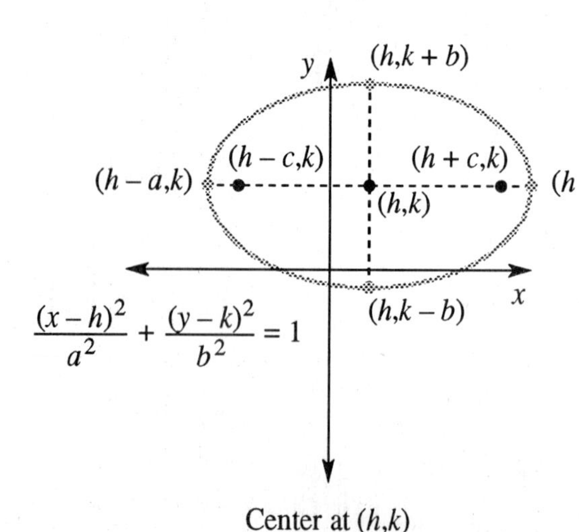

Center at (h,k)
Foci at $(h \pm c,k)$

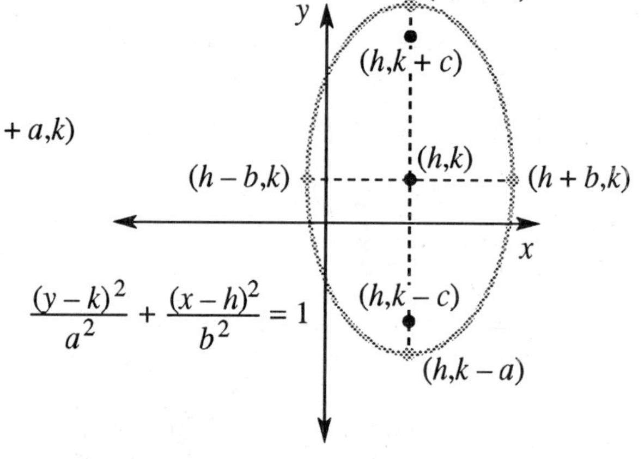

Center at (h,k)
Focus at $(h,k \pm c)$

Parabolas

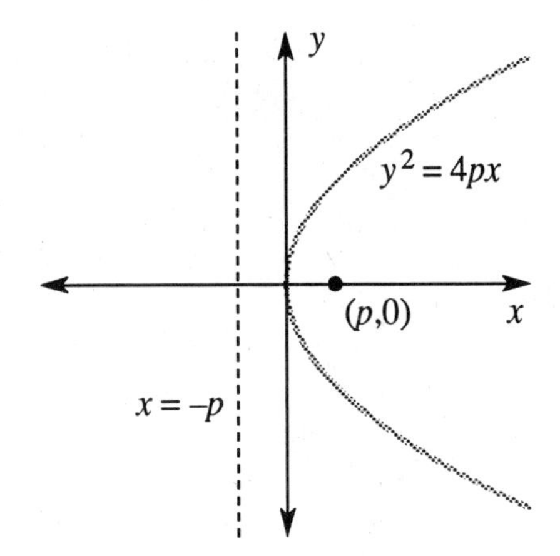

Vertex at $(0,0)$
Focus at $(p,0)$
Directrix : $x = -p$

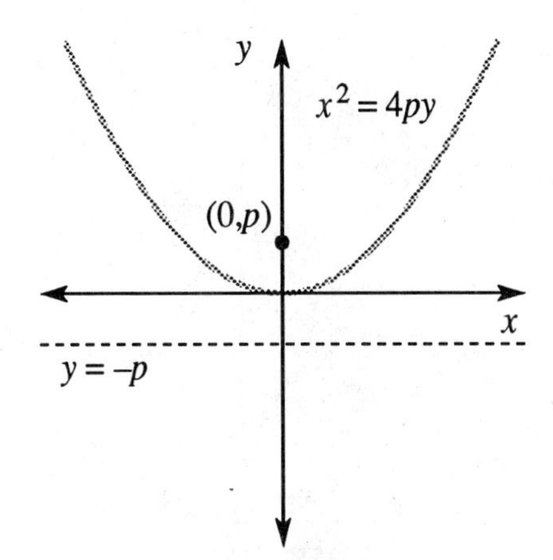

Vertex at $(0,0)$
Focus at $(0,p)$
Directrix : $y = -p$

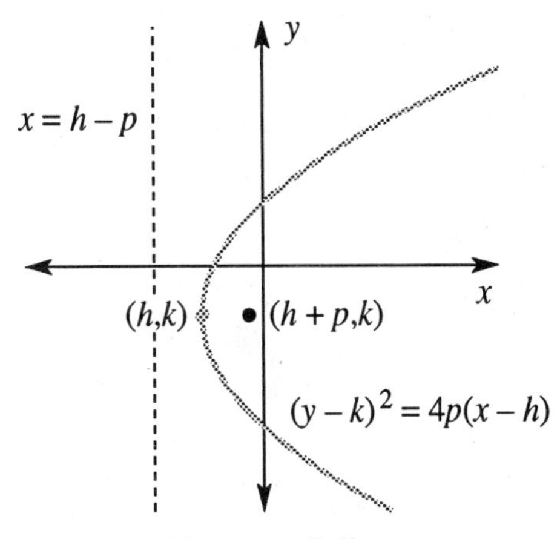

Vertex at (h,k)
Focus at $(h+p,k)$
Directrix : $x = h - p$

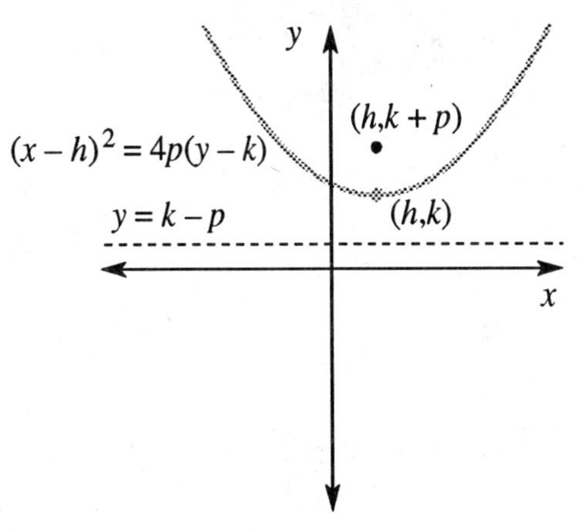

Vertex at (h,k)
Focus at $(h,k+p)$
Directrix : $y = k - p$

Hyperbolas

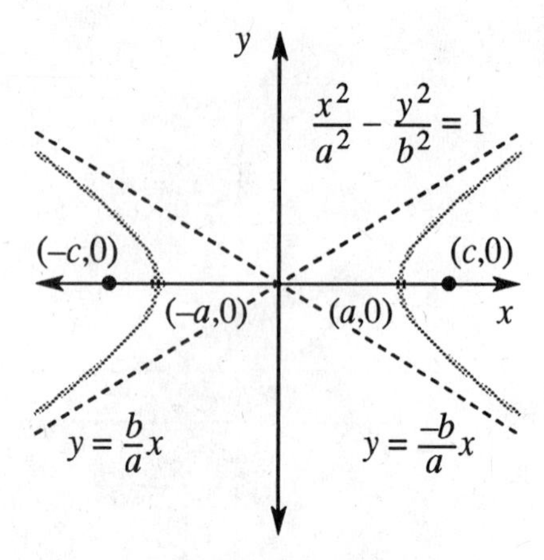

Center at (0,0)
Foci : $(\pm c,0)$
Asymptotes : $y = \pm\frac{b}{a}x$
Vertices at $(\pm a,0)$

$$\text{Eccentricity } e = \frac{\sqrt{a^2+b^2}}{a}$$

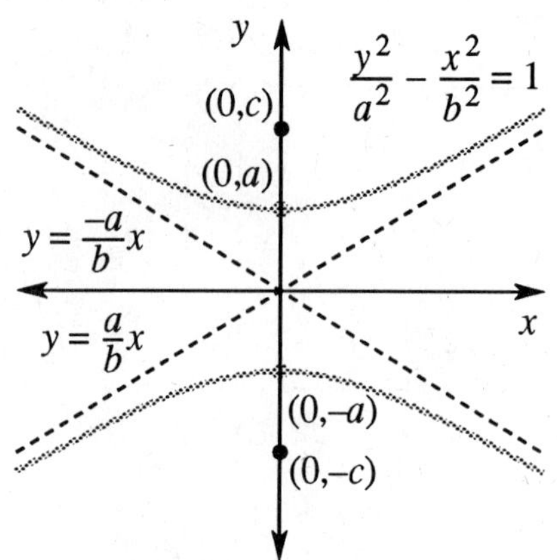

Center at (0,0)
Foci : $(0,\pm c)$
Asymptotes : $y = \pm\frac{a}{b}x$
Vertices at $(0,\pm a)$

$$\text{Eccentricity } e = \frac{\sqrt{a^2+b^2}}{a}$$

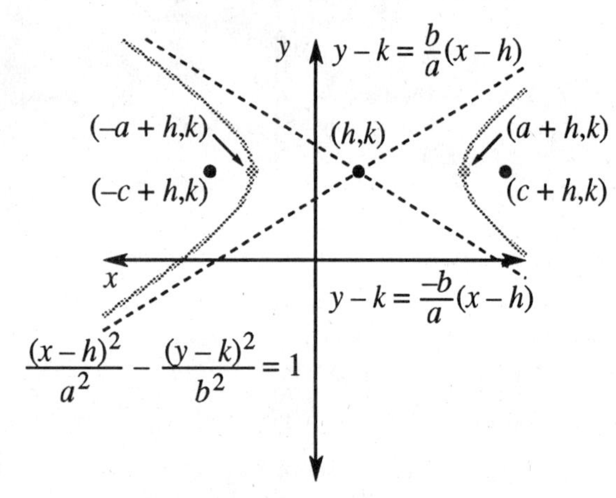

Center at (h,k)
Foci : $(\pm c + h,k)$
Asymptotes : $y - k = \pm\frac{b}{a}(x-h)$
Vertices at $(\pm a + h,k)$

$$\text{Eccentricity } e = \frac{\sqrt{a^2+b^2}}{a}$$

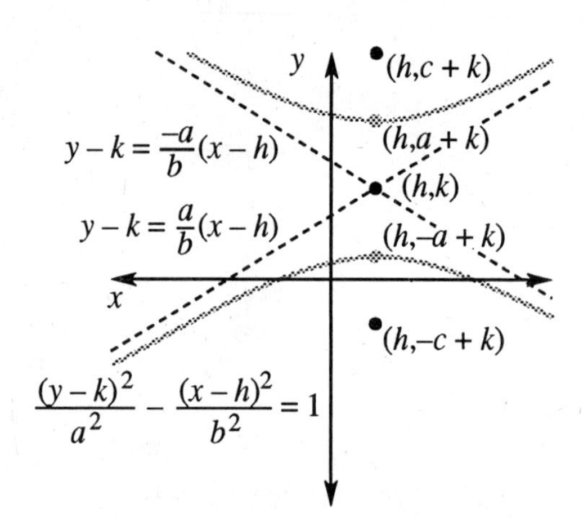

Center at (h,k)
Foci : $(h,\pm c + k)$
Asymptotes : $y - k = \pm\frac{a}{b}(x-h)$
Vertices at $(h,\pm a + k)$

$$\text{Eccentricity } e = \frac{\sqrt{a^2+b^2}}{a}$$

ANSWERS TO SELECTED EXERCISES

Chapter 0

Section 0.1

1. 31. **3.** $\frac{7}{10}$.

5. Those fractions (when written in reduced form) whose denominators have prime factorization $2^n \cdot 5^m$ will have a terminating decimal representation.

7. No. In the process of dividing 22 by 7 by the usual algorithm, 7 is divided into 22, and then into the numbers 10, 30, 20, 60, 40, 50 and then again into 10, 30, etc. These six numbers are the only possibilities. We could never have 70, 80, or more, because we would have a remainder greater than or equal to 7.

9. 10. **11.** $\sqrt{n+1}$.

13. $\frac{\pi}{4}(n+1)$. **15.** $\arcsin\left(\frac{1}{\sqrt{n+1}}\right)$.

17. $= 215.6$ feet.

Section 0.2

1. 3. **3.** 4.

5. 1. **7.** 1.

9. Rewrite to calculate

$$50000000 \cdot 0.0000006 \cdot \tfrac{1}{300} = 30(\tfrac{1}{300}) = 0.1.$$

11. $2(10^8) - 1$. **13.** 1×10^{-99}.

15. $10^{10} - 1$.

17. Approximately half of the distinct numbers a calculator can represent lie between -1 and 1.

Section 0.3

1. $|x+5| \le 3$. **3.** $|x| > 3$.

5. $|x| \ge 0, \quad x \ne -3$. **7.** $|x + \frac{5}{2}| \le \frac{5}{2}$.

9. $|x - \frac{17}{2}| \le \frac{21}{2}$. **11.** $|x| > 3$.

13. $[-3, 3]$.

15. $(-\infty, 1 - \frac{\sqrt{10}}{2}) \cup (-\frac{1}{2}, 1 + \frac{\sqrt{10}}{2})$.

17. $(-\infty, \frac{11}{8}) \cup (\frac{13}{8}, \infty)$. **19.** No real solutions.

21. $(-4, 10)$. **23.** $(-1, 1)$.

25. $(-\infty, -\frac{1}{2}) \cup (\frac{13}{2}, \infty)$.

27. Both open and closed, unbounded.

29. Not an interval.

31. Both open and closed, unbounded.

33. Both open and closed, unbounded.

35. Approximate range for x is $9.997 < x < 10.003$, where $x =$ length of side.

37. $[3.717, 3.723]$; $|x - 3.72| \le .003$.

39. yes.

Section 0.4

1. $P : [\frac{5}{\sqrt{2}}, \infty) \to \mathbb{R}$, $P(\ell) = (2 + \sqrt{2})\ell$.

3. $S : [4, 14] \to \mathbb{R}$, $S(d) = \pi d^2$.

5. Function. **7.** Not a function.

9. Not a function. **11.** Function.

13. $(0, -1)$. **15.** $-\frac{1}{5}$.

17. $\frac{1}{2}$.

19. $a \ne 0$ describes a parabola. $a = 0$ describes a straight line with slope b and y-intercept c.

21. Changing b affects the location of the vertex.

23. If $d > 0$, the graph crosses the x-axis twice. If $d = 0$, the graph touches/crosses the x-axis in one place. If $d < 0$, the graph does not touch the x-axis at all.

25. $a = 1$, $b = -5$. **27.** $a = 4$, $b = -4$.

29. Many answers are possible, such as $a = -6$ and $b = 18$, or, $a = 6$ and $b = -12$.

Section 0.5

1. The line would make a 45° angle with the x-axis.

3. The line would look like the line $x = 0$.

5. $x \approx 1.789$. **7.** $x \approx .775$.

9. $x \approx 2.215$. **11.** $x = 1$.

13. $x \approx 1.496$. **15.** $x \approx 29.563 \pm 90.963i$.

(For some intervals in 17-39, endpoints have been rounded.)

17. $(-\infty, 8.5] \cup [9.5, \infty)$.

19. $(-\infty, -.581) \cup (-.5, 2.581)$.

21. $(-\infty, 1.375) \cup (1.625, \infty)$.

23. No real solutions.

25. $[-.5, 0) \cup (0, .5]$. **27.** No real solutions.

29. $[4.333, 23]$. **31.** $(-.581, 2.581) \cup (3, \infty)$.

33. $(-\infty, 1) \cup (2, \infty)$. **35.** $[-1.162, 5.162]$.

37. $(-\infty, 0) \cup (0, .366]$. **39.** No real solutions.

41. The product of two truth functions will return an output of 1 only when both truth functions are simultaneously true. Hence, multiplication is an appropriate operation to represent AND.

43. After a few zooms in horizontally (by factors of 10), the graph should appear similar to a flat line $y = c$, with $2.7 < c < 2.8$. When you continue to zoom in horizontally, the graph may exhibit some jagged jumps (as you approach the precision limitations of the machine). As you continue to zoom in horizontally, the graph should appear similar to the flat line $y = 1$.

Here's why it happens. For values x very close to 10^{-12}, the effects of the roundoff will vary quite a bit from pixel to pixel, resulting in the jagged jumps. For $x < 10^{-12}$, the base quantity $(1 + x)$ is rounded to *exactly* 1.

Chapter 1

Section 1.1

1. The degree of the resulting polynomial is the sum of the degrees of the original polynomials.

3. Yes. **5.** $(1, 1)$.

7. Odd. **9.** $\frac{2}{1}, \frac{4}{3}, \frac{1}{1}, \frac{2}{3}$.

11. $\frac{3}{2}, \frac{3}{4}, \frac{1}{2}$. **13.** All but $-\frac{1}{1}, \frac{1}{1}$.

15. $\frac{2}{3}$. **17.** $\frac{1}{1}$.

19. $-\frac{2}{1}, -\frac{4}{3}, -\frac{2}{3}, \frac{2}{1}, \frac{4}{3}, \frac{2}{3}$.

21. $y = x^{p/q}$ is an odd function if $D = \mathbb{R}$ or $D = \{x : x \neq 0\}$ and p and q are odd. $y = x^{p/q}$ is an even function if $D = \mathbb{R}$ or $D = \{x : x \neq 0\}$ and p is even. Otherwise, it is neither.

23. a) $p(x) = x^2 + x$. b) $p(x) = (x - 1)^3$.

25. If a is negative, the original graph is translated $|a|$ units to the right.
If a is positive, the original graph is translated a units to the left.

27. The y-intercept of the graph of $y = cf(x)$ is c times the y-intercept of the graph of $y = f(x)$. Changing c doesn't change x-intercept. When $c < 0$, the graph of $y = cf(x)$ is a reflection of the graph of $y = |c|f(x)$ through the x-axis.

29. No. **31.** $\frac{125}{2}$ sec.

33. Over the interval $(0, \frac{125}{4})$.

35. $15,625$ feet.

37. No. The domain for $y = \sqrt[4]{x^2}$ includes values $x < 0$, but the domain for $y = (\sqrt[4]{x})^2$ includes only values $x \geq 0$.

Section 1.2

1. 0. **3.** 1.406.

5. ≈ 1.7. **7.** 1.9194.

9. 1. **11.** 40 years.

13. ≈ 132.9 years. **15.** $6,382,271$ rodents.

17. $\approx \$1,338.23$. **19.** $\approx 14\%$.

21. 5 AM. **23.** noon.

25. $y = 2^{-x}$.

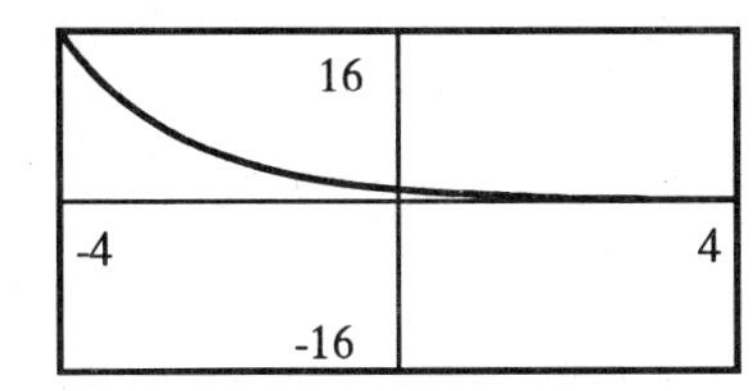

27. $y = -2^{-x}$.

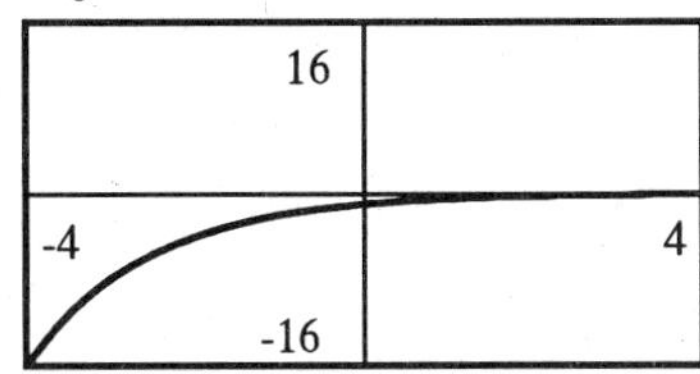

29. $y = \log_2(-x), \quad x < 0$.

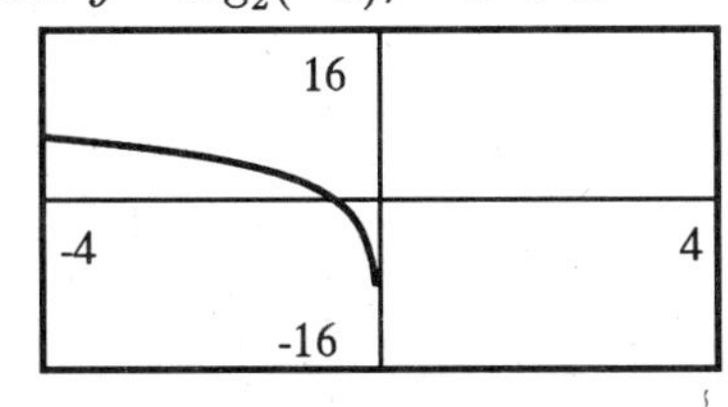

31. $y = -\log_2(x)$.

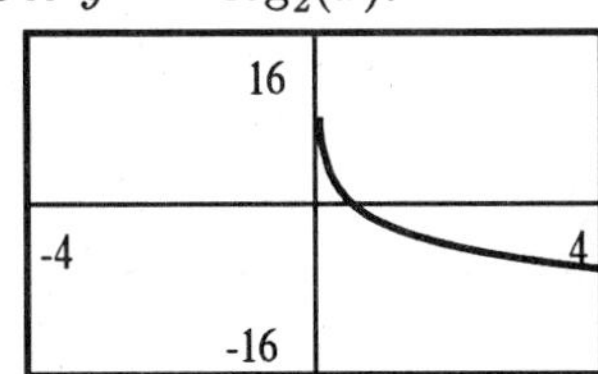

33. $a = 1,\ b = 1$. **35.** $(1, 0)$.

37. $y = a^x$. **39.** $y = a^x$.

Section 1.3

1. $f(x) = \cos(x), \quad f(x) = \sec(x)$.

3. $f(x) = \cos(x), \quad f(x) = \sin(x)$.

5. $|A|$ determines the height or amplitude of the graph of $y = A\sin(x)$. The graph of $y = -A\sin(x)$ is a reflection of the graph of $y = A\sin(x)$ through the x-axis.

7. C shifts the graph of $y = \sin(x)$ $|C|$ units to the right if $C > 0$, and to the left if $C < 0$.

11. $\frac{1}{\pi}$. **13.** 3.

15. $\frac{2\pi}{|B|}$.

17. $|A| + D$. **19.** D.

21. For $C > 0$, the phase shift is C. For $C < 0$, the phase shift is $C + \frac{\pi}{|B|}$.

23. a) $\{0,\ 0.866025,\ -0.866025\}$.

b) $u(t) = \sin(1(2\pi)t)$.

25. a) $\{0,\ -0.951057,\ -0.587785,\ 0.587785,\ 0.951057\}$. b) $u(t) = -\sin(1(2\pi)t)$.

27. a) $\{0,\ -0.433884,\ 0.781831,\ -0.974928,\ 0.974928,\ -0.781831,\ 0.433884\}$.

b) $u(t) = -\sin(3(2\pi)t)$.

29. a) $\{0,\ 0.34202,\ -0.642788,\ 0.866025,\ -0.984808,\ 0.984808,\ -0.866025,\ 0.642788,\ -0.34202\}$.

b) none.

31. It requires more than $2f$ samples per second to reconstruct a signal with frequency f.

Section 1.4

1. $\{x : x \in \mathbb{R} \text{ and } x \neq \pm\sqrt{3}\}$.

3. $\mathbb{R}$.

5. $\mathbb{R}$.

7. $g \circ f \circ h \circ j$.

9. $g \circ k \circ j \circ f$.

11. $h \circ g \circ g \circ g \circ f$ or $h \circ f \circ g$.

13. 1.

15. -6.

17. Undefined.

19. 3.

21. -2.

23. 0, 3.

25. 0.

27.

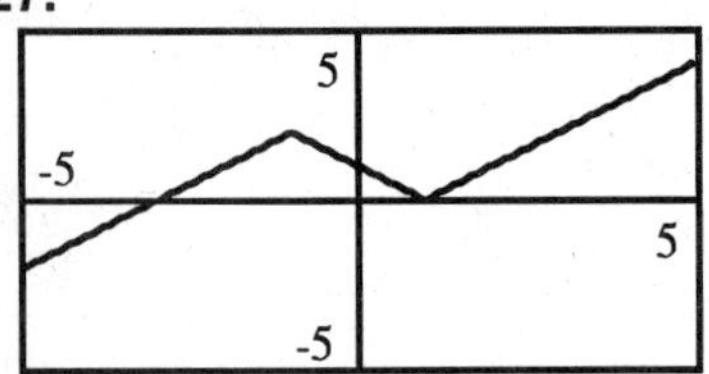

29.

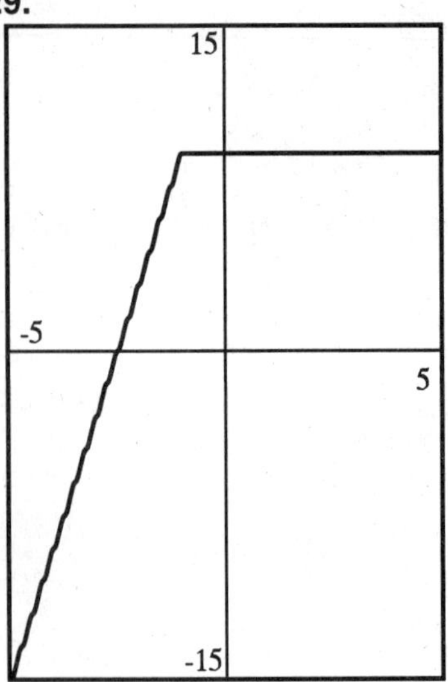

31.

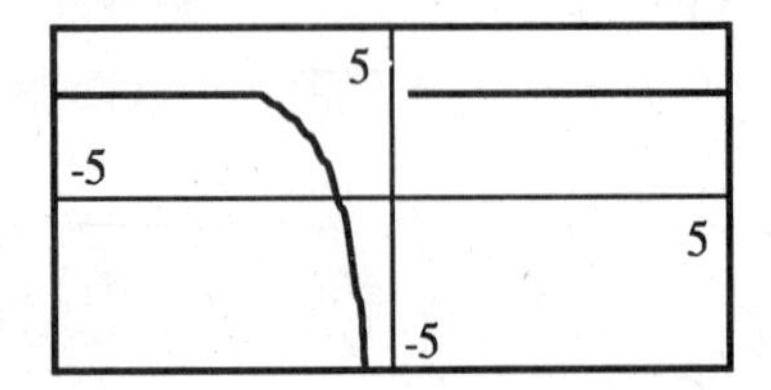

33.

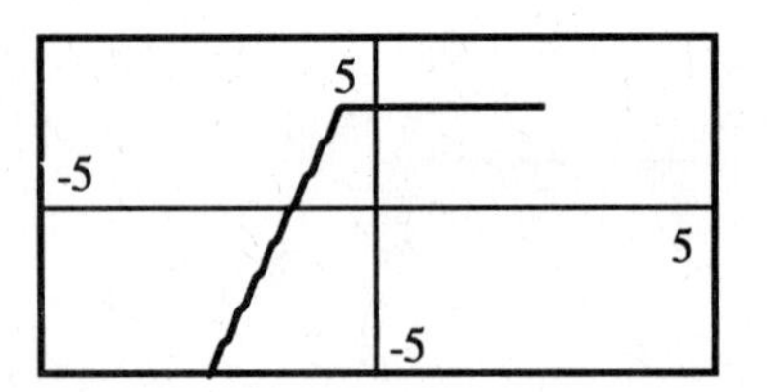

35.

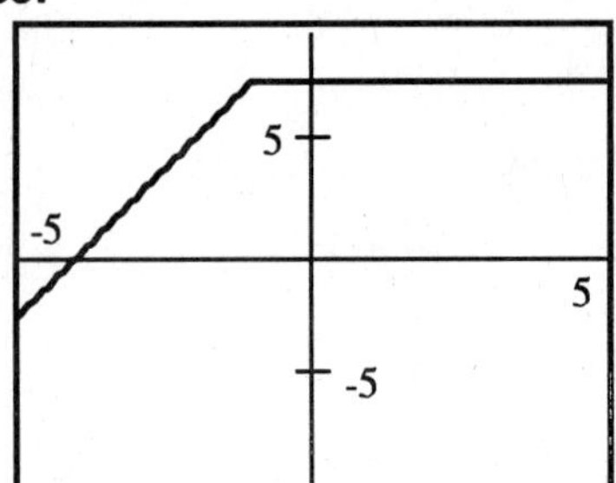

37.

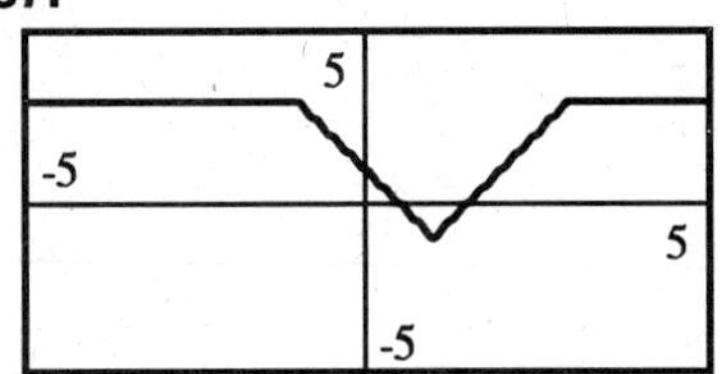

39.

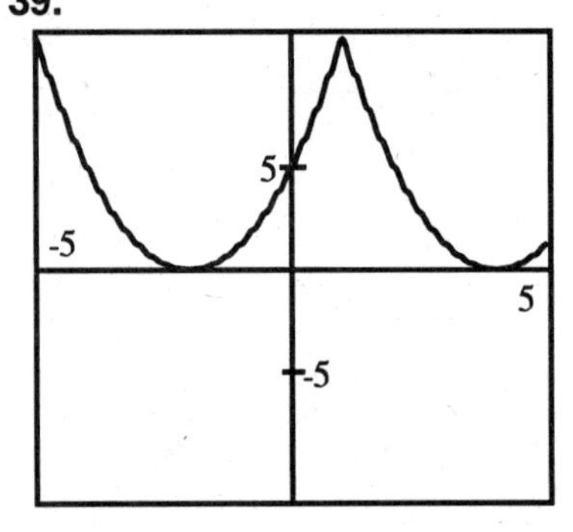

41. For $f(x) = \sinh(x)$, $f(x) = \cosh(x)$, $f(x) = \tanh(x)$, and $f(x) = \operatorname{sech}(x)$, the domain of f is $D = \mathbb{R}$. For $f(x) = \operatorname{csch}(x)$ and $f(x) = \coth(x)$, the domain of f is $D = \{x : x \in \mathbb{R},\ x \neq 0\}$.

45. $f(x) = \sinh(x)$, $f(x) = \tanh(x)$, $f(x) = \operatorname{csch}(x)$, $f(x) = \coth(x)$.

47. $\cosh^2(x) - \sinh^2(x)$

$$= \left[\frac{e^x + e^{-x}}{2}\right]^2 - \left[\frac{e^x - e^{-x}}{2}\right]^2$$

$$= \frac{e^{2x} + 2 + e^{-2x}}{4} - \frac{e^{2x} - 2 + e^{-2x}}{4} = \frac{4}{4} = 1.$$

Section 1.5

1. No inverse.

3. $i^{-1}(y) = y, \quad i^{-1} : \mathbb{R} \to \mathbb{R}.$

5. No inverse.

7. $h^{-1}(y) = \frac{5}{9}(y - 32), \quad h^{-1} : \mathbb{R} \to \mathbb{R}.$

9. If $m = 0$, $f(x) = b$. So for all $x_1 \neq x_2$, $f(x_1) = f(x_2)$, which violates the condition for f to have an inverse.

11. $\left(\frac{b}{1-m}, \frac{b}{1-m}\right)$ **13.** 3.

15. 1. **17.** 3.

19. 2. **21.** $-\frac{\pi}{6}$.

23. $\frac{\pi}{4}$. **25.** $\frac{\pi}{3}$.

27. True for $-\frac{\pi}{2} \leq x \leq \frac{\pi}{2}$.

29. $a = b$.

31. None of the above.

33. None of the above.

35. $y = \text{arccot}(x)$. **37.** None.

39. All are bounded. **45.** $y = \tanh^{-1}(x)$.

47. $y = \text{sech}^{-1}(x)$. **49.** $y = \sinh^{-1}(x)$.

Section 1.6

1. ≈ 277. **3.** ≈ 795.

5. 859. **7.** ≈ 181.659 sec.

9. March.

11. Northern hemisphere.

13. G. **15.** B.

17. I. **19.** E.

21. H. **23.** H.

Chapter 2

Section 2.1

1.

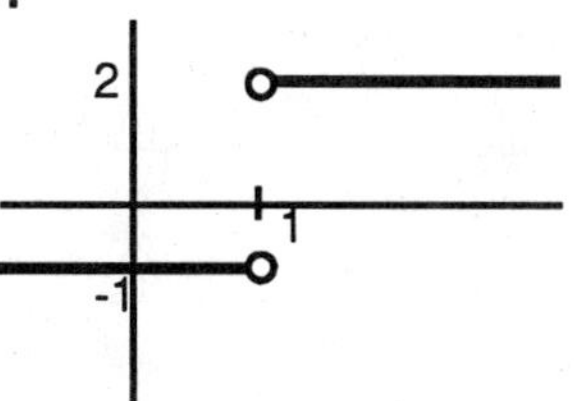

3.

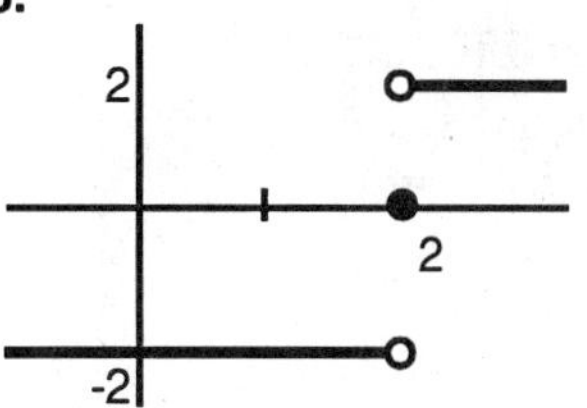

5.

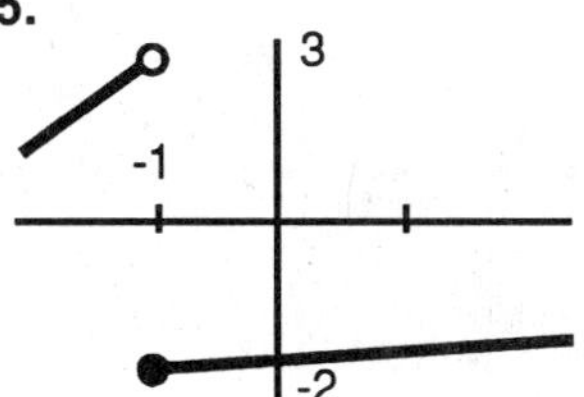

7.

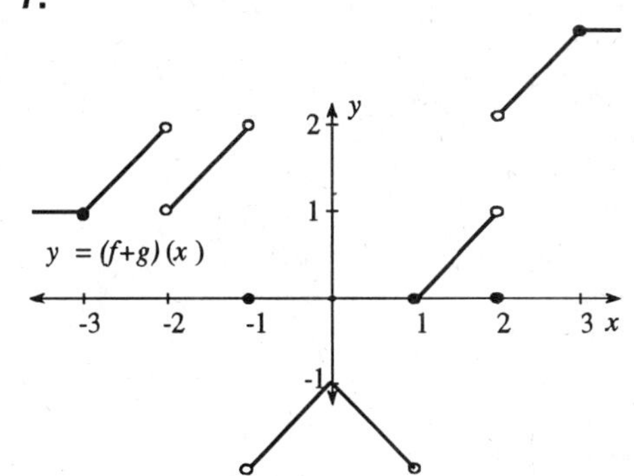

9.

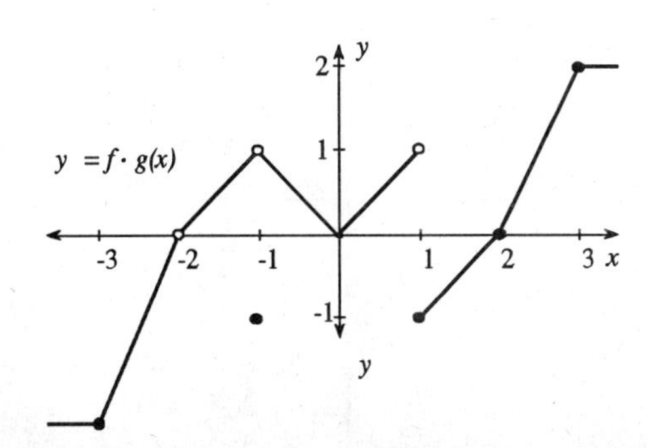

11.

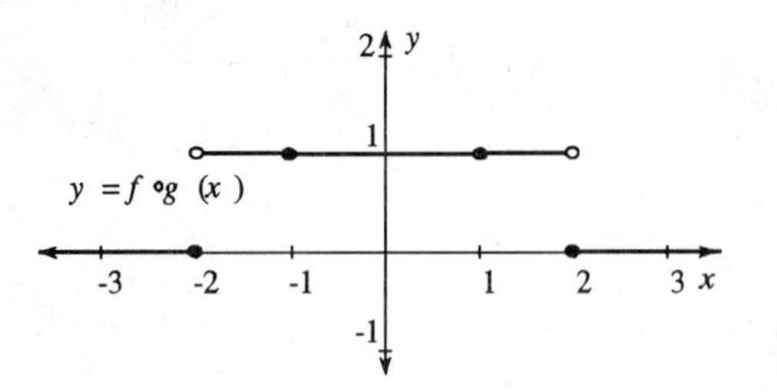

13.

input $x=a$	output $f(a)$	left-hand limit $\lim_{x\to a^-} f(x)$	right-hand limit $\lim_{x\to a^+} f(x)$	limit $\lim_{x\to a} f(x)$	Is f continuous at $x=a$? (yes or no)
-3	-1	-1	-1	-1	yes
-2	undefined	0	0	0	no
-1	1	1	-1	does not exist	no
0	0	0	0	0	yes
1	1	-1	-1	-1	no
2	0	0	0	0	yes
3	1	1	1	1	yes

15.

input $x=a$	output $f(a)$	left-hand limit $\lim_{x\to a^-} f(x)$	right-hand limit $\lim_{x\to a^+} f(x)$	limit $\lim_{x\to a} f(x)$	Is f continuous at $x=a$? (yes or no)
-3	1	1	1	1	yes
-2	undefined	2	1	does not exist	no
-1	0	2	-2	does not exist	no
0	-1	-1	-1	-1	yes
1	0	-2	0	does not exist	no
2	0	1	2	does not exist	no
3	3	3	3	3	yes

17.

input $x=a$	output $f(a)$	left-hand limit $\lim_{x\to a^-} f(x)$	right-hand limit $\lim_{x\to a^+} f(x)$	limit $\lim_{x\to a} f(x)$	Is f continuous at $x=a$? (yes or no)
-3	-2	-2	-2	-2	yes
-2	undefined	0	0	0	no
-1	-1	1	1	1	no
0	0	0	0	0	yes
1	-1	1	-1	does not exist	no
2	0	0	0	0	yes
3	2	2	2	2	yes

19.

input $x=a$	output $f(a)$	left-hand limit $\lim_{x\to a^-} f(x)$	right-hand limit $\lim_{x\to a^+} f(x)$	limit $\lim_{x\to a} f(x)$	Is f continuous at $x=a$? (yes or no)
-3	0	0	0	0	yes
-2	0	0	1	does not exist	no
-1	1	1	1	1	yes
0	1	1	1	1	yes
1	1	1	1	1	yes
2	0	1	0	does not exist	no
3	0	0	0	0	yes

21. b) $\lim_{x\to 0+} f(x) = 0, \quad \lim_{x\to 0-} f(x) = 0.$
c) $\lim_{x\to 0} f(x) = 0.$

23. b) $\lim_{x\to 0+} f(x) = 1, \quad \lim_{x\to 0-} f(x) = -1.$
c) $\lim_{x\to 0} f(x)$ does not exist.

25. b) $\lim_{x\to 0+} f(x)$ does not exist (∞),
$\lim_{x\to 0-} f(x)$ does not exist (∞).
c) $\lim_{x\to 0} f(x)$ does not exist (∞).

27. b) $\lim_{x\to 0+} f(x)$ does not exist,
$\lim_{x\to 0-} f(x)$ does not exist.
c) $\lim_{x\to 0} f(x)$ does not exist.

29. b) $\lim_{x\to 0+} f(x) = 0, \quad \lim_{x\to 0-} f(x) = 0.$
c) $\lim_{x\to 0} f(x) = 0.$

31. b) $\lim_{x\to 0+} f(x) = 0, \quad \lim_{x\to 0-} f(x) = 0.$
c) $\lim_{x\to 0} f(x) = 0.$

33. b) $\lim_{x\to 0+} f(x) = e, \quad \lim_{x\to 0-} f(x) = e.$
c) $\lim_{x\to 0} f(x) = e.$

35. b) $\lim_{x\to 0+} f(x) = -1, \quad \lim_{x\to 0-} f(x) = 0.$
c) $\lim_{x\to 0} f(x)$ does not exist.

Section 2.2

1. Limit exists (3). **3.** Limit exists (4).

5. Limit exists (0). **7.** Limit does not exist.

9. Limit exists (1). **11.** Limit exists (0).

13. Limit exists (0). **15.** Limit exists (4).

17. Limit does not exist.

19. Limit exists $(.1\overline{7})$.

21. Limit exists (0). **23.** Limit exists $(-.3)$.

Section 2.3

1. Continuous.

3. Continuous.

5. Removable discontinuity at 0.

7. Jump discontinuity at 0.

9. Removable discontinuity at 0.

11. f is undefined for $-1 < x < 1$.

13. $\{x : x = n\pi, n$ any integer$\}$.

15. $\{x = \frac{\pi}{2} + n\pi, n$ any integer$\}$.

17. $x = 0$.

19. No jump discontinuity.

21. No jump discontinuity.

23. Jump discontinuity at π.

25. $x = 2$, $x = 3$ are vertical asymptotes.

$\lim_{x\to 2^-} f(x) = -\infty$ $\quad \lim_{x\to 2^+} f(x) = \infty$,

$\lim_{x\to 3^-} f(x) = \infty$, $\quad \lim_{x\to 3^+} f(x) = -\infty$.

27. $x = 1$, $x = -3$ are vertical asymptotes.

$\lim_{x\to 1^-} f(x) = -\infty$, $\quad \lim_{x\to 1^+} f(x) = \infty$,

$\lim_{x\to -3^-} f(x) = \infty$, $\quad \lim_{x\to -3^+} f(x) = -\infty$.

29. $x = \frac{1}{2}$ is a vertical asymptote and the graph has a "hole" at $(-2, \frac{1}{5})$.

$\lim_{x\to 1/2^-} f(x) = -\infty$, $\quad \lim_{x\to 1/2^+} f(x) = \infty$,

$\lim_{x\to -2} f(x) = \frac{1}{5}$.

31. $x = 3$ is a vertical asymptote.

$\lim_{x\to 3^-} f(x) = -\infty$, $\quad \lim_{x\to 3^+} f(x) = \infty$.

33. $x = \frac{3 \pm \sqrt{17}}{2}$ are vertical asymptotes.

Let $a = \frac{3 + \sqrt{17}}{2}$, $\quad b = \frac{3 - \sqrt{17}}{2}$:

$\lim_{x\to b^-} f(x) = -\infty$, $\quad \lim_{x\to b^+} f(x) = \infty$,

$\lim_{x\to a^-} f(x) = -\infty$, $\quad \lim_{x\to a^+} f(x) = \infty$.

35. $x = -2$ is a vertical asymptote.

$\lim_{x\to -2^-} f(x) = -\infty$, $\quad \lim_{x\to -2^+} f(x) = \infty$.

37. $x = 3$ is a vertical asymptote.

$\lim_{x\to 3^-} f(x) = \infty$, $\quad \lim_{x\to 3^+} f(x) = -\infty$.

39. $x = 1$ is a vertical asymptote.

$\lim_{x\to 1^-} f(x) = -\infty$, $\quad \lim_{x\to 1^+} f(x) = \infty$.

Section 2.4

1. 1 or -3.

3. $\frac{\pi}{2}$. $\qquad$ **5.** $-\frac{4}{3}$.

7. f is not continuous on $[-1, 1]$ and, therefore, does not satisfy the hypotheses of the Intermediate Zero Theorem.

9. f is not continuous on the closed interval $[0, 1]$ and, therefore, does not satisfy the hypotheses of the Extreme Value Theorem.

13. $x_1 = 1.5$, $\quad x_2 = 1.75$,
$x_3 = 1.875$, $\quad x_4 = 1.8125$.
Desired accuracy guaranteed in 7 steps;
x_5 is within .01 of a root.

15. $x_1 = .75$, $\quad x_2 = .775$,
$x_3 = .7875$, $\quad x_4 = .78125$.
Desired accuracy guaranteed in 4 steps;
x_2 is within .01 of a root.

17. $x_1 = 2.2$, $\quad x_2 = 2.4$,
$x_3 = 2.3$, $\quad x_4 = 2.25$.
Desired accuracy guaranteed in 7 steps;
x_5 is within .01 of a root.

19. $x_1 = .9875$, $\quad x_2 = 1.11875$,
$x_3 = 1.053125$, $\quad x_4 = 1.0203125$.
Desired accuracy guaranteed in 6 steps;
x_5 is within .01 of a root.

21. $x_1 = 1.65$, $\quad x_2 = 1.375$,
$x_3 = 1.5125$, $\quad x_4 = 1.44375$.
Desired accuracy guaranteed in 7 steps;
x_6 is within .01 of a root.

Section 2.5

1. $\lim_{x\to -\infty} f(x) = 1$, $\quad \lim_{x\to\infty} f(x) = 1$.

3. $\lim_{x\to -\infty} f(x) = 2$, $\quad \lim_{x\to\infty} f(x) = 2$.

5. $\lim_{x\to -\infty} f(x) = 0$, $\quad \lim_{x\to\infty} f(x) = 0$.

7. $\lim_{x\to -\infty} f(x) = 0$, $\quad \lim_{x\to\infty} f(x) = \infty$.

9. $\lim_{x\to -\infty} f(x) = e^{-1}$, $\quad \lim_{x\to\infty} f(x) = e^{-1}$.

11. $\lim_{x\to -\infty} f(x) = -1$, $\quad \lim_{x\to\infty} f(x) = 1$.

13. $\lim_{x\to -\infty} f(x) = \infty$, $\quad \lim_{x\to\infty} f(x) = 0$.

(Viewing windows for ex. 15-29 may vary.)

15. $y = 1$ is a horizontal asymptote.
$[-6000, 6000]$ by $[-3, 3]$.

17. $y = 1$ is a horizontal asymptote.
$[-60000, 60000]$ by $[-3, 3]$.

19. $y = \frac{1}{2}$ is a horizontal asymptote.
$[-60000, 60000]$ by $[-3, 3]$.

21. $y = 1$ is a horizontal asymptote.
$[-60000, 60000]$ by $[-3, 3]$.

23. No horizontal asymptote. $y \approx \frac{x}{8}$.
$[-100, 100]$ by $[-100, 100]$.

25. No horizontal asymptote. $y \approx \frac{x^2}{24}$.
$[-100, 100]$ by $[-10000, 10000]$.

27. No horiz. asy. $y \approx \frac{x^3}{30}$.
$[-500, 500]$ by $[-125000000, 125000000]$.

29. No horizontal asymptote. $y \approx \frac{x}{5}$.
$[-100, 100]$ by $[-100, 100]$.

31. The strategy works because
$\lim_{x\to 0+} \frac{1}{x} = \infty$ and $\lim_{x\to 0-} \frac{1}{x} = -\infty$.

Section 2.6

1. $\delta = .01$. In general, let $\delta = \epsilon$.
Now, whenever $0 < |x - 1| < \delta = \epsilon$,
we have $|(x - 7) - (-6)| = |x - 1| < \delta = \epsilon$.

3. $\delta = .0005$. In general, let $\delta = \frac{\epsilon}{2}$.
Now whenever $0 < |x - (-\frac{1}{2})| < \delta = \frac{\epsilon}{2}$,
we have $\left|\frac{4x^3 + 4x^2 + x}{2x^2 + x}\right| = \left|\frac{x(2x+1)^2}{x(2x+1)}\right|$
$= |2x + 1| = 2|x + \frac{1}{2}| < 2(\frac{\epsilon}{2}) = \epsilon$.

5. $\delta = .00001$. In general, let $\delta = \frac{\epsilon}{1000}$.
Now whenever $0 < |x - 2| < \delta = \frac{\epsilon}{1000}$,
we have $|1000x - 2000| = 1000|x - 2|$
$< 1000 \cdot \frac{\epsilon}{1000} = \epsilon$.

7. $L = 0$; $[-.01, .01]$.

9. Limit does not exist.

11. Limit does not exist.

13. Limit does not exist.

15. $L = 0$; $[-.0065, .0065]$.

17. $L = 0$; $[-.0065, .0065]$.

19. $L = e$; $[-.0065, .0065]$.

21. Limit does not exist.

23. Let $\epsilon > 0$ be given. Let $\delta = \frac{\epsilon}{2}$.
Whenever $0 < |x - a| < \delta = \frac{\epsilon}{2}$,
we have $|2x + 1 - (2a + 1)| = |2x - 2a|$
$= 2|x - a| < 2(\frac{\epsilon}{2}) = \epsilon$.

25. The choice of δ depends on the size of ϵ.

Case 1. Assume $0 < \epsilon < 1$. In this case, choose $\delta = \epsilon/7$. (Note that $\delta < 1$.) Now, whenever $0 < |x - 3| < \delta = \epsilon/7$, we have
$|x^2 - 9| = |(x - 3)(x + 3)| = |x - 3||x + 3|$
$= |x - 3||(x - 3) + 6| \le |x - 3|(|x - 3| + 6)$
$< \delta(\delta + 6) < (\epsilon/7)(1 + 6) = \epsilon$.

Case 2. Assume $\epsilon \ge 1$. In this case, simply choose $\delta = 1/7$. Now, whenever $0 < |x - 3| < \delta = 1/7$, we have
$|x^2 - 9| = |(x - 3)(x + 3)| = |x - 3||x + 3|$
$= |x - 3||(x - 3) + 6| \le |x - 3|(|x - 3| + 6)$
$< (1/7)(\frac{1}{7} + 6) = 43/49 < 1 < \epsilon$.

27. Since $-1 \le \sin(\theta) \le 1$ for any θ,
we have $-1 \le \sin(\frac{1}{x}) \le 1$. Let $x \ge 0$.
Then $-x \le x\sin(\frac{1}{x}) \le x$. Since $\lim_{x\to 0+} -x = 0$
and $\lim_{x\to 0+} x = 0$, we must have
$\lim_{x\to 0+} x\sin(\frac{1}{x}) = 0$ by the Squeezing Principle for limits. Let $x < 0$, then $-x \ge x\sin(\frac{1}{x}) \ge x$.
Since $\lim_{x\to 0-} -x = 0$ and $\lim_{x\to 0-} x = 0$,
we must also have $\lim_{x\to 0-} x\sin(\frac{1}{x}) = 0$ by the Squeezing Principle for limits. Together, these results imply $\lim_{x\to 0} x\sin(\frac{1}{x}) = 0$.

29. For $-\frac{\pi}{2} < x < \frac{\pi}{2}$, $(x \ne 0)$, we have
$0 < 1 - \cos x < (1 - \cos x)(1 + \cos x)$
$= 1 - \cos^2 x = \sin^2(x)$.
Divide each part of the inequality by x.

For $x > 0$, we have

$$0 < \frac{1 - \cos(x)}{x} < \frac{\sin^2(x)}{x},$$

and for $x < 0$ we have

$$0 > \frac{1 - \cos(x)}{x} > \frac{\sin^2(x)}{x}.$$

Chapter 3

Section 3.1

1. 40 mph.

3. speeding up.

5. 1.1 hours.

7. 50 mph at $t = 0.5$ hours,

100 mph at $t = 1.0$ hours.

9. D. **11.** C.

13. ≈ 33.3 mph, 40 mph, 50 mph, ≈ 88 mph.

15. A. **17.** 10 min.

19. 17 min. **21.** 0 min.

23. 3 min. **25.** 15 min.

Section 3.2

1. $y = 3x + 13$.

3. $y = -\frac{1}{2}x - \frac{5}{2}$.

5. $y = -(0.5)(x + 1.5) - 1.75$.

7. $y = -\frac{2}{7}$.

9. $y = \frac{1}{3}(x + 6.5) - 6.5$.

11. yes; no.

13. a)

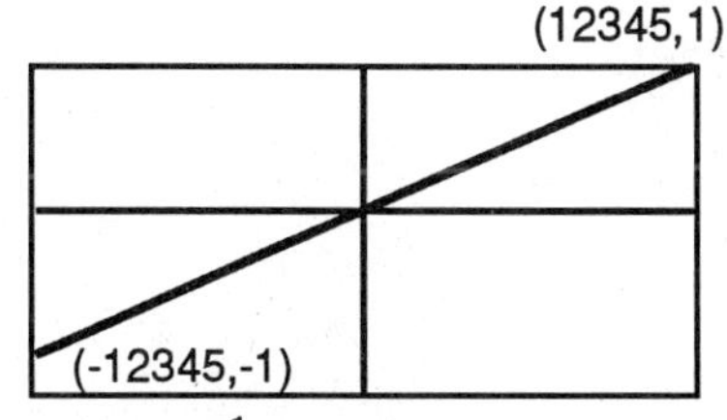

b) $y = \dfrac{1}{12345}x + 0$.

c) $y = \dfrac{1}{12345}(x - 1) + \dfrac{1}{12345}$.

d), e) All calculations yield $m \approx \frac{1}{12345}$ but x_1 gives the most accurate slope when calculated by a machine of limited precision.

15. a)

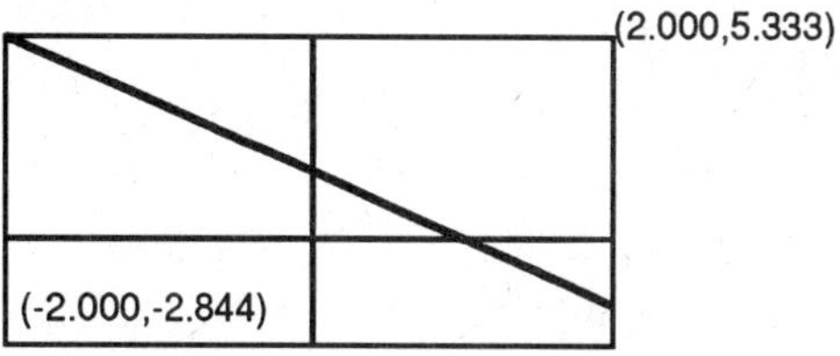

b) $y = -\dfrac{16}{9}x + \dfrac{16}{9}$.

c) $y = -\dfrac{16}{9}(x - 1) + 0$.

d), e) All calculations yield $m \approx -\frac{16}{9}$, but x_1 gives the most accurate slope when calculated by a machine of limited precision.

17. a)

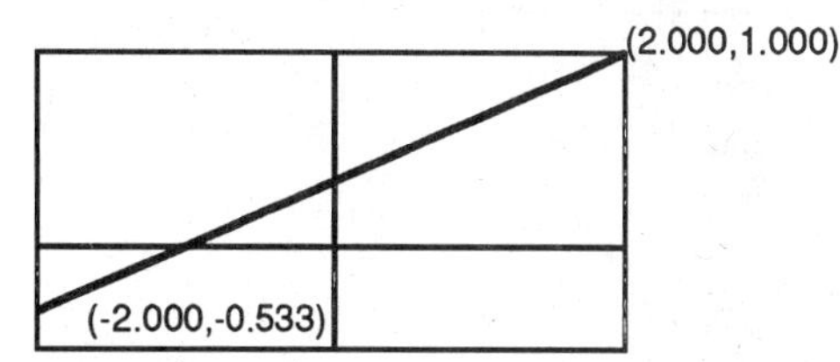

b) $y = \dfrac{1}{3}x + \dfrac{1}{3}$.

c) $y = \dfrac{1}{3}(x - 1) + \dfrac{2}{3}$.

d), e) All calculations yield $m \approx \frac{1}{3}$, but x_1 gives the most accurate slope when calculated by a machine of limited precision.

19. $f(0.5) = 5.715$, $f(1.6) = 3.764$, $f(2.25) = 2.6675$.

21. $m = 2$. **23.** $m = 1$.

25. $m = 0$. **27.** $m = 0$.

29. The function fg is linear over the open intervals $(-1, 1)$ and $(1, 5)$.

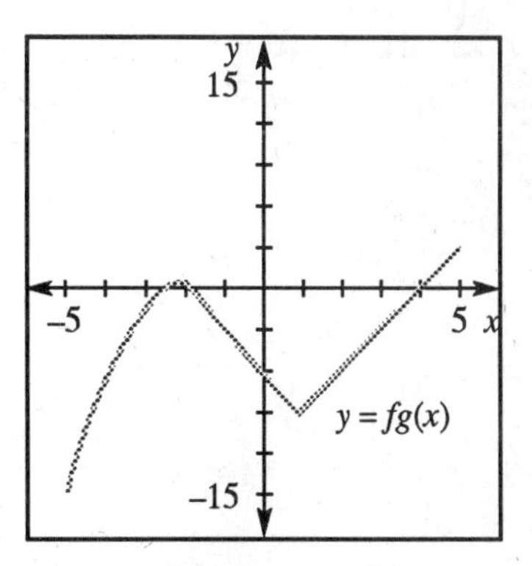

31. $\pi/3$ radians.

33. Let β be the upper right-hand angle between the light ray and the mirror. Since $\alpha+\beta=\pi/2$ and $\theta+\beta=\pi/2$, we can conclude that $\alpha=\theta$.

35. Use $\gamma=\pi-\phi$ and exercise 34.

39. The light is reflected vertically, and has undefined slope.

41.

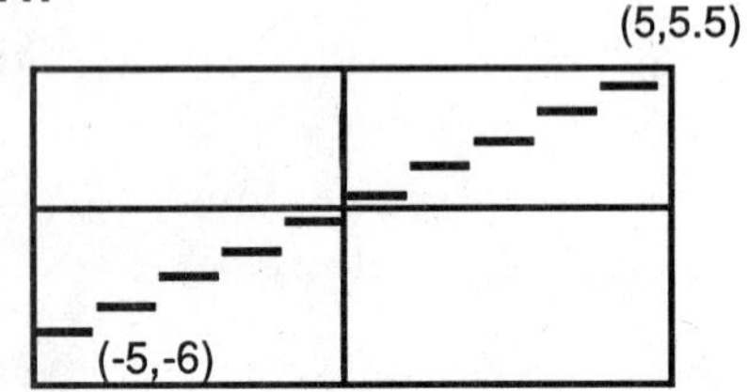

43.

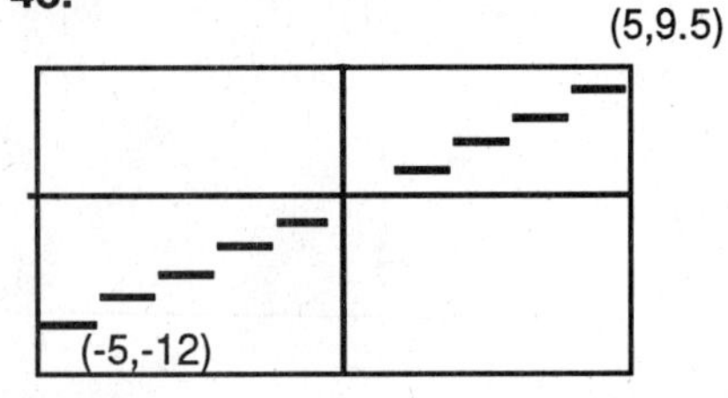

45.

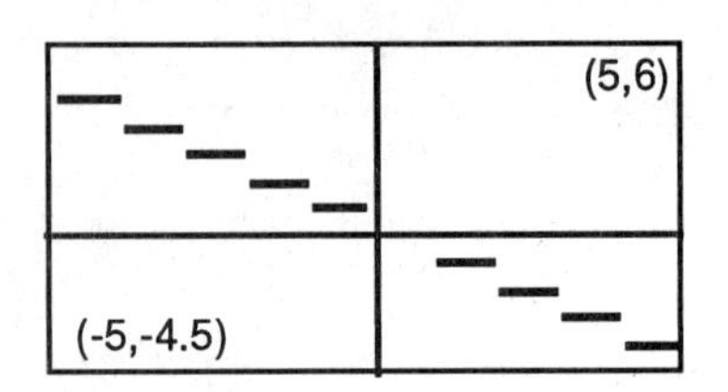

47.

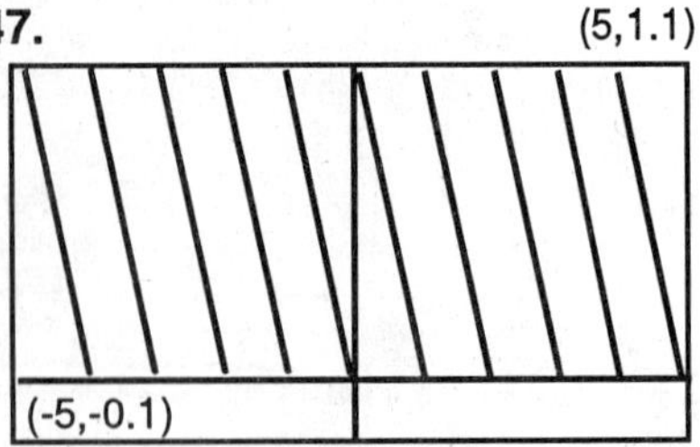

49. For all integers, x.

Section 3.3

1. $f'(1)=\frac{2}{3}$. **3.** $f'(1)=\frac{4}{3}$.
5. $f'(1)=-\frac{1}{2}$. **7.** $f'(1)=\frac{1}{2}$.
9. $f'(1)=2\ln(2)\approx 1.386$.
11. $f'(0)=1$. **13.** $f'(0)=1$.
15. $f'(0)$ is undefined.
17. $f'(0)=0$. **19.** $f'(0)=0$.
21. $f'(1.25)=4$. **23.** $f'(-1.5)=-0.5$.
25. $f'(2.9)=0$. **27.** $f'(6)=0.25$.
29. $f'(1.25)=4$. **31.** $f'(-1.5)=-0.5$.
33. $f'(2.9)=0$. **35.** $f'(6)=0.25$.
37. $f'_-(1.5)=-\frac{2}{5}$, $f'_+(1.5)=\frac{2}{5}$.
39. $f'_-(0)=-1$, $f'_+(0)=1$.
41. $$\frac{1}{2}\left(\frac{f(x_0+h)-f(x_0)}{h}+\frac{f(x_0)-f(x_0-h)}{h}\right)=\frac{f(x_0+h)-f(x_0-h)}{2h}.$$

Section 3.4

For problems 1-19, part c, other guesses are possible.

1. 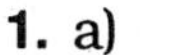

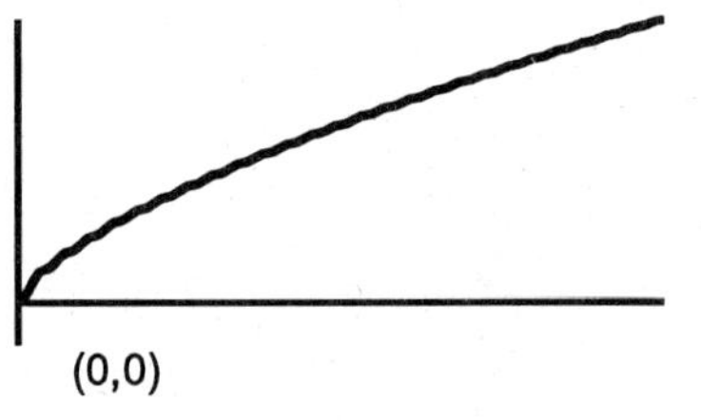

b)

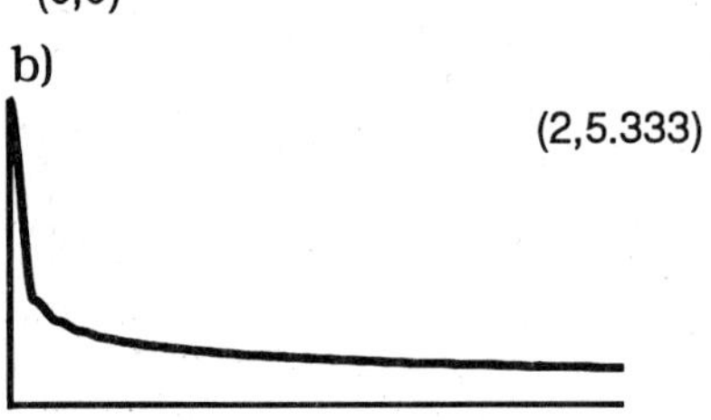

c) $g(x)=\frac{2}{3}x^{-1/3}$.

3. a)

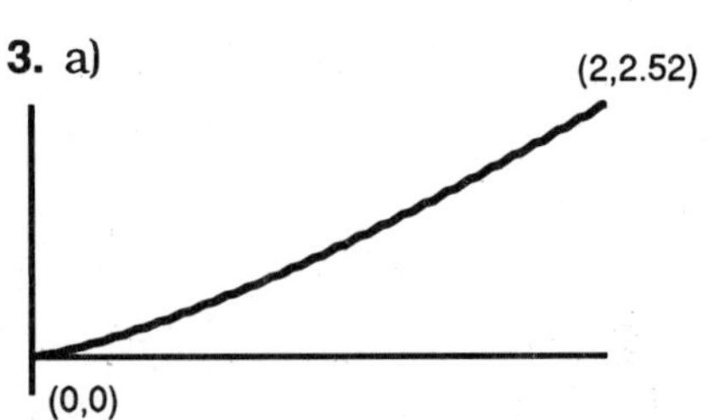

b)

c) $g(x)=\frac{4}{3}x^{1/3}$.

5. a)

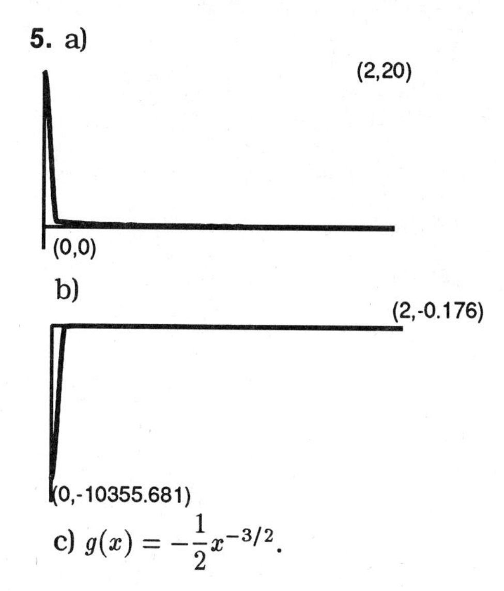

c) $g(x) = -\dfrac{1}{2}x^{-3/2}$.

7. a)

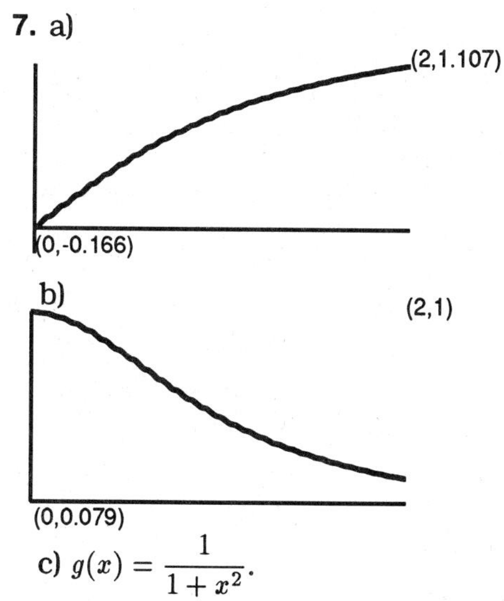

c) $g(x) = \dfrac{1}{1+x^2}$.

9. a)

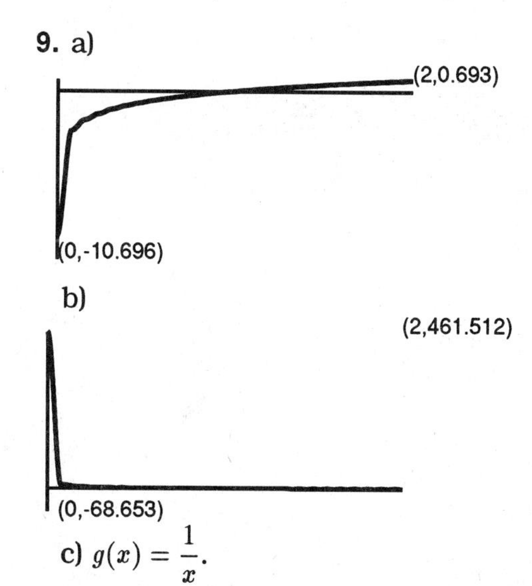

c) $g(x) = \dfrac{1}{x}$.

11. a)

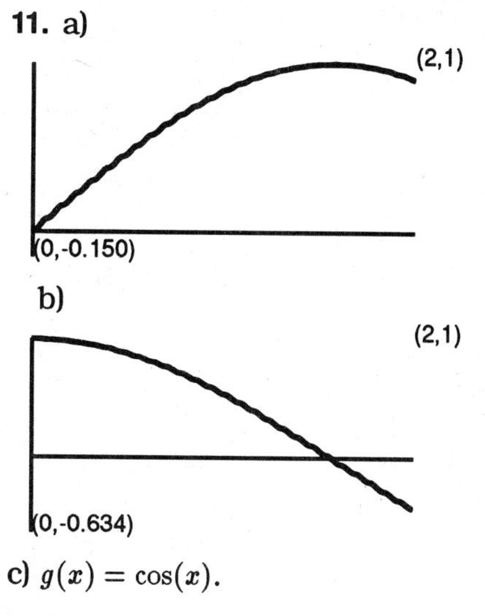

c) $g(x) = \cos(x)$.

13. a)

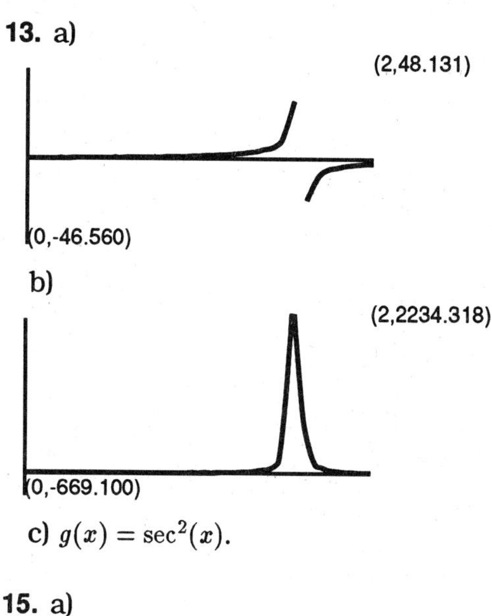

c) $g(x) = \sec^2(x)$.

15. a)

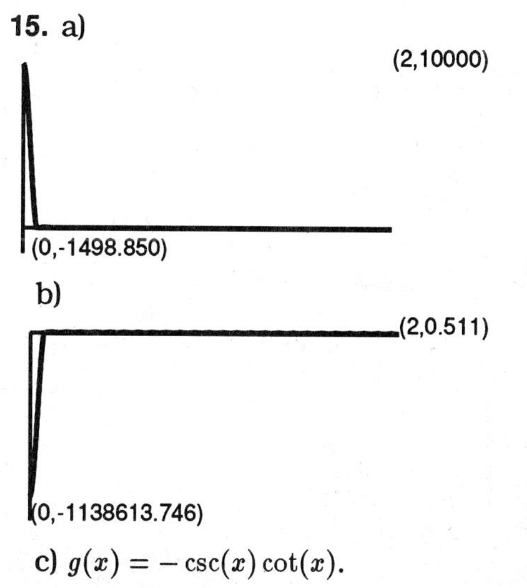

c) $g(x) = -\csc(x)\cot(x)$.

17. a)

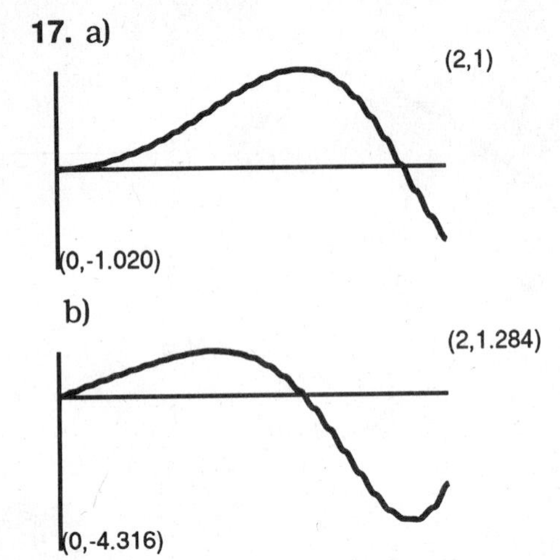

c) $g(x) = 2x\cos(x^2)$.

19. a)

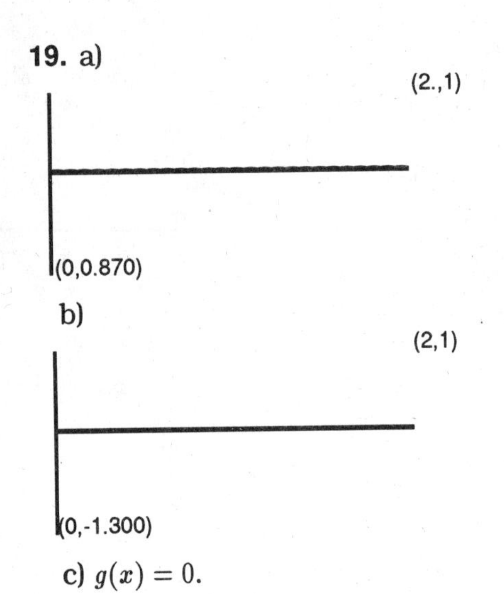

c) $g(x) = 0$.

21.

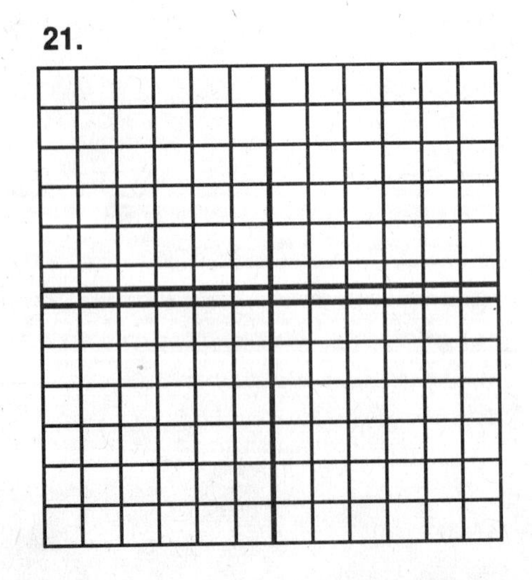

23.

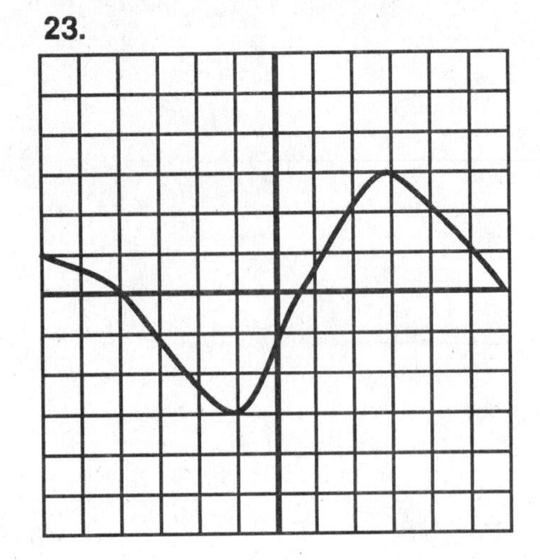

25.

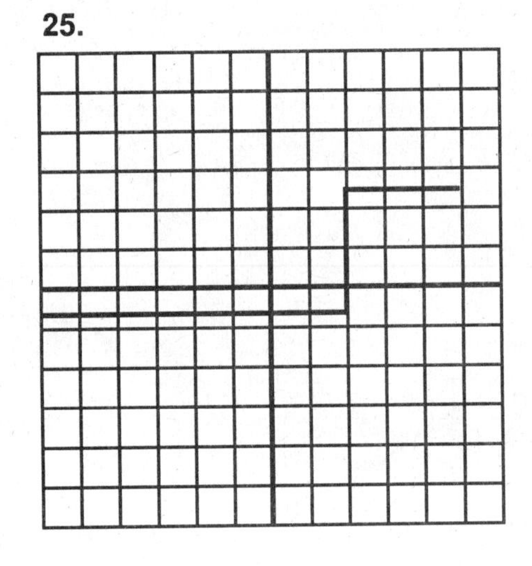

27.

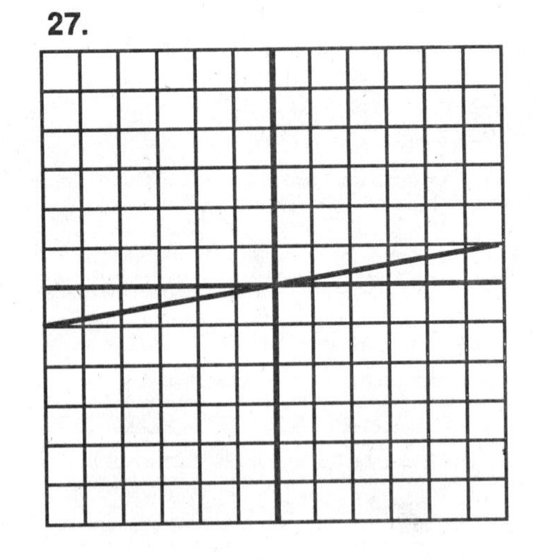

29. 23 and 24. **31.** $f'(x) = -x^{-2}$.

33. $f'(x) = -2x^{-3}$. **35.** $h = 0.000001$.

37.

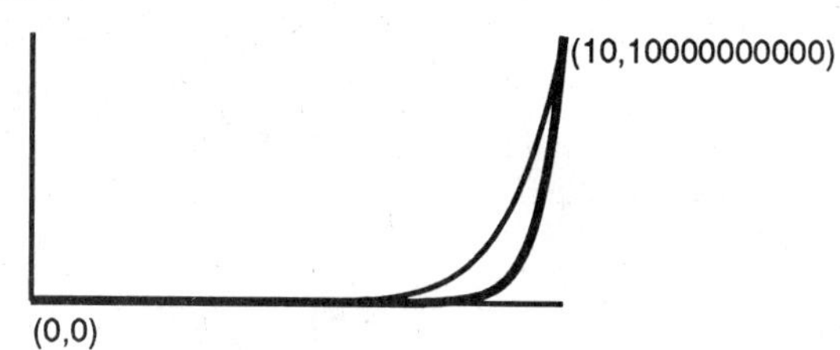

39. $f'(x) = 10^x \ln(10)$, $g'(x) = 10x^9$.

Section 3.5

1. $\Delta V = 16884\pi$ in^3,

$\frac{\Delta V}{\Delta r} = 5628\pi$ in^3 per in.

3. $\Delta V = \frac{4}{3}\pi(3r^2\Delta r + 3r(\Delta r)^2 + (\Delta r)^3)$,

$\frac{\Delta V}{\Delta r} = \frac{4}{3}\pi(3r^2 + 3r(\Delta r) + (\Delta r)^2)$.

5. $\frac{dV}{dr} = 4\pi r^2$.

Both calculations are the same.

7. $\frac{dP}{dx} = 4$; $\left.\frac{dP}{dx}\right|_{x=5} = 4$ cm per cm.

9. $\frac{dy}{dx} = \sqrt{2}$; $\left.\frac{dy}{dx}\right|_{x=5} = \sqrt{2}$ cm per cm

and $\left.\frac{dy}{dx}\right|_{x=3.6} = \sqrt{2}$ cm per cm.

11. $\frac{dz}{dx} = \sqrt{3}$; $\left.\frac{dz}{dx}\right|_{x=2} = \sqrt{3}$ mm per mm.

13. $s(0) = 15$ m.

15. $s(0.3) \approx 14.39$ m.

17. $s(0.99) \approx 8.4$ m.

19. ≈ 10.07 m/s.

21. ≈ -3.97 m/s.

23. $v(0.3) = -4.0374$ m/s.

25. $v(1.49) \approx -20.05$ m/s.

27. $\frac{dv}{dt} = -13.458t$ m/s^2.

29. $c = 12\pi - 6\theta$, $\frac{dc}{d\theta} = -6$,

$\left.\frac{dc}{d\theta}\right|_{\theta=\pi/3} = -6$ in per radian.

Section 3.6

1. $\frac{dy}{dx} = (3x^2 + 6x)(2x^2 + 8x - 5)$
$+(x^3 + 3x^2 + 1)(4x + 8)$.

3. $\frac{dx}{dy} = (5y^4 - 6y^2)(7y^2 + y - 8)$
$+(y^5 - 2y^3)(14y + 1)$.

5. $\frac{dy}{dw} = 2w - 4$.

7. $\frac{dy}{dx} = 2x(3x^3 - x + 1) + (x^2 - 6)(9x^2 - 1)$.

9. $\frac{dy}{dz} = (2z^3 - 5z + 1)(6z^2 + 7)$
$+z((6z^2 - 5)(6z^2 + 7) + (2z^3 - 5z + 1)(12z))$.

11. $\frac{ds}{dt} = 2t - 2t^{-3}$.

13. $\frac{dy}{dx} = -x^{-2} - 2x^{-3} - 3x^{-4}$.

15. $\frac{ds}{dt} = 6t^5 - 6t^{-7}$.

17. $\frac{dT}{dv} = -v^{-2} + 4v^{-3}$.

19. $\frac{dy}{dx} = -2x^{-2} + x^{-4}$.

21. $\frac{dy}{dx} = \frac{4x^2 + 14x - 5}{(4x^2 + 5)^2}$.

23. $\frac{ds}{dt} = \frac{-8t^2 - 30t + 54}{(t^2 - 2t + 3)^2}$.

25. $\frac{dy}{dx} = \frac{-3x + 2}{x^3}$.

27. $\frac{dy}{dx} = \frac{62x}{(2x^2 + 7)^2}$.

29. $\frac{dy}{dx} = \frac{1}{(x + 1)^2}$.

31. $f'(x) = \frac{2^x \ln(2/5) + 3^x \ln(3/5)}{5^x}$.

33. $f'(x) = -\csc^2(x)$.

35. $f'(x) = 2\cos(x) + 7\sin(x)$.

37. $f'(x) = 0$ for $x \neq \frac{n\pi}{2}$, n an integer.

39. $f'(x) = \frac{1}{2}(e^x - e^{-x}) = \sinh(x)$.

Section 3.7

1. $F'(3) = -3.55$.
3. $F'(2) = 6$.
5. $F'(6) = 18$.
7. $F'(1) = 6.5$.
9. $F'(2) = 684$.
11. $F'(3) = 7.5$.
13. $F'(2) = 4.8$.
15. $F'(2) = 36.4$.
17. $F'(4) = -40$.
19. $F'(2) = -0.3e^2$.
21. $F'(4) = 1$.
23. $F'(1)$ is undefined.
25. $F'(3) = -3$.
27. $F'(-2) = -4$.
29. $F'(-3) = 0$.
31. $f'(27) = 0.\overline{037}$.
33. $k'(\sqrt{\pi}) = -2\sqrt{\pi} \approx -3.54$.
35. $f'(\pi/6) = -\sqrt{3}/2 \approx -0.8660$.
37. $\left.\dfrac{d(x^{-5})}{dx}\right|_{x=1} = -5$.
39. $f'(2) = -0.04$.
41. $f'(x) = (2x-1)(x^2+2x-8) + (x^2-x-2)(2x+2)$.
43. $f'(x) = (12x^2+2)(8-9x^3) + (4x^3+2x-5)(-27x^2)$.
45. $f'(x) = 4(x^2-6x+5)^3(2x-6)$.
47. $f'(x) = -\sin(x^2-3x+4)(2x-3)$.
49. $f'(x) = \sec(x^2+6x+8)\cdot \tan(x^2+6x+8)\cdot(2x+6)$.
51. $f'(x) = \dfrac{2(4x+3)}{3(2x^2+3x-2)^{1/3}}$.
53. $f'(x) = \dfrac{-x^3+55x+150}{(x^2+6x+5)^2(x^2-25)^{1/2}}$.
55. $\dfrac{d}{dx}((x^2+1)^4) = 8x(x^2+1)^3$.
57. $\dfrac{d}{dx}(\sqrt[3]{5x^2-17x}) = \dfrac{1}{3}(5x^2-17x)^{-2/3}(10x-17)$.
59. $\dfrac{d}{dx}(\sin(\sin(x)) = \cos(\sin(x))\cos(x)$.
61. $f(x) = x^2$, $x_0 = 5$.
63. $f(x) = x^3$, $x_0 = -1$.
65. $f(x) = 1/\sqrt{x}$, $x_0 = 2$.
67. $\dfrac{d}{dx}(\sin(x^\circ) = \dfrac{\pi}{180}\cos(x^\circ)$.
69. The graph of $y = f(x)$ looks like the graph of the line $y = mx + b$.

Chapter 4

Section 4.1

1. $y = -4x + 5$.
$y = -4(x + \frac{4}{3}) + \frac{311}{27}$.
3. $y \approx 0.5(x - 1.728) - 4.47$.
$y \approx 0.5(x + 1.061) + 4.98$.
5. $(1, 1)$.
7. $y = 3x + 5$.
9. $y = \frac{37}{14}(x-2) + 7$.
11. $y = (4.2)(x - 1.6) + 5.16$.
$y = \frac{-1}{4.2}(x - 1.6) + 5.16$.
13. $y = 16$. $x = -2$.
15. $y = 5(x-1) + 1$.
$y = -\frac{1}{5}(x-1) + 1$.
17. $y = \frac{\sqrt{3}}{2}(x - \frac{\pi}{3}) + \dfrac{3}{4}$.
$y = -\frac{2}{\sqrt{3}}(x - \frac{\pi}{3}) + \dfrac{3}{4}$.
19. $y = 0$. $x = 0$.
21. The best linear approximation is
$g(x) = -6(x+3) + 9$.
$g(-2) = 3$, $f(-2) = 4$,
error = 1.
$g(-4) = 15$, $f(-4) = 16$,
error = 1.
$g(-2.999) = 8.994$, $f(-2.999) = 8.994001$,
error = 0.000001.
$g(-3.001) = 9.006$, $f(-3.001) = 9.006001$,
error = 0.000001.

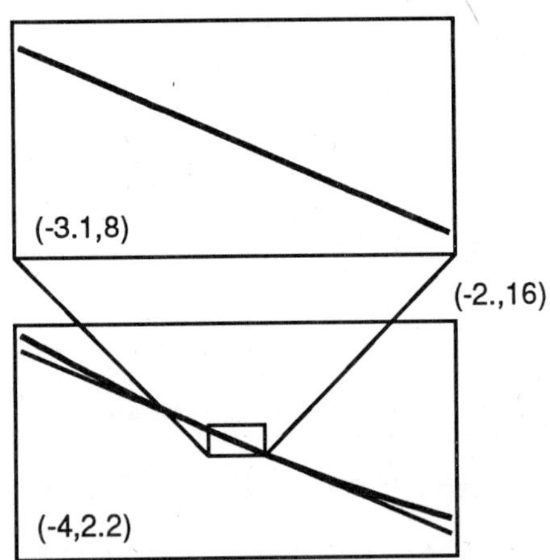

23. The best linear approximation is
$g(x) = -\frac{1}{3}(x+8) + 4$.
$g(-7) = 3.\overline{6}$, $f(-7) \approx 3.659$,

error ≈ 0.007.

$g(-9) = 4.\overline{3}$, $f(-9) \approx 4.327$,

error ≈ 0.007.

$g(-7.999) = 3.999\overline{6}$, $f(-7.999) \approx 3.9997$,

error $\approx 7 \cdot 10^{-9}$.

$g(-8.001) = 4.000\overline{3}$, $f(-8.001) \approx 4.0003$,

error $\approx 7 \cdot 10^{-9}$.

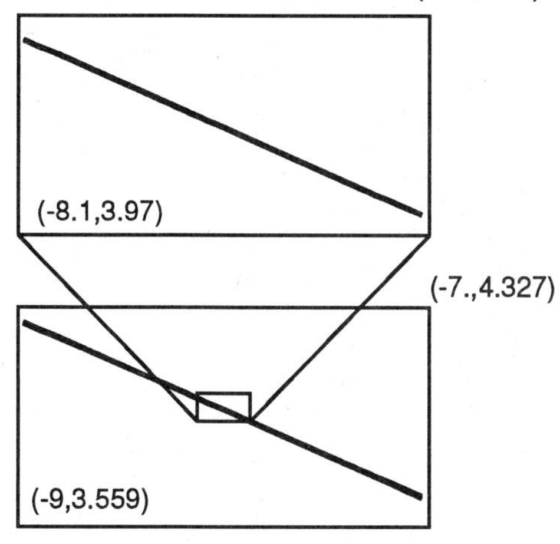

25. The best linear approximation is

$g(x) = \frac{1}{2}(x - \frac{\pi}{3}) + \frac{\sqrt{3}}{2}$.

$g(\frac{\pi}{3} + 1) \approx 1.366$, $f(\frac{\pi}{3} + 1) \approx 0.889$,

error ≈ 0.48.

$g(\frac{\pi}{3} - 1) \approx 0.366$, $f(\frac{\pi}{3} - 1) \approx 0.047$,

error ≈ 0.32.

$g(\frac{\pi}{3} + 0.001) \approx 0.867$, $f(\frac{\pi}{3} + 0.001) \approx 0.867$,

error $\approx 4 \cdot 10^{-7}$.

$g(\frac{\pi}{3} - 0.001) \approx 0.866$, $f(\frac{\pi}{3} - 0.001) \approx 0.866$,

error $\approx 4 \cdot 10^{-7}$.

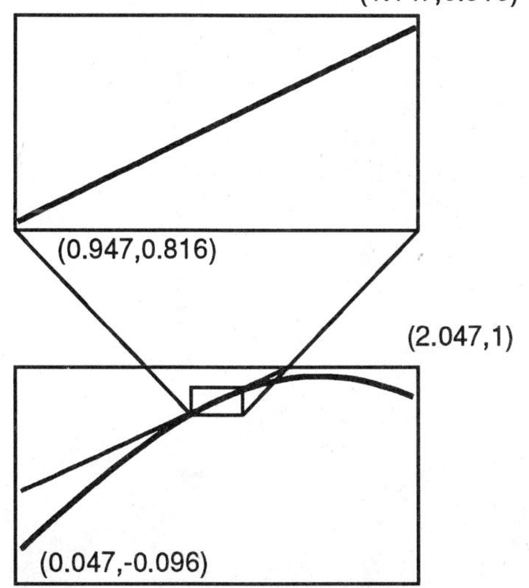

27. The best linear approximation is

$g(x) = 2(x - \frac{\pi}{4}) + 1$.

$g(\frac{\pi}{4} + 1) = 3$, $f(\frac{\pi}{4} + 1) \approx -4.588$,

error ≈ 7.59.

$g(\frac{\pi}{4} - 1) = -1$, $f(\frac{\pi}{4} - 1) \approx -0.218$,

error ≈ 0.78.

$g(\frac{\pi}{4} + 0.001) = 1.002$, $f(\frac{\pi}{4} + 0.001) \approx 1.002$,

error $\approx 2 \cdot 10^{-6}$.

$g(\frac{\pi}{4} - 0.001) = 0.998$, $f(\frac{\pi}{4} - 0.001) \approx 0.998$,

error $\approx 2 \cdot 10^{-6}$.

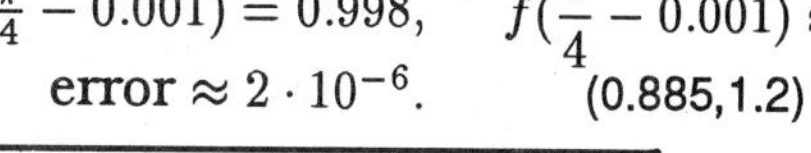

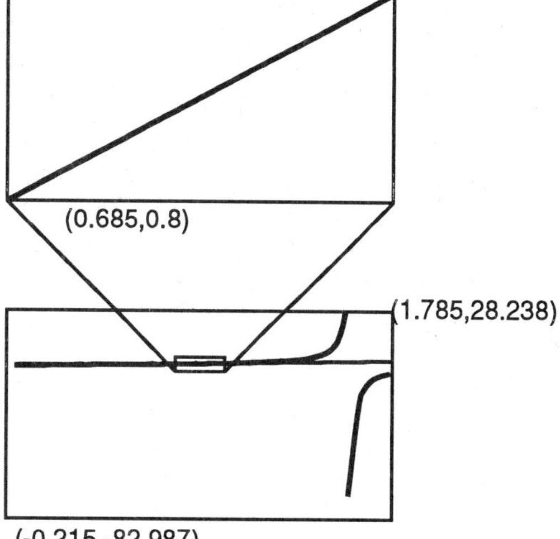

29. The best linear approximation is $g(x) = x$.

$g(1) = 1$, $f(1) = 1$,

no error.

$g(-1) = -1$, $f(-1) = -1$,

no error.

$g(0.001) = 0.001$, $f(0.001) = 0.001$,

no error.

$g(-0.001) = -0.001$, $f(-0.001) = -0.001$,

no error.

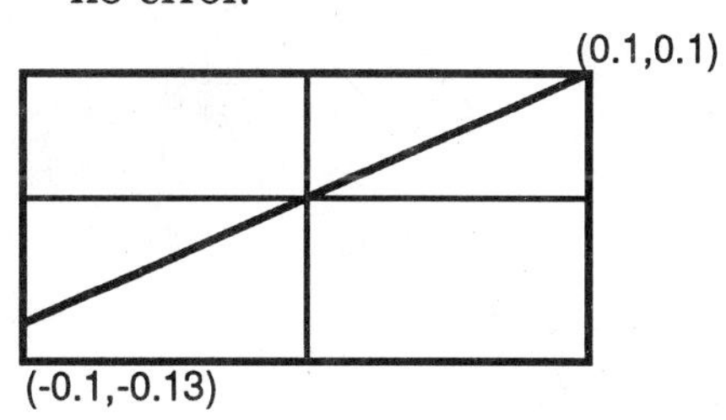

33. $y = \frac{2}{3}(x+3) + 2.25, y = 2(x+1) + 0.25,$
$x = 0, \quad y = -(x-2) + 1, \quad y = -\frac{1}{2}(x-4) + 4.$

35.

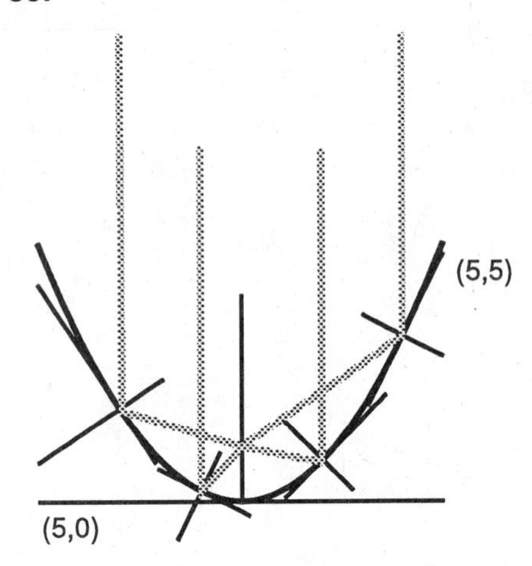

37. $\dfrac{dy}{dx} = \dfrac{x}{2}$, so $\left.\dfrac{dy}{dx}\right|_{x=a} = \dfrac{a}{2}$.

Slope of normal line is $-\dfrac{2}{a}$.

39. Let $y = \left(\dfrac{a^2-4}{4a}\right)(x-a) + \dfrac{a^2}{4}$.

Then $y(0) = -\dfrac{a^2-4}{4} + \dfrac{a^2}{4} = 1.$

Section 4.2

Iterations computed with Newton's method have been rounded to 12 significant digits.

1. $x_0 = 1.5,$ $x_1 = 1.81\overline{6},$
$x_2 = 1.78906727829,$ $x_3 = 1.78885439467,$
$x_4 = 1.788854382,$ $x_5 = 1.788854382.$

3. $x_0 = 0.75,$ $x_1 = 0.775094327327,$
$x_2 = 0.775397451588,$ $x_3 = 0.775397496611,$
$x_4 = 0.775397496611,$ $x_5 = 0.775397496611.$

5. $x_0 = 2.2,$ $x_1 = 2.21505715284,$
$x_2 = 2.21504353349,$ $x_3 = 2.21504353348,$
$x_4 = 2.21504353348,$ $x_5 = 2.21504353348.$

7. $x_0 = 0.9875,$ $x_1 = 0.99978835581,$
$x_2 = 0.99999994026,$ $x_3 = 1,$
$x_4 = 1,$ $x_5 = 1.$

9. $x_0 = 1.65,$ $x_1 = 1.51165749229,$
$x_2 = 1.4959954604,$ $x_3 = 1.49579050291,$
$x_4 = 1.49579046793,$ $x_5 = 1.49579046793.$

11. $x = 7.$

13. Any value $0 < b < \frac{2}{7}$ will do.

15. Any value $b > 0.44.$

17. Most values $0.368 < b < 0.44$ produce chaotic behavior (see illustration).

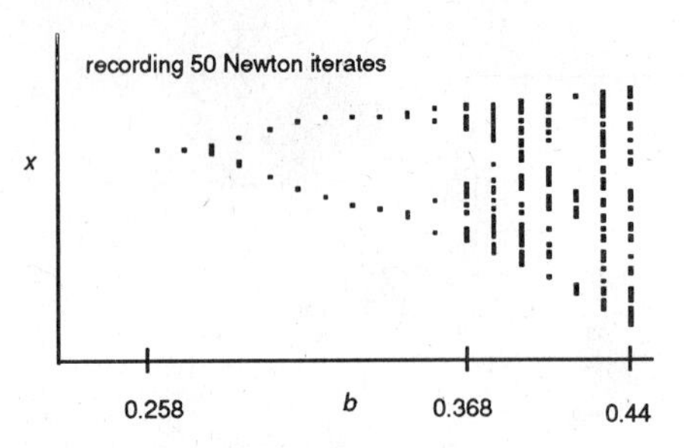

19. $x = 2.02875783811,$
$x = 4.91318043943,$ $x = 7.97866571241.$

21. $x_0 = 1/2.$

23. $1.61803398875,$ $5.$

25. $x_0 = \frac{1}{1},$ $x_1 = \frac{2}{1},$
$x_2 = \frac{3}{2},$ $x_3 = \frac{34}{21},$
$x_4 = \frac{1597}{987},$ $x_5 = \frac{514229}{317811}.$

Section 4.3

1. a)

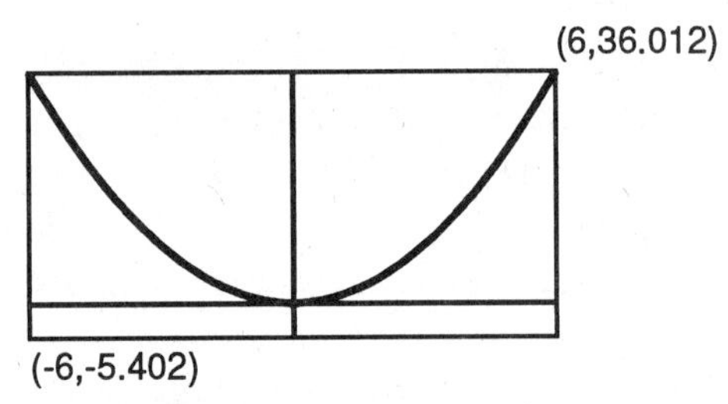

b) Increasing over $(0, 6)$; decreasing over $(-6, 0)$.

c) $f'(x) = 2x.$

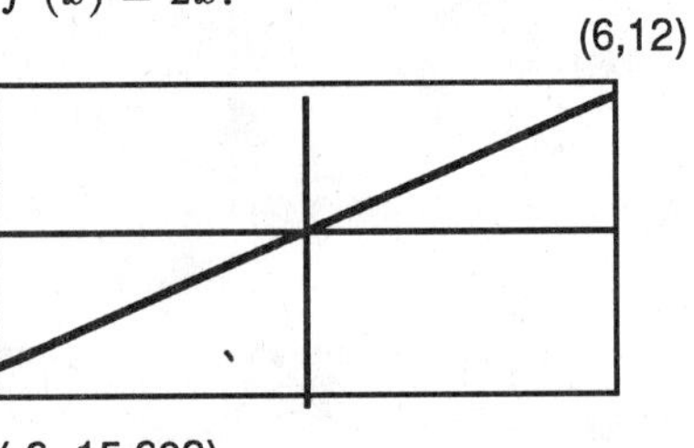

d) Positive over $(0, 6)$; negative over $(-6, 0)$.

e) $x = 0$

f) local minimum at $x = 0.$

3. a)

(6,3.302)

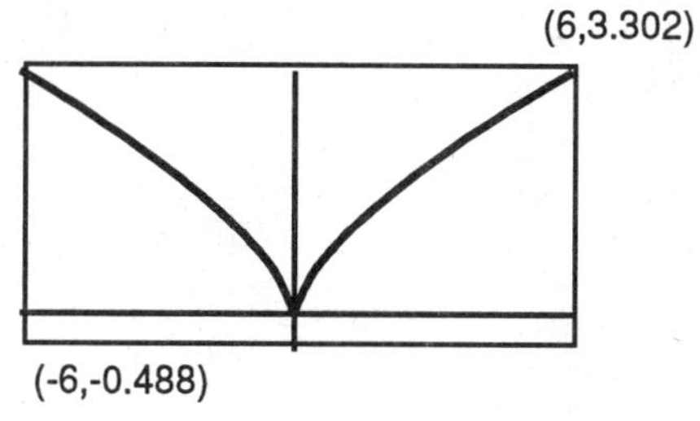

(-6,-0.488)

b) Increasing over $(0,6)$;
decreasing over $(-6,0)$.

c) $f'(x) = \frac{2}{3}x^{-1/3}$.

(6,4.373)

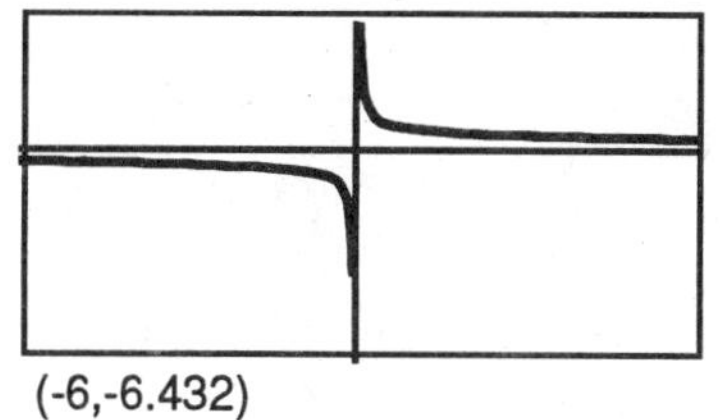

(-6,-6.432)

d) Positive over $(0,6)$;
negative over $(-6,0)$.

e) $x = 0$

f) local minimum at $x = 0$.

5. a)

(6,0.997)

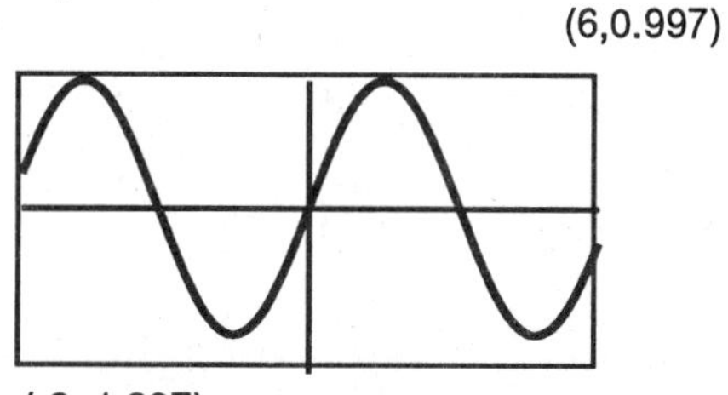

(-6,-1.297)

b) Increasing over $(-6,-\frac{3\pi}{2})$,
$(-\frac{\pi}{2},\frac{\pi}{2})$, and $(\frac{3\pi}{2},6)$.
Decreasing over $(-\frac{3\pi}{2},-\frac{\pi}{2})$ and $(\frac{\pi}{2},\frac{3\pi}{2})$.

c) $f'(x) = \cos x$.

(6,1.000)

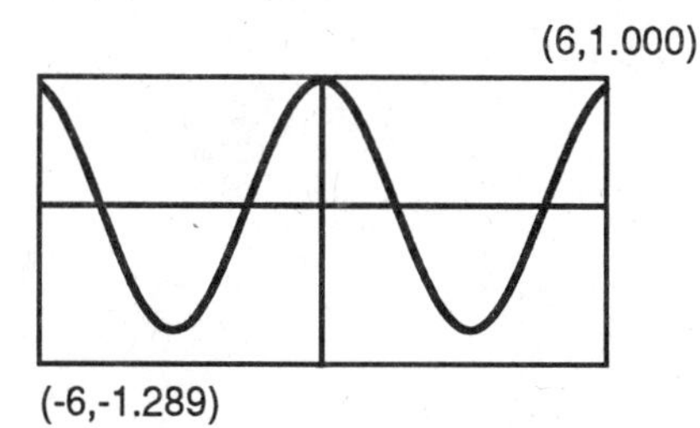

(-6,-1.289)

d) Positive over $(-6,-\frac{3\pi}{2})$,
$(-\frac{\pi}{2},\frac{\pi}{2})$, and $(\frac{3\pi}{2},6)$.
Negative over $(-\frac{3\pi}{2},-\frac{\pi}{2})$ and $(\frac{\pi}{2},\frac{3\pi}{2})$.

e) $x = -\frac{3\pi}{2}$, $x = -\frac{\pi}{2}$,
$x = \frac{\pi}{2}$, $x = \frac{3\pi}{2}$.

f) Local maxima at $x = -\frac{3\pi}{2}$, $x = \frac{\pi}{2}$.
Local minima at $x = \frac{3\pi}{2}$, $x = -\frac{\pi}{2}$.

7. a)

(6,14.027)

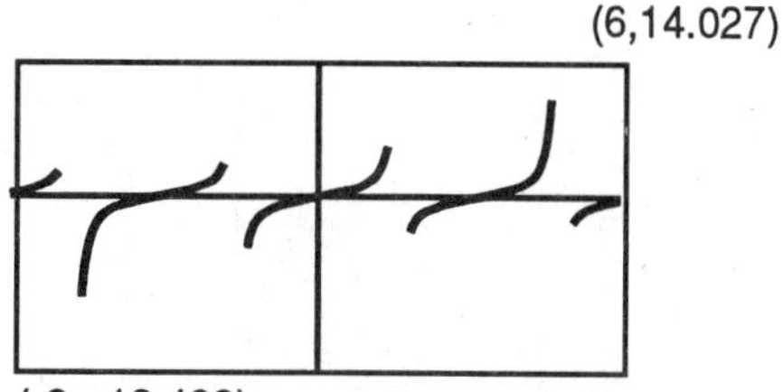

(-6.,-18.466)

b) Increasing over $(-6,-\frac{3\pi}{2})$, $(-\frac{3\pi}{2},-\frac{\pi}{2})$,
$(-\frac{\pi}{2},\frac{\pi}{2})$, $(\frac{\pi}{2},\frac{3\pi}{2})$, and $(\frac{3\pi}{2},6)$.

c) $f'(x) = \sec^2 x$.

(6,100)

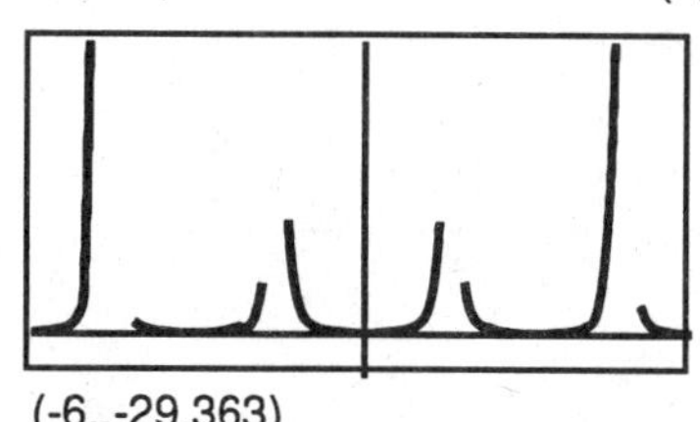

(-6.,-29.363)

d) Positive over same intervals listed in part b).

e) None.

f) See part e).

9. a)

(6,1.431)

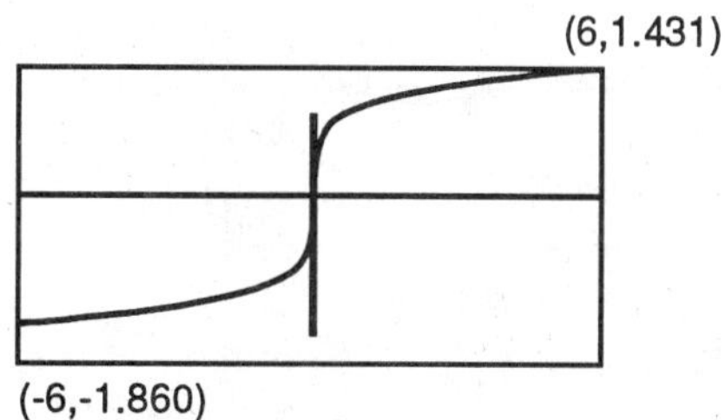

(-6,-1.860)

b) Increasing over $(-6,0)$ and $(0,6)$.

c) $f'(x) = \frac{1}{5}x^{-4/5}$.

(6,87.469)

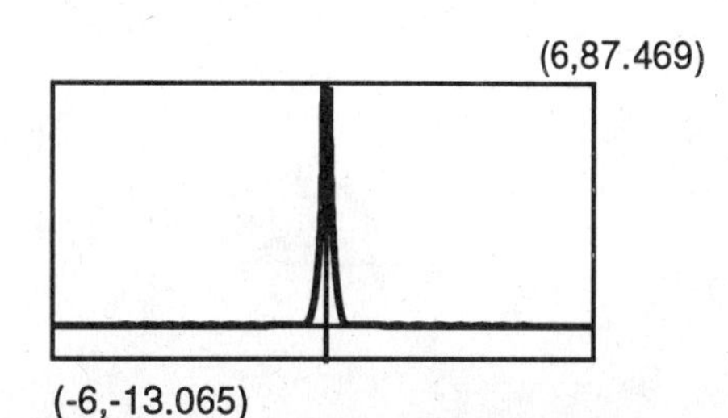

(-6,-13.065)

d) Positive over $(-6,0)$, and $(0,6)$.

e) $x = 0$
f) Neither.

11. a)

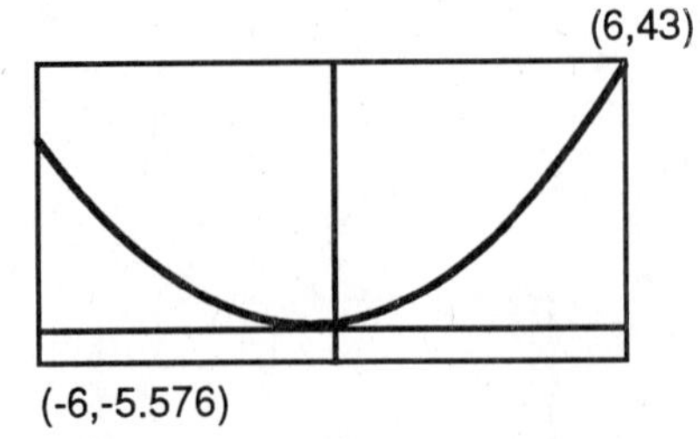

b) Increasing over $(-\frac{1}{2}, 6)$.
Decreasing over $(-6, -\frac{1}{2})$.
c) $f'(x) = 2x + 1$.

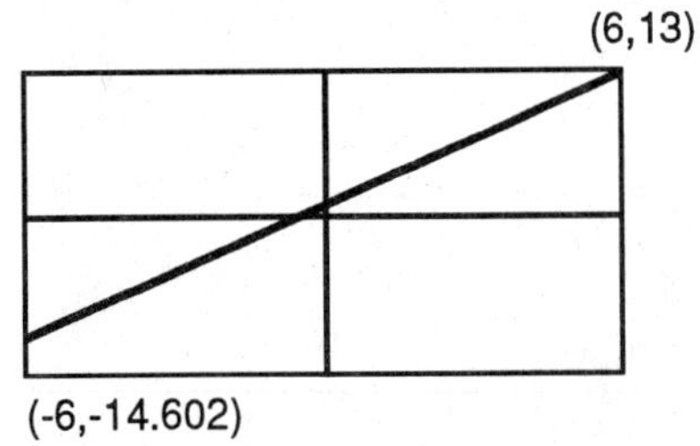

d) Positive over $(-\frac{1}{2}, 6)$.
Negative over $(-6, -\frac{1}{2})$.
e) $x = -\frac{1}{2}$.
f) Local minimum.

13. a)

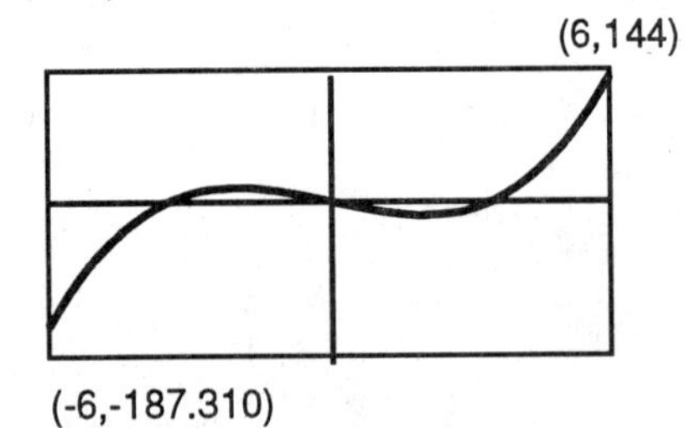

b) Increasing over $(-6, -2)$, $(2, 6)$.
Decreasing over $(-2, 2)$.
c) $f'(x) = 3x^2 - 12$.

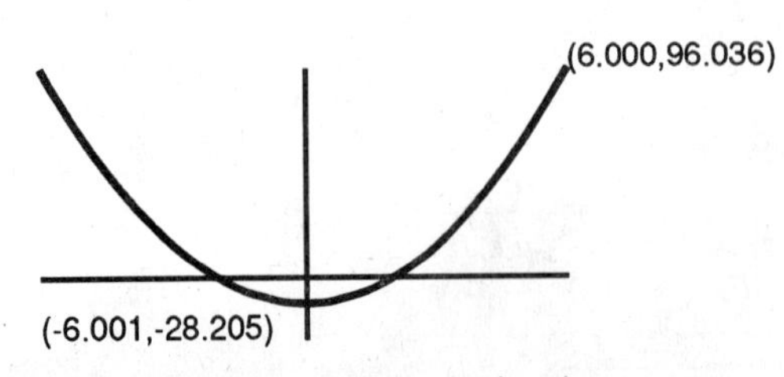

d) Positive over $(-6, -2)$, $(2, 6)$.
Negative over $(-2, 2)$.
e) $x = 2$, $x = -2$.
f) $x = 2$ represents a local minimum.
$x = -2$ represents a local maximum.

15. a)

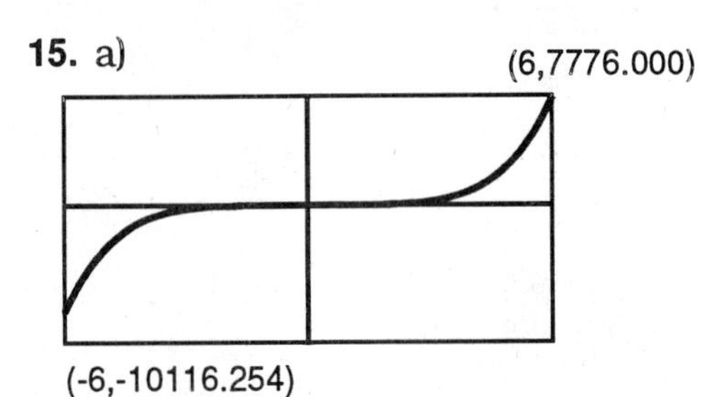

b) Increasing over $(-6, 0)$, $(0, 6)$.
c) $f'(x) = 5x^4$.

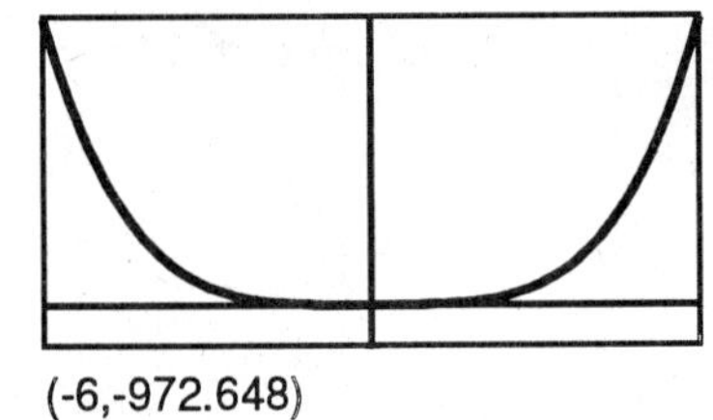

d) Positive over $(-6, 0)$, $(0, 6)$.
e) $x = 0$.
f) Neither.

17. a)

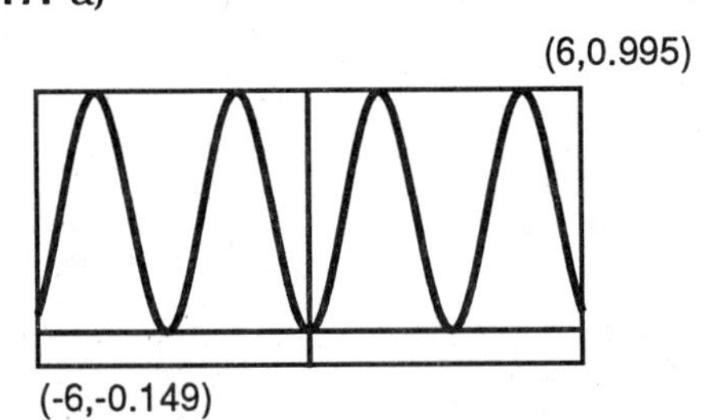

b) Increasing over
$(-6, -\frac{3\pi}{2})$, $(-\pi, -\frac{\pi}{2})$, $(0, \frac{\pi}{2})$, $(\pi, \frac{3\pi}{2})$.
Decreasing over
$(-\frac{3\pi}{2}, -\pi)$, $(-\frac{\pi}{2}, 0)$, $(\frac{\pi}{2}, \pi)$, $(\frac{3\pi}{2}, 6)$.
c) $f'(x) = 2 \sin x \cos x$.

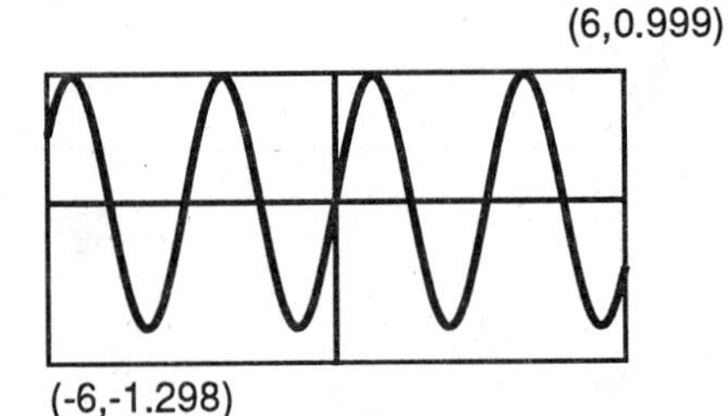

d) Positive over
$(-6,-\frac{3\pi}{2}),\quad(-\pi,-\frac{\pi}{2}),\quad(0,\frac{\pi}{2}),\quad(\pi,\frac{3\pi}{2})$.
Negative over
$(-\frac{3\pi}{2},-\pi),\quad(-\frac{\pi}{2},0),\quad(\frac{\pi}{2},\pi),\quad(\frac{3\pi}{2},6)$.
e) $x=-\frac{3\pi}{2},\quad x=-\pi,\quad x=-\frac{\pi}{2},$
$x=0,\quad x=\frac{\pi}{2},\quad x=\pi,\quad x=\frac{3\pi}{2}$.
f) $x=-\frac{3\pi}{2},\quad x=-\frac{\pi}{2},\quad x=\frac{\pi}{2},\quad x=\frac{3\pi}{2}$
represent local maxima.
$x=-\pi,\quad x=0,\quad x=\pi$
represent local minima.

19. a)

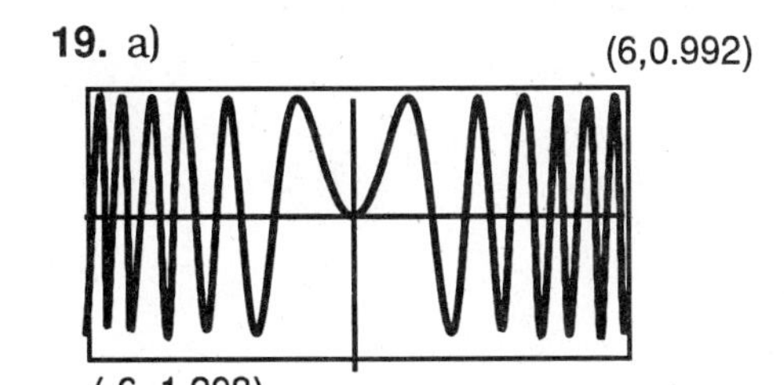

b) Increasing over these intervals:

$(-6,-\sqrt{\frac{21\pi}{2}})$, $(-\sqrt{\frac{19\pi}{2}},-\sqrt{\frac{17\pi}{2}})$,
$(-\sqrt{\frac{15\pi}{2}},-\sqrt{\frac{13\pi}{2}})$, $(-\sqrt{\frac{11\pi}{2}},-\sqrt{\frac{9\pi}{2}})$,
$(-\sqrt{\frac{7\pi}{2}},-\sqrt{\frac{5\pi}{2}})$, $(-\sqrt{\frac{3\pi}{2}},-\sqrt{\frac{\pi}{2}})$,
$(0,\sqrt{\frac{\pi}{2}})$, $(\sqrt{\frac{3\pi}{2}},\sqrt{\frac{5\pi}{2}})$,
$(\sqrt{\frac{7\pi}{2}},\sqrt{\frac{9\pi}{2}})$, $(\sqrt{\frac{11\pi}{2}},\sqrt{\frac{13\pi}{2}})$,
$(\sqrt{\frac{15\pi}{2}},\sqrt{\frac{17\pi}{2}})$, $(\sqrt{\frac{19\pi}{2}},\sqrt{\frac{21\pi}{2}})$.

Decreasing over the following intervals:

$(-\sqrt{\frac{21\pi}{2}},-\sqrt{\frac{19\pi}{2}})$, $(-\sqrt{\frac{17\pi}{2}},-\sqrt{\frac{15\pi}{2}})$,
$(-\sqrt{\frac{13\pi}{2}},-\sqrt{\frac{11\pi}{2}})$, $(-\sqrt{\frac{9\pi}{2}},-\sqrt{\frac{7\pi}{2}})$,
$(-\sqrt{\frac{5\pi}{2}},-\sqrt{\frac{3\pi}{2}})$, $(-\sqrt{\frac{\pi}{2}},0)$,
$(\sqrt{\frac{\pi}{2}},\sqrt{\frac{3\pi}{2}})$, $(\sqrt{\frac{5\pi}{2}}),\sqrt{\frac{7\pi}{2}})$,
$(\sqrt{\frac{9\pi}{2}},\sqrt{\frac{11\pi}{2}})$, $(\sqrt{\frac{13\pi}{2}},\sqrt{\frac{15\pi}{2}})$,
$(\sqrt{\frac{17\pi}{2}},\sqrt{\frac{19\pi}{2}})$, $(\sqrt{\frac{21\pi}{2}},6)$.

c) $f'(x)=2x\cos(x^2)$.

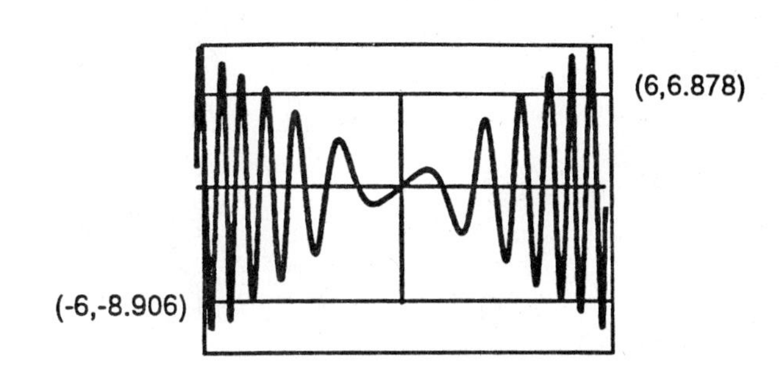

d) Positive over the intervals in part b) where f is increasing; negative over those intervals in part b) where f is decreasing.

e) $x=0$ and $x=\pm\sqrt{\frac{n\pi}{2}}$, where n is an odd integer and $1\le n\le 21$.

f) $x=\pm\sqrt{\frac{n\pi}{2}}$, where $n=1, 5, 9, 13, 17, 21$ represent local maxima.

$x=\pm\sqrt{\frac{n\pi}{2}}$, where $n=0, 3, 7, 11, 15, 19$ represent local minima.

21. Local maxima.
23. Neither.

25. It is a rate of change of arrival time in seconds per feet.
27.

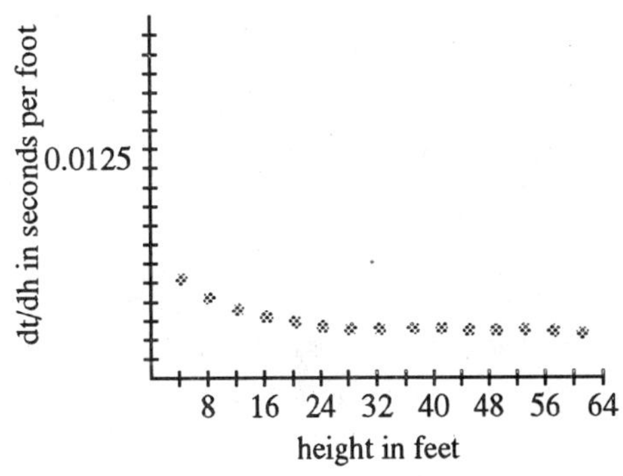

It is asymptotically decreasing;

$$\frac{\sqrt{\frac{h+4}{16}}-\sqrt{\frac{h}{16}}}{4}.$$

29. Approximately June 15.

31. Points of maximum positive and negative rates of change, respectively.
33. Lowest at $t=0$; highest at $t=6.4$.

35. Rising over $(0,2)$, $(4.8, 6.4)$; falling over $(2, 4.8)$.

37. $(6.0, 6.4)$.

39.

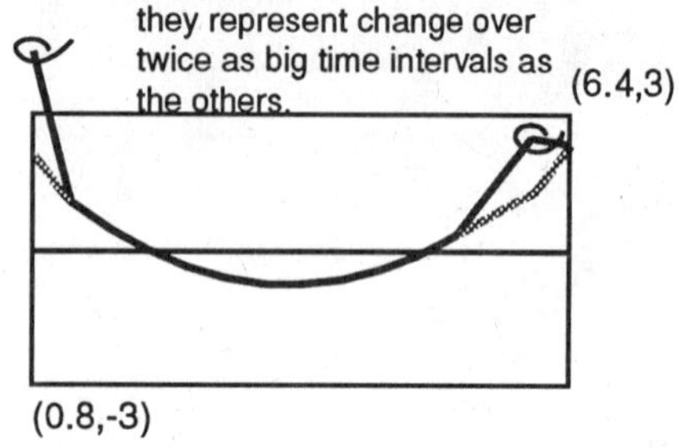

Section 4.4

1. Local maximum at $x = -1/\sqrt{3}$; local minimum at $x = 1/\sqrt{3}$.

3. No critical values.

5. No critical values.

7. Local maxima occur at $x = n\pi$, n an odd integer; local minima occur at $x = n\pi$, n an even integer.

9. Local minimum at $x = 3/2$.

11. $f(1) = 4$ is the abs. max.; $f(-0.75) = -2.125$ is the abs. min.

13. $f(1) = 2$ is the abs. max.; $f(2) = -4$ is the abs. min.

15. $f(0.75) = 0.125$ is the abs. max.; $f(4) = -21$ is the abs. min.

17. $s(0) = 64000$ ft is max. height; $s(60) = 6400$ ft is min. height.

19. $s(0) = 90$ ft is max. height; $s(\sqrt{2700}) = 0$ ft is min. height.

21. Local minimum at $x = 3$.

23. Local maximum at $x = -2$; local minimum at $x = 4$.

25. Local maximum at $x \approx -2/3$; local minimum at $x \approx 11/4$.

27. Critical value at $x = 0$ which is neither a maximum nor a minimum.

Section 4.5

1. $A = \pi h\sqrt{100 - h^2} + \frac{\pi}{2}(100 - h^2)$; Domain $D = (0, 10)$.

3. $V = 72h - \dfrac{h^3}{2}$; Domain $D = (0, 12)$.

5. $V = \dfrac{4\pi r^4}{r^2 - 36}$; Domain $D = (6, \infty)$.

7. $A = \dfrac{16(1 + \sin(\theta/2))^2}{\sin(\theta/2)\cos(\theta/2)}$; Domain $D = (0, \pi)$.

9. $\ell = 24$.

11. ≈ 254 cm^2.

13. ≈ 333 ft^3.

15. ≈ 1810 m^3.

17. ≈ 83 cm^2.

19. 24 in.

Section 4.6

1. See graph for a) and b).

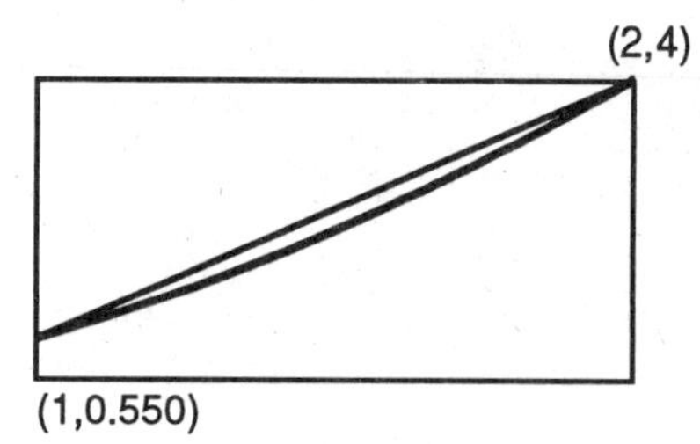

c) $x = 3/2$.

3. See graph for a) and b).

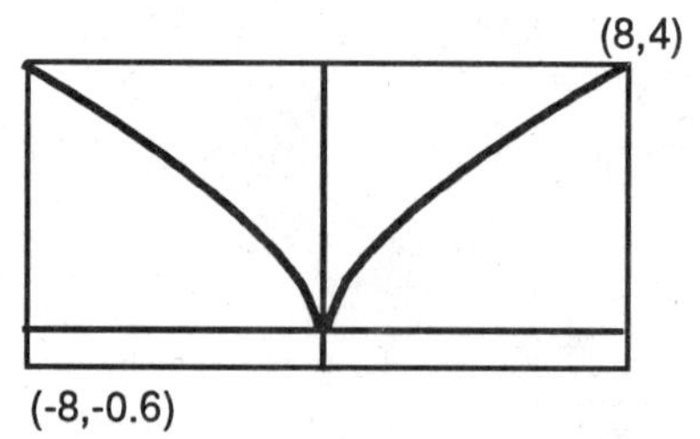

c) None, hypothesis 2 violated.

5. See graph for a) and b).

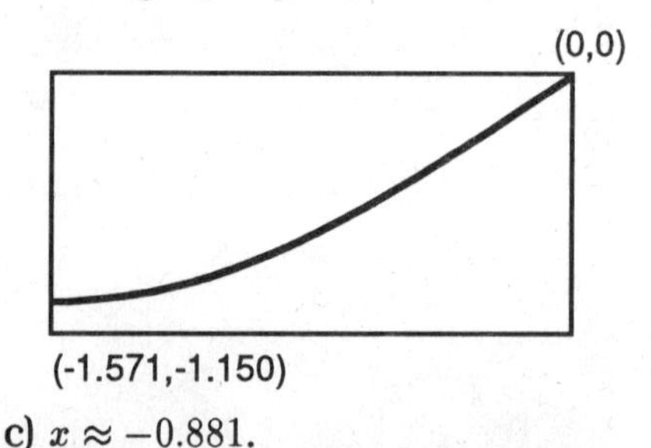

c) $x \approx -0.881$.

7. See graph for a) and b).

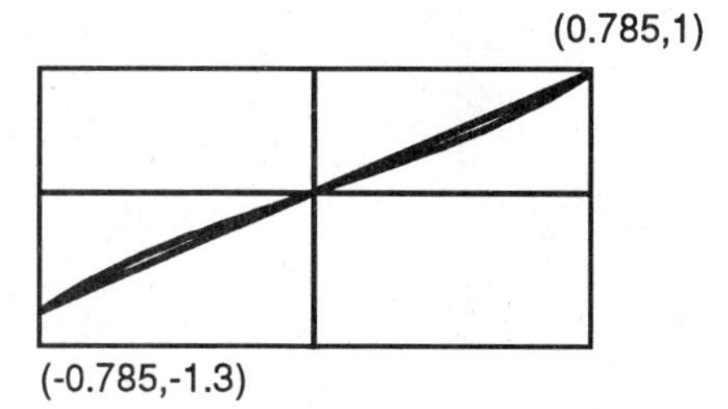

c) $x \approx \pm 0.48$.

9. See graph for a) and b).

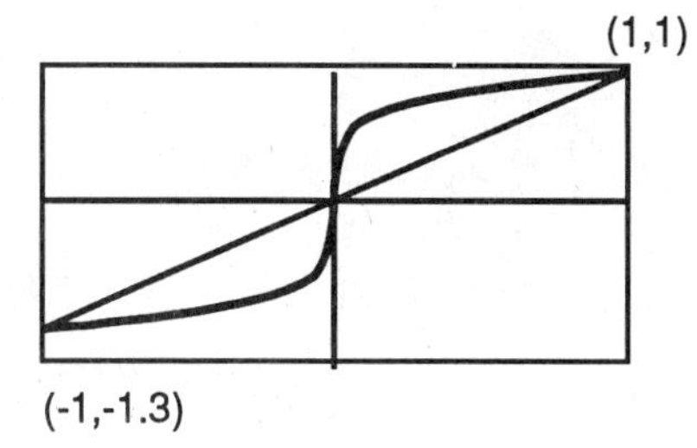

c) $x \approx \pm 0.13$ (hypothesis 2 violated).

11. See graph for a) and b).

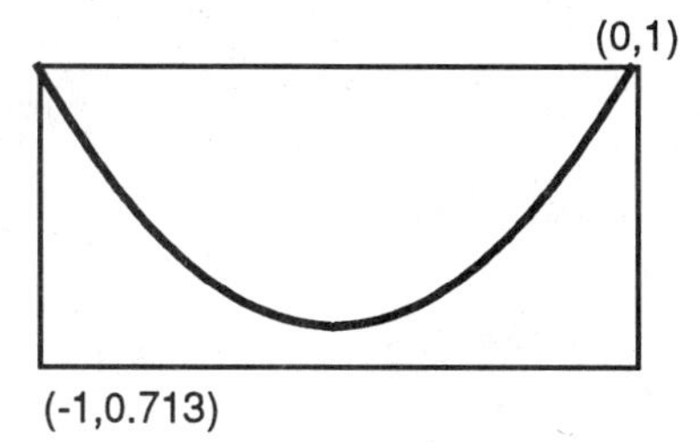

c) $x = -1/2$.

13. See graph for a) and b).

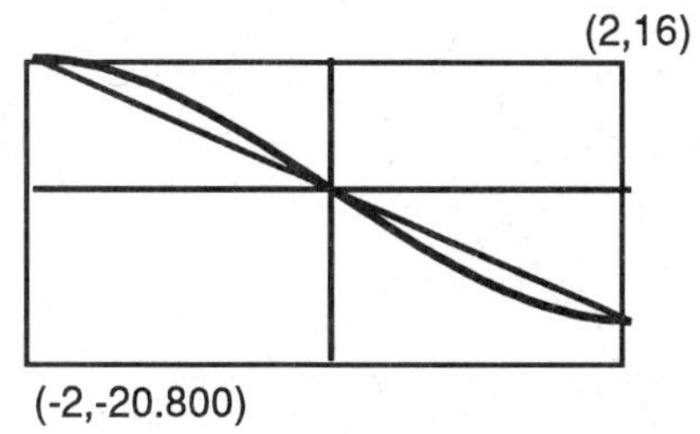

c) $x = \pm 2/\sqrt{3}$.

15. See graph for a) and b).

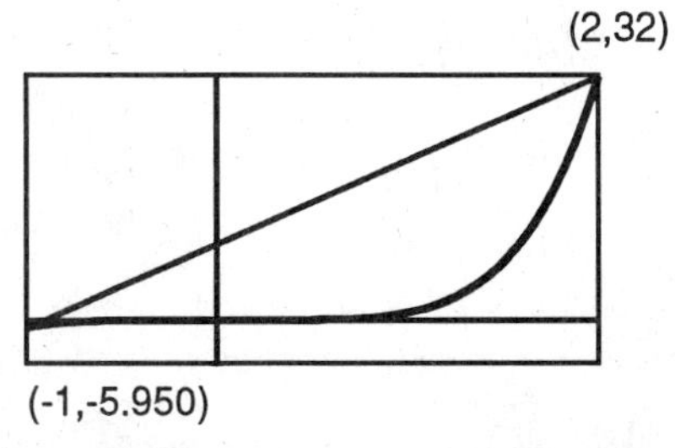

c) $x \approx 1.22$.

17. See graph for a) and b).

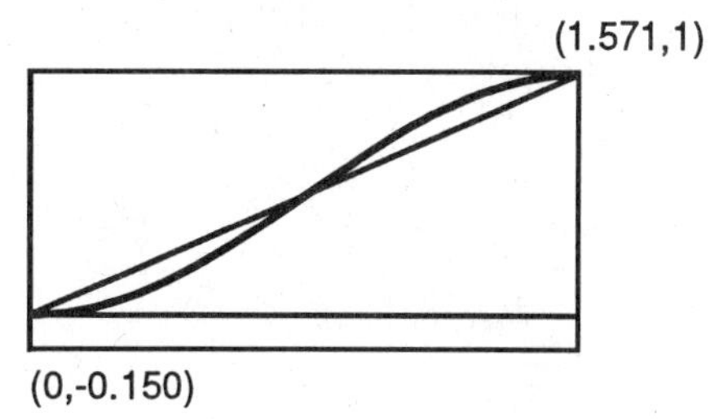

c) $x \approx 0.35$, $x \approx 1.23$.

19. See graph for a) and b).

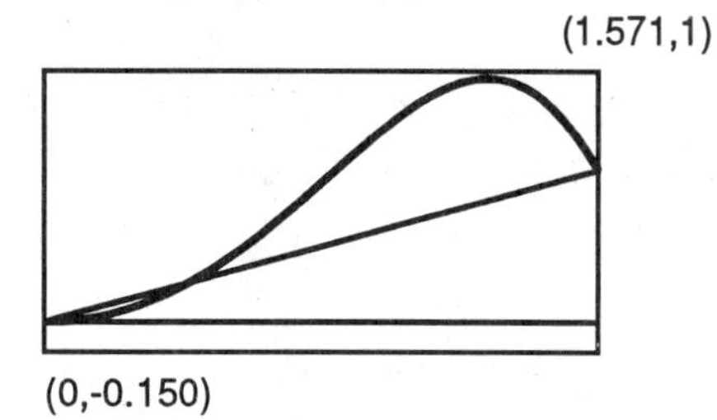

c) $x \approx 0.2$, $x \approx 1.18$.

21. $m = 1/3$ at each point.

23. $m = \frac{1}{12}$ at $x \approx -4.5,\ 1,\ 5.5$.

25. $m = \frac{2}{11}$ at no points.

27. $m = 0$ at $x = 0$.

29. 25 and 28;

hypothesis 2 is violated.

31. See graph.

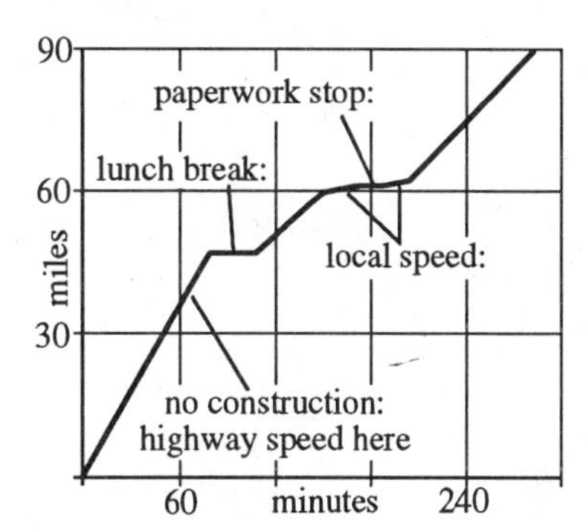

33. Yes.

35. No. He would have had to average 50 mph or more over either the first half of the trip, the second half of the trip, or both.

37. Those positions where the graph appears to be horizontal are likely to correspond to red traffic lights.

39. No, they will hit the second traffic light about half way through the light. Perhaps if they go a quarter of the speed.

Chapter 5

Section 5.1

1. 25 m × 50 m.
3. $\sqrt{\frac{50D}{3}}$ m × $500\sqrt{\frac{3}{50D}}$ m.
5. $\sqrt[3]{V}$ in × $\sqrt[3]{V}$ in × $\sqrt[3]{V}$ in.
7. $(\sqrt{\frac{24S}{T}} + 2S)$ in × $(\sqrt{\frac{24T}{S}} + 2T)$ in.
9. $2/\sqrt{\pi}$ in. **11.** $\pi/3$.
13. ≈ 3.92 cm × 3.92 cm.

15. Cut squares of size ≈ 5.66 cm × 5.66 cm from one side of length 30 cm.
17. $r = \dfrac{10}{8+\pi}$ ft for semicircle and

$\dfrac{20}{8+\pi}$ ft × $\dfrac{20}{8+\pi}$ ft for rectangle.
19. Run 2871 m ground line and 516 m underwater line.

21. For maximum area, entire wire should be made into a circle. For minimum area, use approximately 0.88 m of wire for the circle.
23. $2\pi(1 - \sqrt{2/3}) \approx 1.15$ ($\approx 66°$).

25. ≈ 22.47 ft from the light rated at 200 units.
27. $V/(2r)$.
29. Cylinder: $r = \dfrac{36}{\pi}$ in, $h = 36$ in.
31. \$320 or \$330. **33.** 6 wells.
35. 99 cookie sheets.
37. Cut squares ≈ 2.44 in × 2.44 in from one side of length 12 in.
39. $(0, \infty)$; 5 × 20 × 2,
2 × 8 × 12.5, 1 × 4 × 50.
41. $C = (2.88)x^2 + \dfrac{145}{x}$.

43. ≈ 72.86 cents.

45. The new strategy should be to cut the side of the can so that the height is 12.5 cm and then cut the top and bottom each with a diameter of 6.77 cm from a sheet which is approximately 10.38 cm by 12.5 cm. The cost is approximately 6.45 cents more per can than with the strategy from exercise 44.
47. $\approx 25.75°$, ≈ 15.1 in^2.
49. ≈ 0.14 radians.

Section 5.2

1. $y = \dfrac{1}{x^2}$, $y = 2^x$,
$y = 3^{-x}$, $y = e^{-x^2}$.

3. $y = \sqrt{x}$, $y = 2^x$,
$y = \arcsin(x)$, $y = \arctan(x)$,
$y = \ln(x)$, $y = \log_{10}(x)$.

5. $y = \dfrac{1}{x^2}$, $y = \log_{1/2}(x)$,
$y = 2^x$, $y = 3^{-x}$.

7. $y = \arcsin(x)$, $y = \arccos(x)$,
$y = \arctan(x)$.
9. $y = \sqrt{x}$. **11.** All but $y = x$.
13. $y = -x^4$, $y = x^{5/3}$,
$y = x^{4/3}$, $y = x^4$,
$y = x^3$, $y = x^{7/3}$.
15. $y = x^{2/3}$.
17. $y = x$, $y = |x|$,
$y = -x^4$, $y = x^4$.
19. $y = x^{5/3}$, $y = x^{4/3}$.
21. None; concave up over $(-6, 6)$.
23. $x = -4$, $x = 1/2$;
concave up over $(-6, -4)$ and $(1/2, 6)$;
concave down over $(-4, 1/2)$.
25. $x = 2$; concave up over $(2, 5)$,
concave down over $(-6, 2)$.
27. $x = 0$; concave up over $(0, 6)$,
concave down over $(-6, 0)$.
29. For $y = \sin(x)$ and $y = \tan(x)$:
$x = n\pi$, n any integer;
For $y = \cos(x)$ and $y = \cot(x)$:
$x = \pi + \frac{n\pi}{2}$, n any integer;
For $y = \sec(x)$ and $y = \csc(x)$: none.

31. The degree of $p'(x)$ is one less than the degree of $p(x)$, the degree of $p''(x)$ is two less than the degree of $p(x)$, and so on. The degree of $p^{(n)}(x)$ is zero, meaning that $p^{(n)}(x)$ is constant. Therefore, $p^{(n+1)}(x) = 0$ for all x.

33. $f''(x) = 2/x^3$. So $f''(x) < 0$ for $x < 0$ and $f''(x) > 0$ for $x > 0$. However, $x = 0$ is not an inflection point, because $x = 0$ is not in the domain of f.
35. a) $a(0)$ t/ s^2.

b) None.
c) $s(60) = 6400$ ft.
d) $a(t) = -32$ ft/ s^2 for $0 \le t \le 60$.
e)

37. a) $a(0) = -\frac{1}{15}$ ft/ s^2.
b) None.
c) $s(60) = 30$ ft.
d) $|a(t)| = \frac{1}{15}$ ft/ s^2 for $0 \le t \le 60$.
e)

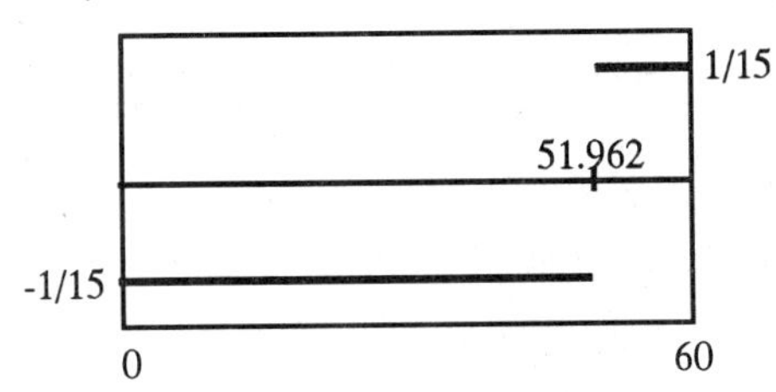

39.

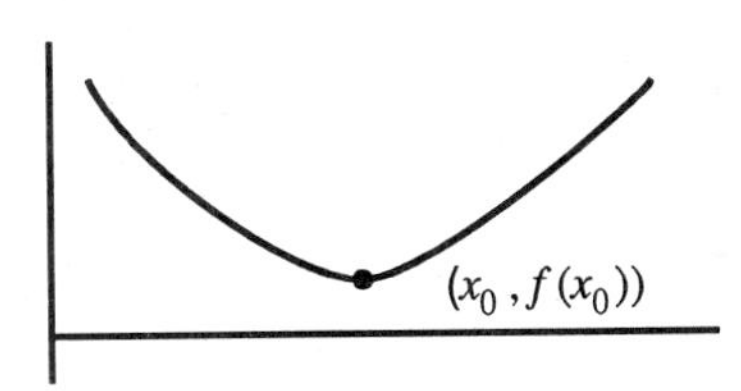

x_0 represents a local minimum.

41.

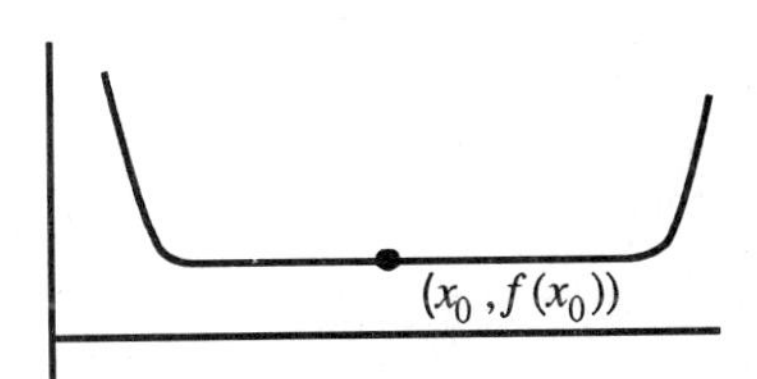

x_0 may represent an inflection point, a local maximum, or local minimum.

43. a) $x = 0, \quad x = 1$.
b) Local maximum at $x = 1$.
c) $(0, 0), \quad (\frac{2}{3}, \frac{16}{27})$.
d) Concave up over $(0, \frac{2}{3})$.
e) Concave down over $(-\infty, 0)$ and $(\frac{2}{3}, \infty)$.

45. a) $x = 0, \quad x = 3$.
b) Local maximum occurs at $x = 0$.
c) $(1, -10), \quad (3, -26)$.
d) Concave up over $(1, 3)$.
e) Concave down over $(-\infty, 1)$ and $(3, \infty)$.

47. a) $x = -1, \quad x = \frac{1}{3}$.
b) Local maximum occurs at $x = -1$.
Local minimum occurs at $x = \frac{1}{3}$.
c) $(-\frac{1}{3}, -\frac{5}{27})$.
d) Concave up over $(-\frac{1}{3}, \infty)$.
e) Concave down over $(-\infty, -\frac{1}{3})$.

49. a) $x = 0$.
b) Local maximum at $x = 0$.
c) None.
d) Concave up over $(-\infty, -2)$ and $(2, \infty)$.
e) Concave down over $(-2, 2)$.

Section 5.3

1. $\frac{dy}{dx} = -\frac{4x}{9y}$. $\quad \left.\frac{dy}{dx}\right|_{(-3/2,\sqrt{3})} = \frac{2}{3\sqrt{3}}$.
Equation of tangent line:
$y = \frac{2}{3\sqrt{3}}(x + \frac{3}{2}) + \sqrt{3}$.
Equation of normal line:
$y = -\frac{3\sqrt{3}}{2}(x + \frac{3}{2}) + \sqrt{3}$.

3. $\frac{dy}{dx} = \frac{3x^2}{2y}$. $\quad \left.\frac{dy}{dx}\right|_{(4,8)} = 3$.
Equation of tangent line:
$y = 3(x - 4) + 8$.
Equation of normal line:
$y = -\frac{1}{3}(x - 4) + 8$.

5. $\frac{dy}{dx} = -1$. $\quad \left.\frac{dy}{dx}\right|_{(1,2)} = -1$.
Equation of tangent line:
$y = -(x - 1) + 2$.
Equation of normal line:
$y = (x - 1) + 2$.

7. $\frac{dy}{dx} = \frac{-y - e^x}{e^y + x}$. $\quad \left.\frac{dy}{dx}\right|_{(0,0)} = -1$.
Equation of tangent line:
$y = -x$.
Equation of normal line:
$y = x$.

9. $\frac{dy}{dx} = \frac{-2xy}{x^2 - 3y^2}$. $\left.\frac{dy}{dx}\right|_{(-3,1)} = 1$.
Equation of tangent line:
$y = (x+3) + 1$.
Equation of normal line:
$y = -(x+3) + 1$.

11. $\frac{dy}{dx} = -\frac{y}{x}$. $\left.\frac{dy}{dx}\right|_{(2,3)} = -\frac{3}{2}$.
Equation of tangent line:
$y = -\frac{3}{2}(x-2) + 3$.
Equation of normal line:
$y = \frac{2}{3}(x-2) + 3$.

13. $\left.\frac{dy}{dx}\right|_{(0,0)}$ is undefined.

15. $\frac{d^2y}{dx^2} = 4$.

17. $\frac{dy}{dx} = -\frac{1}{\sqrt{1-x^2}}$.

19. $\frac{dy}{dx} = \frac{1}{|x|\sqrt{x^2-1}}$.

21. $(8,1)$.

23. $(-2,0)$.

25. $(5,0)$.

27. $(2,0)$ and $(-2,0)$.

29. $(0,a)$.

31. $(\pm a, 0)$.

33. $f'(x) = \frac{3e^x(\arctan(e^x))^2}{1+e^{2x}}$.

35. $f'(x) = \frac{\sec^2(\ln(\sqrt{x}))}{2x}$.

37. $f'(x) = \frac{6x - 3e^{-3x}}{3x^2 + e^{-3x}}$.

39. $f'(x) = 2x\ln(\sin(x)) + x^2\cot(x)$.

41. $f'(x) = \frac{-3x\tan(\ln x) + \sec^2(\ln x)}{xe^{3x}}$.

43. $f'(x) = \frac{-2}{\ln(2)(2+x)(2-x)}$.

45. $f'(x) = -\frac{\ln(5)}{5^x\log_3(3x+2)} - \frac{3}{5^x(\log_3(3x+2))^2(3x+2)\ln(3)}$.

Section 5.4

1. 6π cm/ s.

3. $\frac{dV}{dt} \approx 6734$ cm³/ s, $\frac{dE}{dt} \approx -33.67$.

5. $\frac{df}{dt} = 4x^3\frac{dx}{dt} + 6\cos(\theta)\frac{d\theta}{dt}$.

7. $\frac{df}{dt} = 15x^2\frac{dx}{dt} - \frac{4}{\sqrt{1-y^2}}\frac{dy}{dt}$.

9. $\frac{df}{dt} = \pi\cos(x^2\arcsin(y))\cdot$
$(2x\frac{dx}{dt}\arcsin(y) + \frac{x^2}{\sqrt{1-y^2}}\frac{dy}{dt})$.

11. ≈ 48.8 mph.

13. $\frac{4}{5\pi}$ cm/ s.

15. ≈ -0.00189 m/ min,
≈ -0.00126 m/ min,
$\frac{dh}{dt}$ is not well-defined when $h = 3$.

17. ≈ 0.254 ft/ s.

19. 25.6 min.

21. ≈ 0.2 ft/ min.

23. $\frac{5}{9}$ ft/ min.

25. $\frac{1}{5\pi}$ ft/ min.

27. $\frac{125}{6\pi}$ cm/ s.

29. ≈ 12.3 min.

31. ≈ 1.4 ft/ min.

Section 5.5

1. $\frac{dy}{dx} = \frac{3\cos(t)}{-2\sin(t)}$.
Equation of tangent line:
$y = -\frac{\sqrt{3}}{2}(x-1) + \frac{3\sqrt{3}}{2}$.
Equation of normal line:
$y = \frac{2}{\sqrt{3}}(x-1) + \frac{3\sqrt{3}}{2}$.

3. $\frac{dy}{dx} = 10 - 2t$.
Equation of tangent line:
$y = 4(x-2) + 4$.
Equation of normal line:
$y = -\frac{1}{4}(x-2) + 4$.

5. $\frac{dy}{dx} = \frac{\sin(t) + t\cos(t)}{\cos(t) - t\sin(t)}$.
Equation of tangent line ≈
$y = 0.078(x + \frac{\pi}{3}) + \frac{\pi}{\sqrt{3}}$.
Equation of normal line ≈
$y = -12.8(x + \frac{\pi}{3}) + \frac{\pi}{\sqrt{3}}$.

7. $\frac{dy}{dx} = -\frac{|5-t|}{5-t}$.
Equation of tangent line:
$y = -(x-1) + 4$.
Equation of normal line:
$y = (x-1) + 4$.

9. $\frac{dy}{dx} = \frac{\cosh(t)}{\sinh(t)}$.
Equation of tangent line ≈
$y = 1.04(x - 3.76) + 3.63$.
Equation of normal line ≈
$y = -0.96(x - 3.76) + 3.63$.

11. Negative, counterclockwise.

13. Point of collision: $(0,0)$.
Other points of intersection:
$\approx (-5.22, -1.14)$ and $\approx (6.89, 2.62)$.

15. $x = \sin(t)$, $y = t$ for $-\frac{\pi}{2} \le t \le \frac{\pi}{2}$.

17. $x = \frac{\sin(t)}{\cos(t)}$, $y = t$ for $-\frac{\pi}{2} < t < \frac{\pi}{2}$.

19. $x = \frac{1}{\sin(t)}$, $y = t$ for $-\frac{\pi}{2} < t < \frac{\pi}{2}$.

21. $x = \sin(t)$, $y = \cos(t)$ for $0 \le t < 2\pi$.

23. $x = t$, $y = -t$ for $-1 \le t \le 1$.

25. a) ≈ 27568 ft.
b) ≈ 83.02 s.
c) ≈ 95858 ft.
d) ≈ 1154.66 ft/ s, ≈ −1328.29 ft/ s.

27. a) ≈ 17101 ft.
b) ≈ 65.39 s.
c) ≈ 22226 ft.
d) ≈ 339.9 ft/ s, ≈ −1046.2 ft/ s.

29. $\theta = 0$, $\theta = \frac{\pi}{2}$.

31. No.

33. ≈ 17.4°.

35. ≈ 82 ft.

Chapter 6

Section 6.1

1. 2.5 miles.
3. 12.75 miles.
5. 5.625 miles.
7. 10.625 miles.
9. 2.25 miles.
11. 32 laps (≈ 65.3 mi).
13. ≈ 0.85 hours.
15. 15*th* lap.
17. The other car never catches up, but the gap between the cars narrows between approximately 0.85 and 1.25 hours, and again between approximately 1.6 and 1.8 hours.
21. 24.
23. 20.
25. 97/3.
27. 2π.
29. 10.
31. 13.
33. 5.25.
35. 43/6.
37. 25.
39. 2046.
41. 288.
43. 1.
45. 85.

47. $L_4 = \sum_{n=0}^{n=3} \left(1 + \frac{n}{4}\right)^2 \left(\frac{1}{4}\right)$.

49. $L_{10} = \sum_{n=0}^{9} \left(1 + \frac{n}{10}\right)^2 \left(\frac{1}{10}\right) = 2.185$.

$U_{10} = \sum_{n=1}^{10} \left(1 + \frac{n}{10}\right)^2 \left(\frac{1}{10}\right) = 2.485$.

Section 6.2

1. $\Delta x = 2$; −2, 0, 2, 4, 6, 8;
0, 2, 4, 6, 8, 10; −1, 1, 3, 5, 7, 9.

3. $\Delta x = \frac{5}{8}$;
$7, 7\frac{5}{8}, 8\frac{1}{4}, 8\frac{7}{8}, 9\frac{1}{2}, 10\frac{1}{8}, 10\frac{3}{4}, 11\frac{3}{8}$;
$7\frac{5}{8}, 8\frac{1}{4}, 8\frac{7}{8}, 9\frac{1}{2}, 10\frac{1}{8}, 10\frac{3}{4}, 11\frac{3}{8}, 12$;
$7\frac{5}{16}, 7\frac{15}{16}, 8\frac{9}{16}, 9\frac{3}{16}, 9\frac{13}{16}, 10\frac{7}{16}, 11\frac{1}{16}, 11\frac{11}{16}$.

5. $L_5 \approx 1.11$, $U_5 \approx 1.19$,
avg ≈ 1.15, error ≈ 0.04.

7. $L_5 \approx -0.314$, $U_5 =\approx 0.314$,
avg = 0, error ≈ 0.314.

9. -2.5. **11.** -3.5.

13. -5. **15.** 1.

17. $0,\ 0,\ 0,\ 0$. **19.** $0,\ 0,\ 0,\ 0$.

21. $0,\ -6,\ 2\frac{2}{3}$.

23. $\approx -8,\quad \approx -19,\quad \approx 18$.

25. $\approx 6.5,\quad \approx -1.25,$ undefined over $(5, 6]$.

27. $\approx 3.25,\quad \approx 1.5,\quad \approx -6.25$.

29. 9. **31.** $21/2$.

33. 2. **35.** $-21/2$.

37. 0. **39.** 0.

Section 6.3

1. 2.25 miles. **3.** $t = 23$.

5.

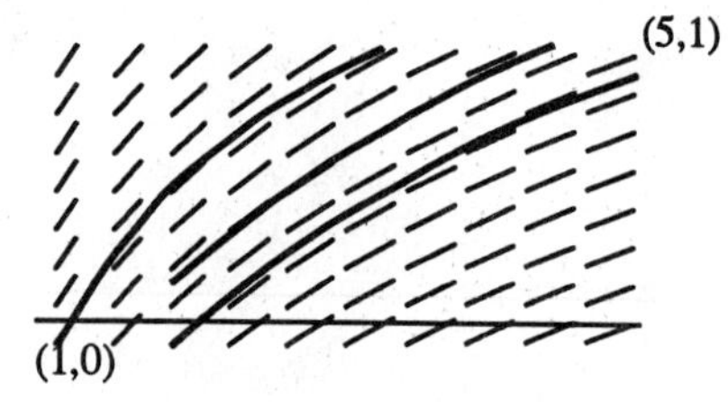

7.

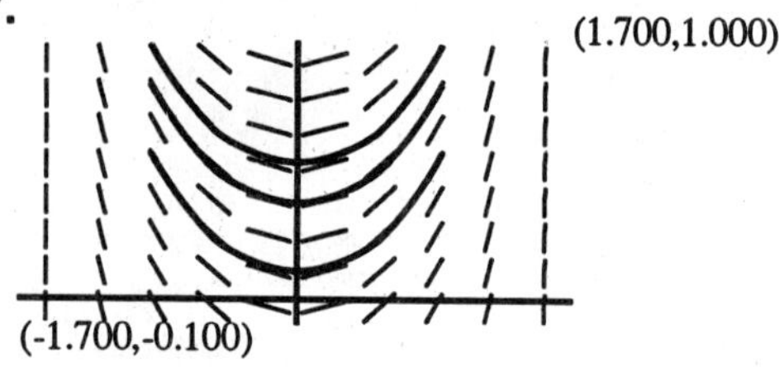

9.

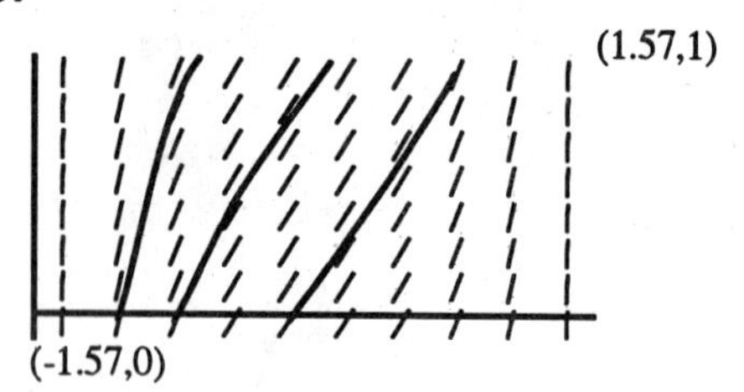

11.

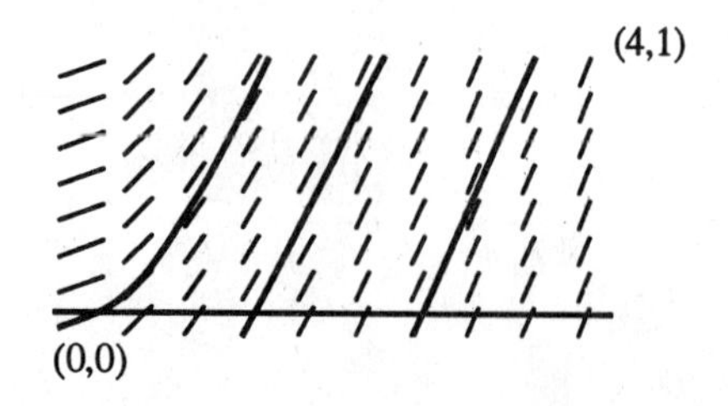

13.

15.

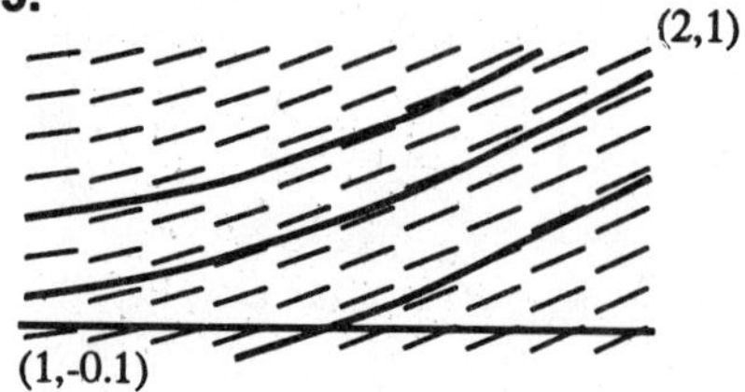

17.

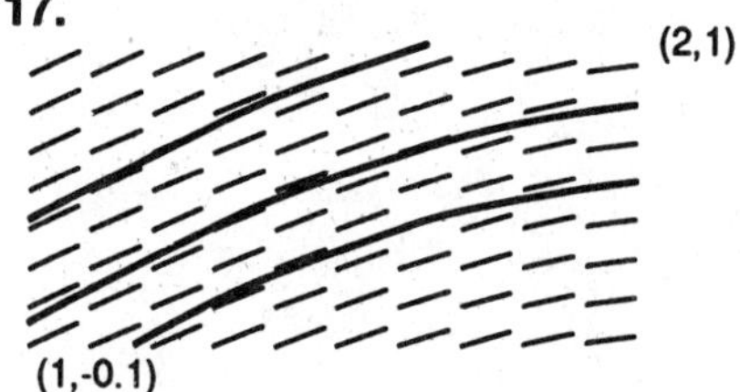

19.

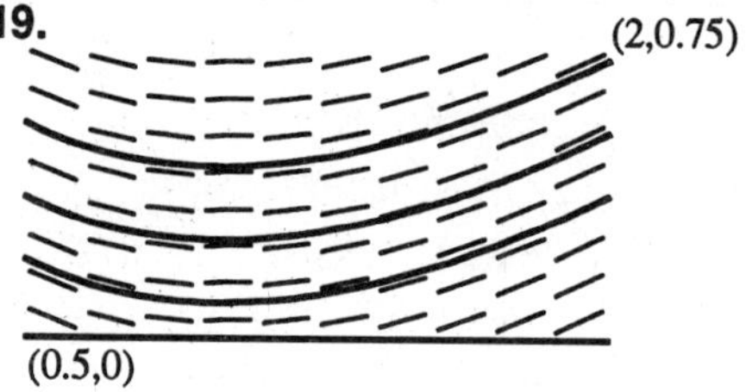

21.

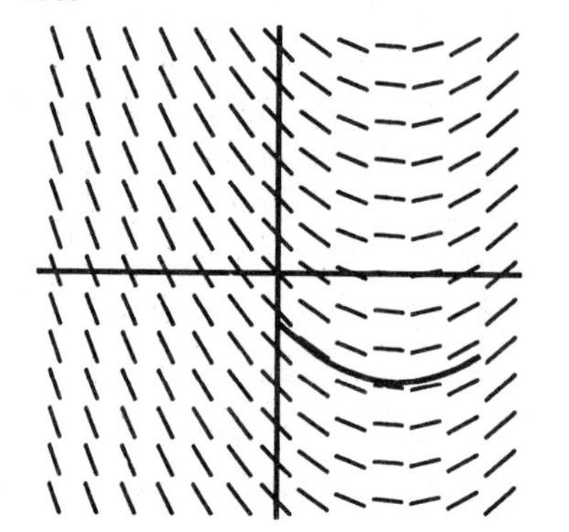

23.

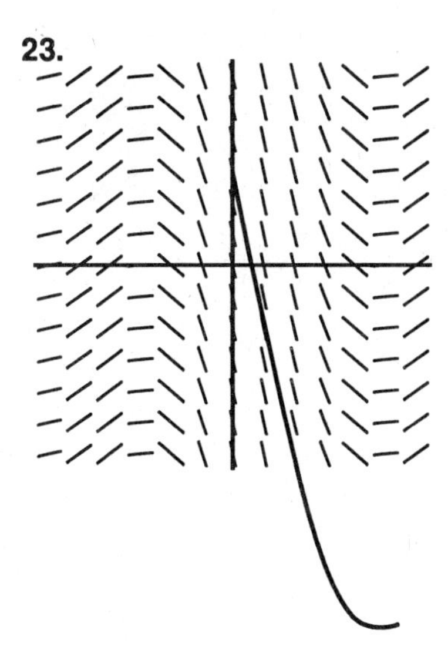

25. 

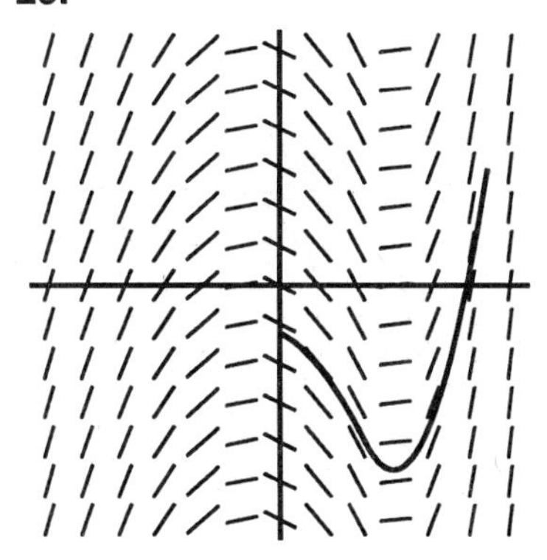

27.

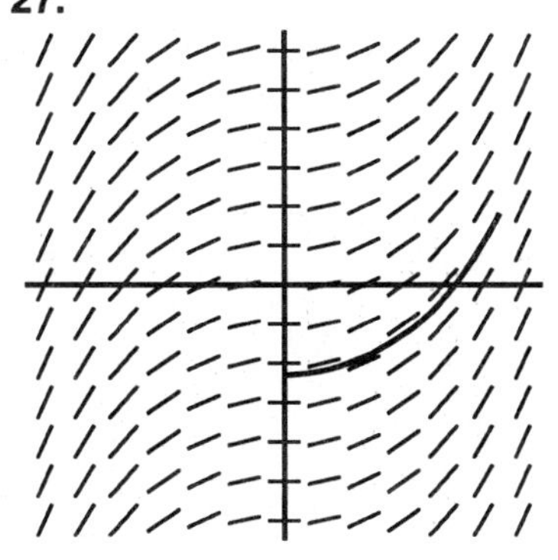

Section 6.4

1. $\dfrac{x^3}{3}+\dfrac{x^2}{2}+x+C.$ **3.** $\dfrac{x^5}{10}+C.$

5. $\dfrac{2}{3}x^{3/2}+C.$ **7.** $6\sqrt{x}+C.$

9. $\dfrac{x^4}{12}+\dfrac{x^{-2}}{6}+C.$ **11.** $\dfrac{3}{10}x^{10/3}+C.$

13. $x+C.$ **15.** $\dfrac{1}{4}\arctan(x)+C.$

17. $e^x-\dfrac{5x^3}{3}+C.$ **19.** $\dfrac{x^2}{2}-\sec(x)+C.$

21. Tables for b and integral values.

0.0	−1.1071				
0.1	−1.0075	1.1	−0.2742	2.1	0.0192
0.2	−0.9098	1.2	−0.2311	2.2	0.0370
0.3	−0.8157	1.3	−0.1920	2.3	0.0535
0.4	−0.7266	1.4	−0.1566	2.4	0.0689
0.5	−0.6435	1.5	−0.1244	2.5	0.0831
0.6	−0.5667	1.6	−0.0950	2.6	0.0965
0.7	−0.4964	1.7	−0.0681	2.7	0.1089
0.8	−0.4324	1.8	−0.0435	2.8	0.1206
0.9	−0.3743	1.9	−0.0208	2.9	0.1316
1.0	−0.3218	2.0	0.0000	3.0	0.1419

23.

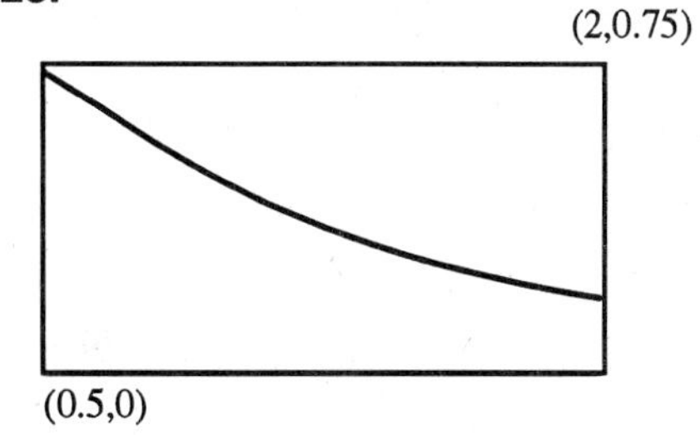

25. Graphs should be the same.

27. $a=0.$

29. $\arctan(0)-\arctan(2)\approx 0-1.107=A(0).$

31. Tables for b and integral values.

0.1	−2.3026	2.1	0.7419
0.2	−1.6094	2.2	0.7885
0.3	−1.2040	2.3	0.8329
0.4	−0.9163	2.4	0.8755
0.5	−0.6931	2.5	0.9163
0.6	−0.5108	2.6	0.9555
0.7	−0.3567	2.7	0.9933
0.8	−0.2231	2.8	1.0296
0.9	−0.1054	2.9	1.0647
1.0	0.0000	3.0	1.0986
1.1	0.0953	3.1	1.1314
1.2	0.1823	3.2	1.1632
1.3	0.2624	3.3	1.1939
1.4	0.3365	3.4	1.2238
1.5	0.4055	3.5	1.2528
1.6	0.4700	3.6	1.2809
1.7	0.5306	3.7	1.3083
1.8	0.5878	3.8	1.3350
1.9	0.6419	3.9	1.3610
2.0	0.6931	4.0	1.3863

35. $f(x)=1/x.$

Section 6.5

1. $\int_1^x 2^{-t^2}\,dt$.

3. $\int_{-\pi}^x \cos^2(t)\,dt$.

5. $\int_{\sqrt{17}}^x \frac{1}{t}\,dt$.

7. $\frac{\sin(2x)}{1+x^2}$.

9. $\frac{x^2\sin(2x)}{1+x^2} + 2x\int_2^x \frac{\sin(2t)}{1+t^2}\,dt$.

11. $\frac{2\sin(2x)}{1+x^2} \int_2^x \frac{\sin(2t)}{1+t^2}\,dt$.

13. $17\frac{1}{3}$.

15. $12\frac{2}{3}$.

17. 4π.

19. $\pi/16$.

21. $A(1) = 0$, $A(5) \approx 0$.

23. $A(1) = 0$, $A(5) \approx -2.3097$.

25. $A(1) = 0$, $A(5) \approx 1.1438$.

27. $A(1) = 0$, $A(5) \approx 0.8035$.

29. Unreasonable since $y = 1/x^2 > 0$ for all x. This does not contradict the Second Fundamental Theorem of Calculus since $y(x) = 1/x^2$ is not continuous on $[-1, 1]$.

Section 6.6

1.

n	left	right	midpt
2	1.05902	1.26612	1.14039
4	1.09970	1.20326	1.14595
8	1.12283	1.17460	1.14733
16	1.13508	1.16097	1.14768
32	1.14138	1.15432	1.14776

3.

n	left	right	midpt
2	−0.78540	0.78540	0
4	−0.39270	0.39270	0
8	−0.19635	0.19635	0
16	−0.098175	0.098175	0
32	−0.049087	0.049087	0

5.

n	left	right	midpt
2	0.88940	0.57334	0.75460
4	0.82200	0.66397	0.74875
8	0.78537	0.70636	0.74730
16	0.76634	0.72683	0.74694
32	0.75664	0.73689	0.74685

7.

n	TRAP	SIMP
2	1.1626	1.1478
4	1.1515	1.1478
8	1.1487	1.1478
16	1.1480	1.1478
32	1.1479	1.1478

$\int_0^1 \sqrt{1+x^2}dx \approx 1.1478$. SIMP gives the best estimate.

9.

n	TRAP	SIMP
2	0	0
4	0	0
8	0	0
16	0	0
32	0	0

$\int_{-1}^1 \arctan(x)dx = 0$. TRAP, SIMP, and the midpoint rule all give the exact value.

11.

n	TRAP	SIMP
2	.73137	.74686
4	.74298	.74683
8	.74587	.74682
16	.74659	.74682
32	.74676	.74682

$\int_0^1 e^{-x^2}\,dx \approx .74682$. SIMP gives the best estimate.

13. ≈ 2.083 mi.

15. 0.0004802142.

17. −5.60303, −5.97073.

19. ≈ -6.0952.

21. 0.

23. −8.

25. 4.7.

27. 3.2.

29. None.

31. In the first picture, construct the tangent line. Two congruent triangles are formed. The area of the lower triangle plus the shaded area (in picture 1.) under the tangent line make up the area of the rectangle when using the midpoint estimate. In this same picture, the area of the upper triangle plus the shaded area under the tangent line make up the area of the trapezoid formed. Since the triangles are all congruent, both estimates are the same. A similar argument holds if we construct the tangent line in picture 3.

33. a) left rectangle.
b) right rectangle.
c) trapezoidal, midpoint, Simpson's.
d) none.

35. a) right rectangle.
b) left rectangle, trapezoidal.
c) none.
d) midpoint, Simpson's.

37. a) right rectangle, trapezoidal.
b) left rectangle.
c) none.
d) midpoint, Simpson's.

39. a) left rectangle.
b) right rectangle, trapezoidal.
c) none.
d) midpoint, Simpson's.

41. a) left rectangle, trapezoidal.
b) right rectangle.
c) none.
d) Simpson's, midpoint.

43. a) right rectangle.
b) left rectangle.
c) midpoint, trapezoidal, Simpson's.
d) none.

45. a) none. b) none.
c) all. d) none.

Section 6.7

1. $\frac{1}{2}\sin(x^2) + C.$ **3.** $\frac{1}{5}\ln|x^5 - 17| + C.$

5. $\frac{1}{20}(2x^3+7)^{5/3} - \frac{7}{8}(2x^3+7)^{2/3} + C.$

7. $-\frac{1}{2}e^{-x^2} + C.$ **9.** $\frac{1}{2}(\ln x)^2 + C.$

11. $-\frac{1}{12}\cos(4x^3+8) + C.$

13. $\frac{(x^3+1)^5}{5} + C.$

15. $\frac{2}{7}(1+\sin(x))^{7/2} + C.$

17. $\frac{2}{3}\sin(6x) + C.$ **19.** $\frac{1}{12}e^{4x^3} + C.$

21. $\frac{2}{5}(1+\sqrt{x})^5 + C.$ **23.** $\tan(\ln(x)) + C.$

25. $\arctan(e^x) + C.$ **27.** $\frac{1}{2}\arctan(\frac{x}{2}) + C.$

29. $\ln|\tan(e^x)| + C.$ **31.** $-\frac{1}{2}e^{\cos^2(x)} + C.$

33. $\frac{(\ln(x)+1)^3}{3} + C.$ **35.** $\frac{(\ln(x))^5}{5} + C.$

37. $\sec(\ln(x)) + C.$ **39.** $4(8+\ln(x))^{1/2} + C.$

41. Let $u = x^2$ and $du = 2x\,dx$.

$$\int_0^{\pi^2} \frac{1}{2}\cos u\,du \approx -.21515.$$

43. Let $u = x^5 - 17$ and $du = 5x^4\,dx$.

$$\int_{-18}^{-16} \frac{1}{5}\frac{1}{u}\,du \approx -.02356.$$

45. Let $u = 2x^3 + 7$ and $du = 6x^2\,dx$.

$$\int_5^{23} \frac{1}{12}\left(\frac{u-7}{\sqrt[3]{u}}\right)du \approx 4.0516.$$

47. Let $u = -x^2$ and $du = -2x\,dx$.

$$\int_{-1}^{-(\ln 2)^2} -\frac{1}{2}e^u\,du \approx -.125.$$

49. Let $u = \ln x$ and $du = \frac{1}{x}\,dx$.

$$\int_0^1 u\,du = \frac{1}{2}.$$

55. Let $u = \arctan x$ and $du = \frac{1}{1+x^2}\,dx$.

Then, we have $\int e^{-u}\cos(4u)\,du$

$$= \frac{e^{-u}}{1+16}(-\cos(4u) + 4\sin(4u)) + C$$

$$= \frac{e^{-\arctan x}}{17}(4\sin(4\arctan x) - \cos(4\arctan x)) + C.$$

57. $\frac{d}{dx}(\sinh(x)) = \frac{e^x + e^{-x}}{2} = \cosh(x).$

$$\int \sinh(x)\,dx = \frac{e^x + e^{-x}}{2} = \cosh(x) + C.$$

59. $\frac{d}{dx}(\operatorname{sech}(x)) = -\operatorname{sech}(x)\tanh(x).$

$$\int \operatorname{sech}(x)\,dx = 2\arctan(e^x) + C.$$

61. $\frac{d}{dx}\tanh(x) = (\operatorname{sech}(x))^2.$

$$\int \tanh(x)\,dx = \ln|\cosh(x)| + C.$$

63. Let $u = \ln(x)$ and $du = \frac{1}{x}\,dx$. Since $\int \operatorname{sech}^2(u)\,du = \tanh(u) + C$, we have

$$\int \frac{\operatorname{sech}^2(\ln(x))}{x} = \tanh(\ln(x)) + C.$$

65. Let $u = 1 + \cosh(x)$ and $du = \sinh(x)\,dx$. Since $\int \frac{1}{u}\,du = \ln|u| + C$, we have

$$\int \frac{\sinh(x)}{1+\cosh(x)}\,dx = \ln|1+\cosh(x)| + C.$$

Chapter 7

Section 7.1

1. $\frac{25}{2}$.
3. 1.
5. 144.
7. 1.
9. $\frac{125}{6}$.
11. ≈ 0.096.
13. ≈ 0.693.
15. ≈ 1.662.
17. $\sqrt[3]{16}$.
19. ≈ 110.
21. 15.
23. 24.
25. 21.
27. 11.5.
29. 5 cans.

Section 7.2

1. 125/3.
3. ≈ 0.393.
5. 1.5.
7. x-axis: ≈ 4.189, y-axis: ≈ 12.566.
9. x-axis: ≈ 24.557, y-axis: ≈ 1.848.
11. x-axis: ≈ 21.401, y-axis: ≈ 27.589.
13. x-axis: ≈ 7.237 y-axis: ≈ 4.842.
15. x-axis: ≈ 3.701, y-axis: ≈ 15.263.
17. $f(x) = \frac{2}{5}x$ over $[0, 10]$; $160\pi/3$.
19. $2\int_0^r \pi(R + \sqrt{r^2 - x^2})^2 - \pi(R - \sqrt{r^2 - x^2})^2\,dx$

$$= 2\pi\int_0^r \Big(R^2 + 2R\sqrt{r^2 - x^2} + (r^2 - x^2)$$

$$-(R^2 - 2R\sqrt{r^2 - x^2} + r^2 - x^2)\Big)\,dx$$

$$= 2\pi\int_0^r 4R\sqrt{r^2 - x^2}\,dx$$

$$= 8\pi R\int_0^r \sqrt{r^2 - x^2}\,dx = 8\pi R(1/4)(\pi r^2) = 2\pi^2 Rr^2.$$

21. 45π.
23. $103\pi/3$.

Section 7.3

1. 3.
3. ≈ 1.087.
5. $-\frac{5}{12}$.
7. ≈ 0.327.
9. doesn't exist.
11. 21π.
13. $\frac{32}{81}$.
15. $\frac{16}{81}$.
17. $\frac{1}{81}$.
19. Answers may vary.
21. This suggests $\approx \frac{21}{30} = 70\%$ of the earth's surface is covered by water.

23. $\sin(x) - \sin(x-1)$. **25.** $\dfrac{2x-3}{2}$.
27. $\frac{1}{2}(\sin(x^2) - \sin((x-1)^2))$.
29. 1/4. The center of the coaster must be at least 2 inches from the edge of the square.
31. $x < \frac{1}{2}$ and $\frac{1}{2}\sin(y) > x$
or $x > \frac{3}{2}$ and $\frac{1}{2}\sin(y) > 2 - x$.
33. $2\ell/(d\pi)$.

Section 7.4

1. $v(t) = \dfrac{t^2}{2} - \dfrac{t^3}{3} - 2$; $s(t) = \dfrac{t^3}{6} - \dfrac{t^4}{12} - 2t + 3$.
3. $v(t) = -\cos(t)$; $s(t) = -\sin(t) + 1$.
5. $v(t) = \frac{2}{3}t^{3/2} - 4$; $s(t) = \frac{4}{15}t^{5/2} - 4t + 2$.
7. Net distance ≈ 2.350.
Total distance ≈ 2.350.
9. Net distance $= 0$.
Total distance ≈ 0.637.
11. Net distance $= 48$ ft.
Total distance $= 80$ ft.

Section 7.5 (answers are approximate)

1. 0.307.
3. 0.779.
5. 0.371.
7. 0.121.
9. 0.113.
11. 26.437.
13. 3.026.
15. 3.090.
17. 10.347.
19. 24.396.
21. 9.293.
23. $4\sqrt{2}$.
25. 1.521.
27. 6.663.
29. 2.973.
31. 0.224.
33. 0.202.
35. 2344.
37. 18.19.
39. 4.436.

Section 7.6

1. 16.
3. 32 in-lbs.
5. 144/7 in-lbs.
7. 15/8 ft-lbs.
9. force $\approx \frac{60}{7}$ lbs,
first spring $\approx 4\frac{6}{7}$ ft, second spring $\approx 5\frac{1}{7}$ ft.
11. ≈ 240 in-lbs.
13. ≈ 3187.5 ft-lbs.
15. ≈ 2800 cm-lbs.
17. ≈ 2099 cm-lbs.
19. ≈ 13647 in-lbs.
21. ≈ 4265 in-lbs.
23. 21875 ft-lbs.
25. ≈ 410156 ft-lbs.
27. $kQ_1Q_2(10^6 - 10^{-1})$.

Section 7.7

1. Converges to 1/2.
3. Converges to 2.
5. Converges to 2.
7. Converges to 100.
9. Diverges.
11. Converges for $p > 1$; diverges for $p \leq 1$.
13. Diverges.
15. Converges to 1/2.
17. Diverges.
19. Converges to 2.
21. Diverges for $p > 0$,
converges to $1/p$ for $p < 0$;
Converges to $1/p$ for $p > 0$,
diverges for $p < 0$.
23. Converges to $\pi/2$. **25.** Diverges.
27. Diverges.
29. Diverges.
31. Diverges.
33. Diverges.
35. Diverges.
37. Diverges for $p \geq 1$,
converges for $p < 1$.
39. Converges to $-\frac{3}{2} + \frac{3}{2}(3)^{2/3}$.

41. Integral diverges. (NOTE: $f(x) = \sec^2(x)$ is not continuous over $[0, \pi]$.)
43. ≈ 1.3.
45. 0.

47. $\dfrac{1}{s^2+1}$.

Chapter 8

Section 8.1

1. $y(x) = 0.5 + \int_0^x e^{-t^2/2}\,dt$, $y(3) \approx 1.750$.

3. $y(x) \approx 0.13(x+5)^{3/2} + 0.031$, $y(3) \approx 2.97$.

5. $y(x) \approx 0.1\left(\frac{x^5}{5} + x^4 + \frac{8x^3}{3} + 4x^2 + 4x\right)$ $+1.19$, $y(3) \approx 26.15$.

7. $y(x) = \arctan(x) + 1 - \frac{\pi}{4}$, $y(3) \approx 1.46$.

9. $x \arcsin(x) + (1-x^2)^{1/2} + C$.

11. $x^3e^x - 3x^2e^x + 6xe^x - 6e^x + C$.

13. $x \arccos(x) - (1-x^2)^{1/2} + C$.

15. $\frac{1}{2}x^2\ln(x) - \frac{1}{4}x^2 + C$.

17. $-x^2\cos x + 2x\sin x + 2\cos x + C$.

19. $x\sin x + \cos x + C$.

21. $\frac{2}{5}x^{5/2}\ln(x) - \frac{4}{25}x^{5/2} + C$.

23. $2x^{1/2}\ln(x) - 4x^{1/2} + C$.

25. $6(x\ln(x) - x) - 3x(\ln(x))^2 + x(\ln(x))^3 + C$.

27. $-\frac{\ln(x)}{x} - \frac{1}{x} + C$.

29. $x^2\sin x + 2x\cos x - 2\sin x + C$.

31. $x\sec x - \ln(|\sec x + \tan x|) + C$.

33. $x\tan x + \ln(|\cos x|) + C$.

35. $-\frac{1}{3}xe^{1-3x} - \frac{1}{9}e^{1-3x} + C$.

37. $\frac{1}{2}x^2\arctan(x) - \frac{1}{2}x + \frac{1}{2}\arctan(x) + C$.

39. $\frac{1}{3}x^3\arctan(x) - \frac{1}{6}x^2 + \frac{1}{6}\ln(1+x^2) + C$.

41. $-\frac{1}{3}x^2(1-x^2)^{3/2} - \frac{2}{15}(1-x^2)^{5/2} + C$.

43. $\frac{1}{2}(x\sin(\ln(x)) - x\cos(\ln(x))) + C$.

45. $x\sinh(x) - \cosh(x) + C$.

47. $\frac{1}{2}e^x(\sin(x) + \cos(x)) + C$.

49. $\frac{1}{6}e^{3x}(\sin(3x) + \cos(3x)) + C$.

Section 8.2

1. Exponential, 6925.
3. Linear, 6360.
5. Exponential, 3658.
7. $y(x) = 42e^{4x-4}$, $(-\infty, \infty)$.
9. $y = x$, $(0, \infty)$.
11. $y(x) = (2\ln(x) + 1 - \ln(4))^{1/2}$, $(\approx 1.2, \infty)$.
13. $y(x) = \ln[(x^2+1))^{1/2}]$, $(-\infty, \infty)$.
15. $y' = 2y$; $y(0) = 3$, $y(0) = -2$.
17. $y' = \ln(125)y$; $y(0) = 25$, $y(0) = 1$.
19. $y' = (x\ln(2))^{-1}$; $y(1) = 0$, $y(1) = 5$.

Section 8.3

1. $\approx 67.5°$.
3. ≈ 88.57; $\approx 79.03°$.
5. ≈ 5.76 years.
7. Second dose after ≈ 3.3 hours,
third and later doses after ≈ 5.2 hours.
9. ≈ 3.14 milligrams, ≈ 3.42 milligrams.
11. ≈ 13.3 years.
13. Bank 1, $\approx 5.28445\%$.
15. ≈ 8.17 lbs/ in^2.

Section 8.4

3.

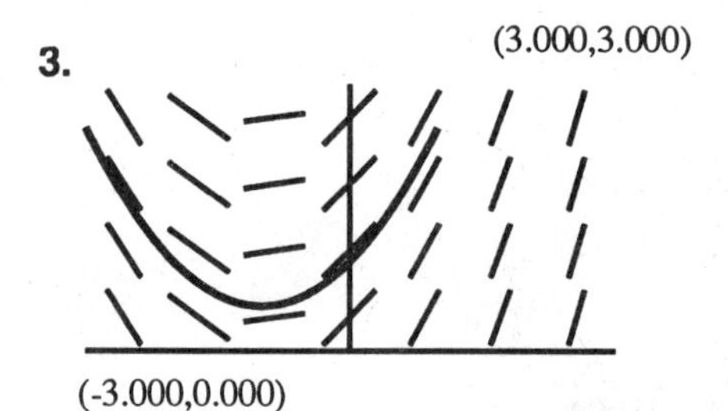

5.

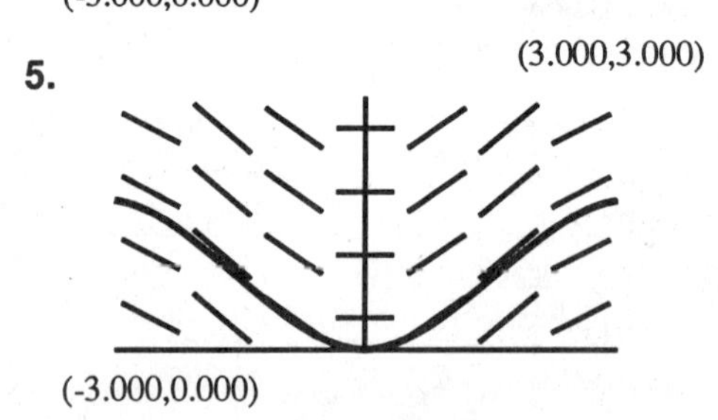

9.

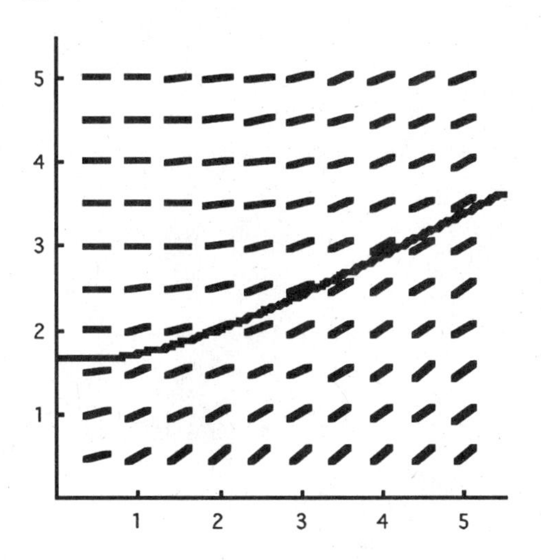

11.

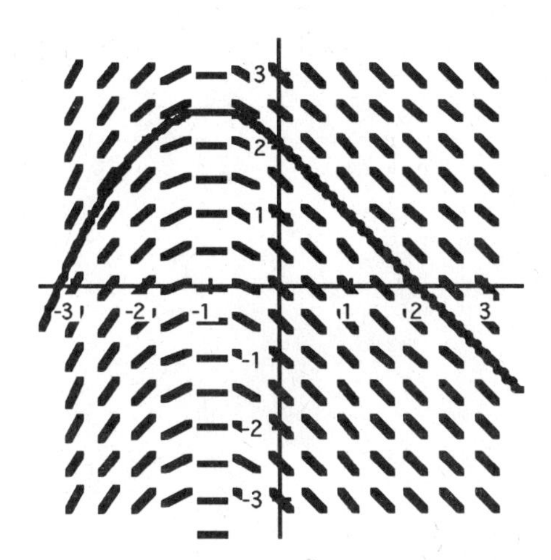

13.

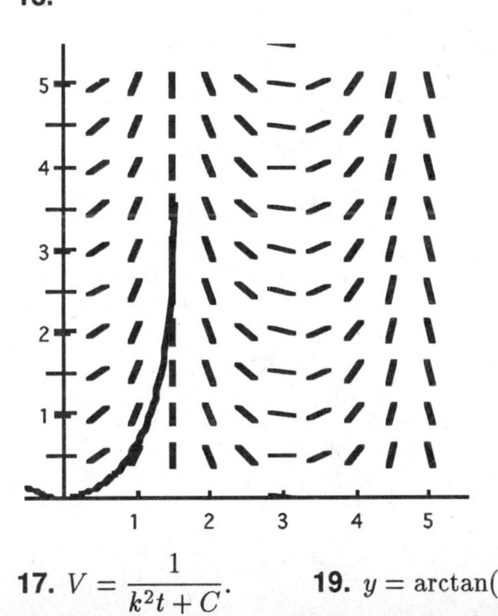

17. $V = \dfrac{1}{k^2 t + C}$.

19. $y = \arctan(x)$.

21. $y = \operatorname{arccot}(x)$.

23. $y = \operatorname{arccsc}(x)$.

25. $y = \ln(x)$.

27. $y(x) = \sqrt[3]{3x + 64}$.

29. $y(x) = \left(\dfrac{3x^2 + 6x + 84}{4}\right)^{2/3}$.

31. $y(x) = -1 + (x^2 + 4)^{1/2}$.

Section 8.5

1. a)

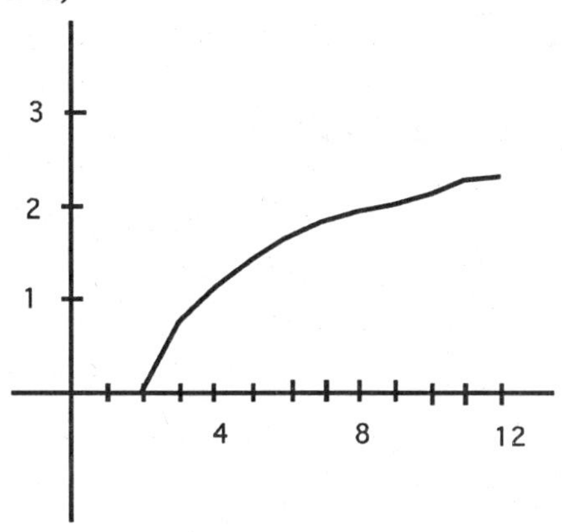

b)

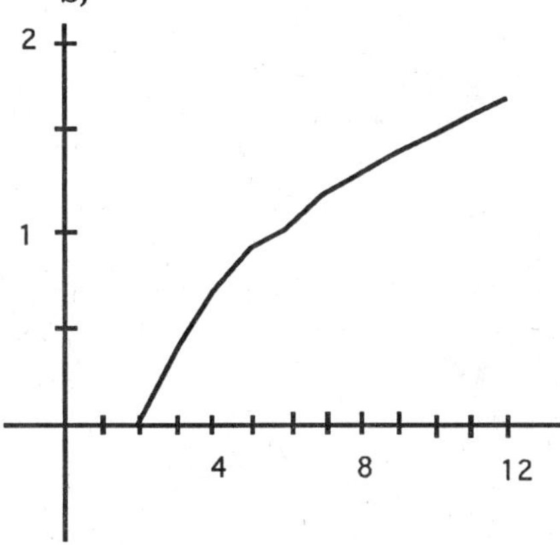

c)

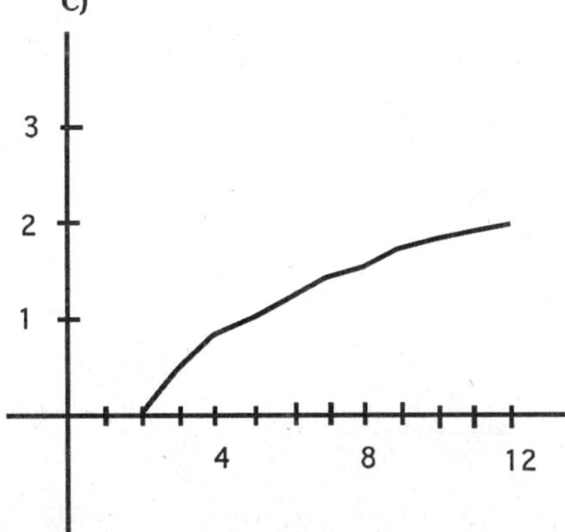

3. a)

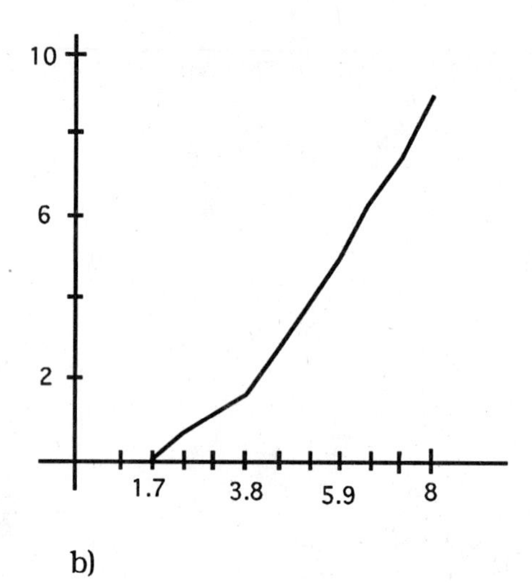

b)

c)

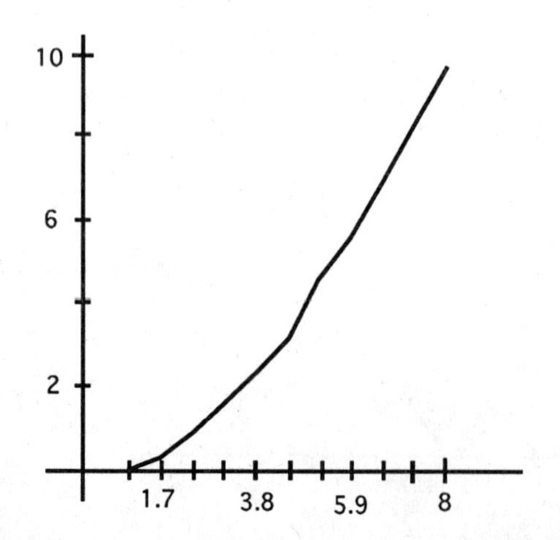

5. a)

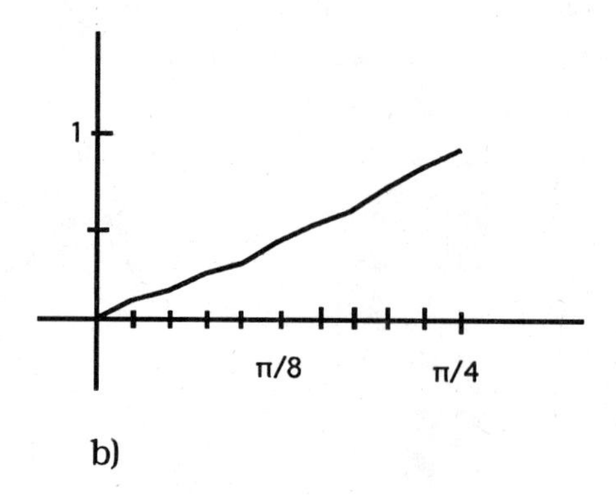

b)

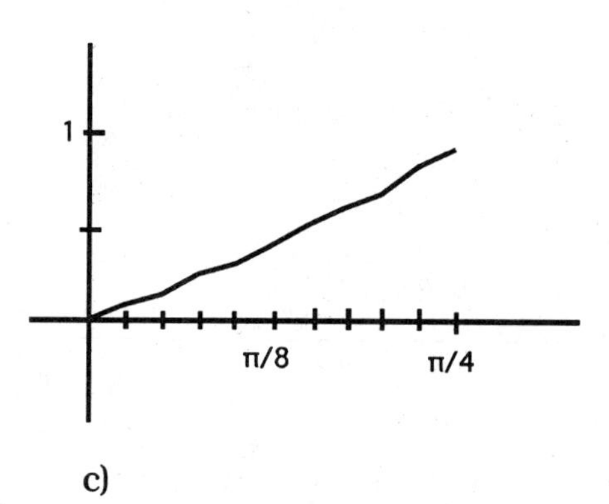

c)

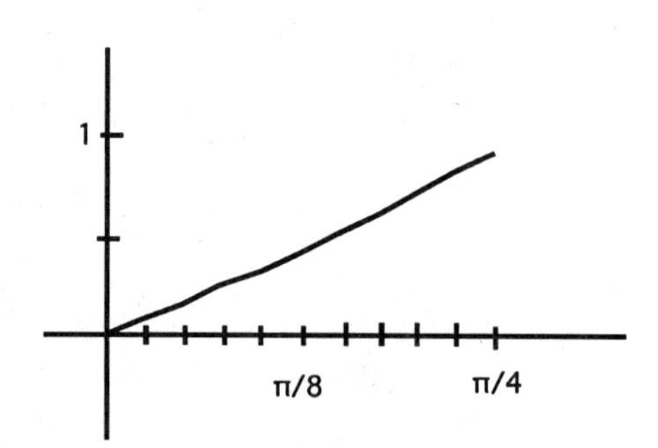

7. Simpson's rule is $\frac{2}{3}$(midpt est) $+\frac{1}{3}\left(\frac{1}{2}(\text{right endpt est} + \text{left endpt est})\right)$.

9. Note that when $x = 1$, $\dfrac{dy}{dx}$ is undefined.

11. $y_1 \approx 1.347$,

$y_2 \approx 1.87$, $y_3 \approx 2.55$,

$y_4 \approx 3.36$, $y_5 \approx 4.29$,

$y(1.2) \approx 2.14$, $y(3) \approx 5.32$.

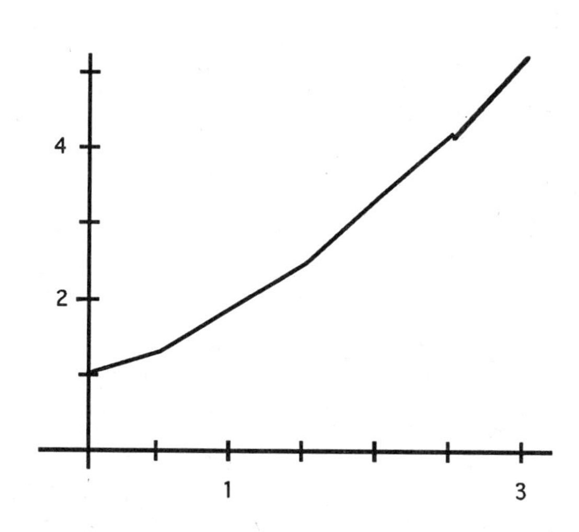

13. $y_1 \approx 0.5$,

$y_2 \approx 1.02$, $y_3 \approx 1.98$,

$y_4 \approx 1.48$, $y_5 \approx 0.97$,

$y(1.2) \approx 1.404$, $y(3) \approx 0.305$.

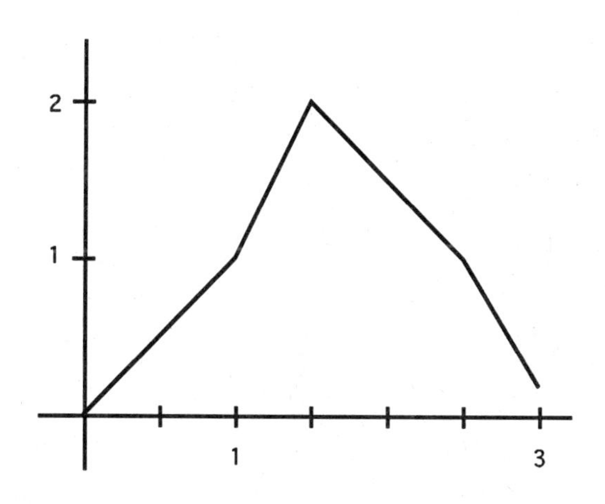

15. $u(t)$ approaches 2. Below are two typical solutions to the differential equation. The first is for the initial condition $u(0) = 1$ and the second is for the initial condition $u(0) = 3$.

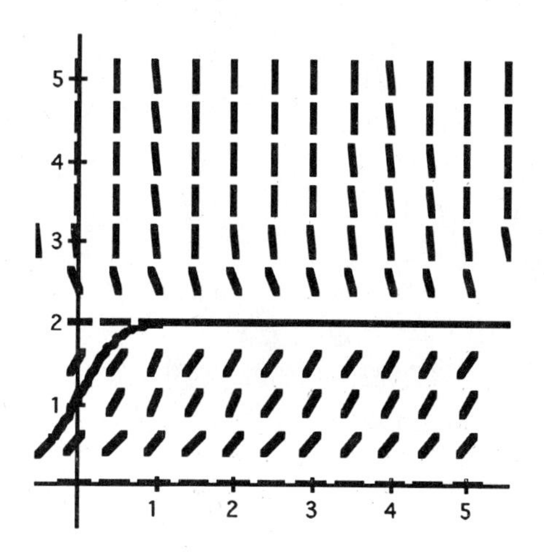

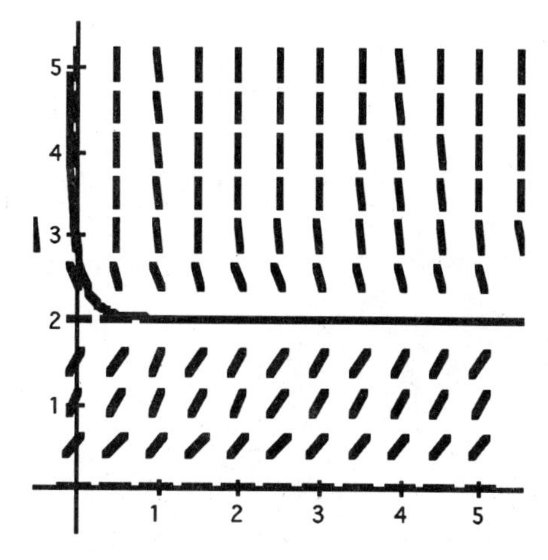

19. ≈ 2.6 hours, $\approx 35.4°$.

21. ≈ 1.35 hours, $\approx 77.7°$.

25. The linear flow rate is the flow rate divided by the cross-sectional area, or

$0.5\ \text{ft}^3/\ \text{s} \cdot 1/(8\ \text{in} \cdot 1\ \text{in}) = 9\ \text{ft}/\ \text{s}$,

so a particle will traverse a 1.5 ft compartment in 1/6 second.

Chapter 9

Section 9.1

1. 0.021, 0.00521, 0.0013, 0.000326, 0.0000814; $M = 1$.
3. 0.167, 0.0417, 0.0104, 0.0026, 0.00065; $M = 1$.
5. 0.0417, 0.0104, 0.0026, 0.000651, 0.000163; $M = 2$.
7. 0.000347, 6.51×10^{-5}, 4.07×10^{-6}, 2.54×10^{-7}, 1.59×10^{-8}; $M = 3$.
9. 0.0556, 0.0347, 0.000217, 0.0000136, 8.48×10^{-7}; $M = 5$.
11. 0.00417, 0.00026, 0.0000163, 1.02×10^{-6}, 6.36×10^{-8}; $M = 12$.

13. $n = 128$. **15.** $n = 512$.
17. $n = 256$. **19.** $n = 8$.
21. $n = 32$. **23.** $n = 16$.

25. The error bound for the trapezoidal rule is 0 because, for any partition of $[a, b]$, the shapes formed are trapezoids.

27. $\dfrac{M''(b-a)^3}{12n^2} = \dfrac{M''(b-a)(b-a)^2}{12n^2} = \dfrac{1}{12}M''(b-a)(\Delta x)^2.$

29. $\dfrac{(1/180)M^{(4)}(b-a)(\Delta x)^4}{(1/12)M''(b-a)(\Delta x)^2} = \dfrac{M^{(4)}}{15M''}(\Delta x)^2.$

31. Many answers.
33. Many answers.
35. $\dfrac{\Delta x}{6}(y_0 + 4y_1 + y_2)$.

Section 9.2

1. $p(x) = x^2$;

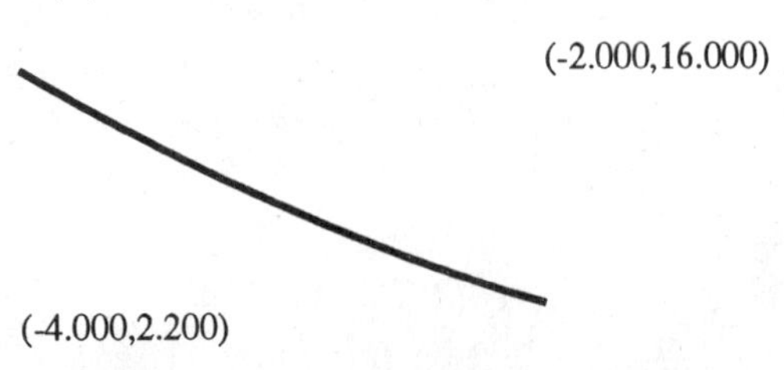

$p(-2) = 4$, $f(-2) = 4$,
$p(-4) = 16$, $f(-4) = 16$,
$p(-2.999) = 8.994001$, $f(-2.999) = 8.994001$,
$p(-3.001) = 9.006001$, $f(-3.001) = 9.006001$,
No errors in the approximations.

3. $p(x) = 4 - \frac{1}{3}(x+8) - \frac{1}{144}(x+8)^2$;

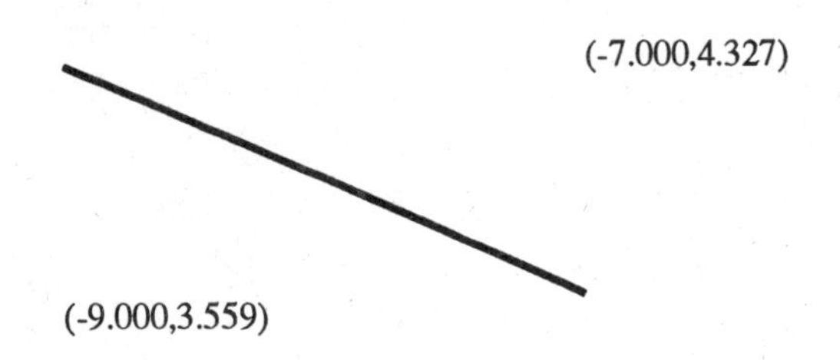

$p(-7) = 3.659\overline{72}$, $f(-7) \approx 3.659306$,
error ≈ 0.0004.
$p(-9) = 4.326\overline{38}$, $f(-9) \approx 4.326749$,
error ≈ 0.0004.
$p(-7.999) \approx 3.99967$, $f(-7.999) \approx 3.99967$,
error $\approx 2 \times 10^{-11}$.
$p(-8.001) \approx 4.0003$, $f(-8.001) \approx 4.0003$,
error $\approx 1 \times 10^{-11}$.

5. $p(x) = x$;

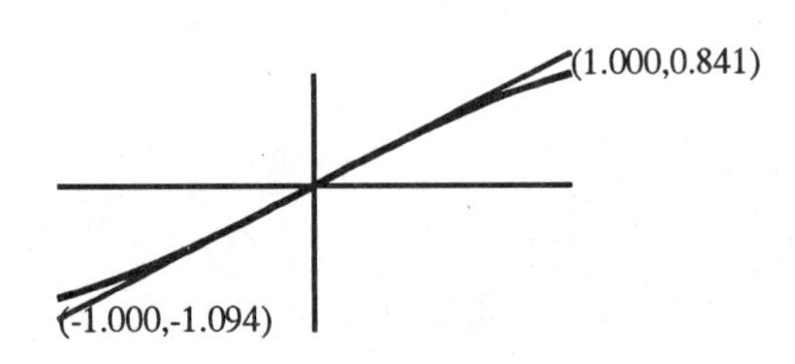

$p(1) = 1$, $f(1) \approx 0.8415$,
error ≈ 0.1585.
$p(-1) = -1$, $f(-1) \approx -0.8415$,
error ≈ 0.1585.
$p(0.001) = 0.001$, $f(0.001) \approx 0.001$,
error $\approx 1.7 \times 10^{-10}$.
$p(-0.001) = -0.001$, $f(-0.001) \approx 0.001$,
error $\approx 1.7 \times 10^{-10}$.

7. $p(x) = 1 + 2(x - \frac{\pi}{4}) + 2(x - \frac{\pi}{4})^2$;

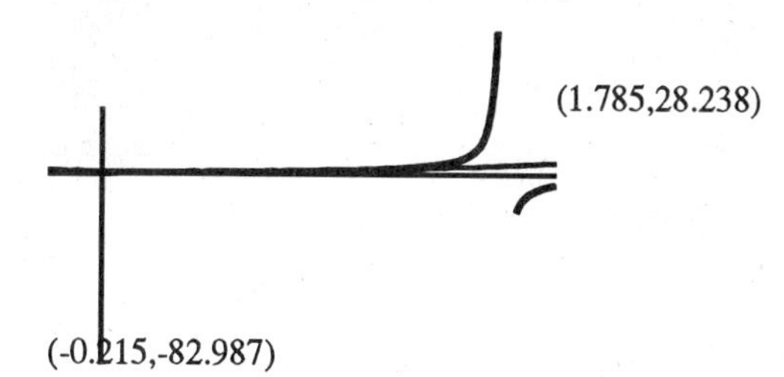

$p(1 + \frac{\pi}{4}) = 5$, $f(1 + \frac{\pi}{4}) \approx -4.588$,
error ≈ 9.6.
$p(-1 + \frac{\pi}{4}) = 1$, $f(-1 + \frac{\pi}{4}) \approx -0.2180$,
error ≈ 1.2.
$p(0.001 + \frac{\pi}{4}) = 1.002002$, $f(0.001 + \frac{\pi}{4}) \approx 1.002002$,
error $\approx 2.7 \times 10^{-9}$.
$p(-0.001 + \frac{\pi}{4}) \approx 0.998002$, $f(-0.001 + \frac{\pi}{4}) \approx 0.998002$,
error $\approx 2.7 \times 10^{-9}$.

9. $p(x) = x$;

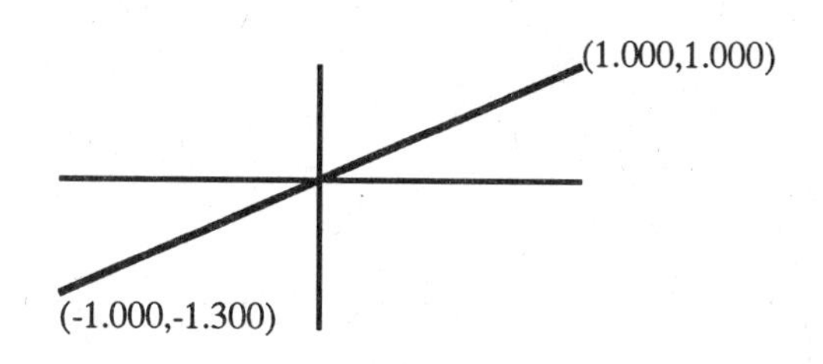

$p(1) = 1$, $f(1) = 1$,
$p(-1) = -1$, $f(-1) = -1$,
$p(0.001) = 0.001$, $f(0.001) = 0.001$,
$p(-0.001) = -0.001$, $f(-0.001) = -0.001$,
No errors in the approximations.

Note: For 11-19, the equations for some circles are approximate.

11. a) $\kappa \approx 0.025$ b) $r \approx 40.24$
c) $(x + 37.5)^2 + (y - 14.5)^2 = (40.24)^2$.

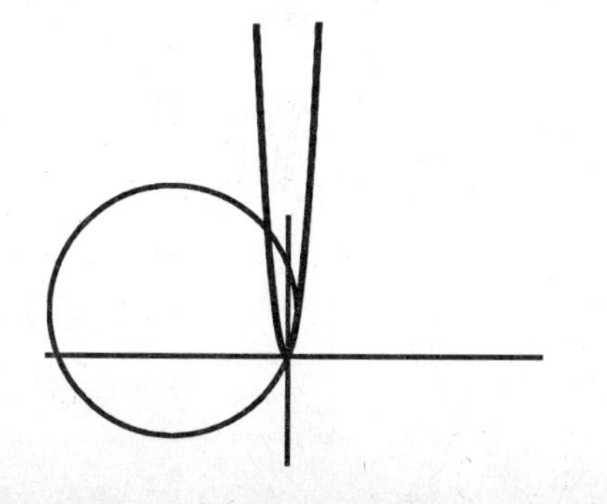

13. a) $\kappa = 12$ b) $r = 1/12$
c) $(x + 2)^2 + (y - \frac{191}{12})^2 = (\frac{1}{12})^2$.

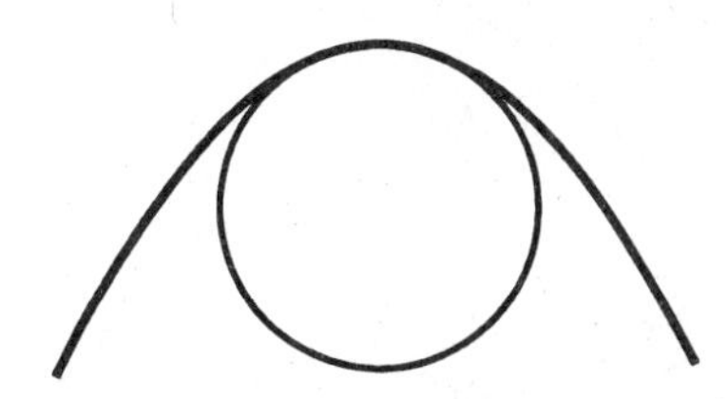

15. a) $\kappa \approx 0.15$ b) $r \approx 6.63$
c) $(x + 5.5)^2 + (y - 2.3)^2 = (6.63)^2$.

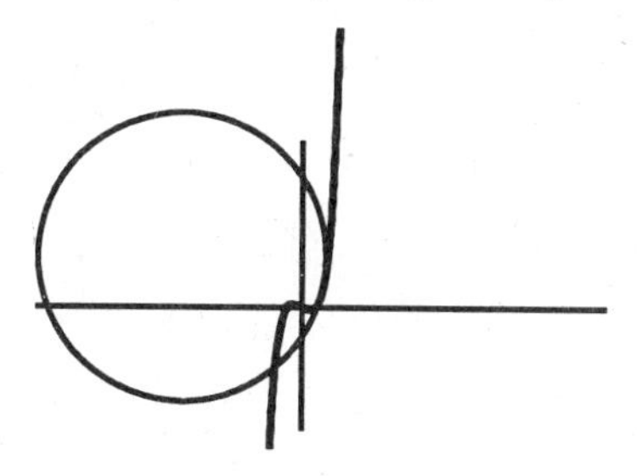

17. a) $\kappa \approx 0.43$ b) $r \approx 2.32$
c) $(x - 2.57)^2 + (y + 1.01)^2 = (2.32)^2$.

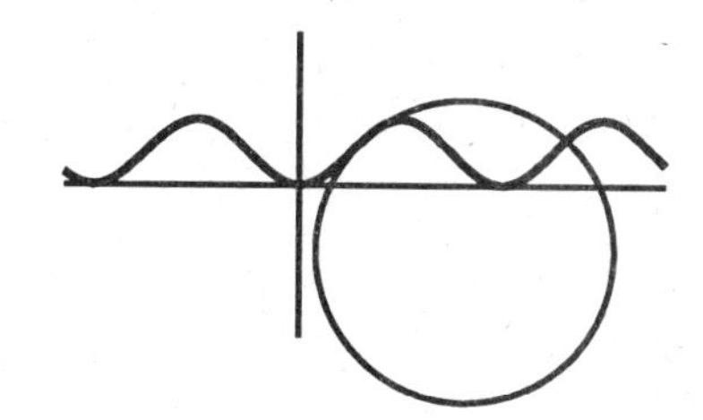

19. a) $\kappa = 2$ b) $r = 1/2$
c) $(x)^2 + (y - 1/2)^2 = (1/2)^2$.

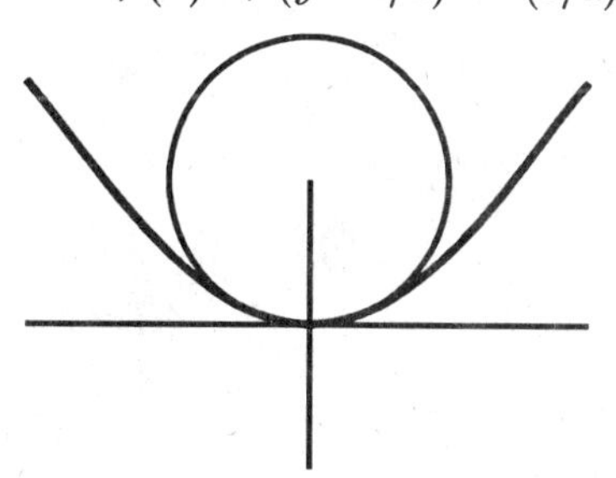

21. $f'(x) = m$ and $f''(x) = 0$,

so $\kappa = \dfrac{0}{(1 + m^2)^{3/2}} = 0$.

23. $\kappa = \dfrac{|f''(x_0)|}{(1+(f'(x_0))^2)^{3/2}} = 0$ since $f''(x_0)$ is 0 ($(x_0, f(x_0))$ is an inflection point). Also note that denominator is never 0.
Since $f''(x_0) = 0$, we have $g(x)$
$= f(x_0) + f'(x_0)(x - x_0) + (1/2)f''(x_0)(x - x_0)^2$
$= f(x_0) + f'(x_0)(x - x_0)$.

25. $g(x) = 2 - (x - 3) - \dfrac{\sqrt{2}}{4}(x - 3)^2$.

27. First, we solve the quadratic equation
$q'(x) = 3ax^2 + 2bx + c = 0$.
$q(x)$ has 2 critical values if $4b^2 - 12ac > 0$,
one critical value if $4b^2 - 12ac = 0$,
and no critical values if $4b^2 - 12ac < 0$.
Solve $q''(x) = 6ax + 2b = 0$ to find $x = -\dfrac{b}{3a}$.
So $(-\frac{b}{3a}, f(-\frac{b}{3a}))$ is the only inflection point.

29. If q has no critical values, then q is always increasing or always decreasing. The graph of q then has minimum steepness only when $q''(x) = 0$, that is, when $x = -b/(3a)$. If q has one critical value, then, solving $q'(x) = 0$, we find $x = (-2b \pm \sqrt{4b^2 - 12ac})/(6a) = -b/(3a)$ since $4b^2 - 12ac = 0$. If q has two critical values, then solving $q'(x) = 0$ we find those values are, as before, $x = \dfrac{-2b \pm \sqrt{4b^2 - 12ac}}{6a}$.
Find the midpoint between the two roots: $x = -b/(3a)$.

Section 9.3

1. $P_5(x) \approx -0.841 + 1.08(x+1) + \dfrac{3.37}{2}(x+1)^2 - \dfrac{4.32}{3!}(x+1)^3 - \dfrac{13.46}{4!}(x+1)^4 + \dfrac{17.29}{5!}(x+1)^5$.

3. $P_5(x) \approx 1 + 2(x - \frac{\pi}{4}) + 2(x - \frac{\pi}{4})^2 + \dfrac{16}{3!}(x - \frac{\pi}{4})^3 + \dfrac{80}{4!}(x - \frac{\pi}{4})^4 + \dfrac{512}{5!}(x - \frac{\pi}{4})^5$.

5. $P_5(x) \approx -1 - 0.5(x - \frac{\pi}{2})^2 - \dfrac{5}{4!}(x - \frac{\pi}{2})^4$.

7. $P_5(x) \approx 0.368 + 0.736(x+1) + 0.736(x+1)^2 + \dfrac{2.943}{3!}(x+1)^3 + \dfrac{5.886}{4!}(x+1)^4 + \dfrac{11.772}{5!}(x+1)^5$.

9. $P_5(x) = 1 + 0.5x^2 - \dfrac{3}{4!}x^4$.

11. 6, 3.1.

13. 15, 0.1. **15.** 9, 1.1.

17. 5, 0.1. **19.** 15, 5.001.

21. $P_3(x) = 1 + (x-1) + 0.75(x-1)^2 + \dfrac{1.25}{3!}(x-1)^3$.

23. $P_3(x) = 1 - 0.5x - 0.4375x^2 - 0.125x^3$.

25. $P_3(x) = 1 + (x-1) + (x-1)^2 + 1.5(x-1)^3$.

27. $P_5(x) = -0.05x^2 + 0.335x^3 - 0.008375x^4 + 0.0001675x^5$.

29. $P_5(x) = x - \dfrac{1}{3}x^3 + \dfrac{2}{15}x^5$.

31. $P_3(x) = -7 + \dfrac{5}{3!}(x-2)^3$.

33. $f(x) = x^2e^{-x}$.

35. Finding the Taylor expansion $f(t + a)$ about $t = 0$ causes the coefficients of each term to be evaluated at $t = a$. Replacing t by $(x - a)$ then gives the correct expansion.

Section 9.4

1. Answers may vary;
$[-0.1, 0.1] \times [-0.002, 0.002]$.

3. Answers may vary;
$[-0.02, 0.02] \times [-1.1 \times 10^{-7}, 8.57 \times 10^{-8}]$.

5. g. **7.** f.

9. f. **11.** f.

13. f. **15.** 1.

17. 2. **19.** 1.

21. 4. **23.** 1.

25. 2, 3. **27.** 4, 5.

29. 3, 4. **31.** 3, 5.

33. 3, 4.

35. The order of agreement is greater than the degree of the polynomial.

Section 9.5

1. 1/2. **3.** 1.
5. 1. **7.** 1.
9. −3/5. **11.** 1/2.
13. 1/2.
15. $\lim_{x\to\infty}(1+\frac{a}{x})^x = \exp(\lim_{x\to\infty} x\ln(1+\frac{a}{x}))$.
Use L'Hôpital's Rule on $\exp\left[\lim_{x\to\infty}\frac{\frac{1}{1+\frac{a}{x}}\cdot\frac{-a}{x^2}}{-\frac{1}{x^2}}\right]$
$= \exp\left(\lim_{x\to\infty}\frac{a}{1+\frac{a}{x}}\right) = \exp(a) = e^a$.
17. ∞. **19.** ∞.
21. 0. **23.** $f(x) = \ln(\ln(x))$, 0.

Section 9.6

The cubic splines determined by the data in exercises 1-4 are shown below.

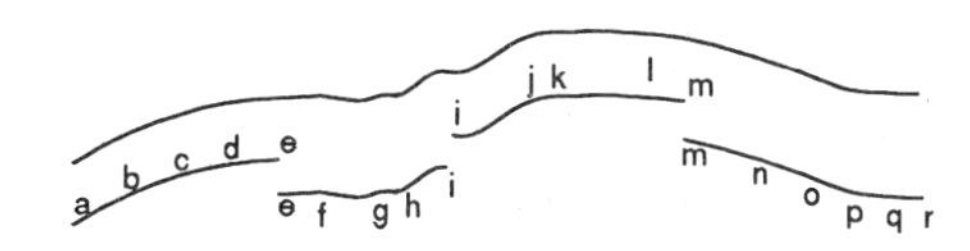

5. As can be seen below, any of the points b, c, or d can be omitted without noticeably altering the curve.

7. As can be seen below, only point l (ell) can be omitted without noticeably altering the curve.

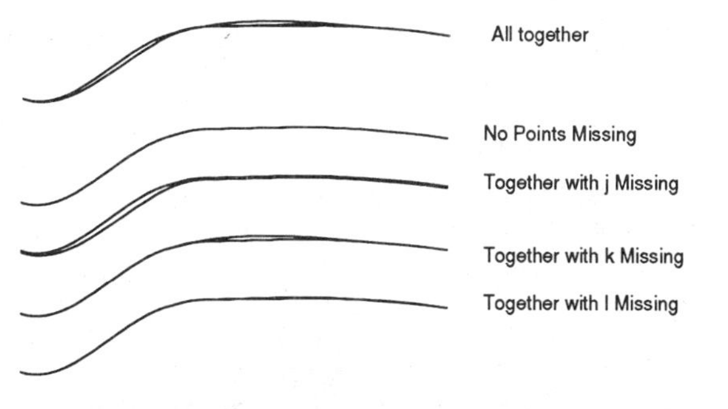

9. No, the curve and the spline approximation match very well.

11. The presence of the "shelf" near point i suggests that other control points were used.

13. Yes, by increasing the slope at point f and decreasing the slope at point g, the resulting spline forms a bump between f and g as shown below:

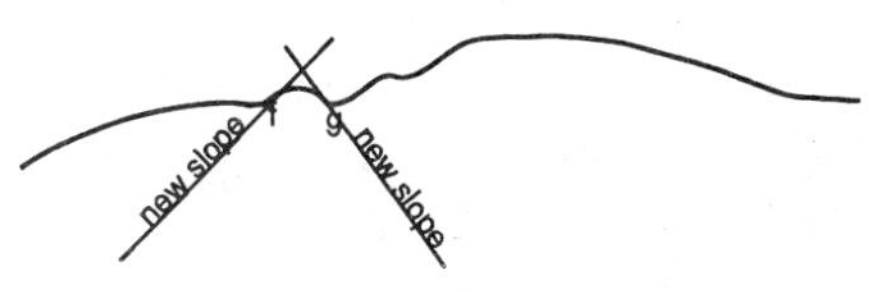

15. A cubic is determined by its value, together with the values of its first, second, and third derivatives, at a point. Since the point b together with the slope at b determine the value and first derivative at b for both the curve from a to b and the curve from b to c, these will automatically agree at b. For b to be superfluous, it must be that the curve from a to b and that from b to c must be part of one and the same cubic curve so the second and third derivatives at b of the curve from a to b must agree with the second and third derivatives at b of the curve from b to c, since they would be derivatives of one and the same cubic.

17. The 15 points are: (−1.81250, 1.03821)
(−1.62500, 0.21191) (−1.43750, −0.48401)
(−1.25000, −1.05469) (−1.06250, −1.50525)
(−0.87500, −1.84082) (−0.68750, −2.06653)
(−0.50000, −2.18750) (−0.31250, −2.20886)
(−0.12500, −2.13574) (0.06250, −1.97327)
(0.25000, −1.72656) (0.43750, −1.40076)
(0.62500, −1.00098) (0.81250, −0.53235)

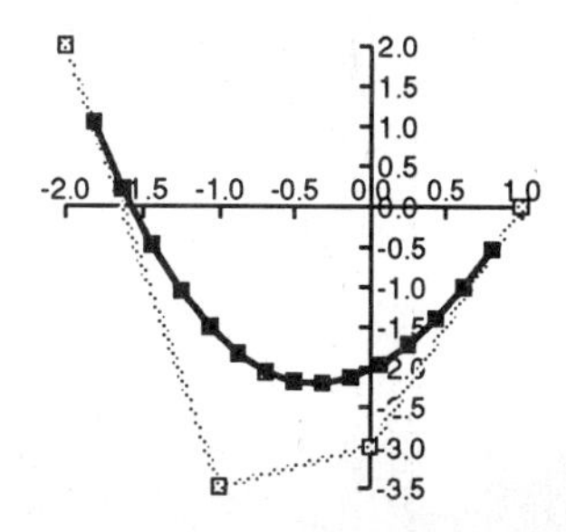

19. The 15 points are: $(-3.56250, -0.64111)$
$(-3.12500, -0.42578)$ $(-2.68750, -0.33350)$
$(-2.25000, -0.34375)$ $(-1.81250, -0.43604)$
$(-1.37500, -0.58984)$ $(-0.93750, -0.78467)$
$(-0.50000, -1.00000)$ $(-0.06250, -1.21533)$
$(0.37500, -1.41016)$ $(0.81250, -1.56396)$
$(1.25000, -1.65625)$ $(1.68750, -1.66650)$
$(2.12500, -1.57422)$ $(2.56250, -1.35889)$

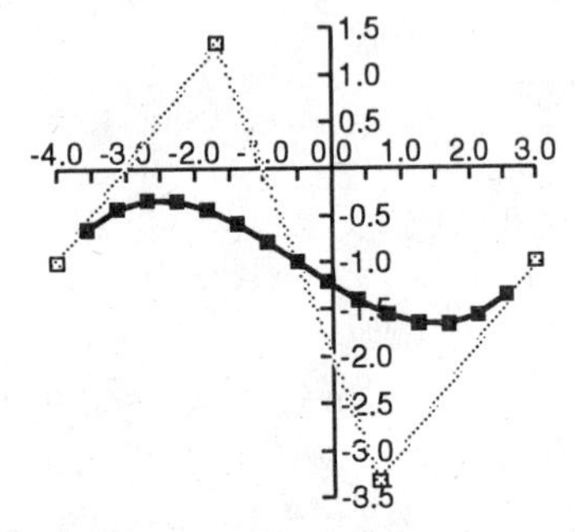

21. The 15 points are: $(2.18750, 2.28516)$
$(2.37500, 2.40625)$ $(2.56250, 2.38672)$
$(2.75000, 2.25000)$ $(2.93750, 2.01953)$
$(3.12500, 1.71875)$ $(3.31250, 1.37109)$
$(3.50000, 1.00000)$ $(3.68750, 0.62891)$
$(3.87500, 0.28125)$ $(4.06250, -0.01953)$
$(4.25000, -0.25000)$ $(4.43750, -0.38672)$
$(4.62500, -0.40625)$ $(4.81250, -0.28516)$

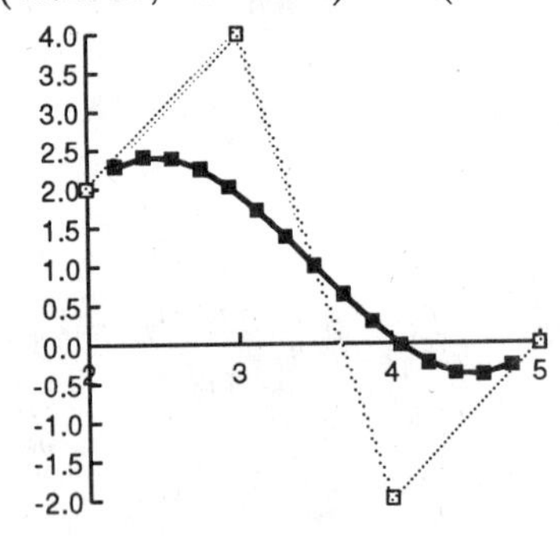

23. $x_n = \dfrac{x_0 + x_1}{2}$ and

$$y_n = \frac{y_0 + y_1}{2} + \tfrac{1}{8}(x_1 m_0 + x_0 m_1 - x_0 m_0 - x_1 m_1).$$

27. For $f(x) = \sqrt{x+1} - \sqrt{x} - 1$, with $x_0 = 2$, $x_1 = 5.5$, we have

spline approximation:
$-.00139473338(x-2)^3 + .0141500181(x-2)^2$
$-.064878256(x-2) - .6821627548$
Taylor approximation:
$-.6821627548 - .064878256(x-2)$
$+.0201379126(x-2)^2 - .0070391666(x-2)^3$

Graphs of approximations:

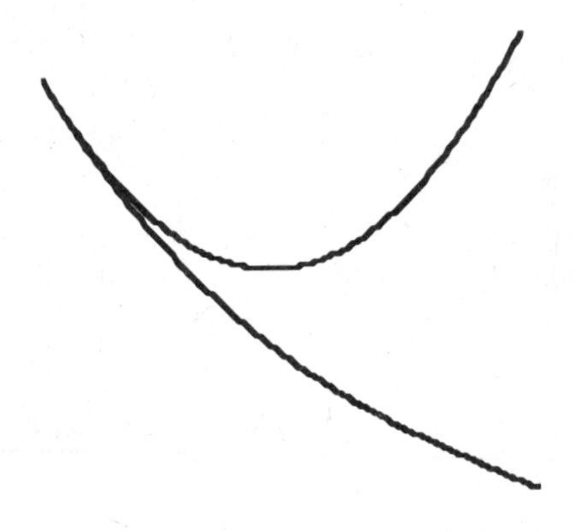

Graphs of the errors:

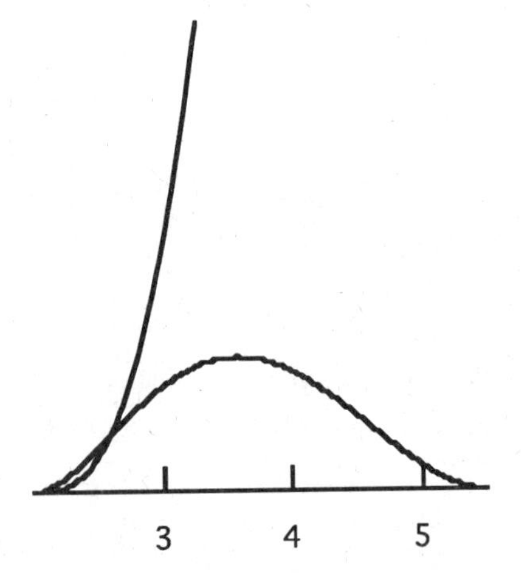

At $x = 4$ the spline is better, and at $x = 2.1$, the Taylor polynomial is better.

29. For $f(x) = x^4$,
with $x_0 = 0$, $x_1 = 1$, we have

spline approximation: $2x^3 - x^2$
Taylor approximation: 0

Graphs of approximations:

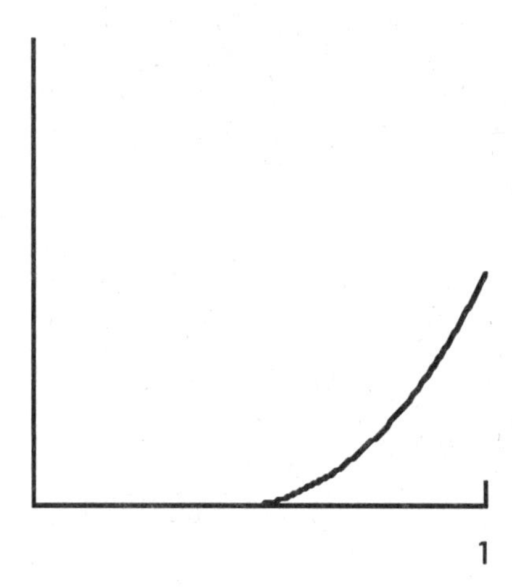

Graphs of the errors:

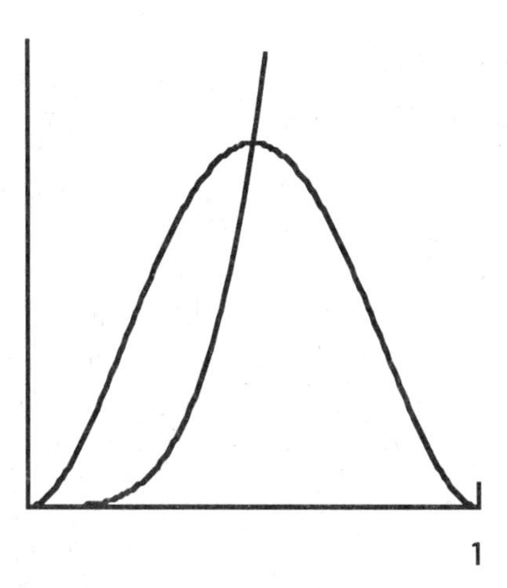

At $x = 0.9$ the spline is better, and at $x = 0.1$, the Taylor polynomial is better.

31. For $f(x) = \tan(x)$,
with $x_0 = 0$, $x_1 = \pi/4$, we have

spline approximation:
$.73522040738x^3 - .22954136412x^2 + x$
Taylor approximation: $\dfrac{x^3}{3} + x$

Graphs of approximations:

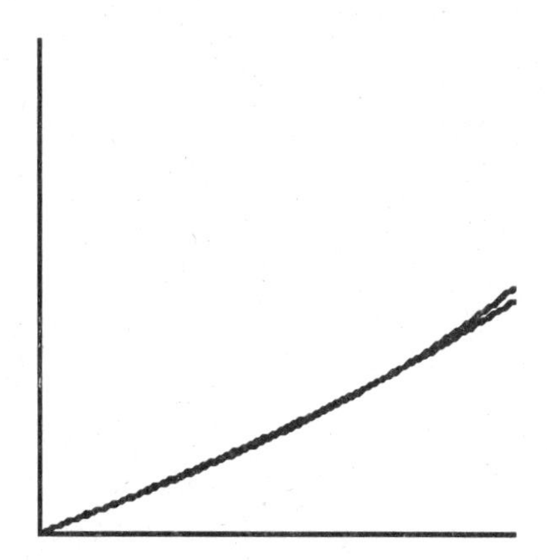

Graphs of the errors:

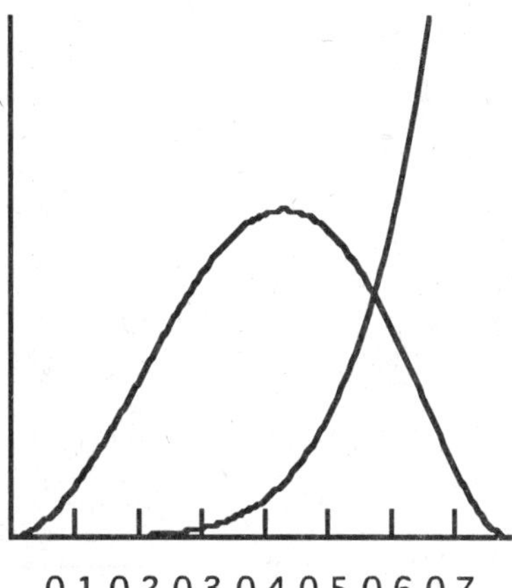

At $x = \frac{7\pi}{32}$, the spline is better, and at $x = \frac{\pi}{8}$, the Taylor polynomial is better.

Chapter 10

Section 10.1

1. $\{3-5n\}_{n=0}^{\infty}$. **3.** $\{\pi\}_{n=0}^{\infty}$.

5. $\{3(-5)^n\}_{n=0}^{\infty}$. **7.** $\{\pi(0)^n\}_{n=0}^{\infty}$.

9. True.

11. False. (Example: $-1, 1, -1, 1, \ldots$.)

13. $\frac{1}{2}, 2, \frac{1}{2}, 2, \ldots$;
bounded, non-monotonic, divergent.

15. $-2, -3.1, -4.01, -5.001, -6.0001$;
unbounded, monotonic, divergent.

17. $0, \frac{3}{2}, \frac{2}{3}, \frac{5}{4}, \frac{4}{5}, \frac{7}{6}, \frac{6}{7}, \ldots$

19. a_{12}.

21. $\{1/n\}_{n=1}^{\infty}$; $\{(1/2)^n\}_{n=0}^{\infty}$; $\{3\}_{n=1}^{\infty}$.

23. $\{n\}_{n=1}^{\infty}$, $\{(3/2)^n\}_{n=0}^{\infty}$, $\{1-2n\}_{n=0}^{\infty}$.

25. $\{(-1)^n\}_{n=1}^{\infty}$, $\{\cos(\frac{n\pi}{4})\}_{n=1}^{\infty}$, $\{\sin(n)\}_{n=1}^{\infty}$.

27. $L=0$, $N=6$.

29. $\left\{\frac{1}{n!}\right\}_{n=0}^{\infty}$ converges faster than $\left\{\frac{1}{2^n}\right\}_{n=0}^{\infty}$.

Section 10.2

1. Converges to $-\frac{1}{4}$. **3.** Converges to $\frac{1}{e-1}$.

5. Diverges. **7.** Converges to $\frac{1}{21}$.

9. Diverges. **11.** Converges to $\frac{3e^2}{3-e}$.

13. Converges to $\frac{5}{6}$. **15.** Converges to $-\frac{1}{3}$.

17. $\sum_{n=0}^{\infty}\left(\frac{14}{17}\right)^n$; $\sum_{n=0}^{\infty}\left(\frac{1}{3}\right)\left(\frac{16}{17}\right)^n$.

19. The first few terms in the sequence are
$1, 2, 2.5, 2.\overline{6}, 2.708\overline{3}, 2.71\overline{6}, 2.7180\overline{5}, 2.71825\ldots,$
$2.71827\ldots, 2.71828\ldots, 2.71828\ldots$
and the sequence converges to e.

21. 42 ft.

23. The total length is 1. $0, \frac{2}{9}$, and $\frac{1}{3}$
are examples of points never erased.

Section 10.3

1. Converges. **3.** Converges.

5. $-.4515$, $.1598$, $-.6795$, $-.8179$.

7. Converges. **9.** Converges.

11. $f(x) = e^{-x}\sin(x)$ is not always positive.

13. $N = 61$; $S_{61} \approx 1.017$;

$$1.01734306175 \le \sum_{n=1}^{\infty}\frac{1}{n^6} \le 1.01734306179.$$

15. $\int_1^b \ln(1+\frac{1}{x})\,dx$

$$= x\ln(1+\tfrac{1}{x})\Big]_1^b - \int_1^b \frac{-1}{1+x}\,dx$$

$$= (x\ln(1+\tfrac{1}{x}) + \ln(1+x))\Big]_1^b$$

$$= b\ln(1+\tfrac{1}{b}) + \ln(1+b) - \ln(2) - \ln(2).$$

$\int_1^{\infty}\ln(1+\frac{1}{x})\,dx$ diverges since

$$\lim_{b\to\infty}(b\ln(1+\frac{1}{b}) + \ln(1+b)) = \infty.$$

(The second term in the limit expression approaches infinity.)

17. $\sum_{n=1}^{\infty}\frac{1}{n}$ diverges but $\left\{\frac{1}{n}\right\}_{n=1}^{\infty}$ converges.

19. $\sum_{n=1}^{\infty}\frac{1}{n}$ and $\sum_{n=1}^{\infty}\left(-\frac{1}{n}\right)$ diverge,

but $\sum_{n=1}^{\infty}\left(\frac{1}{n}+\left(-\frac{1}{n}\right)\right)$ converges.

Section 10.4

1. Converges. **3.** Diverges.

5. Converges. **7.** No information.

9. Converges absolutely.

11. $\lim_{n\to\infty}\left|\frac{1}{(n+1)^p}\left(\frac{n^p}{1}\right)\right|$

$$= \lim_{n\to\infty}\left(\frac{n}{n+1}\right)^p = 1^p = 1 \text{ for all } p.$$

13. Converges absolutely.

15. Converges.

17. Diverges (p-series).

19. Diverges. **21.** Converges.

23. Diverges. **25.** Converges.

27. Diverges (p-series).

29. Diverges. **31.** Diverges.

33. Converges conditionally.

35. Converges.

37. Converges absolutely.

Section 10.5

1. $R = \infty$; $(-\infty, \infty)$.

3. $R = 2$; interval $(1, 5)$.

5. $h(x) = x - \frac{x^2}{2} + \frac{x^3}{3} - \frac{x^4}{4} + \cdots$

$= \sum_{n=1}^{\infty} \frac{(-1)^{n+1} x^n}{n}$; $h(0) = 0$; interval $(-1, 1]$.

7. $|R_{101}| < 0.0098$;

$\ln(2) \approx \sum_{n=1}^{101} \frac{(-1)^{n+1}}{n} \approx 0.698073$;

$\ln(2) \approx 0.693147$, by machine.

9. $\sum_{n=0}^{\infty} \frac{(-1)^n x^n}{n!}$. **11.** $\sum_{n=0}^{\infty} \frac{(-1)^n x^n}{(n+1)!}$.

13. $S_9 \approx 0.4438$.

15. $\dfrac{\frac{x^3}{3!} - \frac{x^5}{5!} + \frac{x^7}{7!} - \frac{x^9}{9!} + \cdots}{x^3 - \frac{x^5}{2!} + \frac{x^7}{4!} - \frac{x^9}{6!} + \cdots}$

$= \dfrac{\sum_{n=1}^{\infty} \frac{(-1)^{n+1} x^{2n+1}}{(2n+1)!}}{\sum_{n=1}^{\infty} \frac{(-1)^{n+1} x^{2n+1}}{(2n-2)!}}$.

Section 10.6

1. $a_0 = 3$, $a_n = a_{n-1} - 5$, $n = 1, 2, 3, \ldots$

3. $a_0 = \pi$, $a_n = a_{n-1}$, $n = 1, 2, 3, \ldots$

5. $a_0 = 3$, $a_n = (-5)a_{n-1}$, $n = 1, 2, 3, \ldots$

7. $a_0 = \pi$, $a_n = 2 \cdot a_{n-1}$, $n = 1, 2, 3, \ldots$

9. $\sqrt{3}$, $\sqrt{3\sqrt{3}}$, $\sqrt{3\sqrt{3\sqrt{3}}}$,

$\sqrt{3\sqrt{3\sqrt{3\sqrt{3}}}}$, $\sqrt{3\sqrt{3\sqrt{3\sqrt{3\sqrt{3}}}}}$, ...

11. 0, -1, -1.54, ...,

-1.57079, ..., -1.570796, ...

13. 0.5, 0.25, 0.0625,

0.00390625, 0.00001525, ...

15. The denominators form the Fibonacci sequence. The numerators form the Fibonacci sequence starting with the second term.

17. $89/55$.

19. 1, 1, 2, 3, 5, 8, 13, 21, 34, 55;

The Fibonacci sequence.

21. $x_1 = 2.100$, $x_2 \approx 1.812$, $x_3 \approx 1.789$.

23. $x_1 \approx 0.773$, $x_2 \approx 0.775$, $x_3 \approx 0.775$.

25. $x_1 \approx 2.226$, $x_2 \approx 2.215$, $x_3 \approx 2.215$.

29. $x_1 \approx 1.699$, $x_2 \approx 1.522$, $x_3 \approx 1.496$.

Appendices

Appendix 1. TRIANGLE TRIGONOMETRY

1. $\frac{5}{13}$.

3. $\frac{13}{12}$.

5. $\frac{5}{12}$.

7. $\frac{\pi}{5} = 36°$.
$\sin(\frac{\pi}{5}) \approx .5878$, $\cos(\frac{\pi}{5}) \approx .8090$,
$\tan(\frac{\pi}{5}) \approx .7265$, $\sec(\frac{\pi}{5}) \approx 1.2361$,
$\csc(\frac{\pi}{5}) \approx 1.7013$, $\cot(\frac{\pi}{5}) \approx 1.3764$.

9. $-\frac{5\pi}{4} = -225°$.
$\sin(-\frac{5\pi}{4}) \approx .7071$, $\cos(-\frac{5\pi}{4}) \approx -.7071$,
$\tan(-\frac{5\pi}{4}) = -1$, $\sec(-\frac{5\pi}{4}) \approx -1.4142$,
$\csc(-\frac{5\pi}{4}) \approx 1.4142$, $\cot(-\frac{5\pi}{4}) = -1$.

11. $\frac{8\pi}{3} = 480°$.
$\sin(\frac{8\pi}{3}) \approx .8660$, $\cos(\frac{8\pi}{3}) = -.5$,
$\tan(\frac{8\pi}{3}) \approx -1.7321$, $\sec(\frac{8\pi}{3}) = -2$,
$\csc(\frac{8\pi}{3}) \approx 1.1547$, $\cot(\frac{8\pi}{3}) \approx -.5774$.

13. $100° = \frac{5\pi}{9}$.
$\sin(100°) \approx .9848$, $\cos(100°) \approx -.1736$,
$\tan(100°) \approx -5.6713$, $\sec(100°) \approx -5.7588$,
$\csc(100°) \approx 1.0154$, $\cot(100°) \approx -.1763$.

15. $270° = \frac{3\pi}{2}$.
$\sin(270°) = -1$, $\cos(270°) = 0$,
$\tan(270°)$ undef., $\sec(270°)$ undef.,
$\csc(270°) = -1$, $\cot(270°) = 0$.

17. $-270° = -\frac{3\pi}{2}$.
$\sin(-270°) = 1$, $\cos(-270°) = 0$,
$\tan(-270°)$ undef., $\sec(-270°)$ undef.,
$\csc(-270°) = 1$, $\cot(-270°) = 0$.

19. angle $C = 100°$,
side $a \approx 4.077$ cm, side $b \approx 5.026$ cm.

21. No triangle possible with given data.

23. side $c \approx 3.6$ inches,
angle $A \approx 33.7°$, angle $B \approx 56.3°$.

25. ≈ 76.84 miles.

27. $\approx 61°$.

29. ≈ 807 meters.

Appendix 2. TECHNIQUES OF INTEGRATION

1. $\sin x - \frac{1}{3}\sin^3 x + C$.

3. $\frac{1}{5}\cos^5 x - \frac{1}{3}\cos^3 x + C$.

5. $\frac{1}{4}\tan^4 x + \frac{1}{6}\tan^6 x + C$.

7. $\frac{1}{5}\tan^5 x - \frac{1}{3}\tan^3 x + \tan x - x + C$.

9. $\tan x - \cot x + C$.

11. $\frac{3x}{8} + \frac{\sin 2x}{4} + \frac{\sin 4x}{32} + C$.

13. $-\frac{1}{5}\cot^5 x - \frac{1}{7}\cot^7 x + C$.

15. $\frac{-1}{1 + \tan x} + C$.

17. $2\arcsin(\frac{x}{2}) - \frac{1}{2}x\sqrt{4 - x^2} + C$.

19. $\frac{\sqrt{x^2 - 25}}{25x} + C$.

21. $\frac{-x}{\sqrt{x^2 - 1}} + C$.

23. $\frac{9}{4}\arcsin(\frac{2x}{3}) + \frac{x}{2}\sqrt{9 - 4x^2} + C$.

25. $\frac{1}{243}(9x^2 + 49)^{3/2} - \frac{49}{81}(9x^2 + 49)^{1/2} + C$.

27. $\frac{1}{2}\arctan\left(\frac{x - 2}{2}\right) + C$.

29. $-2\sqrt{9 - 8x - x^2} - 5\arcsin\left(\frac{x + 4}{5}\right) + C$.

31. $\frac{1}{2}\left(\arctan(x + 2) + \frac{x + 2}{x^2 + 4x + 5}\right) + C$.

33. $\frac{2}{3\sqrt{7}}\arctan\left(\frac{4x - 3}{3\sqrt{7}}\right) + C$.

Appendix 3. METHOD OF PARTIAL FRACTIONS

1. $3\ln|x| + 2\ln|x-4| + C$,
or $\ln|x|^3(x-4)^2 + C$.

3. $6\ln|x-1| + 5/(x-1) + C$.

5. $2\ln|x| - \ln|x-2| + 4\ln|x+2| + C$,

or $\ln\dfrac{x^2(x+2)^4}{|x-2|} + C$.

7. $5\ln|x| - \dfrac{2}{x} + \dfrac{3}{2x^2} - \dfrac{1}{3x^3} + 4\ln|x+3| + C$.

9. $3\ln|x+5| + \ln(x^2+4) + \frac{1}{2}\arctan(x/2) + C$

or $\ln\left((x^2+4)|x+5|^3\right) + \frac{1}{2}\arctan(x/2) + C$.

11. $\ln(x^2+1) - \dfrac{4}{x^2+1} + C$.

13. $\dfrac{x^3}{3} - 9x - \dfrac{1}{9x} - \dfrac{\ln(x^2+9}{2}$
$+\dfrac{728}{27}\arctan\left(\dfrac{x}{3}\right) + C$.

15. $2\ln|x-4| + 2\ln|x+1| - \frac{3}{2}(x+1)^{-2} + C$.

Appendix 4. POLAR COORDINATES

For 1-16, coordinates are approximate.

1. $(1.5, 2.5981)$. **3.** $(1.5, -2.5981)$.

5. $(-\pi, 0)$. **7.** $(0, 0)$.

9. $(5, 53.130°)$; $(5, .92730)$.

11. $(4.2857, -49.4°)$; $(4.2857, -.86220)$.

13. $(4.4429, 45°)$; $(4.4429, \frac{\pi}{4})$.

15. $(1000, 90°)$; $(1000, \frac{\pi}{2})$.

17. a is the radius of the circle and $(a, 0)$ is the center of the circle.

19. $(2a, 0)$ is the furthest right-hand edge of the cardioid. $(0, \pm a)$ are the y-intercepts.

21. $x = a$ is an asymptote. $(a \pm 1, 0)$ are the x-intercepts. For $0 < a \leq 1$, $(0,0)$ is also a point on the graph.

23. $(a \pm 1, 0)$ are x-intercepts. If $a \geq 1$, $(0,0)$ is also a point on the graph. (0 ± 1) are y-intercepts.

25. $(a, 0)$ is the x-intercept. $x = a$ is an asymptote.

27. $e = \frac{1}{3}$: ellipse, $e = 3$: hyperbola.

29. The answers will be the same.

31. The outer tip of each leaf is a distance of a from the origin.

33. Using $\cos(\theta)$ puts the first leaf on the positive x-axis. Using $\sin(\theta)$ puts the center of the first leaf in the direction $\theta = \frac{\pi}{2}k$.

35. If r is an even function of θ, the graphs are identical. If r is an odd function of θ, the graphs are symmetric across the origin.

37. $\sin(\pi-\theta) = \sin(\theta)$, so for any equation with θ only in terms of $\sin(\theta)$ or $\csc(\theta)$, the new and old graphs are identical. $\cos(\pi-\theta) = -\cos\theta$, so for any equation with θ only in terms of $\cos(\theta)$ or $\sec(\theta)$, the new graph is a reflection of the old graph across the origin.

39. If r is an odd function of θ, the new graph is the same as the old graph. If r is an even function of θ, the new graph is a reflection of the old graph across the origin.

41. The new graph is a clockwise rotation of the old graph an angle of $\frac{\pi}{2}$.

43. $(x^2+y^2)^2 - 3x^2y = 0$;
$x(t) = 3\sin(t)\cos^3(t)$,
$y(t) = 3\sin^2(t)\cos^2(t)$.

45. $x^3 + y^2x - 5y^2 = 0$;
$x(t) = 5\sin^2(t)$,
$y(t) = 5\sin^2(t)\tan(t)$.

47. $(x-1)^2(x^2+y^2) - 49x^2 = 0$;
$x(t) = 1 - 7\cos(t)$,
$y(t) = \tan(t) - 7\sin(t)$.

49. $(x^2+y^2-x)^2-9(x^2+y^2)=0$;
$x(t)=(-3+\cos(t))\cos(t)$,
$y(t)=(-3+\cos(t))\sin(t)$.

51. ≈ 2.96. **53.** ≈ 1.68.

55. ≈ 4.84. **57.** ≈ 0.21.

59. ≈ 0.02. **61.** $\frac{3\pi}{2}\approx 4.71$.

63. $\frac{3\pi}{2}\approx 4.71$. **65.** $\frac{3\pi}{2}\approx 4.71$.

67. $\frac{3\pi}{2}\approx 4.71$. **69.** ≈ 0.54.

71. ≈ 0.54. **73.** $\frac{\pi}{8}\approx 0.39$.

75. $\frac{\pi}{12}\approx 0.26$. **77.** $\frac{\pi}{12}\approx 0.26$.

79. $\dfrac{\pi a^2}{4k}$.

Appendix 5. COMPLEX NUMBERS

1. $z\approx 8.06\operatorname{cis}5.23$.

3. $2-7i$.

5. $-34+8i$.

7. With $z_1=6-5i\approx 7.81\operatorname{cis}5.59$,
and $z_2=-4-2i\approx 4.47\operatorname{cis}3.61$,
so $z_1z_2\approx 34.91\operatorname{cis}9.20$.

9. $4\operatorname{cis}(-30°)$.

11. The roots are:
$4\operatorname{cis}(20°)$, $4\operatorname{cis}(60°)$, $4\operatorname{cis}(100°)$,
$4\operatorname{cis}(140°)$, $4\operatorname{cis}(180°)$, $4\operatorname{cis}(220°)$,
$4\operatorname{cis}(260°)$, $4\operatorname{cis}(300°)$, $4\operatorname{cis}(340°)$.

The real root is $4\operatorname{cis}(180°)=-4$.

The conjugate pairs of roots are:
$4\operatorname{cis}(60°)$ and $4\operatorname{cis}(300°)$;
$4\operatorname{cis}(100°)$ and $4\operatorname{cis}(260°)$;
$4\operatorname{cis}(140°)$ and $4\operatorname{cis}(220°)$;
$4\operatorname{cis}(20°)$ and $4\operatorname{cis}(340°)$.

13. 2.

15. $z_1\approx .71+2.12i$, $z_2\approx -.71-2.12i$.

17. $z_1=2$, $z_2=2i$, $z_3=-2$, $z_4=-2i$.

19. $z_1\approx 1.08+1.87i$,
$z_2\approx -2.15$, $z_3\approx 1.08-1.87i$.

Appendix 6. TAYLOR'S FORMULA

1. $x\approx -0.89361$.

3. $x\approx 0.73887$.

5. $x\approx 1.89772$.

7. $x\approx -0.77015$.

9. $x\approx 0.21886$.

11. $R_N(1.2)=\dfrac{f^{(N+1)}(c)}{(N+1)!}(1.2-1)$
is the error term. Now, since
$f^{(N+1)}(c)=\dfrac{(-1)^N N!}{c^N}$ with $1\le c\le 1.2$,
so $|R_N(1.2)|=\left|\dfrac{(-1)^N N!}{c^N(N+1)!}(.2)\right|\le\dfrac{.2}{N+1}$.
When $N=199$, $\dfrac{.2}{N+1}=\dfrac{.2}{200}=.001$,
and $P_{199}(x)=\sum_{n=1}^{199}(-1)^{n+1}\dfrac{(x-1)^n}{n}$.
$P_{199}(1.2)=\sum_{n=1}^{199}(-1)^{n+1}\dfrac{(.2)^n}{n}\approx .18232$
approximates $\ln(1.2)$ within .001.
$P(.2)=\sum_{n=1}^{\infty}(-1)^{n+1}\dfrac{(.2)^n}{n}$ is an alternating series, so the error in $P_N(x)$ is less than or equal to $\dfrac{(.2)^{N+1}}{N+1}$. For $N=3$, $\dfrac{(.2)^4}{4}=.0004<.001$.
Hence, $P_3(.2)=.2-\dfrac{(.2)^2}{2}+\dfrac{(.2)^3}{3}=.182\overline{6}$
approximates $\ln(1.2)$ within .001 as well.

13. $R_N(1)=\dfrac{f^{(N+1)}(c)}{(N+1)!}(1-0)$ is error term.
$f^{(N+1)}(c)=e^c$, where $0<c<1$, so
$|R_N(1)|=|\dfrac{e^c}{(N+1)!}|<\dfrac{3}{(N+1)!}$.
When $N=6$, $\dfrac{3}{7!}\approx .0005952<.001$, and
$P_6(x)=1+x+\dfrac{x^2}{2!}+\dfrac{x^3}{3!}+\dfrac{x^4}{4!}+\dfrac{x^5}{5!}+\dfrac{x^6}{6!}$.
$P_6(1)=1+1+\dfrac{1}{2}+\dfrac{1}{6}+\dfrac{1}{24}+\dfrac{1}{120}+\dfrac{1}{720}$
$=2.7180\overline{5}$ approximates e within .001.

DIFFERENTIATION PRACTICE

1. $\frac{ds}{dt} = 8t + 4.$

3. $\frac{dM}{dw} = \frac{1}{2}w^{-1/2} + 2w^{-3/2} - \frac{9}{2}w^{-5/2}.$

5. $\frac{dy}{dx} = 12x + 5x^{-2} - \frac{4}{3}x^{-5/3}.$

7. $\frac{dN}{dt} = \frac{2}{3}t^{-1/3} + \frac{1}{3}t^{-4/3}.$

9. $\frac{dy}{dr} = 10(5r - 4).$

11. $\frac{dy}{dx} = \frac{1}{\sqrt{2x}}.$

13. $\frac{dy}{dt} = \frac{3}{\sqrt{6t+5}}.$

15. $\frac{dy}{dz} = \frac{4z+4}{3(2z^2+4z+8)^{2/3}}.$

17. $\frac{dy}{dx} = 8x^{1/3} - 2x^{-3/2}.$

19. $\frac{dy}{dx} = \frac{2}{3}t^{-1/3} + \frac{3}{2}t^{-5/2}.$

21. $\frac{dy}{dx} = 7(x^5 - 4x + 8)^6(5x^4 - 4).$

23. $\frac{dL}{dw} = 4(w^4 - 8w^2 + 15)^3(4w^3 - 16w).$

25. $\frac{dy}{dx} = 4x(3x^2 - 1)^3.$

27. $\frac{dT}{ds} = -6(2s^{-4} + 3s^{-2} + 2)^{-7}(-8s^{-5} - 6s^{-3}).$

29. $\frac{dy}{dx} = \frac{1}{3}(3 + 2x^{-2} + 4x^{-3})^{-2/3}(-4x^{-3} - 12x^{-4}).$

31. $\frac{dy}{dx} = 4(7x + (x^2+6)^{1/2})^3(7 + x(x^2+6)^{-1/2}).$

33. $\frac{dA}{dz} = \frac{1}{2}(1 + (1+2z)^{1/2})^{-1/2}(1+2z)^{-1/2}.$

35. $\frac{dA}{ds} = \frac{s}{2}(s^2+9)^{-3/4}(4s+5)^4$
$+16(s^2+9)^{1/4}(4s+5)^3.$

37. $\frac{dy}{dx} = 7(x^2+1)(5x^2+1).$

39. $\frac{dy}{dx} = (2x-5)^{-1/2}.$

41. $\frac{ds}{dt} = \frac{1}{2}(t^2+t+1)^{-1/2}(2t+1).$

43. $\frac{dy}{dx} = 7 + x(x^2+6)^{-1/2}.$

45. $\frac{dx}{dz} = \frac{1}{2}(z^2 + (z^2+9)^{1/2})^{-1/2}$
$\cdot(2z + z(z^2+9)^{-1/2}).$

47. $\frac{dy}{dx} = 18x((x^2-6)^3+1)^2(x^2-6)^2.$

49. $\frac{dy}{dx} = \frac{5x^{3/2}}{2(x+1)^{7/2}}.$

51. $\frac{dy}{dx} = \frac{2(3x^2-5)(62x)}{(2x^2+7)^3}.$

53. $\frac{dy}{dx} = 2(6x-7)^2(8x^2+9)(168x^2 - 112x + 81).$

55. $\frac{dx}{dy} = \frac{3}{2}(y^2-2)^{-1/4}(25y^2 + 2y - 20).$

57. $\frac{dy}{dx} = 3(x^6+1)^4(3x+2)^2(33x^6 + 20x^5 + 3).$

59. $\frac{dy}{dx} = -\frac{2}{3}(7y-2)^{-3}(2y+1)^{-1/3}(28y+25).$

61. $\frac{dA}{dr} = \frac{1}{2}r^{-1/2}(r+1)^{-1/2}(r+2)^{-1/2}(3r^2+6r+2).$

63. $\frac{dy}{dx} =$
$\frac{1}{4}(3x^3 - x + 1)^{-3/4}(x^2-6)^2(81x^4 - 79x^2 + 24x + 6).$

65. $\frac{dy}{dx} = 20x^{3/2} + \frac{21}{2}x^{5/2}.$

67. $\frac{dy}{dx} = \frac{12}{5}(3x+5)^{-1/5}.$

69. $\frac{dy}{dx} = \frac{(-2x^{-3} + (2/3)x^{-2/3})(3x^3 - x + 1)}{2(3x^3-x+1)^{3/2}(x^{-2}+2x^{1/3})^{1/2}}$
$-\frac{(x^{-2}+2x^{1/3})(9x^2-1)}{2(3x^3-x+1)^{3/2}(x^{-2}+2x^{1/3})^{1/2}}.$

71. $\frac{dy}{du} = \frac{-53}{2(7u-9)^{3/2}(2u+5)^{1/2}}.$

73. $\frac{dy}{dx} = \frac{27z^2 - 60z + 5}{(6z+1)^4}.$

75. $\frac{dR}{dw} =$
$\frac{(2w-4)(w+1)(w+3) - (w-1)(w-3)(2w+4)}{((w+1)(w+3))^2}.$

77. $\frac{ds}{dt} = \frac{-48t}{(9t^2+16)^{5/3}}.$

79. $\frac{dy}{dx} = \frac{7(x^2-1)(3x^3 + 50x^2 + 9x - 10)}{(3x+10)^5}.$

81. $f'(x) = \dfrac{-6x^2 - 2x + 3}{e^{x^2}}$.

83. $f'(x) = \frac{10}{3} x \tan^{2/3}(x^2) \sec^2(x^2)$.

85. $f'(x) = 24x \sec^3(4x^2 - 8) \tan(4x^2 - 8)$.

87. $f'(x) = 36x(3x^2 - 5)^2 \tan(3x^2 - 5)^3 \cdot \sec^2(3x^2 - 5)^3$.

89. $f'(x) = -4 \sin^3(\csc x) \cos(\csc x)(\csc x \cot x)$.

91. $f'(x) = 3e^x \tan^2(e^x) \sec^2(e^x)$.

93. $f'(x) = \dfrac{\sec^2(\sqrt{x})}{2\sqrt{x}}$.

95. $f'(x) = 7(e^x + e^{3x})^6(e^x + 3e^{3x})$.

97. $f'(x) = \cos(\frac{1}{x}) + \frac{1}{x} \sin(\frac{1}{x})$.

99. $f'(x) = -\dfrac{3}{2x^2} \sin^{1/2}\left(\dfrac{1}{x}\right) \cos\left(\dfrac{1}{x}\right) e^{\cos x} - \sin^{3/2}\left(\dfrac{1}{x}\right) e^{\cos x}(\sin x)$.

INTEGRATION PRACTICE

1. $\frac{x^2}{2} \arcsin x - \frac{1}{4} \arcsin x + \frac{x}{4}\sqrt{1 - x^2} + C$.

3. $\frac{1}{6} \sin^3(2x) - \frac{1}{10} \sin^5(2x) + C$.

5. $\dfrac{x}{25\sqrt{x^2 + 25}} + C$.

7. $2 \ln|x - 1| - \ln|x| - \dfrac{x}{(x - 1)^2} + C$.

9. $-\sqrt{4 + 4x - x^2} + 2 \arcsin\left(\dfrac{x - 2}{\sqrt{8}}\right) + C$.

11. $\frac{1}{3} e^{2x}(2 \sin(3x) - 3 \cos(3x)) + C$.

13. $-\sqrt{4 - x^2} + C$.

15. $2 \arctan(x^{1/2}) + C$.

17. $\dfrac{10x \sin(5x) - (25x^2 - 2) \cos(5x)}{125} + C$.

19. $\frac{2}{3}(1 + e^x)^{3/2} + C$.

21. $\frac{1}{3} \tan^3 x + C$.

23. $-\frac{1}{4}(8 - x^3)^{4/3} + C$.

25. $\frac{1}{2} e^{2x} - e^x + \ln(1 + e^x) + C$.

27. $\frac{1}{3}(16 - x^2)^{3/2} - 16(16 - x^2)^{1/2} + C$.

29. $x \arctan(5x) - (1/10) \ln|1 + 25x^2| + C$.

31. $\frac{1}{\sqrt{5}} \ln\left|\sqrt{5}x + \sqrt{7 + 5x^2}\right| + C$.

33. $\frac{1}{5}(x^2 - 25)^{5/2} + \frac{25}{3}(x^2 - 25)^{3/2} + C$.

35. $-\frac{1}{4}x^2 e^{-4x} - \frac{1}{8} x e^{-4x} - \frac{1}{32} e^{-4x} + C$.

37. $-\frac{1}{7} \cos(7x) + C$.

39. $x^3 \sin x + 3x^2 \cos x - 6x \sin x - 6 \cos x + \sin x + C$.

41. $24x - \frac{10}{3} \ln|\sin(3x)| - \frac{1}{3} \cot(3x) + C$.

43. $-2\sqrt{1 + \cos x} + C$.

45. $(1/3) \sec^3 x - \sec x + C$.

47. $(1/4)x^4 - 2x^2 + 4 \ln|x| + C$.

49. $\frac{3}{64}(2x + 3)^{8/3} - \frac{9}{20}(2x + 3)^{5/3} + \frac{27}{16}(2x + 3)^{2/3} + C$.

Index

57. $\displaystyle\int \frac{\sqrt{a+bu}}{u}du = 2\sqrt{a+bu} + a\int \frac{du}{u\sqrt{a+bu}}$

58. $\displaystyle\int \frac{\sqrt{a+bu}}{u^2}du = -\frac{\sqrt{a+bu}}{u} + \frac{b}{2}\int \frac{du}{u\sqrt{a+bu}}$

59. $\displaystyle\int u^n\sqrt{a+bu}\,du = \frac{2u^n(a+bu)^{3/2}}{b(2n+3)} - \frac{2na}{b(2n+3)}\int \frac{u^{n-1}}{\sqrt{a+bu}}\,du$

60. $\displaystyle\int \frac{u^n\,du}{\sqrt{a+bu}} = \frac{2u^n\sqrt{a+bu}}{b(2n+1)} - \frac{2na}{b(2n+1)}\int \frac{u^{n-1}du}{\sqrt{a+bu}}$

61. $\displaystyle\int \frac{du}{u^n\sqrt{a+bu}} = -\frac{\sqrt{a+bu}}{a(n-1)u^{n-1}} - \frac{b(2n-3)}{2a(n-1)}\int \frac{du}{u^{n-1}\sqrt{a+bu}}$

62. $\displaystyle\int \frac{du}{u\sqrt{a+bu}} = \frac{1}{\sqrt{a}}\ln\left|\frac{\sqrt{a+bu}-\sqrt{a}}{\sqrt{a+bu}+\sqrt{a}}\right| + C$, (if $a > 0$); $\displaystyle = \frac{2}{\sqrt{-a}}\arctan\sqrt{\frac{a+bu}{-a}} + C$, (if $a < 0$)

Trigonometric Forms

63. $\displaystyle\int \sin^2 u\;du = \frac{1}{2}u - \frac{1}{4}\sin 2u + C$

64. $\displaystyle\int \cos^2 u\;du = \frac{1}{2}u + \frac{1}{4}\sin 2u + C$

65. $\displaystyle\int \tan^2 u\;du = \tan u - u + C$

66. $\displaystyle\int \cot^2 u\;du = -\cot u - u + C$

67. $\displaystyle\int \sin^3 u\;du = -\frac{1}{3}(2+\sin^2 u)\cos u + C$

68. $\displaystyle\int \cos^3 u\;du = \frac{1}{3}(2+\cos^2 u)\sin u + C$

69. $\displaystyle\int \tan^3 u\;du = \frac{1}{2}\tan^2 u + \ln|\cos u| + C$

70. $\displaystyle\int \cot^3 u\;du = -\frac{1}{2}\cot^2 u - \ln|\sin u| + C$

71. $\displaystyle\int \sec^3 u\;du = \frac{1}{2}\sec u\tan u + \frac{1}{2}\ln|\sec u + \tan u| + C$

72. $\displaystyle\int \csc^3 u\;du = -\frac{1}{2}\csc u\cot u + \frac{1}{2}\ln|\csc u - \cot u| + C$

73. $\displaystyle\int \sin^n u\;du = -\frac{1}{n}\sin^{n-1}u\cos u + \frac{n-1}{n}\int \sin^{n-2}u\;du$

74. $\displaystyle\int \cos^n u\;du = \frac{1}{n}\cos^{n-1}u\sin u + \frac{n-1}{n}\int \cos^{n-2}u\;du$

75. $\displaystyle\int \tan^n u\;du = \frac{1}{n-1}\tan^{n-1}u - \int \tan^{n-2}u\;du$

76. $\displaystyle\int \cot^n u\;du = \frac{-1}{n-1}\cot^{n-1}u - \int \cot^{n-2}u\;du$

77. $\displaystyle\int \sec^n u\;du = \frac{1}{n-1}\tan u\sec^{n-2}u + \frac{n-2}{n-1}\int \sec^{n-2}u\;du$

78. $\displaystyle\int \csc^n u\;du = \frac{-1}{n-1}\cot u\csc^{n-2}u + \frac{n-2}{n-1}\int \csc^{n-2}u\;du$

79. $\displaystyle\int \sin au\sin bu\;du = \frac{\sin(a-b)u}{2(a-b)} - \frac{\sin(a+b)u}{2(a+b)} + C$

80. $\displaystyle\int \cos au\cos bu\;du = \frac{\sin(a-b)u}{2(a-b)} + \frac{\sin(a+b)u}{2(a+b)} + C$

81. $\displaystyle\int \sin au\cos bu\;du = -\frac{\cos(a-b)u}{2(a-b)} - \frac{\cos(a+b)u}{2(a+b)} + C$

82. $\displaystyle\int u\sin u\;du = \sin u - u\cos u + C$

83. $\displaystyle\int u\cos u\;du = \cos u + u\sin u + C$

84. $\displaystyle\int u^n\sin u\;du = -u^n\cos u + n\int u^{n-1}\cos u\;du$

85. $\displaystyle\int u^n\cos u\;du = u^n\sin u - n\int u^{n-1}\sin u\;du$

86. $\displaystyle\int \sin^n u\cos^m u\;du = -\frac{\sin^{n-1}u\cos^{m+1}u}{n+m} + \frac{n-1}{n+m}\int \sin^{n-2}u\cos^m u\;du$

$\displaystyle\qquad = \frac{\sin^{n+1}u\cos^{m-1}u}{n+m} + \frac{m-1}{n+m}\int \sin^n u\cos^{m-2}u\;du$

(continued on next page)

Inverse Trigonometric Forms

87. $\int \arcsin u \, du = u \arcsin u + \sqrt{1-u^2} + C$

88. $\int \arccos u \, du = u \arccos u - \sqrt{1-u^2} + C$

89. $\int \arctan u \, du = u \arctan u - \frac{1}{2}\ln(1+u^2) + C$

90. $\int u \arctan u \, du = \frac{u^2+1}{2} \arctan u - \frac{u}{2} + C$

91. $\int u \arcsin u \, du = \frac{2u^2-1}{4} \arcsin u + \frac{u\sqrt{1-u^2}}{4} + C$

92. $\int u \arccos u \, du = \frac{2u^2-1}{4} \arccos u - \frac{u\sqrt{1-u^2}}{4} + C$

93. $\int u^n \arcsin u \, du = \frac{1}{n+1}\left[u^{n+1} \arcsin u - \int \frac{u^{n+1}du}{\sqrt{1-u^2}}\right], \quad n \neq -1$

94. $\int u^n \arccos u \, du = \frac{1}{n+1}\left[u^{n+1} \arccos u + \int \frac{u^{n+1}du}{\sqrt{1-u^2}}\right], \quad n \neq -1$

95. $\int u^n \arctan u \, du = \frac{1}{n+1}\left[u^{n+1} \arctan u - \int \frac{u^{n+1}du}{1+u^2}\right], \quad n \neq -1$

Exponential and Logarithmic Forms

96. $\int ue^{au} du = \frac{1}{a^2}(au-1)e^{au} + C$

97. $\int u^n e^{au} du = \frac{1}{a}u^n e^{au} - \frac{n}{a}\int u^{n-1}e^{au} du$

98. $\int e^{au} \sin bu \, du = \frac{e^{au}}{a^2+b^2}(a \sin bu - b \cos bu) + C$

99. $\int e^{au} \cos bu \, du = \frac{e^{au}}{a^2+b^2}(a \cos bu + b \sin bu) + C$

100. $\int \ln u \, du = u \ln u - u + C$

101. $\int u^n \ln u \, du = \frac{u^{n+1}}{(n+1)^2}[(n+1)\ln u - 1] + C$

102. $\int \frac{1}{u \ln u} du = \ln|\ln u| + C$

Hyperbolic Forms

103. $\int \sinh u \, du = \cosh u + C$

104. $\int \cosh u \, du = \sinh u + C$

105. $\int \tanh u \, du = \ln \cosh u + C$

106. $\int \coth u \, du = \ln|\sinh u| + C$

107. $\int \operatorname{sech} u \, du = \arctan(\sinh u) + C$

108. $\int \operatorname{csch} u \, du = \ln|\tanh \frac{1}{2}u| + C$

109. $\int \operatorname{sech}^2 u \, du = \tanh u + C$

110. $\int \operatorname{csch}^2 u \, du = -\coth u + C$

111. $\int \operatorname{sech} u \tanh u \, du = -\operatorname{sech} u + C$

112. $\int \operatorname{csch} u \coth u \, du = -\operatorname{csch} u + C$

Forms involving $2au - u^2$

113. $\int \frac{\sqrt{2au-u^2}}{u} du = \sqrt{2au-u^2} + a \arccos\left(\frac{a-u}{a}\right) + C$

114. $\int \frac{\sqrt{2au-u^2}}{u^2} du = -\frac{2\sqrt{2au-u^2}}{u} - \arccos\left(\frac{a-u}{a}\right) + C$

115. $\int \frac{du}{\sqrt{2au-u^2}} = \arccos\left(\frac{a-u}{a}\right) + C$

116. $\int \frac{du}{u\sqrt{2au-u^2}} = -\frac{\sqrt{2ua-u^2}}{au} + C$

117. $\int \frac{u \, du}{\sqrt{2au-u^2}} = -\sqrt{2au-u^2} + a \arccos\left(\frac{a-u}{a}\right) + C$

118. $\int \sqrt{2au-u^2} \, du = \frac{u-a}{2}\sqrt{2au-u^2} + \frac{a^2}{2} \arccos\left(\frac{a-u}{a}\right) + C$

119. $\int u\sqrt{2au-u^2} \, du = \frac{2u^2-au-3a^2}{6}\sqrt{2au-u^2} + \frac{a^3}{2} \arccos\left(\frac{a-u}{a}\right) + C$

120. $\int \frac{u^2 \, du}{\sqrt{2au-u^2}} = -\frac{(u+3a)}{2}\sqrt{2au-u^2} + \frac{3a^2}{2} \arccos\left(\frac{a-u}{a}\right) + C$